Suncreens

COSMETIC SCIENCE AND TECHNOLOGY

Series Editor
Eric Jungermann
Jungermann Associates, Inc.
Phoenix, Arizona

1. Cosmetic and Drug Preservation: Principles and Practice, *edited by Jon J. Kabara*
2. The Cosmetic Industry: Scientific and Regulatory Foundations, *edited by Norman F. Estrin*
3. Cosmetic Product Testing: A Modern Psychophysical Approach, *Howard R. Moskowitz*
4. Cosmetic Analysis: Selective Methods and Techniques, *edited by P. Boré*
5. Cosmetic Safety: A Primer for Cosmetic Scientists, *edited by James H. Whittam*
6. Oral Hygiene Products and Practice, *Morton Pader*
7. Antiperspirants and Deodorants, *edited by Karl Laden and Carl B. Felger*
8. Clinical Safety and Efficacy Testing of Cosmetics, *edited by William C. Waggoner*
9. Methods for Cutaneous Investigation, *edited by Robert L. Rietschel and Thomas S. Spencer*
10. Sunscreens: Development, Evaluation, and Regulatory Aspects, *edited by Nicholas J. Lowe and Nadim A. Shaath*
11. Glycerine: A Key Cosmetic Ingredient, *edited by Eric Jungermann and Norman O. V. Sonntag*
12. Handbook of Cosmetic Microbiology, *Donald S. Orth*
13. Rheological Properties of Cosmetics and Toiletries, *edited by Dennis Laba*
14. Consumer Testing and Evaluation of Personal Care Products, *Howard R. Moskowitz*
15. Sunscreens: Development, Evaluation, and Regulatory Aspects. Second Edition, Revised and Expanded, *edited by Nicholas J. Lowe, Nadim A. Shaath, and Madhu A. Pathak*

16. Preservative-Free and Self-Preserving Cosmetics and Drugs: Principles and Practice, *edited by Jon J. Kabara and Donald S. Orth*
17. Hair and Hair Care, *edited by Dale H. Johnson*
18. Cosmetic Claims Substantiation, *edited by Louise B. Aust*
19. Novel Cosmetic Delivery Systems, *edited by Shlomo Magdassi and Elka Touitou*
20. Antiperspirants and Deodorants: Second Edition, Revised and Expanded, *edited by Karl Laden*
21. Conditioning Agents for Hair and Skin, *edited by Randy Schueller and Perry Romanowski*
22. Principles of Polymer Science and Technology in Cosmetics and Personal Care, *edited by E. Desmond Goddard and James V. Gruber*
23. Cosmeceuticals: Drugs vs. Cosmetics, *edited by Peter Elsner and Howard I. Maibach*
24. Cosmetic Lipids and the Skin Barrier, *edited by Thomas Förster*
25. Skin Moisturization, *edited by James J. Leyden and Anthony V. Rawlings*
26. Multifunctional Cosmetics, *edited by Randy Schueller and Perry Romanowski*
27. Cosmeceuticals and Active Cosmetics: Drugs Versus Cosmetics, Second Edition, *edited by Peter Elsner and Howard I. Maibach*
28. Sunscreens: Regulations and Commercial Development, Third Edition, *edited by Nadim Shaath*

Sunscreens

Regulations and Commercial Development

Third Edition

edited by

Nadim Shaath
Alpha Research and Development
White Plains, New York, U.S.A.

Taylor & Francis
Taylor & Francis Group
Boca Raton London New York Singapore

Published in 2005 by
Taylor & Francis Group
6000 Broken Sound Parkway NW
Boca Raton, FL 33487-2742

Printed in the United States of America on acid-free paper
10 9 8 7 6 5 4 3 2 1

International Standard Book Number-10: 0-8247-5794-7 (Hardcover)
International Standard Book Number-13: 978-0-8247-5794-7 (Hardcover)

Library of Congress Cataloging-in-Publication Data is available.

T&F informa

Taylor & Francis Group
is the Academic Division of T&F Informa plc.

Visit the Taylor & Francis Web site at
http://www.taylorandfrancis.com

Preface

The sunscreen industry is achieving remarkable worldwide prominence by responding to the growing need for skin protection with fast-paced innovation. Increased consumer awareness of the harmful effects of sunlight has fueled the demand for improved photo protection. The need for broad-spectrum protection from both UVA and UVB rays has inspired scientists worldwide to research new cosmetic formulations and delivery systems. More effective sunscreen actives, emollients and novel cosmetic and functional ingredients have been regularly added to the formulator's repertoire. Creativity in innovation has been hindered only by regulatory agencies and patent restrictions worldwide. Familiarity with the current restrictive regulations and patent law infringements has become integral to any research effort attempting to provide improved protection to individuals affected by the sun's damaging effects.

This book is designed to help the reader keep pace with the dramatic changes in the sunscreen industry. It provides state-of-the-art research on sunscreen development, evaluation, formulation and regulatory issues with a particular emphasis on the development of consumer sun care products. It features a variety of chapters written by prominent scientists and practitioners from appropriately varied disciplines including academia, industry, the medical community, marketing, the press, scientific organizations and regulatory agencies. These distinguished contributors have shared their latest innovations and knowledge of this ever expanding field in a way that is pertinent to professionals and laymen alike.

The book has 48 chapters that are organized into nine major sections:

I. **Introductory chapters** on the evolution of sunscreens, photo biological aspects, the need for photo protection, the safety of sunscreens and a historical perspective on sun protection.
II. **The Regulatory Aspects** of sunscreens including a chapter from the FDA, European COLIPA, Australian, USA and Japanese

sunscreen regulations, a summary chapter on regulations of sunscreens worldwide and a chapter on the United States Pharmacopeia (USP).

III. **The Ultraviolet Filters** features a chapter on the chemistry and mechanism of action of ultraviolet filters, two chapters on the physical inorganic particulate UV filters, one on the new sunscreen actives and a chapter on the photo stability of ultraviolet filters.

IV. **Cosmetic Formulations** including water proofing strategies, SPF modulation, broad-spectrum formulations, fragrancing sunscreen products, the role of emulsifiers and emollients, natural sun care products and surfactant free sunscreens.

V. **Consumer Products** with UV filters for the beach, daily use, babies and kids, recreational and occupational hazard protection. A chapter on fabrics as UV-radiation filters and another on sunless tanning and tanning accelerators.

VI. **Other Actives in the Sun Care Industry** including antioxidants, green tea polyphenols, botanicals and anti-aging ingredients.

VII. **Commercial Production and Quality Control** procedures for the manufactured sun care products as well as the QC of ultraviolet filters and a chapter on the modern analytical techniques in the sunscreen industry.

VIII. **Analytical Testing Procedures** include *in vivo* and *in vitro* testing procedures of sunscreen cosmetic formulations. The US FDA protocol, the European COLIPA and the International protocols for determining sun protection factors (SPF) are fully described. Balancing UVA and UVB protection, dosimetry of UV radiation and spectral standardization of sources used for sunscreens, *in vitro* models of sunscreen performance and prediction of SPF are discussed.

IX. **Marketing and Information** with chapters on the role of industry publications and technical information as well as recent sunscreen market trends.

This is the first manuscript of its kind on sunscreens that covers technical, regulatory, testing, consumer and commercial aspects of the industry. It gathers information on the production of sunscreen consumer products, safety and the need for photo protection, worldwide regulations, modern analytical techniques for SPF and QC testing, recent trends in research on cosmetic formulations and new ultraviolet filters, actives and cosmetic vehicles. It is a comprehensive manual that incorporates novel advances and newly acquired knowledge in sunscreen research. This assembly of contributing researchers and prominent leaders in the field of sun care protection has produced the most up-to-date and reliable reference guide in sun care available today.

Nadim A. Shaath, Ph.D.
Alpha Research & Development, Ltd.

Acknowledgment

This reference manual has consumed my contributors and I for the last 18 months. To each one of them and their institutions I say, "Thank you." To my wife for actively supporting me and standing beside me since my early teen years I say, "I love you." To my daughter Mona who has co-authored a chapter in this manuscript and has embarked with me on a series of joint publications I say, "You have made me really proud. God bless you." I would also like to thank Mohammad Zureiqi from Alpha Research & Development, Ltd. for his editing, typing and endless communications with my contributors. Finally, a thank you is due to the editors of Marcel Dekker and Taylor & Francis for their patience and continued support.

About the Editor

Dr. Nadim A. Shaath is President of Alpha Research & Development, Ltd., White Plains, New York. He is a frequent speaker and moderator at many scientific meetings and is the author and editor of numerous articles in scientific journals and books. Dr. Shaath is a member of the American Chemical Society, the American Institute of Chemists and the Society of Cosmetic Chemists. He received his B.Sc. (Honors) in Chemistry from the University of Alexandria, Egypt and his Ph.D. degree in Organic Chemistry from the University of Minnesota, Minneapolis. Upon serving three years as a Postdoctoral Fellow in the Medicinal Chemistry Department at the University of Minnesota, he joined the Chemistry faculty at the State University of New York and served as the chairman of the department at SUNY-Purchase. After joining Felton Worldwide as Executive Vice President and Technical Director responsible for the Sunarome sunscreen line, he formed a fragrance, essential oil and sunscreen company, Kato Worldwide/Nickstadt Moeller. Recently he founded Alpha Research & Development, Ltd., a research and consulting firm in the fields of sunscreens and essential oils.

Contributors

Patricia P. Agin *Schering-Plough HealthCare Products Inc., Memphis, Tennessee, USA.*

Nancy Allured *Allured Publishing Corporation, Carol Stream, Illinois, USA.*

Craig A. Bonda *CPH Innovations (an affiliate of the C.P. Hall Company), Chicago, Illinois, USA.*

Mike Brown *The Boots Company plc, Nottingham, UK.*

Stefan Bruening *Cognis Corporation, Ambler, Pennsylvania, USA.*

Felix Buccellato *Custom Essence Incorporated, Somerset, New Jersey, USA.*

Ratan K. Chaudhuri *EMD Chemicals, Inc., Hawthorne, New York, USA.*

Curtis A. Cole *Johnson & Johnson Consumer Products Worldwide, Skillman, New Jersey, USA.*

Christopher Corbett *L'Oréal USA Products, Inc., Clark, New Jersey, USA.*

Gerd Dahms *Institüt für Angewandte Colloidtechnologie, Duisberg, Germany.*

B. L. Diffey *Newcastle General Hospital, Newcastle, UK.*

John C. Dowdy *Rapid Precision Testing Laboratories, Cordova, Tennessee, USA.*

Craig A. Elmets *Department of Dermatology, University of Alabama at Birmingham, Birmingham, Alabama, USA.*

Howard Epstein *Kao Brands—The Andrew Jergens Company, Cincinnati, Ohio, USA.*

Lawrence Evans III *United States Pharmacopeia, Rockville, Maryland, USA.*

Frederick Flores *International Flavors and Fragrances, New York, New York, USA.*

Minoru Fukuda *Shiseido Research Center, Yokohama, Japan.*

Art Georgalas *TRI-K Industries, Northvale, New Jersey, USA.*

Paolo U. Giacomoni *Clinique Laboratories, Melville, New York, USA.*

Anthony D. Gonzalez *Avon Products, Inc., Suffern, New York, USA.*

Kathryn L. Hatch *Agricultural and Biosystems Engineering, The University of Arizona, Tucson, Arizona, USA.*

Bernd Herzog *Ciba Specialty Chemicals Inc., Grenzach-Wyhlen, Germany.*

Julian P. Hewitt *Uniqema Health & Personal Care, Wilton, Redcar, UK.*

Matthew R. Holman *Division of Over-The-Counter Drug Products, Center for Drug Evaluation and Research, Food and Drug Administration, Rockville, Maryland, USA.*

Dietmar Hueglin *Ciba Specialty Chemicals Inc., Basel, Switzerland.*

Ulrich Issberner *Cognis Deutschland GmbH & Co. KG, Duesseldorf, Germany.*

Robert E. Kalafsky *Avon Products, Inc., Suffern, New York, USA.*

Henry T. Kalinoski *L'Oréal USA Products, Inc., Clark, New Jersey, USA.*

Timothy Kapsner *Aveda Corporation, Minneapolis, Minnesota, USA.*

Santosh K. Katiyar *Department of Dermatology, University of Alabama at Birmingham, Birmingham, Alabama, USA.*

Rolf Kawa *Cognis Deutschland GmbH & Co. KG, Duesseldorf, Germany.*

Kenneth Klein *Cosmetech Laboratories, Inc., Fairfield, New Jersey, USA.*

Peter J. Lentini *The Estee Lauder Companies, Melville, New York, USA.*

Edwin D. Leonard, Jr. *Patriot Distributors, Inc., DeLand, Florida, USA.*

Mark Leonard *Cognis Corporation, Ambler, Pennsylvania, USA.*

Kelly Lewellen *Tanning Research Laboratories, Inc., Ormond Beach, Florida, USA.*

Regina Lim *Product Quest, Inc., Daytona Beach, Florida, USA.*

Karl Lintner *Sederma, Paris, France.*

Dennis L. Lott *Tanning Research Laboratories, Inc., Ormond Beach, Florida, USA.*

Kenneth Marenus *Estee Lauder Companies, Melville, New York, USA.*

Romano E. Mascotto *L'Oréal Research, Asnière, France.*

Peter Matravers *Aveda Corporation, Minneapolis, Minnesota, USA.*

Timothy Meadows *Farpoint, Inc., Dallas, Texas, USA.*

Toni F. Miller *Essex Testing Clinic, Verona, New Jersey, USA.*

Emalee G. Murphy *Kirkpatrick & Lockhart LLP, Washington, DC, USA.*

Masako Naganuma *Shiseido Scientific Research Department, Tokyo, Japan.*

Malcolm R. Nearn *Kentlyn, New South Wales, Australia.*

Christopher G. Nelson, Jr. *St. Petersburg, Florida, USA.*

Uli Osterwalder *Ciba Specialty Chemicals Inc., Basel, Switzerland.*

Irwin Palefsky *Cosmetech Laboratories, Inc., Fairfield, New Jersey, USA.*

Patricia Peterson *Aveda Corporation, Minneapolis, Minnesota, USA.*

James P. SaNogueira *Playtex Products, Inc., Allendale, New Jersey, USA.*

Cheryl M. Sanzare *L'Oréal USA Products, Inc., Clark, New Jersey, USA.*

Robert M. Sayre *Rapid Precision Testing Laboratories, Cordova, Tennessee and University of Tennessee Center for the Health Sciences, Memphis, Tennessee, USA.*

David Schlossman *Kobo Products, Inc., South Plainfield, New Jersey, USA.*

Richard J. Schwen *PAREXEL International, Inc., Waltham, Massachusetts, USA.*

Mona Shaath *Alpha Research & Development, Ltd., White Plains, New York, USA.*

Nadim A. Shaath *Alpha Research & Development, Ltd., White Plains, New York, USA.*

Yun Shao *Kobo Products, Inc., South Plainfield, New Jersey, USA.*

Daiva Shetty *Division of Over-The-Counter Drug Products, Center for Drug Evaluation and Research, Food and Drug Administration, Rockville, Maryland, USA.*

William Shields *CCI, Rockledge, Florida, USA.*

Ko-ichi Shiozawa *Aveda Corporation, Minneapolis, Minnesota, USA.*

Joseph W. Stanfield *Suncare Research Laboratories, LLC, Winston Salem, North Carolina, USA.*

David C. Steinberg *Steinberg & Associates, Inc., Plainsboro, New Jersey, USA.*

John P. Tedeschi *Bath & Body Works, Reynoldsburg, Ohio, USA.*

Andrea Tomlinson *Cognis UK, Waltham Cross, UK.*

Christopher D. Vaughan *SPF Consulting Labs, Inc., Pompano Beach, Florida, USA.*

Ismail I. Walele *Finetex, Elmwood Park, New Jersey, USA.*

Glenn Wiener *Tanning Research Laboratories, Inc., Ormond Beach, Florida, USA.*

Carolyn B. Wills *Mary Kay Inc., Dallas, Texas, USA.*

James M. Wilmott *Ridgefield Drive, Shoreham, New York, USA.*

Nabiha Yusuf *Department of Dermatology, University of Alabama at Birmingham, Birmingham, Alabama, USA.*

Contents

Marketing and Information

Introduction

1

Sunscreen Evolution

Nadim A. Shaath

Alpha Research & Development, Ltd., White Plains, New York, USA

HISTORICAL BACKGROUND

In Ancient Egypt the cult of the sun god Ra provided a sun-centered cosmology where Egyptians bowed in worship to the powerful effects of the life-giving sun. The Ancient Egyptians were well aware of the dangers of the sun. Their lands were scorched with heat. Women protected their skin, preferring light skin to dark in their cultural hierarchy of beauty (1). Recent discoveries written on papyri and the walls of several tombs unearthed ingredients and formulations in use in Ancient Egypt specifically addressing issues of sun damage to the hair and skin (2,3).

- *Tirmis* or lupin extract was used to block the rays of the sun and is still used to date to lighten the color of the skin.
- *Yasmeen* or jasmin was used to heal the sun-damaged skin. Recent evidence reveals that jasmin aids in DNA repair at the cellular level.
- *Sobar* or aloe was used to heal sun-damaged skin.
- *Zaytoon* or olive oil was used as a hydrating oil for both skin and hair damaged by overexposure to the sunlight.
- Aquatic lotus oil was used for protection of the skin from the sun.
- *Loze* or almond oil was applied before and after sun exposure to hydrate the sun-damaged skin, improving elasticity and texture.
- Calcite powder and clay were used as ultraviolet (UV) filters similar to the modern day inorganic particulates zinc oxide and titanium dioxide.
- Rice bran extracts were used in sunscreen preparations. Today, gamma oryzanol extracted from rice bran has UV absorbing properties.
- A number of cosmetic ingredients were used to mask and protect the skin and hair from the ravishing rays of the sun (2,3). These included *kohl* (to darken eyes in order to combat sunlight impairment to the retina in the glare of the desert sun), red ochre (to redden and impart a rosy glow in women's makeup mimicking the effect of the sun on the skin), and henna oil (to dye the lips and nails, darken the color of the hair and skin, and protect light skin from the sun). It is interesting to note that lawsone, the active principle of henna, was a Food and Drug Administration (FDA) Category I sunscreen molecule!

In modern times, the first reported use of commercial sunscreens in the world was in 1928 in the USA with the introduction of an emulsion containing two sunscreen chemicals, benzyl salicylate and benzyl cinnamate (4). In the early 1930s, a product containing 10% salol (phenyl salicylate) appeared on the Australian market (5). In the USA, lotions containing quinine oleate and quinine bisulfate appeared in 1935. *p*-Amino benzoic acid (PABA) was first patented in 1943, leading the way for the incorporation of several *para*-amino benzoates in sunscreen formulations (6). During World War II, red petrolatum was used by the US military, which led to extensive use of both inorganic particulates and organic UV absorbers after the war. The US military specifications

(7) issued on July 10, 1951, listed approved sunscreen compounds and the recommended concentrations, namely, glyceryl PABA (3%), and escalol 75A (5%), 2-ethyl hexyl salicylate (Sunarome WMO, 5%), digalloyl trioleate (3%), homomenthyl salicylate (8%), and dipropylene glycol salicylate (4%).

The reader is referred to the chapter written by Giacomoni (8) for a historical perspective on sun protection (also, an interesting perspective on the need for photoprotection).

SKIN CANCER AND THE SOLAR SPECTRUM

According to the Centers for Disease Control and Prevention in Atlanta, the death rate in the USA from melanoma has been growing by ~4% a year. The American Cancer Society reports that there are about 1.5 million new cases of skin cancer diagnosed each year, with about 47,000 cases of melanoma resulting in over 10,000 skin cancer deaths. Of all the reported new malignancies, 80% were basal cell carcinoma, 16% were squamous cell carcinoma, and 4% were malignant melanoma. Most of these cases are a direct result of overexposure to UV radiation (9).

There are three types of UV solar radiation. The most energetic rays are the UV-C (200–280 nm), which are generally filtered out by the ozone layer preventing those deadly rays from reaching the earth's surface. Any significant depletion of the earth's ozone protective layer would pose a hazard that is unimaginable. The second type of UV rays are termed UV-B and they represent a narrow band of rays from 280 to 320 nm with the maximum intensity peaking at ~307 nm. These rays are sufficiently energetic and have been termed as "burning" or "erythemal" rays since they are primarily responsible for the redness associated with sunburn. The third type of UV rays are the UV-A rays, which extend from 320 to 400 nm and by convention have been further subdivided into the shorter UV-A rays, UV-A II (320–340 nm), and the longer UV rays, UV-A I (340–400 nm). See Chapter 13 on the "Chemistry of UV Filters" (10) for the depiction of the solar spectrum and the radiations emitted. These rays have been referred to as the tanning rays since they penetrate deep into the dermis layer of the skin thereby stimulating the formation of melanin, the body's natural defense protective layer. Until the 1970s, they were considered relatively harmless and in many cases were associated with the formation of a healthy tan. Recent evidence, however, has implicated these energetically weaker, yet more penetrating, rays with the higher incidence of skin cancers. Researchers have implicated UV-A radiation with molecular and tissular effects, sagging of the skin, and the introduction of nicks in cellular DNA. Most of the UV-A damage seems to implicate the presence of oxygen and trace metals, hence the increased popularity of using antioxidants and singlet oxygen free radical scavengers.

Protection from UV radiation is paramount. This can be achieved by the avoidance of sun exposure whenever possible, by the wearing of sun protective clothing (11), hats, and UV filtering sunglasses along with the use of adequately formulated sunscreen cosmetic or dermatological preparations. To help the consumers select products that best suit their needs, the FDA and most major country regulatory organizations have adopted several measures and standards (12). In addition to the dissemination of information concerning the harmful effects of prolonged sun exposure, the sun protection factor (SPF) system alerts consumers to the degree of protection required. The water resistance labeling addresses sweating, rub off, and effect of bathing in reducing the efficacy of the product. Also, the UV-A/UV-B labeling system rates products for the type of radiation it reduces. The reader is referred to the next two chapters and the many references cited therein for additional information on the need for photoprotection.

SUNSCREEN PRODUCTS

Sunscreen products worldwide can be classified into three major categories:

1. Daily wear and long-term protective products
2. Tanning products
3. Recreational products

The reader is referred to section entitled "Products with Ultraviolet Filters" in this book for the chapters written on the earlier-mentioned categories and to the chapter by Shaath and Shaath on "Recent Sunscreen Market Trends". Note that the sun care market includes fabrics with UV filters [read Chapter 28 by Hatch (11)] as well as a multitude of after-sun, medicated sunburn treatment products that are outside the scope of this book.

ISSUES AND CHALLENGES FACING THE SUNSCREEN INDUSTRY

A number of issues and challenges face the formulator of cosmetic and pharmaceutical products that contain UV filters.

Regulatory and Safety Issues

In the USA, the FDA has been regulating this industry since August 25, 1978, with the publication of the Advance Notice of Proposed Rulemaking. Sunscreens are considered drugs and cosmetics and therefore must be governed by the FDA-OTC monograph. The final monograph was issued on May 21, 1999, and was to be finalized in May 2001; however, that date has been extended to on or before December 31, 2005 (13).

The regulatory issues that should be addressed include claims, labeling, manufacturing, and quality control for compliance.

Sun Protection Factor

This is an important, but not the only, criterion by which a sunscreen product is evaluated. An *in vivo* test in compliance with the monograph condition has to be met. The many *in vitro* techniques developed are very useful for honing in on the correct formulation, but are not considered legal for compliance with the FDA's monograph protocols (refer to section entitled "Analytical Testing Procedures" for all the *in vivo* and *in vitro* testing procedures). Current FDA regulations allow labeling of sunscreen products to a maximum of 30+, despite the many products currently available with numbers as high as 100. From a cosmetic formulation point of view, increasing the SPF number in a product is governed by simple chemical principles (refer to section entitled "Cosmetic Formulations").

The Region in the UV Spectrum

The next two chapters deal with the need for photoprotection and have adequately covered the issues dealing with UV-A, UV-B, and broad-spectrum protection, including protection from the visible and infrared regions. The protection of the UV-B region is well documented with all the biological *in vivo* analyses available today. UV-A protection testing, on the other hand, is still not yet finalized by the FDA, even though a number of analytical procedures are being discussed and submitted to the FDA by the Cosmetics, Toiletries & Fragrance Association (CTFA), individual companies, and interested scientists.

Water Resistance

The old statements on waterproof sunscreens have been eliminated in favor of water-resistant or more water-resistant claims. The use of polymers and UV filters that have minimal or no water solubility is basic in any formulation addressing this issue. Formulation changes are also necessary to increase its water resistance including favoring water in oil over oil in water formulations.

Photostability and Photoreactivity

A new issue has risen over the last decade questioning the photostability of a few UV filters. The dibenzoyl methane type of sunscreen agents were implicated due to their interconversion between its keto and enol forms; they are known to be less photostable than other molecules in the monograph. This, however, has led to a whole new class of photostabilizers known as triplet–triplet quenchers (14) and a number of patents, most notably by L'Oreal, for the photostabilization of dibenzoyl methane derivatives with octocrylene. It should be noted that any molecule that can photochemically interconvert (*cis–trans*, keto–enol, or other types of photoisomerizations) is subject to some degree of photoinstability. Most derivatives lose some of their efficacy over extended periods of sunlight exposure, even the popular octinoxate and padimate-O. Combinations of octinoxate and avobenzone in particular have also been known to be less photostable.

The benzophenones, octocrylene, the salicylates, and the inorganic particulates are generally photostable molecules.

Photoreactivity is concerned primarily with the inorganic particulates. Among the attributes of metals and their oxides has been their ability to catalyze reactions. Hence, questions relating to the photoreactivity of both zinc oxide and titanium dioxide have recently surfaced. Suppliers have scrambled to assure manufacturers and regulatory agencies of the safety of their products. In general, titanium dioxide is more photoreactive than zinc oxide; however, predispersions and specialized coatings with silica, organics, and aluminum salts have improved these products significantly.

Safety and Stability

Issues of safety are very well defined in the FDA's monograph, COLIPA (Europe) regulations, and other countries' specific regulatory bodies including those of Japan, South Africa, Australia, and New Zealand (12). Basically, a product is in compliance if a UV filter is used at the permissible levels as approved by the regulatory agency in question. All new UV filters must submit New Drug Applications (NDA) to the FDA for approval or file for a Time and Extent Application (TEA) if the ingredient has been in use for more than 5 years in five foreign countries. The finished cosmetic products must be tested, like any other cosmetic or pharmaceutical product, for safety and stability (15). The safety of all ingredients present, their potential interactions with one another, and the packaging must be evaluated.

Sunscreen stability is a major factor contributing to the success of the sunscreen formulation. Thorough long-term stability testing of the experimental formulation needs to be conducted prior to product launch. Degradation of products on exposure to sunlight is a serious problem but the base and packaging materials can also affect sunscreen stability. The solubility of most liquid UV filters is similar to that of the polymers used in many packaging materials. This can result in the UV filter migrating into and degrading the plastic while also reducing the potency of the formulation left behind. The containers must be selected to suit the formulation of the sunscreen. Opaque high-density polyethylene is probably the best container, but there is no universal rule. PET is good for clear products that do not contain certain filters and ingredients.

Manufacturing and Quality Control

Since the FDA classifies all sunscreen products as drugs, the manufacturing sites have to comply with all the applicable regulations and current good manufacturing practices (cGMP) (16). The formulation needs to be submitted for the appropriate battery of tests for SPF and water resistance. The percentage of each active ingredient in every batch manufactured has to be tested and verified by instrumental techniques (GC or HPLC).

Cosmetic Formulation Issues

An entire section of this book (Section V), including nine separate chapters, has been included to address potential problems with formulating sunscreen products containing UV filters.

Formula Types

The vehicle for the UV filter and the delivery system may pose unique problems. Special applications of creams, milks, or lotions require either oil in water (O/W) or water in oil (W/O) emulsions. Other applications include gels, balms, foams, ointments, oils, sprays, or impregnation into fabric, clothing, or polymer applications.

Formula Optimization

The optimization of the formula's SPF, water resistance, and photostability may require the use or avoidance of specific UV filters, polymers, and other ingredients. The mildness, elegance, and cost-effectiveness of a sunscreen product may dictate the selection or elimination of specific ingredients.

Active Ingredients

The heart of any sunscreen product is of course the UV absorber, but other ingredients may well affect the efficacy and performance of sunscreen products. The UV filters permitted in the USA, Europe, Japan, and Australia are listed in Section II of this book.

UV filters may be classified according to the type of protection they offer as inorganic particulates, organic chemical absorbing molecules, or new organic particulates:

1. *Inorganic chemical particulates*: The use of the phrase "physical blockers" should be avoided. These ingredients are chemicals that reflect or scatter the UV radiation. Examples include zinc oxide and titanium dioxide (red petrolatum is no longer in the final FDA monograph). The inorganic chemical particulates, if present in sufficient quantities, will absorb and reflect most UV, visible, and IR rays. They are currently used in conjunction with organic chemical absorbers to achieve high SPFs. *Micronized* forms of these metal oxides are currently available, claiming to enhance sun protection without imparting the traditional opaqueness that is aesthetically unappealing in cosmetic formulations. Other attempts have been made to change the physical form of the inorganic powders or to complex them with organic substances. These metal oxides are marketed in a variety of particle sizes, coatings, dispersions, and suspensions and are currently

widely used in cosmetic formulations. For a review refer to the two chapters on inorganic particulates (17,18).

2. *Organic chemical absorbers*: The term "organic" here should not be confused with organically grown essential oils or other plant derived ingredients. These organic chemical filters absorb the harmful UV radiation. Chemical absorbers are classified into either UV-A or UV-B blockers depending on the type of radiation they protect the skin from. UV-A absorbers are chemicals that tend to absorb radiation in the 320–380 nm region of the UV spectrum (benzophenones, meradimate, and avobenzone). UV-B absorbers are chemicals that absorb radiation in the 290–320 nm region of the UV spectrum (*para*-amino benzoates, salicylates, cinnamates, and camphor derivatives). The best classification of chemical UV absorbers is the one based on the chemical properties of sunscreens (10).
3. *Organic particulates*: For a discussion of this new category of UV filters, the reader is referred to the chapter entitled "New Sunscreen Actives" (19).

Other Ingredients

Sunscreen products, depending on their intended use, contain a multitude of other ingredients. The other types of ingredients that enter into sunscreen products are listed as follows:

1. *Sunless tanners and bronzers*: The only color additive currently approved by the FDA is dihydroxy acetone (DHA). Other tanning accelerators such as tyrosine and its derivatives or tyrosinases are not approved by the FDA as cosmetics. Canthaxanthine marketed as a tanning pill is not allowed by the FDA. It is only approved as a color additive in foods. The reader is referred to the chapter entitled "Sunless Tanning and Tanning Accelerators" (20).
2. *Antiaging, antiwrinkle, and healing products*: The reader is referred to the chapter on antiaging products (21) for a discussion of the ingredients that address the problems associated with aging of the skin, wrinkling, blemishes, acne, chapping of lips and that also contain UV filters. The use of analgesics, aloe, botanicals, antioxidants, essential oils, and extracts in post-sun healing lotions is expanding rapidly.
3. *Sunscreens for hair*: Sun damage to the hair causes the fading of the hair color. It may also cause brittle and dry hair shafts as well as split ends. Products with UV filters have demonstrated their usefulness in addressing some of the problems associated with hair damage. The FDA Category I UV filters are generally used; however, a number of cosmetic ingredient companies supply specialized UV filters specifically designed for the hair. If no SPF is claimed on hair products, non-Category I ingredients may be used, so long as their safety and

efficacy have been demonstrated. Over two decades ago, the concept of quaternary ammonium compounds such as salicylates or cinnamates, that are substantive to the hair and are chemically bonded to UV filters, was introduced. Today, a number of companies offer these products to the industry.

4. *Antioxidants*: Recent research has revealed that free radical scavengers may play an important role in reducing the damage to the skin, especially as it relates to the excessive exposure of UV-A radiation. A multitude of antioxidants, including polyphenols found in green tea and a number of essential oils and plant extracts, are currently being used or suggested for use in many presun, postsun, and during-sun exposure products. The reader is referred to the three chapters in section entitled "Other Actives in the Sun Care Industry" of this book.
5. *Natural ingredients*: It should be noted, at the outset, that any claims of SPF on a product labeled natural sunscreen must contain Category I approved UV filters and be in compliance with all the FDA regulations governing sunscreen products. The use of natural ingredients in the health, aromatherapy, and beauty markets is rapidly expanding. Their use is not only encouraged, they impart substantial benefits to many sunscreen products as well. The reader is referred to the chapter written by the Aveda group (22) for an in-depth discussion of the natural ingredients that improve and boost the SPF, improve solubility of actives, impart aroma therapeutic odors, and address preservation with natural ingredients. It should also be noted here that the term "organic" should refer only to those essential oils or plant derivatives that have been grown organically and are approved by the USDA and its certified organizations.*
6. *Film formers*: A number of very powerful film formers are currently used in sunscreen products to insure water resistance, make them sweat proof, and provide rub-off resiliency. Excellent waterproofing ingredients exist today including the PVP/eicosene copolymer, the octadecene/MA copolymer, and the acrylate copolymers.
7. *Other ingredients for emulsions*: Most of these ingredients are generally not listed under the category of active ingredients. Their presence of course is mainly cosmetic to impart elegance, feel, and functionality, yet their effect on the sunscreen's efficacy may be quite significant. Many studies have demonstrated the effect of emollients in boosting SPF (23). Thickeners, humectants, and emulsifiers have a major effect on the spreading ability of the product on the skin, affecting the thickness of the layer of sunscreen on the skin and its functionality

---

*(a) International Federation for Organic Agriculture Movements (IFOAM), Bundestraus, Gorresstrasse 15, 53113 Bonn, Germany; (b) Organic Farming Research Foundation, PO Box 440, Santa Cruz, CA 95061, USA.

(24). The proper choice of preservative is important not only for insuring safety, microbial elimination, and extension of shelf life, but also for its compatibility with UV actives. For example, formaldehyde donors are not compatible with avobenzone. The reader is referred to the chapter by Klein and Palefski (25) and that by Wilmott (26) on sunscreen products without emulsifiers.

Marketing Issues

Marketing of sunscreen products and skin care products with UV filters poses a serious challenge, considering the rapid advancements in technology, formulations, ingredients, regulations, and information on the causes of skin cancers and the aging process.

The current trends in the marketing of sunscreen products include a shift from tanning to protection, from seasonal products to year-round products, and from beach wear to daily wear. Specific growth trends include products with high SPF, sunless tanning, products for children and kids, products with new biologically active ingredients, and natural ingredients in sunscreen products (27).

SUNSCREEN PRODUCTS FOR THE 21ST CENTURY

The products for sunscreen, lip care, or antiaging that contain UV filters are closely governed by the Final Rule of the FDA in the USA, COLIPA in Europe, and specific country regulations. In the USA and Australia, these products are OTC drugs, whereas in Europe and Japan, they are considered cosmetics. Methods of testing the efficacy of these products have become almost standardized worldwide despite the differences in the protocols between the US FDA and the European COLIPA methods. The UV-A testing procedure, however, is still not finalized in the USA, but in the UK they seem to be content with the Boots star rating system. The challenges of marketing a single product that is sold worldwide still remain due to the slightly differing regulations, most notably on the ultraviolet actives and the testing procedures.

In the last three decades, our knowledge of the chemistry of UV filters and formulations has improved dramatically, enabling the cosmetic chemists to formulate unique and effective sunscreen products. A review of the most important ingredients in the formulation of sunscreen products reveals the areas where we can expect to witness alternative approaches for producing and marketing new and improved products for the 21st century.

UV Filters

Despite the fact that in the USA we only have 16 approved UV filters, several have been recently introduced and improved. The introduction of both zinc oxide and avobenzone has addressed this seriously deficient UV-A protection area. The new micronized forms of both zinc oxide and titanium dioxide, along with the many types of coatings and predispersions, have had a major impact on improving UV-A protection in particular and making more natural claims in some protection products. The photostability of a few of the ingredients, most notably avobenzone, has been significantly improved with well-designed cosmetic formulations and the use of new additives and other quenching ingredients.

The fact still remains that in the USA the process of pursuing an NDA is extremely tedious, time-consuming, and prohibitively costly. The new FDA's TEA establishes criteria and procedures by which OTC conditions may become eligible for consideration on the OTC drug monograph system and that speed up the process of adopting new ingredients or filters approved for use in Europe or other countries. Already three UV filters (amiloxate, enzacmene, and octyl triazone) that have been extensively used in Europe have been considered for approval under this TEA application process. Approval of these three new UV filters in the USA is imminent.

The regulations for approving new UV filters in Europe and Australia are far more progressive than those found in the USA. Recently, a number of new UV filters that address both UV-A and UV-B protection have been introduced in Europe. Among them are filters based on the following chemistry: terphthalidene dicamphor, benzotriazole, phenyl dibenzimidazole, and hydroxy phenyl triazine. The design of many of these new filters has taken on a novel approach for designing more efficient UV-A and broad-spectrum filters while overcoming some of the safety issues such as a few UV filters of low molecular weight (originally designed for maximum solubility in cosmetic formulations) having the tendency to be absorbed in the skin. These new molecules have multiple chromophores with high molecular weight exceeding 500 Da and are thus delivered in cosmetic formulations as insoluble organic particulates, analogous to the delivery of the inorganic particulates of today.

Natural Ingredients

The FDA currently does not recognize natural ingredients and plant extracts possessing UV filtering properties as Category I sunscreen ingredients. Today we can demonstrate that a number of highly effective sunscreen products can be formulated with predominantly natural ingredients, with or without the inorganic particulates. There is a major green movement sweeping the country, hence the need for cosmetic products that are formulated predominantly with natural, organically grown plant ingredients from sustainable and renewable resources. The FDA should take note of this development in view of the fact that the Monograph had been almost finalized in the late 1970s of the last century when the natural and green movement was not yet in bloom. Currently available ingredients that qualify to yield SPF protection and boost existing SPF formulations include extracts of galanga, green coffee, licorice, oat, annatto, and many more natural actives that improve the solubility of UV filters, naturally preserve the formulations, and improve the feel and elegance of natural cosmetics.

Biologically Active Ingredients

Sunscreen products for the 21st century should not only address protection from sunburn, erythema, and redness, but also provide protection from the cellular damage that is causing alarmingly increasing rates of skin carcinomas and melanomas. Today there exist a number of ingredients and protocols, albeit experimental and requiring substantial research, that address a multitude of cellular damage issues, including DNA damage by UV-A, photoaging, immunocompromised skin, free radical generation in the skin, and inflammatory cellular reactions. Their use in daily regimens against the long-term damage of the sun to the skin is crucial.

Cosmetic Formulations

The ingenious cosmetic chemist has to make do with an extremely limited number of approved UV filters. Despite the fact that 21 ingredients were originally permitted, in reality, only eight of them were adequate or available for use. Yet the cosmetic chemist was called upon to produce diverse products that address a number of protection issues, cosmetic elegance, new vehicles, superior performance, higher-SPF products targeted to new sectors of consumers, such as babies, children, teens, sport-oriented individuals, or those seeking self tanners or tanning accelerators. Commercially, the work and the knowledge gained during the last 30 years can be demonstrated by the almost annual double-digit growth of sunscreen, tanning, antiaging, and lip care products. Unfortunately, skin cancer rates continue to rise, and even though this cannot be blamed on the lack of ingenuity or poor cosmetic formulations, it nevertheless begs the issue of relaxing the current regulations to allow for the introduction of new and improved ingredients and sunscreen cosmetic products. The cosmetic chemist in the USA in most of the last century had to make do with only two UV-A filters, namely, oxybenzone (benzophenone-3) and meradimate, both woefully inadequate for efficient UV-A protection. A third ingredient, titanium dioxide, yielded mostly opaque products and has been used predominantly by lifeguards, skiers, mountain climbers, and when brightly colored, for novelty and children's products. Toward the end of the last century several improvements occurred, most notably the introduction of micronized forms of titanium dioxide and zinc oxide (approved in 1998) allowing for more elegant cosmetics that offer clear, nonopaque formulations. Also, Parsol 1789 (avobenzone) was approved in 1996 (it was available since the 1980s exclusively with an NDA approval to Herbert Labs and an amended NDA in the 1990s to Schering-Plough only). Problems of avobenzone with its photoinstability may be partially resolved with quenchers and emollients. More importantly, information regarding the chemistry of the ultraviolet filters, cosmetic formulations, and interactions was widely disseminated since the 1980s, which allowed for more efficient formulations maximizing its SPF potential by the proper selection of emollients, emulsifiers, thickeners, solvents, and other additives (28). The effect of these "other ingredients" on the SPF, and hence the performance of the sunscreen product, was dramatic. Products emerged with SPF labels exceeding 30, utilizing fewer UV filters than their lower SPF counterparts of the 1970s and 1980s. New vehicles (mousse, sprays, gels, towelettes, etc.), new types of emulsions (O/W, W/O, and emulsions that reverse phases), improved thickeners, emollients, emulsifiers, film formers, preservatives, and functional botanical ingredients have all emerged improving the performance and attributes of future sunscreen products.

The issue of new ingredients requiring approval also plagues the sunless tanning and tanning accelerator industry despite the fact that this category is the fastest growing sector in the recreational sunscreen industry. Consumers fearing exposure to sunlight are using tanning accelerators to artificially color their skin and give it the perceived healthy glow. The only approved artificial tanner today is DHA. Ingredients that are safe for developing and stimulating natural melanin or color need to be approved and adopted in the near future to cater to this growing segment of the population.

CONCLUSIONS

The cosmetic industry and dermatologists face major challenges in the future to educate the public about the dangers of excessive exposure to sunlight and to formulate new strategies to address the spiraling incidence of skin cancer and signs of premature aging of the skin (Dan Rather, who normally delivers the news on television, became the news when he dramatically announced to his viewers recently that he is being treated for basal cell carcinoma). Foremost in those strategies would be to formulate safer yet more effective products that reduce significantly the dangers of overexposure to harmful UV radiation.

International regulations need to be eased and harmonized allowing for a single standard worldwide to permit the speedier introduction of new and improved ultraviolet filters and sunscreen products worldwide.

The academic community should actively participate in this domain and form partnerships with dermatologists and sunscreen manufacturers to research the underlying causes of skin cancer from a cellular and molecular biology perspective, unearth markers for early detection, and ultimately assist marketers in producing superior, more natural sunscreen products. New formulations should contain ingredients to address both the direct damage to the skin from sunlight (DNA dimer formation and [6-4]photoproduct formation) and the indirect damage resulting from reactive oxygen species and free radicals.

Analytical and instrumentation scientists are encouraged to develop newer and more advanced techniques for early diagnosis and for more reliable methods of SPF, UV-A, and water resistance testing. The new techniques of photochemistry that are based on the remarkable work of the 1999 Nobel Prize laureate in femtochemistry, Dr. Ahmed Zewail, are now being applied by many scientists for insights into the photostability of DNA and other UV filters.

The botanist working closely with organic chemists should actively research old remedies and new botanical sources for natural sunscreen protection and eventually create better UV filters and other natural ingredients leading to superior sunscreen products.

Ultimately, it is the responsibility of the marketers, the press and the specialized organizations and professional societies to better communicate to the consumer both the dangers of the damaging rays of the sun and the anticipated new discoveries leading to better products and protection. With millions of new cases of skin cancer reported each year due to the excessive exposure to sunlight, we can ill afford to sit idly by while the quality of our lives and its very existence is threatened.

REFERENCES

1. Manniche L. Egyptian Luxuries: Fragrance, Aromatherapy, and Cosmetics in Pharaonic Times. Cairo: The American University in Cairo Press, 1999.
2. Shaath M, Shaath N. Ancient Egyptian Cosmetics, Toiletries and Essential Oils, IFSCC 23rd Congress, Paper 7, Orlando, Florida, 2004.
3. Boulos L. Flora of Egypt. Vols. 1 & 2. Egypt: Al Hadra Publishing, 2000.
4. Patini G. Perfluoropolyethers in sunscreens. Drug Cosmet Ind 1988; 143:42.
5. Groves G. The sunscreen industry in Australia: past, present, and future. In: Lowe NJ, Shaath NA, Pathak MA, eds. Sunscreens: Development, Evaluation, and Regulatory Aspects. 2nd ed. New York: Marcel Dekker, 1997:Chap 12.
6. Safer and More Successful Suntanning. Consumer Guide. New York: Wallaby Pocketbooks, 1979.
7. Kumler W. Action of sunscreen compounds. Perfumer Essential Oil Rev 1952; 12:427.
8. Giacomoni PU. Sunprotection: historical perspective. In: Shaath NA, ed. Sunscreens: Regulations and Commercial Development. 3rd ed. New York: Marcel Dekker, 2005:71–81.
9. Nelson CG, Jr. Photoprotection. In: Shaath NA, ed. Sunscreens: Regulations and Commercial Development. 3rd ed. New York: Marcel Dekker, 2005:19–43.
10. Shaath NA. The chemistry of ultraviolet filters. In: Shaath NA, ed. Sunscreens: Regulations and Commercial Development. 3rd ed. New York: Marcel Dekker, 2005:217–238.
11. Hatch KL. Fabrics as UV radiation filters. In: Shaath NA, ed. Sunscreens: Regulations and Commercial Development. 3rd ed. New York: Marcel Dekker, 2005:557–572.
12. Steinberg DC. Regulations of sunscreens worldwide. In: Shaath NA, ed. Sunscreens: Regulations and Commercial Development. 3rd ed. New York: Marcel Dekker, 2005:173–198.
13. Federal Register. 27666 (May 21, 1999).
14. Bonda CA. The photostability of organic sunscreen. In: Shaath NA, ed. Sunscreens: Regulations and Commercial Development. 3rd ed. New York: Marcel Dekker, 2005:321–349.

15. Schwen RJ. Safety considerations for sunscreens in the USA. In: Shaath NA, ed. Sunscreens: Regulations and Commercial Development. 3rd ed. New York: Marcel Dekker, 2005:55–69.
16. Meadows T. The manufacture of suncare products. In: Shaath NA, ed. Sunscreens: Regulations and Commercial Development. 3rd ed. New York: Marcel Dekker, 2005:699–718.
17. Schlossman D, Shao Y. Inorganic ultraviolet filters. In: Shaath NA, ed. Sunscreens: Regulations and Commercial Development. 3rd ed. New York: Marcel Dekker, 2005:239–279.
18. Shaath NA, Walele II. Inorganic particulate ultraviolet filters filters in commerce. In: Shaath NA, ed. Sunscreens: Regulations and Commercial Development. 3rd ed. New York: Marcel Dekker, 2005:281–290.
19. Herzog B, Hueglin D, Osterwalder U. New sunscreen actives. In: Shaath NA, ed. Sunscreens: Regulations and Commercial Development. 3rd ed. New York: Marcel Dekker, 2005:291–320.
20. Gonzalez AD, Kalafsky RE. Sunless tanning and tanning accelerators. In: Shaath NA, ed. Sunscreens: Regulations and Commercial Development. 3rd ed. New York: Marcel Dekker, 2005:573–599.
21. Lintner K. Antiaging actives in sunscreens. In: Shaath NA, ed. Sunscreens: Regulations and Commercial Development. 3rd ed. New York: Marcel Dekker, 2005:673–695.
22. Kapsner T, Matravers P, Shiozawa K, Peterson P. Formulating natural sun care products. In: Shaath NA, ed. Sunscreens: Regulations and Commercial Development. 3rd ed. New York: Marcel Dekker, 2005:507–521.
23. Shaath NA. On the theory of ultraviolet absorption by sunscreen chemicals. J Soc Cosmet Chem 1987; 82:193.
24. Bruening S, Leonard M, Kawa R, Issberner U, Tomlinson A. Role of emollients and emulsifiers in sunscreen formulations. In: Shaath NA, ed. Sunscreens: Regulations and Commercial Development. 3rd ed. New York: Marcel Dekker, 2005:449–460.
25. Klein K, Palefsky I. Formulating sunscreen products. In: Shaath NA, ed. Sunscreens: Regulations and Commercial Development. 3rd ed. New York: Marcel Dekker, 2005:353–383.
26. Wilmott JM. Surfactant-free sun care. In: Shaath NA, ed. Sunscreens: Regulations and Commercial Development. 3rd ed. New York: Marcel Dekker, 2005:461–491.
27. Shaath NA, Shaath M. Recent sunscreen market trends. In: Shaath NA, ed. Sunscreens: Regulations and Commercial Development. 3rd ed. New York: Marcel Dekker, 2005:929–940.
28. Shaath NA. The chemistry of sunscreens. Cosmet Toil 1986; 101:55–70.

2

Photoprotection

Christopher G. Nelson, Jr.
St. Petersburg, Florida, USA

WHY DO WE NEED PHOTOPROTECTION?

The incidence of sunlight-induced premature aging of the skin and skin cancer is increasing annually. Last year in the USA, over one million new cutaneous malignancies were diagnosed. Approximately 80% of these were basal cell carcinoma, 16% were squamous cell carcinoma, and 4% were malignant melanoma. An estimated 10,250 people died from skin cancer in 2004, of which 7910 died from malignant melanoma. This represents a 4.6% increase over 2003. In 1930, the lifetime risk of an American developing malignant melanoma was 1 in 1500; by 2004, this risk has increased to 1 in 37 (1). The most important preventive factor is protection from ultraviolet (UV) exposure. Most people sustain 80% of their lifetime damage from the sun before age 18; however, UV exposure later in life also contributes by producing cutaneous alterations that allow malignant and premalignant lesions to develop from previous damage, as well as causing damage that leads to premature aging ("photoaging") of the skin (2).

THE SOLAR SPECTRUM

Solar radiation encompasses the entire electromagnetic spectrum, including short, high-energy cosmic and gamma rays, longer lower-energy UV rays, visible light, infrared (IR) radiation, microwaves, and finally radio waves. High-energy waves ($\lambda < 10$ nm) displace electrons from molecules to form ions, and are thus considered *ionizing radiation.* UV, visible, and short IR waves lack the energy required for this process, and are classified as *nonionizing radiation.*

The UV spectrum is divided into vacuum UV ($\lambda = 10$–100 nm), UV-C ($\lambda = 100$–290 nm), UV-B ($\lambda = 290$–320 nm), and UV-A ($\lambda = 320$–400 nm). Further, UV-A is divided into UV-A1 ($\lambda = 340$–400 nm), and UV-A2 ($\lambda = 320$–340 nm).

While the solar spectrum represents a wide range of potential energies and wavelengths, nearly 30–40% of this radiation, including the most harmful portions, is absorbed in the upper layers of the earth's atmosphere by the ozone layer (3). Of the solar radiation reaching the earth, approximately 50% is visible ($\lambda = 10$–400 nm). The ozone layer eliminates virtually all UV radiation below 290 nm. Thus, vacuum UV, UV-C, and the shortest UV-B wavelengths are blocked; conversely, minimal UV-A is filtered. The UV radiation that penetrates the ozone layer and reaches the earth is ~10% UV-B and 90% UV-A at midday (solar noon). The UV-B intensity is highest at solar noon, and declines thereafter. The UV-A intensity remains relatively constant throughout the day (4).

ACUTE SOLAR DAMAGE

Introduction

When exposed to UV radiation, human skin undergoes several changes.

The first response, immediate pigment darkening (IPD), is a transient, brownish-gray coloration of the skin after exposure to UV-A. It begins within 60 s and lasts up to 30 min. Proposed mechanisms of IPD include photo-oxidation of existing melanin and changes in the distribution of epidermal melanocytes (5).

Persistent pigment darkening (PPD) is a longer lasting response of individuals with pigmented skin after exposure to UV radiation. Not only is the melanin, which is already present, further darkened, but the production of new melanin is also enhanced. PPD begins within hours and may last for days to weeks. The proposed mechanism of PPD is UV-A exposure, and while UV-B may have a role, the action spectrum for PPD is not defined for wavelengths shorter than 320 nm (6).

An erythema response may be induced by both UV-A and UV-B. The UV-A response is variable in individuals, and ranges from undetectable to marked. UV-B produces delayed erythema, which appears 3–4 h after exposure and intensifies for 12–24 h. It is often accompanied by pain, pruritus, and the formation of bullae. The minimal erythema dose (MED) is defined as the minimal dose of UV-B needed to produce barely perceptible erythema in a given individual. The 307 nm wavelength is the most efficient for producing erythema (7). The dosage of UV-A to produce erythema (20–70 J/cm^2) is 600–1000 times that required for UV-B (20–1000 mJ/cm^2). Although the intensity of UV-A at noon is typically 10 times that of UV-B, the latter is responsible for 98–99% of delayed erythema development (8).

Mechanism of Acute Photodamage

The biological effects of UV and visible radiation, both acute and long-term, are produced by the absorption of radiation by molecules called chromophores. These molecules have highly characteristic absorption spectra that are dependent upon their structures. After being irradiated, chromophores become "energized" and undergo either molecular reorganization or interaction with nearby molecules. These chemical changes cannot take place unless the specific wavelength for the chromophore is absorbed. The major chromophores of the skin include DNA, proteins, porphyrins, and urocanic acid. Other endogenous chromophores that may absorb UV radiation include NADH/NADPH, tryptophan, riboflavin, and melanin (9).

The action spectra of these chromophores may be influenced by the addition of exogenous photochemically active chromophores (e.g., 8-methoxypsoralen) or by internal entities such as medications or disease states. In fact, organic sunscreens are actually exogenous chromophores that work by attenuating erythemogenic UV radiation.

Current theories for acute photodamage emphasize the importance of DNA absorption of UV radiation. The absorption spectrum for DNA peaks at 260 nm (UV-C), but it also absorbs UV-B and to a lesser degree, UV-A. When UV radiation is absorbed, DNA forms characteristic lesions such as cyclobutane pyrimidine dimers. It has been shown that the action spectra for pyrimidine dimer formation and erythema in human skin are very similar, suggesting that DNA absorption of UV radiation is responsible for acute erythema (10).

Histology of Acute Photodamage

After acute damage by UV radiation, typical histologic changes occur including slight epidermal spongiosis, increase in nuclear diameter and nucleolar size of the keratinocytes, depletion of Langerhans cells, induction of sunburn cells, hyperkeratosis, parakeratosis, acanthosis, and migration of inflammatory cells into the exposed areas (11,12). The inflammatory infiltrate may be mediated by both lipoxygenase products and cytokines such as interleukin-1 (IL-1) (13,14), IL-3 (15), IL-6 (16), granulocyte-macrophage colony stimulating factor (17), and tumor necrosis factor alpha (TNF-α) (18).

Following UV exposure and damage, so-called sunburn cells develop. These sunburn cells are actually necrotic keratinocytes in the epidermis. They are recognized on hematoxylin and eosin staining by their round shapes, pyknotic nuclei, and shrunken glassy eosinophilic cytoplasm. Sunburn cells share many histologic features with apoptotic cells. Apoptosis is an innate programmed cell death pathway, and is important for normal development and tissue homeostasis. Apoptosis plays an important role in eliminating damaged, dysfunctional cells (19). The similarities between apoptotic cells and sunburn cells support the theory that DNA is affected by UV exposure, and also supports the speculation that sunburn cells are an indicator of photocarcinogenic potential (20,21).

CHRONIC SOLAR DAMAGE

Introduction

Chronic exposure to UV radiation accentuates and accelerates many of the changes of intrinsic aging including telangiectasia, blotchy pigmentation, and atrophy as well as loss of the elasticity of the skin. Although hypertrophy of the epidermis is a short-term effect of sun exposure, the consequence of chronic exposure is an exacerbation of age-related atrophy.

Mechanism of Chronic Damage

Tanning of the skin is a consequence of chronic UV radiation exposure, resulting in increased melanin production in melanocytes. While both UV-A and UV-B can cause erythema and tanning, UV-A is much less efficient. UV-B induces tanning by increasing the binding of circulating melanocyte stimulating hormone (MSH) to melanocytes, leading to proliferation, dendritic arborization, and pigment production. Interestingly, these changes occur not only on exposed, but to a lesser extent covered areas of the body (22). Melanin absorbs, reflects, and scatters UV radiation, in addition to functioning as a free radical trap. Melanin is produced from tyrosine through several enzymatically controlled reactions. The rate-limiting step is the conversion of tyrosine into dihydroxyphenylalanine (DOPA) by tyrosine hydroxylase. After its formation, the melanin is incorporated into organelles called melanosomes, which are distributed to surrounding keratinocytes. Some melanosomes remain intact in the keratinocytes as they migrate to become stratum corneum, and others are degraded enzymatically into an amorphous form that deposits in the intercellular spaces. It is this amorphous melanin that undergoes oxidation in the IPD reaction previously mentioned (23). Persons of all skin types have approximately the same number of melanocytes; however, more melanosomes are produced by darker-skinned people accounting for the pigmentation difference. Black-skinned persons have approximately 400 melanosomes per basal epidermal cell, about four times the number in a typical pale Caucasian. The increased number of melanosomes in black skin reduces the penetration of UV-A and UV-B by a factor of 5 and is responsible for a 30-fold increase in MED. Tanning of Caucasian skin induces an increase in melanosomes and a resultant increase in sun protection factor (SPF) between 2 and 4 units. While this increase does afford some photoprotection, the skin is still susceptible to a significant amount of UV radiation induced damage. It is significant that UV-A at high doses (e.g., tanning salons) can produce erythema and melanogenesis, but does not provide the same degree of protection as a naturally acquired UV-B sun tan. The increased melanogenesis induced by UV-A occurs primarily in the basal cell layer without distribution of the melanosomes throughout the entire epidermis as occurs with UV-B. There is therefore no associated SPF increase.

Chronic UV-B exposure causes stratum corneum hypertrophy; it can increase up to six times its original thickness by increased synthesis of basal keratinocytes. The stratum corneum is naturally hypertrophied on the palmar and plantar surfaces, explaining their relative resistance to sun damage. Thickened stratum corneum absorbs or reflects 90–95% of incident UV-B, greatly decreasing the amount that reaches the basal keratinocytes, melanocytes, and superficial dermis (24). It is interesting to note that chronic UV-A exposure does not cause thickening of the stratum corneum, further contributing to the lack of photoprotection offered by a UV-A tan.

Histology of Chronic Damage

Late histologic changes caused by UV radiation include the typical changes of photoaging. Staining with hematoxylin and eosin demonstrates hypertrophy of the stratum corneum and atrophy of the epidermis. The upper dermis displays basophilic degeneration of the dermal collagen, which is separated from the epidermis by a thin band of normal collagen. Within the areas of basophilic degeneration, the bundles of eosinophilic collagen are replaced by amorphous basophilic granular material. With elastic tissue stains, the areas of basophilic degeneration stain like elastic tissue. This elastotic material usually consists of aggregates of thick, interwoven bands in the upper dermis. In severe solar degeneration, the elastotic material becomes more amorphous and may extend into the deeper dermis (25). Damage to the dermal extracellular matrix proteins results in deterioration of the tensile strength of the skin. The exact mechanism of these changes to the collagen and elastic tissue remains elusive, and the exact wavelengths and the respective action spectra for these changes remain to be determined.

OTHER EFFECTS OF PHOTOEXPOSURE

Photosensitive Reaction

A photosensitive reaction is a chemically induced alteration in the skin that makes an individual more sensitive to UV radiation. Following absorption of a specific wavelength, an oral, ingested or topical agent may be chemically altered to produce a reaction ranging from macules and papules, vesicles and bullae, edema, urticaria, to an acute eczematous reaction (26). The two main types of photosensitive reactions are photoxic and photoallergic. Agents that can cause photosensitivity are listed in Table 2.1.

Table 2.1 Agents that may Cause Photosensitivity

- Anticancer drugs
  - Dacarbazine (DTIC-Dome)
  - Fluorouracil (Fluoroplex; and others)
  - Methotrexate (Mexate; and others)
  - Procarbazine (Matulane)
  - Vinblastine (Velban)
- Antidepressants
  - Amitriptyline (Elavil; and others)
  - Amoxapine (Asendin)
  - Desipramine (Norpramin: Pertofrane)
  - Doxepin (Adapin; Sinequan)
  - Imipramine (Tofranil; and others)
  - Isocarboxazid (Marplan)
  - Maprotiline (Ludiomil)
  - Nortriptyline (Aventyl; Pamelor)
  - Protrityline (vivactil)
  - Trimipramine (Smontil)
- Antihistamines
  - Cyproheptadine (Periactin)
  - Diphenhydramine (Benadryl; and others)
- Antimicrobials
  - Antifungals (Fentichlor, Multifungin, Jadit)
  - Demeclocycline (Declomycin; and others)
  - Doxycycline (Vibramycin; and others)
  - Griseofulvin (Fulvicin-UF; and others)
  - Methacycline (Rondomycin)
  - Minocycline (Minocin)
  - Nalidxic acid (NegGram)
  - Oxytetracycline (Terramycin; and others)
  - Sulfacytine (Renoquid)
  - Sulfadoxine-pyrimethamine (Fansidar)
  - Sulfaguanidine
  - Sulfamethazine (Neotrizine; and others)
  - Sulfanilamide
  - Sulfapyridine
  - Sulfasalazine
  - Sulfathiazole
  - Sulfisoxazole (Gantrisin; and others)
  - Tetracycline (Achromycin; and others)
- Antiparasitic drugs
  - Bithionol (Bitrin)
  - Chloroquine (Aralen)
  - Hydroxychloroquine
  - Pyrvinium pamoate (Povan)
  - Quinine
  - Oxybenzone
  - PABA esters
  - *p*-Aminobenzoic acid
- Others
  - Amiodarone (Cordarone)
  - Bergamot oil, oils of citron, lavender, lime, sandalwood, cedar (used in many perfumes and cosmetics; also topical exposure to citrus rind oils)
  - Benzocaine
  - Captopril (Capoten)
  - Carbamazepine (Tegretol)
  - Chloradiazepoxide (Librium)
  - Coal tar and derivatives (containing acridine, anthracene, naphthalene, phenanthrene phenols, thiophene)
  - Contraceptives, oral (Norethynodrel)
  - Cyclamates (calcium cyclamate, sodium cyclohexylsulfamate)
- Antipsychotic drugs
  - Chlorpromazaine (Thorazine; and others)
  - Chlorprothixine (Taractan)
  - Fluphenazine (Pernitil: Prolixin)
  - Haloperidol (Haldol)
  - Perphenazine (Trilafon)
  - Sulfamethizole (Thiosulfil; and others)
  - Sulfamethoxazole (Gantanol; and others)
  - Sulfamethoxazole–trimethoprim (Bactrim, Septra; and others)
  - Thiothixene (Navane)
  - Trifluoperazine (Stelazine; and others)

(*continued*)

Table 2.1 *Continued*

- Triflupromazine (Vesprin)
- Trimeprazine (Temaril)

Diuretics
- Acetazolamide (Diamox)
- Amiloride (Midamor)
- Bendroflumethiazide (Naturetin; and others)
- Benzthiazide (Exna; and others)
- Chlorothiazide (Diuril; and others)
- Cyclothiazide (Anhydron)
- Furosemide (Lasix)
- Hydrochlorothiazide (HydroDIURIL; and others)
- Hydroflumethiazide (Diucardin; and others)
- Methyclothiazide (Aquatensen; Enduron)
- Metolazone (Diulo; Zaroxolyn)
- Polythiazide (Renese)
- Quinethazone (Hydromox)
- Trichlormethiazide (Methahydrin; and others)

Hypoglycemics
- Acetohexamide (Dymelor)
- Chlorpropamide (Diabinese; Insulase)
- Glipizide (Glucotrol)
- Glyburide (DiaBeta; Micronase)
- Tolzamide (Tolinase)
- Tolbutamide (Orinase; and others)

Nonsteroidal anti-inflammatory drugs
- Benoxaprofen (Oraflex)
- Ketoprofen (Orudis)
- Piperacetazine (Quide)
- Prochlorperazine (Compazine; and others)
- Promethazine (Phenegran; and others)
- Thioridazine (Mellaril)
- Naproxen (Naprosyn)
- Phenylbutazone (Butazolidin; and others)
- Piroxicam (Feldene)
- Sulindac (Clinoril)

Sunscreens
- 6-Acetoxy-2,4-dimethyl-*m*-dioxane (preservative in sunscreens)
- Benzophenones
- Cinnamates
- Diethystilbestrol
- Disopyramide (Norpace)
- Dyes (acridine, acriflavine, anthraquinone, eosin, erythrocine, fluorescein, methylene blue, methyl violet, orange red, rose bengal, toluidine blue, trypaflavin, trypan blue)
- Furocoumarins: psoralens (trioxsalen, methoxsalen, psoralen)
- Gold salts (Myochrysine; Solganal)
- Hexachloraphene (pHisoHex; and others)
- Isotretinoin (Accutane)
- 6-Methylcourmarin (used in perfumes, shaving lotions, and sunscreens)
- Mestranol
- Musk ambrette (used in perfumes)
- Quinidine sulfate and gluconate
- Saccharine
- Tattoo dye (red or yellow cadmium sulfide)

Phototoxicity

Phototoxic reactions are the most common type of drug-induced photosensitivity. They resemble an exaggerated sunburn and occur within 5–20 h after the skin has been exposed to a photosensitizing substance (either topically or systemically) and sufficient quantities of UV radiation of the proper wavelength. This is not a form of allergy, and no prior sensitization is necessary. Theoretically, this type of reaction can occur in anyone exposed to sufficient quantities of the offending agent and light; the reaction is dose dependent for both. Phototoxic reactions are commonly caused by UV-A. These reactions may also cause onycholysis (separation of the nail from the nail bed), as the nail bed is particularly susceptible due to a lack of melanin protection (26). Many plants elaborate photoactive substances (e.g., furocoumarins) that can induce phototoxic reactions. These are listed in Table 2.2.

Photoallergy

Photoallergic reactions are mediated by an interaction of drug, light, and the immune system. This is a less common form of drug-induced photosensitivity, and is often caused by UV-B. Photoallergic reactions, unlike phototoxic reactions, represent an immunologic reaction and require a latent period of 24–48 h during which sensitization occurs. They are not dose related (26). If the photosensitizer acts internally, it is called a photodrug reaction; if it acts externally, it is a photocontact dermatitis. The clinical manifestations include pruritus and an erythematous, often papulosquamous, eruption on exposed areas of the skin.

PHOTOSENSITIVITY SKIN DISORDERS

There are several specific skin disorders which are triggered or exacerbated by UV radiation; each has a specific triggering action spectrum, listed below in parenthesis.

Lupus Erythematosus (290–330 nm)

Lupus erythematosus may be exclusively confined to the skin without systemic involvement, as in discoid lupus erythematosus. Systemic lupus may also produce cutaneous manifestations. The clinical findings of both are more prominent on sun exposed skin. Although the action spectrum appears to be predominantly UV-B, UV-A has also been shown to have a role in some individuals (27).

Xeroderma Pigmentosum (290–340 nm)

Xeroderma pigmentosum is an autosomal recessive disorder characterized by a genetic defect in the ability to repair UV radiation induced DNA damage. This reduced ability for DNA repair results in a high incidence of mutations, leading to premature development of nonmelanoma skin cancer as well as malignant melanoma. Typical changes of photodamage also occur, and appear much earlier in life than in unaffected individuals.

Chronic Actinic Dermatitis (290–360 nm)

Chronic actinic dermatitis is seen in older, mostly male patients and presents as erythematous macules and plaques on sun exposed areas. These areas can evolve into lichenified, hypertrophic lesions known as actinic reticuloid.

Table 2.2 Common Plants and Lichens Causing Photodermatitis

Common name	Botanical name	Family
Lime	*Citrus aurantifolia*	Rutaceae
Citron	*Citrus medica* (*C. acida*)	Rutaceae
Bitter orange	*Citrus aurantium*	Rutaceae
Lemon	*Citrus limon*	Rutaceae
Bergamot	*Citrus bergamia*	Rutaceae
Gas plant; burning bush	*Dictamnus albus* (*D. fraxinella*)	Rutaceae
Common rue	*Ruta graveolens*	Rutaceae
Persian lime (Tahitian)	*Citrus aurantifolio*, "Persian" *Phebalium argenteum*	Rutaceae
Cow parsley, wild chervil	*Anthriscus sylvestris*	Umbelliferae
Celery	*Apium graveolens*	Umbelliferae
Giant hogweed	*Heracleum mantegazzianum*	Umbelliferae
Parsnip (garden variety)	*Pastinaca sative* (*P urens*)	Umbelliferae
Cow parsley	*Heracleum sphondylium*	Umbelliferae
Parsnip (wild parsnip)	*Heracleum giganteum*	Umbelliferae
Fennel	*Foeniculum vulgare*	Umbelliferae
Dill	*Anethum graveolens*	Umbelliferae
	Peucedanum ostruthium	Umbelliferae
Wild carrot, garden carrot	*Daucus carota*	Umbelliferae
Masterwort	*Peucedaum ostruthium*	Umbelliferae
	Ammin majus	Umbelliferae
Angelica	*Angelica archangelica*	Umbelliferae
Figs	*Ficus carcia*	Umbelliferae
Milfoil, yarrow	*Achillea millefolium*	Composiate
Stinking mayweed	*Anthemis cotula*	Composiate
Buttercup	*Ranunculus* spp.	Ranunculaceae
Mustard	*Brassica* spp.	Cruciferae
Bind weed	*Convolvulus arvensis*	Convolvulaceae
Agrimony	*Agrimonia eupatoria*	Rosaceae
Goose foot	*Chenopodium* spp.	Cheopodiaceae
Scurfy pea, bavchi	*Psoralea corylifolia*	Leguminosae
St. John's wort	*Hypericum perforatum*	Hypericaceae
	Hypericum crispum	Hypericaceae
	Schinopsis quebrachocolorado	
Red quebracho	*Schinopsia lorentzii*	Anacardiaceae
Lichens	*Parmelia* spp. *Hypogymnia* spp. *Pseudovernia* spp. *Cladonia* spp. *Platismatia* spp. *Physcia* spp. *Umbilicaria* spp. *Cetrania* spp.	Lichen (symbiotic association between fungi and algae) commonly grouped with fungi

Polymorphous Light Eruption (290–365 nm)

Polymorphous light eruption is a common eruption that affects 10–14% of the Caucasian population, with a female predominance. Pruritic papules, macules, vesicles, plaques, and erythema are produced within 2 h to 5 days after sun exposure on unprotected skin.

Hydroa Vacciniforme (290–400 nm)

Hydroa vacciniforme usually starts in the first decade, and has equal sex distribution (28). After exposure to UV-A, a tingling sensation on exposed areas is followed by the development of papules and bullae, which crust and heal with vacciniforme scars. The condition tends to improve with adolescence.

Persistent Light Reaction (290–400 nm)

Most patients who develop a photosensitive dermatitis clear when the offending agent is withdrawn. The subset of persistent light reactors continue to react for months or even indefinitely following UV radiation exposure. The effective mechanism is unknown and may be varied. The persistent nature of the reaction could possibly be due to unknown constant exposure to an offending agent, irrevocable binding of the allergen to dermal protein, or idiopathic.

Solar Urticaria (290–515 nm)

Solar urticaria is a rare disease in which urticaria develops rapidly after exposure to UV radiation. The reaction begins with pruritus within minutes of exposure followed by erythema and urticaria, and usually runs its course in $<$24 h.

Porphyrias (400–410 nm)

Porphyrias are a group of diseases that are caused by inherited or acquired abnormalities in the heme metabolic pathway. Photosensitivity manifests as vesicles, bullae and hypopigmentation, as well as fragility and scarring of the skin. Manifestations are variable depending on the type of porphyria.

Miscellaneous Dermatoses

In addition to xeroderma pigmentosum, other genodermatoses may have photosensitivity, including Bloom's syndrome, Cockayne's syndrome, and Rothman–Thomson syndrome.

Many other dermatoses may be aggravated by UV radiation exposure, including bullous pemphigoid, chronic benign familial pemphigus (Hailey–Hailey disease), cutaneous lymphocytoma, Darier's disease, dermatomyositis, disseminated superficial actinic porokeratosis, erythema multiforme, herpes simplex, Jessner's lymphocytic infiltrate, lichen planus, pellagra, pemphigus, and transient acantholytic dermatosis (Grover's disease).

CARCINOGENESIS RELATED TO PHOTOEXPOSURE

Mechanism of Carcinogenesis

Carcinogenesis due to photoexposure can occur following acute or chronic UV radiation exposure. Carcinogenesis is broadly considered to have three main stages: initiation, promotion, and progression.

Initiation of carcinogenesis likely occurs at a young age in most patients, as 80% of an individual's total lifetime damage is acquired before age 18. Initiation is thought to be caused by DNA absorbing UV radiation, subsequently inducing changes between adjacent pyrimidine bases on one strand of DNA. Cyclopyrimidine dimers, particularly thymine dimers or less commonly, (6-4)-photoproducts may be generated (29). The action spectrum for these changes is maximal at 260 nm (UV-C), although it extends through the UV-B and into the UV-A wavelengths (30,31). These DNA changes are constantly being repaired by nucleotide excision (32). Whenever repair is incomplete, characteristic mutations persist, and if the damage to the genome is great, p53 and its associated proteins will induce apoptosis of the irradiated keratinocyte. If the UV-induced mutations occur in the region containing p53, genomic replication control may be lost. Clonal expansion of these defective keratinocytes may produce an actinic keratosis (33). If the second p53 allele is also mutated, a squamous cell carcinoma may arise. Finally, if the mutations occur in *patched* or other members of the hedgehog signaling pathway, basal cell carcinoma may occur (34,35).

Promotion of carcinogenesis is thought to be mediated by further UV radiation absorption by chromophores. This may lead to the release of reactive oxygen species, singlet oxygen, hydrogen peroxide, and superoxide ion. These reactive species may cause oxidation of lipids and proteins that in turn may affect DNA repair, induce matrix metalloproteinase, produce dyspigmentation, and result in skin aging and carcinogenesis (36). When compared with UV-B, UV-A generates more oxidative stress (37), and is 10 times more efficient than UV-B at causing lipid peroxidation (38). UV-A is more cytotoxic than UV-B (39); it damages DNA by causing strand breaks and oxidation of nucleic acids (39,40). UV-A can inhibit DNA repair (41) and induce matrix metalloproteinase (MMP) synthesis (42), which augments the biologic aggressiveness of skin cancer. UV-B also has an important role in tumor promotion. Following UV-B exposure, fewer T helper-1 (T_H-1), the cell-mediated immunity effector cells, are activated and relatively greater numbers of T helper-2 (T_H-2), the humoral immunity or antibody-producing cells, are generated. This shifts the balance to relative suppression of cell-mediated immunity, resulting in decreased fighting of tumors, viruses, and bacteria. In addition, UV-B radiation interferes with the presentation of antigen by Langerhans cells to T_H-1 cells, but not to T_H-2 cells. Furthermore, there is evidence that suppressor T cells activated by UV-B cause the death of Langerhans cells (43). Signal transduction pathways are activated and synthesis of cyclooxygenase-2 leads to production of prostaglandin E-2 (PGE-2). This produces inflammation, cellular proliferation, and further immunosuppression. Ornithine decarboxylase, the enzyme which downregulates the rate-limiting step in the polyamine biosynthetic pathway, is activated by exposure to UV radiation. Because polyamines regulate cellular proliferation, this allows unregulated cellular proliferation to occur. Thus, UV radiation has a dual role in the pathogenesis of nonmelanoma skin cancer. It not only produces mutations in skin cells, but it facilitates the growth of neoplastic cells by impairing tumor immune surveillance and allowing uncontrolled proliferation of cells.

Finally, in the progression of the premalignant cells to malignancy, additional genetic changes occur, as well as alterations in transforming growth factor beta (TGF-β). UV radiation depletes resident Langerhans cells, which are replaced by macrophages. These macrophages, in turn, preferentially activate T suppressor cells and appear to be responsible for long-term immunosuppression (44). UV-A also generates singlet oxygen, which triggers a cascade including transcription factors AP-1, AP-2, and NFκB. The AP-1 binding couplet contains c-*fos* and c-*jun*, which activates matrix metalloproteinases that are capable of destroying the connective tissue of the skin (45).

Opportunities to Interrupt the Pathway

Now that more of the mechanisms of photocarcinogenesis and photoaging have been elucidated, numerous opportunities to interrupt these pathways are being explored.

Initiation

The initiation stage of carcinogenesis is most effectively interrupted by protecting DNA from UV radiation induced damage. However, small amounts of UV radiation exposure are unavoidable, and even high-SPF sunscreens allow some UV radiation penetration. Additionally, our DNA repair systems cannot be perfect, and some mutant cells inevitably occur. The model for enzymatic repair augmentation has been the easily sunburning, rapidly aging, and cancer prone DNA repair-defective disorder xeroderma pigmentosum. Recently, a topical liposome-encapsulated DNA repair enzyme preparation, T4 endonuclease V, has been reported to dramatically reduce cutaneous malignancy in XP, apparently without adverse effect (46), giving hope for augmenting the repair process by applying a topical agent.

Promotion

Antioxidant therapy has been studied as a possible mechanism to modulate tumor promotion. The skin relies on naturally occurring antioxidants to protect it from oxidative stress generated by sunlight and pollution (47); these antioxidants are both enzymatic and nonenzymatic and react in an interwoven complex harmony. Normal molecular weight nonenzymatic antioxidants include L-ascorbic acid in the fluid phase, glutathione in the cellular compartment, vitamin E in membranes, and ubiquinol in mitochondria (48). Enzymatic antioxidants function predominately in cells. Glutathione peroxidase and glutathione reductase reduce hydrogen peroxide and are important antioxidants in peroxisomes. Copper–zinc superoxide dismutase and manganese superoxide dismutase protect cells from superoxide; additionally, extracellular superoxide dismutase protects the extracellular space from superoxide anion (48). A combination of antioxidants is much more effective than the sum of separate compounds. This synergism is the result of the intricate connections between the antioxidants themselves. If only one of the components is supported, another will soon become the limiting factor. Too much of a single component could even deplete some of the others, resulting in an overall negative effect. This is the case, for example, for high levels of α-tocopherol, which can deplete glutathione and ascorbate, or a large superoxide dismutase increase, which can result in elevated levels of hydrogen peroxide. Providing several different key antioxidants could enhance the complete mechanism (49). Another example is ascorbate, which at high concentrations can act as a pro-oxidant, however, this activity is dependent on the availability of free metal ions, of which the cellular concentration is frequently low (49). In a guinea pig model the iron chelator, 2-furildioxime, in combination with a traditional sunscreen showed a significant increase in SPF, from SPF 4 to SPF 30 when used in a 5% concentration (50). It is also known that α-tocopherol can cause problems due to photoinstability. Its absorption spectrum extends well into the UV range (295 nm) and when skin with a high level of α-tocopherol is irradiated, large numbers of tocopheroxyl radicals are formed that induce lipid peroxidation themselves and deplete other antioxidants, especially glutathione and vitamin C (49). Protective effects against sunburn have been reported for combinations of systemic ascorbic acid (vitamin C) and D-α-tocopherol (vitamin E) (51); topical or oral administration of an extract of *Polypodium leucotomos*, a fern which grows exclusively in the jungles of Honduras, not only prevented sunburn, but also prevented depletion of Langerhans cells (52). Topical green tea polyphenols are effective in preventing sunburn, Langerhans cell depletion and DNA damage (53). Isoflavone genistein (soy) has been shown to inhibit UV-B-induced erythema and inhibited chemical carcinogen-induced reactive oxygen species, oxidative DNA damage, proto-oncogene expression, as well as the initiation and promotion of skin carcinogenesis (54,55).

Another strategy for blocking the promotion stage of carcinogenesis is blocking specific enzymes. Cyclooxygenase-2 is known to increase the production of PGE-2, which leads to cellular proliferation and inflammation (56). Cyclooxygenase can be blocked by nonsteroidal anti-inflammatory drugs (NSAIDs). Diclofenac, one such agent, is available as a topical prescription, approved by the US Food and Drug Administration (FDA) for the treatment of actinic keratoses. As previously noted, ornithine decarboxylase downregulates the rate limiting step in the polyamine biosynthetic pathway; polyamines function to regulate cellular proliferation. Thus, when UV radiation activates ornithine decarboxylase the result is increased cellular proliferation (57).

Ornithine decarboxylase can be blocked by various agents including eflornithine, which is already an FDA approved topical for stopping growth of unwanted hair. This agent also shows promise for treatment of actinic keratoses. Further UV exposure during the promotion stage causes acceleration of all these processes, and thus it is important to block UV radiation during this stage.

Progression

Finally, in the progression stage of carcinogenesis, UV radiation exposure causes additional genetic changes, alternations in TGF-β, and further immunosuppression. Langerhans cell depletion has been shown to be blocked by several antioxidants, as previously noted. The cascade that is set off by singlet oxygen and results in increased matrix metalloproteinases can be partly blocked by retinoic acid (58) and antioxidants (59). Blocking UV radiation exposure during the progression stage is also critical.

IMMUNOPATHOLOGY OF SKIN CANCER—AN APPARENT PARADOX

Most UV-induced skin cancers are highly immunogenic and stimulate a vigorous inflammatory response. In spite of this, they are extremely successful at evading host tumor immunosurveillance mechanisms. In experimental animal models, skin cancers induced by UV-B grow rapidly and eventually kill the host. When these same tumors are implanted into genetically identical mice that have not been exposed to UV radiation, they are promptly rejected and the animals survive. When the tumors are implanted in mice that have been exposed to subcarcinogenic doses of UV-B, this immunologic destruction does not occur (44). Such findings are thought to be caused by a shift in the immunologic balance to suppression of cell-mediated immunity following UV-A exposure, as fewer T_H-1 cells are activated and relatively greater numbers of T_H-2 cells are generated. Thus, the immunologic balance is shifted to the relative suppression of the cell mediated immunity. In addition, antigen presenting cells are destroyed. UV-B radiation also stimulates the production of many different cytokines including IL1-α, IL1-β, IL-6, IL-8, IL-10, IL-12, IL-15, and TNF-α. UV-B also causes the induction of NFκB and it is through the activation of this signal transduction molecule that production of IL-1, IL-6, and TNF-α occurs. IL-10 and TNF-α have been implicated in UV-B-induced immunosuppression. UV-B also causes the release of the neuropeptides substance p and calcitonin gene related peptide (CGRP). It additionally increases the production of pro-opiomelanocortin (PMC) peptides including alpha-MSH (α-MSH). α-MSH and CGRP have both been implicated in UV-B-induced immunosuppression (60).

The minimal dose of UV radiation to cause suppression of cutaneous cell-mediated immunity is much lower than MED. A single exposure of 0.25 and 0.5 MED suppressed contact hypersensitivity response (CHS) by 50% and 80%, respectively (61).

STRATEGIES TO BLOCK UV LIGHT

We know that blocking UV radiation is important to prevent or delay all three phases of carcinogenesis: initiation, promotion, and progression. In reality, there are three main lines of defense to block UV light.

Sun Exposure Avoidance

The first line of defense is to avoid sun exposure whenever possible. The "sunwise precautions" are widely publicized and include limiting exposure from 10:00 a.m. to 4:00 p.m., wearing sunglasses that block 99–100% of the UV light, wearing a hat with a broad brim, seeking shade, and avoidance of sun-lamps and tanning salons. The UV index has been developed to help consumers judge the relative risk of exposure on any given day. It is measured on a scale of 1–10, and is calculated by the National Weather Service using a computer algorithm, which starts with a UV dose rate at the next "solar noon" and incorporates such variables as amount of ozone, clouds, latitude, elevation, and time of the year. This index is widely publicized on radio, television, and in the newspapers, and can also be accessed at: www.epa.gov/sunwise.

Sun Protective Clothing

Our second line of defense is sun protective clothing. More protection is afforded by tighter weaves, repeated laundering, darker colors, and artificial as opposed to natural fibers. Less protection is provided by stretched wet fabrics that are close to the skin. The tightness of the weave can be related with the "hole" effect. In other words, the larger the spaces between the fibers, the more UV radiation can penetrate the fabric. The thicker and closer the fibers, the less light can penetrate. Frequent laundering increases the protection of fabric by shrinking the garment and "plumping up" the fibers. Color is also important; darker shades absorb more UV, and thus black and dark-blue colors are more protective than oranges and reds, which are more protective than pink and light blue. White is the least protective color. The type of fiber is important; organic molecules in synthetic fibers tend to absorb more UV radiation than do cellulosic fibers. Wet fabrics transmit more UV radiation as a result of their refractive index, as well as the reduced scattering effects of their water-filled interstices.

Photoprotection of fabrics is measured by UV protection factor (UPF) and determined by the following formula (62):

$$\mathrm{UPF} = \frac{\Sigma_{280}^{400} E_\lambda B_\lambda \Delta\lambda}{\Sigma_{280}^{400} E_\lambda B_\lambda T_\lambda \Delta\lambda}$$

where E_λ is the solar spectral irradiance, B_λ is the CIE relative erythemal effectiveness values, and T_λ is the spectral transmission.

Solar spectral irradiance values record the intensity of UV radiation at each spectral wavelength that reaches the earth's surface. These were measured in

Albuquerque, New Mexico, on a clear day at noon in July. The relative erythemal effectiveness values compare the effectiveness of each UV wavelength in producing sunburn; these were developed by the International Commission on Illumination (CIE) in 1987. It is important to note that UV-B is 1000 times more erythemagenic than UV-A; therefore the UPF calculation is heavily influenced by the UV-B portion of the spectrum.

Various methods to increase fabric UPF values have been demonstrated. In one study of laundering and dyeing techniques, plain cotton T-shirt fabrics with a low UPF were laundered five times in plain water only, resulting in an increase in UPF from about 5 to approximately 7. Mercerized cloth (cotton treated with sodium hydroxide) has a smaller initial fiber diameter and swells less in laundering. Consequently, it had a lower baseline UPF and less of an increase when washed in plain water. Laundering with plain detergent produced a similar increase in UPF. Multiple washings with detergent plus a UV absorber induced notable increases in the plain cotton T-shirt cloth (from 5 to over 20 UPF), whereas the mercerized cloth increased from 3 to about 12 UPF. Dyeing was also studied and blue dye caused a much greater increase in UPF than yellow. Again, the increase in mercerized was more modest than in untreated cotton fabric (63).

Additives can be utilized to increase the protection of fabrics. A patented fabric has the sunscreen incorporated into the polymer of which it is made. Several chemicals have also been patented and are available as laundry detergents and rinses to add sun protection to fabrics. Furthermore, optical brighteners have been available for many years in most detergents to counteract the yellowing caused by repeated launderings, but have recently been discovered to increase the photoprotection of fabrics. Modern optical brighteners are highly conjugated derivatives of stilbene or benzimidazole; they absorb UV radiation and fluoresce blue. Different specific chemicals are best suited for cotton, polyester, and nylon. The amount of UV radiation they absorb to convert to blue light is significant as demonstrated in a study which showed that repeated washings of both 100% cotton undershirts and knit polo shirts with commercial products containing optical brighteners gave a significant increase in their UPF (64).

Several studies have attempted to address the question of whether UPF and SPF values correlate. When held directly on the skin, *in vivo* SPF tests of fabric were lower than labeled UPF values (65). However, if the fabric is held 1 mm away from the skin, SPF values correlate closely with those of UPF (73). Simulated "*in vivo*" studies of T-shirts on a mannequin upon which was placed a UV-sensitive film showed a variation of a factor of 2 or more depending on location. Areas where the fabric was stretched and closer to the skin such as the upper back and shoulders showed less UPF and areas where the fabric was lax and further from the skin such as the lower back had a higher UPF. In all cases, the UPF measured in this study was higher than the *in vitro* published UPF (66).

Sunscreens

Sunscreens are a very important part of photoprotection, and despite great advances in sunscreen technology, are still an imperfect science. In reality, sunscreens represent our third line of defense against UV radiation. In 1938, the Federal Food, Drug, and Cosmetic Act was passed, establishing the Federal FDA and empowering it with regulatory authority. Among these were the oversight of drugs, defined as anything that prevents or modifies a disease. In 1940, the FDA ruled that sunburn was a disease and therefore sunburn preventives would be regulated as over the counter drugs. For many years, companies were not allowed to make claims of preventing sunburn, and only claims such as "promotes an even tan" were permitted. By the 1970s, dermatologists were beginning to realize the deleterious effects of UV radiation exposure and were recommending sun protection. In 1978, the FDA published an advanced notice of public rule making (ANPR) to regulate the fledgling sunscreen industry. In 1984, the SPF system was adopted, which measured a sunscreen's ability to block UV-B. This entails *in vivo* testing in which 2 $\mu L/cm^2$ of sunscreen are applied on an area of a subject's skin and the relative MED increase is measured. SPF is defined as the ratio between MED of skin with sunscreen vs. MED without the sunscreen. In 1993, the FDA published a tentative final sunscreen monograph (TFM), which included all of the agents approved as sunscreening chemicals, along with their permitted minimum and maximum concentrations. The TFM has had multiple drafts and revisions, and the deadline for its implementation has been repeatedly extended. Previously, the target date of finalization had been December 31, 2002, and of this writing the new target date is January 1, 2005.

As noted, the operational method for determining the UV-B protection is well established and reproducible. However, with recent studies detailing the integral role of UV-A exposure in carcinogenesis as well as photoaging, there has been a great effort to establish a reproducible testing method to quantify UV-A protection. The difficulty lies in the uncertainty of the action spectra for tissue damage by UV-A, both for photodamage and carcinogenesis. No general agreement on a useful end point for damage has been reached. Erythema, which is usually visible on the skin, is weighted toward UV-B exposure. Furthermore, whatever end point is chosen, no single test has been shown to consistently reproduce that biomarker. Among the proposed testing methods for UV-A are assessment of IPD (68), PPD at 2–24 h (69), UV-A-induced erythema (70), erythema induced after topical psoralen application and UV-A exposure (71), UV-A protection factor (APF) in which the smallest UV-A dose to produce minimal erythema or tanning response is compared with and without sunscreen (70), and *in vitro* spectroscopic methods (72) from which is derived the "critical wavelength," the wavelength below which 90% of the UV radiation is absorbed. The American Academy of Dermatology recommends a critical wavelength of 370 nm for sunscreens labeled "broad spectrum" (73). The inability to agree on a single reproducible UV-A testing protocol has seriously delayed the implementation of the TFM, and remains a significant challenge for the future.

SUNSCREENING AGENTS

Sunscreening agents can be divided into organics, which are more soluble and absorb UV radiation, and inorganics, which are less soluble and reflect and scatter the UV radiation.

Organic Sunscreening Agents

Fourteen organic sunscreening agents are listed on the most current version of the TFM. They may be divided into two groups. The first, more efficient at absorbing UV-B, include *para*-amino benzoic acid (PABA) and its esters, salicylates, and cinnamates. Those that absorb better in the UV-A spectrum are benzophenones, anthranilates, and dibenzoyl methanes. Other classes, which are not listed on the TFM, are available outside of the USA. These aromatic compounds absorb a specific portion of the UV radiation spectrum, which is then generally re-emitted at a less energetic longer wavelength, often as heat or light, or may be used in a photochemical reaction such as *cis–trans* or keto–enol photochemical isomerization (74). The organic sunscreening agents are almost always used in combination because no single agent used at currently allowed levels can provide an adequate SPF. In addition, individual organic sunscreening agents have relatively narrow spectra that can be broadened by the synergistic interactions afforded by combinations. Most recently, the combination of organic and inorganic agents has become increasingly popular in sunscreens.

Inorganic Sunscreening Agents

Materials such as titanium dioxide, zinc oxide, iron oxide, barium sulfate, and magnesium oxide remain as particles when introduced into a vehicle because their solubility is very low in acceptable cosmetic preparations. They differ in their capacity to scatter and/or absorb specific wavelengths of light (75). Of these, the two that are listed on the most current version of the TFM and are most commonly used are titanium dioxide and zinc oxide. These agents are often used together with other UV filters to enhance protection in the longer UV and the adjoining visible light range (76). The main problem with such pigmentary powders is that because they are opaque, they appear white on the skin. Iron oxide is sometimes added to improve cosmetic acceptability, and this also has the effect of improving protection in the UV-A and visible light ranges (76).

More recently, both titanium dioxide and zinc oxide have become available as micronized powders. The smaller the particle size, the better the cosmetic acceptability. Micronized titanium dioxide (particle size between 10 and 15 nm as compared with 200–500 nm in nonmicronized forms), creates a shift of photoprotection from the longer UV-A and visible light range toward the UV-B.

Micronized zinc oxide (particle size 60–80 nm as compared with 200–300 nm for the nonmicronized form) protects mainly in the UV-A spectrum, but does not provide the UV-B coverage afforded by micronized titanium dioxide (77).

As particle size is reduced, these agents become less reflective and more absorbing. Their range of protection tends to shift down toward the UV-B. Micronized zinc oxide is more protective than titanium dioxide in the area from 340 to 380 nm. Neither agent is very efficient at absorbing UV radiation above 380 nm (77). Furthermore, titanium dioxide scatters visible light more efficiently, and therefore appears whiter on the skin than does microfine zinc oxide (77). Both agents' ability to scatter light helps them to augment the efficiency of organic sunscreens by effectively increasing the optical path length through the thin layer of sunscreen that is applied to the skin.

Zinc oxide or titanium dioxide used in sunscreen preparations is often coated with other materials such as silicones, fatty acids, or oxides of aluminum, silicone, or zirconium to aid in dispersion. These coatings were developed by the paint industry to reduce particle conglomeration, which improves the distribution of particles when applied as a thin film on a surface. The proper coating provides better compatibility between the particle and the dispersion medium which ultimately improves aesthetics and decreases processing costs. Furthermore, coating may reduce any potential photoactivity of the metal oxides (78).

PROPER USE OF SUNSCREENS

Even when used properly, high SPF sunscreens still transmit some UV radiation. SPF values assume *proper use of sunscreens.* As previously noted, SPF is determined by a very specific operational method involving application of 2 $\mu L/cm^2$ of sunscreen to the skin. Recent studies have shown that most people use less than half of that amount, often only a quarter as much (79,80). At a thickness of 0.5 $\mu L/cm^2$, an SPF of 50 yields a practical SPF of approximately 2 (81). In fact, at 0.5 $\mu L/cm^2$, it is impossible to achieve more than an SPF of 3, regardless of the stated SPF of the sunscreen (81).

SUGGESTIONS FOR THE FUTURE

First and foremost, we need better, more efficient sunscreens. Stable molecules are being developed that disperse energy harmlessly without degrading themselves. Better application systems are being developed along with film forming agents to create a uniform layer of sunscreen on the skin in spite of the normal "peaks and valleys" inherent on human epidermis.

It is also vital to educate the public on the proper use of sunscreens. Most people do not apply enough sunscreen to achieve the stated SPF, and thus higher-SPF sunscreens not used properly may do nothing more than give a false sense of security while allowing enough UV radiation to penetrate to cause damage and immunosuppression. People need to be educated on the proper use of sunscreens, how much to use, and how often to reapply it. The advice to reapply sunscreen every 2–3 h is often given, yet rarely followed. A recent regimen has been described in which sunscreen is applied liberally to exposed areas 15–30 min before going out in the sun, followed by a reapplication of the sunscreen to these same areas 15–30 min after sun exposure begins. Further reapplications are made as necessary after vigorous activity that could remove the sunscreens such as swimming, toweling, sweating, rubbing, etc. This regimen has yielded superior results (82), underscoring the importance of proper sunscreen application.

Finally, despite all of our precautions, it is inevitable that some UV radiation will penetrate and cause DNA damage and immunosuppression. If we cannot avoid or block it out, other options include development of enzyme repair systems, antioxidants used in the correct ratios and balance either topically or systemically or both, and blocking of enzyme systems responsible for increased cellular proliferation, inflammation, and ultimately, carcinogenesis.

REFERENCES

1. American Cancer Society, Facts and Figures 2004.
2. Bergstresser PR, Elmits CA, Takashima A, Mikhtar H. Photocarcinog Photodermatol Photoimmunol Photomed 1995; 11:181–184.
3. Roberts J. Exposure to the sun. In: Auerbach P, ed. Management of Wilderness and Environmental Emergencies. 2nd ed. St. Louis: Mosby, 1989.
4. Gasparro FP, Mitchnick M, Nash JF. A review of sunscreen safety and efficacy. Photochem Photobiol 1998; 68(3):243–256.
5. Coopman SA, Garmun M, Gonzalez-Serva A, Glogau R. In: Arndt K, LeBoit P, Robinson J, Wintroub B, eds. Photodamage and Photoaging: Cutaneous Medicine and Surgery. Philadelphia: WB Saunders, 1996:732–750.
6. Chardon A, Moyal D, Hourseau C. Persistent pigment darkening as a method for the UVA protection assessment of sunscreens. In: Rougier A, Schaefer H, eds. Protection of the Skin Against Ultraviolet Radiations. Paris: John Libbey Euro Text, 1998:131–136.
7. Lowe NJ, Friedlander J. Sunscreens: rationale for use to reduce photodamage and phototoxicity. In: Lowe NJ, Shaath NA, Pathak MA, eds. Sunscreens: Development, Evaluation, and Regulatory Aspects. 2nd ed. New York: Marcel Dekker, 1997:37.
8. Pathak MA. Photoprotection against harmful effects of solar UVB and UVA radiation: an update. In: Lowe NJ, Shaath NA, Pathak MA, eds. Sunscreens: Development, Evaluation, and Regulatory Aspects. 2nd ed. New York: Marcel Dekker, 1997:67.
9. Young AR. Chromophores in human skin. Phys Med Biol 1997; 242:789–802.
10. Young AR, Chadwick CA, Harrison GI, Nikaido O, Ramsden J, Potten C. The similarity of action spectra for thymine dimmers in human epidermis and erythema suggests that DNA is the chromophore for erythema. J Invest Dermatol 1998; 111:982–988.
11. Gilchrest BA, Soter NA, Stoff JS, Mihm MC Jr. The human sunburn reaction: histologic and biochemical studies. J Am Acad Dermatol 1981; 5:411–422.
12. Johnson B. Reactions of normal skin to solar radiation. In: Jarrett A, ed. Physiology and Pathophysiology of the Skin. London: Academic Press, 1984:2414–2492.

13. Gahring L, Baltz M, Pepys MB, Daynes R. Effect of ultraviolet radiation on production of epidermal cell thymocyte: activating factor/interleukin-1 in vivo and in vitro. Proc Natl Acad Sci USA 1984; 81(4):1198–1202.
14. Ansel JC, Luger TA, Lowry D, Perry P, Roop DR, Mountz JD. The expression and odulation of IL-1 alpha in murine keratinocytes. J Immunol 1988; 140(7):2274–2278.
15. Gallo RL, Staszewski R, Sauder DN, Knisely TL, Granstein RD. Regulation of GM-CSF and IL-3 production from the murine keratinocyte cell line PAM 212 following exposure to ultraviolet radiation. J Invest Dermatol 1991; 97(2):203–209.
16. Kirnbauer R, Kock A, Neuner P, Forster E, Krutmann J, Urbanski A, Schauer E, Ansel JC, Schwarz T, Luger TA. Regulation of epidermal cell interleukin-6 production by UV light and corticosteroids. J Invest Dermatol 1991; 96(4):484–489.
17. Nozaki S, Abrams JS, Pearce MK, Sauder DN. Augmentaton of granulocyte/macrophage colony-stimulating factor expression by ultraviolet irradiation is mediated by interleukin-1 in Pam 212 kerartinocytes. J Invest Dermatol 1991; 97(1):10–14.
18. Oxholm A, Oxholm P, Staberg B, Bendtzen K. Immunohistological detection of interleukin-1 like molecules and tumor necrosis factor in human epidermis before and after UVB-irradiation in vivo. Br J Dermatol 1988; 118(3):369–376.
19. Haake AR, Polakowska RR. Cell death by apoptosis in epidermal biology. J Invest Dermatol 1993; 101:107–112.
20. Brenner W, Gschnait F. Decreased DNA repair activity in sunburn cells: a possible pathogenic factor of the epidermal sunburn reaction. Arch Dermatol Res 1979; 266:11–16.
21. Woodcock A, Magnus IA. The sunburn cell in mouse skin: preliminary quantative studies on its production. Br J Dermatol 1976; 95:459–468.
22. Kaplan CA. Suntan, sunburn, and sun protection. J Wilderness Med 1992; 3:173–196.
23. Harber LC, DeLeo VA, Prystowsky JH. Intrinsic and extrinsic photoprotection against UVB and UVA radiation. In: Lowe NJ, Shaath NA, eds. Sunscreens: Development, Evaluation, and Regulatory Aspects. New York: Marcel Dekker, 1990:359–378.
24. Lowe NJ, Freidlander J. Sunscreens: rationale for use to reduce photodamage and phototoxicity. In: Lowe NJ, Shaath NA, Pathak MA, eds. Sunscreens: Development, Evaluation, and Regulatory Aspects. 2nd ed. New York: Marcel Dekker, 1997.
25. Heilman ER, Friedman RJ. Degenerative diseases and perforating disorders. In: Elder D, ed. Lever's Histopathology of the Skin. 8th ed. Philadelphia: Lippincott-Raven, 1997:341–351.
26. Litt JZ. Drug Eruption Reference Manual. New York: The Parthenon Publishing Group, 2002:422–423.
27. Johnson JA, Fusaro RM. Broad spectrum photoprotection: the role of tinted auto windows, sunscreens, and browning agents in the diagnosis and treatment of photosensitivity. Dermatology 1992; 185:237–241.
28. Sonnex TS, Hawk JLM. Hydroa vacciniforme: a review of 10 cases. Br J Dermatol 1998; 118:101–108.
29. Pinnell SR. Cutaneous photodamage, oxidative stress, and topical antioxidant protection. J Am Acad Dermatol 2003; 48(1):1–19.
30. Young AR, Potten CS, Nikaido O, Parsons PG, Boenders T, Ramsden JM, Chadwick CA. Human melanocytes and keratinocytes exposed to UVB and UVA in vivo show comparable levels of thymine dimers. J Invest Dermatol 1998; 111:936–940.
31. Kielbassa C, Epe B. DNA damage induced by ultraviolet and visible light and its wavelength dependence. Methods Enzymol 2000; 319:436–445.

32. Goukassian D, Gad F, Yaar M, Ellen MS, Nehel US, Gilehrest BA. Mechanisms and implications of the age-associated decrease in DNA repair capacity. FASEB J 2000; 14:1325–1334.
33. Zeigler A, Johnson AS, Leffell DJ, Simon JA, Sharma HW, Kimmelman J, Remingtion L, Jacks T, Brash DE. Sunburn and p53 in the onset of skin cancer. Nature 1994; 372:773–776.
34. Bale AE, Yie KP. The hedgehog pathway and basal cell carcinomas. Hum Mol Genet 2001; 10:757–762.
35. Maszerbaum, Beech J, Epstein EH Jr. Ultraviolet radiation mutagenesis of hedgehog pathway genes in basal cell carcinomas. J Invest Dermatol Symp Proc 1999; 4:41–45.
36. DeBuys HV, Levy SB, Murray JC, Madey DC, Pinnell SR. Dermatologic aspects of cosmetics: modern approaches to photoprotection. Dermatol Clin 2000; 18(4):577–590.
37. Danpure HJ, Tyrell RM. Oxygen-dependence of near UV (365 nm) lethality and the interaction of near UV and X-rays in two mammalian cell lines. Photochem Photobiol 1976; 23:171–177.
38. Morlieve P, Moysan A, Tirache I. Action spectra for UV-induced lipid peroxidation in cultured human skin fibroblasts. Free Radic Biol Med 1995; 19:365–371.
39. de Gruiji FR. Photocarcinogenesis: UVA vs. UVB. Singlet oxygen, UVA and ozone. Methods Enzymol 2000; 319:359–366.
40. Wenczl E, Pool S, Timmerman AJ, Vanderschaus GP, Roza L, Schothorst AA. Physiologic doses of ultraviolet irradiation induce DNA strand breaks in cultured human melanocytes as detected by means of an immunological assay. Photochem Photobiol 1997; 66:826–830.
41. Parsons PG, Hayward IP. Inhibition of DNA repair synthesis by sunlight. Photochem Photobiol 1985; 42:287–293.
42. Fisher GJ, Choi HC, Bata-Csorgo Z, Shao Y, Datta S, Wang ZQ, Kang S, Voorhees JJ. Ultraviolet irradiation increases matrix metalloproteinase-8 protein in human skin in vivo. J Invest Dermatol 2001; 117(2):219–226.
43. Bergstresser PR. Ultraviolet imunosuppression. Prog Dermatol 2000; 34(3):1–12.
44. Cooper KD. UV-induced skin cancers and photoimmunology. In: Mukhtar H, Elmets CA, eds. Photocarcinogenesis: Mechanisms, Models and Human Health Implications. Photochem Photobiol 1996; 63(4):355–447.
45. DeBuys HV, Levy SB, Murray JC, Madey DL, Pinnell SR. Modern approaches to photoprotection. Dermatol Clin 2000; 18(4):577–590.
46. Yarosh D, Klein J, O'Connor A, Hawk J, Rafal E, Wolf P. Effect of topically applied T4, endonuclease V in liposomes on skin cancer in xeroderma pigmentosum: a randomized study. Xerderma Pigmentosa Study Group. Lancet 2001; 357:926–929.
47. Tiele JJ, Dreher F, Packer L. Antioxidant defense system in skin In: Elsner P, Maibach HI, eds. Cosmeceuticals: Drugs vs. Cosmetics. New York: Marcel Dekker, 2000:145–187.
48. Pinnell SR. Cutaneous photodamage, oxidative stress, and topical antioxidant protection. J Am Acad Dermatol 2003; 48(1):1–19.
49. Steenvoorden DPT, Beijersberger van Henegouwen GMJ. The use of endogenous antioxidants to improve photoprotecton. Photochem Photobiol B: Biology 1997; 41:1–10.
50. Bissett DL, McBride JF. Synergistic topical photoprotection by a combination of the iron chelator 2-furildioxime and sunscreen. J Am Acad Dermatol 1996; 35(4):546–549.

51. Eberlain-Konig B, Placzek M, Przybilla B. Protective effect against sunburn of combined septemic ascorbic acid (vitamin C) and D-α tocophenol (vitamin E). J Am Acad Dermatol 1998; 38(1):45–48.
52. Gonzalez S, Pathak MA, Cuevas J, Villarrubia VG, Fitzpatrick TB. Photodermatol Photoimmunol Photomed 1997; 13:50–60.
53. Elmets CA, Singh D, Tubesing K, Matsoi M, Katiyar S, Mukhtar H. Cutaneous photoprotection from ultraviolet injury by green tea polyphenols. J Am Acad Dermatol 2001; 44(3):425–432.
54. Wei H, Bowen R, Barnes S, Cai Q, Wang Y. Antioxidant and anticarcinogenic properties of the soybean isoflavone genistein. Proc Soc Exp Biol Med 1995; 208:124–130.
55. Wei H. Photoprotective action of isoflavone genistein Models mechanisms and revelance to clinical dermatology. J Am Acad Dermatol 1998; 39(2):271–272.
56. Wilgus TA, Parrett ML, Ross MS, Tobes KL, Robertson FM, Oberyszyn TM. Inhibition of ultraviolet induced cutaneous inflammation by a specific cycloxygenase-2 inhibitor. Adv Exp Med Biol 2002; 507:85–92.
57. Fischer SM, Conti CJ, Uner J, Aldaz CM, Lubet RA. Celecoxib and difluoromethylornithine in combination have strong therapeutic activity against UV-induced skin tumors in mice. Carcinogenesis 2003; 24(5):945–952.
58. Fisher GJ, Wang ZQ, Datta SC, Varani J, Kang S, Voorhees JJ. Pathopysiology of premature skin aging induced by ultraviolet light. N Engl J Med 1997; 337(20):1419–1428.
59. Kang S, Chung JH, Lee JH, Fisher GJ, Wan YS, Duell EA, Voorhees JJ. Topical *N*-acetyl cysteine and genistein prevent ultraviolet-light-induced signaling that leads to photoaging in human skin in vivo. J Invest Dermatol 2003; 120(5):835–841.
60. Scholzen TE, Kalden DH, Brzoska T, Fisbeck T, Fastrich M, Schiller M, Bohm M, Schwartz T, Armstrong CA, Ansel JC, Luger TA. Expression of proopiomelanocorin peptides in humas dermal microvascular endothelial cells: evidence for a regulation by ultraviolet light and interleukin-1. J Invest Dermatol 2001; 116(5):829.
61. Kelly DA, Young AR, McGregor JM, Seed PT, Potten CS, Walker ST. Sensitivity to sunburn as associated with susceptibility to UVR-associated suppression of cutaneous cell-mediated immunity. J Exp Med 2000; 191:561–566.
62. American Association of Textile Chemists and Colonists. Test Method 183, 2000.
63. Wang SQ, Kopf AW, Marx J, Bogdan A, Polsky D, Bart RS. Reduction of ultraviolet transmission through cotton T-shirt fabrics with low ultraviolet protection by various laundering methods and dyeing: clinical implications. J Am Acad Dermatol 2001; 44:767–774.
64. Stone J, Kim J, Hatch K. Proceedings of the International Textile and Apparel Association Conference, Kansas City, MO, 2001.
65. Gambichler T, Avermaete A, Bader A, Altmeyer P, Hoffmann K. Ultraviolet protection by summer textiles: ultraviolet transmission measurements verified by determination of the minimal erythema dose with solar-simulated radiation. Br J Dermatol 2001; 144(3):484–489.
66. Gies HP, Roy CR, McLennan A, Diffey BL, Pailthorpe M, Driscoll C, Whillock M, McKinlay AF, Grainger K, Clark I, Sayre RM. UV protection by clothing: an intercomparison of measurement and methods. Health Phys 1997; 73(3):456–464.
67. Ravishankar J, Diffey B. Laboratory testing of UV transmission through fabrics may underestimate protection. Photodermatol Photoimmunol Photomed 1997; 13(5–6):202–203.

68. Kaidbey KH, Barnes A. Determination of UVA protection factors by means of immediate pigment darkening in normal skin. J Am Acad Dermatol 1991; 25:262–266.
69. Moyal D, Chardon A, Kollias N. Determination of UVA protection factors using the persistent pigment darkening (PPD) as the end point. Part 1. Calibration of the method. Photodermatol Photoimmunol Photomed 2000; 16(6):45–249.
70. Cole C, van Fossen R. Measurement of sunscreen UVA protection: an unsensitized human model. J Am Acad Dermatol 1992; 26:178–184.
71. Lowe NJ, Dromgoole SH, Sefton J, Bourget T, Weingarten D. Indoor and outdoor efficacy testing of a broad spectrum sunscreen against ultraviolet A radiation in psorlen-sensitized subjects. J Am Acad Dermatol 1987; 17:224–230.
72. Diffey BL, Tanner PR, Matts PJ, Nash JF. In vitro assessment of the broad-spectrum ultraviolet protection of sunscreen products. J Am Acad Dermatol 2000; 43(6):1024–1035.
73. Position Statement. An UVA protection of sunscreens. Am Acad Dermatol 2000.
74. Shaath NA. Evolution of modern sunscreen chemicals. In: Lowe NJ, Shaath NA, Pathak MA, eds. Sunscreens: Development, Evaluation, and Regulatory Aspects. 2nd ed. New York: Marcel Dekker, 1997:3–34.
75. Kaye ET, Levin JA, Blank IH, Arndt KA, Anderson RR. Efficacy of opaque photoprotective agents in the visible light range. Arch Dermatol 1991; 127:351–355.
76. Roelandts R. Shedding light on sunscreens. Clin Exp Dermatol 1998; 23:147–157.
77. Pinnell SR, Fairhurst D, Gillies R, Mitchnick MA, Kollias N. Microfine zinc oxide is a superior sunscreen ingredient to microfine titanium dioxide. Dermatol Surg 2000; 26:309–314.
78. Gasparro FP, Mitchnick M, Nash JF. A review of sunscreen safety and efficacy. Photochem Photobiol 1998; 68(3):243–256.
79. Autier P, Boniol M, Severi G, Dore JF. European organization for research and treatment of cancer melanoma co-operative group: quantity of sunscreen used by European students. Br J Dermatol 2001; 144(2):288–291.
80. Neale R, Williams G, Green A. Application patterns among participants randomized to daily sunscreen use in a skin cancer prevention trial. Arch Dermatol 2002; 138:1319–1325.
81. Wulf HC, Stender IM, Lock-Andersen J. Sunscreens used at the beach do not protect against erythema: a new definition of SPF is proposed. Photodermatol Photoimmunol Photomed 1997; 13(4):129–132.
82. Diffey B. When should sunscreen be reapplied? J Am Acad Dermatol 2001; 45(6):882–885.

3

A Perspective on the Need for Topical Sunscreens

B. L. Diffey

Newcastle General Hospital, Newcastle, UK

OBSERVABLE CUTANEOUS EFFECTS OF SUN EXPOSURE

Ultraviolet (UV) radiation exhibits a number of effects on skin, both beneficial and undesirable. The purpose of sun protection should be to minimize the likelihood of adverse effects without undue detriment to the beneficial effects. The biological effects of UV on skin are summarized below.

Production of Vitamin D

The only well-established beneficial effect of solar UV on the skin is the production of vitamin D_3. The skin absorbs UV-B radiation in sunlight to convert sterol precursors in the skin, such as 7-dehydrocholesterol, to vitamin D_3. Vitamin D_3 is further transformed by the liver and kidneys to biologically active metabolites such as 25-hydroxyvitamin D; these metabolites then act on the intestinal mucosa to facilitate calcium absorption, and on bone to facilitate calcium exchange. There is some suggestion that an enzyme involved in vitamin D metabolism may protect against colon, breast, and prostate cancer (1).

Tanning

A consequence of exposure to solar UV, which still seems to be socially desirable, is the delayed pigmentation of the skin known as tanning, or melanin pigmentation. Melanin pigmentation of skin is of two types: (i) constitutive—the color of the skin seen in different races and determined by genetic factors only and (ii) facultative—the reversible increase in tanning in response to sun exposure.

While vitamin D production and tanning are, or may be perceived to be, a desirable consequence of sun exposure, the remaining three—sunburn, skin cancer, and photoaging—are universally recognized to be adverse effects of sun exposure.

Sunburn

Erythema, or redness of the skin due to dilatation of superficial dermal blood vessels, is one of the commonest and most obvious effects of UV exposure ("sunburn"). Following exposure to solar UV radiation, there is usually a latent period of 2–4 h before erythema develops. Erythema reaches maximum intensity between 8 and 24 h after exposure, but may take several days to resolve completely. If a high enough exposure has occurred, the skin will also become painful and edematous, and blistering may result.

Skin Cancer

The three common forms of skin cancer, listed in order of seriousness, are basal cell carcinoma (BCC), squamous cell carcinoma (SCC), and malignant melanoma (MM). Around 90% of skin cancer cases are of the nonmelanoma variety (BCC and SCC), with BCCs being approximately four times as common as SCCs. Exposure to solar UV radiation is considered to be a major etiological factor for all three forms of cancer (2).

Photoaging

The clinical signs of a photoaged skin include dryness, deep wrinkles, accentuated skin furrows, sagging, loss of elasticity, mottled pigmentation, and telangiectasia (3,4). Chronic solar exposure is the major environmental insult that contributes to photoaging and is quite distinct from chronological, or intrinsic, aging.

SUNSCREEN USE AND THE SUN PROTECTION FACTOR

Topical sunscreens act by absorbing or scattering UV radiation and are widely available for general public use as a consumer product.

By far the most common reason for using sunscreens, cited by 80% of people in one survey (5), was to protect against sunburn. Other reasons why people use sunscreens are because they (6):

- Know the dangers of sun exposure
- Perceive themselves at high risk of skin cancer
- Know people who have had skin cancer
- Want Protection against aging and wrinkling
- Wish to extend time in the sun
- Have previously had skin cancer

Equally important, the reasons why people choose not to use sunscreens are because (6):

- They have skin that does not burn easily
- They already have a "protective" tan
- They are not outdoors enough to warrant use
- Sunscreens are a nuisance and greasy to apply
- Sunscreens are expensive
- Sunscreens retard the desired tan
- They use other sun protective measures
- They forget

The protection provided by a sunscreen is expressed by its sun protection factor (SPF). It is popularly interpreted as how much longer skin covered with sunscreen takes to burn compared with unprotected skin (5). A more appropriate definition of the SPF is that it is the ratio of the least amount of UV energy required to produce a minimal erythema on sunscreen protected skin to the amount of energy required to produce the same erythema on unprotected skin (7). At the start of the 1990s most commercially available sunscreen products had SPFs less than 10 but by 2000 most manufacturers produced products with factors of 15–30, and it is not uncommon to find products claiming a factor of 50 or higher.

HOW LARGE SHOULD THE SPF BE TO PREVENT SUNBURN?

Sunscreens are used principally to prevent sunburn. The magnitude of sunscreen SPF required to achieve this goal can be determined given knowledge of the local UV climatology, the user's behavior outdoors, and their personal susceptibility to sunburn.

Maximum daily ambient UV levels, expressed in units of standard erythema dose (SED), under clear summer skies are about 70 in the tropics, 60 at midlatitudes approximating to those of southern Europe, and 45 for northern European latitudes (8). The SED is a measure of erythemal UV radiation and is equivalent to an erythemal effective radiant exposure of 100 J/m^2 (9).

These maximum ambient exposures will not be received by people simply because it would be unrealistic to lie in the unshaded sun all day without moving. An extreme sunbather might spend half the time supine and half the time prone, resulting in a maximum exposure on much of the body surface of 50% of ambient. For upright subjects engaging in a variety of outdoor pursuits such as gardening, walking, or tennis, the exposure relative to ambient on commonly exposed sites, for example, chest, shoulder, face, forearms, and lower legs, ranges from ~20% to 60% (10). So, someone who is on vacation in southern Europe, for example, would receive a daily exposure of no more than 20 SED over much of the body surface. Since an exposure of 2–4 SED is necessary for a minimal erythema on the previously unexposed buttock skin in the most common northern European skin types (II/III) (11), a photoprotective device (sunscreen or clothing) need only possess an SPF of 10 or more to give a sunburn-free vacation. And for tropical sun exposure, a protection factor of 15 or higher should be more than adequate for all-day exposure.

If then, sunscreens of SPF 15 are sufficient to protect against sunburn even for all-day exposure in tropical sunshine, why are people who usually or always use a high-factor (≥15) sunscreen more likely to report sunburn than those who rarely or never use sunscreen (12,13)?

That the protection achieved is often less than that expected is explained by a number of reasons (14):

- People normally apply much less sunscreen than the amount used in the testing process to determine a product's SPF.
- Sunscreen is normally spread haphazardly and not uniformly.
- So-called "physical" sunscreens containing mineral pigments like zinc oxide can leave a white film on the skin and, as a consequence, people may be encouraged to apply less.
- Sunscreens can be removed by water immersion, sand abrasion, and toweling.
- Sunscreen may not be reapplied appropriately.

All of these factors mean that, as a rule of thumb, the protection achieved is typically about one-third of the rated SPF (14). So, in order to achieve 15-fold protection, an SPF50 rated sunscreen needs to be applied.

HOW HIGH SHOULD THE SPF BE TO GIVE A WORTHWHILE REDUCTION IN LIFETIME RISK OF SKIN CANCER?

For people living in countries with large seasonal changes in ambient UV radiation (both UV-B and UV-A), such as those in northern Europe, the northern part of the USA, and Canada, exposure to sunlight is either *adventitious* (generally summer weekdays and the six winter months) or *elective* (generally summer weekends and summer vacation). The contribution to annual UV exposure from these two types of exposure is typically 30% and 70%, respectively (15).

Estimates of the risk of inducing skin cancer from exposure to UV radiation require knowledge of dose–response relationships and the relative effectiveness of different wavelengths (known as an *action spectrum*) in sunlight in causing skin cancer. Data on dose–response relationships and action spectra are available to some extent to allow quantitative estimates of the risk of nonmelanoma skin cancer (NMSC) incidence, but presently not for malignant melanoma. The best estimate for the action spectrum for NMSC resembles that for erythema (16).

Application of multivariate analysis to population-based epidemiology of NMSC has shown that, for a group of subjects with a given genetic susceptibility, age and environmental UV exposure are the two most important factors in determining the relative risk. This has led to a simple power law relationship, in which the lifetime risk can be approximated to (17):

$$\text{Risk} \approx (\text{annual UV dose})^{\beta}$$

The symbol β is a numerical constant associated with the specific type of NMSC and is normally derived from surveys of skin cancer incidence and ultraviolet climatology.

If sunscreen use is limited to elective sun exposure, and it is assumed that the protection achieved is one-third of the SPF rating, the lifetime risk of NMSC relative to a non-sunscreen user is simply

$$\{0.3 + 0.7/[\text{SPF}/3]\}^{\beta}$$

where SPF is the *rated* SPF. For the purpose of examining the predicted benefit of sunscreen use on relative lifetime risk of NMSC, an exemplary value of 2 will be used for β (18). If sunscreens rated at SPF5, SPF15, or SPF50 are used, the previous expression indicates that the corresponding reduction in lifetime risk of NMSC, compared with no sunscreen use during elective exposure, is one-half, one-fifth, and one-tenth, respectively. More sophisticated models of NMSC risk are available than the simple approach used here, but in essence use of these is unlikely to change dramatically these general estimates of the effect that sunscreens used during intentional sun exposure can have in modifying the lifetime risk of skin cancer.

IS DAILY USE OF SUNSCREENS OF BENEFIT?

"Consumers want more and more UV protection in their daily skin care products to prevent everything from wrinkles to cancer" (19). This quotation from a consumer publication is now received wisdom by most beauty journalists and has stimulated many cosmetic companies to incorporate UV absorbing chemicals into facial moisturisers designed for daily use. Provided the daily use of topical products containing UV filters does no harm and considering the potential health benefits, manufacturers and others may argue that these products are in a small but measurable way providing a positive impact.

There is limited evidence indicating that daily application of a high-factor (SPF > 15) sunscreen may prevent SCC (20) and contribute to the prevention of solar elastosis (21). However, these two studies were carried out in Queensland and Texas, respectively, both areas of high insolation, and the conclusions may not necessarily be transferable to people living in countries of low insolation, such as those in northern Europe and the northern part of America. In a review of sunscreen safety and efficacy (22), it was concluded that the current list of commonly used organic and inorganic active ingredients have favorable toxicological profiles and do not pose a concern for human health. However, it is known that, although uncommon, UV absorbers in sunscreens are now the commonest cause of positive photopatch tests (23). Concern has been raised about systemic absorption of sunscreens after topical application (24), cellular toxicity (25,26), impact on vitamin D synthesis (27), and estrogenic activity (28), although the significance of these reports to human health consequences of sunscreen use remains circumspect.

A number of case–control studies on cutaneous melanoma showed significantly higher risks among sunscreen users (6). Although these studies could be taken to suggest an increase in the risk of melanoma due to sunscreen use, they are difficult to interpret because of problems of positive confounding (e.g., people who are at most risk of burning and most likely to develop melanoma are also most likely to use sunscreens) and negative confounding (e.g., sunscreen users may also use other methods of sun protection such as clothing).

While these concerns are insufficient to stop the use of sunscreens as part of a sun protection strategy, they do suggest that perhaps there is an optimal use of topically applied UV filters beyond which the benefit of further use may be both unnecessary and unjustified, especially in the context of people living in countries not known for their sunny climate.

In an analysis combining the relative exposures during different periods of the year with topical sun protection used during one or more of these periods, it was possible to estimate an "equivalent age" (29). This can be taken as the age by which someone using no sunscreen during adulthood (from age 18 until age 70) would receive the same cumulative sun exposure as another person engaging in a specific sunscreen-use strategy throughout their adult life. Implicit in this calculation is that other sun protection measures (including none) are the same in both the sunscreen users and the non-sunscreen users and that the protection afforded by the sunscreen is assumed to be one-third of the SPF rating (see earlier). The calculated equivalent ages are summarized in Table 3.1

The conclusion from these calculations is that, in terms of reducing the cumulative UV exposure (assumed to be a surrogate for photoaging), a significant benefit can be achieved by using a sunscreen during summer holidays and outdoor leisure activities at summer weekends. For example, use of SPF15 sunscreen products during holidays and summer weekends can reduce the lifetime UV dose by an equivalent of almost 30 years of unprotected exposure. However, whether the product is SPF15 or SPF30 makes little difference to chronic exposure (although it would be expected to be important in reducing the risk of sunburn). Supplementing this by daily use of a product incorporating UV filters during summer weekdays may reduce the equivalent age by an additional 8 years or so. Virtually no benefit is gained from using UV protective products from October to March in latitudes beyond 50°.

A STRATEGY FOR SUNSCREEN USE

In summary, the following strategy is proposed for a rational approach to the application of topical sunscreen agents for people living in countries not known for their sunny climate:

- No need for UV protection in autumn and winter (October through March in the northern hemisphere).
- Daily skin care (incorporating UV filters of SPF8–15) in spring and summer (April through September) when exposure is largely adventitious or unintentional.
- Sunscreen application (SPF > 30) on sunny holidays and long periods outdoors on summer weekends.

Adoption of this strategy should lead to the following outcomes:

- Prevention of sunburn.
- Giving about the same lifetime UV exposure as a 35-year-old who behaves in a similar way with regard to sun exposure but who uses no sunscreen.

Table 3.1 Calculated Equivalent Ages

	Rated SPF		
Cumulative use	8	15	30
Summer holiday	60	58	56
+Summer weekend	47	41	37
+Summer weekday	41	33	28
+October–March	38	28	23

- Reduction in the risk of NMSC by at least fivefold relative to a nonuser of sunscreen.
- Delay in the signs of photoaging.
- Ensuring a moderate exposure to sunshine, especially in late summer and early autumn, to maintain vitamin D status during the winter months.

Finally, it goes without saying that for white-skinned people living in tropical and subtropical regions (roughly in the latitude band 30°N to 30°S) there are sound climatological and biological reasons for adopting year-round sun protection behavior, which would include the use of sunscreens.

REFERENCES

1. Holick MF. A perspective on the beneficial effects of moderate exposure to sunlight: bone health, cancer prevention, mental health and well being. In: Giacomoni PU, ed. Sun Protection in Man. Amsterdam: Elsevier Science BV, 2001:11–37.
2. International Agency for Research on Cancer. IARC Monographs on the Evaluation of Carcinogenic Risks to Humans, Vol. 55. Solar and UV Radiation. Lyon: International Agency for Research on Cancer, 1992.
3. Leyden JJ. Clinical features of ageing skin. Br J Dermatol 1990; 122:1–3.
4. Gilchrest BA. Photodamage, Oxford: Blackwell Science, 1995.
5. Health Education Authority. Sunscreens and the Consumer. London: Health Education Authority, 1996.
6. International Agency for Research on Cancer. IARC Handbooks of Cancer Prevention: Volume 5 Sunscreens. Lyon: International Agency for Research on Cancer, 2001.
7. Department of Health and Human Services FDA, USA. Sunscreen drug products for over the counter use: proposed safety, effectiveness and labelling conditions. Fed Reg 1978; 43(166):38206–38269.
8. Roy C, Gies H, Toomey S. Monitoring UV-B at the Earth's surface. Cancer Forum 1996; 20:173–179.
9. CIE Standard. Erythema Reference Action Spectrum and Standard Erythema Dose. CIE S 007/E-1998. Vienna: Commission Internationale de l'Éclairage, 1998.
10. Diffey. BL Human exposure to ultraviolet radiation. In: Hawk JLM, ed. Photodermatology. London: Arnold, 1999:5–24.
11. Harrison GI, Young AR. Ultraviolet radiation-induced erythema in human skin. Methods 2002; 28:14–19.
12. Dixon H, Shatten R, Borland R. Reaction to the 1995/1996 SunSmart Campaign: results from a epresentative household survey of Victorians. In: SunSmart Evaluation Studies No 5. Melbourne: Anti-Cancer Council of Victoria, 1997:70–96.
13. Ling T-C, Faulkner C, Rhodes LE. A questionnaire survey of attitudes to and usage of sunscreens in northwest England. Photodermatol Photoimmunol Photomed 2003; 19:98–101.
14. Diffey BL. Sunscreens: use and misuse. In: PU Giacomoni, ed. Sun Protection in Man. Amsterdam: Elsevier Science BV, 2001:521–534.
15. Diffey BL. Human exposure to solar ultraviolet radiation. J Cosmet Dermatol 2002; 1:124–130.

16. de Gruijl FR, van der Leun JC. Estimate of the wavelength dependency of ultraviolet carcinogenesis in humans and its relevance to the risk assessment of a stratospheric ozone depletion. Health Phys 1994; 67:319–326.
17. National Radiological Protection Board. Health Effects from Ultraviolet Radiation. Report of an Advisory Group on Non-ionising Radiation. Documents of the NRPB. Vol. 13, No. 1. 2002:253–268.
18. Diffey BL. An analysis of the risk of skin cancer from sunlight and sunbeds in subjects living in northern Europe. Photodermatology 1987; 4:118–126.
19. Hickey JP. UV protection in skin care. Happi Mag, September 1999.
20. Green A, Williams G, Neale R, Hart V, Leslie D, Parsons P, Marks G, Gaffney P, Battistutta D, Frost C, Lang C, Russell A. Daily sunscreen application and beta carotene supplementation in prevention of basal-cell and squamous-cell carcinomas of the skin: a randomised controlled trial. Lancet 1999; 354:723–729.
21. Boyd AS, Naylor M, Cameron GS, Pearse AD, Gaskell SA, Neldner KH. The effects of chronic sunscreen use on the histologic changes of dermatoheliosis. J Am Acad Dermatol 1995; 33:941–946
22. Gasparro FP, Mitchnick M, Nash JF. A review of sunscreen safety and efficacy. Photochem Photobiol 1998; 68:243–256.
23. Ibbotson SH, Farr PM, Beck M, Diffey BL, Ferguson J, George GA, Green C, du P Menagé H, Murphy GM, Norris PG, Rhodes LE, White IR. Photopatch testing: methods and indications. Br J Dermatol 1997; 136:371–376.
24. Hayden CGJ, Roberts MS, Benson HAE. Systemic absorption of sunscreen after topical application. Lancet 1997; 350:863–864.
25. Dunford R, Salinaro A, Cai L, Serpone N, Horikoshi S, Hidaka H, Knowland J. Chemical oxidation and DNA damage catalysed by inorganic sunscreen ingredients. FEBS Lett 1997; 418:87–90.
26. Butt ST, Christensen T. Toxicity and phototoxicity of chemical sun filters. Radiat Prot Dosim 2000; 91:283–286.
27. Nowson CA, Margerison C. Vitamin D intake and vitamin D status of Australians. Med J Aust 2002; 177:149–152.
28. Schlumpf M, Cotton B, Conscience M, Haller V, Steinmann B, Lichtensteiger W. *In vitro* and *in vivo* estrogenicity of UV screens. Environ Health Perspect 2001; 109:239–244.
29. Diffey BL. Is daily use of sunscreens of benefit in the UK? Br J Dermatol 2002; 146:659–662.

4

Safety Considerations for Sunscreens in the USA

Richard J. Schwen
PAREXEL International, Inc., Waltham, Massachusetts, USA

REQUIREMENTS FOR SAFETY TESTING OF SUNSCREENS

In the USA, sunscreens are classified as drugs based on their ability to prevent injury to the skin after exposure to ultraviolet radiation (UVR). Because of their proven safety and ease of use by consumers, the Food and Drug Administration (FDA) has allowed them to be marketed over the counter (OTC), provided they comply with the OTC monograph specifying active ingredients, concentrations, use, and labeling (1). These criteria are based upon safety and efficacy data submitted by industry during the sunscreen monograph development process initiated back in 1972. The 1978 Tentative Final Monograph listed 21 ingredients, which changed to the current list of 16 with the 1996 approval of the New Drug Application (NDA) for avobenzone (2).

Importantly, any new sunscreen active ingredient, or even an old sunscreen used inconsistent with the OTC monograph, technically results in FDA classification of that product as an unapproved new drug. Clinical testing thus requires an Investigational New Drug (IND), and marketing requires approval of an NDA containing sufficient data on quality, safety, and efficacy. Due to the high cost of such R&D programs, companies usually enter the sunscreen market with products compliant with the OTC monograph. Indeed, only one new sunscreen active ingredient (avobenzone) has been approved using the NDA process since the inception of the OTC monograph process in 1972 (2). Thus, the regulatory classification of sunscreens as drugs in the USA, while protecting the public, also effectively represents an economic barrier to development of new active ingredients.

While the OTC monograph allows sunscreen marketing without a submission, the Food, Drug and Cosmetic Act still requires the marketer to provide assurance that its products are safe in humans prior to marketing. Indeed, safety concerns have led to the withdrawal of several OTC sunscreen formulations and active ingredients. Unexpected interactions among formulation components, skin irritation in certain subsets of patients, and unexpected sensitization responses have unfortunately led to safety "surprises" in the marketplace. Thus, confirmation of the safety of otherwise OTC-compliant products is needed even though no additional data need to be filed with FDA prior to marketing. This burden on the company to assure safety prior to marketing also applies to "purely" cosmetic compounds, which are even less regulated compared to the OTC monographed drugs like sunscreens.

The present chapter is a review of the safety issues associated with sunscreen development, and a summary of the safety testing models available (*in vitro*, animal, and human). This chapter also provides perspective on the development and evaluation of safety data in terms of the risk/benefit of sunscreens.

PARAMETERS AFFECTING SUNSCREEN SAFETY

Sunscreen safety in the marketplace is affected by the chemical structure, as well as environmental, and use factors that may affect their toxicity. Environmental and use factors include those that have the potential to produce reactive species (e.g., light exposure leading to phototoxicity), and those that may affect dermal and systemic exposure. Factors known to affect dermal and systemic exposure, and therefore toxicity of a sunscreen include actual applied dose, treatment frequency, hydration of the skin, sites of the body treated, total body surface area treated, treatment of compromised skin (e.g., abrasions, sunburn), effect of sweating, exposure of the skin to water during bathing, and the potential for concomitant treatment with other topical products. Variables also include demographic differences in skin characteristics such as race, age, and gender (3). The impact of any one of these variables upon a product's toxicity is potentially significant. In practice, safety programs usually address the primary and most significant variables, and in the process generate a range of safety data that captures or "brackets" the impact of other less significant variables upon the risk assessment. This approach usually allows the less significant variables to be addressed via "paper" arguments regarding their potential impact upon safety.

The convenient grouping of approved sunscreens into organic and inorganic categories reflects not only their chemistry, but also their general mechanism of efficacy and potential for toxicity. Organic sunscreens are the most popular types with many ingredients approved for use in the OTC monograph (1). The mechanism of action of the organic sunscreens relates to the activation of double bond electrons in the molecule by UV-B radiation, followed later by emission of the energy as low-energy and less-damaging light and heat (4). This same proposed mechanism of efficacy against UV-B radiation, however, is also a concern from the toxicology standpoint, since this same activation could theoretically lead to generation of reactive intermediates. In practice, however, the approved organic active ingredients show a high level of safety even with prolonged use.

On the other hand, the approved inorganic sunscreens (titanium dioxide and zinc oxide) are largely biologically inert. These minimally absorbed, microfine inorganic particles accomplish their efficacy by remaining on the surface of the skin and reflecting UV light, thus acting as an effective sunblock. The action spectrum shows that these inorganic compounds are most effective in the UV-A range, thus they find common use in combination with UV-B-absorbing organic sunscreens to provide broad-spectrum protection.

SAFETY PROGRAMS REQUIRED FOR SUNSCREEN PRODUCTS

Safety programs for sunscreen products usually fall into three main categories, based upon intended use of the data from the program: (a) safety programs for the company's internal R&D decision-making, (b) traditional safety programs to confirm safety of OTC monograph-compliant products, and (c) full safety programs for new sunscreen active ingredients (full NDA programs). The predictiveness, extent, and cost for these three types of programs can vary significantly. Programs designed for internal decision-making often include *in vitro* models used as part of a screening program for selection of ingredients and formulations (see following text). These models may not be accepted by FDA as validated predictors of safety in humans, and often carry a higher risk of false positives and false negatives. The company usually uses these faster and cheaper models to collect data to be used for optimizing the formulation, and often later conducts the longer-term, more expensive, confirmatory safety studies using validated FDA-accepted models.

On the other hand, safety programs for OTC monograph-compliant products usually employ more predictive, traditional *in vivo* safety models to confirm lack of key dermal toxicities: skin irritation, eye irritation, and delayed contact hypersensitivity. Typically the ingredients' safety is already well characterized, and the studies are conducted to confirm there are no unexpected toxicities for that particular formulation. Similar programs are conducted for primarily cosmetic products containing approved sunscreens (e.g., hair care products, lipstick, and makeup). The obligation to confirm safety is still with the manufacturer, and the goal is to provide assurance that there are no surprises in the marketplace.

The third category is more extensive since FDA considers new sunscreen actives to be new drugs. In practice, these programs include assessment of safety in several categories including genotoxicity, drug transport and disposition (absorption, distribution, metabolism, and excretion; ADME), dermal safety, systemic safety, and special safety (reproduction, teratology, carcinogenesis). Important variables that affect toxicity are also addressed, including the exposure to light (phototoxicity, photoallergy, photocarcinogenesis), the effect of skin variability (age, gender, race), and parameters affecting drug transport (e.g., treatment of compromised skin, location of treatment site). Studies typically proceed in the order of *in vitro*, *in vivo* (animal), and *in vivo* (human), often with studies conducted concurrently in order to expedite the overall program. Separate studies are usually conducted on the drug substance (active ingredient) and drug product (complete formulation) in order to assess intrinsic toxicity of the active as well as toxic behavior in a more realistic exposure matrix. Study design often includes placebo and positive controls in order to confirm the study validity and to "benchmark" the results with marketed products to help put the results in perspective. For the special toxicity studies in the areas of reproduction, teratology, and carcinogenesis, only the active ingredient is tested, and positive controls are typically not included. Broader assessment of safety may include assessment of accidental misuse or abuse situations (oral toxicity, eye irritation). Usage studies include testing in large numbers of subjects who are provided "final" labelled product with the instructions for use, with subsequent measurement of product consumption and consumer comments. These studies help predict actual variability in exposure (and safety) in the future marketplace, since subjects often do not follow instructions on use.

For new sunscreen ingredients, the amount of safety data required for marketing authorization varies by country and regulatory authority (5). One of the realities is that some countries classify sunscreens as cosmetics, and require less safety data for marketing authorization compared to the USA. If marketed earlier outside the USA, the safety data collected from these markets may subsequently be submitted to FDA under Material Time and Extent provisions, in order to support marketing authorization in the USA (5).

SAFETY TESTING MODELS FOR SUNSCREEN PRODUCTS

Protocols for safety testing can be found in a variety of resources (6–8). Critical for design of a safety program are: (a) specific objectives for the program, (b) the regulatory requirements for the studies in the program, (c) the relevant scientific and medical information related to the issue at hand, and (d) the corporate ethics and acceptable risk/benefit for that product in the marketplace. A description of the key models used to evaluate the safety issues common to sunscreen products follows. Included are comments on their endpoints and relevance in a safety program. As noted, compliance with the OTC monograph eliminates the need to file data with the FDA, and studies are conducted mainly for internal confirmation. On the other hand, development of a new sunscreen active ingredient in the USA would lead to conduct of not only *in vitro*, but the *in vivo* animal and human studies listed below as well.

In Vitro Models

Sunscreen drug development programs usually employ *in vitro* models for safety assessment due to significant savings in terms of cost and time when compared to standard *in vivo* safety models. Common models are shown in Table 4.1. While *in vitro* results are least relevant to safety assessment in humans, they play a particularly important role in the safety screening process since poor performing ingredients can be eliminated early, thus avoiding unnecessary exposure to animals and humans.

Sunscreens not only need to protect the consumer from the genotoxic effects of UVR, but themselves need to be devoid of genotoxic effects. While approved OTC sunscreens do not need to be tested, new sunscreen candidates usually undergo a battery of tests, each with its own advantages, disadvantages and limitations. *In vitro* models used to assess potential for genetic damage include the reverse mutation (Ames) test in bacteria, and the mouse lymphoma test in mammalian cells. The ability of a chemical or formulation to induce broader scale genetic damage in chromosomes is assessed in the mouse micronucleus assay, which measures the more macroscopic histological changes in chromosomes after *in vivo* treatment of mice. A positive response suggesting mutagenic potential is cause for concern and usually triggers either more extensive testing or rejection of the new sunscreen candidate.

In addition to these classical genotoxicity tests, other more investigative models have also been developed to screen for genotoxic potential, as well as photogenotoxic potential. These models include direct incubation with DNA, bacteria, and yeast, either with or without radiation (9). While not definitive measures of safety, these models streamline the screening process and are usually followed up with testing in the more validated, *in vivo*-relevant safety models. Indeed the lack of correlation of some *in vitro* results with effects in humans points to the need to interpret results from *in vitro* models with caution. This is due to the fact that *in vitro* models cannot emulate the *in vivo* dynamics of drug exposure, absorption, metabolism, and elimination from the treatment site, all of which have the potential to affect toxicity.

Table 4.1 Common *In Vitro* Safety Models

In vitro safety model	Endpoint	Rationale for use
Genotoxicity		
Ames mutagenesis	Point mutation (bacteria)	Gene mutation test (bacterial, *in vitro*)
Mouse lymphoma	Point mutation and chromosomal abberations (mammalian)	Gene mutation test (mammalian, *in vitro*)
Mouse micronucleus (*in vivo*)	Chromosomal damage	Gross genetic damage (*in vivo*)
Photogenotoxicity	Mutagenicity (Ames) after exposure of product to light	Measures light activation to a mutagenic species
Cytotoxicity	Cell death *in vitro* via neutral red uptake	Detects general cell toxicity
Photocytotoxicity	Cell damage after exposure of cells to product and light	Detects potential for light-activation to acutely toxic species
In vitro ocular tolerance (cytosensor microphysiometer, tissue equivalent assay (TEA), *ex vivo* rabbit eye or bovine corneal models)	Cell toxicity as a function of dose and time	*In vitro* models for potential for eye irritation
In vitro skin penetration	Transport of chemical through skin samples	Drug transport will allow assessment of systemic exposure

Investigative models have also been developed for prediction of a compound's potential for producing skin irritation, as assessed by direct cell damage *in vitro*. Accordingly, *in vitro* cytotoxicity assessment is a relatively quick means of obtaining data suggestive of irritation potential. The model includes treatment of mammalian cells (fibroblasts or keratinocytes) *in vitro* with the chemical, and measuring cellular uptake of a dye, which is indicative of cell damage (10). Photocytotoxicity employs a similar model, with the inclusion of exposure to UVR to simulate the solar spectrum. Indeed, use of this model has found acceptance in the European Union, due to its strong correlation with *in vivo* photoirritation (11). In order to identify the potential for ocular toxicity early in the program, the cytosensor method, the tissue equivalent assay (TEA), or the *ex vivo* rabbit ocular toxicity models may be used. The cytosensor method determines the metabolic rate via production of acid metabolites in murine fibroblasts, whereas the TEA model measures mitochondrial metabolism in epithelial cells via the dye stain MTT. *In vitro* corneal cell toxicity may also be assessed in isolated bovine corneal cells (10).

An important element of any topical drug program, including sunscreens, is the assessment of dermal drug transport. These models are used to measure absorption and potential for systemic toxicity. Skin penetration, and potential for systemic toxicity, is of course not a desired trait for sunscreens. Drug transport can be assessed *in vitro* using skin samples from animals or humans, with the transport ultimately depending upon many factors including the physical and chemical characteristics of the drug (12). In the standard model, drug is applied topically to a skin sample layered over a diffusion cell, and the amount of drug passing through the skin sample and into the lower diffusion chamber is quantified (13). Drug design for sunscreens includes considerations such as molecular weight, lipophilicity, and polarity to minimize drug transport through the stratum corneum, the rate-limiting factor in drug transport through the skin. *In vitro* and *in vivo* assessment of drug transport is critical to the overall risk assessment of the compound or formulation, since these are the data used to make estimates of systemic exposure and toxicity in all of the organ systems other than the skin.

For reliable use in a sunscreen development program, each of these *in vitro* models should be first validated in terms of their ability to predict response in man. Ultimately, this is accomplished through generation of data that establish reproducible and consistent comparison of response. From a practical standpoint, different compounds and classes of compounds are tested in each model. More rigorous data will be required by FDA in the event screening models are used in a drug submission. The search for validated methods is warranted however, due to the benefits such systems may play in development programs in terms of speeding the screening of candidates, and reduction of the need for testing in animals and humans.

In Vivo Dermal Safety Testing in Animals

In vivo dermal safety testing in animals represents the next stage of safety assessment, and is conducted to obtain data more relevant to humans. Key models include those listed in Table 4.2.

In vivo assessment of new candidates for sunscreens typically includes primary skin irritation in animals. The rabbit is the traditional animal model, with both abraded and unabraded skin tested. The more expensive minipig may be used since its skin characteristics model humans better than either rabbits or rodents with thinner skin and higher hair density. Treatment duration can be from a few days to several weeks, and it is important to prevent the animal from removing the test product from the treatment site. Indeed, mice without restraint can ingest the majority of a topically applied product in a matter of minutes (14). In traditional topical skin irritation studies, animals are initially

Table 4.2 *In Vivo* Dermal Safety Models—Animals

In vivo dermal safety—animals	Model (endpoint)	Rationale for use
Skin irritation	Rabbit patch testing (erythema, edema, scaling)	*In vivo* model for acute skin irritation
Phototoxicity	Rabbit patch model with light activation (acute erythema, edema, scaling)	Light activation to irritating species
Delayed contact hypersensitivity	Local lymph node assay (LLNA) or guinea pig maximization (erythema, edema)	Potential for sensitization
Photoallergy	Sensitization models with inclusion of light (erythema, edema)	Light activation to potentially sensitizing agent
Eye irritation	Rabbit low-volume eye test or rabbit Draize test (erythema, inflammation)	Confirmation of *in vitro* positive results
Subchronic dermal toxicity	Rabbit or rodent dermal model, typically 28-day study (dermal and systemic safety endpoints)	Assess topical and systemic safety after repeat topical doses
Dermal carcinogenicity	Rodent model and other new *in vivo* models (onset and incidence of tumors).	Confirmation of positive genotoxicity results
Photocarcinogenicity	Rodent model, typically hairless mouse (onset and incidence of light-induced tumor production)	Confirmation of positive photogenotoxicity results

shaved, treated daily, and skin irritation is assessed by grading on a visual scale for erythema, edema, and scaling. Dose-ranging, by varying concentration or volume applied, is included in order to identify the highest non-irritating dose. As human data are obtained later in the program, the *in vivo* animal models are reviewed to identify which is most predictive of humans for that particular product. This "validated" model is then used in the future for further optimizing the formulation.

Phototoxicity studies assess the potential of the light to produce irritating species in mice previously treated with topical formulation. In the typical model, hairless mice are treated topically, with one group subsequently exposed to simulated solar light. The ability of light to shift the dose-response curve for skin irritation (erythema, edema) is an index of whether light interacts with the product to produce irritating species. Organic sunscreens, which actually absorb UV light, have the theoretical potential to produce reactive species as they release this energy into the surrounding dermal tissues.

For detection of delayed contact hypersensitivity, the mouse local lymph node assay (LLNA) is now the preferred *in vivo* model of choice due to cost and relevance of the data to humans (15). In LLNA, the test material is painted on the ear of mice daily for three consecutive days. The local lymph nodes are harvested on day 6 to determine if lymphocyte cell proliferation has taken place above a predetermined stimulation index of threefold. In the guinea pig maximization test, shaved guinea pigs are treated daily for 3 weeks (induction phase) with the highest nonirritating dose previously determined in separate skin irritation studies. After a 2-week rest phase, the animals are dosed and graded for erythema and edema at 24 and 48 h (challenge phase), with positive responders rechallenged after a second rest period to confirm the result (16). Photoallergy is assessed in a similar model, except that exposure to the compound and light is included during the induction phase. A positive response during the challenge phase indicates that the compound has the ability to produce photoreactive species that can induce a sensitization response.

Assessment of the potential for eye irritation is important for new actives and formulations due to the potential for the eye to be accidentally exposed to the product. The standard model is the Draize eye irritation test in rabbits, using both rinsed and nonrinsed treatment groups. Irritation is graded using a scale that takes into account several parameters. An improvement over the Draize model is the low-volume eye irritation test, which is predictive of responses in humans but less stress for the animals (17). As noted earlier, the development of predictive *in vitro* methods for eye irritation have significantly reduced the use of animals.

Subchronic dermal toxicity assessment is usually a later-stage toxicity model, which assesses not only dermal but systemic toxicity as well. The typical species is the rat, with treatment duration of 28 days or longer in the standard toxicity protocol. Animals are shaved at intervals and treated daily, with periodic assessment of dermal (erythema, edema, scaling) and systemic toxicity (behavioral effects, food consumption, body weight). At the end of the study, animals are sacrificed, and systemic safety is assessed by standard parameters (gross pathology, organ weights, histopathology, hematology, serum chemistry, urinalysis). As with other *in vivo* models, ingestion must be minimized in order to attribute any observed toxicity to dermal exposure. Observations in treated and control animals (placebo formulation) are compared to confirm any drug-related toxicities.

Dermal carcinogenicity and photocarcinogenicity represent the late-stage animal safety studies for new sunscreen actives. The need for these studies is based upon the potential for chronic exposure of humans to the candidate sunscreen. The typical animal model includes treatment of hairless mice daily for 2 years, with assessment of any dermal tumors in terms of onset and frequency, as well as assessment of tumor production at sacrifice. Photocarcinogenicity is assessed in a similar model except with inclusion of simulated solar radiation. Pilot studies are conducted to allow for selection of proper dose ranges and to assure adequate survival in the main study to assure statistical validity. Protocols for these very expensive and long-term studies are discussed with FDA in advance, and as with other toxicity studies follow the relevant guidelines of the International Conference on Harmonization (ICH) (18).

In Vivo Systemic Safety Testing in Animals

Sunscreens are selected for their efficacy properties as well as their dermal safety, lack of systemic absorption, and lack of systemic toxicity. Virtually any systemic toxicity of a sunscreen would present an unacceptable risk/benefit situation. This is because the level of risk deemed "acceptable" is very low due to the fact that other relatively safe products are already available, and since use will occur in an uncontrolled OTC market environment. Subchronic dermal toxicity, as noted earlier, is a model used to assess both local (dermal) as well as systemic safety of the compound. Other key models for assessment of systemic safety of new actives and formulations are given in Table 4.3.

Table 4.3 Key Models for Assessment of Systemic Safety—Animals

Systemic safety—animals	Model (endpoint)	Rationale for use
Acute oral toxicity	Rodent and nonrodent (acute symptoms and lethality after acute exposure)	Assess safety after accidental ingestion or high systemic dose
Subchronic dermal or oral toxicity	Rodent and nonrodent repeat dose studies (behavioral effects, gross pathology, histopathology, serum chemistry, urinalysis)	Identifies target organ toxicities after prolonged high systemic exposure, and provides key data for the risk assessment
Teratology	Rodent and nonrodent models (malformations *in utero*)	Determines potential for toxicity to the fetus and offspring
Reproduction	Rodent models (impairment of reproductive capacity, using multiple endpoints)	Determines potential for toxicity to reproductive system of male and female
Dermal pharmacokinetics and absorption, distribution, metabolism, and excretion (ADME)	Rodent and nonrodent (drug dermal transport, and distribution, metabolism, and excretion)	Determines systemic exposure, fate of absorbed drug in the body, and key data for risk assessment

Acute oral toxicity is typically assessed in mice or rats, and is a broad indicator of the potential systemic toxic effects of the drug candidate. The classic parallel-design LD_{50} model has been replaced with an increasing dose model that is less demanding in terms of animal use. In a full toxicology program, acute toxicity assessment is usually followed by subchronic oral toxicity, which typically ranges in duration from 28 to 91 days and includes the systemic parameters noted above for subchronic dermal toxicity studies.

Teratology and reproductive toxicity are two additional elements of a program designed to assess the systemic toxicity of a new drug candidate on offspring and reproductive success. Teratology studies assess the effect of systemic drug on the embryo and fetus, and are usually conducted in two species (rodent and nonrodent). The number and types of malformations are compared in control and treatment groups using a dose–response design. Reproductive toxicity studies assess the effect of drug on male and female reproductive organs, and reproductive performance. In peri- and postnatal toxicity studies, pregnant females are treated prior to, during, and after pregnancy to assess effects on the offspring. Protocols vary according to program needs, but all are designed to identify a no-effect level in order to allow for a proper risk assessment.

Percutaneous drug absorption and its distribution, metabolism, and excretion (ADME) are typically evaluated in rodents treated topically with radiolabeled drug. Radiolabel is measured in urine, feces, treated site on the skin, and in the organs of the remaining carcass to confirm the amount of drug absorbed and tissue distribution. Metabolites in blood and urine are usually quantified, and gross assessment of drug absorption is determined by measuring percent of dose recovered in urine and feces. For many compounds, percutaneous absorption in rodent models provides an overestimate of drug transport in man, based on the rodent's thinner skin and higher hair density. As the program progresses, data are obtained in several species, including humans, and the animal model most representative of exposure and metabolite profiles in humans is identified. This species is then given special attention in the risk assessment, since it is presumed to better reflect and predict potential toxicities in humans due to these similarities.

In Vivo Dermal and Systemic Safety Testing in Humans

Safety testing of sunscreens in humans should normally be a confirmation of the encouraging results obtained in prior *in vitro* and animal testing. While *in vitro* and *in vivo* animal data are useful, they never completely predict responses in humans. Studies in humans should not only confirm safety, but they should also be designed to predict safety in the larger population. Accordingly, human safety testing programs often include smaller-sized studies to confirm response, followed by larger studies to detect low-frequency responses in key demographic groups (race, age, skin type). Larger numbers of subjects are required to reliably detect low-frequency responses. Indeed, a frequency of 1% incidence of a significant toxicity such as delayed contact hypersensitivity (two responders in a group of 200 subjects) would translate to 10,000 people affected per 1 million users. The company is thus faced with design of larger studies to minimize surprises and unnecessary risk in the future marketplace, where the costs associated with termination of a program are much higher.

Key human safety models for sunscreens are shown in Table 4.4.

Acute and subchronic skin irritation are usually assessed over small areas on the back or arms using both unoccluded (open) and occluded (patched) treatment areas. Unoccluded sites resemble the actual use situation in the marketplace, where volatile formulation ingredients are allowed to evaporate. Occlusion, on the other hand, represents a worst-case situation where the applied material is allowed to better penetrate the stratum corneum via hydration of the skin under the occluded patch. In both models, erythema, edema, and other elevated responses are assessed as the primary indicators of skin irritation.

Delayed contact hypersensitivity (dermal sensitization) in humans is assessed using the human repeat insult patch test (HRIPT). A 3-week induction

Table 4.4 Key Models for Assessment of Safety—Humans

Dermal and systemic safety—humans	Model (endpoint)	Rationale for use
Acute skin irritation	Acute patch testing under occlusive or semiocclusive patches (acute erythema, edema)	Confirm dermal nonirritating dose in humans
Subchronic skin irritation	21-day cumulative patch test (acute erythema, edema)	Confirm nonirritating dose after repeat dose in humans
Delayed contact hypersensitivity	Human repeat-insult patch test (HRIPT) (prolonged erythema and edema after challenge phase)	Provides confirmation that drug is of low sensitization potential in humans
Human phototoxicity	Acute patch model with simulated solar radiation (acute erythema, edema)	Confirmation of lack of phototoxicity in humans
Human photoallergy	HRIPT-type model with solar radiation (prolonged erythema and edema after challenge phase)	Confirmation of lack of photoallergy in humans
Human dermal pharmacokinetics and absorption, distribution, metabolism, and excretion	Human dermal model (blood/urine levels of drug and key metabolites)	Confirms actual systemic exposure in humans, and provides key data for systemic risk assessment

phase, using a nonirritating concentration and occlusion, is followed by a 2-week rest, then a challenge phase (7). A positive response is represented by a prolonged erythema/edema at a naïve treatment site. Typically, 100–200 subjects are used in order to detect low-frequency positive responses.

Phototoxicity and photoallergy studies in humans employ similar models as the skin irritation and HRIPT models described in the preceding text, except that simulated solar radiation is included in the treatment phase. The models include appropriate controls for the formulation excipients and the presence of light, so that any positive response is due to light interaction with the drug.

RISK ASSESSMENT AND SAFETY TESTING OF SUNSCREENS

Results from the safety studies mentioned earlier allow for a risk assessment for a new sunscreen candidate. This is done by calculating the no observable adverse effect level (NOAEL) from animal studies, and comparing it to the level of exposure estimated for humans. This NOAEL/human dose ratio is the safety margin for the product, and it is calculated separately for each toxicity endpoint. Although FDA has not defined a minimally acceptable safety margin, this NOAEL/human dose ratio would traditionally be at least 100-fold. Of this, a 10-fold margin is included to account for species variability between animals and humans, with a further 10-fold margin added to account for variability in response within the human population. Indeed, it is appropriate that FDA not set a defined minimal acceptable ratio, since the appropriate ratio would vary depending on the toxic effect, the frequency of the effect in the population, the variability in actual dose applied in the marketplace, the benefit to the consumer (i.e., risk acceptance), and many other considerations. However, for a drug product in the sunscreen category, a conservative acceptable safety margin ratio of 100-fold is reasonable since there are adequate sunscreens already available on the market, with known and acceptable safety and efficacy. For marketed active ingredients, the safety margins are actually much higher in order to assure safety of subjects in an uncontrolled OTC market use situation.

For the safety models described, the validation of all models is critical since false positives and false negatives can lead to missed opportunities or unpleasant safety surprises in the market. Ideally, a properly validated model should demonstrate a dose-response, and provide a rank-ordering of "actives" that corresponds to the rank order of the safety of these compounds in humans.

CONCLUSION

By design, sunscreens provide protection from UV-B and UV-A by either absorbing or reflecting this UV radiation. Accordingly, the risk assessment of a new sunscreen candidate should include the benefits of blocking UV-A and UV-B, as well as the actual safety profile of the sunscreen itself. FDA's acceptance of the safety of currently marketed sunscreens was determined during the OTC monograph process, which included a review of all available safety data on many actives. For 15 of the existing actives, and one new active approved under an NDA, the conclusion was that the risk to humans for these actives was very low in an OTC use scenario. Most "new" sunscreen products actually include these previously approved OTC active ingredients, thus safety testing is more limited, does not need to be filed with FDA, and is performed by the company to confirm there are no unexpected toxicities for their particular formulation.

On the other hand, a truly new sunscreen active ingredient must be subjected to the extensive safety testing described in the previous sections, since it would be classified as an unapproved new drug with IND and NDA filing requirements. From a toxicology perspective, this database provides the data needed for a proper risk assessment to protect subjects during clinical testing, and to protect consumers in the future marketplace. To date, R&D activity has shown that few companies have been willing to pursue this expensive and long-term investment, but perhaps the growing demand for safe and even more effective UV-A and UV-B sunscreens will provide the needed financial incentive.

REFERENCES

1. Code of Federal Regulations Title 21, Section 352.10. Sunscreen active ingredients. Revised as of April 1, 2003. Final Rule May 21, 1999.
2. Approved Drug Products with Therapeutic Equivalence Evaluations, US Department of Health and Human Services, Food and Drug Administration, 1996.
3. Robinson MK. Population differences in acute skin irritation responses. Race, sex, age, sensitive skin and repeat subject comparisons. Contact Dermatitis 2002; 46(2):86–93.
4. Shaath NA, ed. Sunscreens: Regulations and Commercial Development. 3rd ed. New York: Marcel Dekker, 2005.
5. Steinberg DC. Regulations of sunscreens worldwide. In: Shaath NA, ed. Sunscreens: Regulations and Commercial Development. 3rd ed. New York: Marcel Dekker, 2005:173–198.
6. OECD Guidelines for the Testing of Chemicals. Vol. 1. Paris: Organization for Economic Co-operation and Development, 1993.
7. Haschek WM, Rousseaux CG. Handbook of Toxicologic Pathology. New York: Academic Press, 1991.
8. Niesink RJM, Vries J, Hollinger MA. Toxicology Principles and Applications. New York: CRC Press, 1996.
9. Marrot L, Belaidi JP, Chaubo C, Meunier JR, Perez P, Causse C. An in vitro strategy to evaluate the phototoxicity of solar UV at the molecular and cellular level: application to photoprotection assessment. Eur J Dermatol 1998; 8:403–412.
10. Nohynek GJ, Schaefer H. Benefit and risk of organic ultraviolet filters. Regul Toxicol Pharmacol 2001; 33:285–299.
11. Opinion concerning basic criteria for the in vitro assessment of percutaneous absorption of cosmetic ingredients. EU Scientific Committee on Cosmetic Products and Non-Food Products Intended for Consumers. June 23, 1999.

12. Kasting GB, Filloon TG, Francis WR, Meredith MP. Improving the sensitivity of in vitro skin penetration experiments. Pharm Res 1994; 11(12):1747–1754.
13. Franz TJ. Percutaneous absorption and the relevance of in vitro data. J Invest Dermatol 1975; 64(3):190–195.
14. Schwen RJ. Drug development, quality of data, and meetings with the FDA. Presented at the Australian Biotechnology Association Meeting, Brisbane, Australia, Nov 2002.
15. Kimber I, Dearman RJ, Basketter DA, Ryan CA, Gerberick GF. The local lymph node assay: past, present and future. Contact Dermatitis 2002; 47(6):315–328.
16. Buehler EV, Newmann EA, Parker RD. Use of the occlusive patch to evaluate the photosensitive properties of chemicals in guinea pigs. Food Chem Toxicol 1985; 23(7):689–694.
17. Gettings SD, Lordo RA, Demetrulias J, Feder PI, Hintze KL. Comparison of low-volume, Draize and in vitro eye irritation test data. I. Hydroalcoholic formulations. Food Chem Toxicol 1996; 34(8):737–749.
18. New Horizons and Future Challenges. Sixth International Conference on Harmonisation, Osaka, Japan, Nov 15, 2003.

5

Sunprotection: Historical Perspective

Paolo U. Giacomoni
Clinique Laboratories, Melville, New York, USA

Life expectancy in Europe and North America has increased by a factor of 3 in the last three centuries. One of the paradoxical consequences of increasing life span has been that chronic exposure to small, not immediately life-threatening insults accumulates as physiological changes later in life, which are unpleasant at best and life-threatening at worst. This is particularly true for the changes provoked by solar radiation.

THE SUN AND HUMANS IN THE PAST

Some of the beneficial and harmful effects of solar radiation have been known since antiquity, at least in the surroundings of the Mediterranean Sea. The beneficial effects of the sun, its necessity for the survival of the human species, were so clear to the humans in these regions, that the cult of the God Sun was developed that lasted several thousand years in ancient Egypt. This cult perpetuated itself, under different aspects, until the development of Mithraism and his philosophical influence upon the newly born Christian religion.

One would think that the adoration of the sun was shared by the ancient Greeks. They had a predilection for Apollo, the driver of the chariot of the sun, and indeed, when thinking of ancient Greeks, the image comes to mind of naked athletes or warriors, as sculpted in marble or painted on vases. A naive conclusion from these observations could be that ancient Greeks were not worried by solar radiation. Yet, the observation of other paintings or the reading of Greek literature convinces us that this is not the case.

First of all, tan was not palatable to ancient Greeks. Hera, the "first lady" of the Olympos, is repeatedly described in the Iliad as having white arms.

In the description of Ulysses' adventures, Homer says that while Princess Nausicaa and her friends wait for the linen to dry, they swim in the sea. And after the bath they apply olive oil to their bodies, have a sort of picnic, and then, after having thrown away the veils covering their heads, they play ball.

This means that these young women want to be unimpeded when playing ball, but that before the game, for the picnic, they had dressed themselves up and had covered their heads because they knew that men prefer women with white skin, as well as because they were aware of the scorching effects of the sun.

The care taken by women in ancient Greece to protect themselves against the burning rays of the sun is apparent in Antigone's words: "I see a woman. She comes toward us, mounted on a young mare. On her head, a thessalian hat with large brims covers her face to protect her against the sun".

Vase paintings, too, reveal that ancient Greeks were aware of the dangers linked to sun exposure. At the Metropolitan Museum of Arts in New York, one finds documented evidence in favor of the above statement. On a vase of the 5th century BC, the Trojan prince Paris is depicted as a young shepherd. He wears a coat and a hat with a large brim. The other masculine figures in the painting are also wearing full body-covering coats. This seems to indicate that when not racing or fighting, men tended to cover their bodies. Yet, not all of the warriors were necessarily naked. A painting of the 4th century BC portrays the combat of Greeks and Amazons, with fully dressed warriors. In a more peaceful painting from the 6th century BC the painter portrays the participants in a wedding procession as fully dressed men and women. Because of the mild climate of Greece, those clothes were not intended to protect against the cold, so the last interpretation we are left with is that those clothes and hats were meant to protect against the sun.

Similar paintings can be found on Greek vases in every archeological museum.

The most concise, yet precise, description of the harmful effects of the sun is given by Xenophon. Between 400 BC and 398 BC he was one of the officers committed to bringing back to Greece a battalion of 10,000 Spartan mercenaries from central Mesopotamia (today's Iraq), where they were fighting an unsuccessful war and were at risk of becoming slaves. Upon crossing a snow-covered mountain in Armenia, he noticed the effects of freezing temperatures and of the albedo of snow. He writes: "Soldiers who lost the use of the eyes, blinded by the snow, or who lost their toes because of the cold, were abandoned. In order to protect the eyes against the albedo from the snow, they kept a black fabric before the eyes, and in order to protect their feet, they kept moving continuously". From this we learn that as early as the beginning of the 4th century BC, Greek mercenaries knew the cause–effect relationship between the albedo of the snow and the impairment of the eye, as well as the possibility of avoiding it by reducing the number of photons reaching the eye.

Etruscans were not afraid of working in the fields and chasing game under the sun. They painted scenes of every day life with men wearing coats and hats. They painted themselves as tanned men, but their women were always painted as white. Only dancers were naked. The Romans, too, seem to have preferred white skin for their loved ones (be they boys or girls). Yet, what remains of their writings, filtered by the Christian monks of the middle age, does tell us much about their philosophical and political views but very little about how they protected their skin against solar radiation.

The superficial researcher does not find much to read about sun protection in the writings from the low Roman Empire through the Middle Ages and Renaissance until the late 18th century. The *Interpretatio Arabicorum Nominum* by Andrea Alpago, first published in Venice in 1527 as an appendix to Avicenna's *Canon* does not contain one single word about ingredients able to protect against the damage caused by the sun.

In the 500 pages or so of the two volumes of Hufeland's *Art of Increasing Human Life Span*, published in Jena (Germany) in 1796, avoiding exposure to sunlight is not quoted as a way to improve, if not life span, at least the quality of the skin. It has to be noted, though, that the skin was known to be an important organ of the body and Hufeland uses about 10 pages in describing methods for taking care of one's skin. One of the possible reasons for not laying emphasis on the consequences of excessive exposure to solar radiation is that at the end of the 18th century in Germany, 80% of the human beings did not live beyond the age of 30, and only 6% lived longer than 60 years: physiologists and doctors had yet to understand the essence of microbial infection and were not yet ready to tackle dermatological issues.

In these same times, British aristocrats and Swiss scientists discovered an interest in gratuitous physical activity and the pleasure of climbing mountains. The Mont Blanc became fashionable. In 1786 Paccard and Balmat reached the top of the Mont Blanc. Thirty years later, Countess Henriette d'Angeville climbed the Mont Blanc. After having reached the top, she observed the guides who helped her in the climbing: one's lips were bleeding and his face was covered with "droplets", another had a visual impairment, a third one had black lips, covered with blisters. Curious about her own situation, she took a mirror from her bag and noticed that she had a swollen nose and lips, the white of her eyes was all red and crossed by darker red veins, her skin was as if grilled, and purple colored from the chin to the roots of the hair.

This is to say that by the end of the 18th century, centuries-long popular knowledge and newly acquired aristocratic experience agreed on the fact that exposure to solar radiation is harmful. What happened in the next century to justify the craze about sunbathing which still lasts today?

EXPERIMENTAL EVIDENCE OF BENEFICIAL AND HARMFUL EFFECTS OF SOLAR RADIATION

In the 19th century, the Industrial Revolution moved large amounts of the population from the country to the cities, and the standards of living dropped dramatically. In particular, instead of working or playing in the fields, children were compelled to work hard in factories, lived in poorly equipped houses, and were deprived of milk, and they developed rickets. The Polish physician Sniadecki (1768–1838) realized that children living in rural areas around Warsaw did not develop rickets. He concluded that it was the lack of exposure to sunlight that caused the high incidence of rickets in Warsaw, and postulated that this was also the cause for the high incidence of rickets in the highly industrialized cities of northern Europe. It took 70 years for T.A. Palm, a British physician, to draw the same conclusions in 1890, upon observing that children had a high risk of developing rickets in the cities of Great Britain, whereas children living in equally squalid yet sunlit conditions in India did not develop the disease. He concluded that sunbathing could have beneficial effects in avoiding rickets, and recommended it to the medical community. In 1919 the German physician Huldschinsky treated rickets with radiation from a mercury lamp and suggested that UV was responsible for the curative effect. [For a detailed account on rickets and its cure, see Ref. (1).]

In the meanwhile, Finsen (the 1903 Nobel Prize winner) was experimenting in treating phototherapy diseases as diverse as small pox, tuberculosis, and lupus erythematosus. A strong positive image became associated with sunlight, irrespective of the observations by Dubreuilh or Unna indicating that farmers develop skin cancer in sun exposed zones, whereas city dwellers are rarely affected (2) or that sailors exposed a long time to sunlight develop "sailor's skin", a condition characterized by erythema, pigmentation, and hyperkeratosis, and have a chance of developing skin cancer (3).

At the turn of the century, in the time of the triumphant Belle Epoque, British aristocrats and dandies "discovered" the French Riviera, invented outdoor sports, praised physical activity, and as an accessory, developed a tan. The Belle Epoque ended catastrophically with World War I. Men were sent to the front and for many years all the work in farms and factories was performed by women. This has greatly contributed to the social emancipation of women. Could it be that it also pushed women into the sun, and won them over to the psychological pleasure of displaying a tan similar to the one of dandies and aristocrats? Whatever the reason, in the 1930s the tan became a must. According to Driscoll (4), "the French fashion designer Coco Chanel is credited with promoting suntanning as a fashion statement at this time. Thus, by the 1930s, it became fashionable to wear more revealing swimming costumes to develop a slight tan, which was also a statement that a tanned person was rich enough to afford a holiday in the sun". And to spread the fashion of tanning beyond the borders of the affluent class, the French government promulgated in 1936 a law establishing the principle of paid vacations: the employee was paid during the days off. France has a few thousand kilometers of coasts and the rush to the sea was generalized. So, about 65 years ago, exposure to solar radiation became a mass phenomenon in Europe. Everybody immediately noticed what was first published by Widmark in 1889 (5), that exposure to ultraviolet provokes erythema, and the necessity for a sunscreen was immediately felt.

UV-B, THE BAD GUY

The use of a specific glass type to filter ultraviolet radiation showed at least two spectral regions called UV-A (wavelength above 320 nm) and UV-B (wavelength below 320 nm) and that the UV-B part of the spectrum was responsible for erythema [for details about this subject, see Ref. (6)].

The advent of molecular biology after World War II provided scientific paradigms to understand the effects of ultraviolet radiation. Monochromatic UV-C lamps (emitting ultraviolet radiation at 254 nm) were used to induce mutagenesis in simple organisms, to study the photochemistry of DNA damage and the enzymology of DNA repair. The absorption spectrum of DNA spans the full UV-C and UV-B spectra, and UV-B itself was suspected of being carcinogenic. Later, experiments with laboratory rodents confirmed that UV was to be considered a full carcinogen, with UV-B playing the role of tumor initiator because of its capability to generate cyclobutane-type and (6-4)pyrimidine dimers, and UV-A playing the role of tumor promoter because of its capability to promote irritations. Being unable to generate pyrimidine dimers, though, UV-A was considered for many years to be harmless.

At that time, therefore, sunscreens only absorbed UV-B, known as erythemogenic radiation. Many sunscreens were phototoxic and photounstable. Often they were more damaging than protecting. To this, one can add the photosensitizing concoctions prepared by unskilled merchants and self-appointed pharmacists. In the following 50 years, sunscreen technology improved and it not only provided a protection against UV-B, but also paradoxically helped to point out that UV-A was also harmful to cells and tissues. The first hint of this conclusion came from the epidemiologic observation that after years of exposure to solar radiation notwithstanding the use of anti-UV-B sunscreens, the skin of sun worshippers became severely damaged, sagging, elastotic.

EXPERIMENTAL EVIDENCE FOR UV-A INDUCED DAMAGES

Experiments performed with cultured cells in the 1960s and the 1970s seemed to indicate that UV-A had the capability to introduce nicks in cellular DNA. Yet the purist could always argue that the radiation used was contaminated by UV-B radiation and that the calculation of the quantum yield of nicking was therefore impossible. The advent of simple and double monochromators allowed the investigation of the biological effects of UV-A to proceed free of this criticism. At the end of the 1980s, work with laboratory rodents indicated clearly that UV-A had molecular and tissular effects. Bissett et al. (7) pointed out the role of repeated UV-A irradiations in the sagging of the skin, which was not achieved with UV-B radiation. Balard and Giacomoni (8) pointed out that ultraviolet from solar simulators (UV-B + UV-A) could induce the drop in the level of NAD in the epidermis, which could not be obtained by the use of only UV-B radiation on cells in culture. Last but not least, Brunet and Giacomoni (9) pointed out that UV-A dramatically enhanced the small induction of heat shock genes provoked in the epidermis by UV-B. A couple of years later it was understood that DNA damage was inflicted by UV-A only in the presence of oxygen and a transition metal (10). This damage, therefore, manifested itself as being oxidative in nature. These results, therefore, paved the way to the use of antioxidants in cosmetics and in sun care to avoid the indirect damages caused by UV-A, such as oxidative nicking of DNA, peroxidation of lipids, production of singlet oxygen, and so forth.

WHY ANTI-UV-A SUNSCREENS?

Oxidative damage is but one of the effects of UV-A. Studies with laboratory rodents have opened the path to the understanding of UV-induced immune depression, carcinogenesis, photodamage, and photoaging.

In 1977, Fisher and Kripke (11) observed that rodents did not reject a tumor graft if they were previously irradiated with huge doses of UV. This seminal paper marked the beginning of the era of photoimmunology. Besides the use of ultraviolet to help in grafting tumors in laboratory rodents, it was observed that a previous exposure to UV impaired the responses of contact hypersensitivity and delayed-type hypersensitivity in mice and rats. The mechanisms involved in these phenomena have been the objects of bitter disputes in the scientific community over the years. It seems that one of the reasons for the conflicting results could be found in the fact that, like erythema, the immune depression is a threshold phenomenon, and that different mice strains have different threshold values, the differences being as large as a factor of 4 (12).

Ultraviolet radiation impairs immune response in humans by increasing the activity of suppressor T-cells (13). Although exposure to UV-B prior to vaccination does not impair the production of antibodies at a normal rate (14), exposure to UV-B impairs the delayed-type hypersensitivity response. Broad spectrum (UV-B + UV-A) sunscreen seem to protect the sensitivity response better than only UV-B sunscreens, thus pointing out a role for UV-A in the establishment of immune suppression (15).

The depression of the immune response in humans is likely to be the consequence of the reduction of Langerhans cell count in the epidermis successive to exposure to UV. Indeed UV irradiation generates haptens and it can be expected that antigen presenting cells just migrate to lymph nodes at a higher than normal rate because of the large number of haptens they encounter. One could also speculate that the impairment of the hypersensitivity response might well be an evolutionary advantage because it reduces the risk of anaphylactic shock induced by excess haptens. The interest in the immune depression provoked by ultraviolet radiation was aroused by the fact that UV-B sunscreens were unable to fully protect laboratory rodents, as well as human volunteers, against immune suppression. From this phenomenon two things were to be learned: first, that UV-A plays a role in photoinduced immune suppression and second, that the threshold for triggering the immune suppression is smaller than the threshold for triggering erythema. Thus, the protection factor afforded by a sunscreen to the immune response is smaller than the protection factor afforded against erythema.

ANTI-UV-B AND ANTI-UV-A SUNSCREENS

The large attention devoted to UV-A should not make one forget that UV-B is mutagenic, immune-suppressive, and cancerogenic. To point out the important role of the biological effects of UV-A, one does not need to lessen the dangers of UV-B. The cell damaging potential of UV-B and its capability to produce sunburn cells are instrumental in triggering an inflammatory response, now recognized as one of the most important factors of skin aging (16). So, UV-B should not only be feared because of its immune-suppressive, mutagenic, cancerogenic, and erythemal (burning) properties, but also because it plays a role in damaging the extracellular matrix and eventually all of the skin. The quantum yield of DNA damage by UV-A is smaller than the one of UV-B, but the count of UV-A photons in sunlight is 20 times larger than the count of UV-B, and the damage to the extracellular matrix induced by UV-A (mostly singlet oxygen driven) is incredibly larger than the one triggered by UV-B, which is generally absorbed by the DNA in keratinocytes.

It is therefore necessary to couple anti-UV-B sunscreens with anti-UV-A sunscreens. The sunscreens should also be associated with scavengers of singlet oxygen, which is now accepted as the major reactive species of oxygen involved in the indirect damages provoked by ultraviolet (17,18). This recommendation is all the more important because all sunscreens, being substances able to absorb radiation around 300–350 nm, have the unwelcome capability to transfer their excitation energy to oxygen. By doing so, they increase the level of singlet oxygen and the rate of production of oxidative damages.

BEYOND SPF

Notwithstanding all the progresses in biochemistry, molecular biology, and dermatology, we still assess the protection offered by a sunscreen with methods having two major potential flaws: the end point is the erythema, and the ultraviolet radiation is UV-B.

Among the physiological responses to solar radiation, erythema is the simplest to assess. Clinical observation is sufficient to differentiate between erythemas of different degrees of severity. Erythema only appears if the delivered UV dose is above a threshold. This contributed to the decision to use it as the end point of choice for determining the protective effects of sunscreens. Indeed the clinical analysis of erythema allows one to estimate with a certain precision, the numerical factor by which a topically applied sunscreen is able to reduce the delivered UV dose.

Methodologically, the use of the intensity of the erythema for evaluating UV-protecting capabilities of specific compounds suffers from one major flaw. Indeed, inhibitors of the erythemal response such as vaso-constrictive or anti-inflammatory drugs could be believed to provide protection against UV-induced damage, whereas they only inhibit the reaction triggered by the damage, that is, erythema. This type of objection extends to all the proposed methods to assess the protection offered by specific compounds against UV, which rest on the quantitative analysis of a physiological reaction to damage instead of on the assessment of the damage itself. Indeed, the inhibitors of the response under scrutiny might be mistaken for protecting agents.

From a practical point of view, in the past, the use of erythema as an endpoint has been a valuable tool in facilitating the evaluation of the efficiency of new sunscreens. However, recent progress in photobiology indicates that, irrespective of the methodological flaw discussed above, the exclusive use of erythemal data might be dangerously misleading. Indeed, physiological responses to solar radiation as crucial as UV-induced immune depression have threshold values different from those relative to the onset of erythema, and DNA damage is linearly dependent on UV dose, without the threshold effect.

Ideally, one should assess the protective effect of specific compounds by evaluating the damages inflicted by the same dose of radiation (with identical spectral distribution) in the presence or in the absence of the protecting agent. The evaluation of the molecular damage inflicted by solar radiation on human skin is of course a difficult task, which requires invasive techniques. The only possibility one is left with is to assess the kinetic of removal of one easy-to-measure damage and of a physiological response after exposure to UV in the presence or in the absence of protecting agents.

THE FUTURE: NEW STRATEGIES FOR DEFENSE

Reducing the number of photons impinging on target organs is a way to reduce photodamage and its consequences, but there is more to sun protection than just wearing clothes or sunscreens. It should be possible to stimulate cellular self-defense against outside aggressions. Fifteen years ago one of my graduate students observed that messenger RNA for heat shock proteins accumulates in epidermis after exposure to UV (9). We decided to point out in her doctoral dissertation that "if the expression of these proteins has a beneficial effect for UV irradiated epidermis, we could look for a gratuitous inducer of their genes and thus prepare the epidermis to a subsequent irradiation to protect it against deleterious effects of solar radiation". In our minds, the concept of "gratuitous induction", so helpful 30 years earlier in the understanding of the mechanism of negative control of gene expression, had found an application in photobiology!

In the last 10 years or so it has been shown that the response of human cells to UV is not limited to constitutive DNA repair and pigmentation, but also encompasses poly-ADP-ribosylation, expression of heat shock proteins, accumulation of p53 protein, induction of the cytochrome P-450 associated system of detoxification, and expression of other defense proteins. One could therefore propose treatments to "help" the cells induce their defense systems before going out in the sun. It is essential, of course, that the induction of defense mechanisms be obtained by harmless treatments, as it is essential that the assessment of the negative consequences of an aggression be obtained by measuring the damage, not the defensive response to the aggression itself. Indeed, when protecting agents are screened for their activity by measuring the extent of a particular defense response, any inhibitor of that defense response can be mistaken for a protecting agent.

By topical application of xenobiotics it is now possible to improve the rate of repair of DNA and to stimulate melanin production. It is also possible to induce the expression of heat shock proteins and of heme-oxygenase. It is possible, too, to reactivate the Embden–Meyerhof pathway interrupted when poly-ADP ribosylation depletes the cell of NAD, thus avoiding cell death because of the lack of energy. UV-induced immune suppression deserves a different approach. Boosting the immune response might have undesirable consequences. It is therefore crucial that, when dealing with the impairment of hypersensitivities, one confines oneself to the protection of specific targets and to the repair of specific molecules, without inducing an overall boosting of the immune system.

THE FUTURE: NEW AGGRESSORS?

Last but not least, we might ask if we are sure to have searched all the spectrum for harmful radiations. It is well known that the edge of violet light is harmful to the retina, it is well known that blue light impairs catalase. Specific wavelengths in the visible spectrum inhibit the synthesis of melatonin. Excess infrared might enhance an inflammatory response. This is to say that it should not be excluded that even the friendly visible light is endowed with harmful action. Of course, there is no reason to panic, we have been living with visible and infrared radiation for millennia, but learning about the molecular, enzymatic, and photochemical effects of visible and infrared rays might be helpful to the progress of science and beneficial for general health.

REFERENCES

1. Holick MF. A perspective on the beneficial effects of moderate exposure to sunlight: bone health, cancer prevention, mental health and well being. In: Giacomoni PU, ed. Sun Protection in Man. Amsterdam: Elsevier, 2001:11–37.
2. Dubreuilh W. Epitheliomatoses d'origine solaire. Ann Dermatol 1907; 8:387.
3. Unna PG. Die Histopathologie der Hautkrankheiten. Berlin: Verlag von August Hirschwald, 1894.
4. Driscoll CMH. Artificial protection against solar radiation: fabrics. In: Giacomoni PU, ed. Sun Protection in Man. Amsterdam: Elsevier, 2001:457–486.
5. Widmark J. Über den Einfluss des Lichtes auf die Haut. Hygiea Festband, 1889.
6. Urbach F. The negative effects of solar radiation: a clinical overview. In: Giacomoni PU, ed. Sun Protection in Man. Amsterdam: Elsevier, 2001:39–67.
7. Bissett DL, Hannon DP, Orr TV. Wavelength dependence of histological, physical and visible changes in chronically UV-irradiated hairless mouse skin. Photochem Photobiol 1989; 50:763–769.
8. Balard B, Giacomoni PU. Nicotinamide adenosine dinucleotide level in dimethylsulfate-treated or UV-irradiated mouse epidermis. Mutat Res 1989; 219:71–79.
9. Brunet S, Giacomoni PU. Heat shock mRNA in mouse epidermis after UV irradiation. Mutat Res 1989; 219:217–224.
10. Audic A, Giacomoni PU. DNA nicking by ultraviolet radiation is enhanced in the presence of iron and of oxygen. Photochem Photobiol 1993; 57:508–512.
11. Fisher MS, Kripke ML. Systemic alteration induced in mice by ultraviolet light irradiation and its relationship to ultraviolet carcinogenesis. Proc Natl Acad Sci USA 1977; 74:1688–1692.
12. Kim TH, Ananthaswami HN, Kripke ML, Ulrich SE. Advantages of using hairless mice versus haired mice to test sunscreen efficacy against photoimmune suppression. Photochem Photobiol 2003; 78:37–42.
13. Hersey P, Haran G, Hasic E, Edwards A. Alteration of T-cell subset and induction of suppressor T-cell activity in normal sujects after exposure to sunlight. J Immunol 1983; 131:171–174.
14. Sleijffers A, Garssen J, De Gruijl FR, Boland GJ, Van Hattum J, Van Vloten WA, Van Loveren H. Influence of ultraviolet B exposure on immune response following hepatitis B vaccination in human volunteers. J Invest Dermatol 2001; 117:1144–1150.

15. Moyal DD, Fourtanier A. Efficacy of broad-spectrum sunscreens against the suppression of the elicitation of delayed-type hypersensitivity response in humans depends on the level of ultraviolet A protection. Exp Dermatol 2003; 12:153–159.
16. Giacomoni PU, Rein G. Factors of skin aging share common mechanisms. Biogerontology 2001; 2:219–229.
17. Girotti AW. Lipid photo-oxidative damage in biological membranes: reaction mechanisms, cytotoxic consequences, and defense strategies. In: Giacomoni PU, ed. Sun Protection in Man. Amsterdam: Elsevier, 2001:231–250.
18. Davies MJ, Truscott RJW. Photo-oxidation of proteins and its consequences. In: Giacomoni PU, ed. Sun Protection in Man. Amsterdam: Elsevier, 2001:251–275.

Regulatory Aspects

6

The Role of FDA in Sunscreen Regulation

Matthew R. Holman and Daiva Shetty
*Division of Over-The-Counter Drug Products,
Center for Drug Evaluation and Research,
Food and Drug Administration,
Rockville, Maryland, USA*

This chapter describes how the Food and Drug Administration (FDA) regulates products containing sunscreen active ingredients. FDA regulates these products based on the Code of Federal Regulations (CFR), which derives from the

Federal Food, Drug, and Cosmetic Act (the Act), legislation enacted by Congress. Discussion will begin with differentiation of drug and cosmetic products according to the CFR. Then, the remainder of the chapter will focus on sunscreen drug products. The two mechanisms under which sunscreen drug products can be regulated will be compared and contrasted. Because the most common regulatory mechanism for marketing sunscreen drug products is the over-the-counter (OTC) drug monograph system, the OTC sunscreen drug monograph will be used to explain this system. Finally, two mechanisms by which an OTC drug monograph can be amended will be described.

DIFFERENTIATING DRUG, COSMETIC, AND DRUG–COSMETIC PRODUCTS

To understand whether a particular product is a drug, cosmetic, or drug–cosmetic product, FDA refers to the definitions of a drug and a cosmetic stated in the Act. In Section 201(g) of the Act, a drug is defined as follows:

(A) articles recognized in the official United States Pharmacopeia, official Homeopathic Pharmacopeia of the United States, or official National Formulary, or any supplement to any of them
(B) articles intended for use in the diagnosis, cure, mitigation, treatment, or prevention of disease in man or other animals
(C) articles (other than food) intended to affect the structure or any function of the body of man or other animals
(D) articles intended for use as a component of any articles specified in clause (A), (B), or (C)

In Section 201(i) of the Act, a cosmetic is defined as follows:

(1) articles intended to be rubbed, poured, sprinkled, or sprayed on, introduced into, or otherwise applied to the human body or any part thereof for cleansing, beautifying, promoting attractiveness, or altering the appearance
(2) articles intended for use as a component of any such articles; except that such term shall not include soap

These definitions define drug and cosmetic products, and FDA considers any product that falls under both of these definitions as a combination drug–cosmetic product.

Based on these definitions, FDA regulates all products containing a sunscreen active ingredient and bearing a sunburn protection or prevention claim as drugs. As described in 21 CFR 700.35, FDA regulates products containing a sunscreen active ingredient but not bearing a sunburn protection or prevention claim as cosmetics. For example, these products include those that contain a sunscreen active ingredient to protect product color. Furthermore, some products regarded as drugs are also regulated as cosmetics by FDA. Combination drug–cosmetic sunscreen products are abundant because many sunscreen drug products contain colorants, moisturizers, and other beautifying components and bear cosmetic claims. For example, a product labeled with an SPF value and labeled for the relief of dry skin is a drug–cosmetic (sunscreen–moisturizer) product.

REGULATORY MECHANISMS FOR MARKETING SUNSCREEN DRUG PRODUCTS

Because nearly all sunscreen drug products are sold OTC, this section will focus on the mechanisms under which OTC sunscreen drug products can be marketed. An OTC sunscreen drug product, whether it is also a cosmetic or not, can be marketed under a new drug application (NDA) or the OTC drug monograph system, more specifically, the OTC sunscreen monograph. Although nearly all sunscreen products in the marketplace are marketed under the OTC sunscreen monograph, it is important to understand both mechanisms. Both mechanisms require that sunscreen products be manufactured under current good manufacturing practices (cGMPs) as defined in 21 CFR Part 210. In addition, all OTC drug products must comply with the labeling content and format requirements of 21 CFR 201 Subpart C.

New Drug Application

Although there are some similarities in marketing under an NDA and the OTC sunscreen monograph, many differences exist between the two routes (Table 6.1). An NDA requires FDA approval before the sunscreen product can be introduced into the OTC market. A drug manufacturer must submit data in an NDA demonstrating that the product is safe and effective as a sunscreen for use by consumers without the assistance of a healthcare professional. The data are reviewed within time frames specified in the Prescription Drug User Fee Amendments of 2002 (PDUFA III). For a standard NDA, FDA approval is given within 10 months.

At the time that an NDA is submitted to FDA, the drug manufacturer must submit a user fee. In 2003, the user fee for a typical NDA was $573,500. An NDA is considered confidential by FDA. FDA does not release any information, including the receipt of an NDA, until the review is complete. At this time, FDA's determination of approvability becomes public, but the data contained in the NDA remain confidential.

Only after FDA approves a sunscreen product as safe and effective can a drug manufacturer market the product. Moreover, the drug manufacturer can only market the exact formulation that FDA has approved with the exact labeling that FDA has approved. Any change in formulation, labeling, manufacturing process, and so on, that deviates from that approved in the NDA must be approved by FDA before the manufacturer can make the change. The manufacturer must

Table 6.1 Comparison of Two Regulatory Mechanisms for Marketing an OTC Sunscreen Drug Product

OTC drug monograph	NDA
No FDA pre-approval before marketing	FDA pre-approval based on clinical trials demonstrating adequate evidence of safety and efficacy as well as detailed manufacturing data are required before marketing
No fees required to market product	PDUFA user fees required when NDA submitted
Any interested parties can market product with the same active ingredients for the same indications	Exclusivity and patent protection may prevent other interested parties from marketing a product with the same ingredients for the same indications
No deadline associated with publication of a final monograph	Specific review deadlines
Only considers active ingredients as long as the inactive ingredients in a product are safe and do not interfere with the effectiveness of the active ingredients (21 CFR 330.1(e))	Based on the final formulation
Rulemaking process is public and comments and data submitted to FDA are placed on public display in Division of Dockets Management	Information submitted to FDA is confidential, but FDA reviews of the application are available to the public after approval

submit an NDA supplement supporting the desired change. NDA supplements do not have user fees associated with them unless FDA has to review clinical data.

NDA products can be protected from competition from similar products by patent protection, exclusivity, or both. NDA products can be patented, preventing anyone except the patent holder from manufacturing a drug with the same active ingredient(s) for the same indication(s). Patent protection is provided only for those products that have been granted a patent by the U.S. Patent and Trade Office. Under certain circumstances, FDA may protect an NDA product from competition after patent expiration. FDA grants marketing exclusivity to compensate for the significant amount of time that it can take to bring a drug into the market from its initial discovery.

The description given above applies to all NDA products, including those classified as "NDA deviations." An NDA deviation is an NDA that uses an OTC drug monograph to support its approval (21 CFR 330.11). The NDA deviation allows a drug manufacturer to submit an NDA that only contains data related to how the conditions of use of an OTC drug product differ from the applicable OTC drug monograph(s). For example, a drug manufacturer could submit an

NDA for an OTC sunscreen product that complies with the sunscreen monograph except that the product includes labeling not found in the monograph. The NDA could reference the sunscreen monograph to support the safety of the active ingredients and simply submit data supporting the additional labeling. An NDA deviation can only reference a final monograph. Also, a product marketed under an NDA deviation must follow the reporting requirements of the NDA regulations.

OTC Drug Monograph System

Marketing a sunscreen product under the OTC drug monograph is significantly different from marketing the product under an NDA (Table 6.1). Sunscreen products marketed under the monograph do not require FDA approval before marketing. Prior to marketing, a sunscreen manufacturer only has to list its sunscreen product according to 21 CFR Part 207. FDA has a compliance office that is responsible for ensuring that all OTC drug products comply with the registration and listing requirements as well as cGMP and applicable OTC regulations, including OTC drug monographs. For sunscreen products, the compliance office monitors products for appropriate active ingredients at the allowed concentrations, labeling consistent with the monograph, and accurate SPF values according to the testing requirements of the OTC sunscreen drug monograph.

As discussed later in this chapter, OTC drug monographs are based on active ingredients and not on the final formulation. Thus, in contrast to OTC drug products marketed under NDAs, OTC drug products marketed under OTC drug monographs have the flexibility of changing formulations without FDA pre-approval. There are two major requirements regarding ingredients:

1. The active ingredient(s) or combination of active ingredients must be allowed under an OTC drug monograph.
2. The inactive ingredients must be safe and not diminish the effectiveness of the active ingredient(s).

For this reason and because the rulemaking process to create an OTC drug monograph is public, there is no exclusivity associated with products marketed under an OTC drug monograph.

DESCRIPTION OF THE OTC DRUG MONOGRAPH SYSTEM

The OTC sunscreen monograph is used to illustrate the OTC drug monograph system. In 1972, FDA created the OTC drug monograph system as a means to examine all of the OTC drug products in the marketplace to determine whether they were safe and effective. The OTC drug monograph system was designed to be a public process in which all of the active ingredients, rather than the final formulations, for a particular therapeutic category, such as sunscreen, were evaluated for safety and efficacy. The basis of the OTC drug monograph system is a three-step public rulemaking process:

1. Advanced Notice of Proposed Rulemaking (ANPR)
2. Tentative Final Monograph (TFM)
3. Final Monograph (FM)

As the process moves forward, each step builds upon and is a continuation of the previous step. The development of the OTC sunscreen monograph will be used as an example to explain this process.

Advisory Panel Review

In 1972, FDA appointed 17 independent advisory review panels consisting of expert scientists, together with consumer and industry representatives, to review the safety and efficacy of the marketed OTC drug products. Thus, the OTC monograph system only included active ingredients present in products on the market prior to its inception in 1972. FDA later changed this limitation to include active ingredients present in products on the market prior to May 1975. An external Advisory Review Panel on OTC Topical Analgesic, Antirheumatic, Otic, Burn, and Sunburn Prevention and Treatment Products (the Panel) evaluated sunscreen drug products. The Panel was charged with determining whether each active ingredient in a sunscreen product was safe and effective for use as a sunscreen. To accomplish this task, the Panel assigned each active ingredient to one of three categories:

- Category I: generally recognized as safe, generally recognized as effective (GRAS, GRAE)
- Category II: not generally recognized as safe, not generally recognized as effective (not GRAS, not GRAE)
- Category III: more data need to be submitted; cannot determine safety and effectiveness

A sunscreen active ingredient could fall into any of these categories during the initial review. A separate assessment was made for efficacy and safety. For example, the Panel found bornelone as safe (i.e., Category I for safety), but did not have sufficient data to determine its effectiveness (i.e., Category III for effectiveness). In addition, the panel recommended labeling, including therapeutic indications, dosing, and warnings.

After the Panel met, FDA published the ANPR for OTC sunscreen products in the *Federal Register* on August 25, 1978 (63 FR 38206). The ANPR announced FDA's intent to create the OTC sunscreen monograph. In addition, the ANPR included the Panel Report, which contained the Panel's conclusions on whether each active ingredient was Category I, II, or III for safety and effectiveness. The ANPR included a 90 day comment period, in which any interested party could submit comments to FDA regarding the Panel's conclusions.

Tentative Final Monograph

In the *Federal Register* of May 12, 1993 (58 FR 28194), FDA published an advanced notice in the form of a Tentative Final Monograph for Sunscreen Drug Products for OTC Human Use. This TFM was based on FDA's evaluation of the Panel's findings and consideration of public comments submitted in response to the ANPR. The TFM was FDA's preliminary position regarding the safety and effectiveness of particular active ingredients as well as acceptable labeling and final formulation testing (i.e., SPF testing). Similar to the ANPR, the TFM included a 90 day comment period. Regulations [21 CFR 330.10(a)(7)(iii) and (iv)] also allow 12 months to submit new data and an additional 60 days to submit comments on the new data.

Final Monograph

The Final Monograph for Sunscreen Drug Products for Over-The-Counter Human Use was published on May 21, 1999. It was based on the FDA's consideration of public comments on the proposed TFM, and new data and information on sunscreen drug products submitted to the FDA. Unlike a TFM, an FM typically does not have a comment period. However, an FM has an effective date. In the case of the OTC sunscreen FM, an effective date was included, but the FDA later stayed the effective date, so the FM is not yet implemented. The FM was stayed because it deals with UV-B protection and FDA wants to include UV-A protection, which FDA will incorporate in a future rulemaking (*Federal Register* 66, pp. 67485–67487). Therefore, manufacturers can comply with the FM, but they are not required to. After the FM becomes effective, any OTC sunscreen drug product marketed in the USA under the monograph must meet all regulatory specifications listed in the FM. Pre-approval by the FDA to market an OTC sunscreen product is not required if the regulatory standards described in the monograph are met.

Description of an OTC Drug Monograph

OTC drug monographs contain several components including, but not limited to, the following:

- General provisions
- Active ingredients
- Labeling
  - Indications for the product
  - Warnings
  - Drug interaction precautions
  - Directions for use
  - Specialized labeling
  - Professional labeling
- Testing procedures

FDA refers to each of these components as conditions of use. The conditions of use found in a monograph are those that FDA has found to be GRASE.

To understand the components of an OTC drug monograph, the OTC sunscreen drug monograph will be described. The first section of the monograph describes its purpose, certain definitions, and their abbreviations. The second section of the monograph lists acceptable sunscreen active ingredients and their concentrations that can be used in the finished OTC drug product. There are a total of 16 sunscreen active ingredients listed in this section. Each of these ingredients can be marketed within the concentration specified for each ingredient, if the finished product provides a minimum SPF value of not less than 2 as measured by the testing procedures specified in the monograph. This section also identifies active ingredients that are allowed to be combined with other active ingredients.

The labeling section describes the two parts of an OTC drug product label: principal display panel (PDP) and Drug Facts panel. The PDP is the part of the label that is most likely to be displayed or examined by consumers at a retail site. Every manufacturer has the liberty of designing their labels. However, there is certain information that is required to be displayed on the PDP. The PDP of a sunscreen drug product is required to have a statement of identity or the established name of the drug and must identify the product as a "sunscreen". The PDP must also list the product's SPF value. If the product satisfies the water resistant sunscreen product testing procedures as specified in the monograph, the PDP must include a statement about its water resistance.

The Drug Facts panel must be displayed on the outer package of all OTC drug products and is usually displayed on the back of the outer package. It has to meet the requirements specified in the monograph as well as the requirements specified in 21 CFR 201 Subpart C. The Drug Facts panel has a number of required headings:

- *Active ingredient(s)*: This section must list all active ingredients, their concentrations, and their statement of identity as a "sunscreen".
- *Uses*: This section lists the indications for the particular product. The only indication allowed under the monograph is the prevention of sunburn. Also, sunscreen products that satisfy water resistance testing have to list the time period of their efficacy after the water activity, perspiration, or sweating.
- *Warnings*: This section contains a number of subheadings used to describe contraindications, drug–drug interactions, as well as other information about possible adverse events associated with the drug or the condition that it treats.
- *Directions*: This section defines how to use the product, including the amount of the drug to be used and the frequency. Specific instructions are usually given for pediatric age groups.

Additional information on product performance may be added under the heading *Other information* or anywhere outside the Drug Facts panel.

Following labeling, the FM specifies finished product testing procedures. This is an important part of the FM and describes the conditions and procedures for determining the SPF value and water resistance of a product. The testing procedures provide a detailed description of the standard (control) sunscreen composition and preparation, light source (solar simulator), sunscreen application, subject irradiation, and calculations for determination of SPF value.

AMENDING AN OTC DRUG MONOGRAPH

A drug manufacturer or any other party may wish to alter the conditions of use in an OTC drug monograph. For example, a manufacturer may wish to market a drug product with an active ingredient concentration higher than the upper limit listed in an OTC drug monograph. There are two mechanisms by which a drug manufacturer or any other interested party can amend an OTC drug final monograph:

- Citizen petition
- Time and extent application (TEA)

Neither of these mechanisms require that any additional fees other than the drug registration and listing fee be paid to FDA. However, there are many differences between these two mechanisms.

Citizen Petition

The citizen petition (petition) process is described in 21 CFR 10.30. A petition can be submitted to FDA at any time to amend a TFM or FM for any OTC drug category. A petition is used to submit data and comments after the comment and data periods have expired following publication of an ANPR, TFM, or FM. A petitioner can request that FDA amend any condition of use allowed by an OTC drug monograph (see previous section). One limitation to amending conditions of use allowed by an OTC drug monograph is that the condition must have existed in the marketplace prior to 1975.

The FDA must issue a response to the petition within 180 days. However, this response is often an interim response because FDA typically cannot complete the review of a petition within this time frame. After FDA reviews a petition, it either grants or denies the petition. If FDA grants a petition, the appropriate OTC drug monograph is amended by the publication of a rulemaking in the *Federal Register*. If FDA denies a petition, FDA sends the petitioner a letter explaining why the petition was denied.

Time and Extent Application

The TEA is a regulatory process that allows conditions of use not found in the OTC marketplace prior to 1975 to be considered for inclusion in an OTC drug monograph. FDA created the TEA to allow conditions of use to meet the marketing "for a material time" and "to a material extent" requirements of Section 201(p) of the Act. These requirements must be met for a condition of use to be GRASE. Thus, a TEA can be used in two situations:

- Conditions of use found in drug products sold in the USA under NDAs
- Conditions of use found in products sold outside the USA

The second situation can describe various types of products marketed as OTC drug products or cosmetic drug products in other countries. Products regulated as drug products in the USA may not be regulated as drug products in other countries even though similar testing requirements are necessary for marketing (e.g., sunscreens are regulated as cosmetics in the UK and as drug products in the USA).

The basic requirement for submission of a TEA is that a condition of use be marketed for a minimum of five continuous years in the same country and in sufficient quantity (21 CFR 330.14). The TEA is essentially a two-step process:

1. TEA submission to determine eligibility
2. Submission of safety and effectiveness data and review of the data by FDA

During the first step, an applicant submits information related to the marketing experience of a condition. Initially, the TEA is considered confidential, similar to an NDA. FDA reviews the marketing information to determine whether the condition has been marketed for a material time and to a material extent. If the condition does not meet these requirements, the applicant is sent a letter stating that the condition is ineligible to be included in the OTC drug review and explaining the reason(s) for this decision. In this case, the letter is put on public display, but the TEA remains confidential.

If the condition is eligible to be included in the OTC drug review, FDA publishes a notice of eligibility in the *Federal Register* and a request for data. FDA's review of the TEA and the redacted TEA are put on public display. This leads to the second step in the TEA process, which are FDA review of safety and effectiveness data. After FDA reviews the data, FDA publishes a rulemaking in the *Federal Register*. The rulemaking contains FDA's conclusions regarding whether the condition is Category I, II, or III for safety and effectiveness. If the condition is found to be GRASE (Category I), the applicable OTC drug monograph(s) will be amended to allow the condition to be marketed.

7

The Final Monograph

Emalee G. Murphy
Kirkpatrick & Lockhart LLP,
Washington, DC, USA

HISTORY AND SCOPE OF THE REGULATION

The US Food and Drug Administration (FDA) published the Final Rule for Sunscreen Drug Products for Over-the-Counter Human Use on May 21, 1999,[1] and the resulting regulation (or monograph) is codified in 21 Code of Federal Regulations (CFR), Parts 352.1–352.77, 310.545, 700.35, and 740.19. The Rule establishes the conditions under which a sunscreen is "generally recognized as safe and effective" and not misbranded for its intended use by identifying the authorized monograph sunscreen active ingredients, their permitted combinations, and any limitations on their use; establishes the required label statements and format for all sunscreen drug products; and sets forth the official test method to determine sun protection factor (SPF) values and performance claims such as "water resistant/very water resistant". A major regulatory advantage of compliance with the Final Rule is that sunscreen products formulated and labeled in accordance with the Final Rule and that also comply with other general requirements for over the counter (OTC) drug products and facilities[2] may be placed on the US market without further FDA review and are not subject to new drug approval procedures.

The Final Rule is the result of over 20 years' deliberation by FDA and interested parties on the legitimate scientific and legal grounds for regulating sun protection products, which at one time were viewed by many as no more in the drug category than were sun bonnets. The evolution of the Rule, its scope, and history, including the agency's legal rationale for sunscreen drug regulations, are best elucidated in the preambles to FDA's Advance Notice of Proposed Rulemaking (ANPR), the Proposed Rule, and its various amendments. Although some originally questioned FDA's classification of sunscreens as drugs,[3] the agency's rationale was predicated on prior Trade Correspondence issued in the 1940s, in which it had clearly differentiated sun tanning products as cosmetics and sunburn protection products as drugs.[4] In the preamble to the Proposed Rule, FDA explained its decision to apply the drug sunscreen requirements to cosmetic products bearing sunscreen claims as well as to traditional "beach" sunscreens, stating,

> Sunscreen products are marketed with various intended uses, such as (1) beach products for occasional use to protect consumers from extreme

[1]64 Fed. Reg. 27666 (May 21, 1999).

[2]For example, Drug Establishment Registration and Drug Listing Requirements set forth at 21 Code of Federal Regulations (CFR) 207; Current Good Manufacturing Procedures for Finished Pharmaceutical Products set forth at 21 CFR 211; OTC drug labeling requirements at 21 CFR 369; and color additive regulations for drug products at 21 CFR parts 73 and 74.

[3]See Cosmetic, Toiletry, and Fragrance Association comments, 1978 (Docket 78N-0038).

[4]Trade Correspondence No. TC-61 (February 15, 1940) stated that a product promoted for prevention of damage from the sun is a drug, and a product that is promoted solely for the purpose of acquiring an even tan can be considered a cosmetic. The Final Rule includes a provision that revokes TC-61 as the regulation supersedes the Trade Correspondence.

> sunlight conditions, (2) tanning products to aid consumers in acquiring a tan, and (3) non-beach products for daily use to protect consumers from chronic exposure to sunlight (e.g., make-up preparations and lipsticks). Although these intended uses are different, the agency considers each one a drug use.
>
> Beach products are considered drugs because they prevent sunburn, protect the skin against harm from the sun, and prevent skin damage through overexposure to the sun. In addition, consumers equate these products with mitigating harmful effects from the sun. For these reasons, sunscreen beach products are drugs under section 201(g)(1)(B) [of the Federal Food, Drug, and Cosmetic Act]. Such products are also drugs under section 201(g)(1)(C) because they affect the body's physiological response to solar radiation (i.e., they lessen the erythema reaction). Tanning products that contain sunscreens are drugs because they prevent a sunburn ... and affect melanogenesis .... Non-beach sunscreen products are drugs because they prevent lip or skin damage ... as well as freckling, and uneven skin coloration .... [5]

FDA further clarified its view of sunscreen drug identity by stating,

> When an ingredient can be used for either drug or cosmetic purposes, its regulatory status is determined by objective evidence of the distributor's intent ... this includes, but is not limited to, the representations made by the manufacturer or distributor in the labeling or promotion of the product. The agency believes that the inclusion of a sunscreen active ingredient in a product that is intended or promoted to protect the consumer's skin from the harmful effects of the sun brings the product within the statutory definition of a drug .... Such intent may be derived from labeling, promotional material, advertising, and any other relevant source [including] the consumer's intent in using the product .... The agency believes that all products containing a sunscreen active ingredient and claiming to protect the consumer from the sun or to enhance the consumer's ability to obtain an effect from sun exposure (i.e., a tan) must be regulated as drugs in order to ensure the effectiveness of the sunscreen ingredient ... [with a few select exceptions ...] such products may also be regulated, *but not solely*, as cosmetics.[6] (Emphasis added.)

Accordingly, products that contain one or more active sunscreen products and are represented as intended to protect the skin from the sun, including the use of words such as "sunscreen", "sun block", "sunshield" and phrases such as

---

[5]56 Fed. Reg. 28194, 28195 (May 12, 1993). The Federal Food, Drug, and Cosmetic Act (FDC Act) defines a drug as "an article intended for use in the diagnosis, cure, mitigation, treatment, or prevention of disease" or "intended to affect the structure or any function of the body". 21 USC 321(g) (2003).

[6]56 Fed. Reg. 28204, 28205.

"helps to acquire an even tan" and "protects against premature skin aging", are regulated as drugs. Furthermore, FDA concluded that references to "tanning" in product labeling are so closely allied with sun protection that sun tanning lotions without sunscreens are required to bear a warning statement, discussed below. Shampoos, hair conditioners, hair sprays, nail polishes and similar products may contain a sunscreen for nontherapeutic use and will not be regulated as drugs as long as the labeling clearly describes the nontherapeutic nature of the sunscreen. For example, an appropriate explanatory phrase on the label might state, "This product contains a sunscreen to protect the hair from damage caused by the sun" or "Contains a sunscreen to protect product color".

FDA issued the Final Rule as part of the agency's ongoing review of nonprescription drug active ingredients the OTC Drug Review.[7] The procedures for the Review started with an initial call for data in support of the safety and efficacy of particular sunscreen active ingredients, which were evaluated by a specially appointed panel of independent experts, the Advisory Review Panel on OTC Topical Analgesic, Antirheumatic, Otic, Burn, and Sunburn Prevention Drug Products. To be included in the OTC Drug Review program, the drug substance must have been on the US market as a sunscreen agent prior to December 4, 1975.[8] The Panel's task was to assess the information voluntarily submitted by interested parties and to give FDA its written views on the safety and effectiveness of each active ingredient as a sunscreen agent. Importantly, the OTC Review Panel was tasked to assess only the active sunscreen agents; inactive ingredients used in OTC drug products are beyond the scope of the Review. Inactive ingredients in OTC drug products are generally unregulated, except that they must be safe and suitable for their intended use and must not interfere with the product effectiveness or with analyses to determine the identity, strength, quality, or purity of the active ingredient(s).[9]

The agency published the unaltered Panel Report as the ANPR to establish a monograph for OTC drug sunscreen products in the August 25, 1978, *Federal Register*,[10] and provided interested parties the opportunity to comment. The preamble to the ANPR is a valuable source of information on the products and active sunscreens then on the US market, the studies and literature used by the Panel to make its safety and effectiveness decisions (all of which are available from FDA through the Freedom of Information Act procedures), and the initial discussions of UV radiation characteristics and the most appropriate product sunscreen efficacy testing methodology, for which at that time no uniform standard procedure existed.

[7]The review of nonprescription active ingredients was mandated by the 1962 New Drug Amendments to the Federal Food, Drug, and Cosmetic Act which, in brief, required that all drug products be evaluated for safety and effectiveness.

[8]21 CFR 330.13(a).

[9]21 CFR 330.1(e).

[10]43 Fed. Reg. 38206 (August 25, 1978).

The subsequent Notice of Proposed Rulemaking for OTC Drug Sunscreen Products (the Proposed Rule or Proposal) that was issued in the May 12, 1993, *Federal Register*[11] reflects FDA's initial response to the significant advances in sunscreen marketing, safety, and technology developed during the years between 1978 and 1993. In one of the agency's most controversial decisions, FDA proposed to limit the maximum SPF value to SPF 30. FDA also proposed that the SPF value appear on the product principal display panel of all sunscreen products and eliminated the minimum levels of active sunscreen ingredients, except for sunscreen actives in combination with another sunscreen or any other active ingredient.[12] The Proposal also confirmed that all sunscreens included in an OTC final monograph must be adequately and publicly characterized in a United States Pharmacopoeia (USP) monograph. FDA simplified sunscreen labeling terminology; shortened and consolidated the required label statements; and addressed claims such as "antiaging", "premature aging of the skin", "accelerates tanning", and other similar representations that had proliferated in sunscreen labeling since the publication of the original ANPR. In addition, the Proposal further clarified the methodology used to determine the effectiveness of sunscreen products and sunscreen products represented as "water resistant" or "very water resistant".

The Proposal reflected FDA's ongoing concerns about sunscreen safety and effectiveness. For example, information pertaining to the safety of Padimate A led to its deletion from the list of sunscreens in the Proposed Rule, while information concerning the effect of nitrosating agents in sunscreens such as Padimate O was investigated and resolved.[13] During the 15 years between 1978 and the long-awaited publication of the Proposal in 1993, FDA continued to address issues such as sunscreen testing methodology in separate *Federal Register* notices and at FDA-sponsored meetings.[14] Following public comment on the

[11]58 Fed. Reg. 28194 (May 12, 1993).

[12]FDA eliminated the minimum levels of sunscreen ingredients for single drug category products because the effectiveness of a sunscreen product is not measured merely by the amounts of active in the product.

[13]The Proposed Rule describes the methodology developed by FDA and the industry to identify and determine the quantitative presence of the new nitrosamine, *n*-methyl-*N*-nitrosaminobenzoate octyl ester (NMPABAO). As the presence of NMPABAO in sunscreen drug products containing Padimate O also depends upon the presence of a nitrosating agent, such as the preservative 2-bromo-2-nitro-1, 3-propandiol, FDA concluded that Padimate O could be safely used in formulations without direct or indirect nitrosating agents. Although FDA set no limits for the presence of NMPABAO in sunscreen products, the agency suggested a maximum limit of 500 ppb and requested comment. The Final Rule did not include any maximum limit for NMPABAO.

[14]After having extended the comment period from November 24, 1978 to December 26, 1978, FDA reopened the administrative record in March 1980 45 Fed. Reg. 18403 (March 21, 1980), to permit consideration of information filed with FDA after the original submission period ended. Testing methods for sunscreen finished products and claims were the most significant issues. FDA reopened the administrative record once again in 1987 in order to hold a public meeting to discuss the recommendations of the Panel on testing and claims issues. 52 Fed. Reg. 3598 (September 4, 1987).

Proposed Rule, FDA reopened the administrative record in 1994 to solicit comments on an amendment to the Proposal that would eliminate five sunscreen active ingredients for which there appeared to be no public interest in developing USP monographs.[15] Altogether, 6 of the original 21 ingredients proposed as safe and effective in the ANPR did not appear in the Final Rule.[16] In 1996, FDA amended the Proposed Rule to add the ingredient avobenzone as a single active sunscreen agent and in combination with certain other active sunscreens,[17] and in 1998, FDA proposed to include zinc oxide as a single ingredient and in combination with any other proposed active sunscreen, except avobenzone.[18] Both avobenzone and zinc oxide are included in the Final Rule.

In addition to modifying the list of proposed active sunscreen ingredients, FDA also reopened the administrative record twice to consider issues related to the safety and effectiveness of OTC drug sunscreen products and ingredients. The agency announced a public meeting in 1994 to discuss ultraviolet A (UV-A) radiation claims[19] and again in 1996 to announce a public meeting on the photochemistry and photobiology of sunscreens.[20] FDA's conclusions concerning UV-A testing are not included in the Final Rule and, according to the agency, will be discussed in future issues of the *Federal Register*. In the interim, the preamble to the Final Rule indicates that UV-A labeling may continue in accordance with the Proposed Rule.[21] In that document, FDA suggested that in certain circumstances, UV-A labeling may be appropriate if the ingredient(s) used in a product has an absorption rate that extends to 360 nm or above in the UV-A range. Although UV-A effectiveness and testing was beyond the scope of the original Advisory Panel evaluation, the Panel did evaluate a combination of lawsone with dihydroxyacetone, which it stated had been shown as effective against both UV-B and UV-A radiation (to 400 nm). Because the agency believes that information about UV-A protection is important to consumer health and safety, it acknowledged that the lawsone/dihydroxyacetone combination could bear claims to UV-A protection, as could any other monograph sunscreen active ingredient able to demonstrate UV-A protection in the 360–400 nm

---

Until May 26, 1988, FDA accepted comments on new information submitted in connection with the public hearing discussion. FDA's Proposed Rule appeared in the May 12, 1993 *Federal Register*. 58 Fed. Reg. 29194.

[15]59 Fed. Reg. 29706 (June 8, 1994).

[16]Padimate A (eliminated for safety reasons), digalloyl trioleate, ethyl 4-[bis(hydroxypropyl) aminobenzoate], glyceryl aminobenzoate, lawsone with dihydroxyacetone, red petrolatum, and diethanolamine methoxycinnamate.

[17]61 Fed. Reg. 48645 (September 16, 1996).

[18]63 Fed. Reg. 56584 (October 22, 1998).

[19]59 FR 16042 (April 5, 1994).

[20]61 Fed. Reg. 42398 (August 15, 1996).

[21]64 Fed. Reg. 27666 at 27667.

range.[22] In its discussion of UV radiation claims, the agency noted that the radiation that reaches the earth is in the UV portion (290–400 nm) of the sun's spectrum, and that any other claims to protection from visible light or infrared light are inconsistent with this and would cause any product so represented to be considered an unapproved new drug.

The public hearing announced by FDA in 1996 and the subsequent discussion of the photochemistry and photobiology of sunscreens addressed, among other issues, the safety and efficacy of micronized titanium dioxide and the question whether the micronized version of the ingredient should be considered a new drug substance. FDA rejected the notion that the micronized ingredient should be considered a new drug. Interestingly, data submitted to FDA in connection with the public hearings on the subject indicated that micronized titanium dioxide absorbs short-wavelength UV radiation and reflects and scatters long wavelengths, thereby functioning similarly to chemical UV-B radiation sunscreens.

KEY PROVISIONS OF THE FINAL MONOGRAPH

The key provisions in the Final Sunscreen Rule are the identification of permitted active ingredients and combinations, uniform labeling of sunscreens, and clarification of permitted performance claims and of the test methods to determine sunscreen effectiveness against radiation in the UV-B range. This section describes these provisions in summary.

Permitted Active Sunscreen Ingredients

Sunscreen active ingredients, as defined in the Final Rule, are those ingredients listed in the regulation in 21 CFR 352.10 that "absorb, reflect, or scatter radiation in the UV range at wavelengths from 290 to 400 nanometers". The following ingredients and maximum concentrations are permitted for use as sunscreen active ingredients, provided that the finished product provides a minimum SPF value of not less than SPF 2 as measured by the testing procedures set forth in the monograph. These ingredients are the subjects of USP monographs, and the new drug names indicated for some of the ingredients reflect the USP established name of the ingredient. Any future sunscreen active ingredient listed in the Final Rule must likewise be the subject of a monograph published in the USP.

Ingredients Listed in 21 CFR 352.10

(a) Aminobenzoic acid (PABA) up to 15%
(b) Avobenzone up to 3%
(c) Cinoxate up to 3%
(d) Reserved

---

[22] 58 Fed. Reg. 28194 at 28232.

(e) Dioxybenzone up to 3%
(f) Homosalate up to 15%
(g) Reserved
(h) Menthyl anthranilate up to 5% (now Meridamate)
(i) Octocrylene up to 10%
(j) Octylmethoxycinnamate up to 7.5% (now Octinoxate)
(k) Octylsalicylate up to 5% (now Octisalate)
(l) Oxybenzone up to 6%
(m) Padimate O up to 8%
(n) Phenylbenzimidazole sulfonic acid up to 4% (now Enzulisole)
(o) Sulisobenzone up to 10%
(p) Titanium dioxide up to 25%
(q) Trolamine salicylate up to 12%
(r) Zinc oxide up to 25%

Active Ingredient Combinations

The following sunscreens may be combined with each other in a single product when used in the prescribed concentrations. The Final Rule sets no minimum concentration levels, but the amount of each active ingredient in a combination must contribute a minimum SPF of at least 2 to the finished product. In addition, the finished product must have a minimum SPF of not less than the number of sunscreens in the combination, multiplied by 2.

Sunscreen Active Ingredient Combination Pattern A

Any of the following ingredients may be combined up to the indicated maximum concentrations:

(a) Aminobenzoic acid (PABA) up to 15%
(c) Cinoxate up to 3%
(e) Dioxybenzone up to 3%
(f) Homosalate up to 15%
(h) Menthyl anthranilate up to 5%
(i) Octocrylene up to 10%
(j) Octylmethoxycinnamate up to 7.5%
(k) Octylsalicylate up to 5%
(l) Oxybenzone up to 6%
(m) Padimate O up to 8%
(n) Phenylbenzimidazole sulfonic acid up to 4%
(o) Sulisobenzone up to 10%
(p) Titanium dioxide up to 25%
(q) Trolamine salicylate up to 12%
(r) Zinc oxide up to 25%

Sunscreen Active Ingredient Combination Pattern B

The following ingredients may be combined up to the indicated maximum concentrations:

(b) Avobenzone up to 3%
(c) Cinoxate up to 3%
(e) Dioxybenzone up to 3%
(f) Homosalate up to 15%
(i) Octocrylene up to 10%
(j) Octylmethoxycinnamate up to 7.5%
(k) Octylsalicylate up to 5%
(l) Oxybenzone up to 6%
(o) Sulisobenzone up to 10%
(q) Trolamine salicylate up to 12%

Ingredients for Combination Sunscreen–Skin Protectant Products

The Final Rule provided for combination sunscreen–skin protectant products without specifying the specific permitted ingredient combinations allowed. Since publication of the Final Sunscreen Rule, FDA has issued the Final Rule for OTC Drug Skin Protectant Products for Human Use,[23] which sets forth the following permitted sunscreen–skin protectant combinations:

Combinations of Sunscreens and Skin Protectant Ingredients

Any sunscreen ingredient may be combined with any of the following skin protectant ingredients:

(a) Allantoin, 0.5–2%
(d) Cocoa butter, 50–100%
(e) Cod liver oil, 5–13.56%, in accordance with Section 347.20(a)(1) or (a)(2), provided the product is labeled so that the quantity used in a 24 h period does not exceed 10,000 U.S.P. units vitamin A and 400 U.S.P. units cholecalciferol
(g) Dimethicone, 1–30%
(h) Glycerin, 20–45%
(i) Hard fat, 50–100%
(k) Lanolin, 12.5–50%
(l) Mineral oil, 50–100%; 30–35% in combination with colloidal oatmeal in accordance with § 347.20(a)(4)
(m) Petrolatum, 30–100%
(r) White petrolatum, 30–100%

[23]Final Monograph for Skin Protectant Drug Products, 68 Fed. Reg. 33362 (June 4, 2003), codified at 21 CFR 347.20(d).

LABELING REQUIREMENTS

The Final Rule simplifies and consolidates the required labeling for sunscreen products. The SPF value, which must appear on the principal display and front panels of the sunscreen immediate and outer containers, is limited to SPF 30 "Plus" (or " + ") and the original five product category designations (PCD) have been reduced to three. Use of the PCD language in labeling is optional:

Chart 1—Product Category Descriptions

Minimal sun protection product	(Provides an SPF value of 2 to under 12)
Moderate sun protection product	(Provides an SPF value of 12 to under 30)
High sun protection product	(Provides an SPF value of 30 or above)

Permitted claims for products in the three PCD categories include:

Chart 2—Permitted Claims for Product Category Descriptions

SPF 2 to under 12	"Provides minimum/minimal protection against sunburn/sunburn and tanning" or "For skin that sunburns minimally"
SPF 12 to under 30	"Provides moderate protection against sunburn/sunburn and tanning" or "For skin that sunburns moderately"
SPF 30 or 30+	"Provides high protection against sunburn/sunburn and tanning" or "For skin that sunburns easily"

The Proposed Rule would have limited sunscreen SPF values to 30. Many comments requested that FDA either set no limit on sunscreen SPF values or that the limit be set at SPF 50. These comments suggested that higher SPF value products are needed to protect the consumer from increased lifestyle and environmental exposure to the sun, because sensitive-skinned persons may burn even with SPF 30 products. Furthermore, comments suggested that higher SPF values could be achieved through formulation changes rather than through increased concentrations of active ingredients, although information available at that time did not support any relationship between high SPF values and safety concerns. Other comments noted that limiting SPF values would stifle sunscreen product development and preventative health benefits, such as increased protection from UV radiation-induced photoimmunosuppression. On the other hand, many argued that the proposal to limit SPF values to 30 would stop the promotional "bidding war" surrounding high SPF value products.

FDA struck a compromise by permitting higher SPF formulations while limiting the labeled SPF value to 30+. While the agency agreed on the need for higher SPF products and acknowledged the apparent lack of safety issues, it was concerned that the testing methods developed to determine lower SPF values might not be able to accurately and reproducibly determine higher SPF values. Furthermore, the incremental increase in protection provided by an SPF 30 product and an SPF 50 product is not easily evident to the consumer due to the nonlinearity of the SPF rating system. Nevertheless, the agency encouraged interested parties to continue development of test methods suitable for assessing the effectiveness of high SPF products and to submit test data in support of such methods to FDA. In fact, FDA has indicated that test methodology and the related search for appropriate terminology to describe the benefits afforded by higher SPF products will be the subject of a future *Federal Register* notice.

As previously stated, the Final Rule greatly simplified (and limited) the general labeling requirements for OTC drug sunscreen products. In part, this was undoubtedly in response to the publication of FDA's regulation to standardize all OTC drug labels by establishing a uniform format for the presentation of required label statements.[24] The drug facts panel format adopted by FDA leaves little room for lengthy product descriptions and the final language of the sunscreen monograph seems to be designed to accommodate this more restricted labeling concept. Despite urgent requests by industry, with the exception of lip products, FDA made no distinction in the Final Rule between labeling requirements for "beach" products and those for products normally marketed as cosmetics and formulated with sunscreens for daily sun protection.

The exceptions for lipsticks and lip balms are limited and include provisions to omit the otherwise required statements, "For external use only" and "When using this product, keep out of eyes. Rinse with water to remove". In addition, the directions to apply the product "generously", "liberally", "smoothly", or "evenly" and to "ask a doctor about use for children under 6 months" are not required for lip products. FDA also notes that the modified drug facts panel labeling permitted that certain small containers by 21 CFR 201.66(d)(10) be used for sunscreen products labeled for use only on specific small areas of the face, such as the lips, nose, ears, or around the eyes.

With these exceptions, all sunscreens must bear the following information required by the Final Rule and other labeling regulations applicable to OTC drugs generally.[25]

On the Principal Display Panel

1. The established name of the drug (if any) and the identification "sunscreen"

---

[24]64 Fed. Reg. 13254 (March 17, 1999), codified at 21 CFR 201.66.

[25]21 CFR 201.1–201.323, 21 CFR 310.

2. The SPF value up to 30 (and for products with SPF values higher than 30), the designation 30 plus or 30+
3. If applicable, the statement "Water/Sweat Resistant" or "Water/Perspiration Resistant" or "Very Water/Sweat Resistant" or "Very Water/Perspiration Resistant"

If a "water resistant" or a "very water resistant" claim is made for the product, the labeled SPF must be the value obtained after the product has been tested using the water- resistant or very water-resistant testing procedures outlined in the regulation. There is no special test method for perspiration claims, as these are supported by data generated from the water resistance trials. Regardless of the product's properties, water resistance claims are optional even if the product passes the testing.

In the Drug Facts Panel

1. Under the heading "Active Ingredient", the name of the drug ingredient and its percentage in the product and the purpose "Sunscreen".
2. Under the heading "Uses", the statements "Helps prevent sunburn" and, for example, "Higher SPF gives more sunburn protection". If applicable, the statements "Retains SPF after [40]/[80] minutes of activity in the water/sweating/perspiring". In addition, the Uses section of the panel may also include a reference to the SPF-related Product Category Description claims (see chart 2 given earlier).
3. Under the heading "Warnings", the statements **"Keep out of reach of children"**, "For external use only", "When using this product, keep out of eyes. Rinse with water to remove", and "Stop use and ask a doctor if rash or irritation develops and lasts".
4. Under the heading "Directions", the statements, "Apply generously/liberally/smoothly/or evenly [insert an appropriate time interval if a waiting period is needed] before sun exposure and as needed", and "Children under 6 months of age, ask a doctor". In addition, the Directions section of the panel may delete the phrase "as needed" above and substitute "Reapply as needed or after towel drying, swimming/sweating/perspiring".
5. The following optional statements may appear in the drug facts panel under the heading "Other Information" or anywhere outside the panel: a reference to the applicable product performance claim (see chart 2) and/or the statement, "Sun Alert: Limiting sun exposure, wearing protective clothing, and using sunscreens may reduce the risks of skin aging, skin cancer, and other harmful effects of the sun".
6. Under the heading "Inactive Ingredients", a declaration of the excipients in the product, listed in alphabetical order in the product, except that in the case of products also regulated as cosmetics, the

ingredients should be declared in the order of predominance in the product.[26]

7. Under the heading "Questions", the panel may also include a telephone number or address for further information.

Example Sunscreen Drug Facts Panel

DRUG FACTS

Active Ingredients	***Purpose***
Titanium Dioxide (10%)	Sunscreen
Zinc Oxide (5%)	Sunscreen

Uses

- Helps prevent sunburn
- Higher SPF gives more sunburn protection
- Retains SPF after 40 minutes of activity in the water
- Provides moderate protection

Warnings

For external use only

When using this product

- Keep out of eyes. Rinse with water to remove

Stop use and ask a doctor if

- rash or irritation develops and lasts

Keep out of reach of children. If swallowed, get medical help or contact a Poison Control Center right away.

Directions

- Apply generously and uniformly before sun exposure, repeat application every two hours and after swimming.
- Children under 6 months of age: ask a doctor

Inactive Ingredients: LIST IN ALPHABETICAL ORDER

The Final Rule also addresses the labeling of products represented both as sunscreens and as skin protectants and permits statements of identity, indications, warnings, and directions for use applicable to each product type to be combined to eliminate duplications. Where time intervals or age limits related to use of the product as a sunscreen or skin protectant differ, the directions for the combination product may not recommend any dosage that exceeds that of any individual ingredient in the applicable monographs or provide for use by any age group lower than the highest minimum age limit in an individual monograph. The principal display panel of a combination sunscreen/skin protectant product

[26]21 CFR 201.10.

must include the required statements for both product types, for example, "Sunscreen/Skin Protectant; SPF 20; Very Water-Resistant".

Example Sunscreen/Skin Protectant Drug Facts Panel

DRUG FACTS

Active Ingredients	***Purpose***
Titanium Dioxide (10%)	Sunscreen
Zinc Oxide (5%)	Sunscreen
Glycerin (30%)	Skin Protectant

Uses

- Helps protect against sunburn
- Higher SPF gives more sunburn protection
- Retains SPF after 40 minutes of activity in the water
- Provides moderate protection
- Temporarily protects and helps relieve chapped or cracked skin

Warnings

For external use only

When using this product

- Keep out of eyes. Rinse with water to remove

Do not use on

- deep or puncture wounds
- animal bits
- serious burns

Stop use and ask a doctor if

- rash or irritation develops and lasts more than 7 days or clears up and occurs again within a few days

Keep out of reach of children. If swallowed, get medical help or contact a Poison Control Center right away.

Directions

- Apply generously and uniformly before sun exposure, repeat application every two hours and after swimming.
- Children under 6 months of age: ask a doctor

Inactive Ingredients: LIST IN ALPHABETICAL ORDER

LABELING CAVEATS

The Final Rule clarifies the agency's position on specific other product performance claims for sunscreens including claims for antiaging and photoaging effects; tanning acceleration; melanin and antioxidant effectiveness; sunless tanning products; "chemical-free", "PABA-free", and "natural" ingredient claims; extended protection claims; and some claims that were previously included as acceptable indications in the Proposed Rule, such as "protection from freckles and uneven skin tone".

Antiaging/Antiphotoaging

The only statement permitted by the Final Rule related to antiaging and photoaging is the voluntary Sun Alert statement:

> **Sun Alert**: Limiting sun exposure, wearing protective clothing, and using sunscreens may reduce the risks of skin aging, skin cancer, and other harmful effects of the sun.

Variations in the statement will cause the product to be misbranded. In addition, an OTC sunscreen drug that uses "antiaging" language in the labeling to suggest any unapproved therapeutic or physiologic effect would "likely be subject to regulatory action as an unapproved new drug".[27] Products without sunscreen ingredients or sunscreening claims but which use "antiaging" language in labeling or in the product name would not fall within the OTC sunscreen drug category. However, depending on the claims made and the circumstances of distribution, FDA could also consider such a product to be an unapproved new drug. As a practical matter, FDA has tended to rigorously enforce use of unacceptable claims on products clearly within established OTC drug categories, including sunscreens.

Tanning Accelerators, Melanin and Antioxidants

The preamble to the Final Rule addresses FDA's view that products represented to accelerate or stimulate the tanning process or to stimulate the production of melanin in the body are unapproved new drugs because the intended use of the product is to affect the structure or function of the body. Products represented to contain melanin as a sunscreen ingredient are likewise unapproved new drugs because melanin is not included in the Final Rule as a safe and effective sunscreen ingredient. In addressing label references to antioxidants and free radicals, FDA acknowledges protection claims attributed to antioxidants in some cosmetic product labeling and intends to address them on a case-by-case basis.

Warnings for Tanning Products without Sunscreens

Products represented solely as cosmetics, such as sunless tanning products, moisturizers for use during or after sun exposure, and "bronzers" to impart color without tanning or to enhance tanning in some other way and which do not contain sunscreens, must include the warning statement required under the Final Rule by new section 21 CFR 740.19, namely:

> **Warning**—This product does not contain a sunscreen and does not protect against sunburn. Repeated exposure of unprotected skin while

[27]64 Fed. Reg. 27666 at 27673.

tanning may increase the risk of skin aging, skin cancer, and other effects to the skin even if you do not burn.

"Chemical-free", "Natural", and "PABA-free" Ingredients

The terms "chemical-free", "non-chemical", and "natural" have been applied to some products containing mineral sunscreens, such as titanium dioxide and zinc oxide. FDA states in the Final Rule that all sunscreen products contain active and inactive ingredients obtained through some chemical process or formulated into the finished product by a chemical process. Therefore, the use of these terms to describe either the sunscreen ingredient or the finished product is likely to be unacceptable. However, FDA intends to review such claims on a case-by-case basis.

FDA agrees that consumers are familiar with the term "PABA" and might not recognize the compendial (USP) name, "aminobenzoic acid", and to eliminate the term "PABA" from sunscreen labeling could cause some consumers to use a product to which they have an allergy and to suffer adverse health effects. Therefore, FDA concludes that wherever the ingredient "aminobenzoic acid" appears in the labeling of an OTC drug sunscreen product, "including labeling that notes the absence of this ingredient", the descriptive term "PABA" must immediately follow the established name. A product that is marketed as "PABA-free" is now required to state that the product is "Aminobenzoic acid (PABA)-free".

Extended Protection Claims

Some comments on the Proposed Rule suggested that the "very water resistant" claim be expanded beyond the 80 min test period for products that can show such extended efficacy. FDA acknowledges in the Final Rule that data submitted do indicate that under testing conditions, some products may retain their SPF values for up to 270 min. However, as no usage data were submitted to refute the Advisory Panel's contention that 80 min is an appropriate upper exposure limit, FDA opted to retain the 80 min test protocol. Thus, a claim for extended water resistance is outside the Final Rule and would be subject to review under a new drug application. FDA noted that it would revisit the question should it receive usage data indicating consumer patterns of more than 80 min of water exposure. In addition, references to "prolonged exposure time", originally present in the Proposed Rule, are omitted from the final product category descriptions because, as FDA states in the preamble to the Final Rule, these claims could send the wrong message about the dangers of even suberythmal, nonburning sun exposure.

Freckles and Uneven Skin Tone

The Proposed Rule would have allowed sunscreen-containing makeup preparations, lip products, and skin preparations to be represented as effective in the prevention of "lip damage", "freckling", or "uneven skin tone". However, these indications have been dropped from the Final Rule on the basis that the SPF testing predicts protection only from UV-B sunburn, and because freckling, skin tone and lip damage may be attributable to UV-A, as well as to UV-B, radiation. FDA noted that it would revisit the question of such claims when specific supportive data are provided or a specific clinically relevant final formulation test is developed.

TESTING SUNSCREEN EFFICACY

The test methodology outlined in the Final Rule applies only to the efficacy of a product in protecting against UV-B sunburn exposure and is considered relevant only for sunscreens with lower SPF values. As stated in the Preamble to the Final Rule, the proposed test method for measuring values up to SPF 30 "represents at this time a straightforward, well-understood, and sound method for measuring these values".[28] Nevertheless, FDA discussed its concerns that data from the test methods currently authorized may not adequately assess the efficacy of sunscreens with SPF values above 15. Because test methodology in this area is evolving, FDA intends to work with interested parties in the development of accurate methods for assessing high SPF value products and will, if appropriate, address this issue in a future *Federal Register* proposal. FDA is also working with interested parties to develop methodology to assess the effectiveness of UV-A sunscreens and to investigate whether sunscreens operative against UV-A radiation might also help to protect against premature skin aging, photoaging, and wrinkling. The agency intends to explore these issues in a future issue of the *Federal Register* when it completes the UV-A portion of the sunscreen monograph.[29]

FDA recognizes that the formulation or mode of administration of some products may require modification of the testing procedures and that alternative methods, such as automated or *in vitro* methods, may be used. However, any proposed modification or alternative procedures must be submitted to FDA as a Citizen's Petition[30] and accompanied by data to support the modification or data showing that the alternative methodology produces results of equivalent accuracy. In the meantime, the testing procedure described in the Final Rule, including procedures for determining "water resistant" and "very water resistant" claims, will be used as the standard by which SPF value claims will be measured. A detailed discussion of the UV-B sunscreen product test methodology is included elsewhere in this volume.

WHAT OF THE FUTURE?

At the time of writing, FDA has indicated its intention to take action in several unfinished areas. These include developing a test method for determining the

---

[28]64 Fed. Reg. 27666 at 27680.

[29]64 Fed. Reg. 27666 at 27677.

[30]See 21 CFR 10.30 for the rules governing submission of Citizen's Petitions.

effectiveness of UV-A sunscreens and the appropriate claims for such products, in particular, claims that might link premature skin or photoaging protection to UV-A sunscreen use. At the same time, FDA has indicated that it will consider whether a "negative" claim may be necessary to alert consumers about sunscreen products that do not provide UV-A protection. FDA also continues to work on developing a suitable test method for evaluating claims to high SPF protection from UV-B radiation, which when completed, may allow for the use of SPF values higher than 30+ in sunscreen product labeling. Other items open for future consideration are the required specific reapplication directions to sunscreen users and the extended protection claims based on data to indicate that consumers stay in the water longer than 80 min, the current limit for "very water resistant" claims.[31]

In order to address these and other issues, FDA has extended the effective date of the Final Rule until December 31, 2005[32] (with the exception of those parts that require the warning statement for cosmetic preparations that contain sunscreen ingredients for nontherapeutic uses (21 CFR 700.35) and cosmetic suntanning preparations that do not contain any sunscreen active ingredients).

In an earlier *Federal Register* notice also extending the effective date and reopening the administrative record, FDA identified eight areas in which it is seeking further data and information.[33]

FDA Requests for Information and Comment

1. Whether to adopt a specific spectral power distribution pattern and require that solar simulators be filtered to provide a continuous emission spectrum from 290 to 400 nm with the following percentage of erythema-effective radiation in each specified range of wavelengths. This modification would be intended to eliminate conditions that may cause overestimation of SPF value for high-SPF sunscreens.

Wavelength (nm)	*Percent erythema effectiveness*
290	0.1
290–310	46–67
290–320	80–91
290–330	86.5–95
290–340	90.5–97
290–350	93.5–99

[31]See November 17, 2000 letter from Charles Ganley, MD, Director, Division of OTC Drug Evaluation, CDER, FDA to Martin A. Weinstock, MD, PhD, Chairman, Skin Cancer Advisory Group and Mary O'Connell, Director, Skin Cancer Initiatives (Docket 78N-0038).

[32]66 Fed. Reg. 67485 (December 31, 2001).

[33]65 Fed. Reg. 36319 (June 8, 2000).

2. Whether to replace the current specifications in Section 21 CFR 352.71 of the Final Rule limiting to 5% the amount of a solar simulator's total energy output that can be contributed by wavelengths longer than 400 nm and substituting a limit on the total radiation delivered to the skin for all wavelengths. The purpose of the modification would be to limit the total energy delivered to the skin so that skin temperature does not reach a point that influences the UV dose reciprocity relationship during the long exposure times needed to test high-SPF sunscreens.
3. Additional data on the suitability of an analytical method related to the use of one or more specific control preparations to test high-SPF sunscreen drug products (SPF values of 15 and greater).
4. Whether the high-performance liquid chromatography assay is suitable both for the currently authorized homosalate SPF 4 standard and for SPF 15 standard, including a validation package documenting specificity, accuracy, limit of detection, linearity, precision, and reproducibility of the method. The purpose of the modification would be to replace the spectrophotometric assay presently designated in Section 21 CFR 352.70(c) of the Final Rule.
5. Whether the number of currently identified SPF 20–25 test subjects should be increased in tests for SPF values over 30.
6. Whether the current exposure dose format for MED determination is adequate for sunscreens with SPF values over 30. The current procedure is described as a series of seven exposures administered to the protected test sites to determine the MED of protected skin, consisting of a geometric series of five exposures, where the middle exposure is placed to yield the expected SPF, plus two other exposures placed symmetrically around the middle exposure. The purpose of the inquiry is to solicit comment on the agency's concern that widely spaced geometric progression offers less accuracy in the upper SPF range and may produce overestimated SPF values in high-SPF test preparations.
7. Whether the labeled SPF limit of 30+ should be eliminated and how to communicate in product labeling the level of sun protection associated with high-SPF sunscreen drug products. FDA also requested comments on the use of professional labeling for health practitioners, about the value of high-SPF products, and about valid indications.
8. Whether the practical limitations of current test equipment and subject patience can be overcome, because testing high SPF preparations necessitates the use of longer UV radiation exposure time, often several hours. FDA asks what the total exposure times would be for testing preparations with estimated SPF values of 60 and higher and what the practical limit in terms of an SPF value might be.

In the area of UV-A testing, FDA has received information related to *in vitro* methodology to determine the potency of UV-A protection in sunscreens and a recommendation for a UV-A Index representing the broadness and the amplitude of UV-A protection for consumer labeling.[34] Other comments to FDA on UV-A testing and labeling advocate using a combination of both *in vitro* critical wavelength testing (with a claim threshold of 370 nm) and an *in vivo* method showing at least a fourfold increase in protection from persistent pigment darkening or in the protection factor in the UV-A range. Products that meet both test criteria would be labeled as "broad spectrum".[35]

Other comments submitted to FDA express the need for prescription sunscreen products,[36] the need for photostability data for all sunscreen products,[37] and the infringement of FDA on First Amendment Freedom of Speech ensuing from the limit on SPF values and the restrictive nature of the uniform OTC drug labeling regulation.[38] The Cosmetic, Toiletry, and Fragrance Association (CTFA) has requested exemption for topical products with no dosage limits, such as sunscreens, from the proposed regulations requiring bar code labeling on all drug products,[39] and has requested off-label listing of inactive ingredients in the case of small package OTC drug products, including, for example, lip products containing sunscreens.[40]

CONCLUSION

Despite its official title, the 1999 *Federal Register* document is by no means a "Final" Rule governing OTC drug sunscreen products. The comprehensive monograph for both UV-B and UV-A sunscreen protection labeling and testing that FDA had hoped to publish by the end of 2002 is now scheduled for the end of 2005 and many of the issues and disagreements discussed above must be resolved prior to publication. The history of the sunscreen monograph spans more than three decades, if one begins with the 1972 commissioning of the original Panel of Experts by FDA. During that time, perceptions of public health priorities, technical advances, consumer practices, and marketing visibility have changed. While at the time of writing there is still no truly "Final"

[34]See November 12, 2002, letter to FDA from Beiersdorf AG (Docket 78N-0038).

[35]See April 1, 2002, letter to FDA from the American Dermatology Association (Docket 78N-0083).

[36]See Citizen Petition of February 13, 2003, to FDA from Robert Sayer, PhD and Ramon Fusaro, MD, PhD and FDA's June 13, 2003, response soliciting additional information on the potential use of the New Drug Application procedures or OTC monograph professional labeling as possible methods for adding additional sunscreen indications (Docket 03P-0067).

[37]See Citizens Petition of August 13, 2003, from TRLI to FDA (Docket 78N-0038).

[38]See October 28, 2002, letter to FDA from the Cosmetic, Toiletry, and Fragrance Association (Docket 02N-0209).

[39]See June 12, 2003, letter to FDA from CTFA, (Docket 02N-0204).

[40]See September 2, 2003, letter to FDA from CTFA, (Docket 78N-021P).

Sunscreen Rule, FDA and sunscreen manufacturers, testers, and users have created enough flexibility within the OTC Drug Review to consider and incorporate modifications to the original proposals that address these developments in an ongoing manner. The most important challenge for the future will be to maintain a similar flexibility in accommodating the addition of new ingredients, new indications, and new scientific insights, which are inevitable and foreseeable events. Balancing FDA's charge to protect public health by assuring safe and effective drug products with the consumer's "right to know" and the commercial interests of industry remains the chief challenge for the future, not only as it relates to the sunscreen monograph, but also for the entire OTC drug industry.

8

Regulatory Aspects of Suncreens in Europe

Romano E. Mascotto
L'Oréal Research, Asnière, France

DEFINITION OF ULTRAVIOLET FILTERS

In Europe, sunscreen products are considered cosmetics, as their function is to protect the skin from sunburn. The European Economic Community (EEC) has issued a directive to its member states relating to cosmetic products.[1] Article 1 says

> A "cosmetic product" means any substance or preparation intended for placing in contact with the various external parts of the human body or with the teeth and mucous membranes of the oral cavity with a view exclusively or principally to clean them, perfuming them or protecting

[1]OJ of European Communities Number L262/170 (September 27, 1976).

> them in order to keep them in good condition, change their appearance or correct body odours.

Because of this definition there is a need to differentiate between the legal status of sunscreen in European countries and that in the USA, Canada, and Australia, where they are considered OTC products.

THE EEC DIRECTIVE PUBLISHED NOVEMBER 28, 1983

The Third Amendment[2] gives the definition and a list of ultraviolet (UV) filters that cosmetic products may contain. This list is divided into two parts: UV filters that are fully permitted and those that are provisionally permitted. Through successive Adapting Commission Directives[3] the provisional list has been voided, transferring the approved substances to the fully permitted list and adding new permitted UV filters. It is no longer accepted by the European Commission to provisionally register new UV filters.

The chemical nomenclature used is International Nomenclature for Cosmetic Ingredients (INCI) and requires interpretation into trade names, which are commonly understood by a cosmetic chemist. This is tabulated in Table 8.1. The maximum concentrations, other limitations, and requirements and warnings that must appear on the label are also listed in the table. The numbers prefaced with "S" indicate COLIPA numbers (COLIPA—The European Cosmetic Toiletry and Perfumery Association, representing the cosmetic industry in those European countries that are members of the European Union). A definition of UV filters is given in the preamble of the Annex VII ECC Directive:

> UV filters are substances which, contained in cosmetic sunscreen products, are specifically intended to filter certain UV rays in order to protect the skin from certain harmful effects of these rays. These UV filters may be added to other cosmetic products within the limits and under the conditions laid down in this Annex.

Other UV filters not listed in the table can be used for product protection (stabilizing colors, and so forth).

The status of permitted UV filters has been reviewed by the EEC working party dealing with the safety of cosmetic products, called the Ad Hoc Working Party on Cosmetic Directive (AHWP). This group consists of member state governments, as well as representatives from industry and consumer groups. As this working party contains a mix of people, not necessarily scientifically trained, they are being advised by the Scientific Committee on Cosmetology and Non Food Products (SCCNFP) set up by the EEC Commission. Committee members are independent eminent scientists, mainly dermatologists and toxicologists from

[2]OJ of European Communities Number L332/38 (November 11, 1983).

[3]SCCNFP/0690/03 Final (and annexes).

Table 8.1 UV Filters That Cosmetic Products May Contain

COLIPA Ref. No.	EEC Ref. No.	INCI name	Maximum authorized concentration (%)	Other limitations and requirements	Conditions of use and warnings which must be printed on the label	Trade names, other chemical or trivial names
S1	1	PABA	5			PABA; Paramino l; Pabacidum; Amben; Pabanol
S57	2	Camphor benzalkonium methosulfate	6			(3-(4′-Trimethylammonium-benzylidene)-ibornan-2-one-methylsulfate; mexoryl SO
S12	3	Homosalate	10			Homomenthyl salicylate; 3,5,5-trimethyl cyclohexyl salicylate; Filtrosol A; benzoic acid 2-hydroxy-3,3,5 trimethyl cyclohexylester; Kemester HMS
S38	4	Benzophenone-3	10		Contains oxybenzone[a]	2-Hydroxy-4-methoxy-benzophenone; Uvistat 24; Uvinul M40; Eusolex 4360; Cyasorb UV-9; Spectrasorb UV-9; benzophenone-3 (CTFA); Neo-Heliopan BB; oxybenzone; Uvasorb Met
S45	6	Phenylbenzimidazole sulfonic acid	8 (as acid)			Eusolex 232; Novantisol; Neo-Heliopan Hydro/USP; Parsol HS

(*continued*)

Table 8.1 *Continued*

COLIPA Ref. No.	EEC Ref. No.	INCI name	Maximum authorized concentration (%)	Other limitations and requirements	Conditions of use and warnings which must be printed on the label	Trade names, other chemical or trivial names
S71	7	Terephthalylidene dicamphor sulphonic acid	10 (as acid)			Mexoryl SX; ecamsule
S66	8	Butyl methoxydibenzoylmethane	5			Parsol 1789; 4-*t*-butyl-4′-methoxy dibenzoyl methane; Eusolex 9020
S59	9	Benzilidene camphor sulfonic acid	6 (as acid)			3-(4′-sulfobenxylidene) camphor; Mexoryl SL
S32	10	Octocrylene	10 (a)			Uvinul N-539 T;. Eusolex OCR; Escalol 597; Neo-Heliopan 303/USP
S72	11	Polyacrylamidomethyl benzylidene camphor	6			Mexoryl SW
S28	12	Ethylhexyl methoxycinnamate	10			Parsol MCX; Neo-Heliopan AV; *p*-methoxycinnamic acid 2-ethylhexyl ester; Sunarome OMC; Uvinul MC80; Escalol 557 L
S3	13	PEG-25 PABA	10			Ethoxylated PABA ethyl ester; Lusantan 25 (ethoxylated-ethyl-4-aminobenzoate)
S27	14	Isoamyl *p*-methoxycinnamate	10			Isopentyl-4-methoxycinnamte; Neo-Heliopan E 1000
S69	15	Ethylhexyl triazone	5			Uvinul T-150

S73	16	Drometrizole trisiloxane	15		Mexoryl XL
S78	17	Diethyl hexyl butamido triazone	10		
S60	18	4-Methylbenzilidene camphor	4		3-(4′-Methylbenzylidene)-D-1-camphor; Eusolex 6300; Eusolex 8021 (part); Parsol 5000
S61	19	3-Benzylidene camphor	2		3-Benzylidene camphor; Mexoryl SD; Ultren BK; Ultraoyd
S13	20	Ethylhexyl salicylate	5		Octyl salicylate (CTFA) UV; Sunarome WMO; benzoic acid; 2-hydroxy-2-ethylhexyl ester; Neo-Heliopan OS/BP; Neo-Heliopan OS/USP
S8	21	Ethylhexyl dimethyl PABA	8		Sunarome PLUS-Arlatone UV-B; octyldimethyl PABA; Escalol 507, Padimate O; Eusolex 6007; 2-ethylhexyl-*p*-dimethyl amino benzoate; Escalol 507
S40	22	Benzophenone-4 (acid) Benzophenone-5 (Na Salt)	5 (a)		2-Hydroxy-4 methoxy-benzophenone-5-sulfonic acid and salt Uvinul MS-40; benzophenone-4 (CTFA); Uval; Cyasorb UV-S-5; Syntase 230

(*continued*)

Table 8.1 *Continued*

COLIPA Ref. No.	EEC Ref. No.	INCI name	Maximum authorized concentration (%)	Other limitations and requirements	Conditions of use and warnings which must be printed on the label	Trade names, other chemical or trivial names
S79	23	Methylene bis-benzotriazoyl tetramethylbutylphenol	10			Tinosorb M
S80	24	Disodium phenyl dibenzyimadazole tetrasulfonate	10 (a)			Neo-Heliopan AP
S81	25	Bis-ethylhexyloxyphenol methoxyphenyl triazine	10			Tinosorb S
S74	26	Polysilicone-15	10			Parsol SLX
S75	27	Titanium dioxide	25			Eusolex T-2000

Note: The zinc oxide (S76) dossier has been submitted in 2003 to the SCCNFP for evaluation; the use of the product is temporarily permitted.
[a]The concentration corresponds to the acidic form.

different countries. They study and review the data provided to them from various sources, including different government health boards, associations, industry, hospitals, databases, and others. Their mission is to form an opinion on the safety of chemical substances used in cosmetics under normal conditions of use and then publish their findings and decision in a report which can be found in the SCCNFP website.[4]

Meanwhile, the cosmetic industry, through the EU Countries Trade Association, COLIPA, plays an important role in securing a reasonable list of permitted UV filters and continues to collect, review, and present data and information on usage.

The individual countries' trade associations deal with the regulatory bodies of their own governments. COLIPA has not only contributed to the preparation of a sensible definition and list of UV filters but has also been collecting safety data on the chemicals and presented them to the EEC commission in the required format. COLIPA has a subcommittee on sun products that deals with sunscreens and UV filters and teams working on sun protection factor (SPF) measurement, water resistance, UV-A protection, and photostability methods.

There is a standard procedure for adding substances to the list of UV filters. This procedure is laid down in Article 8 (2) of the EEC Cosmetic Directive, which reads: "the amendments necessary for adapting Annexes II to VII to technical progress shall be adapted in accordance with the same procedure, after consultation of the Scientific Committee for Cosmetology and Non Food Products at the initiative of the Commission or of a member State".

This, in practice, means that if a new cosmetic ingredient, for example, UV filter, is discovered, the following action needs to be taken:

- COLIPA sends a written request to the EEC commission, supported by file with safety data on the ingredient.
- EEC commission also submits the summary of the file to the working party of Cosmetic Directive (AHWP).
- SCCNFP presents a written opinion to the EEC commission.
- This opinion is then circulated to all members of AHWP.
- The AHWP discusses the proposed addition to the list, usually in the presence of an industry expert. This procedure takes time, usually two or more meetings.
- In case of a favorable attitude by EEC member states' delegates, the EEC commission then prepares an official proposal for an amending Commission Directive.
- The proposal is sent to the Committee for Adaptation for Technical Progress (CATP), which is then convened by the EEC commission.
- CATP discusses the proposed amendment and approves or rejects it by qualified majority voting.

[4]See footnote 3.

- In case of approval, the EEC commission then prepares the amending directive; this is signed by an EEC commissioner and officially distributed to all EEC member states and subsequently in the Official Journal (OJ) of the European Communities.

In 2003 the European commission asked the SCCNFP to evaluate the UV filters listed without a complete dossier, namely S1, S57, S12, S38, and S45. The European and American industries responded positively and will submit the complete status of the art safety information[5] before the end of 2005 as requested.

NON-EU COUNTRIES' REGULATORY STATUS

Most of the non-EU countries (e.g., Sweden, Turkey, and Switzerland) largely follow the EU directive as a code.

SUN PROTECTION MEASUREMENTS

In 1994 Colipa published an SPF test method and introduced new techniques to characterize and specify the emission spectrum of the UV source and to colorimetrically select the skin type of the volunteers. COLIPA, the Japan Cosmetic Industry Association (JCIA), and South Africa Cosmetic, Toiletry, and Fragrance Association (CTFA) decided to harmonize and improve the SPF method at the Malta Mutual Understanding Conference in 2000. Major changes to improve the reproducibility of the measured SPF are

- Application procedure of the product on the skin including a training CD-ROM for cream lotion and powder application
- Reading of the unprotected and protected minimal erythema dose
- Strict definition of the quality of the filtered UV spectrum
- Requirement for a periodical monitoring of the UV lamp by a qualified expert
- Tightened %RCEE limits in the spectral range 290–320 nm (85–90%)
- Reduction of dose progression to 12% for SPF $\geq$ 25
- Reduction of the statistical criterion (95% CI $\leq \pm 17\%$)

A joint agreement on the new "International Sun Protection Factor (SPF) Test Method" was reached in October 2002.

A COLIPA new recommendation (No. 11) on SPF labeling has been published in 2002; the limitation of the SPF numbers to be labeled is intended to facilitate the understanding of the consumer.

---

[5]See footnote 3.

The recommendation states

> The mean value from the test is rounded down to any whole number in the SPF Classification Table shown below, and this number is the maximum SPF to be labeled. SPF test results should not be rounded up to the nearest number in the classification table. The following Categories and SPF numbers are recommended. Indication of products Categories may be useful and should be optional.
>
> | Type | SPF |
> |---|---|
> | Low | 2–4–6 |
> | Medium | 8–10–12 |
> | High | 15–20–25 |
> | Very high | 30–40–50 |
> | Ultra | 50+ |
>
> The maximum SPF labeled should be SPF 50+ (for a product to be labeled as SPF 50+ the mean SPF measured must have been SPF 60 or above). The SPF numbers labeled are restricted to those and only those shown in the table. The term *sunblock* should no longer be used.
> All labeling should comply by 31 December 2005.

COLIPA actively works on the UVA protection measurement method; the mandate of the project team is to develop an *in vitro* method validated against the *in vivo* persistent pigment darkening (PPD) method. *In vivo* PPD method will be authorized as an alternative.

Future labeling will be based on a ratio between the *in vivo* SPF number and the PPD result and the results will be expressed on labeling as a class in order not to introduce a new number for UVA protection that can be misleading for the consumer.

FUTURE

In recent years, epidemiological evidence has accumulated data that indicate that skin cancer and degenerative skin changes (e.g., aging) are partly related to excessive exposure to UV rays. Cosmetic manufacturers tend to use UVA and UVB filters in many products, not only those that are used to prevent sunburn.

This gives the cosmetic scientists reason to believe that UV filters and other substances that have the ability to filter out UV light will become even more important in reducing the risk of premature skin aging and skin cancer. Further regulatory restriction would only harness flexibility and innovation. Guidelines, rather than regulations, would be respected. The consumer's safety is the main obligation of a manufacturer and, therefore, the scientific and ethical approach to sunscreens should be left with the experts.

9

Regulation of Sunscreens in Australia

Malcolm R. Nearn
Kentlyn, New South Wales, Australia

INTRODUCTION

Sunscreens are regulated as therapeutic goods in Australia. Given Australia's claim to have the highest incidence of skin cancer in the world, this seems very reasonable. People from countries where UV-B radiation is less intense and of shorter duration may consider this unnecessary; however, Australians well understand the need to protect skin against sun exposure and they expect their interests to be properly protected by the implementation of appropriate controls of the quality of the sunscreens they buy and use. This is best achieved in Australia by dealing with sunscreens as therapeutic goods.

Since 1983 the Australian Standard (later to become the Australian/New Zealand Standard) entitled "Sunscreen Products—Evaluation and Classification" (AS/NZS 2604)[1] has provided descriptions of the techniques for measuring the ability of sunscreens to protect skin against UV radiation. It also provides performance standards that a product must achieve if it is to comply with the Standard. Further, it states the requirements for the labeling of sunscreens that comply with the Standard. Although compliance with Australian Standards is voluntary, the Sunscreen Standard has been underpinned by regulations issued by the Therapeutic Goods Administration (TGA) that make compliance with the current edition, AS/NZS 2604:1998, enforceable in many respects. The main regulatory framework for sunscreens is the Therapeutic Goods Act 1989, the regulations of which are administered by the TGA. Generally, sunscreens are "listed" therapeutic goods, meaning that the sponsor (usually the marketer) must supply certain information and assurances before the TGA will grant permission to market by issuing an Australian Listing (Aust L) number. (However, there are some exceptions to this general rule; these exceptions are explained below.) The onus is on the sponsor to ensure that the sunscreens they make and distribute to the market meet the necessary standards of quality and effectiveness. The TGA has the power to intervene if the marketed sunscreens do not meet the required standards.

The regulation of sunscreens as therapeutic goods differs slightly from that of other therapeutic goods, and in some respects is more flexible. For instance, stability testing may be conducted according to "Guidelines for Stability Testing of Sunscreens".[2] Also, there is a modified Code of Good Manufacturing Practice for sunscreens that is available on the TGA website.[3]

---

[1]Australian/New Zealand Standard® Sunscreen products—Evaluation and Classification. Standards Australia, 286 Sussex Street, Sydney, NSW 2000, Australia and Standards New Zealand, Level 10, Standards House, 155 The Terrace, Wellington 6001, New Zealand.

[2]Guidelines for Stability Testing of Sunscreens April 1994. Compiled by the Australian Society of Cosmetic Chemists (ASCC), the Cosmetic Toiletry, Fragrance Association of Australia (CTFA), The Nutritional Foods Association of Australia (NFAA), and the Proprietary Medicines Association of Australia (now the Australian Self-Medication Industry [ASMI]. www.asmi.com.au.

[3]Australian Code of GMP for Therapeutic Goods—Sunscreen Products 1994. www.tga.gov.au/docs/html/gmpsunsc.htm.

The regulations and their interpretation by officers of the TGA change from time to time, so it is prudent to refer to the TGA's very helpful website[4] to remain abreast of the current situation.

THE REGULATORY FRAMEWORK

In Australia the Commonwealth Government's Department of Health and Ageing is responsible for the safety and efficacy of therapeutic goods and devices (and other matters). The Act of Parliament that covers these activities is the Therapeutic Goods Act 1989,[5] which is a general statement of the requirements for the manufacture and marketing of therapeutic goods. The objective of the Act is to ensure the quality, safety, effectiveness, and availability of therapeutic goods within Australia and for export from Australia and import into Australia. The Therapeutic Goods Act is given effect by a series of regulations that are updated from time to time in the light of changing needs. (One might add that the implementation of the regulations, and particularly guidelines, is a matter of individual interpretation of officers of the TGA, so that seemingly minor changes can evolve in use.) The administration of these regulations is conducted by the TGA.

Therapeutic goods may be either medicines or medical devices. Medicines may be categorized as prescription only (meaning that to obtain them the customer must take a doctor's prescription to a pharmacist who will dispense it) or nonprescription. Nonprescription medicines may be "complementary medicines" or "over-the counter (OTC) medicines". Complementary medicines are "traditional" or "alternative" medicines; they include vitamin, mineral, herbal, aromatherapy, and homoeopathic products.

OTC medicines and complementary medicines may be either registrable or listable. Registrable medicines must be registered with the TGA by completing the necessary application forms and sending them to the TGA with the relevant fees and evidence of safety, efficacy, stability, and specifications. This information is then evaluated and the sponsor (person or company submitting the information) is duly informed of the decision. On the other hand, applications to market a listable product receive minimal evaluation by the TGA at the time of application. The onus is on the sponsor to possess the information relating to efficacy, stability, safety, and specifications. However, the TGA normally checks that the labels comply with the relevant regulations before issuing marketing permission. Also, the sponsor must give a written (and legally binding) assurance that the necessary data relating to efficacy have been obtained prior to marketing. From time to time the TGA conducts an audit of such listing

[4]www.health.tga.gov.au.tga.

[5]Therapeutic Goods Act 1989, Act No. 21 of 1990 (includes amendments up to Act No. 3 of 1999). www.dhs.vic.gov.au/nphp/publicvations/legislation/implement_opt/an2-7.pdf. (For further amendments see the TGA website.)

applications to determine if the necessary efficacy and other data have been obtained. If the sponsor does not have the data then TGA can cancel the listing (marketing permission) of that product and may suspend or cancel the license of the sponsor to manufacture and market that product, or indeed any therapeutic product.

All prescription-only, registrable, and listable therapeutic goods must be manufactured in premises that have been *licensed* by the TGA (see figure).

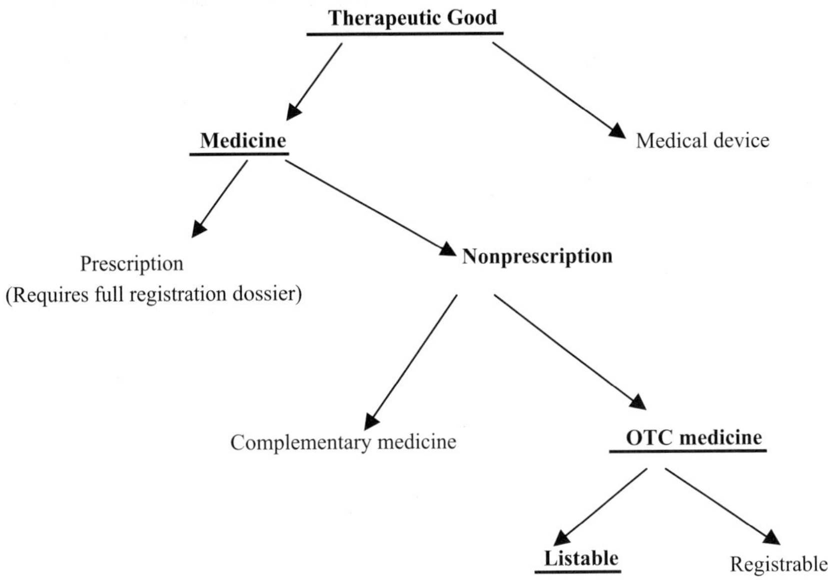

Generally, sunscreens are listable therapeutic goods in Australia:

1. Listable sunscreens are those sunscreens or moisturizers containing sunscreens that make SPF claims where the SPF = 4 or greater, and do not make prohibited claims. Labels must comply with the Therapeutic Labeling Order TGO 69, the Therapeutic Goods Advertising Code, and the current edition of the Sunscreen Standard AS/NZS 2604. For further details see the section on labeling of sunscreens. Sunscreens having SPFs of less than 4 (i.e., 3 or 2) are listable if they contain certain ingredients of animal origin (the reason for this is concern about the potential to transmit transmissible spongiform encephalopathies).
2. Sunscreens must be *registered* with the Australian Register of Therapeutic Goods (ARTG) if they are included in the Schedule of Pharmaceutical Benefits (PBS). The PBS is a scheme whereby the Government provides a subsidy for a medicine that is included in

the PBS when a doctor's prescription is provided by the patient to the dispensing pharmacist. Currently, the patient will pay up to A$23.10 or A$3.70 for holders of concession cards (e.g., pensioners). Sunscreens must also be registered if in addition to making sunscreening claims they make other therapeutic claims. A sunscreen product must be registered if it contains a sunscreen active that is not included in the current list (see later). Registration is far more onerous (and expensive) because a full registration package must be submitted for evaluation by the TGA.

3. Sunscreens are *exempt* from the need for listing or registration and manufacture in licensed premises when the SPF is 3 or less and the product does not contain certain ingredients of animal origin. However, these sunscreens are still medicines and must comply with the TGA regulations for labeling of therapeutic goods.
4. Tinted, unmedicated lip preparations, including lipsticks, are *excluded* (i.e., not therapeutic) even if they make sunscreen claims but do not make other therapeutic claims. Other cosmetics without therapeutic claims (other than "with sunscreen") and without SPF claims or equivalent on the label are also excluded. Excluded sunscreens are regulated as cosmetics by the National Industrial Chemicals Notification and Assessment Scheme (NICNAS) and The Australian Competition and Consumer Commission.

TEST METHODS

The test methods for sunscreen efficacy are set out in the Australian/New Zealand Standard AS/NZS 2604. The SPF test method has much in common with the COLIPA method, although there are subtle differences. It may be purchased from Standards Australia.[6]

In addition to the SPF test method three methods are described for measuring UV-A transmission between 320 and 360 nm. Method 1—solution method is applicable to products that dissolve completely in a solution of dichloroethane (12.5%), cyclohexane (37.5%), and isopropanol (50%). Following serial dilution the absorbance of the sunscreen in a 1 cm path length UV–VIS spectrophotometer cell should be equivalent to 8 μm of the undiluted product. Method 2—thin film method is applicable to products that do not dissolve in the solvent. An 8 μm of sunscreen product is sandwiched between two quartz plates and this assembly is positioned adjacent to the measuring device of a UV–VIS spectrophotometer. Method 3—plate method is applicable to all sunscreens. The transmittance of a 20 μm layer of the sunscreen product is measured using a UV–VIS spectrophotometer with integrating sphere. The broad-spectrum

[6]See footnote 1.

requirement for the sunscreen Standard AS/NZS 2604-1998 is that the sunscreen sample must not transmit more than 10% of any wavelength between 320 and 360 nm when tested by methods 1 or 2 and not more than 1% when tested by method 3.

All three methods tend to grossly exaggerate UV-A protection because they do not take into account the roughness of the skin—the true film thickness of the sunscreen on skin is much lower. Method 2 also has another defect that is due to the failure of an ordinary spectrophotometer to capture light that is scattered after passing through the sample. Method 1 also has another defect because it does not take account of spectral shifts due to solvent effects.

THE LISTING PROCESS

Sunscreens may be listed on the ARTG either by completing a written application or electronically through the Electronic Listing Facility (ELF).[7]

ELF allows the sponsor to create applications and draft applications, and to list a sunscreen product on the ARTG. When preparing the entry you can view the label checklist to ensure that you are not making a prohibited claim. You can also find out whether the ingredients you propose to use are already included in the ARTG (and thus permitted). Currently, ELF is not entirely foolproof, and the use of a local regulatory affairs consultant may make the process easier. Also, TGA currently has a local ELF Help Desk (1800 773 312).

NEW CHEMICALS

New chemicals for listable or registrable sunscreens must be included in the ARTG. Many are already registered, but if a new material is to be registered an application for inclusion, together with the appropriate information (and fees, of course), must be sent to the Business Unit of the OTC Medicines Branch of the TGA. The information is reviewed by OTC Medicines toxicologists and then by an independent expert committee, the Medicines Evaluation Committee.

New Excipients (Nonactive Ingredients)

Before a new excipient (i.e., one that is not currently included in the ARTG) can be used in a sunscreen it must be cleared for use by TGA. The sponsor should

[7]Electronic Listing Facility. www.health.gov.au/tga/docs/html/elfuserg.htm (for guidance and training on the use of ELF).

provide the following information:[8]

1. Evidence that it is included in the CTFA International Cosmetic Ingredient Dictionary (page number and reference should be quoted).
2. Assurance that it is not included in the current edition of Annex II of the EEC Cosmetic Directive 76/768. This is the list of substances that an EEC cosmetic may *not* contain.
3. Assurance that the excipient has been approved by the relevant regulatory agency in one or more of the following countries: Sweden, Canada, USA, Canada, UK, or Netherlands, or (less desirably).
4. Assurance that there have been market-place sales of comparable products containing the excipient in one of the above countries for at least 2 years.
5. Acute oral toxicity: LD50—animal or alternative equivalent.
6. Irritation study—skin, animal, or alternative method.
7. Sensitisation study—skin, animal, or alternative method. In addition, the following may be required in individual cases:
8. Eye irritation study
9. *In vitro* mutagenicity (Ames) test
10. *In vitro* percutaneous absorption test

That is, to register a new excipient the sponsor will have to provide the information set out in (1)–(7) and may be required to provide in addition the information set out in (8)–(10). In principle, you may be able to market a product containing the new excipient if the information set out in (1)–(4) is provided and the sponsor undertakes to provide the information in (5)–(7) within 6 months, but this is considered to be inadvisable, particularly if evaluation by the TGA of the data in (5)–(7) leads them to ask for any or all of the data in (8)–(10).

Other sources of information that will be considered are publications in the Cosmetic Ingredient Review and acceptance by NICNAS. (New chemicals other than therapeutic ingredients must be cleared by NICNAS.)

New Sunscreen Actives

The data needed to support the approval of a new sunscreen active are based on those needed for the approval of a new sunscreen active in the EU. TGA has adopted the European guidelines for each test method. However, subtle

[8]Australian Regulatory Guidelines for OTC Medicines (ARGOM.) Published by TGA July 1, 2003. 10.9–10.10. www.tga.gov.au/docs/html/listguid.htm.

differences in interpretation often mean that the EU registration dossier will not suffice to achieve registration in Australia. In particular, the TGA takes the view that it is not possible to interpret toxicology data without properly designed and conducted toxicokinetic studies. It is possible that absorption of the active by the oral route may be lower than absorption by the dermal route. Thus, a substance may be systemically toxic by the dermal route but not by the oral route.

Another point of difference concerns skin penetration. If it is sufficiently low in practice the EU may waive the need for certain tests. But how do they decide what is "sufficiently low"? Furthermore, the toxicologists in TGA take the view that *in vitro* skin penetration studies may not duplicate *in vivo* studies. On the other hand, TGA is aware of the need for new improved sunscreen actives and will accept sound arguments for not conducting certain tests, such as carcinogenicity tests.

Details of the requirements for registration of a new sunscreen active are given in the Australian Regulatory Guidelines for OTC Medicines.[9] Below is a summary of the guidelines. (Note that these are not intended to be prescriptive.)

- Photostability—UV absorbance spectra. The sunscreen active must be photostable and in addition it may be necessary to show that the new active does not interact with (e.g., destabilize) other sunscreen actives with which it might be used. The TGA probably has in mind the interaction between methoxycinnamates and avobenzone.
- Acute toxicity (oral and dermal).
- Skin irritation; relevant human studies are acceptable.
- Phototoxicity.
- Eye irritation.
- Skin sensitization; relevant human studies are acceptable.
- Photosensitization.
- Toxicokinetics (oral, dermal, and ADME [absorption, distribution, metabolism, and excretion] studies).
- Repeat dose toxicity (oral and dermal)—3–6 month data.
- Genotoxicity and photomutagenicity (tests in bacteria and mammalian cell lines, photomutagenicity in bacteria, photomutagenicity in a chromosomal aberration test and an *in vivo* chromosome aberration assay).
- Reproductive toxicity, including assessment for fertility and developmental effects, and endocrine disruption assays.
- Carcinogenicity and photocarcinogenicity—or a justification for not supplying the data.
- Interaction potential—that is, it may be necessary to show that the new active does not interact with other approved sunscreens.

---

[9]See footnote 8.

PERMITTED SUNSCREENS ACTIVES AND THEIR MAXIMUM ALLOWED DOSAGES

Australian approved name (AAN)	Other names	Maximum concentration (%)
Aminobenzoic acid	4-Aminobenzoic acid (PABA)	15
Isoamyl methoxycinnamate	Isopentenyl-4-methoxycinnamate; isoamyl-4-methoxycinnamate	10
Butyl methoxy dibenzoyl methane	1-(4-tert-butylphenyl)-3-(4-methoxyphenyl)propane-1, 3-dione; avobenzone	5
Cinoxate		6
Dioxybenzone	Benzophenone 8	3
	Ethoxylated ethyl-4-aminobenzoic acid; PEG 25 PABA	10
Padimate O	2-Ethylhexyl-4-dimethylaminobenzoate	8
Octyl methoxycinnamate	Octinoxate	10
Octyl salicylate	2-Ethylhexyl-salicylate, octisalate	5
Homosalate	Homomenthyl salicylate	15
Menthyl anthranilate	Menthyl 2-aminobenzoate, meradimate	5
4-Methylbenzylidene camphor	3-(4-Methylbenzylidene)-D-L camphor	4
Octocrylene	2-Cyano-3,3-diphenyl acrylic acid, 2-ethylhexyl ester	10
Octyl triazone		5
	Alpha-(2-oxoborn-3-ylidene)toluene-4-sulfonic acid and its salts	6 (as acid)
Oxybenzone	Benzophenone-3	10
Phenylbenzimidazole sulfonic acid	Ensulizole	4
	N,N,N-Trimethyl-4-(oxoborn-3-ylidenemethyl)anilinium methyl sulfate	6
Benzophenone-4	Sulizobenzone	10
	Sulisobenzone sodium, benzophenone 5	10
Ecamsule	Terephthalylidene dicamphor sulfonic acid	10
Titanium dioxide		25
Triethanolamine salicylate	Octisalate	12
Zinc oxide		[a]
Methylene bis-benzotriazolyl tetramethylbutyl phenol	Tinosorb M	10
Drometrizole trisiloxane	Mexoryl XL	15

[a]An upper limit of 20% had been set, but it is understood that this limit may be removed.

SUNSCREENS ACTIVES UNDER REVIEW

The following sunscreen actives are under review and cannot be used until that review is complete.

AAN	Other names	Maximum concentration
Benzophenone		To be determined
Benzophenone-2		To be determined
Isopropylbenzyl salicylate		To be determined
Salicylic acid salts	Salicylic acid salts (K, Na, time and extent application [TEA])	To be determined

LICENSING OF PREMISES

Premises where therapeutic goods are processed, including manufacture, filling, labeling, sterilizing, QC testing, packing, storage, or release, must be licensed by the TGA. Application forms can be downloaded from the TGA website.[10] If the production process is conducted at several different premises, each of them must be licensed, except where the production involves the same kinds of goods under the same management, including QA management. Another exception relates to temporary storage of raw materials or work-in-progress in other locations before returning to the (licensed) warehouse. If the sunscreen is manufactured overseas the premises must also be licensed; the requirements are described in the Standard for Overseas Manufacturers.[11] The license is normally granted for a limited number of applications. For instance, a license to manufacture a sunscreen would not entitle the company to manufacture sterile goods unless other conditions are met.

If a sunscreen manufactured outside Australia is to be imported into Australia, it must have been manufactured in therapeutic premises that are satisfactory to TGA. However, this does not apply to sunscreen actives—the onus is on the manufacturer of sunscreen formulations to ensure that the sunscreen actives they use in listable and exempt sunscreens have been made to appropriate standards.

In the application for a license all steps in the process must be described in general terms. Also, the range of dosage forms and devices must be described.

[10]Application for a License to Manufacture Therapeutic Goods. http://www.health.gov.au/tga/docs/pdf/gmpapp.pdf.

[11]Guidelines on Standard for Overseas Manufacturers. 13th ed., July 2003. http://health.gov.au/tga/docs/pdf/gmpsom13.pdf.

LABELING OF SUNSCREENS

The labels of listed, registered, and exempt sunscreens must comply with the following:

- The Labelling Order (TGO 69). This 48 page document can be downloaded from the TGA website.[12] TGO 69 deals with the general requirements for labeling all medicines. Of relevance to sunscreens are
  - Application and exemptions
  - Interpretation
  - Label requirements, particularly 3(1) General, 3(2) Particulars to be included on the label, 3(3) Particulars to be included on the main label, 3(9) Preparations for skin or mucous membranes, 3(14) Directions for use, 4 Expression of quantity, 7 Permitted storage conditions, First schedule. Note that these requirements also cover goods imported into Australia.
- The Therapeutic Advertising Code[13] (see later).
- AS/NZS 2604/1998, which is the current version of the Australian/New Zealand Standard "Sunscreen Products—Evaluation and Classification". It may be bought from Standards Australia.[14] AS/NZS 2604 distinguishes between *primary sunscreens*, the main purpose of which is to protect against the harmful effects of ultra violet rays, and *secondary sunscreens*, for which the main purpose is moisturizing or some other nontherapeutic function and sunscreening is secondary. For each category there are mandatory requirements and secondary requirements.

Mandatory Requirements for Primary Sunscreens

- Label protection factor (SPF as it appears on the pack) cannot be higher than the measured SPF rounded down to the nearest whole number, and it cannot be greater than 30+.
- The label protection factor must appear clearly on the main label.
- Clear and adequate directions for use must appear on the container.
- The names of all actives must be given on the container.

Optional Requirements for Primary Sunscreens

- Category description (as appropriate to the label SPF).
- Broad spectrum on the main label (but if you claim broad spectrum the sunscreen must pass the appropriate test for broad spectrum).

---

[12]Therapeutic Goods Order TGO 69. www.tga.gov.au/docs/html/tgo69.htm.

[13]Therapeutic Goods Advertising Code. Published by the Therapeutic Goods Advertising Code Council (TGACC), Private Bag 938, North Sydney, NSW 2059, Australia. www.tgacc.com.au/code_gloss_files/Code_2003-07-16.pdf.

[14]See footnote 1.

- Water resistant on the main label (but if you claim water resistant the sunscreen must pass the appropriate test for water resistant).

Mandatory Requirements for Secondary Sunscreens

- Label protection factor (SPF as it appears on the pack) cannot be higher than the measured SPF rounded down to the nearest whole number, and it cannot be greater than 30+.
- The label protection factor must appear clearly on the pack, but not necessarily on the main label.
- Clear and adequate directions for use must appear on the container.
- The names of all actives must be given on the container.

Optional Requirements for Secondary Sunscreens

- Category description (as appropriate to the label SPF).
- Broad spectrum (but if you claim broad spectrum the sunscreen must pass the appropriate test for broad spectrum).
- Water resistant (but if you claim water resistant the sunscreen must pass the appropriate test for water resistant).

ADVERTISING OF SUNSCREENS

Advertising (and labeling) of sunscreens must comply with the Therapeutic Goods Advertising Code[15] which is issued by the Therapeutic Goods Advertising Code Council. This Code sets out the general requirements and restrictions on advertising therapeutic goods. Advertisements for therapeutic goods are required to be approved, and this is undertaken before the advertisement is made public. For sunscreens (and certain other therapeutic goods) the proposed advertisement is sent for clearance to Advertising Services, Australian Self-Medication Industry.[16]

There are some items that specifically relate to sunscreens:

- For most therapeutic goods advertisements should not lead people to believe that harmful consequences may result from the therapeutic good not being used. **Sunscreens are specifically exempt from the provisions of this clause.**
- In general, an advertisement for therapeutic goods *must not* be directed to minors. **Sunscreens (and certain other products) are exempt from this restriction.**
- In general, any representation regarding the treatment, cure, or prevention of a neoplastic disease (e.g., cancer) is a *prohibited representation*.

[15]See footnote 11.

[16]Advertising Services, Australian Self-Medication Industry Level 4, 140 Arthur Street, North Sydney 2060, Australia.

However, prevention of skin cancer through the use of sunscreens is not a prohibited representation.

- SPF 30+ broad-spectrum sunscreens can make the following claims:
  - "Can aid in the prevention of premature aging of the skin" or words to that effect.
  - May assist in preventing some skin cancers; may reduce the risk of some skin cancers—provided that the need for avoidance of prolonged exposure to the sun and the importance of protective hats, clothing, and eyewear are highlighted.

THE COSMETIC/THERAPEUTIC INTERFACE

The National Coordinating Committee on Therapeutic Goods has published "Cosmetic Claims Guidelines".[17] These set out a series of examples of claims that can be regarded as cosmetic, claims that are unacceptable for a cosmetic (but not necessarily unacceptable for a medicine), and claims that are borderline (unacceptable unless sufficiently modified to provide a cosmetic implication). Two examples are particularly relevant to sunscreens.

Example 1

It is acceptable to claim that a cosmetic may cover up age spots and dark pigmented areas, but any reference to fading of age spots (depigmentation, bleaching of skin) would be regarded as a therapeutic claim. Claims that the product may temporarily reduce the depth of wrinkles by moisturization would require further explanation to demonstrate the cosmetic nature of the claim. (In these contexts the reader should bear in mind that any therapeutic claim in addition to a normal sunscreening claim would require that the product be submitted for full registration.)

Example 2

Allowable cosmetic claims include that the product gives the skin a bronze (suntanned) appearance; that it prevents, protects against drying effects of the sun; and that it moisturizes the skin; "with sunscreen" is only acceptable for a cosmetic if there is no statement of SPF number, sunscreen category description, or other therapeutic claim. The following are therapeutic claims: helps protect the skin from the harmful effects of the sun; SPF; accelerates/activates suntan; pretan accelerator; allows you to stay in the sun x times longer; screens (blocks) (filters) out some of the sun's UV (UV-A/UV-B/UV-C) (harmful) rays. (Most of these are claims that are allowed for a listable sunscreen, of course, but a claim of tan acceleration may well require that the product be

[17] National Coordinating Committee on Therapeutic Goods Australia (NCCTG). Cosmetic Claims Guidelines. 3rd ed., May 9, 1997. www.health.gov.au/hsh/tga/tga.htm.

submitted for registration.) A claim that the product gives the darkest tan with less time in the sun, or that it enhances tan, may be regarded as therapeutic unless otherwise qualified to show that it is a cosmetic.

The features that distinguish acceptable cosmetic claims are either that they refer solely to a cosmetic property (such as moisturizing) or that they relate to the illusion of a property (look, feel). The probable justification for these allowed claims is that cosmetics are supposed to be designed to disguise, cover up, or otherwise superficially change the appearance of skin (and hair or teeth). If the effect that is claimed implies a physiological response from the skin it is more likely to be considered to be a therapeutic claim.

CONCLUSIONS

Sunscreens in Australia are regulated as therapeutic goods. Although the process of listing them on the ARTG is quick, because the onus is placed on the sponsor (marketer) to self-regulate (make sure that the sunscreen product and its labeling and advertising comply with the relevant regulations), the TGA has the power to determine whether the manufacturer and marketer are complying with the regulations. These regulations are developing and evolving. Some of the changes that are likely are as follows. Australia and New Zealand are harmonizing their laws and regulations (Trans Tasman Harmonisation) relating to therapeutic goods (and other areas), so that artificial barriers to trade can be minimized. The Australian New Zealand sunscreen standard (AS/NZS 2604) has been reopened to consider possible changes to the broad-spectrum part of the Standard. While there are some areas of disagreement it is probably true to say that (a) there is an acceptance that the current test methods are inadequate and (b) any new method is unlikely to involve *in vivo* measurement of UV-A protectiveness. Some people in the industry would like to see secondary sunscreens regulated as cosmetics and are lobbying the authorities to this end, but other industry bodies are opposed to this. Some of the industry guidelines are fairly old and may need to be reviewed.

NICNAS is the body that registers all new chemicals, other than therapeutic ingredients. Thus, it affects cosmetics rather than listed, registered, or exempt sunscreens. Many people in the cosmetics industry believe that NICNAS places a dead hand on Australian industry. By its insistence on registering every new ingredient, even if it has been through a similar process in other countries, it denies Australian industry the access to new ingredients and thus the ability to create new products that can compete overseas. A working party has been set up to consider the regulation of “chemicals of low concern” such as cosmetic ingredients.

10

Legal and Regulatory Status of Sunscreen Products in Japan

Minoru Fukuda
Shiseido Research Center, Yokohama, Japan

Masako Naganuma
Shiseido Scientific Research Department, Tokyo, Japan

OUTLINE

There is now worldwide awareness of the chronic and acute damage to human skin caused by the ultraviolet (UV) rays in sunlight. Nevertheless, people of different nationalities have differing skin responses, differing concerns about the consequences of exposure, and differing attitudes to suntan and sunburn. Surveys show that Japanese women are most anxious about pigmentation, so their prime expectation of sunscreen products is to prevent skin pigmentation. Pigmentation is caused by not only UV-B but also UV-A, so sunscreen products for the Japanese market should have both UV-B and UV-A protective potencies.

The market for sunscreen products in Japan has been increasing year by year, and the protective efficacy has also been improved. Sun protection factor information (such as SPF) has been given on products in Japan since 1981. Japan Cosmetic Industry Association (JCIA) standard SPF test methods were issued in 1992, and revised in 1999, and it was decided that the highest SPF which could be labeled on sunscreen products would be 50+. The move towards international harmonization of legal and regulatory requirements for cosmetics has led to international agreement on unified SPF measurement methods among Japan, EU and South Africa. The latest JCIA SPF measurement method in 2003 was based on this agreement.

In addition to UV-B, UV-A plays an important role in photoaging. In 1996 the JCIA measurement standards for UV-A protection efficacy came into effect. In Japan, the regulation of cosmetics was changed dramatically in April 2001. Allowed UV absorbers which can be used for preventing UV damage to skin are limited to those in positive lists in the new regulation. The above changes are discussed, together with prospects for sunscreen products in Japan.

INTRODUCTION

The chronic and acute damage to human skin caused by the UV rays in sunlight has attracted attention both in Western society and in Japan, although to different extents. The necessity of sunscreen to prevent such damage has always been recognized in both cultures. However, Japanese and Caucasians differ in skin color and sensitivity to UV rays and also in attitudes toward suntan and sunburn. Therefore, their expectations of what sunscreen products should do likewise differ. Further, legal and regulatory requirements covering the manufacture of sunscreen products differ from one country to another.

In this chapter, we will describe the response of Japanese skin to UV rays, the attitude of Japanese people to UV exposure, and the characteristics they expect of sunscreen products. The legal and regulatory framework for sunscreen products, SPF testing methods, and PA (protection grade of UV-A) testing methods in Japan will be introduced, and we will describe the labeling methods adopted by the Japan Cosmetic Industry Association (JCIA). Furthermore, we discuss the harmonization process leading to The International SPF Testing

Method agreed upon by JCIA, The European Cosmetic Toiletry and Perfumery Association (COLIPA), and Cosmetic, Toiletry and Fragrance Association of South Africa (CTFA/SA), and comment on subjects for future discussion.

JAPANESE SKIN CHARACTERISTICS AND ATTITUDE TO UV

Billions of people live on the earth, and each has his or her own skin color. In humans, skin color depends on the quantities of melanin and oxygenated or reduced hemoglobin present in the skin, as well as on the skin's thickness and water content. Among these factors, the quantity of melanin, which is distributed in the skin, determines its fairness or darkness, and greatly influences the human complexion. At the same time, melanin plays a part in reducing the damage that UV rays cause in the skin. This means that a person's color determines his or her degree of resistance to UV, which is one measure of the adaptability of people to the earth's environment. Moreover, skin color influences not only attitudes toward UV, but also attitudes toward prevention of UV damage.

The so-called "sun belt zone" circling the equator, where people are exposed to high levels of UV rays, is part of the torrid or subtropical zone; the people who live there are generally dark-skinned. In the middle latitudes away from the Equator, where sunlight contains moderate levels of UV, the majority of inhabitants have yellowish skin tones. People with white skin live in high latitudes, far from the equator.

The Japanese live in an island country, which extends from latitude 25°N to latitude 45°N, and ethnically belong to the Mongolian peoples. They have yellowish skin with moderately developed melanin productivity. The gradations of skin color of the Japanese vary widely from fair to dark. Most of those with fair skin have skin brightness and hue similar to those of Caucasians; those with dark skin have aspects in common with Negroes (1). In our classification of the back skin colors of the Japanese by visual evaluation in addition to the colorimetric parameters of value, chroma, and hue, the colors observed are divided basically according to the parameters of value (V) and chroma (C), and arranged within the spectrum from fair through dark skin (2) (Fig. 10.1). Naturally there are differences in sensitivity to erythema and tanning between Japanese and Caucasians, and even among Japanese individuals with various skin tones. Figure 10.2 compares the process of tanning between Japanese and Caucasians by means of measurement of the minimal erythema dose (MED)/minimal melanogenesis dose (MMD) ratio using sunlight as the light source (2–5). The results showed that the Caucasians tanned hardly at all even when erythema had been induced to some degree by a single sunlight exposure; the Japanese were more prone to tan than the Caucasians.

As regards the seasonal variation of facial skin color, skin color started to become darker in spring and was darkest in August (Fig. 10.3) (6). It became fairer from autumn to winter and was brightest in March. At the same time, the pigmentation at various sites on the same person were determined. Interestingly,

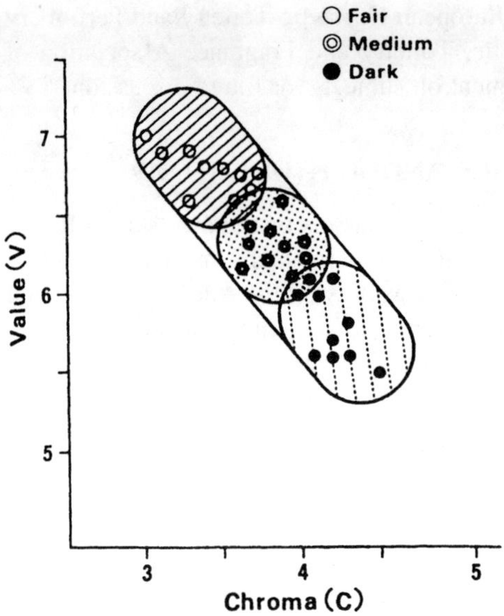

Figure 10.1 Distribution of skin color in Japanese people.

the extent of variation was larger on the pigmented than on the nonpigmented sites, though the variations were the same between pigmented and nonpigmented sites. Therefore, pigmented sites stood out from the surrounding skin color.

The skin types of Japanese are shown in Fig. 10.4 (7). This survey was conducted by companies belonging to the JCIA on 2500 persons (1258 females and 1242 males). The skin type was investigated using modified Fitzpatrick skin type (8) by means of questionnaires. The ratios of skin types I, II, and III are 18.2%, 28.0%, and 29.8%, respectively. About 76% persons thought that their skin first turned red, and 76% of them thought it then became dark.

Furthermore, in a questionnaire on skin troubles in Japanese females, pigmented spots and freckles occupied the top spot and wrinkles came second. Figure 10.5 shows the results of a survey of 5211 Japanese women in 1995. In addition, Yoshii (9) reported that the ratio of pigmentation or pigmented spots among Japanese females reporting skin troubles was 69% and the ratio of wrinkles was 53%. On the other hand, the ratio of pigmentation was 20–40% and the ratio of wrinkles was 40–60% in the USA, UK, and Germany. There was no difference in the ratio of persons who were troubled with wrinkles. Japanese females were characteristically very worried about pigmentation. Since Japanese women have higher levels of melanin productivity and they have medium-colored skin, pigmentation is relatively prominent on their skin.

Next, we investigated the attitude of Japanese women to UV (Fig. 10.6) in 2002. The level of awareness of UV was divided into five grades: very concerned, moderately concerned, no opinion, slightly concerned, unconcerned. The ratios

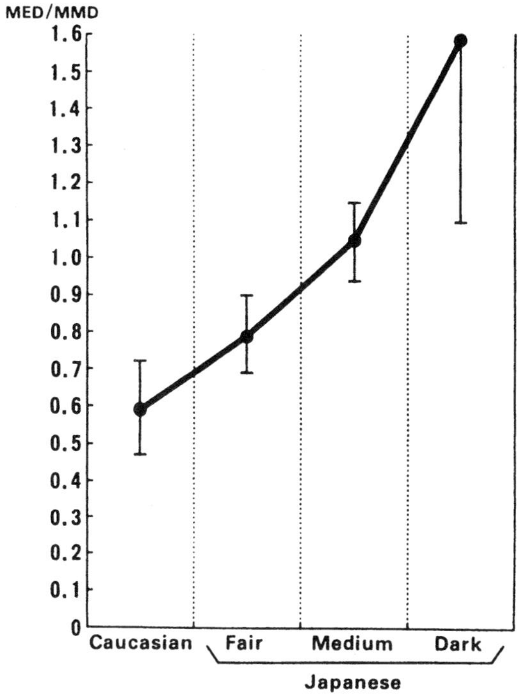

Figure 10.2 Tanning capacity of Japanese of various skin colors and Caucasians.

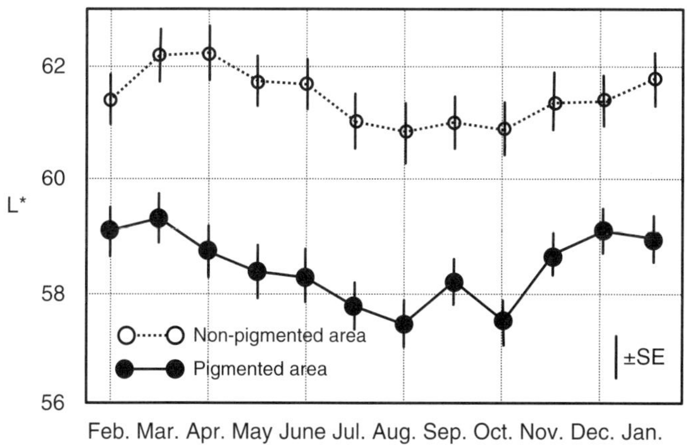

Figure 10.3 Monthly change in L^* in pigmented and nonpigmented areas on Japanese women's faces.

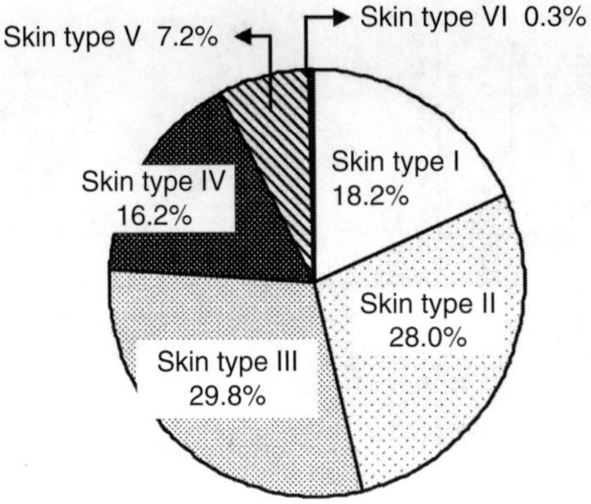

Figure 10.4 Distribution of skin types in Japanese people (data from JCIA for 2500 persons).

of very concerned and moderately concerned were 38.2% and 47.9%, respectively. Therefore, over 90% of Japanese females were concerned about UV exposure. The main reasons for this were given as follows: (1) UV elicits pigmentation or pigmented spots (57%) and (2) UV induces tanning (13%). Only 8.1% of persons mentioned skin cancer, which is the main concern of Caucasians.

In Japan, fair skin has been considered from ancient times to be an essential factor in beauty. There is an old saying, "A fair complexion hides seven defects". Following this traditional aesthetic sense, skin coloration and UV reactivity in terms of pigmentation and pigmented spots are the focus of Japanese women's thinking about UV.

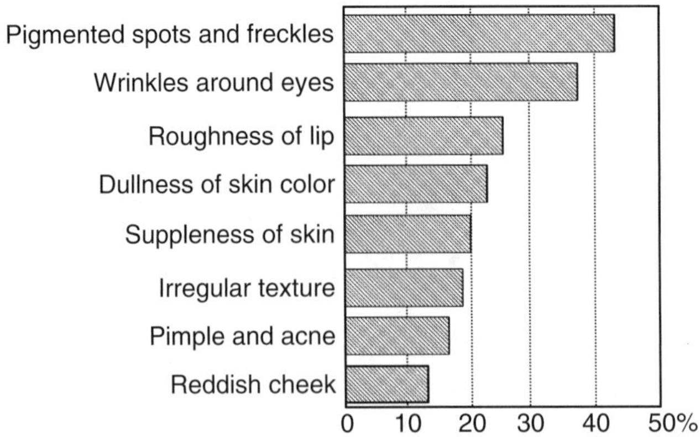

Figure 10.5 Skin troubles in Japanese women. A total of 5211 Japanese women were surveyed by means of questionnaires in 1995.

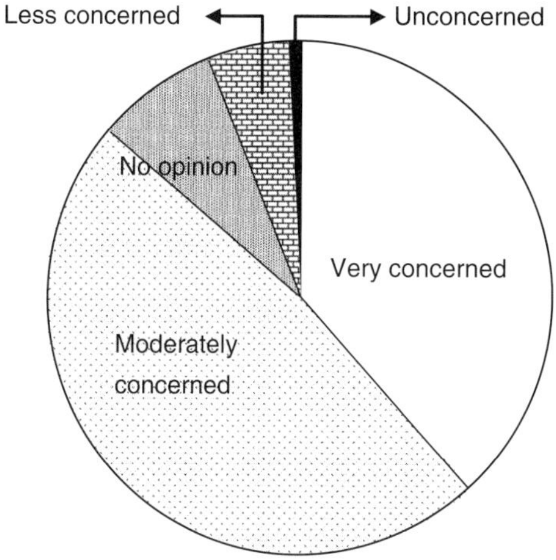

Figure 10.6 The attitude of Japanese women to UV.

THE SUNSCREEN CHARACTERISTICS DESIRED BY JAPANESE

Cosmetic products with a UV-protective effect first appeared in Japan in 1981. Before then, partly as a result of advertising posters showing beautifully tanned women in swimsuits, it had been fashionable to get a tan by sunbathing at the beach. However, young women often became excessively sunburned or pigmented in their eagerness to become tanned in a short time. At the same time, many people disliked tanning on the face. In this situation, product labeling enabled consumers to use sunscreens to the best effect for their own purposes and according to their particular skin sensitivity to UV.

Later, it was realized that not only UV-B, but also UV-A damaged the skin, and also that skin exposed to UV rays showed early photoaging phenomena. In particular, UV-A aggravated and induced pigmented spots and freckles. Therefore, many products that had both UV-B and UV-A protective effectiveness appeared on the Japanese market. Since 1996, both SPF and PA have been labeled on the packaging of sunscreen products. Protection of the body in addition to the face became of increasing concern. Annual cosmetics sales for the last 10 years are shown in Fig. 10.7. The sales of total skin care products have increased only slightly, whereas those of sunscreen and suntanning products have increased rapidly.

In 1998, the favorable mention of sunbathing disappeared from the advice for mothers and babies supervised by the Ministry of Health, Labor and Welfare. Furthermore, material to educate the public about the need for UV protection was published in 2003 by the Ministry of the Environment. Consequently, sunscreens for babies and children have become available. This means that the consumers of sunscreen products cover the whole range of age. In addition, there are special

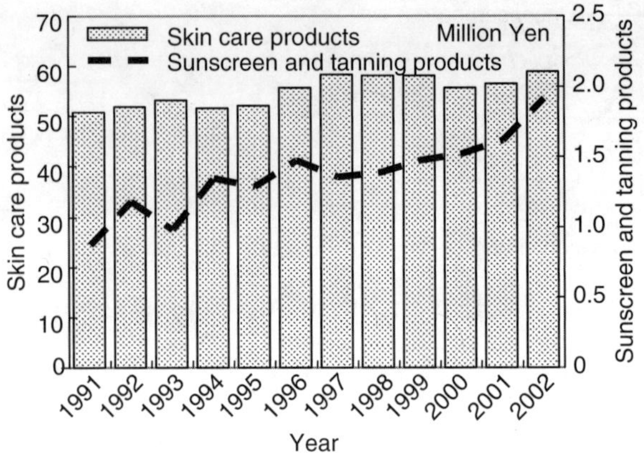

Figure 10.7 Sales of sunscreen and suntanning products and total skin care products in the Japanese market.

sunscreen products such as sunscreens for acned skin which do not contain comedogenic ingredients and sunscreens for sensitive skin or babies' skin which do not contain UV absorbers, perfume, paraben, or coloring materials.

Thus, with the popularization of UV protection and due to warnings by dermatologists that daily exposure to UV rays can accelerate aging of the skin, UV care has become part of the daily routine throughout the year. Accordingly, nowadays UV-protective products include daily milky lotions and other basic cosmetics and makeup products, in addition to sunscreens. The report showed a high ratio of users of foundation in Japan compared with Caucasian females (9). Virtually all foundations for summer use now have a function for UV protection.

In Japan, seasonal changes in climate are very distinct (Fig. 10.8). The Japanese summer is characterized by high temperature and humidity. Therefore, people prefer more astringent cosmetics and foundation cakes for wet or dry use. Perspiration and sea bathing require a high level of water resistance. Two-layer emulsions with high SPF and high water resistance have been introduced as sunscreens. The use of products with high water resistance has been accompanied by the development of special cleansing products.

In addition, Japanese skin is more sensitive to stimulation by cosmetics and other products than is that of Caucasians. This is an important point that should be taken into account in the design, development, and sale of sunscreens.

THE REGULATION OF SUNSCREEN PRODUCTS AND THE DEVELOPMENT OF UV-PROTECTIVE AGENTS

The regulatory requirements for sunscreens differ from country to country. In the USA, Canada, and Australia, sunscreens are over-the-counter drugs. On the other

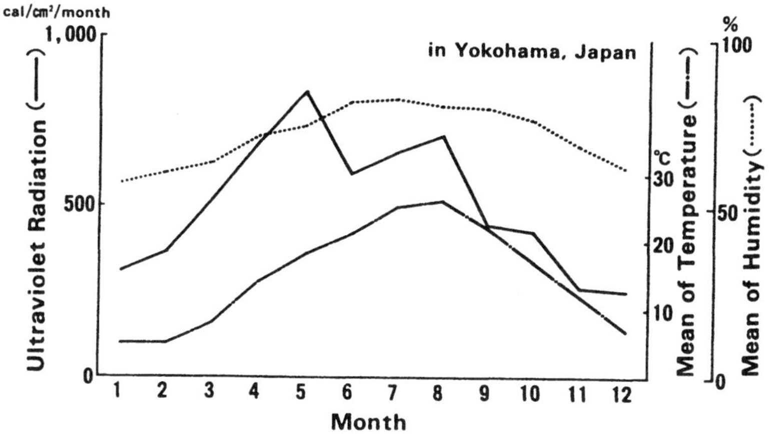

Figure 10.8 Seasonal variations in UV radiation, temperature, and humidity.

hand, they are treated as quasi-drugs in China, Korea, and Taiwan. Furthermore, they are cosmetics in Japan under The Pharmaceutical Affairs Law, as is the case in Europe. The Pharmaceutical Affairs Law underwent major revision on April 1, 2001. Before this time, cosmetic manufacturers made cosmetics by using only ingredients that were permitted by the government. However, since then it is permitted to combine any ingredients in cosmetics except for materials in three groups, and materials on a negative list, which includes active drugs, hormones, and so on. The three groups are UV absorbers, coal-tar dyes, and preservatives, and in these categories, only ingredients on the positive list can be used. UV absorbers on the positive list are shown in Table 10.1.

There are 27 UV absorbers and 1 mixture of two UV absorbers on the positive list. Before 1990, the material most popular with Japanese manufacturers on the basis of safety and effectiveness was octyl dimethyl PABA. However, some problems with safety were reported, and it rapidly disappeared from the Japanese market. Now octyl methoxycinnamate is the most widely used UV-B absorber and butyl methoxydibenzoylmethane (avobenzone: Parsol 1789) (10) is the most widely used UV-A absorber.

The UV absorbers initially developed absorbed UV under 320 nm. Many of the absorbers in Table 10.1 are UV-B absorbers. The Japanese have also shown an interest in the harmful effects of UV-A, especially in its tanning effect. UV-A rays penetrate the skin more deeply than UV-B rays (11), and reach the earth in high doses (12,13). Normally, our skin is exposed to greater amounts of UV-A than UV-B rays. Several experiments have proved that chronic exposure of skin to UV-A rays causes abnormalities in the connective tissue of the dermis (14,15) and accelerates the harmful effects of UV-B, such as carcinogenesis (16). Furthermore, it has become clear that the UV

Table 10.1 Positive List for UV Absorbers in Japan (Revised Version in 2002)

Groups	UV absorber	Maximum concentration (%)			Brand name
		Japan	COLIPA	FDA	
PABA derivatives	PABA p-aminobenzoic acid	4	5	15	
	Octyl dimethyl PABA	10	—	8	Escalol 507
	Pentyl dimethyl PABA	10	—	—	Escalol 506
Cinnamic acid derivatives	Octyl methoxycinnamate	20	10	7.5	Parsol MCX NeoHeliopan AV Escalol5 57 Eusolex 2292 Uvinul MC80
	Octanoate	10	—	—	Sunguard B
	Cinoxate	5	—	3	
	Diisopropyl methyl cinnamate	10	—	—	
	Isopentyl trimethoxycinnamate trisiloxate	7.50	—	—	Sun shelter SP
	Ferulic acid	10	—	—	
Benzophenone derivatives	Benzophenone-3 Oxybenzone	5	10	6	Neoheliopan BB Escalol 567 Eusolex 4360 UvinuI M40 ASL24
	Benzophenone-5	10	—	—	
	Benzophenone-4 (Sulisobenzone)	10	—	10	Uvinul MS40

	Benzophenone-6	10	—	—	Uvinul D49
	Benzophenone-9	10	—	—	Uvinul DS49
	Benzophenone-1	10	—	—	Uvinul 400
	Benzophenone-2	10	—	—	Uvinul D50
	4-(2-beta-glucopyranosiloxy) propoxy-2-hydroxybenophenone	5	—	—	
Salicylic acid derivatives	Homomenthyl salicylate (Homosalate)	10	10	15	
	Octyl salicylate (2-ethylhexy salicylate)	10	5	5	NeoHeliopan OS Escalol 587
dibenzoylmethane derivatives	Butyl Methoxydibenzoylmethane	10	5	3	Parsol 1789 Eusolex 9020
	Terephthalylidene sulfonic acid	10	10 (as acid)	—	Mexoyl SX
	Phenylbenzimidazole Sulfonic Acid	3	8 (as acid)	4	Parsol HS NeoHeliopan Hydro Eusolex 232
	2-ethylhexyl dimethoxybenzylidene dioxoimidazolidine propionate	3	—	—	Softshade
Others	1-(3,4-dimethoxyphenyl)-4,4-dimethl-1,3- entanedione	7	—	—	
	Octocrylene	10	10 (as acid)	10	NeoHeliopan 303 Escalol 597 Uvinul N539
	Octyl triawne	5	5	—	Uvinul T150
	Drometrizole trisiloxate	15	15	—	Mexorvul XL

rays which induce chloasma, a source of concern for Japanese women, cover the range from UV-A to UV-B, and that the main causative wavelength lies in the UV-A region (17). Some attempts have been made to develop effective UV-A absorbers, and butyl methoxydibenzoylmethane was introduced into Japanese sunscreen products in 1986 (18). Recently, Mexsoryl SX has been added to the positive list.

Some of the requirements for applications to add a newly developed UV absorber to the positive list are shown in Table 10.2. The requirements include data on origin, background of discovery, use in foreign countries, physical and chemical properties, and safety. Submitted materials will be discussed in a council, which will approve an absorber, if they consider that it is safe and useful. Then the applicant can use it in sunscreens or other cosmetics.

The foregoing discussion has dealt with UV absorbers. Next, we will consider UV-scattering agents in the form of inorganic powders as UV-protective cosmetic materials. The scattering effects of several kinds of inorganic powders are shown in Fig. 10.9. Superior UV-preventive effects were observed with titanium oxide, ferrous oxide, and zinc oxide. As ferrous oxide is colored, it cannot be used in large amounts in sunscreens. It is advantageous that inorganic powders are not allergenic and do not have absorption peaks at visible wavelengths. However, they scatter not only UV, but also visible light. Therefore, skin to which inorganic powder has been applied looks pale or white.

Table 10.2 Data Required in Application for Approval of UV Absorbers for the Positive List

Data on origin, background of discovery, use in foreign countries, etc.	Data on origin and background of discovery Data on use in foreign countries Data on characteristics and comparison with other UV absorbers
Data on physical and chemical properties	Data on determination of structure Data on physical and chemical properties
Data on safety	Data on acute toxicity Data on subacute toxicity Data on reproductive effects Data on skin irritation Data on chronic toxicity Data on skin sensitization Data on phototoxicity Data on photosensitization Data on eye irritation Data on genotoxicity Data on human patch test Data on absorption, distribution, metabolism, excretion

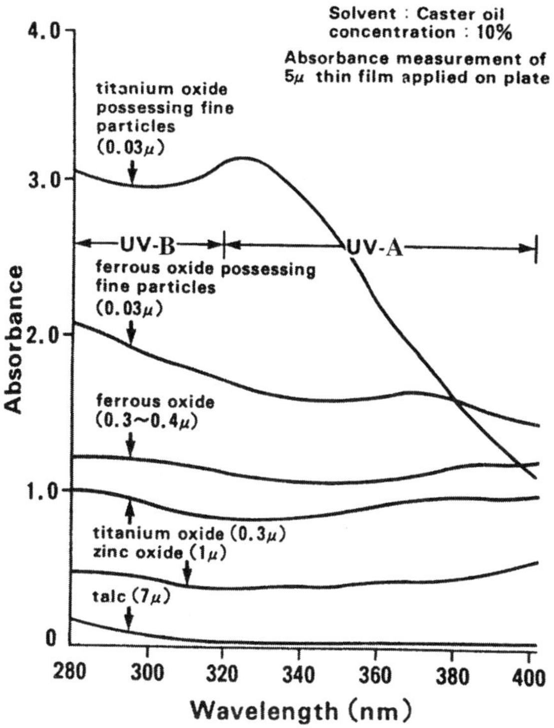

Figure 10.9 UV protective effect *in vitro* of UV scattering agents.

In order to improve the texture of cosmetics using these inorganic powders, while taking advantage of their UV-protective effect, attempts have been made to change the forms of the powders or to prepare complexes of several inorganic powders or combinations of inorganic powder and organic substances (19). The UV-protective effect of inorganic powder varies with the diameter of the particle. Titanium oxide, with a particle size of under 0.05 μm in diameter, has a high UV-protective effect and does not block visible rays (20). It does not have a conspicuous color when applied to the skin, which is an advantage. Since titanium oxide has poor spreadability, procedures such as adding spherical nylon particles were devised in order to overcome this drawback (21). An oxide complex of silicon and titanium was also developed; this complex has a superior UV-intercepting effect and improved transparency to visible rays. Moreover, it is possible to process inorganic powders containing UV absorbers to optimize the UV-protective effect.

Recently, zinc oxide powders have been used in sunscreens (19). Zinc oxide powders are good protectors against UV-A without blocking visible light (22). This has the advantage that treated skin does not look white. Furthermore, various formulations have been tried. Figure 10.10 shows zinc oxide particles in the form of petals. The use of wet preparation methods allows control of the

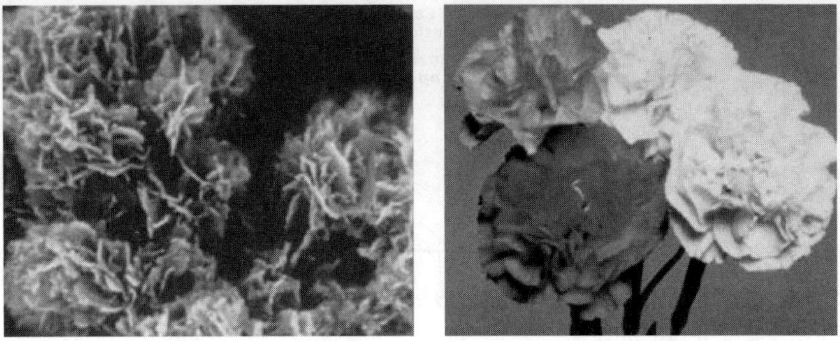

Figure 10.10 Newly developed zinc oxide formulation (left) and carnations (right).

diameter of particles and figures, and the petals are formed as secondary agglomerations. Primary particles of the zinc oxide have weak cohesive force, and when they are applied on the skin they spread uniformly over the skin. This characteristic improves the passage of visible light and the protective efficacy against UV. The development of UV-protective agents, including scattering powders, has made rapid progress, and every year new sunscreens using new protective agents appear on the market in Japan.

As mentioned earlier, safety and a potent UV-protective effect are essential factors for sunscreens sold in Japan. Therefore, UV absorbers and UV-scattering agents are usually incorporated in sunscreens in various combinations rather than as a single ingredient in large amounts.

DEVELOPMENT OF EFFECTIVENESS, LABELING, AND TESTING OF SUNSCREEN PRODUCTS IN JAPAN

SPF Testing Methods in Japan

Since the US FDA released "Sunscreen Drug Products for Over-the-Counter Human Use" in 1978 (8), many sunscreen products labeled with the SPF value have been put on sale in the USA and Europe. In Japan, Shiseido first introduced sunscreens labeled with Sun Care Shi-Suu 2,4,6, which means SPF, as an indicator of UV protection efficacy into the market in 1981.

In 1991 JCIA established the Standard SPF Test Method (23) based on the concept that the SPF value indicated on sunscreen products should be standardized, permitting product comparison. The method served as a criterion for product selection based on extensive measurement of UV-protective effects, and was designed to be as consistent as possible with the worldwide trend toward uniformity in UV protection efficacy evaluation. The JCIA Standard SPF Test Method came into effect in January 1992.

Since then, labeled SPF values have tended to increase from year to year (Fig. 10.11) (24). In 1999 the highest SPF number of a product on the Japanese

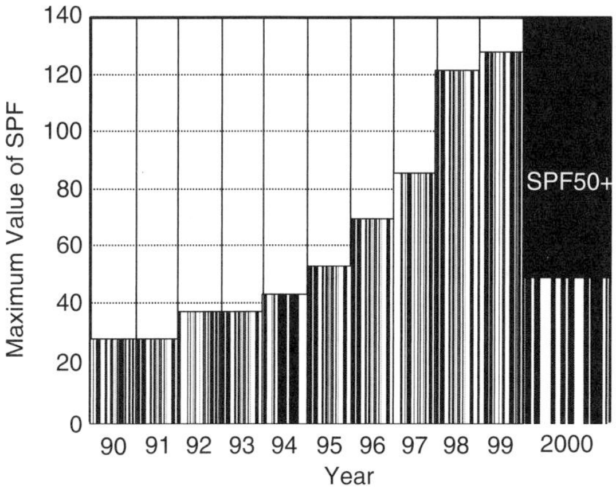

Figure 10.11 Annual changes in maximum labeled SPF in the Japanese market.

market was 123. A variety of products appeared bearing extremely high labeled SPF values, which were beyond the range expected when the JCIA Standard Test Method was implemented, and it became evident that there was a possibility of large disparities in measured SPF.

The Expert Committee on SPF of the JCIA set out to revise the JCIA Method in October 1997. They concluded that the conditions of measurement should be revised to increase the accuracy at high SPF values, and the international situation should be taken into account, considering that an upper limit had been imposed on labeled SPF values in the USA, Australia, and New Zealand. As a result, the conditions of SPF measurement were partially revised, and the upper limit of labeled SPF values was set at SPF50+. There are two reasons for the decision to fix SPF50+ as the upper limit of the labeled values: (1) measurement errors become greater when a certain magnitude of measured values is exceeded and (2) a sunscreen product with SPF of 50 is considered sufficient for protecting the skin from sunburn. Taking into account persons with hypersensitivity to UV and regions where people are exposed to very strong UV, however, it was decided that SPF50+ may be labeled on products that clearly have a higher UV protection efficacy than SPF50. The JCIA's Standard SPF Test Method, which was established in November 1991, was changed to the 1999 Revised Version (25), to take effect from January 1, 2000. From 2000 the maximum SPF label number has remained at 50+ in the Japanese market.

Today the idea of SPF labeling has been accepted throughout the world. The USA, Australia, New Zealand, Europe, South Africa, China, South Korea, Taiwan, South America, and Japan all have similar SPF testing methods. Nevertheless, some differences of detail, for example, in testing conditions, remain. Are these important? If Shiseido of Japan wants to export sunscreen to the USA or Europe, it is necessary to do SPF testing and SPF labeling of the sunscreen all over again, using the US FDA method and COLIPA method, respectively. The situation is similar when a US or European company wants to export to Japan. This wastes time and resources for retesting and relabeling of SPF on sunscreen products.

To find out how the different testing conditions for SPF determination among the countries would affect the SPF values of sunscreen products, 15 laboratories under JCIA, COLIPA, and CTFA/Australia (CTFA/AS) measured SPF values of the same two standard sunscreens using their own testing methods. This was the so-called international ring test (26). Interestingly, the SPF values of each of the standard sunscreens obtained by the various testing methods were not statistically significantly different.

Table 10.3 shows the results from one laboratory that measured SPF values of the two sunscreens in Caucasian volunteers and Asian volunteers (Japanese and Chinese) living in the USA. Untreated MED of Caucasian people is about 30% smaller than that of Asian peoples with the same skin type II. However, the differences in SPF values of 8% homosalate lotion (SPF4 standard) and Sunscreen A between Caucasians and Asians were not significant.

These data suggest that existing differences in the precise SPF testing conditions, including the races of volunteers, may not need to be taken into account in setting an international framework for SPF testing.

Then JCIA, COLIPA, CTFA of America (CTFA), CTFA/AS, and CTFA/SA got together at the International SPF Harmonization Conference held in April 2000 in the Republic of Malta (27). The representatives called for a thorough scientific examination of the feasibility of developing an International SPF Test Method. Representative experts of JCIA, COLIPA, CTFA, and CTFA/SA gathered in Brussels in September 2000, and started to discuss concretely every detail of the SPF test methods.

By way of meetings in Tokyo (October 2001), Brussels (February 2002), and Tokyo (August 2002) and three international teleconferences, basic agreement on an International SPF Test Method was reached between JCIA, COLIPA, and CTFA/SA in October 2002, at a meeting in Johannesburg.

Table 10.3 SPF and MED of Two Types of Sunscreen for Caucasians and Asians Living in the USA

	Skin type	n	8% HMS (SPF 4)		Sunscreen A		Untreated MED (J/cm^2)	
			SPF	SD	SPF	SD	MED	SD
Caucasians	I–III	20	3.6	0.5	11.9	2.8	0.98	0.12
	II	18					0.98	
Asian	II–III	20	3.7	0.6	10.4	1.6	1.5	0.28
(Japanese 19 + Chinese 1)	II	8					1.3	

Note: HMS is homomenthyl salicylate.

Finally, the International SPF Test Method was promulgated in English in March 2003 (28).

In Japan, we translated the English version into Japanese as the "Japan Cosmetic Industry Association SPF Test Method—2003 Revised Version," adding some further local requirements, for example, the expiry date and labeling method of SPF value. This new method came into effect in Japan on June 1, 2003 (29). Table 10.4 compares the major testing conditions between the International SPF Test Method (JCIA Standard SPF Test Method—2003 Revised Version), the JCIA Standard SPF Test Method (1999 version), and the US FDA SPF Test Method (1999). A major feature of the International SPF Test Method is that it specifies clearly the SPF test conditions which the JCIA method 1999 version, COLIPA's method, the US FDA's method, and the AS/NZ method had adopted.

Measurement Standards for UV-A Protection Efficacy in Japan

UV-A causes darkening of the skin immediately after exposure [immediate pigment darkening IPD)], and in the event of exposure to large amounts of UV-A, this darkening seems to be transformed to delayed pigment darkening. There are also reports that UV-A increases the sensitivity of the skin to UV-B. In addition to these acute responses, UV contributes to skin cancer and to aging of the skin, typified by blotches and wrinkles. The relative contributions of UV-A and UV-B to these various reactions are not known, but the effects of the deep penetration of UV-A cannot be ignored.

Japanese are more prone to tanning than Caucasians. While Americans and Europeans expect sunscreens to allow them to tan safely, Japanese expect them to prevent tanning, exactly the opposite expectation.

At present, SPF is the only universal parameter that is used for judging the effect of sunscreens in the markets. This SPF, however, indicates the protective effect against erythema mainly caused by UV-B, but not that against tanning, which is the most serious problem for Japanese women. Under these circumstances, the labeled "UV Protection" in product claims is not always adequate, so there is a need to clarify whether a product protects against UV-A or UV-B, and to what extent it protects against each.

Throughout the world, the SPF value acts as an index that the consumers use for product selection. With respect to an index or measurement method for UV-A protection, however, a uniform measurement method has not yet been established on a national or industry-wide level, although several papers on the subject have been published, and studies are under way in various countries. Throughout the world, products display various numerical values or marks indicating their efficacy for UV-A protection, but because there was particular concern that a uniform measurement method had not been established in Japan and these numerical values might cause confusion among consumers in their product selection, it has been decided not to display the level of UV-A protection on sunscreens.

Table 10.4 SPF Test Methods: International Method, JCIA Methods (2003 Revised Version and 1999 Version), and FDA Method (1999 Version)

		International method and JCIA method (2003 revised version)	JCIA method (1999 version)	US FDA method (1999 version)
1	Selection of volunteers	Questionnaire; medical check by professional; World Medical Association Declaration of Helsinki	Questionnaire	Questionnaire
2	Skin type and test area	Phototype, colorimetric method; back	Phototype; back	Phototype; back
3	Number of test subjects	Minimum 10, maximum 20 (a maximum of 5 results may be excluded)	Minimum 10	Minimum 20 (maximum subjects 25)
4	Statistical criterion	95% CI $<$ 17% of mean SPF	SE less than 10% by mean SPF	
5	Standard sunscreen	P1 (DIN standard SPF 4) P2 (CTFA recommended SPF 12) P3 (JCIA standard SPF 15) P7 (FDA and JCIA standard SPF 4) $2 < SPF < 20$: can choose all $SPF > 20$: choose P2 or P3	$2 < SPF < 20$: choose P3 or P7 $SPF > 20$: choose P3	P7
6	Acceptance limits of standards	$3.9 < P1 < 4.4$ $10.7 < P2 < 14.7$ $13.2 < P3 < 17.4$ $3.8 < P7 < 4.7$	$11.8 < P3 < 18.6$ $3.2 < P7 < 5.0$	$3.191 < P7 < 5.749$ The 95% confidence interval for the mean SPF must contain the value 4.
7	Product quantity and application	$2.00\ mg/cm^2 \pm 2.5$; CD-ROM	$2\ mg/cm^2$ or $2\ m/cm^2$	$2\ mg/cm^2$
8	Drying time	Start exposure sequence between 15 and 30 min after application	Quickly after 15 min	At least 15 min

9	Test areas	Minimum 30 cm^2, maximum 60 cm^2 (1 cm between adjacent application sites)	Minimum 20 cm^2 (1 cm between adjacent application sites)	Minimum 50 cm^2
10	Solar simulator	Xenon lamp; %RCEE acceptance limits <290 nm: <1.0% 290–300 nm:2.0–8.0% 290–310 nm:49.0–65.0% 290–320 nm:85.0–90.0% 290–400 nm:100% Total irradiance without an excessive feeling of heat or pain	Xenon arc solar simulator with a continuous spectrum similar to sunlight	Solar simulator which emits continuous spectrum from 290 to 400 nm similar to sunlight at sea level from the sun at a zenith angle of 10° <290 nm:<1% of its total energy >400 nm:<5% of its total energy
11	Criteria for solar simulator	Recommend to check with spectroradiometric measurement.	UV radiometer and erythema response	Spectroradiometer system, or equivalent instrument
12	Uniformity of beam	Within 10% for a large-beam UV source	—	Good uniformity (within 10%)
13	Exposure subsites	Minimum 0.5 cm^2 more than 1 cm^2 is recommended .8 cm between each exposure subsite	Minimum 0.5 cm^2, more than 1 cm^2 is recommended	Minimum 1 cm^2
14	Number of subsites	Minimum 5	No mention	7
15	Incremental progression of UV	Expected SPF < 25: 1.25 Expected SPF > 25: 1.12 Smaller ratio may be used	Expected SPF <20:1.25 Expected SPF <30:1.50 Expected SPF >30:1.10	Untreated: 1.25 <8:0.64, 0.80, 0.90, 1.0, 1.1, 1.25, 1.56 >8, <15:0.69, 0.83, 0.91, 1.0, 1.09, 1.20, 1.44 >15:0.76, 0.87, 0.93, 1.0, 1.07, 1.15, 1.32

(continued)

Table 10.4 *Continued*

		International method and JCIA method (2003 revised version)	JCIA method (1999 version)	US FDA method (1999 version)
16	MED	The lowest UV dose that produces the first perceptible unambiguous erythema with defined borders appearing over most of the field of UV exposure, 16–24 h after UV exposure	The minimum UV dose that produces a minimally perceptible erythema in almost the entire field of radiation (2/3 or more) 16–24 h after irradiation	The first perceptible redness reaction with clearly defined borders 22–24 h
17	MED assessment	MEDu, MEDp, and MED of standard sample are evaluated on the same day in a blind manner	MEDu and MEDp are recommended to be evaluated on the same day by some evaluators	MEDu, MEDp, and MED of standard sample are evaluated on the same day in a blind manner
18	Expression of MED	mJ/cm^2 or MED unit or time (s)	No mention	J/m^2
19	SPFi and SPF	SPFi = MEDpi/MEDui SPF is calculated as the arithmetical mean of all SPFi	SPFi = MEDpi/MEDui SPF is calculated as the arithmetical mean of all SPFi	SPFi = MEDpi/MEDui SPF is calculated as the arithmetical mean of all SPFi

20	Labelling SPF	No mention	Integral numbers, discarding fractions of the mean; the upper limit of SPF labeling is 50; SPF 50+ if the SPF is 50 or more and the lower limit of the 95% confidence interval is 51.0 or more	Maximum value less than 95% confidence interval
21	Reporting	Information to be included in test report is shown	No mention	No mention
22	Rejection of test data	In case the MED could not be determined	No mention	In case the MED could not be determined

UV-A protection has so far been studied mainly for the purpose of clinical treatment of patients sensitive to UV-A (30) or in patients sensitized to UV-A by oral or topical application of 8-MOP (31), trimethylpsoralen (32), or tetracycline (33) for the treatment of psoriasis vulgaris and vitiligo.

However, although the methods used are effective in clinical practice, it is not possible to compare the UV-A-protective effect of sunscreens quantitatively when experimental facilities are different, due to differences in the sensitivity of the subjects and in the action spectra. It may be dangerous to expose healthy volunteers artificially photosensitized to UV-A by application of psoralen compounds, and this would be ethically unacceptable.

We have attempted to use IPD as an indicator of UV-A protection efficacy (34,35). IPD is a temporary brown-gray to brown-black coloration observed in human skin immediately after exposure to UV-A. This reaction was originally reported by Hauser (36). Thereafter, it was discovered that IPD is due to a photo-oxidation reaction in which a colorless melanin precursor is oxidized to generate a pigmented product (37). It was further discovered that IPD occurs on exposure to visible light (36,38) and that this response is an effective index for measuring UV-A protection in healthy human skin (10,18,34,35,39). Because it occurs with a relatively small dose of UV-A and fades quickly, it is believed that IPD is suitable as a response index for measuring UV-A protection in Japanese subjects. However, we encountered the following problems:

1. Because it fades so rapidly, the darkening response immediately after UV-A exposure varies widely among individuals, and stable PFA (protection factor against UV-A) values are difficult to obtain.
2. When tests are performed on sunscreen, especially makeup products, 2 or 3 min elapse after UV-A exposure while the skin is wiped with skin cleaner, and from a practical standpoint, observation immediately after exposure is impossible.
3. Determination should be done by several experienced observers, but in the periods of time required for two or three observers to make observations one after the other, the darkening response disappears.

When time course observations of IPD were made in an attempt to overcome these problems using four types of UV-A light sources, it was discovered that by 2 h or more after exposure the rate of fading slowed down and became stable (Fig. 10.12) (40). It was then determined that stable values could be obtained when PFA values were calculated by using the response at 2–4 h after exposure as an index (40).

It is believed that the measurement of UV-A protection by using the IPD response 2–4 h after exposure as an index is a suitable method. It is not appropriate to designate the response that occurs 2–4 h after exposure as IPD, because it is different from the immediate response after exposure. Therefore, after considerable discussion it was decided that from the standpoint of a response that ultimately persists, this response should be called persistent pigment

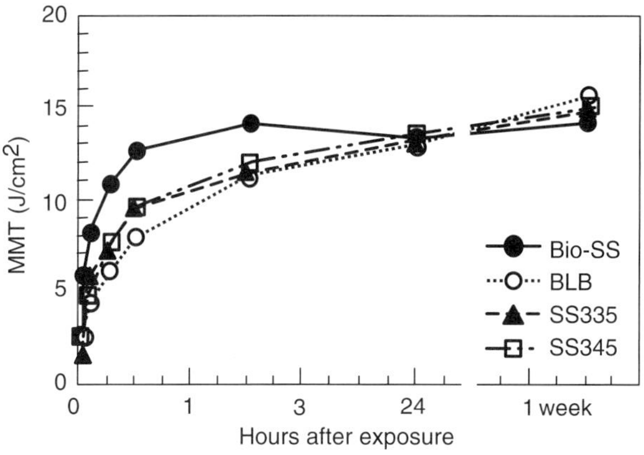

Figure 10.12 Time course of MMT determined with various types of light sources. Bio-SS: biosolar simulator (Watanabe Shoukou) with UVA filter; BLB: fluorescent lamp (Toshiba) with Schott WG335 (2 mm); SS335: solar simulator model 600 (Solar Light Co.) with Schott UG11 and Schott WG335 (2 mm); SS345: solar simulator model 600 (Solar Light Co.) with Schott UG11 and Schott WG345 (2 mm).

darkening (PPD), and the minimum dose of UV-A necessary for inducing this response should be called the minimal persistent pigment darkening dose (MPPD). PFA values are obtained as a ratio of MPPD in protected skin to MPPD in unprotected skin. We determined PFA values of standard sunscreen in Japanese volunteers of various skin types. As shown in Fig. 10.13, the PFA values of standard sunscreen showed no statistically significant differences among the volunteers with the five skin types. However, we could not decide whether there

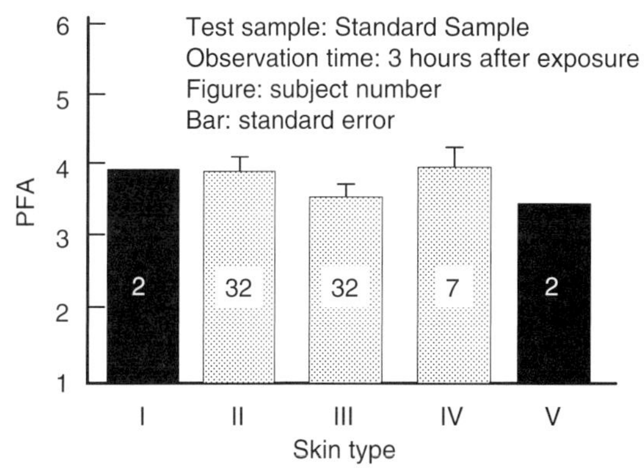

Figure 10.13 Relationship between skin types of volunteers and PFA values of standard sunscreen.

were differences in PFA between skin types II–IV and skin types I and V because the number of volunteers with skin types I and V was too small.

The main differences in test conditions between the SPF test method and the UV-A protection test method standardized by JCIA are summarized in Table 10.5. The JCIA method for measuring UV-A protection efficacy seems to be excellent. Its major advantages are (1) it is possible to obtain a test result in a short time, (2) there is no injury to volunteers, (3) it is also safe for the examiners, (4) it shows good reproducibility, and (5) it has high precision. There were no obvious disadvantages.

Development of Sunscreen Labeling for UV Protection Efficacy in Japan

Before 1986, the labeling of sunscreen products for UV protection efficacy was only done in terms of expressions such as "excellent UV protection", "strong UV protection", etc. in Japan. This was insufficient for consumers to select an adequate sunscreen, and such labeling was regarded as unreliable by consumers.

Shiseido put the first sunscreen products labeled with the quantitatively measured SPF and UV-A protection levels on sale in Japan. As shown in Fig. 10.14, the former was expressed as Suncare-Shisuu in 1981 by Shiseido and the latter as one of a set of protection grades, namely, A, AA, and AAA, in 1986.

Other companies also followed in the footsteps of Shiseido. At that time there were no Japanese standards for labeling or for testing, so some confusion arose. Currently, we have the following standards of labeling on sunscreens for SPF and PA.

The arithmetic mean of SPF values determined in subjects is the SPF value for the sample. The SPF values are expressed in integral numbers, discarding fractions. However, SPF is expressed as SPF 50+ if the SPF for the sample is over 50 and the lower limit of the 95% confidence interval is 51.0 or more, or as SPF 50 if the lower limit of the 95% confidence interval is <51.0. The PFA is a value that measures UV-A protection in terms of protection against skin darkening 2–4 h after exposure. The SPF uses the erythema response as the index of protection, and in that respect it is quite different from the PFA. More especially, because SPF is an index of the extent to which reddening can be controlled, it can be regarded as giving an approximate guide to the effect in actual situations. In the case of UV-A, however, even when we use darkening as an index, it is impossible to prevent darkening through UV-A protection alone, and it is difficult to link the response of the skin to a protective effect that can actually be seen by consumers. Moreover, the values differ if the index is changed (35). For example, when the immediate darkening, which occurs directly after UV-A exposure, is used as an index rather than PPD, different PFA values are obtained. Nevertheless, although the values themselves may vary, it is believed that they all yield similar results concerning the relative strength or weakness of the protection.

Table 10.5 JCIA Standards for SPF Test Method and UV-A Protection Efficacy Test Method

		SPF test method (2003 revised version)	UVA protection efficacy test method
1	Selection of volunteers	Questionnaire; medical check by professional; World Medical Association Declaration of Helsinki	Questionnaire
2	Skin type and test area	Phototype, colorimetric method; back	Phototype; back
3	Number of test subjects	Minimum 10, maximum 20 (a maximum of five results may be excluded)	Minimum 10
4	Statistical criterion	95% CI < 17% of mean SPF	SE less than 10% by mean PFA
5	Standard sunscreen	P1 (DIN standard SPF4) P2 (CTFA recommended SPF12) P3 (JCIA standard SPF15) P7 (FDA and JCIA standard SPF4) 2 < SPF < 20: can choose all SPF > 20: choose P2 or P3	Cream containing 5% 4-*tert*-butyl 4′-methoxydibenzoylmethane and 3% 2-ethylhexyl *p*-methoxycinnamate
6	Product quantity and application	2.00 mg/cm^2 ± 2.5; CD-ROM	2 mg/cm^2 or 2 m/cm^2
7	Light source	Solar simulator (xenon lamp); %RCEE acceptance limits <290 nm: <1.0% 290–300 nm: 2.0–8.0 % 290–310 nm: 49.0–65.0% 290–320 nm: 85.0–90.0% 290–400 nm: 100% Total irradiance without an excessive feeling of heat or pain	Continuous UVA spectrum similar to sunlight; ratio of UVA/UVA = 8–20%. UV ray shorter than 320 nm shall be excluded

(*continued*)

Table 10.5 *Continued*

		SPF test method (2003 revised version)	UVA protection efficacy test method
8	Incremental progression of UV	Expected SPF < 25: 1.25 Expected SPF > 25: 1.12 Smaller ratio may be used.	1.25<
9	MED and MPPD	The lowest UV dose that produces the first perceptible unambiguous erythema with defined borders appearing over most of the field of UV exposure, 16–24 h after UV exposure	The minimum UV dose that produces slight darkening over essentially the whole radiation field within 2 to 4 h after exposure.
10	SPF and PFA	SPFi = MEDpi/MEDui SPF is calculated as the arithmetical mean of all SPFi	PFAi = MPPDpi/MPPDui PFA is calculated as the arithmetical mean of all PFAi
11	Labeling	Integral numbers, discarding fractions of the mean; the upper limit of SPF labeling is 50; SPF 50+ if the SPF is 50 or more and the lower limit of the 95% confidence interval is 51.0 or more	2 < PFA < 4: PA+ 4 < PFA < 8: PA++ 8 < PFA: PA+++ PA shall be placed together with SPF
12	Reporting	Information to be included in test report is shown	No mention
13	Rejection of test data	In case the MED could not be determined	In case the MPPD could not be determined

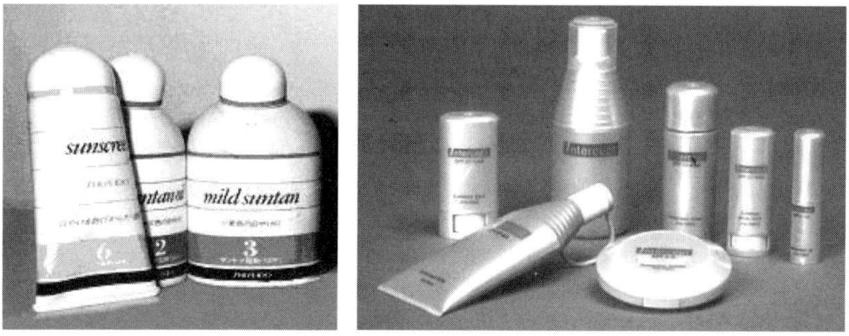

Shiseido Sunscreen in 1981
(Suncare-Shisuu 2,3,6)

Intercept Sunscreen in 1986
(UVA Protection Grade,A,AA,AAA)

Figure 10.14 First labeling products of the quantitative efficacies for UV-A and UV-B protection in Japan.

Therefore, a classification scheme rather than numerical values was adopted for expressing UV-A protection. The method of classification was based on the following considerations:

1. The difference in UV-A protection must be clear from the measured values. For expressing the effectiveness we chose cutoff points of 2, 4, and 8 based on the fact that the value "2 or more" differs by at least three geometric progression increments ($1.25 \times 1.25 \times 1.25 = 1.95$) from the value of "1" given for no effect, and in the same manner each class differs from the next by at least three geometric progression increments.
2. The meaning of the classification must be clear. The protection doubles for each step of increase in the classification.

In recognition of the fact that the labels must be simple, clear, and easy for consumers to understand, PA was selected as the expression for UV-A protection, and the classes of protection are expressed by +, ++, and +++.

"PA+" indicates that the product offers protection against UV-A, "PA++" indicates that the product offers considerable protection against UV-A, and "PA+++" indicates that the product offers the greatest protection against UV-A. There are no sunscreens having only UV-A protection efficacy without UV-B protection efficacy. Therefore, a restriction has been imposed such that the labeling of the level of UV-A protection is combined with SPF values as shown in Fig. 10.15.

PROBLEMS FOR THE FUTURE

One goal of cosmetics scientists is to be able to protect the skin against aging, that is, to reduce or delay the signs of skin aging. Recovery and maintenance

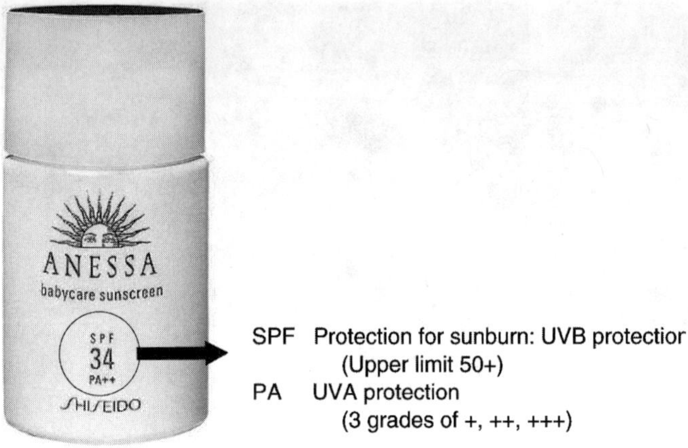

Figure 10.15 Example of labeling of UV-A and UV-B protection efficacies in Japan.

of “fresh skin” is a common desire of all people. Aging phenomena in the skin include pigmented spots, wrinkles, yellow skin, flabby skin, and tumors. These skin changes are most commonly observed in the sites usually exposed to sunlight, especially the face. They are collectively designated as photoaging, and are considered to be caused mainly by cumulative UV exposure and external stimulation. The most important countermeasure to photoaging of skin is defense of the skin against UV rays. The simplest method is a change of life style to avoid unnecessary sunburn and suntan. Measures such as wearing sunglasses, long-sleeved shirts, and a hat, putting up a parasol, and using sunscreens are effective. Recent study has indicated that UV-B and UV-A accelerate skin aging, and that both must be intercepted in order to prevent skin aging. Therefore, the protective efficacy of sunscreens is a very important function for consumers.

Skin care cosmetics for daily use as well as those for leisure use are also required to have a sun protective function. Accordingly, there is a continuing need for new UV-A and UV-B absorbers which can be used in sunscreens in appropriate amounts, and which at the same time are safe enough for use on people with sensitive skin (41).

The dosages of sunscreens are determined not only by the safety levels of UV absorbers, but also by the solubility of the absorbers in the base or solvent. High solubility in cosmetics bases and solvents such as oil, alcohol, and water is an essential factor for cosmetics ingredients.

Furthermore, UV absorbers must be water resistant. Since most sunscreens are used on the beach or in the mountains in summer, UV absorbers would lose their practical value if they were easily dissolved by seawater or perspiration. In other words, UV absorbers have little practical value if they are not water resistant, even if they have high UV absorbance. Therefore, development of UV absorbers having superior water resistance as well as a UV-protective

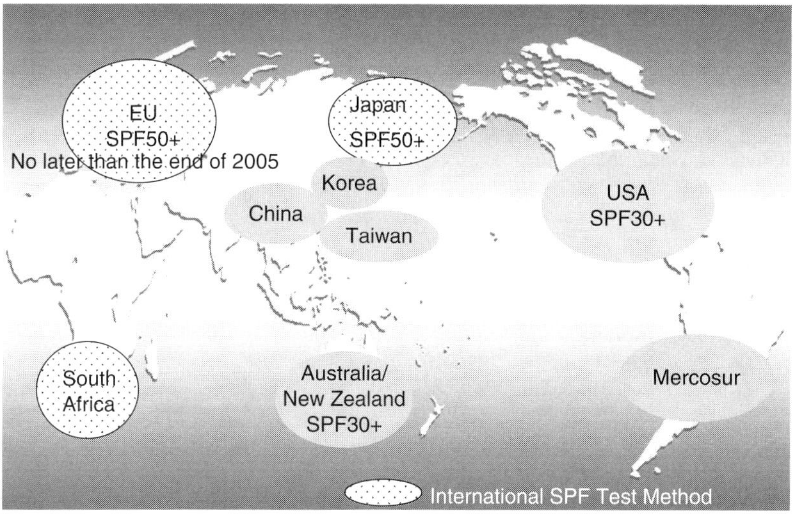

Figure 10.16 SPF test methods and upper limits of SPF labeling on sunscreen products around the world.

effect, safety, and high solubility is highly desirable. The need for protection from UV-A is evident from the established dermal toxicity of UV-A. Therefore, measures on an international scale should immediately be taken to develop a method of evaluating UV-A blocking and to identify UV-A absorbers.

Figure 10.16 shows the international status of SPF values and test methods. The upper limits of labeled SPF numbers on sunscreen products in Japan, EU, USA, and Australia/New Zealand are different. Further, although the differences in SPF test methods among these countries and areas are not major, there are still small differences in testing conditions, and differences in the ways of expressing SPF also remain an issue.

These differences, which are scientifically insignificant, result in economic loss and delay. In the near future, international harmonization of SPF test methods and labeling methods should be promoted, including UV-A protection and water resistance testing methods for sunscreen products.

REFERENCES

1. Morikawa F, Nakayama Y, Iikura T, Nakajima K, Ohta S, Ishihara M. The application of photographic techniques for the differentiation of the location of melanin pigment in the skin. In: Fitzpatrick TB et al., ed. Biology and Diseases of Dermal Pigmentation. Tokyo: University of Tokyo Press, 1981:231–244.
2. Fukuda M, Nagashima M, Munakata A, Nakajima K, Ohta S. Effect of biological and physical factors on ultraviolet erythemal and pigmentary response. J Soc Cosmet Chem Jpn 1979; 13:20–28.

3. Fukuda M, Naganuma M. Sunscreen. In: Takase Y et al., ed. Cutaneous Aging. Tokyo: Seiji Shoin, 1985:369–381.
4. Fukuda M, Naganuma M, Maeda K. Protection against cutaneous aging induced by repeating sun exposure. In: Kligman AM et al., ed. Cutaneous Aging. Tokyo: University of Tokyo Press, 1988:589–605.
5. Fukuda M, Nakajima K. Sunscreen. J Jpn Cosmet Sci Soc 1981; 5:73–82.
6. Mizugaki M, Naganuma M, Fukuda M. Seasonal skin color variation of the pigmented area on the female face measured by remote color sensing system. J Jpn Cosmet Sci Soc 1997; 21:185–189.
7. Fukuda M. Self-reported skin type of Japanese. J Jpn Cosmet Sci Soc 1991; 15:103–105.
8. Food and Drug Administration. Sunscreen drug products for over-the-counter-human use. Fed Reg 1978; 43:38206–38269.
9. Yoshii T. The survey about female attitude against their skin and the character of their skin—the international comparison of surveys conducted in Japan, US, Europe and Asia. J Jpn Soc Cutan Health. 2003; 50:68–74.
10. Fukuda M, Naganuma M, Iwai M, Nakayama Y. Protection to UVA-induced skin reaction by ultraviolet absorbers. J Soc Cosmet Chem Jpn 1988; 22:5–9.
11. Everett MA, Yeargers E, Sayre RM, Olson RL. Penetration of epidermis by ultraviolet rays. Photochem Potobiol 1966; 5:533–542.
12. Fukuda M, Naganuma M, Nakajima K. Ultraviolet radiation of sunlight in Japan. Acta Dermatol (Kyoto) 1987; 82:551–558.
13. Naganuma M, Hara E, Yagi E, Fukuda MM. Seasonal variation of solar UV dose. J Soc Cosmet Chem Jpn 1991; 25:15–20.
14. Kligman LH, Akin FJ, Kligman AM. The contributions of UVA and UVB to connective tissue damage in hairless mice. J Invest Dermatol 1985; 84:272–276.
15. Poulsen JT, Staberg B, Wulf HC, Brodthagen H. Dermal elastosis in hairless mices after UV-B and UV-A applied simultaneously, separately or sequentially. Br J Dermatol 1984; 110:531–538.
16. Stanberg B, Wulf HC, Klemp P, Poulsen T, Brodthagen H. The carcinogenic effect of UVA irradiation. J Invest Dermatol 1983; 81:517–519.
17. Toda K, Ohta M. Female facial melanosis. In: Fitzpatrick TB et al., ed. Biology and Diseases of Dermal Pigmentation. Tokyo: University of Tokyo Press, 1981:225–229.
18. Fukuda M, Naganuma M, Nakajima K. Laboratories studies on UVA protection with Parsol A. Nishinihon J Dermatol 1987; 49:88–94.
19. Fukuda M, Takata S. The evolution of recent sunscreens. In: Altmyer P, Hoffman K, Stucker M, eds. Skin Cancer and UV Radiation. Berlin: Springer-Verlag, 1997:266–275.
20. Inomata Y, The application of nanoparticles to the skin care products. Frag J 2003; 31(8):55–62.
21. Tokubo K. Application of powders to cosmetics—their protection and reform of their function. Fragr J 1986; 80:60–66.
22. Kurosawa T. Recent trends and prospective problems of sunscreen agents. Fragr J 1999; 29(5):14–19.
23. JCIA. Japan Cosmetic Industry Association Standard Sun Protection Factor Test Method. JCIA, 1991.
24. Fukuda M. Where is SPF war going to?—Should we set the upper limit on labeled SPF values? Proc Jpn Comm Sunlight Prot 1999; 9:35–42.

25. Fukuda M, Arai S, Kawai M, Suzuki T, Naganuma M, Okada T, Masaki H, Motoyosi T. Sunscreens and UV protection—SPF & PA. 1999 revised version. JCIA, 2000:1–59.
26. COLIPA. Reports on the International Multi-Centered SPF Ring Test. December 1996.
27. Fukuda M. Recent 10 years on sunscreen cosmetics in Japan. Proc Jpn Comm Sunlight Prot 2001; 11:93–103.
28. CTFA/SA, COLIPA, JCIA. International Sun Protection Factor (SPF) Test Method. 2003.
29. Fukuda M, Asano H, Kawai M, Naganuma M, Hirose O, Matsue K, Mouri K. Sunscreens and UV protection—SPF and PA. 2003 revised version. JCIA, July 25, 2003.
30. Rice EG. Dihydroxyacetone naphthoquinone protection against photosensitivity. Dermatologica 1976; 153:38–43.
31. Jarratt M, Hill M, Smiles K. Topical protection against long wave ultraviolet A. J Am Acad Dermatol 1983; 9:354–283.
32. Parrish JA, Pathak MA, Fitzpatrick TB. Prevention of unintentional overexposure in topical psoralen treatment of vitiligo. Arch Dermatol 1971; 104:281–283.
33. Dahlen RW, Shapiro SI, Berry CZ, Schreiber MM. A method for evaluating sunscreen protection from longwave ultraviolet. J Invest Dermatol 1970; 55:164–169.
34. Fukuda M, Naganuma M. The sunscreen industry in Japan: past, present, and future. In: Lowe NJ, Shaath NA, eds. Sunscreen: Development, Evaluation and Regulatory Aspects. New York: Marcel Dekker, 1990:173–194.
35. Naganuma M, Fukuda M. Development of testing method for UVA protection. J Jpn Soc Cutan Health 1992; 29:291–298.
36. Hauser T. Uber spezifische Wirkungen des Langwelligen Ultravioletten lichts auf die menschliche haut. Strahlen-therapie 62, 1938:315–322.
37. Sawamura D, Sato S, Kiuchi H, Hashimoto I, Katabira Y. UVA induced darkening of lower epidermal cells as an in vitro system of immediate pigment darkening (IPD) and mechanisms of IPD. J Dermatol 1986; 13:101–107.
38. Pathak MA. Riley FC, Fitzpatrick TB. Melanogenesis in human skin following exposure to longwave UV and visible light. J Invest Dermatol 1964; 39:435–443.
39. Kaidbey K. Determination of UVA protection factors by means of immediate pigment darkening in normal skin. J Am Acad Dermatol 1991; 25:262.
40. Naganuma M, Fukuda M, Arai S, Kawai M, Suzuki T, Hirose O, Masaki H, Motoyosi K, Yoshii T. Standard test method for classification and labeling of sunscreen having UVA protection efficacy in Japan. J Soc Cosmet Chem Jpn., 1997; 31:420–427.
41. Rapaport M. Patch testing in Japanese subjects. Contact Dermatitis 1984; 11:93–97.

11

Regulations of Sunscreens Worldwide

David C. Steinberg
Steinberg & Associates, Inc., Plainsboro, New Jersey, USA

Sunscreens are regulated throughout the world either as cosmetics or as over-the-counter (OTC) drugs that do not require a governmental preapproval, or as OTC drugs that require a preapproval before they are placed on the market. Regardless of how they are regulated, all of these product regulations are very similar concerning sunscreens! Each country has a preapproved list of permitted UV filters, an accepted method of running efficacy by SPF determination, and regulated labels. Some countries have approved methods for UV-A claims and water-resistance testing.

This chapter will cover the approved UV filters in the USA, EU, Japan, and Australia, their maximum use level, correct ingredient designation, and how new filters are approved. There is also a master cross-reference list by INCI designation. The different SPF test methods will be described along with the formulations of reference standards, current approved UV-A methods, water-resistant testing, labeling requirements, and finally a brief review of current Good Manufacturing Procedures (cGMPs) for the USA.

OVERVIEW OF REGULATIONS AND PERMITTED UV FILTERS

The USA regulates sunscreens as OTC drugs under the Final Monograph issued May 21, 1999. For a complete copy see http://www.fda.gov/cder/otcmonographs/Sunscreen/sunscreen_FR_19990521.pdf.

Japan regulates sunscreens as cosmetics as of March 31, 2002.

The European Union regulates sunscreens as cosmetics under the Cosmetic Directive 76/768/EEC. These can found at http://pharmacos.eudra.org/F3/cosmetic/pdf/vol_1en.pdf.

Australia regulates sunscreens as OTC drugs under the Therapeutic Goods Act of 1989, which require preapproval before being allowed on the market. There is an exemption of products that claim an SPF of 3 or less.

ACTIVE INGREDIENTS

The permitted list of UV filters is the cornerstone for formulating sun protection products. The USA permits the fewest UV filters with Japan, the EU, and Australia having many more approvals.

The USA

As of October 1, 2003, there are 16 permitted filters in the USA. Table 11.1 lists these by their drug name and the maximum permitted level. These actives must meet the specifications found in the United States Pharmacopoeia. All sunscreens can be used with any other sunscreen with the exception of avobenzone. This is permitted to be used only with the following other permitted filters: cinoxate, dioxybenzone, octinoxate, octisalate, homosalate, oxybenzone, octocrylene, sulisobenzone, and trolamine salicylate. If you use two or more UV filters in a product, each must add a minimum SPF of 2 to the total. So a product with one filter must have a minimum SPF of 2, for two filters it must be 4, for three filters it must be 6, and so on.

Japan

Japan changed their regulations in 2002 and moved sunscreens into the category of cosmetics from quasi-drugs. They established a positive list for permitted UV filters and permitted concentrations. These are allowed in four separate categories of use: all cosmetics (Table 11.2), rinse-off no mucous membrane application,

Table 11.1 US Permitted Filters

UV filter drug name	Maximum concentration (%)
Aminobenzoic acid	15
Avobenzone	3
Cinoxate	3
Dioxybenzone	3
Homosalate	15
Meridamate	5
Octocrylene	10
Octinoxate	7.5
Octisalate	5
Oxybenzone	6
Padimate O	8
Ensulizole	4
Sulisobenzone	10
Titanium dioxide	25
Trolamine salicylate	12
Zinc oxide	25

Table 11.2 UV Filters Allowed in Japan in all Cosmetics

UV filter INCI name	Maximum content (per 100 g)
Homosalate	10
Glyceryl ethylhexanoate dimethoxycinnamate	10
PABA and its esters	4 total
Butyl methoxydibenzoylmethane	10

leave-on no mucous membrane application; and rinse-off and leave-on cosmetics which can be applied to mucous membranes (Table 11.3).

EU Permitted Filters

All UV filters must be preapproved and listed in Annex VII (Table 11.4).

Australian Approved UV Filters

Australia has a permitted list of UV filters and also requires all filters to obtain an Australian approved name (AAN) before use (Table 11.5).

SUMMARY OF ACTIVES

Table 11.6 summarizes by INCI name the approvals by country by concentration for sunscreen application.

APPROVAL PROCESS FOR NEW ACTIVE INGREDIENTS

USA

Before 2002, the only method available to approve a new active was the very complex and costly New Drug Application (NDA) process. Here, a manufacturer would submit the new active in a formulation along with extensive safety and efficacy testing. The FDA would approve this and send a letter to this submitter allowing them to sell this new drug with the FDA's stated rules, *for this particular formulation only*. If the manufacturer wanted to use this active in a different formulation, they were required to submit a supplementary NDA. Only this company could use this active. A producer of the active could obtain an NDA but that would put them in the finished goods business! After at least 2 years on the market, the holder of the NDA could then petition the FDA to reopen the Final Monograph to allow this active. If the FDA approves this request, then anyone could use this active in any Monograph compliant formulation. Since 1978, with the original publication of the Proposed Rules for Sunscreens

Table 11.3 UV Filters Allowed in Japan Depending on the Type of Cosmetic

UV filter	Type 1	Type 2	Type 3
Glucopyranoxy propylhydroxy benzophenone	5	5	NA[a]
Ethylhexyl salicylate	5	10	NA
Diisopropyl methyl cinnamate	0.5	10	NA
Cinoxate	∞[c]	5	5
Benzophenone-6	10	10	NA
Benzophenone-9	10	10	NA
Benzophenone-1	10	10	NA
1-(3,4-dimethoxyphenyl) 4,4-dimethyl-1,3-pentanedione[b]	7	7	NA
Ethylhexyl dimethoxybenzylidene dioxoimidazolidine propionate	3	3	NA
Benzophenone-2	10	10	0.05
Terephthalidene dicamphor sulfonic acid	10	10	NA
Ethylhexyl triazone	5	5	NA
Isopentyl trimethoxycinnamate trisiloxane	7.5	7.5	2.5
Pentyl dimethyl PABA	10	10	NA
Ethylhexyl dimethyl PABA	10	10	7
Isopropyl methoxycinnamate, diisopropyl methoxycinnamate esters (mixture)	10	10	NA
Ethylhexyl methoxycinnamate	20	20	8
Benzophenone-3	∞[c]	5	5
Benzophenone-4	10	10	0.1
Benzophenone-5	10	10	1
Phenylbenzimidazole sulfonic acid	3	3	0
Ferulic acid	10	10	NA
Octocrylene	10	10	NA

[a]NA = not allowed.
[b]No INCI designation.
[c]∞ = no limit.
Note: Categories of use: type 1—rinse-off, no mucous membrane application; type 2—leave-on, no mucous membrane application; type 3—rinse-off and leave-on cosmetics which can be applied to mucous membranes.

by the FDA, only avobenzone was approved by this very complicated method. This has been a major issue between industry and the FDA.

In 1999, the FDA proposed new rules for allowing foreign safety and efficacy data to be used for possible approval of any OTC drug active or to increase the permitted level. This rule was finalized in January 2002. It is known as Time and Extent Application (TEA).

TEA is a three-part process. The first part is a submission by either a user or a seller of the active of a formal application showing a minimum of five

Table 11.4 UV Filters Permitted in the EU (Annex VII)

COLIPA No.	Chemical name as used in the directive	Maximum concentration (%)
S 1	4-Aminobenzoic acid	5
S 3	Ethoxylated ethyl-4-amino benzoate	10
S 8	2-Ethylhexyl-4-dimethyl-aminobenzoate	8
S 12	Homosalate	10
S 15	2,4,6-Trianolino-(*p*-carbo-2′-ethylhexyl-1′oxy)-1,3,5-triazone	5
S 16	Drometrizole trisiloxane	15
S 17	Benzoic acid, 4,4′-[[6-[[4-[[(1,1-dimethylethyl) amino]carbonyl]phenyl] amino]1,3,5-triazine-2-4-diyl]bis-bis(2-ethylhexyl)] ester	10
S 19	3-Benzylidene camphor	2
S 20	2-Ethylhexyl salicylate	5
S 27	Isopentyl-4-methoxycinnamate	10
S 28	2-Ethylhexyl-4-methoxy-cinnamate	10
S 32	2-Cyano-3,3-diphenyl acrylic acid, 2-ethylhexyl ester	10
S 38	Oxybenzone (warning label required—“contains oxybenzone if over 0.5%”)	10
S 40	2-Hydroxy-4-methoxybenzo-5-sulfonic acid	5
S 45	2-Phenylbenzimidazole-5-sulfonic acid and its potassium, sodium, and triethanolamine salts	8
S 57	*N,N,N*-Trimethyl-4-(2-oxoborn-3-ylidenemethyl) anilinum methyl sulfate	6
S 59	alpha-(2-Oxoborn-3-ylidene)toluene-4-sulfonic acid and its salts	6
S 60	3-(4′-Methylbenzylidene)-D-1-camphor	4
S 66	1-(4-*tert*-Butylphenyl)-3-(4-methoxyphenyl) propane-1,3-dione	5
S 71	3,3′-(1,4-Phenylenedimethylene)-bis-(7,7-dimethyl-2-oxobicyclo-[2.2.1] hept-1-ylmethanesulphonic acid) and its salts	10
S 72	Polymer of *N*-{(2 and 4)-[2-oxoborn-3-ylidene) methyl]benzyl}acrylamide	6
S 74	Benzylidene malonate polysiloxane	10
S 75	Titanium dioxide	25
S 76	Zinc oxide	25
S 79	2,2′-Methylene-bis-(6-(2*H*-benzotriazol-2-yl)-4-(1,1,3,3-tetramethylbutyl)phenol)	10
S 80	2,2′-(1,4-Phenylene)bis)-1*H*-benzimidazole-4,6-disulfonic acid, monosodium salt	10
S 81	2,4-Bis-{[4-(2-ethyl-hexyloxy)-2-hydroxy]-phenyl}-6-(4-methoxyphenyl)- (1,3,5)-triazine	10
S 83	Benzoic acid, 2-[4-(diethylamino)-2-hydroxybenzoyl]-hexyl ester (expressed as acid)	10

Table 11.5 UV Filters Permitted in Australia by Their Required Name

AAN	INCI name	Maximum concentration (%)
Aminobenzoic acid	PABA	15
Isoamyl methoxycinnamate	Isoamyl *p*-methoxycinnamate	10
Benzophenone-2*	Benzophenone-2	*
Butyl methoxydibenzoylmethane	Butyl methoxydibenzoylmethane	5
Cinoxate	Cinoxate	6
Dioxybenzone	Benzophenone-8	3
Octyl methoxycinnamate	Ethylhexyl methoxycinnamate	10
Octyl salicylate	Ethylhexyl salicylate	5
Homosalate	Homosalate	15
Isopropylbenzyl salicylate*	Isopropylbenzyl salicylate	*
Menthyl anthranilate	Menthyl anthranilate	5
4-Methylbenzylidene camphor	4-Methylbenzylidene camphor	4
Octocrylene	Octocrylene	10
Octyl triazone	Ethylhexyl triazone	5
None	Benzylidene camphor sulfonic acid	6
Oxybenzone	Benzophenone-3	10
Phenylbenzimidazole sulfonic acid	Phenylbenzimidazole sulfonic acid	4
None	Camphor benzalkonium methosulfate	6
*	Salicylic acid salts	*
Benzophenone-4	Benzophenone-4	10
None	Benzophenone-5	10
Ecamsule	Terephthalylidene Dicamphor sulfonic acid	10
Titanium dioxide	Titanium dioxide	25
Triethanolamine salicylate	TEA salicylate	12
Zinc oxide	Zinc oxide	20
Methylene bis-benzotriazolyl tetramethylbutylphenol	Methylene bis-benzotriazolyl tetramethylbutylphenol	10
Drometrizole trisiloxane	Drometrizole trisiloxane	15

Notes: None—must apply for AAN before it can be used. The asterisks denote sunscreens currently under review—no new products containing these will be permitted until the review is completed.

consecutive years of use of this UV filter (the rules for a TEA cover all drugs, not just UV filters) as a nonprescription product in a foreign country. After this submission is reviewed and meets the FDA's requirements, the FDA issues a notice in the *Federal Register* that this first part has been approved. Rejected

Table 11.6 Cross-Reference of all UV Filters by INCI Designation

INCI designation	USA	Japan	EU	Australia
1-(3,4-Dimethoxyphenyl) 4,4-dimethyl-1,3-pentanedione		7		
3-Benzylidene camphor			2	
4-Methylbenzylidene camphor	[c]		4	4
Benzophenone-1		10		
Benzophenone-2		10		[a]
Benzophenone-3	6	5	10	10
Benzophenone-4	10	10	5	10
Benzophenone-5		10		10
Benzophenone-6		10		
Benzophenone-8	3			3
Benzophenone-9		10		
Benzylidene camphor sulfonic acid			6	6
Bis-ethylhexyloxyphenol methoxyphenyl triazine			10	
Butyl methoxydibenzoylmethane	3	10	5	5
Camphor benzalkonium methosulfate			6	6
Cinoxate	3	5		6
Diethylamino hydroxybenzoyl hexyl benzoate			10	
Diethylhexyl butamido triazone			10	
Diisopropyl methyl cinnamate		10		
Disodium phenyl dibenzimidazole tetrasulfonate			10	
Drometrizole trisiloxane			15	15
Ethyl PABA		4		
Ethylhexyl dimethoxybenzylidene dioxoimidazolidine propionate		3		
Ethylhexyl dimethyl PABA	8	10	8	8
Ethylhexyl methoxycinnamate	7.5	20	10	10
Ethylhexyl salicylate	5	10	5	5
Ethylhexyl triazone	[c]	3	5	5
Ferulic acid		10		
Glucopyranoxy propylhydroxy benzephenone		5		
Glyceryl ethylhexanoate dimethoxycinnamate		10		
Glyceryl PABA		4		
Homosalate	15	10	10	15
Isoamyl *p*-methoxycinnamate	[c]		10	10
Isopentyl trimethoxycinnamate trisiloxane		7.5		

(*continued*)

Table 11.6 *Continued*

INCI designation	USA	Japan	EU	Australia
Isopropyl methoxycinnamate		10		
Menthyl anthranilate	5			5
Methylene bis-benzotriazolyl tetramethylbutylphenol			10	10
Octocrylene	10	10	10	10
PABA	15	4	5	15
PEG-25 PABA			10	10
Pentyl dimethyl PABA		10		
Phenylbenzimidazole sulfonic acid	4	3	8	4
Polyacrylamidomethyl benzylidene camphor			6	
Polysilicone-15			10	
TEA[b]-salicylate	12			12
Terephthalylidene dicamphor sulfonic acid		10	10	10
Titanium dioxide	25	No limit	25	25
Zinc oxide	25	No limit	b	20

[a]Under review, no new approvals are expected until this is complete.
[b]Permitted as a color.
[c]TEA (Time and Extent Application) submitted.

applications are not made public. After this announcement, there is a request for submission of safety and efficacy data for the UV filter alone and this filter formulated into sunscreens. This data can come from suppliers or users anywhere it is permitted. After the FDA reviews these submissions, another announcement is made in the *Federal Register* stating the intention of the FDA to amend the Final Monograph to allow this new ingredient. After a comment period, this then becomes an approved filter for everyone to use.

So far (as of October 1, 2003), three filters have been approved through step 1: amiloxate (INCI isoamyl methoxycinnamate), enzcamene (4-methylbenzylidene camphor), and ethylhexyl triazone (no drug name as of this writing).

Japan

Under the new cosmetic regulations, there is a positive list of UV filters. To be approved and placed on this list requires a formal submission to the Minister of Health, Labor and Welfare (MHW), Examination and Administration Section, Medicine Bureau, who after reviewing your submission will approve or reject or request additional data. The submission must include the chemistry of the filter including thc method of production and purity. You need to submit data as to its efficacy and whether it is for UV-A, UV-B, or both. If the filter has been approved in any other market, this information must be included along with maximum use levels and any restrictions. If the chemistry is similar to that of other sunscreens, this comparison is also required.

Safety testing includes single-administration toxicity, repetitive administration toxicity, reproductive development toxicity, skin primary irritation, continuous skin irritation, sensitivity, phototoxicity, photosensitization, eye irritation, genetic toxicity, human patch test on Japanese subjects, and data on absorption, distribution, metabolism, and excretion.

All data must be submitted on official forms in Japanese.

European Union

The Scientific Committee Cosmetics and Non-Food Products (SCCNFP)[a] reviews submissions (usually coordinated by The European Cosmetic, Toiletry and Perfumery Association [COLIPA]) and then makes recommendations to the European Commission. If approved, they are added to the Cosmetic Directive as an Adaptation of Technical Progress and the filter is added to Annex VII.

The test required for submission by SCCNFP can be found at http://europa.eu.int/comm/food/fs/sc/sccp/out185_en.pdf.

Australia

The Medicines Evaluation Committee advises the Therapeutic Goods Administration (TGA) on the regulation of OTC medicines (including sunscreens) in Australia.

The following studies should be submitted:

- Acute oral toxicity
- Acute eye irritation
- Skin sensitization
- Acute dermal irritation
- Toxicokinetics—an *in vivo* determination of dermal and oral absorption is needed to establish systemic exposure via both routes and to enable the interpretation of the toxicity studies
- Genotoxicity testing—in bacterial and mammalian cell lines, photomutagenicity test in bacteria, photomutagenicity in a chromosomal aberration test, and an *in vivo* chromosome aberration assay
- Reproductive toxicity testing—for assessment of developmental and fertility effects
- Photostability
- Subchronic oral toxicity
- Carcinogenicity—*in vivo* carcinogenicity and photocarcinogenicity bioassays or justification for not providing these studies; a justification could be based around issues such as
  - The expected pattern of use (identify possible low exposure)

[a]This committee has been replaced in 2004 by the Scientific Committee on Consumer Products (SCCP).

Results of mutagenicity studies
Lack of similarity to existing molecules with known carcinogenic activity
Low persistence in the skin
Low *in vivo* absorption
Lack of photosensitization or phototoxic potential
Proven photostability
Lack of possible adverse effects on the skin (change to epidermis/dermis)

Another issue that should be addressed is the potential for interaction with other commonly used UV filters, since sunscreen products generally contain more than one active ingredient. These are new requirements as Australia use to automatically allow any UV filter permitted in the USA or the EU.

TESTING OF SUNSCREENS

Sun protection factor (SPF) is the universal method to describe efficacy of sunscreens. SPF is the ratio of the length of time you can be exposed to UV (mainly B) radiation with the sunscreen divided by the same amount of radiation without the sunscreen. The FDA in its Final Monograph describes the US method. COLIPA and Japan Cosmetic Industry Association (JCIA) (trade associations) have adopted methods for the EU and Japan. Australian methods are adopted by TGA from the latest Australian/New Zealand Standards.

Table 11.7 compares these four methods.

REFERENCE STANDARDS

USA

The FDA in their Final Monograph establish the following as the reference standard formulation:

Part A	
Lanolin	5.00
Homomenthyl salicylate	8.00
White petrolatum	2.50
Stearic acid	4.00
Propylparaben	0.05
Part B	
Methylparaben	0.10
EDTA disodium	0.05
Propylene glycol	5.00
Triethanolamine	1.00
Purified water	74.30

Procedure: Heat both phases to 77–82°C with constant stirring until the contents of each phases are solubilized. Add A to B slowly while stirring. Cool.

Table 11.7 Comparison of the Four Methods

Parameter	EU	USA	Australia	Japan
Date	October 1994	May 21, 1999	1998	January 1992
UV definition	UV-C 200–280 UV-B 280–320 UV-A 320–400	UV-B 290–320 UV-A 320–400	UV-B 290–320 UV-A 320–400	UV-B 290–320 UV-A 320–400
Selection of volunteers	Medical—informed consent Technical–visual, colorimetry	Questionnaire, informed consent	Questionnaire, personal interview	Questionnaire
Exclusion criteria	Pregnant, lactating, medication, dermatological problems, abnormal response, UV-A suntan	Medical history, abnormal skin response, medication	Photosensitizing medication, skin disease, abnormal response to UV, allergies	Photodermatitis, photosensitizing, medication
Skin type	Phototypes I, II, III	Phototypes I, II, III	Phototypes I, II, III	Phototypes I, II, III
Test area	Back	Back	Back	Back
Age limitation	18–60 years	—	—	>18 years
Frequency	5 times/12 month period	—	—	—
Number of subjects	10–20—statistical criterion	20 data = 25 subjects	= 10	= 10
Statistical criterion	95% CI < 20% mean SPF	—	SEM = 7% SPF	SEM = 10% SPF
Reference standard	P1 2.7%OMC SPF = 4 P2 7% ODP, 3% OB, SPF = 12 P3 3% OMC, 0.5% AVB, 2.78% PBIS SPF = 15	8% HS SPF = 4.47	8% HS SPF = 4 P3 3% OMC, 0.5% AVB, 2.78%PBIS SPF = 15	8%HS SPF = 45 5% AVB, 3% OMC For UV-A

Acceptance limits for standards	—	±SD 95% CI includes value of 4.0	With 25% of nominal value, applicable to each subject	—
Quantity applied	2.00 ± 0.04 mg/cm^2	2 mg/cm^2	2.0 mg/cm^2 or μL/cm^2 ±5%	
Mode of delivery	Weight (by loss), fingercot, no loss, droplets, gentle rubbing	Fingercot (oil, lotion: syringe; gel, butter: warmed)	Weight, fingerstall, validated method; uniform thickness	Fingertip, weight or volume–viscosity
Test site	≥35 cm^2 randomized	≥50 cm^2 randomized	≥30 cm^2	≥20 cm^2
Drying time	As soon as possible after 15 min	≥15 min	≥15 min 20–25°C air-conditioned	≥15 min
Solar simulator	Continuous spectrum, erythemal efficacy similar to that of standard Sun	Continuous emission spectrum 290–400 nm, similar to sunlight at sea level, 10° zenith angle, <1% energy <290 nm <5% energy >400 nm	<1% energy <290 nm; no peaks in UV-B, continuous spectra in UV-A; Xe preferred (150–6000 W) + WG 320/1 mm (2% at 300 nm) + dichroic mirror or IR filter	Xenon arc; continuous spectrum similar to sunlight in UV-B; energy <290 nm smallest
UV monitoring	Radiometer (280–400 nm)	Spectroradio metry	—	UV radiometer
Flux uniformity	15% (min—max)/subsite	Within 10%/subsite	—	Constant and uniform flux
Number of exposure sites	At least 5	≥3; 5 for MEDu, 7 for MEDp	≥5	—

(*continued*)

Table 11.7 *Continued*

Parameter	EU	USA	Australia	Japan
Progression of doses	25% geometric	1.25 SPF <8: 0.64–1.56 exp. SPF X SPF 8–15: 0.69–1.44 X SPF >15: 0.76–1.32 X	≤26% (geometric) ≤ 12% for SPFe ≥ 25	25% (geometric) smaller for high SPF
Exposure site: minimum size	Minimum 0.5 cm^2 Recommended ≥1 cm^2	≥1 cm^2	≥1 cm^2	≥0.5 cm^2
Skin response	erythema	erythema	erythema	erythema
Observation time-post exposure	16–24 h	22–24 h	16–24 h	16–24 h
Minimal erythema	First perceptible unambiguous redness, with clearly defined borders	Smallest dose of energy that produces redness reaching site at 22–24 h postexposure	Minimum quantity of radiant energy to produce the first detectable reddening of fair human skin	Minimum UV dose that produces minimally perceptible erythema at most radiation fields

MED determination	Simultaneous, paired, visual, or colorimetric evaluation	Blind MEDus previous and same day	Visual only, same observer and similar manner for MEDu and MEDp	Visually—one or two trained evaluators. MEDu/MEDp simultaneously or not; same manner
MED expression	Energy (mJ/cm^2) or time (s)	$E_{eff} = \Sigma V_i(\lambda)^* I(\lambda)$ J/m^{2}effective	Energy or time	—
Individual SPFi definition	MEDpi/MEDui	MEDps (J/m^2)/ MEDus (J/m^2)	MEDp/MEDu	MEDp/MEDu
Validation of individual result	Not the lowest dose in the series	Rejection: no erythema/ ps or μs Subject noncompliant	SPFi–SPF of std 4 $\leq$ 25%	MED not recognized at protected or unprotected site
SPF definition Variability	Arithmetical mean of SPFi and 95% CI with n volunteers	Arithmetical mean x of SPFi SD, A = t.s./v_n with n volunteers	SPF mean of SPFi, one decimal point, labeled to lowest integer (SEM $\leq$7% mean SPF)	Arithmetical mean x of SPFi Lower integral number

Note: OMC = Octyl methoxycinnamate; ODP = Octyl dimethyl PABA; OB = Benzophenone-3; AVB = Butyl methoxydibenzoylmethane; PBIS = Phenylbenzimidazole sulfonic acid; HS = Homosalate.

This standard can be obtained from Cosmetech Laboratories (1-973-882-5151) (www.Cosmetech.com).

European Union

COLIPA lists three different formulations as standards.

P1 Low SPF Standard:

Phase 1	
Propylene glycol stearate, SE (Tegin P)	1.0
Mineral oil (liquid paraffin WPM 24)	5.0
Stearic acid	1.5
Octyl methoxycinnamate (Parsol MCX)	2.7
Cetearyl alcohol (Lanette O)	0.4
Propylparaben	0.1
Phase 2	
Methylparaben	0.1
Triethanolamine	0.8
Glycerin (85%)	4.0
Carbomer (Carbopol 934P)	0.1
Water	84.3

Heat phases 1 and 2 to 75°C. Add phase 1 to 2 with stirring. Cool to 30°C. SPF = 4.0–4.4.

P2 High SPF Standard (CTFA/JCIA Standard):

Phase 1	
Lanolin	4.5
Cocoa butter	2.0
Glyceryl stearate, SE	3.0
Stearic acid	2.0
Octyl dimethyl PABA (Escalol 507)	7.0
Benzophenone-3 (Uvinul M40)	3.0
Phase 2	
Water	71.6
Sorbitol	5.0
Triethanolamine	1.0
Methylparaben	0.3
Propylparaben	0.1
Phase 3	
Benzyl alcohol	0.5

Melt Phase 1 and heat to 80–85°C. Heat phase 2 to 80–85°C. Add phase 1 to phase 2 with a homogenizer. Cool to 50°C and add phase 3. SPF = 11.5–13.9

P3 High SPF Standard (Bayer Standard C202/101):

Ingredients	*Percentage w/w*
Part 1	
Cetostearyl alcohol BP (and) PEG-40 castor oil (and) Sodium cetearyl sulfate	3.15
Note: As the source may affect the end product, this is Emulgade F (Henkel, INCI—cetearyl alcohol [and] PEG-40 castor oil [and] sodium cetearyl sulfate)	
Deceyl oleate	15.0
Octyl methoxycinnamate	3.0
Butyl methoxy dibenzoylmethane	0.5
Propyl hydroxybenzoate BP (INCI—propylparaben)	0.1
Part 2	
Water purified BP (INCI-water)	53.57
Phenylbenzimidazole sulfonic acid	2.78
Sodium hydroxide (45% solution) BP	0.9
Methyl hydroxybenzoate BP (INCI—methylparaben)	0.3
Disodium edetate BP (INCI—disodium EDTA)	0.1
Part 3	
Water purified BP	20.0
Carbomer	0.3
Note: As the grade of carbomer used may affect the end product, the grade equivalent to carbomer 934P should be used	
Sodium hydroxide (45% solution) BP	0.3

Procedure: Heat part 1 to 75–80°C. Heat part 2 to 80°C (if necessary boil until solution is clear and cool to 75–80°C). Add part 1 into part 2 while stirring part 2. Prepare part 3 by dispersing carbomer in water (by stirring with rotor/stator dispersator), then add sodium hydroxide for neutralization. Add part 3 to parts 1 and 2 while stirring and homogenize for about 3 min. Adjust pH to 7.8–8.0 with sodium hydroxide or lactic acid while stirring until cooled to room temperature.

The mean SPF $\pm$ 2 standard deviations should fall between 12.5 and 18.5. This product should be stored below 20°C and used within 1 year of preparation.

Japan

Japan uses the COLIPA P2 as a standard.

Australia

Australia has two reference standards for SPF.

1. Homosalate Reference Product:

Part A	
Wool fat BP	5.00
Homosalte	8.00
Paraffin soft white BP	2.50
Stearic acid	4.00
Propyl hydroxybenzoate BP	0.05
Part B	
Methyl hydroxybenzoate BP	0.10
Disodium edetate BP	0.05
Propylene glycol BP	5.00
Triethanolamine BP	1.00
Water purified BP	74.30

Procedure: Heat parts A and B separately to between 77°C and 82°C with constant stirring until the contents of the bath are solubilized. Add part A to part B while stirring. Cool down to room temperature. The mean SPF $\pm$ 2 standard deviations should fall between 4 and 5.

2. P3 Reference Standard:

This is identical to the COLIPA high SPF reference.

UV-A TESTS

USA

At the time of writing (October 1, 2003), the FDA had not issued proposed regulations for UV-A testing and claims. These are expected in the Spring of 2005 and will probably be finalized in 2006.

European Union

The EU has no COLIPA method or any recognized method. Companies are free to substantiate their UV-A protection claims by any published method. Popular method include the *in vitro* critical wavelength and the Boots Star System methods.

Japan

The first country approved, official method to define UV-A protection is the Japanese method, which came into effect on January 1, 1996. This method states that SPF is a worldwide recognized method to give consumers a general idea of protection against UV-B radiation. They have proposed another ratio called PFA (protection factor of UV-A). This is an *in vivo* test.

To develop PFA values, testing is performed on a minimum of 10 human subjects of skin types I, II, or IV (always burns easily, tans minimally; burns moderately, tans gradually; burns minimally, always tans well, respectively).

The standard is a cream with 5% avobenzone and 3% octinoxate. The light source is continuous spectra UV-A with a filter to prevent radiation below 320 nm. The radiation should be of a ratio similar to sunlight in the UV-A range. This ratio is 8–20% of UV-A II (320–340 nm) to UV-A I (340–400 nm).

There is a minimal persistent pigment darkening dose (MPPD), which is a slight darkening over the field of 0.5 cm^2, that persists or occurs within 2–4 h of exposure. This is read by at least two trained operators.

The PFA is defined as the ratio of the MPPD with protection over the MPPD without protection:

$$\text{PFA} = \frac{\text{MPPD protection}}{\text{MPPD without protection}}$$

The method to express this ratio is

2 to <4	PA +	Protection against UV-A
4 to <8	PA++	Considerable protection
8 or more	PA+++	Greatest protection

Labels will look like the following:

1. SPF 10 PA+

or

2. SPF 10 PA+

The UV-A test standard formulation is

Part A	
Water	57.13
Dipropylene glycol	5.00
Potassium hydroxide	0.12
Trisodium edetate	0.05
Phenoxyethanol	0.3

Part B	
Stearic acid	3.0
Glyceryl stearate, SE	3.0
Cetostearyl alcohol	5.0
Petrolatum	3.0
Glyceryl tri-2-ethylhexanoate	15.0
2-Ethylhexyl *p*-methoxycinnamate	3.0
4-*tert*-Buty-4′-methoxydibenzoylmethane	5.0
Ethylparaben	0.2
Methylparaben	0.2

Heat A and B to 70°C. Add B to A to emulsify.

Australia

Australia tests for UV-A protection using an *in vitro* method. The sunscreen is dissolved in a solvent mixture of dichloromethane, cyclohexane, and isopropanol. The transmission of the sample is run using a spectrophotometer from 320 to 360 nm. There must be at least 90% absorption to claim UV-A protection. If the sunscreen is not clear in the solvent, an alternative method using a thin film is used.

WATER RESISTANCE TESTS

The FDA has a published test and Australia Standards also has a method that is required to be used there.

USA

The Final Monograph changed the water resistance testing from the Tentative Final Monograph (TFM). The complete test can be found in the Final Monograph. In general, the sunscreen is applied and then the subjects are put into 23–32°C water in a pool, whirlpool, or Jacuzzi. There is then a 20 minutes immersion time with moderate activity followed by 20 minutes of rest (with no toweling of the site of application). Another 20 minutes of immersion with moderate activity is then followed by air drying and running of the SPF test. The SPF that is found can then be put on the label and the product labeled "water resistant". For the claim "very water resistant" the immersion is four times 20 minutes.

Australia

Australia permits two methods for determining water resistance. The mean protection factor of the sunscreen is determined after immersion of the test subject for not less than 40 minutes in either a swimming pool (method 1) or a spa bath (method 2).

Method 1—swimming pool immersion:

This is for an indoor pool at temperatures between 23°C and 28°C and a pH of 6.8–7.2. It should be protected from significant direct sunlight.

Procedure: The SPF is determined by the Australian method. The test subjects are engaged in moderate swimming activity for not less than 40 minutes according to this schedule:

Moderate swimming	20 minutes
Rest period (no toweling of test sites)	5 minutes
Moderate swimminutesg	20 minutes

The time claimed does not include the rest periods. When time to be claimed is >40 minutes, the schedule should consist of 20 minutes of activity followed by 5 minutes of rest. After the conclusion of the swimming, the subjects should dry themselves in the air for not less than 15 minutes. SPF is then run again.

Method 2—spa pool immersion:

The spa should be indoors and protected from direct sunlight and have a pH between 6.8 and 7.2. The temperature should be maintained at 33 ± 2°C. For every 20 minutes of immersion of test subjects, the water should be circulated for 16 minutes and the air agitated for 4 minutes. The time should be the same as for swimming pools, and the subjects should sit facing the center of the spa and sit so that the water jets do not impinge directly on the test sites.

Tested SPF after immersion	Maximum water resistance claimable
At least 2, but <4	Should not be claimed
At least 4, but <8	40 minutes
At least 8, but <15	80 minutes
At least 15, but <20	2 hours
At least 20, but <25	3 hours
>25	4 hours

THE LABELING OF SUNSCREENS

It is critical to understand that *no dual labeling* of sunscreens is permitted in the four major markets. The USA and Australia treat sunscreens as drugs while Japan and the EU consider them as cosmetics. You cannot label a product a drug and also label it as a cosmetic for a different market. So you may have the same formulation, but you must use separate labels.

USA

The labeling of sunscreens in the USA includes front and back panel labels, permitted and prohibited claims, and correct nomenclature.

Front panel

You are required to identify the product as a sunscreen and also state the SPF. The maximum SPF permitted is 30+.

You may list Product Performance Statements with these categories or descriptions:

SPF 2 to under 12 (minimal or minimum sunburn protection)
SPF 12 to under 30 (moderate sunburn protection)
SPF 30 or above (high sunburn protection)

You are required to have the net contents on the front in the lower 30% of the label.

The following claims are prohibited:

Shields from the sun
Blocks out the rays of the sun
Prevents or protects against freckling
Prevents or protects against wrinkling
Prevents or protects against redness or uneven coloring of the skin
Protects against UV-A/UV-B
Shields against specific factors that accelerate the signs of skin aging
Protects against premature aging, skin aging, skin lesions, and skin cancer (with or without stating "due to the sun" in the labeling of the product)
PABA-free
Sunblock
Natural
Chemical-free
Nonchemical
Extended wear
All-day protection
IR radiation protection claims

You may say: "aminobenzoic acid (PABA)-free". You may claim on the front label "Water resistant" or "Very water resistant" if your product passes the FDA tests.

Back panel

You are required to have a "Drug Facts" panel.

Example:

Drug Facts	
Active Ingredients	***Purpose***
Avobenzone 3.0%	Sunscreen
Octinoxate 5.2%	"
Octisalate 2.0%	"
Oxybenzone 2.8%	"
Uses • helps prevent sunburn • higher SPF gives more sun protection • retains SPF after 40 minutes of activity in water	
Warnings For external use only	
When using this product keep out of eyes. Rinse with water to remove	
Stop use and ask a doctor if rash or irritation develops and lasts	
Keep out of reach of children, if swallowed, get medical help or contact a Poison Control Center right away	
Directions • apply generously 30 minutes before sun exposure and as needed • children under 6 months of age: ask a doctor • reapply as needed or after towel drying, swimming or sweating	
Other information Sun alert: Limiting sun exposure, wearing protective clothing, and using sunscreen may reduce the risk of skin aging, skin cancer, and other harmful effects of the sun	
Inactive ingredients Water, Diethylhexyl Naphthalate, Glycerin, Polyglyceryl-3 Methyl Glucose Distearate, Butylene Glycol, Isopropyl Myristate, C30-38 Olefin/Isopropyl Maleate/MA Copolymer, Stearyl Alcohol, Disodium EDTA, Carbomer, Triethanolamine, Phenoxyethanol, Methylparaben, Ethylparaben, Propylparaben Butylpararben, Isobutylparaben	
Questions? 1-800-123-4567 between 9 am and 5 pm EST	

For information on Drug Facts labeling go to http://www.fda.gov/cder/Offices/OTC/drugFacts.htm

or contact Hirschhorn & Young Graphics (1-212-246-4695) for their book *Simplified FDA OTC Label Requirements Guidelines*.

Sunscreens must list their active ingredients using drug names followed by the percentage in the formulation. The only permitted purpose is sunscreen. Under

"Uses" you are required to say "Helps prevent sunburn" or "Higher SPF gives more sunburn protection". Optionally, if you pass the water resistant (or very water resistant) test, you can say, "Retains SPF after 40 (80) minutes of activity in the water". Finally you may list the Product Performance Statements mentioned earlier.

Required warnings and directions are spelled out in the Final Monograph. Under other information you may state, using these exact words: "Sun alert: limiting sun exposure, wearing protective clothing, and using sunscreens may reduce the risks of skin aging, skin cancer, and other harmful effects of the sun".

Inactive ingredients must be listed using INCI nomenclature in descending order of predominance to 1%, provided you make cosmetic claims on the front label. If you make no cosmetic claims whatsoever, you must list the inactive ingredients by their drug name in alphabetical order. If the ingredient does not have a recognized drug name, it is advisable to make some cosmetic claim and follow the cosmetic labeling described earlier.

All sunscreens must have Drug Facts labels no later than May 16, 2005. Sunscreens placed on the market after January 1, 2002, also should have Drug Facts labels. Products on the market before this date and that make a UVA protection claim are not required to have Drug Facts labels until the FDA announces it is required.

There are also a special exemption and special label requirements for products applied to a small area of the face such as lipsticks.

European Union

As sunscreens are regulated as cosmetics the labeling rules follow their cosmetic regulations. You must have an address in the EU on your label. You must have an ingredient declaration using INCI names in descending order of predominance—note there are no "active" ingredients in cosmetics, nor can you state percentages. Finally, you must substantiate all claims. So SPF, UV-A, or water-resistant claims require proof in your Product Information Package.

Australia

Australia requires the listing of the actives using AAN and the maximum concentration present. They also require listing of the preservatives used and their percentages.

You must give your TGA approval number listing it like this: AUST L (insert number). Other required information includes storage conditions, expiration date (which is required for all products regardless of stability testing), batch number, the name and address of the marketer of the product, and the SPF.

Optional claims permitted are "Broad spectrum", providing the SPF is at least 15 and you pass the Australian UV-A test; you are allowed to claim water resistance up to 4 h providing you pass the Australian water resistant test.

For products with an SPF of 30+ you may claim "May assist in preventing some skin cancers" or "Reduces the risk of some skin cancers". You will also need to include "The need for avoidance of prolonged exposure to the sun", and "The importance of wearing protective clothing, hats, and eyewear".

You may make reference to protection against sun induced skin aging.

Japan

Besides the listing of UV-A claims as stated in the UV-A section, Japan requires all cosmetics to now have complete ingredient disclosure in descending order of predominance in Japanese symbols.

MANUFACTURE OF SUNSCREENS

Regardless of country, sunscreens must be produced under current cGMPs. In the USA these can be found in 21 CFR Sections 210 and 211. The major requirements are listed below:

1. *Quality unit*: Quality control and quality assurance must be independent of production. Approval or rejections of all procedures, raw materials, packaging, labeling, and in-process materials of drug products must not be decided by anyone reporting to production. If the product is produced outside your facility (contract manufacturer), you must have independent QC supervision. All responsibilities and procedures must be in writing.
2. *Personnel*: All personnel must be qualified by education and experience to comply with cGMPs. There must be adequate supervision and training in cGMPs, skills, and Standard Operating Procedures (SOPs), and there must be documentation of this training and effectiveness.
3. *Facilities and utilities*: The design and construction of the facilities must be such that they ensure cGMP compliance. There must be adequate space to prevent mix-ups and contaminations. Housekeeping must be adequate with written procedures and adequate training. Special areas of concern include heating, ventilation and air conditioning, dust control, and microbiological control.
4. *Equipment*: The equipment must be qualified for its intended use. Written documentation of maintenance, calibration, and cleaning and change procedures is needed. Cleaning procedures must be validated and monitored.
5. *Control of materials*: You should have specifications, vendor qualifications, incoming controls, QC release, shelf life, storage, and dispensing controls.
6. *Water*: You need specifications, a validated system, and monitoring procedures.
7. *Master production and control records*: These must be approved by the Quality unit and must have adequate specificity of materials,

equipment, formulation, process steps, and parameters to ensure a reproducible product.

8. *Packaging and labeling controls*: This is a major FDA inspection concern. How do you prevent label mix-ups?
9. *Investigations*: How to handle deviations, out of specifications, and corrective actions.
10. *Prevention of contamination*: Raw material qualifications, QC of incoming materials, storage of materials, personnel controls such as hygiene, clothing, and practices, process controls, equipment cleaning and verification, cleaning validation, facility design, environmental controls, and housekeeping.
11. *Laboratory controls*: Specifications, sampling and testing procedures, method validation, reference standards, instrument maintenance and calibration, record keeping, and stability program.

The FDA does not require SPF be run on each batch. What is required is the analysis of the actives for the level that was used to determine the SPF. The amount of each filter must be $100 \pm 5\%$ of the original amount. This is the same criterion as that for determining expiration dating. If your formulation is stable for 3 years and the actives are present again at the $100 \pm 5\%$ level, you are not required to have an expiration date. If you use accelerated stability testing for this, you should periodically compare this with real time retained samples.

12

Sunscreen Products: The Role of the US Pharmacopeia

Lawrence Evans III

United States Pharmacopeia, Rockville, Maryland, USA

INTRODUCTION

A major function of the United States Pharmacopeia (USP) is the development of monographs containing public standards for articles such as prescription/nonprescription drugs, dietary supplements, and excipients. These standards help to ensure that the public receives quality medicines and supplements.

Since 1972, the Food and Drug Administration (FDA) has made a concerted effort to develop regulations for over-the-counter (OTC) drug products. On May 21, 1999, their efforts came to fruition for OTC sunscreen products with the publication of the final rule (1) (21 CFR 352.10). Often referred to as the final monograph for sunscreens, it should not be confused with a *USP* monograph. The regulation lists the active ingredients allowed in sunscreen products and describes test specifications and label requirements. As part of the final rule, FDA required that each active ingredient have a *USP* monograph.

Below is the list of sunscreen active ingredients (former titles in parentheses) included in part 352.10 of the final rule.

a. Aminobenzoic acid
b. Avobenzone
c. Cinoxate
d. [Reserved]
e. Dioxybenzone
f. Ensulizole (phenylbenzimidazole sulfonic acid)
g. Homosalate
h. [Reserved]
i. Meradimate (menthyl anthranilate)
j. Octinoxate (octyl methoxycinnamate)
k. Octisalate (octyl salicylate)
l. Octocrylene
m. Oxybenzone
n. Padimate-O
o. Sulisobenzone
p. Titantium dioxide
q. Trolamine salicylate
r. Zinc oxide.

Two positions are labeled "Reserved" for the possible addition of diethanolamine methoxycinnamate and Lawsone with dihydroxyacetone, the inclusion of which depends solely on the development of *USP* monographs.

This chapter describes the role of USP in the regulation of sunscreens, beginning with the mission of USP, followed by a historical look at the organization and ending with a review of *USP* monographs for the sunscreen active ingredients. Each of these topics will be discussed to show how USP works to provide public standards for sunscreen active ingredients. This information is also broadly applicable to drug substances and products for various therapeutic categories.

THE US PHARMACOPEIA

Mission

The mission of the USP is "to promote the public health and benefit practitioners and patients by disseminating authoritative standards and information developed by its volunteers for medicines, other health care technologies, and related practices used to maintain and improve health and promote optimal health care quality" (2).

History

The US Pharmacopeial Convention is the only major nongovernment pharmacopeia in the world. It evolved from a group of 11 physicians who met in 1820 to lay the foundation for the first *United States Pharmacopeia*, a compendium of 217 "well-established drugs" (3). Beginning in 1880, the pharmacopeia was transformed from a book of recipes to one containing product standards (4). At that time, USP published the pharmacopeia in 10-year intervals until 1942, after which the organization switched to 5-year intervals. In 1975, USP acquired the *National Formulary* and began publishing it with the *USP* as a single unit titled the *United States Pharmacopeia and National Formulary* (*USP–NF*) (5). In 2002, USP reached another milestone by making *USP–NF* an annual publication.

Legal Recognition

Federal laws recognize the *USP* and *NF* as official compendia of the USA. Early acknowledgment was given in the Drug Import Act of 1848, when federal legislation recognized the *USP* as an official compendia (6). Both the 1906 Federal Food & Drugs Act and the 1938 Federal Food, Drug, and Cosmetic Act (FD&C Act) mention *USP* and *NF* strength, quality, and purity as enforceable standards (7,8). The FD&C Act uses the term "official compendium" in reference to the official *USP* and the official *NF* and their Supplements. Also, the FD&C Act made compliance with *USP* and *NF* compendial standards enforceable by FDA under its adulteration and misbranding provisions. In order for a drug not be declared adulterated and misbranded, it must conform to all of the requirements of its monograph and other relevant portions of the compendia. Any variations in strength, quality, or purity must be stated on the article's label (8).

United States Pharmacopeia and National Formulary

USP–NF are the largest and most comprehensive compendia in the world. Comprising more than 3800 drug substance, drug product, dietary supplement, and excipient monographs, *USP–NF* is organized into two primary sections, *USP* and *NF*, each of which has similar subsections. *USP* is subdivided into seven subsections:

- Front Matter (mission, preface, people, admissions, and a commentary)
- General Notices
- Monographs
- General Chapters
- Reagents, Indicators, and Solutions
- Tables
- Dietary Supplement Monographs.

The front matter of *USP* includes the organization's mission statement and the preface, which briefly gives the history and rules and procedures of the not-for-profit organization. Also found in this section are lists of the people involved (e.g., Expert Committee members, USP staff), admissions to *USP–NF*, and a commentary section. The admissions sections lists official title changes, revisions appearing in the current edition not included in the previous edition, articles that appeared in the previous edition but were not included in the current edition, and articles admitted by Supplement. Supplements represent additional means of publishing revisions to the *USP–NF* between its annual editions. The commentary section includes responses to public comments and proposals.

The General Notices and Requirements section contains summaries of the basic information regarding the interpretation and application of the standards; tests, procedures, and acceptance criteria; and other requirements in the *USP–NF*. When specific information is not given in a monograph, the requirements set forth in the General Notices are applied. Exceptions to the general notices and chapters are noted in the individual monograph and are given precedence.

Monographs make up the bulk of *USP*. Each monograph consists of the specification plus additional information for an official article, that is, a substance or preparation that can meet public standards for strength, quality, and purity. A typical monograph consists of the official title, descriptive information, definition, packaging and storage instructions, labeling instructions, reference standards information, and the monograph's specification, which includes the monograph tests, procedures, and acceptance criteria.

General Chapters help reduce duplication of text by creating standard procedures and sometimes acceptance criteria applicable to a broad number of monographs and other general chapters. They can be broadly classified as either General Tests and Assays or General Information. The two can be distinguished by their assigned chapter number: General Tests and Assays are numbered below 1000 (e.g., ⟨831⟩ *Refractive Index*). General Information Chapters are numbered above 1000 (e.g., ⟨1225⟩ *Validation of Compendial Methods*). The latter are interpretive documents that are not required in conformity testing, although they can become so if they (or a part of them) are referenced in a monograph and/or they are adopted by reference in law or regulation.

They can also become mandatory if a manufacturer or compounding professional includes them in internal product or process standards.

The reagents, indicators, and solutions section includes general tests for reagents, reagent specifications, indicators required in monograph procedures, and descriptions of test, buffer, colorimetric, and volumetric solutions. The Tables section contains a number of reference tables provided as supplemental information such as container specifications for dispensing capsules and tablets, description and solubility information, and standard atomic weights as recommended by the International Union of Pure and Applied Chemistry.

The final section of the *USP* is dedicated to dietary supplement monographs. Dietary supplement ingredient and product monographs follow the same format as drug substance and product monographs.

The *NF* contains sections essentially identical to *USP* without the Dietary Supplements section. Several sections of *NF*, such as the front matter, most General Chapters, and the reagents sections, reference those of *USP* in order to avoid duplication. The primary difference between *USP* and *NF* is the scope of these monographs. The *NF* contains monographs for excipients. A minority of these articles can also be drug substances and are cross-referenced to the *USP*.

USP Reference Standards

A reference standard is a highly characterized chemical that is suitable for use in performing the test procedures that appear in *USP–NF*. They are used to test compliance/noncompliance with monograph requirements. USP reference standards are developed through a collaborative effort involving USP, FDA, and industry and/or academic laboratories. To guarantee integrity, the process involves extensive testing by multiple groups, a rigorous approval process conducted by the USP Reference Standards Committee, appropriate packaging, and fulfillment of numerous quality control requirements prior to release for distribution (7).

Standards-Setting Body

The standards-setting body of USP is the Council of Experts, consisting of 62 Expert Committee chairs who are elected at the USP quinquennial Convention (2) from a pool of candidates developed by the Convention's Nominating Committee. After the primary election, a further election occurs to populate each Expert Committee with its members. Taken together, the Council of Experts and its Expert Committees comprise approximately 650 volunteers who set the standards in the *USP–NF* and also contribute value-added information for the *USP-DI*. The Expert Committees are organized into divisions, each of which has its own Executive Committee with responsibilities that differ from those of the Council's Executive Committee (2).

Monograph Development and Revision Process

Overview

The development of new monographs and revision of existing monographs are exceptional processes that involve public comment and interaction between USP and stakeholders. USP's bimonthly journal of standards development and official compendial revision, *Pharmacopeial Forum* (*PF*), is the vehicle for public review and comment. Manufacturers and interested parties voluntarily submit proposals to USP for consideration by the appropriate Expert Committee for review, after which the Committee approves the proposals for publication in *PF*. If there are no adverse comments, the proposal becomes official in *USP–NF*. If there are significant comments requiring revision of the proposal, republication in *PF* is necessary. The process is a dynamic one that is governed by an unbiased set of procedures developed to establish public standards.

Contributors

There are several contributors to the revision process, but the one constant is the USP staff liaison in the Information and Standards Department at USP. Each liaison is responsible for one or more Expert Committees. As the title implies, liaisons serve as an interface for industry, government, the Expert Committees, and other pharmacopeias (Fig. 12.1). Liaisons also are technical experts for the numerous monographs for which they are responsible. Other contributors to the revision process include stakeholders, FDA, and the public. Manufacturers, contract laboratories, and trade organizations primarily make up the stakeholders group and initiate the majority of the requests for revision submitted to USP. At each of its centers, FDA has a person responsible for interactions with USP.

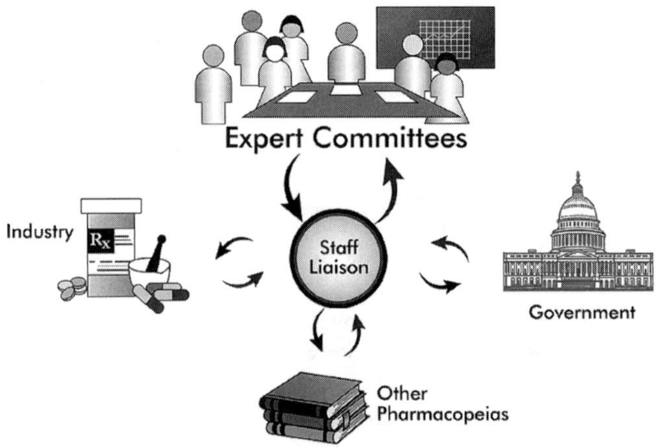

Figure 12.1 Contributors to the USP standard setting process.

The Center for Drug Evaluation and Research and Development is the only center with a compendial staff that reviews proposals published in *PF* and submits comments that reflect the views of the agency.

Revision Process

The procedures that govern the review process are depicted in the flow chart in Fig. 12.2. The process is initiated upon receipt of a proposal to develop a new monograph or revise an existing monograph. Prior to forwarding it to the Expert Committee, the USP staff liaison reviews the submitted proposal to ensure it is technically sound, includes all pertinent supporting information (e.g., validation data), and is formatted in *USP–NF* style. Review of most of the active sunscreen ingredient monographs falls under the responsibility of the Pharmaceutical Analysis 6 (PA6) Expert Committee.

Once the Expert Committee concludes that the request for revision is acceptable, approval is given to publish it in *PF* for public review and comment. Significant comments are forwarded by the USP liaison to the Expert Committee for review. If the Expert Committee concludes that the comments are not significant and no additional revisions are required, the proposal becomes official and is published in either an *Interim Revision Announcement*, a *Supplement* to the *USP–NF*, or the *USP–NF*. If the Expert Committee concludes the comments are significant, a revised proposal is published in *PF*, including comments and response.

Guideline for Submitting Revisions

USP has available for complimentary download from its website (www.usp.org) the *Guideline for Submitting Requests for Revision to the USP–NF*. The purpose of the Guideline is to provide interested parties with a tool to help draft optimal submissions and reduce delays in the process. The Guideline comprises an introduction, glossary, addenda, and chapters describing the requirements for drug substance and product monographs.

The Guideline outlines the procedures involved in the development of a new monograph as well as the information to assist sponsors in submitting the needed information. In an effort to make the process paperless, USP invites interested parties to submit revision proposals electronically. In addition, an overview of the Guideline's organization is given to help navigate users through the document. Arguably one of the most useful features of the Guideline is its glossary. In an era when nomenclature varies globally and terms such as *test*, *procedure*, and *method* sometimes are all used interchangeably in the same context, USP works to promote consistency in nomenclature as a means of facilitating communication.

Chapters 1–4 are core elements of the Guideline. Information needed to submit revision proposals for noncomplex actives, which include drug substance and products, biological/biotechnological-derived substances, excipients, and vaccines, is given. Each chapter describes the requirements such as name,

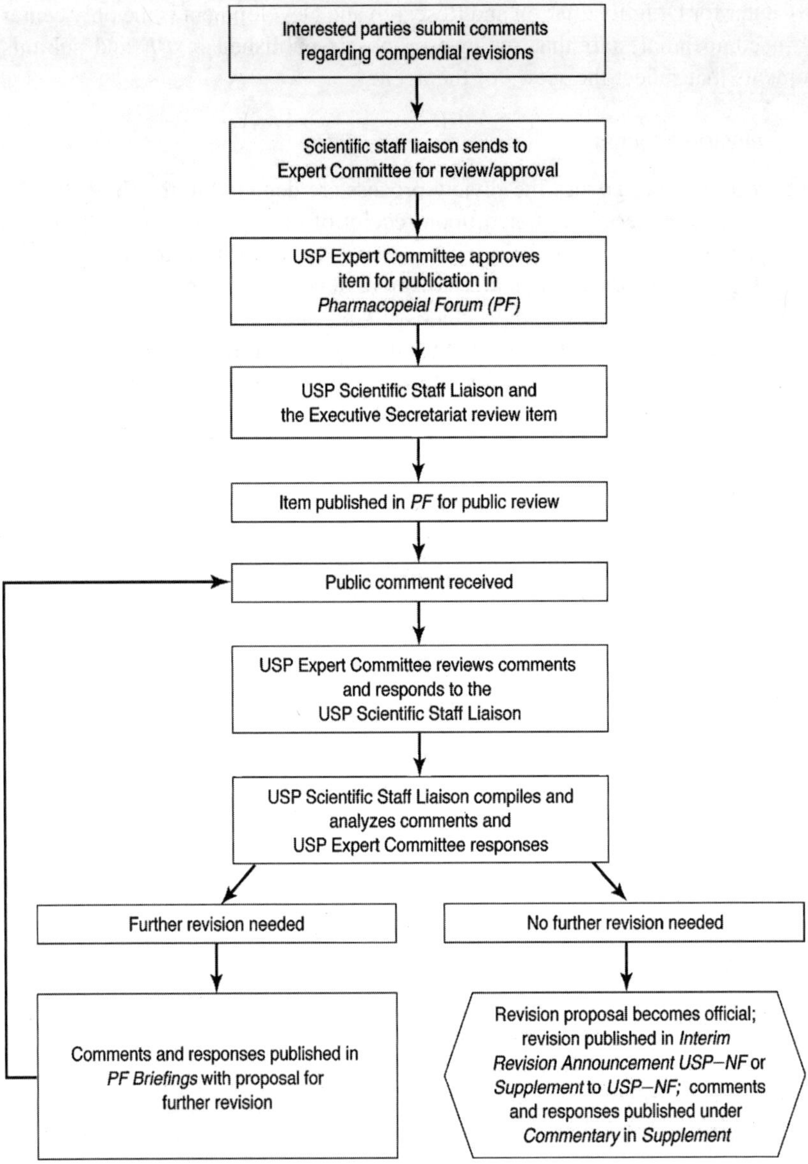

Figure 12.2 Public review and comment process for standards development [from Ref. (2)].

assay, test for impurities, identification of active moiety when applicable, and a host of other requirements for each of the types of monographs mentioned. For active ingredients used in sunscreen products, the requirements to revise this class of actives are found in chapter one, Noncomplex Actives.

The Addenda section of the Guideline consists of templates for drug substance, tablets, capsules, and excipient monographs. These models are designed to help a sponsor in drafting monograph proposals into *USP–NF* format and are supplemental to the validation data supplied with a revision proposal. USP's intent with the Guideline is to provide another tool to increase the efficiency of the revision process.

Pharmacopeial Forum

As mentioned earlier, *PF* is the vehicle for public review and comment. Each issue of *PF* routinely includes sections that describe policies, give information on reference standards, and list cancelled proposals, to name a few. Three sections of special interest are Previews, In-Process Revision, and *Interim Revision Announcements* (*IRAs*). New monographs and revisions to existing monographs can appear in any of these sections. However, each section represents a different stage in the process of becoming official. Generally, there is a 60-day public comment period for items published as In-Process Revision. Parties who are unable to provide comments prior to this deadline can submit an "Intent to Comment Form" that gives an intended date by which comments will be submitted. Items appearing in Previews are not scheduled to become official and may or may not advance to In-Process Revision status. Examples of items often published in this section are:

- Proposed new monographs of articles that are available from multiple sources
- Controversial items requiring an extended public comment period
- Items at an early stage of consideration, such as new technology.

USP plans to begin including a comment date in Preview proposals. Proposals appearing as In-Process Revision are items scheduled for official implementation. This usually includes proposals to revise new and existing monograph specifications or proposals that have graduated from the Previews section. Interim Revision Announcements are a mechanism to make revisions official between Supplements to *USP–NF*. Published in *PF* with official dates of implementation, they are the only items in this publication that are official. Thus *PF* is a valuable source of immediate and future revisions relevant to industry, regulatory agencies, and the public.

USP MONOGRAPHS FOR SUNSCREEN ACTIVE INGREDIENTS

In the tentative final monograph for OTC sunscreen products published in the *Federal Register* in May 1993, FDA proposed 20 Category I (generally recognized as safe and effective) ingredients for use in OTC sunscreen drug products, of which several did not have *USP* monographs (10). A year later, FDA published a proposal to amend the tentative final monograph to include only the 15 active ingredients for which *USP* monographs existed or for which there was an expressed interest in developing *USP* monographs (11). To achieve this goal, FDA encouraged the Nonprescription Drug Manufacturers and the Cosmetic, Toiletry, and Fragrance Associations to work with USP to develop monographs for these ingredients. Nine ingredients were chosen by the associations as materials of interest for *USP* monographs. No interest was expressed for the five remaining ingredients (digalloyl trioleate, ethyl 4-[bis(hydroxypropyl)] aminobenzoate, glyceryl aminobenzoate, lawsone with dihydroxyacetone, and red petrolatum), and they were deleted from the tentative monograph (11). Avobenzone and zinc oxide were later added to the list of active ingredients by means of separate amendments (12,13). A *USP* monograph had already been established for zinc oxide. Since the publication of the final monograph, cinoxate was removed from *USP 26–NF 21* and is the lone active ingredient on the list without a *USP* monograph (2).

In addition to the ingredients listed in 21 CFR 352.10, *USP–NF* contains product monographs (e.g., aminobenzoic acid gel) that incorporate some of these ingredients (2). There are also monographs in *USP–NF* for ingredients not identified in 352.10 but which are used in sunscreen products outside the USA (e.g., dihydroxyacetone).

USP Monographs for Active Ingredients Identified in 21 CFR 352.10

A *USP* monograph for a sunscreen substance follows a standard format. The definition of the substance appears under the name, followed by universal and specific tests as needed. According to the Guideline, USP has adopted the International Conference on Harmonisation (ICH) approach, which requires four universal tests and additional specific tests depending on the article. The universal tests are Description, Identification, Assays, and Impurities Test. In current *USP* monographs, impurities are generally handled by either the test for Related Substances or Chromatographic Purity. In the Description and Solubility section of *USP–NF*, some of the active sunscreen ingredients are described as liquids and oils. Several others are described as powders, but only the monographs for avobenzone and aminobenzoic acid have a melting point specification. Homosalate, meradimate, octocrylene, octinoxate, octisalate, padimate O, and trolamine salicylate are liquids and oils that have a refractive index specification. With the exception of sulisobenzone, all other ingredients described as powders have either a loss on drying or loss on ignition test.

Most of the monographs for ingredients identified in 21 CFR 352.10 have two identification test procedures, infrared (IR) absorption and ultraviolet (UV) absorption. The monographs for octocrylene, sulisobenzone, and trolamine salicylate have only the UV identification requirement, and homosalate requires only an IR procedure. The monographs for zinc oxide and titanium dioxide incorporate chemical procedures.

The majority of the Assay test procedures for sunscreen active ingredients are either titration or gas chromatography (GC). Although the monographs for dioxybenzone and oxybenzone have UV assays, trolamine salicylate is the only ingredient with a liquid chromatography assay procedure. Most ingredient monographs with a chromatographic assay procedure also have a Chromatographic Purity test. In addition to these tests, additional test requirements can be found in the individual monographs.

Since their introduction into *USP–NF*, most of the sunscreen active ingredient monographs have undergone little, if any, revision. Even fewer revisions have occurred in the *USP* monographs of those ingredients that preceded the final sunscreen monograph (e.g., zinc oxide). The most notable revision came in the form of a name change for six ingredients. The revision, which had an adoption date of September 1, 2002 (18 months after the official publication date), included ingredients listed and not listed in 21 CFR 352.10. The United States Adopted Names (USAN) Council proposed simpler and more convenient chemical names relative to those provided in the original proposals submitted to USP. It is the policy of the USP Nomenclature and Labeling Expert Committee to adopt such USAN names when available for the titles of *USP* monographs. The names (former name in parenthesis) of the ingredients that changed were amiloxate (isoamyl methoxycinnamate); ensulizole (phenylbenzimidazole sulfonic acid); enzacamene (methyl benzylidene camphor); meradimate (menthyl anthranilate); octinoxate (octyl methoxycinnamate); and octisalate (octyl salicylate) (14).

Octocrylene, octisalate, and octinoxate are the only ingredients listed in 21 CFR 352.10 for which monograph revisions have been made in recent years. A significant revision to the octocrylene monograph was the addition of a Chromatographic Purity test for individual and total impurities (15). A revision to Identification Test A was also included in the revision proposal. A subsequent proposal to increase the individual impurity limit was published and was based on the typical impurity level found in material in commerce (16). The monograph for octisalate underwent similar revisions: Identification Test A was revised and a test for Chromatographic Purity was introduced, later followed by a revision to lessen the overly restrictive individual and total impurities limits that had been previously enacted (17,18).

USP Monographs for Ingredients not Identified in 21 CFR 352.10

Amiloxate, enzacamene, and dihydroxyacetone are active sunscreen ingredients not included in 21 CFR 352.10 but which have *USP* monographs. The monographs of each are very similar to those included in 21 CFR 352.10. Two identification tests are given for each, including IR tests. The dihydroxyacetone monograph uses thin-layer chromatography (TLC) as the second identification test, whereas UV is the second identification test in the amiloxate and enzacamene monographs. GC is the technique of choice for assay in the amiloxate and enzacamene monographs, but a conventional titration is used for dihydroxyacetone. TLC is used to determine impurities present in dihydroxyacetone, whereas a GC procedure is employed in the amiloxate and enzacamene monographs.

Aside from the nomenclature revisions, there have been no other revisions to any of the three monographs mentioned in this section, probably because they are not included in 21 CFR 352.10. This is likely to change because FDA has made both amiloxate and enzacamene eligible for consideration based on information provided in their respective Time and Extent Applications (TEAs) (19).

CONCLUSION

The objective of this chapter was to discuss the role of USP in helping to assure the quality of sunscreen ingredients. The final FDA OTC sunscreen monograph, the adjustment in names by USAN, and continuous improvement from USP's Council of Experts in sunscreen monographs offer a good example of positive stakeholder interactions to make available valuable products for consumers, patients, and practitioners. The combined approach conserves manufacturer and regulator resources. It fulfills the general purpose of USP's two official compendia extending back in time almost 200 years. The role of the USP will continue to expand as the number of active ingredients added to 21 CFR 352.10 continues to increase.

APPENDIX

Octinoxate Monograph (From Ref. 2)

Former title: Octyl Methoxycinnamate

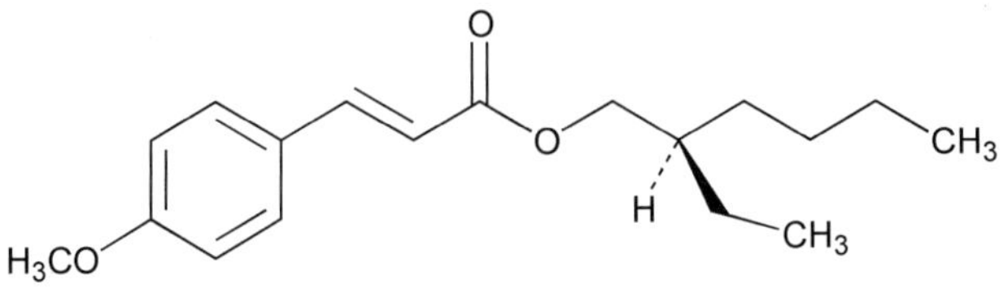

$C_{18}H_{26}O_3$ 290.40
2-Ethylhexyl 3-(4-methoxyphenyl)-2-propenoate.
2-Propenoic acid, 3-(4-methoxyphenyl)-, 2-ethylhexyl ester. [*5466-77-3*].

Octinoxate contains not less than 95.0 percent and not more than 105.0 percent of $C_{18}H_{26}O_3$, calculated on the as-is basis.

Packaging and storage—Preserve in tight containers, in a cool place.
USP Reference standards ⟨11⟩—*USP Octinoxate RS.*

Identification—

A: *Infrared Absorption* ⟨197F⟩.
B: *Ultraviolet Absorption* ⟨197U⟩—
Solution: 5 μg per mL.
Medium: alcohol.

Specific gravity ⟨841⟩: between 1.005 and 1.013.
Refractive index ⟨831⟩: between 1.542 and 1.548.

Acidity—Transfer 5 mL of Octinoxate to a suitable container, add 50 mL of alcohol, and mix. Add 4 drops of phenolphthalein TS, and titrate with 0.1 N sodium hydroxide: not more than 0.8 mL is consumed.

Chromatographic purity—

System suitability solution—Prepare a solution of benzyl benzoate and USP Octinoxate RS in acetone containing about 50 mg of each per mL.

Test solution—Transfer about 5 mL of Octinoxate to a 100-mL volumetric flask, dilute with acetone to volume, and mix.

Chromatographic system (see *Chromatography* ⟨621⟩)—Proceed as directed in the *Assay*, but chromatograph the *System suitability solution.*

Procedure—Inject a volume (about 1 μL) of the *Test solution* into the chromatograph, record the chromatogram, and measure the responses for all the peaks. Calculate the percentage of each impurity in the portion of Octinoxate taken by the formula:

$$100(r_i/r_s),$$

in which r_i is the peak response for each impurity; and r_s is the sum of the responses for all the peaks: not more than 0.5% of any individual impurity is found; and not more than 2.0% of total impurities is found.

Assay—

Internal standard solution—Transfer about 25 mL of benzyl benzoate to a 500-mL volumetric flask, dilute with acetone to volume, and mix.

Standard preparation—Dilute an accurately measured quantity of *USP Octinoxate RS* quantitatively, and stepwise if necessary, with *Internal standard solution* to obtain a solution having a known concentration of about 50 mg per mL.

Assay preparation—Transfer about 5 mL of Octinoxate, accurately measured, to a 100-mL volumetric flask, dilute with *Internal standard solution* to volume, and mix.

Chromatographic system (see *Chromatography* ⟨621⟩)—The gas chromatograph is equipped with a flame-ionization detector and a 0.32-mm × 25-m column that contains coating G1. The carrier gas is helium, flowing at a rate of about 2 mL per minute. The chromatograph is programmed as follows. Initially the temperature of the column is equilibrated at 80°, then the temperature is increased to 300° over a period of 10 minutes, and maintained at 300° for 10 minutes. The injection port temperature is maintained at 250°, and the detector is maintained at 300°. Chromatograph the *Standard preparation*, and record the peak responses as directed for *Procedure*: the relative retention times are about 0.68 for benzyl benzoate and 1.0 for octinoxate; the resolution, *R*, between benzyl benzoate and octinoxate is not less than 20; the column efficiency is not less than 65,000 theoretical plates; and the relative standard deviation for replicate injections is not more than 2.0%.

Procedure—Separately inject equal volumes (about 1 µL) of the *Standard preparation* and the *Assay preparation* into the chromatograph, record the chromatograms, and measure the responses for the major peaks. Calculate the quantity, in mg, of $C_{18}H_{26}O_3$ in the portion of Octinoxate taken by the formula:

$$100C(R_u/R_s),$$

in which C is the concentration, in mg per mL, of *USP Octinoxate RS* in the *Standard preparation*; and R_u and R_s are the peak response ratios of octinoxate to benzyl benzoate obtained from the *Assay preparation* and the *Standard preparation*, respectively.

REFERENCES

1. Office of the Federal Register, Federal Register, 64(98), Rules and Regulations, 1999: 27666–27693.
2. The United States Pharmacopeia, 26th rev. and The National Formulary, 21st ed. Rockville, MD: The United States Pharmacopeia Convention, 2003.
3. The United States Pharmacopeia, 1st rev. The United States Pharmacopeia Convention, 1820.
4. The United States Pharmacopeia, 6th rev. The United States Pharmacopeia Convention, 1880.
5. The United States Pharmacopeia, 20th rev. and The National Formulary, 15th ed. Rockville, MD: The United States Pharmacopeia Convention, 1980.
6. Drug Import Act of 1848, 9 Stat., 1848.
7. Federal Food & Drugs Act of 1906, Public Law 59-384, 34 Stat. 768, 1906.

8. Federal Food, Drug & Cosmetic Act of 1938, Public Law 75-717. 52 Stat. 1040, 1938.
9. USP: People, Programs, Policies, and Procedures, 2000–2005. Rockville, MD: The United States Pharmacopeia Convention, 2002.
10. Office of the Federal Register, Federal Register, 58(90), Proposed Rules, 1993: 28194–28296.
11. Office of the Federal Register, Federal Register, 59(109), Proposed Rules, 1994: 29706–29707.
12. Office of the Federal Register, Federal Register, 61(180), Proposed Rules, 1996: 48645–48655.
13. Office of the Federal Register, Federal Register, 63(204), Proposed Rules, 1998: 56584–56589.
14. Pharmacopeial Forum 2000; 26(3).
15. Pharmacopeial Forum 2001; 27(5):3028.
16. Pharmacopeial Forum 2002; 28(4):1170.
17. Pharmacopeial Forum 2001; 27(5):3027–3028.
18. Pharmacopeial Forum 2002; 28(5):1420.
19. Office of the Federal Register, Federal Register, 68(133), Notices, 2003: 41386–41387.

Ultraviolet Filters

13

The Chemistry of Ultraviolet Filters

Nadim A. Shaath
Alpha Research & Development, Ltd., White Plains, New York, USA

INTRODUCTION

The recent evidence linking ultraviolet-A (UV-A) rays to serious damage beyond the fashionable and sought-after tan is daunting (1). These and other important findings have prompted the cosmetic industry to create new sunscreen products that would afford the consumers more efficient protection. Since the cosmetic industry began formulating a myriad of new sunscreen active agents into an array of functional products, it has become necessary for the cosmetic chemist to know more about the chemical structure and reactivity of UV filters and their potential interaction with other ingredients in the sun care cosmetic formulations.

This chapter first reviews the electromagnetic spectrum and the ultraviolet rays responsible for most of the skin damage and its associated disease and discomfort. The UV filters are then classified according to their structure–activity relationship and the attributes of each are highlighted. The mechanism of sunscreen action is presented and the effect emollients have on the functionality of sun care formulations is discussed. Finally, the features of the UV filters of the future are outlined.

THE ELECTROMAGNETIC SPECTRUM

Human skin and hair are constantly subjected to solar radiation (2). The radiation emitted by the sun is of an electromagnetic character and differs from other forms of electromagnetic radiant energy in its spectrum, as described by its energy (E), wavelength (λ), or the frequency (ν). Electromagnetic radiation is energy governed by the following relationship:

$$E = h\nu$$

where E = energy (ergs), h = Planck's constant = 6.62×10^{-27} erg/s, and ν = frequency (cycles per second [cps] or Hertz [Hz]).

An important physical relationship governing the properties of electromagnetic waves is described by the following equation:

$$\nu = c/\lambda$$

By substituting the second equation into the first, we arrive at the all important equation governing the action of sunlight on humans where the energy (E) and the wavelength (λ) have a reciprocal relationship as shown below:

$$E = hc/\lambda$$

where c = speed of light = 3.0×10^{10} cm/s and λ = wavelength (cm or m).

The above relationship reveals that the wavelength increases as the energy associated with it decreases and vice versa. Thus, the UV-B region of the spectrum (290–320 nm) will have higher energies associated with it than the UV-A region (320–400 nm) (see Fig. 13.1). The significance of this relationship

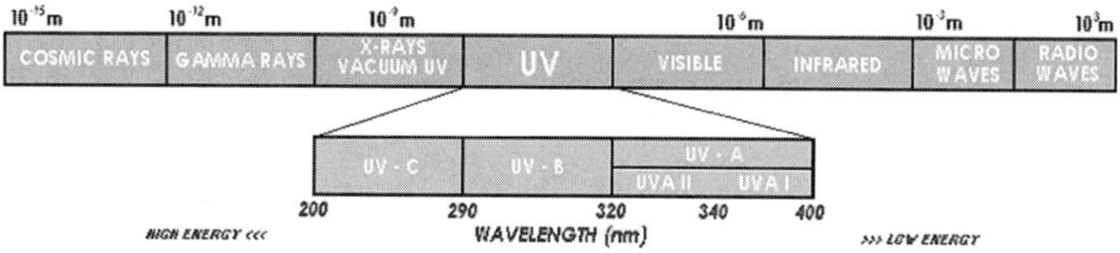

Figure 13.1 The electromagnetic spectrum of radiant energy.

between energy and wavelength will become more evident when the effects of UV radiation on the skin are discussed.

Solar radiation that is visible to the eye is only a very small segment of the total range of the electromagnetic waves and can roughly be divided into three regions:

- *Electrical rays*, which include wireless, Hertzian, radiowaves and microwaves. These rays are generally longer wavelengths (measured in meters) and have much lower energies associated with them than the harmful UV rays.
- *Optical rays*, which are subdivided into infrared, visible, and UV rays.
- *X-rays, gamma rays, and cosmic rays* have short wavelengths measured in 10^{-9}–10^{-15} m and are obviously high in energy and extremely damaging rays.

In the optical region, the UV rays have the shortest wavelengths and the highest energies associated with them. These rays are sufficiently energetic to cause photochemical reactions, resulting in both immediate and delayed damage to the skin and hair, termed the *photochemical effect*. The visible region or the *light effect* is where the rainbow of the colors of the spectrum is exhibited (violet to red). The longest wavelength (hence, lower energy) is the infrared (IR) region, which is responsible for the *heat effect*. The UV rays, which have been demonstrated to be the most damaging to humans, can be further subdivided into three regions, namely, the UV-A, UV-B, and UV-C.

The most damaging of the UV radiations is the UV-C, also called the *germicidal region*, has the highest energy associated with it (the lower wavelengths, 200–290 nm). Fortunately, the harmful rays of the UV-C and of course those that are higher, namely, X-rays, gamma rays, and cosmic rays are filtered by the stratospheric ozone layer; thus, none of these rays reach the earth's surface. The depletion of this layer through the continued use of chlorofluorohydrocarbons (CFCs) poses a major threat to mankind if left unabated. Nevertheless, artificial light sources (tanning salons, mercury arc, or welding arcs) do contain some UV-C radiation and should be used only with adequate protection. It is the UV-A and UV-B regions that are not completely filtered out by the ozone layer and are sufficiently energetic to cause damage to the skin and hair.

The UV-B rays, also called the *burning or erythemal rays* with wavelengths ranging from 280 to 320 nm, is responsible for most of the immediate damage to the skin, resulting in erythema or sunburn, and subsequent long-term damage if the skin is left unprotected.

The UV-A region extends from 320 to 400 nm and is further subdivided into UV-A I from 340 to 400 nm and UV-A II from 320 to 340 nm. Parish et al. (3) list many reasons why the UV rays are extremely important and should be dealt with:

1. The amount of solar UV-A reaching the earth's surface is enormously greater than that of UV-B.
2. Photosensitivity reactions (phototoxicity and photoallergy) are mostly mediated by UV-A.
3. High doses of UV-A can cause redness to human skin; moreover, UV-A may potentiate or add to the biological effects of UV-B.
4. The development of sunscreens that effectively block or diminish the highly erythemogenic UV-B permits prolonged sun exposures; however, many of these sunscreens do not significantly alter the amount of UV-A reaching the skin.
5. UV-A is transmitted by most window glass and many plastics that do not transmit UV-B.
6. Recent studies suggest that UV-A can affect cells and microorganisms.
7. There is experimental and epidemiological evidence to suggest that solar UV-A is one of the possible etiological agents for certain kinds of cataracts in humans.

For these and more reasons protection from the UV-A rays is crucial in any photoprotection regimen.

EFFECT OF UV RADIATION ON THE SKIN

The skin, which is the largest organ of the body, has several functions including the regulation of body temperature, protection from the environment, partial regulation of water loss and retention, and serves as a temporary storage site for glucose when blood glucose is elevated. Other biochemical properties associated with the skin are melanin formation, epinephrine stimulation of the sweat glands and the regeneration of viable epidermal cells (4).

The skin is composed of three layers: the epidermis, including the stratum corneum, the dermis, and the hypodermis (see Fig. 13.2). The dermis contains melanocytes, which generate the melanin pigment responsible for the color of the skin. Exposure to rays with wavelengths in the UV-A region will stimulate the formation of melanin, which acts as a protective layer on the skin. The skin is shown along with the amount of UV radiation that penetrates each layer. UV radiation near 300 nm (UV-B) penetrates both the stratum corneum and the epidermis and is sufficiently energetic to cause severe burning (erythema)

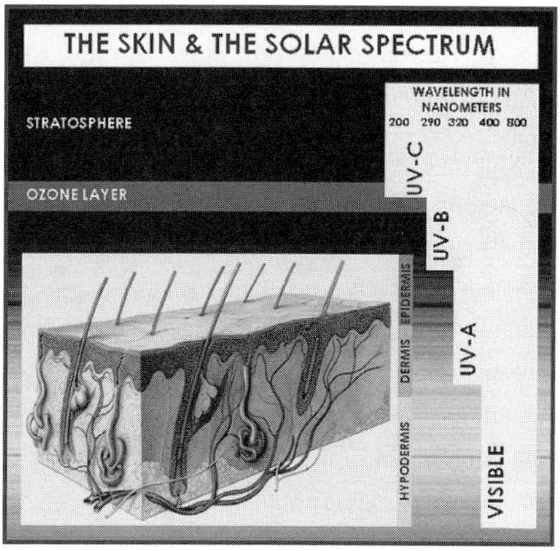

Figure 13.2 Schematic representation of light penetration into the skin.

of the skin, especially in fair-skinned individuals. Radiation with wavelengths longer than 350 nm starts penetrating the dermis thereby stimulating the formation of melanin and producing a tan that protects the skin from immediate sunburn. Although UV-A rays are of lower energy than the UV-B rays, the fact that they can penetrate further into the hypodermis, causes elastosis (loss of structural support and elasticity of the skin) and other skin damage, potentially leading to the skin cancers we observe rising in epidemic proportions today.

CLASSIFICATION OF UV FILTERS

There are three types of UV filters:

1. Organic UV absorbers
2. Inorganic particulates
3. Organic particulates.

This chapter deals primarily with the organic UV absorbers. The inorganic particulates are dealt with in Chapter 14 and the new organic particulates are dealt with in Chapter 15.

The relationship between chemical structure and efficacy of UV filters is clearly evident as documented in this chapter.

Sunscreens have originated from both academic and industrial research laboratories with completely diverse uses. The cost, safety, and marketability of the new filters have had a dramatic influence on the evolution of the current approved list of sunscreen chemicals, regardless of their efficacy, degree, and nature of their protection.

In the USA, the recently approved Category I list of sunscreen chemicals (5) lists 16 UV filters, 14 of which are organic UV filters (that absorb UV rays) and two inorganic particulates (that both absorb and reflect UV rays). No organic particulates have been approved as Category I ingredients in the USA. The ingredients along with their approved percentage, the λ_{max} and extinction coefficient (ε) are shown in Table 13.1.

Table 13.1 FDA-OTC Panel Category I Sunscreens

Sunscreen	Approved %	λ_{max} (ethanol) (nm)	Extinction coefficient (ε) (ethanol)
A. Organic absorbers			
UV-A absorbers			
Avobenzone	3	357	30,500
Oxybenzone	6	325	9,400
Sulisobenzone	10	324	8,400
Dioxybenzone	3	327	10,440
Meradimate	5	336	5,600
UV-B absorbers			
PABA	15	290	14,000
Cinoxate	3	305	11,000
Octocrylene	10	303	12,600
Ocinoxate	7.5	310	23,300
Octisalate	5	307	4,900
Homosalate	15	306	4,300
Padimate-O	8	307	27,300
Ensulizole	4	310	26,000
Trolamine salicylate	12	298	3,000
B. Inorganic particulates			
Zinc oxide	25	Broad spectrum	
Titanium dioxide	25	Broad spectrum	

This list of UV filters, with the exception of avobenzone and the micronized forms of zinc oxide and titanium dioxide, reflects the knowledge that dates back to the early 1970s. They do not represent the most recent advances in UV filter design. Currently, any sunscreen supplier wishing to introduce a new UV filter must either go through a costly and time-consuming New Drug Application (NDA) to the US Food and Drug Administration (FDA) or hope for the reopening of the monograph for additional sunscreen approvals before its anticipated adoption date in 2005. Unlike medical drugs, for which the return on investment may be in the hundreds of millions of dollars, sunscreen chemicals do not afford substantial returns to the companies producing them. The cost to obtain an NDA is estimated to be several million dollars with a waiting period exceeding 3 years. This is prohibitive for most manufacturers embarking on research designed to produce new and innovative UV filters.

A promising alternative to the NDA process is the FDA's Time and Extent Application (TEA) (Chapter 6) that established criteria and procedures by which over-the-counter (OTC) conditions may become eligible for consideration in the OTC drug monograph system. Three new ingredients, namely amiloxate, enzacamene, and octyl triazone are under review for potential inclusion in the list of approved sunscreens in the USA.

The European Economic Community (EEC) member countries have established a body called COLIPA (Chapter 39) that effectively regulates the sunscreen industry. The cost in both time and the production of the necessary safety toxicological data is reasonable, allowing for more new introductions and innovations. Japan (Chapter 10) and Australia (Chapter 9) have similar, less costly measures for the adoption and introduction of new sunscreen agents.

Seven new ingredients have been recently approved for use in Europe (Chapter 16):

1. BEMT (*bis*-ethylhexyloxyphenol methoxyphenyl triazine [S81])
2. DTS (drometrizole trisiloxane [S73])
3. DBT (dioctyl butamido triazone [S78])
4. EHT (ethyl hexyl triazone [S69])
5. DHHB (diethylamino hydroxbenzoyl hexyl benzoate)
6. BDHB (*bis*-diethylhydroxybenzoyl benzoate)
7. BBET (*bis*-benzoxzoylphenyl ethylhexylimino triazine).

Many of the new UV filters being designed in Europe have followed a novel new approach to the conventional organic UV absorbers. They generally contain multiple chromophores and are occasionally grafted onto a polymer backbone. The molecular weights of most of these molecules exceed 500 Da and a few of them have been supplied as microfine organic particulates in 50% aqueous dispersions in the same manner as the new microfine inorganic particulates of today.

Herzog and coauthors have recently described the broad spectrum UV filter (BEMT) (6). To illustrate the general new trends in the synthesis of new molecules, the molecular structure of BEMT is shown here:

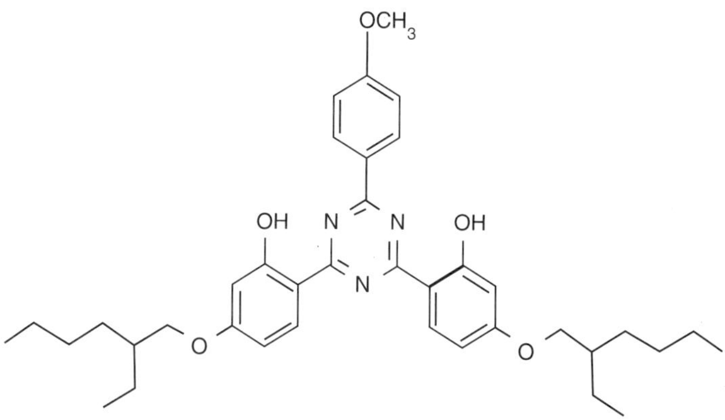

It is evident that broad-spectrum absorbance is attained due to the extended resonance delocalization through the full aromatic molecule. The *ortho* substituents extend the electron transfer through hydrogen bonding between the phenolic group and the nitrogen in the heterocylic ring. The *para*-methoxy substituent in BEMT with its electron-donating capability lowers the energy requirements even further, thereby extending the absorption λ_{max} into the longer UV-A. The water resistancy in BEMT is achieved by the two hydrophobic ethyl hexyl substituents.

The organic chemical UV filters approved in the USA today can be classified as derivatives of the following classes of compounds:

1. PABA and *p*-aminobenzoates
2. Salicylates
3. Cinnamates
4. Benzophenones
5. Anthranilates
6. Dibenzoyl methanes
7. Camphor derivatives
8. Miscellaneous chemicals.

The above classes of organic molecules will be reviewed below to illustrate the relationship between their chemical structures, the UV absorbance activity and their physico-chemical properties.

PABA and *p*-Aminobenzoates

Para-amino benzoic acid (PABA) has an absorption maxima at 290 nm and a moderate molar extinction coefficient of 14,000. Its chemical structure reveals the presence of two reactive functional groups; namely, amino and carboxylic acid moieties, substituted in a *para* orientation on the benzene nucleus as shown:

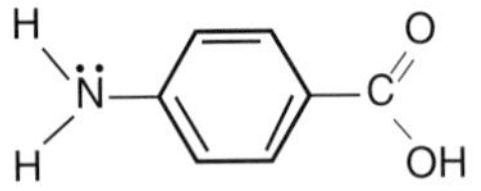

This particular configuration of an electron-releasing group ($-NR_2$) substituted *para* to an electron acceptor group ($-COOH$) allows for the efficient electron delocalization shown here:

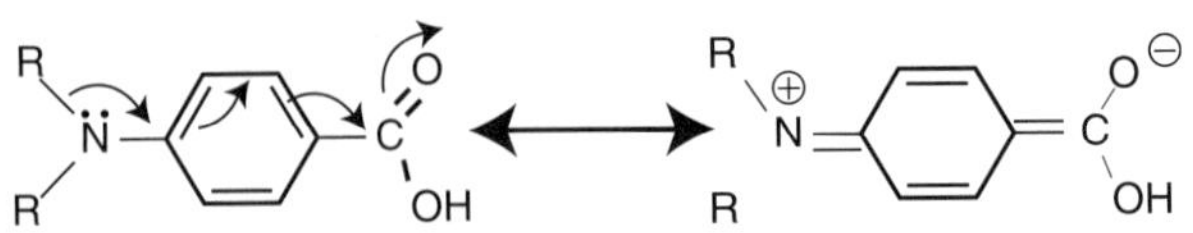

Quantum chemical calculations have revealed that this electron delocalization energy corresponds to the electronic transitions associated with the UV-B region of the solar spectrum (7). Unfortunately, the presence of these two extremely polar groups, the amino and carboxylic acid, situated away (*para*) from one another contributes to a number of problems that render the use of this product commercially less appealing, namely:

1. Free amines tend to oxidize rapidly in air and thereby produce off colors.
2. Amines and acids are extremely polar groups that tend to hydrogen bond intermolecularly as shown:

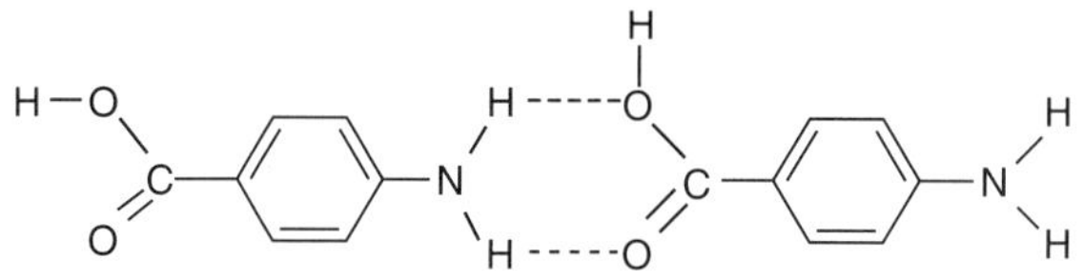

   This intermolecular hydrogen bonding leads to the increased association of the molecules, thereby producing a crystalline physical state. This crystal structure poses various constraints on the liberal use of the product in cosmetic formulations. A suitable emollient will be required to ensure the rapid and continuous dissolution of PABA in the formulation.
3. The presence of both the polar amine and carboxylic acid group promotes the water solubility of the sunscreen chemical in the finished cosmetic formulation owing to the excessive hydrogen bonding with emollients.
4. Excessive hydrogen bonding between PABA and polar emollients, leads to a dramatic solvent effect (7). This solvent effect will shift the λ_{max} by 27 nm from 293 nm in nonpolar solvents to 266 nm in polar solvents. Such solvent effects have a major influence on the efficacy of the UV filter in cosmetic formulations.
5. The carboxylic acid and amine substituents cause the molecules to be subject to pH changes in the formulation.

In addition to the foregoing chemical limitations of PABA, several recent reports have cast doubt on its safety as a UV filter (8) hence it has experienced a major decline in its worldwide use as a sunscreen agent.

Researchers in the field of sunscreens responded to the consumers need for better UV filters, and several sunscreens based on the strength of the PABA moiety emerged. A sunscreen was designed to protect both the amino and carboxylic acid grouping from pH changes and potential chemical reactions. Padimate-O the only other PABA derivative that is on the Category I listing was until recently the workhorse of UV filters. It represented the ultimate in sunscreen design as the intermolecular association leading to the many of the undesirable properties listed above was decreased. This change in structure resulted in a UV filter that is a liquid instead of a crystalline solid and also decreased the problems associated with the primary amine and the carboxylic acid group outlined above. Its molar extinction coefficient is one of the highest found in a UV-B filter in the USA, reaching 27,300. The extinction coefficient is double that of PABA. Even though it is still subject to solvent affects, the shifts reported are from 300 nm in nonpolar solvents to 316 nm in polar solvents, values that are well within the UV-B range. Reports of its photoinstability have been cited in the literature (9) and its commercial use worldwide has decreased significantly.

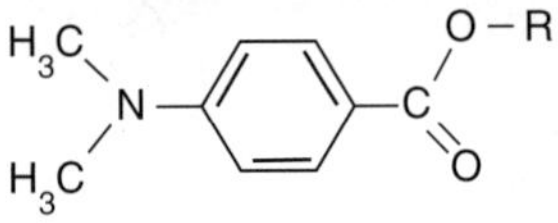

Salicylates

Salicylates were the first UV filters ever used in sunscreen preparations (10). Several of these derivatives have enjoyed substantial sales worldwide including octisalate (S.-13 in Europe), homosalate (S.-12 in Europe), and the water-soluble trolamine salicylate (S.-9 in Europe).

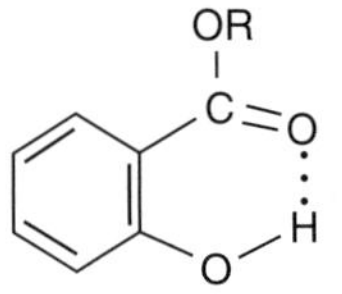

R = 2-ethyl hexyl:octisalate

R = homomenthyl:homosalate

R = triethanolamine:trolamine salicylate

The salicylates as a group, are *ortho*-disubstituted compounds with a spatial arrangement permitting internal hydrogen bonding within the molecule itself as shown in the chemical structure, exhibiting a UV absorbance of about 300 nm. The hydrogen bonding possible in the salicylates lowers the energy requirements for the compound's electrons to be promoted to its photochemically excited state as shown here:

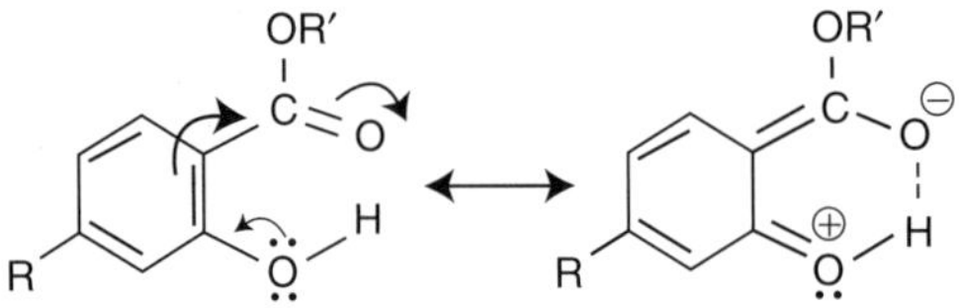

The salicylates have the ideal UV-B sunscreen range of 300–310 nm, nevertheless, for precisely the same reason, namely the *ortho* relationship, they have a much lower extinction coefficient. The *ortho* relationship of the phenolic group to the bulky carboxylic ester grouping causes crowding and strain on the molecule as a whole. To counterbalance this steric strain, the two groups deviate ever so slightly from planarity. Any minor deviation from planarity of the molecule causes a lowering of the extinction coefficient because the symmetry will dictate whether an electronic transition is allowed or forbidden. A discussion of such rules is beyond the scope of this chapter; however, the interested reader is referred to the many excellent monographs on the topic (11).

The salicylates are excellent solubilizers of crystalline UV filters such as the benzophenones and avobenzone. They are mild and stable ingredients with an excellent safety record, despite their continued use for more than 50 years. This is predominantly due to this unique *ortho*-disubstituted chemical structure. The two active groups, the hydroxyl and the carboxylic acid groups, are intramolecularily hydrogen bonded to one another rendering their electrons less available for interaction with other ingredients or with biological substrates found on the skin.

For water-soluble sunscreens, trolamine salicylate is commercially available and approved for use worldwide. It is known to boost the sun protection factor (SPF) of cosmetic formulations owing to their substantivity to the skin and is also used in hair preparations.

Cinnamates

Cinnamates, most notably octinoxate, are currently the most popular sunscreens protecting the UV-B rays of the electromagnetic spectrum. In fact, there were over a dozen cinnamate derivatives on the European COLIPA lists and three are approved for use in the USA. A fourth molecule, amiloxate, is currently under review through the TEA process (Chapter 6). The structure following the next paragraph reveals remarkable similarity to octinoxate where the ester is an amyl grouping instead of the octyl group.

The cinnamates have an extra unsaturation conjugated to both the aromatic ring and the carbonyl portion of the carboxylic ester. This configuration permits the electron delocalization to occur throughout the octinoxate molecule. The energy corresponding to this electronic transition has a wavelength of about 310 nm and a fairly strong molar extinction coefficient (>23,000). For practical purposes, this molecule is insoluble in water, making it suitable for most water-resistant sunscreen formulations.

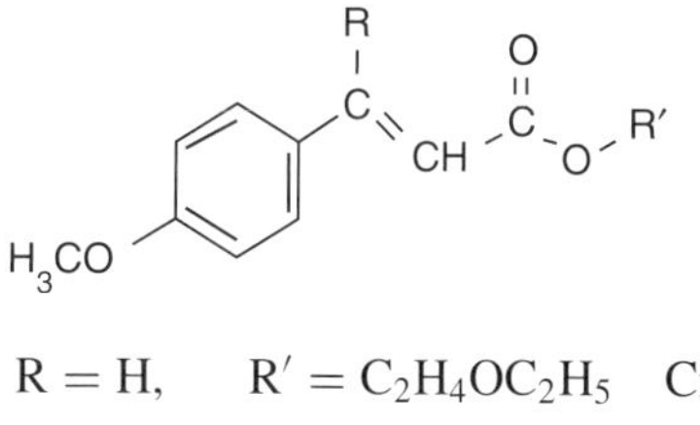

R = H, $R' = C_2H_4OC_2H_5$ Cinoxate

R = H, $R' = C_8H_{17}$ Octinoxate

R = H, $R' = C_5H_{17}$ Amiloxate

R = CN, $R' = C_8H_{17}$ Octocrylene

Octinoxate, on the other hand, is subject to *cis–trans* isomerism and it is known to lose some of its efficacy due to this photoinstability. Other reports also suggest the lowering of the SPF values of formulations in combination with avobenzone. Despite these reports, octinoxate has had an excellent safety record and remains as the most popular UV filter in use worldwide.

Another cinnamate approved for use today is octocrylene (ethyl hexyl cyano diphenyl acrylate) with a λ_{max} of 303 nm and an extinction coefficient of 12,600. It is approved for use in the USA at levels up to 10%. It found increased use after L'Oreal published its findings that octocrylene increases the photostability of formulations containing avobenzone (Chapter 17). The third molecule, Cinoxate has had limited use in cosmetic formulations in the USA.

Benzophenones

The benzophenones are the only class of compounds that belong to the aromatic ketone category. Avobenzone is a diketone with unique chemical properties and the rest of the 14 Categtory I ingredients are esters, acids, or their salts.* Resonance delocalization in benzophenones as in all the other classes of compounds discussed earlier, is aided by the presence of an electron releasing group in either the *ortho* or *para* position or both. The electron-accepting group in this case, the carbonyl group itself, participates in the resonance delocalization process shown next,

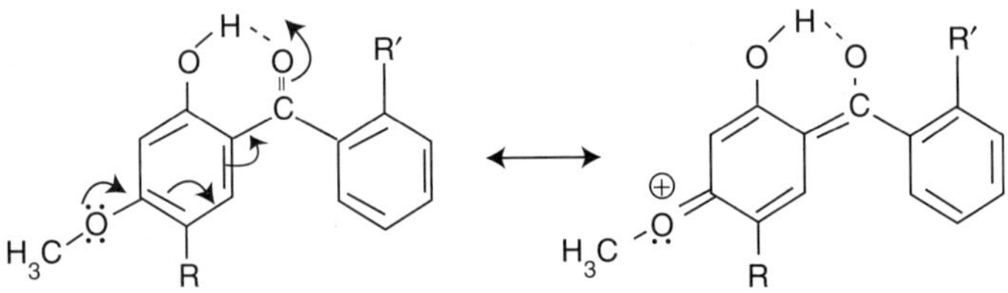

R = H	R′ = H	Oxybenzone
R = H,	R′ = OH	Dioxybenzone
R = SO_3H,	R′ = H	Sulisobenzone

Aromatic ketones, unlike the esters encountered earlier, will resonate more easily, thereby requiring a lower quantum of energy for the electronic transition resulting in a higher wavelength (exceeding 320 nm) hence their use as UV-A filters.

The drawback in using benzophenones as UV filters is due to various factors:

- Aromatic ketones are chemically different from esters. Metabolically, esters unlike ketones may be hydrolyzed *in vivo*, producing by-products that the body can metabolize (a detoxification mechanism). It has been

*Even though dibenzoyl methane derivatives are arylakyl ketones, they exhibit their UV-filtering effect through a *keto–enol* tatomerism, which is not possible in benzophenones.

reported that patients developed statistically more allergic reactions to oxybenzone than to PABA (12).

- These products are, without exception solids, and are generally difficult to handle and to dissolve in cosmetic formulations.
- Their UV absorption reveals two maxima, one around 290 nm (UV-B) and the other is generally <330 nm, which is a value barely into the UV-A region.

Anthranilates

Anthranilates, or *ortho*-aminobenzoates, are an interesting class of UV filters. Meradimate, is on the US FDA Category I listing.

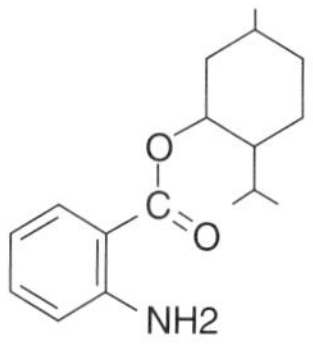

Meradimate

This class of compounds offers an elegant example on the effect of chemical structure on UV absorbance characteristics. This effect, termed here the *ortho effect*, has been observed in numerous organic compounds. Meradimate, has a λ_{max} of 336 nm, whereas padimate-O, a *para*-disubstituted aminobenzoate has a λ_{max} of only 307 nm.

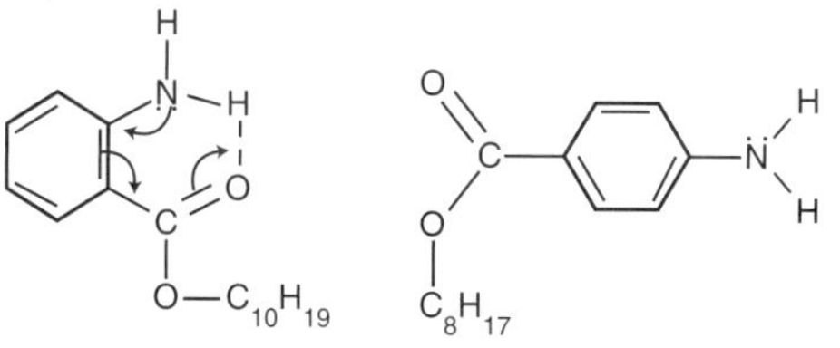

Meradimate (λ_{max} 336 nm)

Padimate-O (λ_{max} 307 nm)

This dramatic 29-nm shift in the maximum absorption is clearly due to the ease in electron delocalization in the *ortho*-disubstituted compounds for which the geometry allows for this "through space" assistance. This also results in a lower molar extinction coefficient in the anthranilates than that of the *para*-amino benzoates, in a manner analogous to that described for the salicylates. Again, the steric crowding in the *ortho*-disubstituted compound causes the molecule to deviate from coplanarity, thereby reducing the intensity of the absorbance.

Anthranilates, as with salicylates, are stable and safe compounds to use owing to this *ortho*-disubstituted relationship and, as in salicylates, do not exhibit any significant solvent shift effects in cosmetic formulations (7).

Dibenzoylmethanes

Dibenzoylmethanes, or substituted diketones, are a relatively new class of UV filters. Only one has now received approval for use in the USA (avobenzone), whereas three are approved for use in Europe.

This group of UV filters exhibits properties resulting from a *keto–enol* tautomerism (Chapter 17). The *keto* form of these compounds actually has a λ_{max} of about 260 nm. However, the *enol* form has a λ_{max} exceeding 350 nm, making them suitable candidates for UV-A protection.

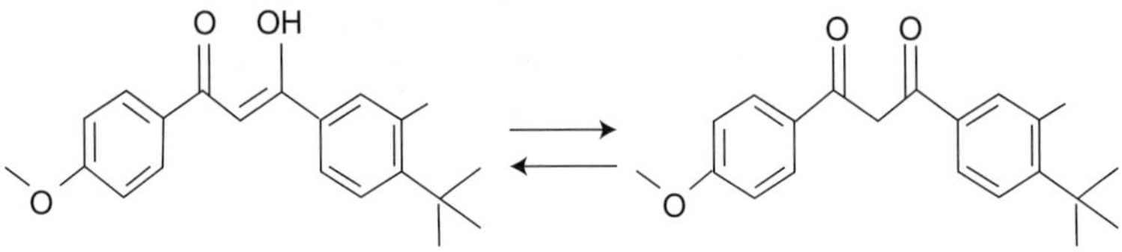

Enol: $\lambda_{max} \sim 350$ nm Keto: $\lambda_{max} \sim 260$ nm

Butyl methoxydibenzoyl methane (avobenzone)

Dibenzoyl methane derivatives have exceptionally high molar extinction coefficients (>30,000). However, they suffer from possessing low photostability. In several reports (13), the photoisomerization of various sunscreen chemicals have been listed. Avobenzone is reported to be relatively photolabile if improperly formulated in cosmetic vehicles. Triplet–triplet quenchers have been introduced to stabilize the molecule (a patent by L'Oreal uses octocrylene for its stabilization) and a number of emollients and ingredients are purported to stabilize the more desirable *enol* form of the molecule.

Camphor Derivatives

Six bicyclic compounds are approved for use in the EEC member countries and only one, Enzacamene is currently being considered for use in the USA through the TEA process.

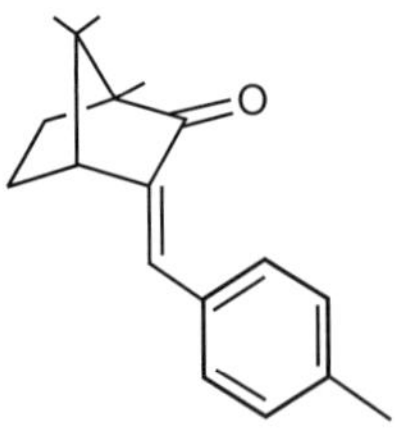

4-Methyl benzylidinecamphor (enzacamene)

Most of the bicyclic derivatives are solids and have a high molar extinction coefficient generally >20,000 and absorb in the UV-B range of 290–300 nm. They all owe their photostability (14) to the resonance delocalization in the molecule, shown here:

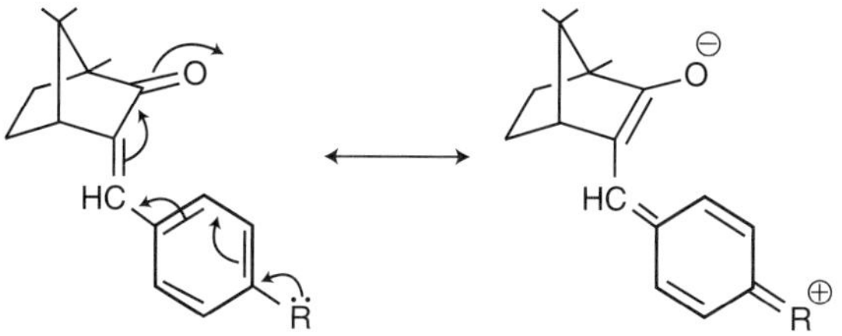

Miscellaneous Compounds

2-Phenyl benzimidazole-5-sulfonic acid (ensulizole) has some water solubility, is a high melting white powder, is affected by pH changes and is used in limited quantities in the USA. It has a moderate to high extinction coefficient of 26,000 and its λ_{max} is about 310 nm.

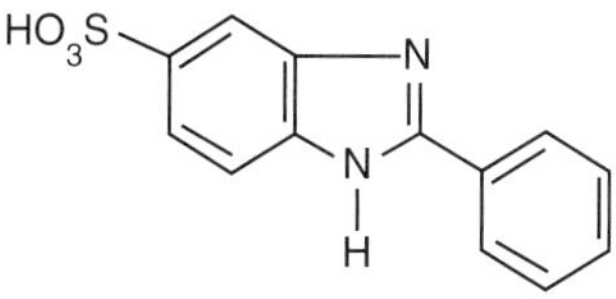

Ensulizole

The inorganic particulates have currently received an inordinate amount of attention and we have devoted two chapters to review their chemistry and applications (Chapters 14 and 15).

Also, several new organic particulates have recently been approved in Europe and their chemistry is reviewed by Herzog et al. (Chapter 16).

MECHANISM OF SUNSCREENING ACTION

UV filters are generally aromatic compounds conjugated with an electron-receiving group (e.g., a carbonyl group) or conjugated with a double bond (X) and an electron-releasing group (an amine, a hydroxyl, or a methoxyl group) that is substituted in the *ortho* or *para* position of the aromatic ring (7) as shown:

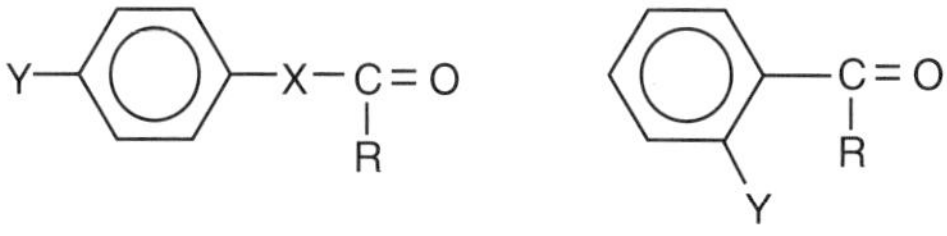

para-Disubstituted UV absorbers   *ortho*-Disubstituted UV absorbers

Chemicals of this configuration absorb the harmful short-wave (high-energy) UV rays (200–400 nm) and convert the remaining energy into innocuous longer-wave (lower-energy) radiation (>400 nm). Quantum mechanical calculations have shown that the energy of the radiation quanta present in the UV-B and UV-A regions lies in the same order of magnitude as that of the resonance energy of electron delocalization in aromatic compounds. Thus, the energy absorbed from the UV radiation corresponds to the energy required to cause a "photochemical excitation" in the sunscreen molecule. In other words, the sunscreen chemical is excited to a higher energy state from its ground state by absorbing this UV radiation. As the excited molecule returns to the ground state, energy is emitted that is lower in magnitude than the energy initially absorbed to cause the excitation (longer wavelengths).

The longer wavelength radiation is emitted in one of several ways (see Fig. 13.3). If the loss in energy is quite large, that is, the wavelength of the emitted radiation is of sufficient length that it lies in the infrared region, then it may be perceived as a mild heat radiation on the skin. This minuscule heat effect is undetected because the skin receives a much larger heat effect by being directly exposed to the sun's heat. If the emitted energy lies in the visible region, then it may be perceived as either a fluorescent or a phosphorescent effect. This is common in the imidazoline-type sunscreen for which a slight bluish haze may be observed on the skin or in cosmetic formulations. In the extreme case, the emitted radiation is sufficiently energetic (lower wavelength) that it may cause a fraction of the sunscreen molecule to react photochemically. *Cis–trans* or *keto–enol* photochemical isomerization has been observed in some organic molecules, causing a mild shift in the λ_{max} of the chemical (15).

Effect of Vehicle on the Efficacy of UV Filters

Cosmetic vehicles may have a profound effect on the efficacy of UV filters and their formulations. The pH, λ_{max}, and extinction coefficient (ε) directly influence the SPF and the stability of cosmetic formulations.

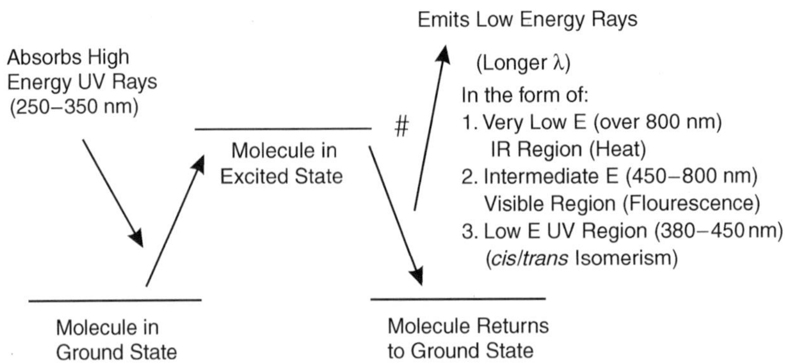

Figure 13.3 Schematic representation of the process in which a sunscreen chemical absorbs ultraviolet radiation.

pH Effects on UV Filters

The UV absorption spectra of acidic and basic compounds may be affected by pH. In acidic compounds, the use of alkaline conditions ($pH > 9$) will assist in the formation of anions that tend to increase delocalization of electrons (16). This electron delocalization would decrease the energy required for the electronic transition in the UV spectrum; hence, a bathochromic shift is observed (longer wavelength or λ_{max}). For example, phenols in an alkaline environment will experience this anticipated bathochromic shift owing to the formation of the phenolate anion. This phenolate anion will participate in resonance delocalization of electrons.

Acidic conditions ($pH < 4$) will assist in the formation of cations with aromatic amines. A hypsochromic shift towards the lower wavelength occurs because the protonation of the unbound loan pair of electrons with acid would prevent any resonance delocalization of the electrons. Thus aniline, for example, forms the anilinium cation at low pH and a considerable hypsochromic shift occurs.

Thus, UV filters such as PABA, sulisobenzone, zinc oxide, and ensulizole experience pH changes in their formulations. Care must be exercised when handling cosmetic formulations containing these UV filters that are affected by pH changes.

Effect of Emollients on the Efficacy of UV Filters

Solvent shifts in sunscreen chemicals due to their combinations with a variety of emollients have been observed (7). The use of different emollients in cosmetic formulations may profoundly influence the effectiveness of a sunscreen chemical. The shifts in the UV spectrum are due to the relative degrees of solvation by the emollient in the ground state and the excited state of the chemical. To predict the effect the emollient has on a particular chemical, the interaction (mostly hydrogen bonding) between the emollient and the sunscreen chemical must be understood.

The solvation of polar sunscreens (e.g., PABA) with polar solvents such as water or ethanol will be quite extensive. This extensive solvation stabilizes the ground state, thereby inhibiting electron delocalization. The net result would be a hypsochromic shift to lower wavelengths as depicted in Fig. 13.4 (case A). For less polar sunscreen compounds, such as padimate-O, the solvent–solute interaction (hydrogen bonding) is different because the excited state is more polar than the ground state. The net result is stabilization of the excited state by polar solvents. This then lowers the energy requirements for the electronic transition; hence, a higher λ_{max} would be expected, and a bathochromic shift occurs as shown in Fig. 13.4 (case B) and Table 13.2.

For sunscreen compounds such as salicylates and anthranilates, they are subject to the "ortho" effect, which supersedes other resonance delocalization effects for the observed UV transitions. The six-membered ring formation

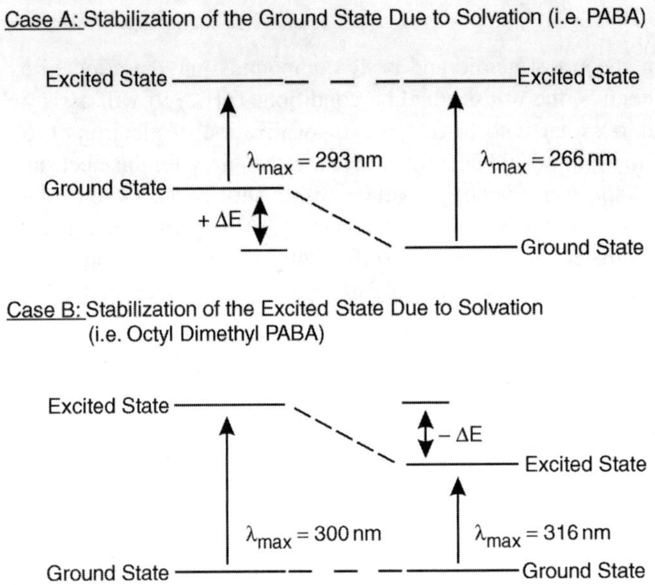

Figure 13.4 Energy diagram depicting the stabilization of the ground state and the excited state.

reduces the energy requirements for the electronic transition in the molecule by loosening the electrons in the carbonyl group that is conjugated to the aromatic ring.

This lower-energy transition is reflected in a higher than usual λ_{max}. Most of the available electrons are involved in the six-member cyclic arrangement and

Table 13.2 Summary of UV Absorption Data of Sunscreens in Combination with Polar and Nonpolar Solvents

Sunscreen	$\Delta\lambda$ ($\lambda_2 - \lambda_1$)	λ_1 max nonpolar	λ_2 max polar	Extinction coefficient (ε)
PABA	−27	293	266	14,000
Dioxybenzone	−26	352	326	10,440
Sulisobenzone	−10	334	324	8,400
Oxybenzone	−8	329	321	9,400
Octisalate	−2	308	306	4,900
Homosalate	−2	310	308	4,300
Meradimate	+2	334	336	5,600
Avobenzone	+9	351	360	30,500
Padimate-O	+16	300	316	27,300
Ocinoxate	+23	289	312	23,300

are not available for interaction with the solvent molecules. Thus, salicylates and anthranilates do not exhibit any significant solvent shifts.

Effects on the Extinction Coefficient

The value of the extinction coefficient (ε) is the basis of how the effectiveness of the sunscreen chemical is assessed. Therefore, chemicals with a high extinction coefficient are more efficient in absorbing the energy of the harmful UV radiation than chemicals with a lower extinction coefficient.

All the electronic transitions for any compound may be characterized as *symmetry allowed* or *symmetry forbidden* (17). Symmetry-allowed transitions generally have high extinction coefficients, and symmetry-forbidden transitions have lower extinction coefficients. Nevertheless, trends in extinction coefficients for sunscreen chemicals can be arrived at qualitatively by studying both the spatial requirements and the electronic transition responsible for the observed UV spectrum. The degree of resonance delocalization in a molecule gives a clear indication as to its λ_{max} and a qualitative prediction of its extinction coefficient is possible.

The more efficient the electron delocalization in a molecule, the higher its extinction coefficient. Compare, for example, padimate-O and homosalate. In padimate-O, the two substituents on the benzene ring are in a *para* relation, whereas the two substituents in the homosalate are in a sterically hindered *ortho* relation. In *ortho*-disubstituted aromatic compounds, the two groups are close to one another, causing a deviation from planarity. The slightest deviation from coplanarity will significantly reduce resonance delocalization; hence, a lower extinction coefficient is observed in homosalate compared with padimate-O. For the same reason, octisalate and homosalate (both *ortho*-disubstituted) have lower extinction coefficients than the *para*-disubstituted compounds. Increased conjugation, allowing for more efficient resonance delocalization, will also result in higher extinction coefficients. For example, the extinction coefficient of ethylene is 15,000, that of 1,3-butadiene is 21,000, that of 1,3,5-hexatriene is 35,000, and for the highly conjugated molecule, β-carotene, it is 152,000 (18). The new UV filters originating in Europe have multiple chromophores and therefore increased conjugation resulting in extinction coefficients exceeding 40,000 (Chapter 16).

THE FUTURE OF UV FILTERS

The ultimate sunscreen chemical should ideally have the following characteristics:

1. It should absorb the harmful UV radiation in the region 280–380 nm. If a broad-spectrum protection is not possible by using one sunscreen chemical, then the use of two or more ingredients that filter the

280–320 nm (UV-B region) and the 320–380 nm (UV-A region) radiation, may be necessary.

2. It should possess a large molar extinction coefficient (ε) at its λ_{max}. Values exceeding 25,000 would be extremely desirable. This would afford the maximum possible protection with the least amount of sunscreen in the cosmetic formulations. The new molecules currently designed in Europe have multiple chromophores with unusually high extinction coefficients.
3. The UV filters should have good solubility in emollients. Solid sunscreens such as the benzophenones, avobenzone, camphor derivatives, and PABA require special care to solubilize in formulations and insure that they do not crystallize out on the skin. To insure the stability of the sunscreen formulation, the UV filters must remain dissolved throughout allowing for a reasonable shelf life. Inorganic and organic particulates with silicone backbones have to be suspended properly in the formulation and the phase in which they are incorporated in is chosen carefully to allow for maximum stability.
4. The λ_{max} and the molar extinction coefficient (ε) should not be affected by solvents. Excessively polar sunscreen chemicals are stabilized by polar solvents, thereby lowering the energy requirements of the ground state of the sunscreen. This in turn will cause a hypsochromic shift (to shorter wavelengths) in polar solvents. On the other hand, sunscreens that are not too polar in their ground state but more polar in their photochemical excited states, will experience a bathochromic shift (to longer wavelengths) in polar solvents. The ideal sunscreen would be one in which the polarity of the ground state and that of the photochemically excited state are similar in nature. Hence, a hypsochromic shift (owing to the solvent stabilization of the ground state) will be counterbalanced by the bathochromic shift (owing to the solvent stabilization of the photochemically excited state).
5. It should have excellent photostability and be photochemically inert. If isomerization such as *cis–trans* or *keto–enol*, is possible in the molecule, then the degradation quantum yields should be low, indicating that the isomerization is reversible. The addition of specific emollients or quenchers may be necessary to insure their photostability in the formulation. Inorganic particulates should be produced commercially with the least amount of photo-chemical reactivity possible. This may include choosing the type of mineral carefully, the specific coating and the type of dispersant.
6. For water-resistant formulations, the sunscreen should be practically insoluble in water. Water-soluble sunscreens will still have a role to play in the sunscreen formulations, such as in hair preparations or when boosting the SPF is required.

7. It should not be toxic, comedogenic, sensitizing, or phototoxic.
8. It should be compatible with cosmetic vehicles and ingredients, and be easy to use and handle.
9. Since UV filters constitute a significant portion of the cosmetic formulation, occasionally exceeding 15% of the formula, then it may also be desirable to have the sunscreen impart additional characteristics such as emolliency, moisturizing, or possibly imparting a pleasant aroma that can cover base notes in formulations that are fragrance-free.
10. It should not discolor the skin, stain clothing, cause stinging sensations, deposit crystals, cause drying of the skin, or produce off-odors when applied to the skin or hair.
11. The UV filter should be available isomerically pure, be chemically stable for prolonged storage, and be chemically inert to other cosmetic ingredients.
12. The ideal sunscreen should be inexpensive to use.
13. It should be compatible with most packaging material.
14. Sunscreen molecules should be adequately protected with patents and intellectual property. Patents should cover their combinations with other UV filters, emollients, quenchers, or additives.
15. Ultimately, the UV filter should be approved worldwide by official regulatory agencies with the fewest restrictions on levels used or combinations that are disallowed.

The foregoing conditions are obviously a wish list for the theoretically ideal sunscreen candidate. Unfortunately, no sunscreen chemical on the market today can claim to possess all of these properties. Nevertheless, the sunscreen chemicals available, whether through deliberate design or through serendipity, have provided the cosmetic chemist with a reasonable arsenal of UV filters that are effective, possess a number of the "ideal" properties and have only a few undesirable effects.

CONCLUSIONS

Our understanding of how sunscreens absorb and/or repel the harmful UV rays is extensive. The relationship of chemical structure and efficacy of UV filters was clearly demonstrated through the review of all the currently available UV filters, as well as recent reports on new chemicals possessing unique sunscreen capabilities. The evolution of modern sunscreen chemicals, although still not complete, has nevertheless produced an impressive array of UV filters that have been incorporated into a multitude of products used in our daily lives such as moisturizers, creams, lotions, towelettes, and shampoos.

The future will witness new applications for which sunscreens may be used requiring more effective, substantive sunscreen chemicals that have fewer drawbacks and limitations. This calls for additional extensive research and resources devoted to this effort by chemical and cosmetic institutions and commercial firms, newer more effective testing procedures to ensure the safety of UV filters at the anticipated expanded usage levels, and the reasonable relaxation of regulations by governmental and regulatory agencies to allow for the speedier adoption of novel UV filters.

REFERENCES

1. Gasparro F, Mitchnick M, Nash J. A review of sunscreen safety and efficacy. Photochem Photobiol 1998; 68(3):243.
2. Parish J. The scope of photo medicine. In: Regan J, Parish J, eds. The Science of Photo Medicine. New York: Plenum Press, 1982:3–17.
3. Parish J, Anderson R, Urbach F, Pitts D. The Spectrum of Electromagnetic Radiation: UV-A. New York: Plenum Press, 1978:5–6.
4. Marzulli F, Maibach H. Dermatoxity. 2nd ed. New York: McGraw-Hill, 1983:32.
5. Federal Register, 27666 (May 21, 1999).
6. Mongiat S, Herzog B, Deshayes C, Konig P, Osterwalder U. Cosmet Toilet 2003; 118(2):47–54.
7. Shaath NA. On the theory of ultraviolet absorption by sunscreen chemicals. J Soc Cosmet Chem 1987; 38:193.
8. Kligman AM. The identification of contact allergens by human assay: III. The maximization test: a procedure for sunscreening and rating contact sensitizers. J Invest Dermatol 1966; 47:393–409.
9. Gasparro F. UV-induced photoproducts of *para*-aminobenzoic acid. Photodermatology 1985; 2:151.
10. Patini G. Perfluoropolyethers in sunscreens. Drug Cosmet Ind 1988; 143:42.
11. Jaffe HH, Orchin M. Theory and Application of Ultraviolet Spectroscopy. New York: John Wiley & Sons, 1964.
12. Davis D. Cosmet Insiders Rep 1988; 7:1–2.
13. Beck I, Deflander A, Lang G, Arnaud R, Lemaire J. Study of the photochemical behavior of sunscreens benzylidene camphor and derivatives. Int J Cosmet Sci 1981; 3:139–152.
14. Beck I, Deflander A, Lang G, Arnaud R, Lemaire J. Study of the photochemical behavior of sunscreens benzylidene camphor and derivatives II. Photosensitized isomerization by aromatic ketones and deactivation of the 8-methoxy psoralin triplet state. J Photochem 1985; 30:215.
15. Liem DH, Hilderink LTH. UV absorbers in sun cosmetics 1978. Int J Cosmet Sci 1979; 1:341–361.
16. Morrison R, Boyd R. Organic Chemistry. 7th ed. Boston: Pearson, Allyn and Bacon, 2003.
17. Streitwiezer A Jr. Molecular Orbital Theory for Organic Chemists. New York: John Wiley & Sons, 1961.
18. Scott AI. Interpretations of the Ultraviolet Spectra of Natural Products. New York: Pergamon Press, 1964.

14

Inorganic Ultraviolet Filters

David Schlossman and Yun Shao
Kobo Products, Inc., South Plainfield, New Jersey, USA

EVOLUTION AND PERSPECTIVES

Evolution of Inorganic Ultraviolet Filters

The popularity of inorganic ultraviolet (UV) filters with consumers and formulators results from their effectiveness and safety. It is disclosed in JP Application

No. 1981-161,881 that when 0.1–40% of ultrafinely divided titanium oxide with a particle size of 10–30 nm, which has been rendered hydrophobic, is blended into cosmetic base materials, it transmits visible light but reflects and scatters the harmful UV rays (1).

There are no known allergies to physical sunscreens (2). Contrarily, there has been much data gathered from clinical studies that some organic sunscreens cause photoallergies, are skin sensitizers, and can penetrate through the dermis into the blood stream. The photostability of organic sunscreens varies and they may become degraded unless they are stabilized or encapsulated.

Physical sunscreens, particulates, inorganic UV filters, inorganic sunscreens, micronized pigments, micro, nano, ultrafine and mineral pigments are all terms that which will be used interchangeably in this chapter to describe attenuation grades of titanium dioxide and zinc oxide. Nowadays, many global brands are formulated with particulates as the sole sunscreen agent to attenuate UV radiation in baby and infant care products, and they are frequently contained in combination with organics in children's products and daily wear products for the face, lips, and eyes.

Notwithstanding their safety, there are some drawbacks to formulating sunscreens with inorganic pigments. The usual factors impairing demand are higher formulation costs and poor esthetics, including diminished spreading, moisturizing, besides the so-called whitening effect.

Titanium Dioxide and Zinc Oxide

Companies are permitted by the FDA to make a broad-spectrum protection label claim with either titanium dioxide or zinc oxide (3). During the past few years, there has been a shift to zinc oxide from titanium dioxide as more consumers are paying attention to warnings from dermatologists about the harmful effects of UV-A radiation and are favoring products with higher UV-A protection. Studies have been published in dermatologic journals in the USA, which report that micronized zinc oxide absorbs more UV light in the long-wave UV-A spectrum (340–380 nm) than micronized titanium dioxide (4,5). It is also popular because of its superior transparency since it has a lower refractive index than titanium dioxide, 2.0 compared with 2.7. Schering-Plough introduced during 2003, under their brand Coppertone KIDS® an SPF 50 UV-A/UV-B sunscreen lotion with zinc oxide. The FDA permits up to 25% of titanium dioxide and zinc oxide to be used in sunscreen products in the USA, however, these particulates may not be formulated together with butyl methoxy dibenzoyl methane (avobenzone), an organic UV-A sunscreen (3). In Europe, the COLIPA has yet to recommend zinc oxide be listed as a sunscreen active (6). MHW permits combinations of micronized pigments and avobenzone in Japan.

Perspectives for Inorganic UV Filters

Increased global competition in the personal care industry has enabled elegant formulations to be developed internationally. Today's micropigments as supplied, are finer in particle size, contain a narrower particle size distribution, have an improved physical and chemical stability, and are easier to disperse. During his presentation at the 2003 Florida SCC Sunscreen Symposium, David Steinberg remarked that the approval by the FDA of combinations of avobenzone together with micronized pigments should be forthcoming in the new sunscreen monograph (7). Demand for micropigments in the USA should increase after that. The future demand for titanium dioxide and zinc oxide pigments will in fact be influenced by the impending monograph, particularly the regulations on measuring UV-A (and a broad-spectrum sun protection claim), and whether SPF 30+ becomes the maximum amount of sun protection that can be claimed. Competition from new organic filters, broad spectrum organic particulates like methylene bis-benzotriazolyl tetramethylbutylphenol, and a further understanding of UV damage on skin structures will also influence demand (8).

PHYSICAL AND CHEMICAL PROPERTIES OF TITANIUM DIOXIDE AND ZINC OXIDE

General Properties

Titanium Dioxide

Titanium is the ninth most common element in the earth's crust. In nature, it exists only in combinations with other elements such as oxygen. Three titanium-containing ores are of commercial importance: ilmenite, rutile, and anatase. Ilmenite is a composite of oxides of iron and titanium and has a formula of $FeTiO_3$ or $FeOTiO_2$. Titanium dioxide content of ilmenite ranges from 45% to 60%. Important deposits are located mainly in Brazil, India, and Canada.

Naturally occurring rutile and anatase are not pure and contain various amounts of metals including those that pose health hazards to humans. Therefore, commercial TiO_2 is always synthesized. Although rutile and anatase have the same chemical identity, they are different in their crystalline structure. Anatase has a regular octahedral crystal lattice while rutile has a tetragonal one. Another type of titanium dioxide is called brookite, which forms an orthorhombic crystal. However, brookite has no commercial importance.

Out of the aforementioned three forms of titanium dioxide, rutile is the most thermally stable. When anatase and brookite are heated at a very high temperature, they convert into rutile, in which unit cell the atoms are more densely packed. Rutile and anatase have somewhat different physical and chemical properties, because of their difference in crystal lattice. Some of the properties are listed in Table 14.1.

Chemically, titanium dioxide is very stable. It is stable towards acids and bases except very concentrated strong acids. It is insoluble in all organic solvents. Therefore, it is considered to be essentially inert in all of its applications. It is very safe to use and has replaced many other white pigments, because of its inertness and insolubility.

Table 14.1 Physical Properties of Titanium Dioxide

Parameter	Rutile	Anatase
Density (g/cm^3)	4.2	3.9
Hardness (Mohs)	6–7	5.5–6
Refractive index	2.76	2.52
Dielectric constant	114	48
Melting point (°C)	1855	Converts into rutile

Zinc Oxide

Zinc ranks 24th in abundance but never occurs free in nature. Zinc is never found as the free metal but there are a number of important ores such as sphalerite (zinc blende, zinc sulfide, ZnS), smithsonite (zinc carbonate, $ZnCO_3$), zincspar (also zinc carbonate, $ZnCO_3$), and marmatite (zinc sulfide, ZnS, containing some iron sulfide, FeS). Zinc is widespread around the world. Important deposits are located in North America and Australia.

Pure zinc oxide (ZnO) is typically a white or yellow-white powder. Crystalline zinc oxide has a hexagonal crystal structure. Zinc oxide is produced by oxidizing zinc vapor in burners or by precipitation from zinc salt. The source of the zinc vapor is either impure zinc oxide or purified zinc metal. Zinc vapor generated from purified zinc metal will provide the highest purity zinc oxide that can be used in personal care products (9–11). Physical properties of zinc oxide are listed in Table 14.2.

Unlike titanium dioxide, zinc oxide is slightly soluble in water. The reported water solubility of zinc oxide ranges from 1.6 mg/L (29°C) to 5 mg/L (25°C). An important conversion in water is the hydrolysis of zinc oxide to zinc hydroxide. The reported water solubility of zinc hydroxide ranges from 2.92 mg/L (18°C) to 15.5 mg/L (29°C). The rate of conversion of zinc oxide to zinc hydroxide is dependent on various factors, the most important of which is temperature.

Although zinc oxide is not reactive in most conditions where practical applications are employed, its reactivity needs to be noted to avoid misuse. It can adsorb carbon monoxide and carbon dioxide and react with carbon dioxide in moist air generating zinc carbonate. Zinc oxide and zinc hydroxide are amphoteric. They can react with acid to form zinc salts or with alkali to form zincates.

Table 14.2 Physical Properties of Zinc Oxide

Parameter	Value
Density (g/cm^3)	5.7
Hardness (Mohs)	4
Refractive index	1.99
Dielectric constant	1.7–2.5
Melting point (°C)	1975

Isoelectric Point

When a pigment is dispersed in a liquid, the stability of the dispersion is affected by the electrical charge on the pigment surface, which gives an electrostatic repulsion to keep particles apart. The classic method to measure the surface charge is zeta potential. This is typically done in a polar solvent and the zeta potential is measured as the pH of the medium changes. Isoelectric point (IEP) is obtained when a pH is such that zeta potential is zero, that is, the surface of the particles is neutral. The IEP of pure titanium dioxide is 3.8 and that for zinc oxide is 9. For various reasons, TiO_2 is coated with alumina or silica. The IEP is then altered and determined by the nature of the coating. With alumina coating, the IEP shifts to a higher pH of 7. With silica coating, the IEP shifts to a lower pH of 2.1, which renders the surface negatively charged in most applications. The surface charge can be greatly changed and increased by the adsorption of polymeric electrolytes. As a result, polymeric electrolytes are frequently used in pigment dispersion.

In a nonaqueous medium, the surface charges of TiO_2 and ZnO are much less. Since TiO_2 and ZnO are often coated with organic compounds when they are dispersed in a nonaqueous medium, the effect of surface charge on the stability of dispersion is less important and the steric repulsion becomes a predominant factor in stabilizing the dispersed particulate.

Photocatalytic Activity

Both TiO_2 and ZnO are semiconductors whose electrons can be excited with energy and promoted from valence band to the conducting band in which the electron can move around the atomic structure. The energy gap between the two bands is 3.06 eV for rutile and 3.20 eV for anatase corresponding to a long-wavelength absorption edge of 420 and 390 nm, respectively. Light with a shorter wavelength has enough energy to excite the electrons in the valence band and therefore can be absorbed by TiO_2. When the electrons are promoted to the conducting band, they can migrate away from the original lattice and, therefore, create hole–electron pairs. The electrons and holes react with dissolved oxygen, surface hydroxyl groups and absorbed water to form hydroxide and superoxide radicals that can be responsible for many side reactions (Fig. 14.1).

$$\mathrm{TiO_2 + UV\ light \longrightarrow e^- + hole^+} \qquad \text{(Rxn. 1)}$$

$$\mathrm{e^- + O_2 \longrightarrow O_2^-} \qquad \text{(Rxn. 2)}$$

$$\mathrm{hole^+ + OH^- \longrightarrow \cdot OH + TiO_2} \qquad \text{(Rxn. 3)}$$

$$\mathrm{e^- + Ti^{4+} \longrightarrow Ti^{3+}} \qquad \text{(Rxn. 4)}$$

Figure 14.1 Reactions involved in the photocatalytic activity of TiO_2.

When O_2 is excluded, reaction 2 cannot proceed. Instead reaction 4 will take place. At such a state the electrons can absorb visible light and cause graying. This phenomenon can occur to a TiO_2 containing product that is packed in an airtight, transparent package.

The band gap for zinc oxide is 3.35 eV, which corresponds to a wavelength of ~380 nm. Under UV irradiation, reactions 1–3 listed in Fig. 14.1 for titanium dioxide also take place in zinc oxide. Reaction 4 will not occur due to the nature of the zinc chemistry. Therefore, graying caused by UV absorption does not occur to zinc oxide.

Scientists at Kemira Corporation studied the difference in photocatalytic activity between ultrafine rutile and anatase. The sample was dispersed in melamine–formaldehyde resin and the drawdown of the paste was exposed to UV light for 3 min. The relative photocatalytic activity was determined by measuring the darkening of the paste induced by the reduction of Ti^{4+} to Ti^{3+}. Based on data obtained, they concluded the following.

- Rutiles are much more light resistant than anatase crystals
- Calcination of crystals greatly improves light stability
- A heavy inorganic posttreatment is the key to improving their light stability (Kemira Pigments, personal communication, 2003).

Kobayashi and Kalriess conducted a quantitative study on the photodecomposition of gaseous acetaldehyde in the presence of various grades of TiO_2 and ZnO (12). The rate constant of the first-order reaction was calculated from measured data and was used to indicate the level of the photocatalytic activity. Some interesting data are presented in the Table 14.3.

The experimental data confirmed that rutile is much more photostable than anatase. Zinc oxide is more stable than titanium dioxide, but the level of its photocatalytic activity cannot be ignored.

Researchers at Sakai reported suppressed photochemical activity of their micronized zinc oxide (SF-20) with an organosiloxane treatment. They found that a 10% slurry of this zinc oxide in white petrolatum after 9 h exposure under a 365-nm UV lamp had decreased yellowing (13). Reduced zinc ion

Table 14.3 Rate Constant of the First-Order Reaction

Sample	Size (nm)	Treatment	Rate
TiO_2 (anatase)	410	None	4.76
		2% Methicone	<0.01
TiO_2 (70% rutile)	21	None	3.70
TiO_2 (rutile)	30–50	Alumina	0.13
		3% Lecithin	0.033
ZnO	15–35	None	1.83
		3% Methicone	<0.01

bleeding was reported by treating micro zinc oxide with silica by Showa Denka under alkaline (1% ammonia, pH 11.7) or acidic (0.012% nitric acid, pH 2.7) conditions. Once the soluble zinc concentration rises in a cosmetic formulation containing fatty acids, the viscosity of the formulation increases and eventually gelation occurs (14). The photocatalytic activity of zinc oxide can be almost completely suppressed if the pigment is coated first with an inorganic coating, and is secondarily coated with an organic compound.

The test methods described above for measuring the photocatalytic activity and many others reported in literature are often too complicated for a cosmetic chemist to perform. A few industrial methods have then been developed during the past few years. These methods are indeed very useful for quick comparison study to screen different types of titanium dioxide, although indirect and not analytically quantitative.

Glycol Method

A sample of the inorganic sunscreen is mixed with propylene glycol. The mixture is preferably milled on a Hoover Muller or a bench-top mill. The paste obtained is placed on a white chart and is then covered with a glass plate. The edges of the glass plates are sealed so that the paste is isolated from the air. The sample is then exposed to sunshine or UV light for a certain period of time. The change of color of the paste before and after the exposure can be assessed visually or quantified instrumentally (15).

Vitamin Method

In this method, a sample of the inorganic sunscreen, 1% solution of ascorbyl monopalmitate in decaglyceryl monolaurate, and propylene glycol monocaprylate are mixed completely. The paste is drawn down on a white chart. The color is then compared to the blank sample in which no ascorbyl monopalmitate is added (15).

Optical Behaviors

When light hits a particle, it can be reflected, scattered, or absorbed. A simple equation for the interaction of light with a particle is expressed in Fig. 14.2, where I_t is intensity of transmitted light, I_0 is the intensity of incident light; I_r, I_s, and I_a are the intensities of the reflected, scattered, and absorbed light, respectively. For submicrometer particles, the specular reflection is often very small. Scattering and absorption are the major attenuation mechanism and the predominance is related to the particle size and the chemical composition.

$$I_t = I_0 - (I_r + I_s + I_a)$$

Figure 14.2 Equation describing the interaction of light with a particle.

Scattering

The scattering from molecules and very tiny particles (<0.1 wavelength) is predominantly Rayleigh scattering. When the particle size is at the same magnitude as the wavelength, Mie scattering predominates. This scattering produces a pattern like an antenna lobe, with a sharper and more intensely forward lobe for larger particles (Fig. 14.3).

For attenuation grade TiO_2, the scattering follows Mie theory and the intensity of scattering (I_s) can be expressed as in Fig. 14.4, where N is the number of the particles, I_0 is the intensity of the incident light, d is the diameter of the particle, λ is the wavelength of the incident light, and m is the relative refractive index, which is defined as the ratio of the refractive index of the particle over that of the medium in which the particle is (16,17).

As shown in Mie's equation, the intensity of scattering is proportional to the sixth power of the particle diameter and therefore, a large particle is much more efficient in scattering. At a given weight, Nd^3 is constant. Thus, scattering is proportional to the third power of the particle diameter. As a result, in order to reduce the scattering of visible light (the whitening effect), the reduction of the top size in a distribution is important, even more so than to reduce the mean particle size. On other hand, when the size is reduced too much to minimize the whitening, the dominance of scattering of UV light will give way to absorption.

Another important factor in Mie's equation is the relative refractive index. In most sunscreen products, the media (like oils) have a refractive index of 1.33–1.6. When rutile TiO_2 with a refractive index of 2.76 is used, the relative refractive index is about 1.8. If ZnO is used instead, its lower reactive index of 1.99 will result in a relative refractive index of about 1.3. According to the Mie's law, TiO_2 will be nearly three times effective in scattering light.

Absorption

As aforementioned, light with wavelength <420 nm has enough energy to excite the electrons in the valence band and therefore can be absorbed by rutile TiO_2. The theoretical calculation has shown, however, the absorption of UV at longer wavelength is weak and gradually reaches a plateau at 360 nm (Fig. 14.5). TiO_2 is not considered as an efficient UV-A, especially UV-A II,

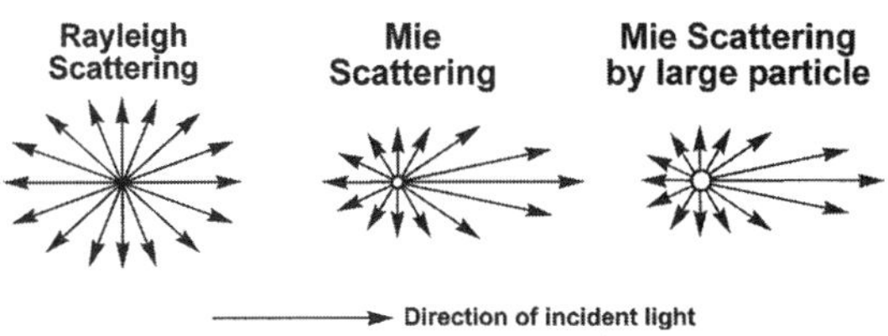

Figure 14.3 Scattering patterns for Mie and Rayleigh scattering.

$$I_s \propto \frac{Nd^6}{\lambda^4} * \left[\frac{m^2 - 1}{m^2 + 2}\right]^2 * I_0$$

Figure 14.4 Equation of Mie scattering.

absorber, but is an efficient UV-B absorber. The attenuation of UV-A by TiO_2 mainly takes places via scattering (18).

Since the band gap wavelength of zinc oxide is longer than that of titanium dioxide, ZnO absorbs broader spectrum range of UV light than TiO_2. Moreover, due to the difference in electron energy states (i.e., band structure), the UV cutoff is sharper for ZnO than for TiO_2.

The absorption is a function of the number of atoms that interact with the light in its pathway. For a single photon, the size has no effect on the absorption. In reality, however, when the particle size is reduced, there will be more particles that become available to interact and hence absorb the UV light. Due to this increase in the interactions, smaller particle size will result in a stronger UV absorption when the weight of TiO_2 or ZnO is fixed (19). The limitation on the particle size, however, is quantum behavior, which occurs when the size of the particle is close or smaller than the exciton Bohr diameter (20), which is about 5 nm. Neither TiO_2 nor ZnO on the market has a size even close to this dimension yet, which means that the smaller the particle size, theoretically, the better the UV absorption (Fig. 14.6).

MANUFACTURERS OF INORGANIC ULTRAVIOLET FILTERS

As mentioned earlier, commercial TiO_2 is always synthesized. Tayca, ISK, Sumitomo Cement, and Sakai, the dominant global manufacturers of micronized pigments all have their factories in Japan. Kemira, another important producer of micronized titanium dioxide, is located in Finland. Manufacturers are listed in Table 14.4.

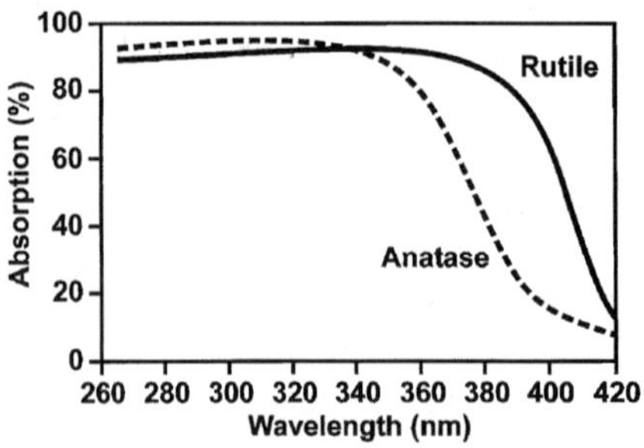

Figure 14.5 Calculated UV absorption curves for rutile and anatase TiO_2.

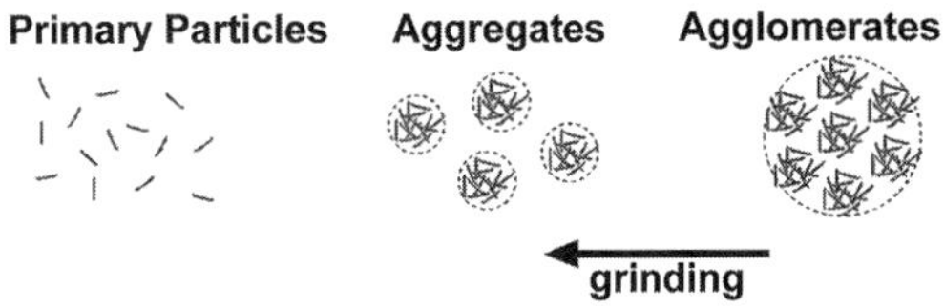

Figure 14.6 Particle size and transparency.

Production of Micronized Titanium Dioxide

Titanium dioxide pigments are typically made from one of two chemical processes (21). The sulfate process is used by the majority of micro titanium producers including Tayca, the largest global supplier of rutile-based micronized titanium dioxide (Tayca Corporation, personal communication, 2000). In this process, the titanium ores are reacted with sulfuric acid resulting in a titanyl sulfate intermediate. Sachtleben manufactures anatase grades of TiO_2 from naturally occurring ore. The ore is converted to a soluble form using highly concentrated sulfuric acid (22). The chloride process is newer. It produces pigments by reacting titanium ores with chlorine gas at 900°C to obtain titanium tetrachloride. Hydrolysis of these titanium salts and calcination are necessary production steps to obtain a rutile pigment. Rutilization catalysts such as Al^{3+} and aluminum chloride enable the process to occur at lower temperatures. This is important to avoid excessive particle growth and pigment discoloration (21).

Tioxide Group PLC patented a particulate material consisting of a noncalcined titanium dioxide. The particles are acicular in shape within the range of 10–150 nm. They are coated with an oxide or hydrous oxide layer of alumina and silica and contain an organic dispersing agent selected from the family of compounds consisting of substituted carboxylic acids and soap bases such as polyhydroxy stearic acid (23).

Table 14.4 Manufacturers of Micronized Titanium Dioxide

Manufacturer	Trade name	Internet address
Degussa	P-25	www.degussa.com
Ishihara Sangyo Kaisha, Ltd.	TTO	www.iijnet.or.jp/itc-fmp/
Kemira Pigments Oy	UV Titan	www.kemira.com/pigments
Rhodia	Mirasun	www.rhodia.com
Sachtleben	Hombitec	www.sachtleben.de/h/e/hom/0000e.html
Showa Denka	Maxlight	www.sdk.co.jp/chemicals/index.html
Tayca Corporation	MT Series	www.tayca.co.jp/english/file/04/04_02.html
Titan Kogyo	STT	www.titankogyo.co.jp
Uniqema	Solaveil, Tioveil	www.uniqema.com/pc

Alternatively, particles of titania can be prepared by decomposition or hydrolysis of suitable titanium compounds. High-temperature hydrolysis of an organic titanium compound such as titanium alkoxide can be used. Oxidation or hydrolysis in the vapor state of titanium halides under appropriate conditions can also be used (24). Degussa manufactures a fumed titanium dioxide of high purity (see www.degussa.com).

Manufacturers of Micronized Titanium Dioxide

Kemira, ISK, and Sachtleben are manufacturers of both pigmentary and micronized grades of titanium dioxide for personal care products. Micronized titanium dioxide is supplied at a particle size of approximately 1/10 of the particle size of pigmentary titanium dioxide (24). Commercially available micropigments range in particle size of 10–60 nm and attenuate a broad range of UV light. Titan Kogyo and Showa Denka both offer micronized titanium dioxide pigments larger than 100 nm (25,26).

ISK manufactures their micronized titanium dioxide by a proprietary method, which is neither the sulfate nor the chloride process. Rutile, anatase, and combinations of both are produced. ISK distinguishes their grades as made by either the calcination or wet process. Wet process grades are superior in dispersibility, but calcined grades have superior physical and chemical stability (ISK, personal correspondence, 1995). ISK also offers different shapes such as spherical, dendrite, and spindle (27). They have also developed a titanium dioxide balloon that consists of micronized titanium particles, but feels smoother than micronized titanium dioxide (28). The shell wall was found to be too fragile to permit any commercial applications besides loose powders (Toshiki Pigment Co. Ltd., personal correspondence, 2000).

Kemira produces rutile grades by the sulfate process (Kemira Pigments, personal correspondence, 2003). The optical properties are mainly developed in the crystallization and/or calcination process steps during their manufacturing process of 20 nm titanium dioxide (29). Rhodia, Sachtleben, Titan Kogyo, all supply an anatase crystal and Degussa supplies a mixture of anatase and rutile. Anatase reflects more UV light as opposed to a rutile crystal that absorbs more UV light (30).

Typical Specifications of Micronized Titanium Dioxide

Consideration of the particle size and surface treatment are important in selecting a grade of micronized titanium dioxide for a given application. Popular grades are included in Table 14.5.

Production and Manufacturers of Micronized Zinc Oxide

The different production techniques to produce nanosized zinc oxide can be summarized as follows:

- Vapor techniques (e.g., combustion synthesis, gas condensation, plasma synthesis)

Table 14.5 Micronized Titanium Dioxide—Typical Specifications

Supplier	Grade	TiO_2 (%)	Crystal form	Primary particle size (surface area—BET)	Surface treatment
Degussa	P-25	$\geq$99.5	Anatase	21 nm (50 $\pm$ 15 m^2/g)	None
EMD	Eusolex T-2000	76–82	Anatase	10–15 nm	Alumina, dimethicone
ISK	TTO S-4	>82	Rutile	15 nm	AHSA[a]
ISK	TTO S-3	>82	Rutile	15 nm	Alumina
ISK	TTO V-3	>82	Rutile	10 nm	Alumina
Kemira	UV Titan M170	>75	Rutile	14 nm	Alumina, methicone
Kemira	UV Titan M262	>85	Rutile	20 nm	Alumina, dimethicone
Sachtleben	Hombitec L5	75–85	Anatase	(80–160 m^2/g)	Silica, silicone
Showa Denka	Maxlight TS-04	64	Unknown	35 nm	Silica
Tayca	MT-100T	>80	Rutile	15 nm	AHSA[a]
Tayca	MT-500B	>96	Rutile	35 nm	Alumina
Tayca	MT-100Z	>73	Rutile	15 nm	AHSA[a]
Titan Kogyo	STT 65C-S	96.5	Anatase	(64 m^2/g)	None

[a]Aluminum hydroxide and stearic acid.

- Liquid techniques (e.g., chemical precipitation, hydrothermal processing, sol–gel processing)
- Solid state techniques (e.g., mechanochemical processing).

Manufacturers are listed in Table 14.6.

According to Innes et al., the major issues to overcome in the production of nanopowders are controlling the growth of the particles and then stopping the newly formed particles from agglomerating once formed. Hard agglomerates of zinc oxide are formed when they are manufactured by vapor techniques. This is because the nanoparticles are created by the rapid solidification of a liquid or vapor into a gaseous medium. The particles will have a higher surface energy than particles made by other methods and will be more reactive. These more reactive surfaces will aid the formation of hard agglomerates and thus individual particles will be more difficult to disperse (21).

Advanced Nano Technologies' mechanochemical processing uses a high-energy dry milling to induce chemical reactions during ball–powder collisions to form nanoparticles in a solid state matrix. Agglomeration is minimized by ensuring the particles are encapsulated on formation by a solid diluent (typically NaCl). The mean particle size is 25 nm with a standard deviation of 3.3 nm (31). Nanophase manufactures micronized zinc oxide by a vapor technique (see www.nanophase.com).

Table 14.6 Manufacturers of Zinc Oxide

Manufacturer	Trade name	Internet address
Advanced Nano Technologies	Zinclear	www.ant-powders.com/zinclear.htm
BASF	Z-Cote	www.basf.com
Elementis Specialties	Nanox	www.elementis-specialties.com
Zinc Corporation of America	USP-1	www.zinccorp.com
Nanophase	NanoGuard	www.nanophase.com
Sakai	Finex	www.sakai-chem.co.jp
Showa Denka	Maxlight ZS	www.sdk.co.jp/chemicals/index.html
Sumitomo Cement	ZnO series	www.socnb.com/index_e.html
Tayca Corporation	MZ Series	www.tayca.co.jp/english/file/04/07_03.html
Haarmann and Reimer	ZnO Neutral	www.symrise.com

Manufacturers of micronized zinc oxide are included in Table 14.6. The most popular grades that are sold are ZnO-350 in Japan, manufactured by Sumitomo Osaka Cement, and Z-Cote HP-1 supplied by BASF in the USA.

Typical Specifications of Micronized Zinc Oxide

As with micronized titanium dioxide, particle size and surface treatment of micronized zinc oxide are important factors in selecting a grade to formulate. Popular grades supplied to the personal care market by the leading manufacturers are listed in Table 14.7.

SURFACE TREATMENT

Background

The physical and chemical stability of micronized pigments were discussed in the section titled "Physical and Chemical Properties of Titanium Dioxide and Zinc Oxide." Therefore, it should be of no surprise that surface treatments add value to micronized pigments. As a matter of fact, multiple coatings have become a standard industrial practice and are known to be very effective. They are of paramount importance for compatibility in formulation, photostability for years, and mechanical properties (32). Surface treatments are produced by micropigment manufacturers and by companies specializing in organic surface treatments. Treatment specialists include Daito Kasei and Miyoshi Kasei in Japan, and US Cosmetics and Kobo Products in the USA. Several popular treatments are listed in Table 14.8. It is imperative to use a coated TiO_2 or ZnO for a sunscreen application to ensure the stability of the product.

Table 14.7 Micronized Zinc Oxide—Typical Specifications

Supplier	Grade	ZnO (%)	Primary particle size (Surface area—BET)	Surface treatment
ANT	Zinclear	–	25 nm	Stearic acid
BASF	Z-Cote	98	$<$200 nm	None
Elementis	Nanox 200	$>$99	60 nm (17 m^2/g)	None
Sakai	Finex SF-20	$>$99	60 nm (20 m^2/g)	None
Showa Denka	ZS-032	80	31 nm	Silica
Sumitomo Cement	ZnO-350	$>$99	35 nm	None
Tayca	MZ-700	$>$99	10–20 nm	None
Tayca	MZ-500	$>$99	20–30 nm	None
Tayca	MZ-300	$>$99	30–40 nm	None

Surface Properties of Micronized Pigments

Small particle size TiO_2 or ZnO are preferred for beach and daily wear applications, to reduce skin whitening accordingly. The photocatalytic activity, however, becomes much greater since the surface area of the pigment particle

Table 14.8 Popular Surface Treatments of Micronized TiO_2 and ZnO

Manufacturer/supplier	Grade	Type	Surface treatment	Description
BASF	Z-Cote HP-1	ZnO	Trimethoxy caprylyl silane	Hydrophobic
Degussa	T-805	TiO_2	Trimethoxy caprylyl silane	Hydrophobic
EMD	Eusolex® T-2000	TiO_2	Alumina, dimethicone	Hydrophilic
EMD	Eusolex® T-S	TiO_2	Alumina, stearic acid	Lipophilic
Ishihara	TTO S-4	TiO_2	Aluminum hydroxide, stearic acid	Lipophilic
Ishihara	TTO S-3	TiO_2	Alumina	Hydrophilic
Ishihara	TTO 51-C (calcined)	TiO_2	Aluminum hydroxide, stearic acid	Lipophilic
Kemira	M170	TiO_2	Alumina, methicone	Hydrophobic
Kemira	M262	TiO_2	Alumina, dimethicone	Hydrophobic
Kobo	ZnO-XZ-MS4	ZnO	Methicone	Hydrophobic
Kobo	R10-TiO_2-TTS7	TiO_2	ITT/TCS crosspolymer	Lipophilic
Sachtleben	Hombitec L5	TiO_2	Silica, silicone	Hydrophobic
Sakai	Finex-K2	ZnO	Zinc silicate, silica	Hydrophilic
Showa Denka	Maxlight TS-04	ZnO	Silica	Hydrophilic
Showa Denka	Maxlight ZS-032	ZnO	Silica	Hydrophilic

increases one magnitude faster with a drop in size (33). Therefore, the surface of a micronized or ultrafine pigment must be treated to suppress this activity to minimize or eliminate potential side reactions that can occur to other ingredients in a formula. The anatase form of titanium dioxide is more reactive than the rutile form, and calcined grades less reactive than wet processed grades as reviewed earlier. Rhodia reported anatase to be a better substrate for an optimal surface treatment (34).

A separate issue with decreasing particle size to be discussed further is agglomeration. The larger specific surface areas are thus the reactive surface area for the formation of aggregates, agglomerates, and flocculates (and also adsorption processes). The forces of attraction that cause aggregates are explained more fully in the section on particle size under the heading "Influence of Particle Size on UV Attenuation by TiO_2 and ZnO."

TiO_2 surface properties have been summarized by Sachtleben Chemie GmbH as follows:

1. Primary particle size or specific surface area
2. The presence of acidic and basic hydroxyl groups
3. The moisture absorbed
4. The surface charge (resulting from defects, dopings, unsaturated valencies and the adsorption of ions).

The surface of untreated titanium dioxide pigments is polar or hydrophilic and may be characterized significantly by oxygen ions and by the pronounced hydration and accumulation of hydroxyl ions (22). Pigments have air voids trapped between particles and absorb moisture on their surface to reduce their energy state (21).

Inorganic/Organic Surface Treatments

Surface treatments of micronized pigments are broadly classified as inorganic and organic. Inorganic surface treatments are paramount to both the pigments physical and chemical stability and heat stability, as was noted earlier by scientists at Kemira. Alumina, silica, and zirconia are the widely used inorganic surface treatments. Zirconia is not allowed in Europe. Inorganic treatments are typically formulated by the manufacturers as part of the crystal, or they can be added as a posttreatment. Calcination of the treatment results in the bonding of the treatment to the pigment surface, but the high temperature requirements cause the particle size to increase. Organic surface treatments like alkoxy titanates, silanes, and methyl polysiloxanes react with and displace the water of hydration absorbed on a pigment surface modifying it from hydrophilic to hydrophobic or lipophilic. Organic surface treatments benefit the particles' physical and chemical stability and promote wetting and steric stabilization in a carrier.

Popular Surface Treatments for Micronized Pigments

Tayca Corporation characterizes their surface-treated micronized titanium dioxide as hydrophilic or hydrophobic (34). Tayca supplies micronized pigments coated with inorganic and organic surface treatments, such as alumina, silica, aluminum stearate, dimethicone, and methicone (35). The organic treatments are applied by a wet process to minimize the aggregation of particles. Inorganic treatments are either calcined or produced by a wet process. Aluminum hydroxide and aluminum stearate have been the most popular combination for surface treating micronized titanium dioxide. Treatments may be classified as a lipophilic treatment, because it enhances the wetting of the pigment in an ester (36). Researchers at Estee Lauder claimed a novel organic dispersion comprised of this surface-treated micronized titanium dioxide and a suitable branched chain ester without the use of a dispersing aid (37). In the ester isononyl isononanoate, a dispersion consisting of 65% of Tayca's MT-100T can be milled without a dispersant (38). Kemira utilizes wet milling to break down aggregates and treats the surface with alumina to improve stability, and dimethicone to render the surface property of its micronized titanium dioxide to hydrophobic (29).

Surface Treatments of Micronized Titanium Dioxide or Zinc Oxide for Use with Avobenzone

Outside of the USA, combinations of inorganic UV filters and avobenzone are allowed. It is necessary to have a uniform and densely coated pigment to maintain the activity of the avobenzone, because it reacts with metal ions. Tayca's MT-100Z and Kemira's M262 have both an inorganic and organic surface treatment, which makes their pigments compatible with avobenzone. Showa Denka uses a liquid phase deposition method to coat zinc oxide (and also titanium dioxide) with a thin layer of silica (14). Sakai offers a grade coated with zinc silicate and silica. These treated pigments have been found to be compatible with avobenzone (39).

Hydrophilic Surface Treatments for Micronized Pigments

Alumina and silica are hydrophilic treatments that enhance the dispersability and stability of the micronized pigment in an aqueous phase. Hydrophilic treatments like polysaccharides, polyacrylates, and polyether silanes have been promoted with limited success.

Selecting the Proper Surface Treatment

Popular surface treatments have distinct benefits and drawbacks. It is important to consider the needs of the formula before deciding on the best treatment. Schlossman and Shao measured the premix viscosities of hydrophobic and lipophilic treatments in esters, hydrocarbons and silicone fluids to determine their dispersibility in multimedia (40). Popular surface treatments of micronized pigments are detailed in Table 14.8.

Proper surface treatment is essential for:

- No aggregation
  - Achieve transparency
- Homogeneous dispersion
  - Ease of formulation
  - Ability to disperse in formulation
  - Stability
- Stable dispersion
  - No dispersing agents required (22).

Popular surface treatments of micronized pigments are detailed in Table 14.8.

INFLUENCE OF PARTICLE SIZE ON UV ATTENUATION BY TiO_2 AND ZnO

The theoretical calculations were reviewed in the section titled "Physical and Chemical Properties of Titanium Dioxide and Zinc Oxide." In the following section, experimental data from practical applications of micronized pigments will be reviewed and examined.

Particle Size

Many studies on the influence of the particle size on UV attenuation by inorganic sunscreens have been reported in literature, but the term "particle size" was seldom clearly defined. This often causes confusions when cosmetic chemists try to apply the reported study result in real practice. Thus, it is necessary to clarify the definition of particle size before undertaking the discussion about the influence of the particle size on UV attenuation by inorganic sunscreens.

As shown in Fig. 14.6, both TiO_2 and ZnO powders consist of primary particles that are crystalline structures held together by atomic or molecular bonding. The primary particle size is determined by process conditions when TiO_2 or ZnO crystals are forming and will not be affected by the subsequent processing during their applications. The primary particles always aggregate to form secondary particles due to their high surface energy such as van der Waals force, electrostatic force, hydrogen bonding of surface hydroxyl groups, and water bridging between the primary particles. These forces for the aggregation get stronger as the primary size decreases and the specific surface area increases. The aggregates in turn group to form agglomerates, the structure of which is often loose and easy to break with mechanical force. Because the sizes of either agglomerate and aggregate can vary depending on the dispersion status of the particles and are not considered the intrinsic property of a particular grade of TiO_2 or ZnO, the manufacturers often choose to report only the primary particle size, which is either measured by using an electron microscope or calculated from the measured specific surface area. Since the primary particles have a size much smaller than the wavelength of UV light and always form aggregates, they do not interact with light independently. As a result, the size of the aggregates rather than primary particle size should be used to characterize TiO_2 or ZnO in actual application.

In practice, the particle size is often measured by using a light scattering size analyzer. The powder or dispersion sample is diluted to a usually low concentration in an appropriate solvent. The scattering intensity of laser light by the particles in the sample is recorded, calculated, and transformed into particle size distribution from which mean particle size and standard deviation can be derived. Although the dilution in the sample preparation may alter the particle size in the actual product to some extent, the discrepancy has been generally accepted until a better analytical method becomes available. In the following sections, the term of particle size will be used to represent the mean particle size.

Influence of Particle Size on UV Attenuation

Titanium Dioxide

Particle size and UV/visible transmittance: For sunscreen application, attenuation grade titanium dioxide and zinc oxide with a primary particle size of less than 100 nm are used to minimize the whitening. Although the primary particle size of these materials can be as small as 10 nm, the agglomeration is so severe that an efficient milling of the pigment is always necessary to disperse the particles. Otherwise, the advantage of a small size will not be displayed. A common practice is to grind a predispersion of either TiO_2 or ZnO. The primary particle size becomes the key factor in deciding the highest possible transparency when the dispersion is properly formulated and milled. In a study by Schlossman, four types of titanium oxide with similar metal soap treatment but different primary particle sizes were milled in fairly well controlled conditions and the properties of all dispersions were compared. The particle sizes are listed in Table 14.9 and the UV/visible transmittance curves are shown in Fig. 14.7.

Table 14.9 Particle Size of TiO_2 Dispersions

Sample	PPS (nm)	PS (nm)
1	15	125.3
2	35	154.1
3	100	251.1
4	180	263.4

Note: PPS, primary particle size; PS, particle size measured.

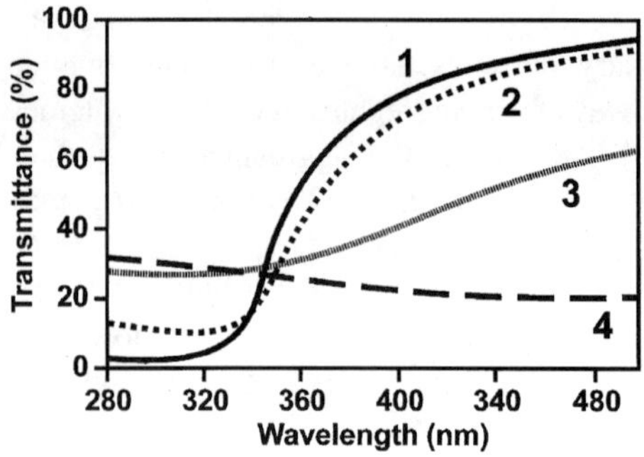

Figure 14.7 Transmittance curves of TiO_2 dispersions in isononyl isononanoate; primary particle sizes: 1 = 15 nm; 2 = 35 nm; 3 = 100 nm; 4 = 180 nm (TiO_2 concentration: 0.001% in $CHCl_3$).

It is very clear from the transmittance curves in Fig. 14.7 that transmittance of visible light (>400 nm) is much higher when the particle size is smaller. This result was easily confirmed by comparing the drawdown of the dispersions on a glass plate. When the particle size of TiO_2 dispersion is >200 nm, like samples 3 and 4, the curves appears to be rather flat across both UV and visible regions. These TiO_2 samples cannot be used to make sunscreen lotions as they will be too whitening and UV attenuation will be too weak (38).

Both samples 1 and 2 have high transmittance in visible range and are suitable for sunscreen lotions. Sample 1 has smaller size and the transmittance under 320 nm is also lower indicating that sample 1 will give a high SPF when TiO_2 use level is the same. However, sample 2 has a lower transmittance in almost the entire UV-A range (335–400 nm). As a result, it is predicted that it will give a better PFA (protection factor for UV-A) score.

Theoretical calculation by Stamatakis et al. (41) and experimental data from Sakamoto et al. (42) showed that the attenuation of UV light with a wavelength of 300 nm (UV-B) increases as the size decreases but that of UV light with a wavelength of 350 nm (UV-A) decreases if the particle size is 100 nm or smaller. Therefore, it became clear for TiO_2 that:

1. UV-B attenuation is predominately due to its absorption, which increases as the particle size decreases.
2. UV-A attenuation is predominately due to scattering by TiO_2. Particle size needs to be controlled to maximize the attenuation without causing whitening.

Particle size and sun protection factor: Scientists at Tayca and Tri-K Industries, Inc. compared the sun protection factor (SPF) values of both o/w (oil in water) and w/o (water in oil) sunscreen lotions using either straight TiO_2 powder or milled TiO_2 dispersion (43). The TiO_2 had a primary particle size of 15 nm and was coated with aluminum hydroxide and stearic acid. The particle size of TiO_2 in dispersion was about 0.4 μm. The size of TiO_2 powder in emulsion was not reported but was probably over 1 μm. The *in vitro* test results clearly demonstrated the advantages of using a preground TiO_2 dispersion—up to 70% increase in SPF value (Fig. 14.8). Similar results have been reported by other researchers in literature (44).

In vivo study on the relationship of the particle size of TiO_2 and the SPF of the corresponding sunscreen lotions was reported by Schlossman et al. (38). The results are listed in Table 14.10. It is evident that SPF depends on the particle size and the smaller size yields higher SPF.

Particle size and PFA: Table 14.11 lists the *in vivo* PFA test results for sun lotions using different sized TiO_2 (38). As mentioned above, TiO_2 attenuates UV-A mainly by scattering. As a rule of thumb, the maximum scattering at a particular wavelength occurs when the diameter of a particle is half of the wavelength to be scattered (45). In addition, the scattering intensity by a bigger and heavier particle is much stronger than by a smaller one. The particles in formula A are too small to be effective in scattering UV-A. The particles in B are bigger and are very effective in scattering UV-A. Therefore, when the size of TiO_2 is well controlled, it can be very effective in attenuating both UV-B and UV-A, providing a broad-spectrum protection. This type of TiO_2 can be especially useful in formulating color cosmetics with sun protection claims.

Zinc Oxide

Particle size and UV/visible transmittance: In Schlossman's study, four types of ZnO were dispersed and milled under the same conditions. The particle sizes are listed in Table 14.12 and the transmittance curves are shown in Fig. 14.9. Unlike TiO_2, ZnO dispersions are rather transparent even when the size is quite large. ZnO absorbs UV light more uniformly, and it has a sharp cutoff that starts around 375 nm and shifts slightly to a shorter wavelength as

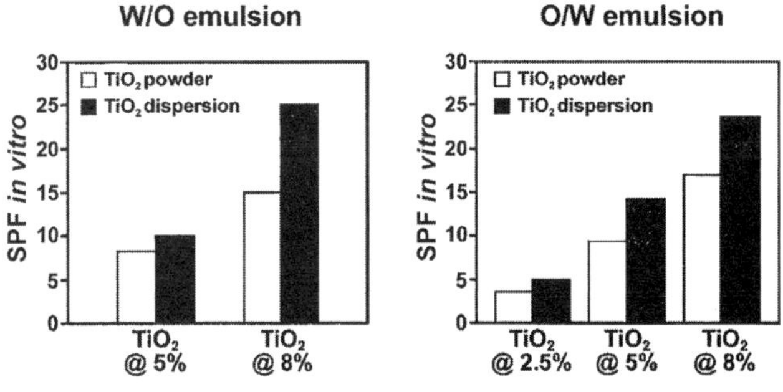

Figure 14.8 *In vitro* SPF of TiO_2 in W/O and O/W emulsions: comparison of straight TiO_2 powder and ground TiO_2 dispersion.

Table 14.10 *In vivo* SPF Test Results of TiO_2-Containing Sunscreen Lotions

Formula type	PPS (nm)	Dispersion PS (nm)	Active (%)	SPF (UV-B)
O/W	15	125.3	10.49	50.0
O/W	15	125.3	10.49	41.2
W/O	15	132.1	10.49	37.5
W/O	15	132.1	8.74	37.5
	35	194.6	1.96	
W/O	15	132.1	6.24	30.5
	35	194.5	4.23	
W/O	35	154.1	10.29	28.4
O/W	15	MT-100T powder	7.80	9.60

Note: 15 nm TiO_2 is MT-100T; 35 nm TiO_2 is MT-500B (from Tayca Corporation). PPS, primary particle size; PS, particle size measured; SPF, sun protection factor.

the particle size gets smaller. The UV curves in Fig. 14.9 also show that the smaller the primary particle size (PPS) the less UV light is transmitted across the entire UV-B region and most of the UV-A region, indicating a better broad-spectrum protection (38).

In *in vitro* PFA testing such as critical wavelength and UV-A/UV-B ratio, the relative attenuation power in UV-B and UV-A is more heavily weighted than the absolute attenuation power. As a result, sample 1 could give a lower PFA score than sample 4 whose attenuation is more evenly distributed through 290–400 nm. In *in vivo* SPF testing, the results can be opposite. Therefore, the selection of a suitable grade of ZnO will depend on the test method chosen.

Particle size, SPF, and PFA: Table 14.13 lists the *in vivo* SPF and PFA test scores for sunscreen lotions that contain ZnO of different particle sizes. Obviously, as the particle size decreased the SPF increased dramatically. The PFA scores also increased as the size decreased to 35 nm. However, the UV-A/UV-B ratio obtained *in vitro* indicates that large particle size ZnO has a better UV-A protection.

Because ZnO is not considered to be a potent UV-B attenuator, it is often used in combination of other organic sunscreens. Therefore, the study on

Table 14.11 *In vivo* PFA Scores of TiO_2-Containing Sunscreen Lotions

Formula type	PPS (nm)	Dispersion PS (nm)	Active (%)	PFA (UVA)
A (O/W)	15	125.3	10.49	4.5
B (O/W)	15	154.1	10.29	6.75

Note: PPS, primary particle size; PS, particle size measured.

Table 14.12 Particle Size of ZnO Dispersions

Sample	PPS (nm)	PS (nm)
1	20	228.3
2	~60	246.0
3	~100	263.6
4	~200	292.2

Note: PPS, primary particle size; PS, particle size measured.

sunscreen products containing only ZnO, especially by the *in vivo* method, is limited. More investigations are needed to obtain a better understanding of UV attenuation behavior of ZnO in cosmetic formulations and the optimum particle size.

Characterization of TiO_2 and ZnO Dispersions

Although the particle size is a useful parameter to predict the UV attenuation power of TiO_2 and ZnO, extinction ratio can be sometimes more informative about their efficacy. In the measurement of UV/visible spectrum, sample of TiO_2 (or ZnO) powder or a dispersion is usually diluted to a level at which the maximum absorbance is <2. Figures 14.10 and 14.11 show the typical absorption curves for TiO_2 and ZnO, respectively. It should be noted that absorbance here measures the total amount of UV attenuated by the sample through scattering or absorption. The absorbance thus has a different physical meaning from that of absorption discussed previously. Once an absorption curve is obtained, the extinction coefficient can be calculated as in Fig. 14.12.

As a generally accepted industrial practice, the extinction coefficients at the following wavelengths are selected to represent the UV/visible spectrum

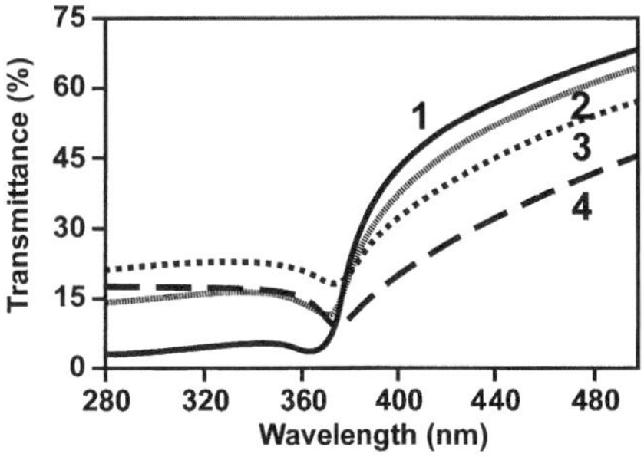

Figure 14.9 Transmittance curves of ZnO dispersions in isononyl isononanoate; primary particle sizes: 1 = 20 nm; 2 = ~60 nm; 3 = ~100 nm; 4 = <200 nm (ZnO concentration: 0.005% in $CHCl_3$).

Table 14.13 *In vivo* SPF and PFA Scores of ZnO-Containing Sunscreen Lotions

Formula type	PPS (nm)	Dispersion PS (nm)	Active (%)	SPF (UV-B)	PFA (UV-A)	UV-A/UV-B Ratio
W/O	20	130.0	14.10	25.0	3.1	
O/W	20	228.2	14.97	16.2	7.5	0.70
W/O	20	228.2	14.97	14.0	7.5	0.72
W/O	~100	263.0	16.00	12.6	5.83	0.83

Note: PPS, primary particle size; PS, particle size measured.

of TiO_2:

- 308 nm: maximum erythemal effectiveness
- 360 nm: middle of UV-A region
- 524 nm: blue end of visible light.

Therefore, the ratio of extinction coefficients at 308 and 524 nm is used to indicate the UV-B protection and the transparency. Within the same spectrum, the ratio of extinction coefficient is the same as the ratio of the absorbance at the same wavelengths. The larger the ratio is, the higher the transparency and the SPF are. On the other hand, the ratio of extinction coefficients at 308 and 360 nm is used to indicate that attenuation in UV-B vs. that in UV-A. A lower ratio often indicates a broader-spectrum protection.

The extinction coefficient ratios and the absorption peak positions of TiO_2 with various particle sizes are listed in Table 14.14. The ratios of both 308/360 and 308/524 increase substantially as the particle size reduces; a clear indication that the TiO_2 is getting more transparent and attenuation shifting further toward UV-B. The ratio of 308/364 corresponding to a size of 110 nm or smaller is so high that a very weak UV-A protection is predicated. It is worthy to be noted that the maximum absorption shifts to UV-C region, which may negate its efficacy in UV-B too. Since TiO_2 dispersion with such a small size has been on the market

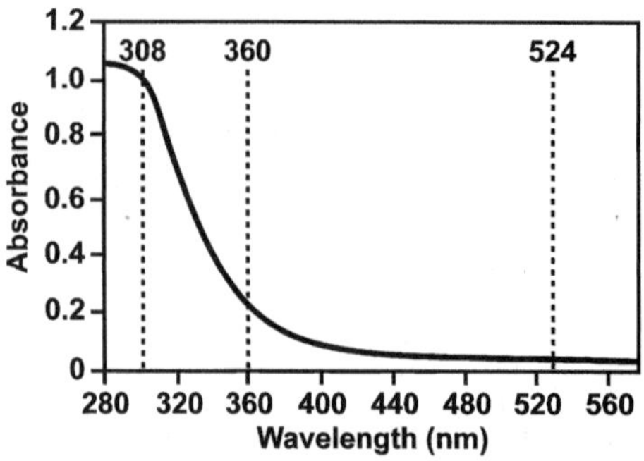

Figure 14.10 UV absorbance curve of TiO_2.

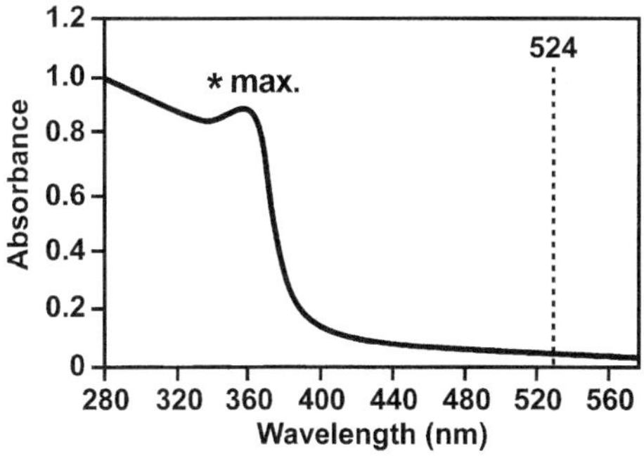

Figure 14.11 UV absorbance curve of ZnO.

for only the past few years, a conclusive correlation of particle size and SPF/PFA awaits more investigation. In general, TiO_2 of such a particle size can be used in combination with UV-A sunscreen agents to achieve a very transparent and yet a broad-spectrum protection.

For ZnO, the absorbance below the cutoff wavelength is rather uniform indicating an even attenuation of both UV-A and UV-B. Therefore, the selection of wavelength to represent an UV/visible spectrum is:

- λ_{max}: overall UV attenuation
- 524 nm: blue end of visible light.

The ratio of extinction coefficients at the maximum absorption and at 524 nm is used to indicate the UV-A and UV-B protection and the transparency of a ZnO product. Some experimental data are presented in Table 14.15.

It can be seen from the data that the extinction coefficient ratio of 308/360 is almost equal to 1.0 indicating that ZnO is a both UV-A and UV-B absorber. As the size goes down to 130 nm or lower, the extinction ratio of λ_{max}/524 nm can be very high. As a matter of fact, when ZnO with a particle size of 110 nm was used in a sunscreen lotion, almost two SPF units were achieved from each percent of ZnO. The maximum absorption shifts downward as far as 360 nm when the size decreases. In *in vitro* UV-A testing, the lower λ_{max} would, as previously discussed, fare worse. In *in vivo* UV-A testing, the UV-A I (320–360 nm) region is more responsible for generating erythema, the outcome was also worse. Therefore, it is very likely that a medium particle size is an optimum size for shielding UV-A when it is measured *in vivo*. Again, both the particle size and the test method have been considered when selecting a proper grade of ZnO.

$$\text{Extinction coefficient} = \frac{\text{Absorbance}}{\text{Active \%} \times \text{Path length}}$$

Figure 14.12 Equation for extinction coefficient.

Table 14.14 Particle Size, Extinction Ratio, and Absorption Peak of TiO_2

Particle size (nm)	Ext. ratio 308/360	Ext. ratio 308/524	λ_{max} (nm)
100	7.0–8.0	70–90	275
110	4.5–5.5	50–55	280–290
130	3.4–3.9	11–26	290–305
150	2.0	9.0	300
150	2.0	17	313
250	1.1	2.6	318

DISPERSION OF INORGANIC ULTRAVIOLET FILTERS

Objectives of the Dispersion Process

Pigment Processing: *Physico-chemical principles* by J. M. Oyarzún, is an excellent reference (46) on pigment dispersion. He defines pigment dispersion as a stepwise process whose objective is to produce a stable and uniform dispersion of finely divided pigment particles, that is, aggregates and primary particles, in an application medium. The key elements of the process are further defined to be mechanical breakdown, wetting, and stabilization. In order to achieve mechanical breakdown it is necessary to use energy to break down the cohesive forces, the intermolecular forces of attraction that hold the solid particles together. The cohesion forces acting between the structure units of pigment agglomerates are essentially physical in nature and not accomplished by chemical bonding. The surface forces of particles with microscopic dimensions are stronger than coarse grain particles like sand.

Mechanical breakdown may be achieved with a high shear or a high-speed disperser. The dispersion formulation typically consists of a micropigment, surface treatment, dispersant, and a carrier medium. The surface treatment is paramount for prewetting the pigment in the carrier and decreasing the absorption of the dispersant by the pigment. The dispersant aids in the wetting and stabilizes the particles in the carrier. Fig. 14.13 shows the role of the surface treatment and dispersant in the premix of a 15 nm micronized titanium dioxide in

Table 14.15 Particle Size, Extinction Ratio, and Absorption Peak of ZnO

Particle size (nm)	Ext. ratio 308/360	Ext. ratio 308/524	λ_{max} (nm)
110	1.0	34	360
130	1.1	27	358
190	0.9	7.8	371
260	0.9	4.1	375

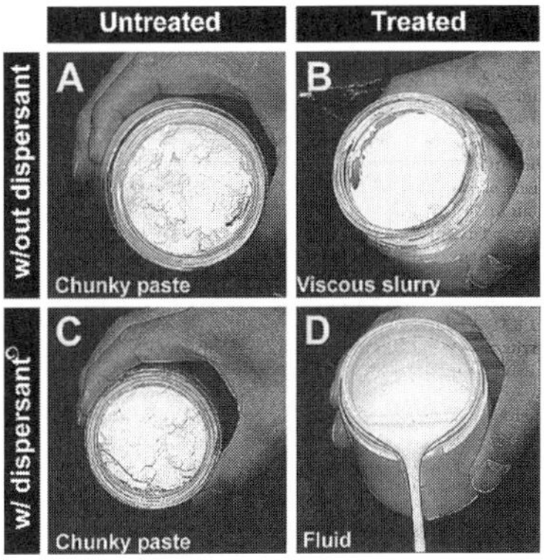

Figure 14.13 Surface treatment and prewetting of the pigment.

cyclopentasiloxane (36). The dispersion formulation must be well suited for the mechanical process. The pigment solids and viscosity of the premix dispersion dictate the choice of mill.

Index of Agglomeration

Dispersion processing becomes more problematic when the pigment is getting finer (22). The index of agglomeration was proposed by Schlossman and Shao as the ratio of the dispersion particle size over the primary particle size (47). It can be observed from Table 14.16 that pigments having a smaller primary particle size contain larger indices of agglomeration. Modifying the components of the dispersion formula will influence the pigment grind, meaning the dispersion particle size and the index of agglomeration. Table 14.17 lists the particles sizes for four distinct dispersion formulations containing UV-Titan M170, a micronized titanium dioxide from Kemira.

Table 14.16 Influence of Primary Particle Size on the Index of Agglomeration

PPS (nm)	Type	PS (nm)	Index of agglomeration
10	TiO_2	110	11
15	TiO_2	143	9.5
20	TiO_2	143	7.2
20–30	ZnO	145	5.8
35	TiO_2	179	5.1
120	ZnO	250	1.3

Note: PPS, primary particle size; PS, particle size measured.

Table 14.17 Influence of Dispersion Formulation on the Index of Agglomeration (Primary Particle Size is 14 nm for All Dispersions)

Dispersion formulation	PS (nm)	Index of agglomeration
Iododecane and polyhydroxystearic acid (60% solids)	172	12.3
Iododecane and polyhydroxystearic acid (50% solids)	110	7.9
C12–15 alkyl benzoate and polyhydroxystearic acid	165	11.8
Cyclopentasiloxane and PEG-10 dimethicone	165	11.8

Note: PS, particle size measured.

Advantages of Dispersions

The demand by formulators for dispersions instead of powders is increasing. The desired particle size (and attenuation) can be more readily obtained with a dispersion of micronized pigments, because the concentration of particulates in an oil or aqueous phase of a finished product formulation is likely to be too low to provide enough particle to particle interaction to break apart agglomerates and aggregates. The whitening effect can thus be minimized by formulating with dispersions, because large particles that scatter visible light can be milled finer. Producers of finished products are often poorly equipped with the proper dust collection devices or mills to handle fine particle size pigments. Powerful and specialized mixing equipment may be needed to wet these pigments, because they are hard and dense, and possess a higher specific gravity.

Incorporating Micronized Pigments and Dispersions into Formulations

The process of dispersion takes place on the solid/liquid interface between the pigment surface and the dispersion fluid (22). Suitable vehicles include oils/esters, surfactants, glycols, silicone fluids, and water (48). A procedure often followed by companies that make their own dispersions will be to make a predispersion of the pigment in the carrier contained in the formulation. This predispersion can be stored until it is needed to produce the finished formulation. An 80/20 mixture of titanium dioxide with barium sulfate coated with stearic acid dispersed in isooctyl stearate is an example of a dispersion formula without a dispersing aid (1). Dispersions are supplied to the personal care market either as thick pastes or as low viscosity fluids. Pastes are more easily added to formulations by diluting the pigment solids with more of the same carrier and dispersant. Low viscosity fluids, for example, with viscosities under 30,000 cP, are typically added directly to the oil or aqueous phase.

Producers of Dispersions

Uniqema began marketing their Tioveil dispersions during the late 1980s. Their original product line featured aqueous and ester based 40% solids titanium dioxide dispersions. They patented an oil dispersion comprising particles of titanium dioxide having an average size of 10–150 nm surface treated with alumina, silica, and an organic dispersing aid in an oil carrier. The organic dispersing aid claimed comprises monoesters of fatty acid alkanolamides and carboxylic acids wherein the fatty acids have from 6 to 22 carbon atoms, or is a polyhydroxy carboxylic acid or an ethoxylated phosphate monoester (49).

In 1995, Kobo Products, Inc. entered the personal care market with High Solids® dispersions. The Kobo titanium dioxide dispersions were typically thick pastes, as high as 65% solids, and were mainly ester based and incorporated a polyglyceryl ester, Hexaglyn PR-15 from Nikko Chemicals, as a dispersing aid. The micronized titanium was coated with aluminum hydroxide and stearic acid. Their zinc oxide dispersions also contained Hexaglyn PR-15 and were over 70% solids. It contained a titanate treated zinc oxide pigment to prewet the particles in esters. The dispersion particle size was optimized by formulating with a high pigment concentration (38). Collisions of pigment particles occur inside the mill. Lower solids dispersions are not sufficiently viscous to grind the particles in this type of mill.

New milling systems proposed initially for inks have been used to grind low-viscosity dispersions. The viscosity of the milled dispersion formula, containing pigment, surface treatment, dispersant (and possibly a resin) has to be less than 10,000 cP. Kobo supplies these dispersions as High Speed™ dispersions. Typically, the micropigment is hydrophobized with a silicone treatment, and a silicone polyether copolymer can be used as a dispersant. Polyhydroxystearic acid is a suitable dispersing aid that is effective to formulate dispersions with a low viscosity. Kobo offers a 50% dispersion of Kemira M170 in isododecane that has a viscosity of 20 cP. During 2003, Shao and Schlossman coauthored a paper comparing micropigment dispersions made with silicone polyether copolymers, silicone/acrylate copolymers, and polyhydroxystearic acid (50).

Uniqema and Degussa have recently introduced aqueous based dispersions of hydrophobic micronized titanium dioxide. Aqueous-based dispersions of hydrophobic titanium dioxide are purported to be sterically stable and tolerate formulations over a wide range of pH (51,52). Tioxide patented an aqueous dispersion of particulate zinc oxide coated with amorphous silica, by mixing an alkali metal silicate, an acid, and a stabilizing agent (53). They have also patented a mixed oxide dispersion comprising an oil, particles of zinc oxide between 5 and 150 nm, particles of titanium dioxide between 5 and 150 nm, and an organic dispersing aid (54).

Suppliers of dispersions in water, esters, and silicone fluids are listed in Table 14.18.

FORMULATIONS

Guidelines

Sunscreen compositions are formulated in the form of a cream, lotion, or oil. The active agent when present on skin must be resistant to chemical or photodegradation

Table 14.18 Suppliers of Micropigment Dispersions

Supplier	Dispersion	Active	Active (%)	Surface treatment/dispersant	Carrier
ANT	Zinclear 40CCT	ZnO	40	Stearic acid/polyhydroxystearic acid	Caprylic/capric triglyceride
Elementis	Nanox® Gel 200	ZnO	55	Polyhydroxystearic acid	C12–15 alkyl benzoate
EMD	Eusolex® T-Aqua	TiO_2	30	Alumina/sodium Metaphosphate	Water
EMD	Eusolex® T-45D	TiO_2	45	Alumina, dimethicone/polyglyceryl-6 polyricinoleate	Isononyl isononanoate
Ishihara Sangyo	TSK-5	TiO_2	30	Silica	Water
Kobo	High Speed™ CM3K50XZ4	ZnO	45	Methicone/PEG-10 Dimethicone	Cyclopentasiloxane
Kobo	High Solids® IN60S4	TiO_2	48	Aluminum hydroxide/stearic acid	Isononyl isononanoate
Kobo	High Solids® INH73MZ	ZnO	70	Isopropyl titanium triisostearate/ polyglyceryl 6-polyricinoleate	Isononyl isononanoate
Kobo	High Speed™ PM1P65M170	TiO_2	48.75	Methicone/polyhydroxystearic acid	Isohexadecane
Kobo	High Speed™ TNP50ZCL	ZnO	50	Triethoxy caprylyl silane/ polyhydroxystearic acid	C12–15 alkyl benzoate
Kobo	High Speed™ TNP55VTTS	TiO_2	41	ITT/TCS crosspolymer/ polyhydroxystearic acid	C12–15 alkyl benzoate
Rhodia	Mirasun ® TiW60	TiO_2	29–36	Silica (15%), alumina (5%)	Water
Uniqema	Tioveil AQ	TiO_2	<40	Alumina, silica/Na polyacrylate	Water
Uniqema	Tioveil FIN	TiO_2	<50	AS and alumina/polyhydroxystearic aicd	C12–15 alkyl benzoate

to absorption through the skin, and to removal by perspiration, skin oil, or water. It must be odorless and nonstaining to the skin or clothing (55). Consumer research studies indicate that a sunscreen formulation should rub in easily, leave the skin nonsticky, and above all should be invisible on the skin after application (1).

Emulsifiers and Additives

Novel emulsifiers, dispersants, thickeners, and film formers have enabled sunscreen formulators to create more elegant formulators, improve emulsion stability, and boost SPF. Shin-Etsu, a leading supplier of silicone fluids in Japan, has introduced new silicone compunds for surface treatments and new surfactants that have contributed to the marketing of fluid water-in-silicone emulsions with good spreading that may contain pigment loadings over 30% (56,57).

The SPF of sunscreen products containing micronized titanium dioxide can be increased with the addition of beeswax (58). Nearn et al. described an O/W sunscreen composition containing 0.5% to about 5% by weight of microfine titanium dioxide having a particle size less than 100 nm and containing a dispersing agent in an amount sufficient to stabilize the emulsion, comprising a long chain saturated primary alcohol having an average of from about 25 to about 45 carbon atoms in the long chain, ethoxylated or unethoxylated (59). L'Oreal described a storage-stable, ultrafine O/W emulsion prepared by phase inversion containing an inorganic nano pigment, the oily phase of said emulsion ranging from 100 to 1000 nm (60,61). Nicoll et al. patented a sunscreen emulsion containing a mixture of hydrophilic and hydrophobic titanium dioxides with an average particle size <100 nm and comprising a silicone surfactant (62). Dahms patented O/W and W/O emulsions consisting of low levels of emulsifiers or low HLB emulsifiers (<6), in combination with aqueous or oily dispersions of metallic oxides with dispersing aids (63–65).

According to E.M. Merck, the guidelines that should be observed in formulating with Eusolex® grades of micronized titanium dioxide are as follows (66):

- Use nonionic (polymeric emulsifiers)
- Use nonpolar or polar solvents
- Use polar emollients in the presence of organic UV filters
- Use best pH.

Determining Suitable Levels of Actives

The active amount of inorganic sunscreens in a formula is close to 20% in Japan (as reported in a market survey by Sakai during the late 1990s) and is estimated to be 5% in the USA and in Europe. Climate, industry, consumer preferences, and regulations are the major reasons for these differences. In Japan, the MHW only recently limited the maximum SPF claim to 50+, and restricts the amount of organic sunscreen at 20%. Asian consumers are more tolerant of skin whitening and, in some instances, some whitening is preferred. In addition, Japanese formulations may contain shaker balls in the package to help redisperse the particles before application to the skin.

Foundations and Daily UV Lotions

The addition of micronized titanium dioxide to liquid foundations to obtain SPF 15 and higher is common. Typically, a 15 nm micronized titanium dioxide is combined together with pigmentary titanium dioxide to balance coverage and protection. Iron oxides, while not approved as an active inorganic sunscreen, will boost the SPF of a make-up formula by approximately 0.5 SPF units per weight. Broad-spectrum protection is more readily obtained in a foundation where coverage and color are permitted than a skin care product, because pigmentary titanium dioxide and iron oxides both attenuate UV-A. Zinc oxide is sometimes added to boost UV-A. Companies also formulate with a medium-sized micronized titanium dioxide pigment between 20 and 35 nm, because they will provide more UV-A and the amount of whitening is tolerable in their formulation. Schlossman compared five marketed foundations labeled with SPF 10–20 and found they all had critical wavelengths over 380 nm (67). It is difficult to make foundations for all skin types that will not be ashy looking.

Kemira's M262 and Tayca's MT-500H and MT-500T are promoted for their UV-A protection and have been found by the authors to have good light stability and low reactivity. Kobo has formulated an SPF 44 water-in-silicone foundation (with 13% active titanium dioxide) with a silicone based dispersion of M262 (47). Both titanium dioxide and zinc oxide have been used by cosmetic firms like Estee Lauder, P&G, and L'Oreal to offer daily UV protection in skin care products.

Formulating with Zinc Oxide

The chemical property of zinc oxide needs to be taken into consideration especially when an untreated zinc oxide is used in the aqueous phase. Even when the zinc oxide is used in the nonaqueous phase, the zinc cation can bleed into an aqueous phase over time and impair the long-term stability. A common caution in formulating a ZnO-containing product is to avoid or to minimize the use of anionic emulsifier or thickener such as carbomers. Combinations of zinc oxide and titanium dioxide are more likely to be W/O formulations, because of their different isoelectric points. Coating micronized titanium dioxide and zinc oxide with silica or silicates may stabilize them sufficiently to be formulated together in water. Showa Denka and Sakai manufacture such kinds of treatments in Japan. Applications are limited outside of Japan, however, because the selling prices of these ingredients are very high. SunSmart successfully patented and marketed in the USA a sunblock with micronized zinc oxide said particles having an average particle diameter $<0.2\ \mu m$ and containing <20 ppm lead, <3 ppm arsenic, <15 ppm cadmium, and <1 ppm mercury (68).

Obtaining Broad-Spectrum Protection

Kemira has studied formulations with UV-Titan M262 combined with zinc oxide or methoxy dibenzoyl methane. The UV-A protection provided by UV-Titan can be improved to maximum protection, four stars (****), by combining UV-Titan M262 with zinc oxide or low levels of avobenzone (33), as shown in Table 14.19.

It is claimed in JP 60-231607 that an antisuntan cosmetic containing a combination of 1–30 wt% of ultrafine zinc oxide (average particle size of 10–60 nm), a UV light absorber (a derivative of benzophenone, benzoic acid, salicylic acid, or cinnamic acid, etc.) and a UV light scattering agent (titanium dioxide, kaolin, or calcium·carbonate) can be formulated to shield completely the UV light (69).

Tanner et al. patented a novel sunscreen composition containing <5% of micronized titanium dioxide or zinc oxide in combination with avobenzone and a stabilizing organic filter to achieve a broad spectrum protection with good transparency (70).

SunSmart patented, in the USA, a physical sunscreen with micronized zinc oxide having an average particle diameter <0.2 μm and containing <20 ppm lead, <3 ppm arsenic, <5 ppm cadmium, and <1 ppm mercury (68). They successfully market in the USA their Z-Cote®(Z-Cote at the time of this writing is a registered trademark of the BASF Corporation). A sunscreen with a UV-A/UV-B ratio over 0.8 can be formulated using Z-Cote, because it is effective at scattering long-wavelength UV-A light. Notwithstanding, there are scientists in the USA who prefer to formulate with zinc oxides of smaller particle size because of their superior transparency and higher UV absorption.

Cole et al. claimed a synergistic combination of titanium dioxide having a particle size <∼35 μm and zinc oxide having a particle size <∼50 μm; the said titanium dioxide and zinc oxide being present in a weight ratio of from about 1 : 25 to 10 : 1 and the total of said titanium dioxide and zinc oxide comprising from about 4.0% to about 25% of the total composition to protect the skin from the harmful effects of sunlight (71). Researchers at Boots described a sunscreen composition containing a blend of 15 nm titanium dioxide between

Table 14.19 SPF Value and UV-A/UV-B Ratio Measured for W/O Emulsions

UV filter(s)	SPF *in vitro*	UV-A/UV-B ratio
5% M262	16	0.68
5% ZnO	4	0.85
5% M262 + 5% ZnO	22	0.82
3% M262	8	0.67
0.5% BMDBM	1	UV-A only
3% M262 + 0.5% BMDBM	8	0.80

10–70% and 30–90% of another grade of titanium dioxide with a primary particle size of between 30 and 50 nm. It is substantially transparent on skin and has a UV-A/UV-B ratio in the range of 0.25–0.60 (72).

Approximately 3.5% Eusolex® T-2000 is claimed in formulation to be sufficient to meet the Australian UV-A standard requirements (66).

Sample Formulations

W/O Waterproof Sunscreen Formula SPF 30+

Phase A

Cetyl PEG/PPG-10/1 dimethicone (and) polyglyceryl-4-isostearate (and) hexyl laurate (Abil WE 09/Goldschmitd)	5.00%
Isononyl isononanoate (Wickenol 151/Alzo)	6.00%
Cyclomethicone (DC 345 Fluid/Dow)	7.50%
Cetyl dimethicone (Abil Wax 9801/Goldschmitd)	3.00%
Methyl glucose sesqustearate (Glucate SS/Amerchol)	0.50%
Dioctyl malate (Ceraphyl 45/ISP Van Dyk)	2.00%

Phase B

Micronized titanium dioxide (and) stearic acid (and) aluminum hydroxide (and) isononyl isononanoate (IN60TS/Kobo)	21.33%

Phase C

Deionized water	51.07%
Polycarbamyl polyglycol ester (Aculyn 44 C1/Rohm & Haas)	2.50%

Phase D

Sodium chloride	0.50%
Phenoxyethanol (and) methylparaben (and) ethylparaben (and) propylparaben (and) butylparaben (Uniphen P-23/Induchem)	0.60%

Manufacturing procedure

Premix Aculyn 44 into water under propeller at ambient temperate

When Aculyn 44 is fully dissolved, add premixed phase D to phase C

Heat phase A to 75°C and cool to 65°c

Add phase B to phase A under homogenization

Return to propeller mixing and add premixed Phases C and D to phases A and B.

O/W Sunscreen Lotion SPF 27

Phase A

Demineralized water	58.05%
Glyceryl methacrylate (Lubrajel MS/Barnet)	1.00%
Tetrasodium EDTA (Versen 220/Dow Chemicals)	0.10%

Phase B

Butyl octyl salicylate (Hallbright BHB/C.P. Hall)	6.00%
Monoglyceryl citrate (Dadex MGC/Eastman Kodak)	0.50%
Avobenzone (Parsol 1789/Givaudan-Roure)	1.50%
PVP hexadecane copolymer (AntaronV216/ISP)	2.00%
Cyclomethicone (SF1202/GE Silicones)	3.00%
Phenyl trimethicone (SF1550/GE Silicones)	1.00%
Shea butter (Cetiol SB-45/Henkel)	1.00%
Hydrogenated lecithin (Lecithin W/D/Henkel/CLR)	0.25%
Cetyl alcohol (and) glyceryl stearate (and) PEG-75 stearate (and) ceteth 20 (and) steareth-12 (Emulsynth Delta/Gattefosse)	4.00%
Methyl glucose sesquistearate (Glucate SS/Amerchol)	1.00%
Homosalate and titanium dioxide (and) aluminum hydroxide (and) stearic acid (HS40S4/Kobo)	18.00%

Phase C

Urethane/C1-20 Alkyl PEG Copolymer (Acculyn 44/Rohm & Haas)	2.00%

Phase D

Diazolidinyl urea (and) iodopropynyl butyl carbamate (Germall Plus Liquid/ISP)	0.60%

Manufacturing procedure

Mix Phase 1 in the order listed and heat to 75°C
Heat items of phase B till 78°C, mix till all dissolved
Then add HS40S4, homogenize till smooth and homogeneous
Heat to 75–78°C if need be after homogenization
Add phase B to phase A, continue mixing for 10 min, then add phase C
Switch to homogenizer and homogenize for 15 min
Switch to sweep mixing and cool to 40°C, then add phase D
Continue mixing while cooling to 30°C.

Sunscreen Cream Gel

Phase A

Deionized water	38.10%
Carbomer (Carbopol 980 2% solution/Noveon)	20.00%
Glycereth-26 (Liponic EG-1/Lipo)	3.00%
Butylene glycol	0.25%
Disodium EDTA	0.10%

Phase B

C12-15 alkyl benzoate (and) titanium dioxide (and) alumina (and) polyhydroxystearic acid (and) ITT/TCS crosspolymer (TNP55VTTS/Kobo)	10.00%

Caprylic/capric triglyceride (Liponate GC-K/Lipo)	5.00%
Benzophenone-3 (Uvinul M 40/BASF)	5.00%
Ethylhexyl salicylate (Escalol 587/ISP Van Dyk)	5.00%
Cetearyl alcohol (and) ceteareth-20 (Lipowax D/Lipo)	2.50%
Glyceryl stearate (and) PEG-100 stearate (Arlacel 165/Uniqema)	1.75%
Stearyl alcohol	1.00%
Sillicone (DC 200-100/Dow Corning)	1.00%
Ethylhexyl methoxycinnamate (Uvinul MC 80/BASF)	7.50%

Phase C

Triethanolamine 99% (q.s. to pH 6.5–7)	1.80%

Phase D

Ascorbyl glucoside (AA2G/Siberhegner)	2.00%

Phase E

Germaben II/ASP Sutton	1.00%

Manufacturing procedure

Mix phase A ingredients and heat to 65°C
Mix phase B ingredients and heat to 65°C until the titanium dioxide is dispersed
Add phase B to phase A
Add phase C and cool to 45°C
Add phases D and E, cool with mixing to room temperature.

Sprayable O/W Sunscreen SPF 15+

Phase A

Deionized water	69.80%
Butylene glycol	3.00%
Phenoxyethanol (and) methylparaben (and) ethylparaben (and) butylparaben (and) propylparaben (and) isobutylparaben (Phenonip/NIPA Labs)	1.00%

Phase B

C14–22 alcohols (and) C12–20 alkyl glucoside (Montanov L/SEPPIC)	4.50%
C12–15 alkyl benzoate (and) zinc oxide (and) polyhydroxystearic acid (and) triethoxy caprylsilane (TNP50ZSI/Kobo)	19.00%
Squalane (Phytolane LS/DD Chem Co)	1.00%
Tridecyl stearate (Liponate TDS/Lipo)	1.00%
Tocopheryl acetate (Vitamin E Acetate/BASF)	0.20%

Phase C

Acrylamides copolymer (and) mineral oil (and)
C13–14 Isoparafin
(and) polysorbate 85 (Sepigel 501/SEPPIC) 0.50%

Manufacturing procedure

In main kettle, combine phase A ingredients and heat to 78–80°C with moderate speed propeller mixing
Heat phase B to 80°C and mix until uniform
Add phase B to phase A with medium speed propeller mixing; mix for 15 min or until emulsification is complete
Begin cooling batch
At 40°C add phase C to batch and mix well
Cool to 25°C.

REGULATIONS, CLAIMS, TOXICITY, AND TESTING

The landscape for new formulations containing micronized pigments has been shaped as much by government regulations, testing, and labeling standards (e.g., there are different specifications for purity between Japan and the USA), and by toxicological and ecological concerns. As was mentioned earlier, the FDA does not allow titanium dioxide or zinc oxide to be used with avobenzone. Titanium dioxide labeled as attenuation grade for sunscreens must meet the requirements of USP 24 for purity. The starting pigment is required to be 99.0% TiO_2 calculated on the ignited basis. The specification for loss on ignition is 13% after drying. Attenuation grade material may contain suitable coatings, stabilizers, and treatments to assist formulators. All tests and assays are conducted on uncoated, untreated material (73).

In Europe, the SCCNFP (Scientific Committee for Cosmetic Products and Non-food Products) adopted a favorable opinion on the safety of micronized titanium dioxide for use in cosmetic products at a maximum concentration of 25%. Micronized titanium dioxide is required to pass the purity requirements of E171 laid down in the EEC directive concerning foodstuffs and coloring matters (74). Acceptance of zinc oxide as an active sunscreen agent in the near future, however, is uncertain, because of concerns with the mutagenicity and genotoxicity of zinc and its salts (6).

Recently, titanium dioxide has been selected for examination under Proposition 65 in California as a potential carcinogen (see www.OESHA.ca.gov/prop65/CRNR/notices/statelisting/proritizationnotice). There are other concerns with zinc oxide manufacturers (ZOPA) over their waste streams causing aquatic toxicity.

Inorganic UV filters are nonpenetrating making them suitable for use on children and others with sensible skin. Lansdown and Taylor studied the percutaneous absorption of zinc oxide and titanium dioxide on rabbit skin (75).

SUMMARY

Inorganic UV filters have been marketed for over 25 years. The UV attenuation performance of inorganic sunscreens in a finished product is influenced by their particle size. Advancements in particle technology have enabled the production of ultrafine particles and there are more specialty grades to choose from. Notwithstanding, scientists continue to search for the optimum particle size that can completely shield all UV-A/UV-B and be transparent on all skin types. It is not as simple as formulating with the smallest particle in all applications because, while very fine particles offer unprecedented transparency, the maximum attenuation by titanium dioxide shifts to UV-C, and UV-A attenuation by zinc oxide becomes weaker (or we can say their UV-A/UV-B attenuation is likely to be worse). The authors have recently tested *in vivo* a formulation containing 15 nm titanium dioxide and 60 nm zinc oxide. The SPF and PFA data showed that this was a promising combination to obtain a high SPF/PFA score in formulations containing solely inorganic UV filters.

Multiple surface treatments for particles are responsible for improving their physical and chemical stability and promoting their wetting and stability in dispersions. New surfactants, dispersants and dispersions are all contributing to improvements in efficacy.

The advances in surface treatment have enabled the development of particles with outstanding physical and chemical stabilty, and the restrictions on their combination with avobenzone need to be eliminated. It would also make sense to reexamine the USP specifications, because it is well known that the inorganic coating gives the particle its physical stability. Conceptually, it makes sense to decrease the purity requirements from 99% to a lower amount for attenuation pigments. This would allow for a heavier alumina coating in the crystal, and maybe there would be more grades of micronized titanium dixoide produced by the chloride process.

The outlook for physical sunscreens remains promising, as evidenced by the furious pace that new raw materials have become available to the personal care industry. Competition between traditional suppliers and startup nanotechnology companies will ensure a continuation of new and promising inorganic UV filters for years to come.

REFERENCES

1. Bhat G, Lindemann R, Martin KO, Naik Satam P. Johnson and Johnson Consumer Products. US Patent 5,028,417, 1991.
2. American Academy of Dermatology Public Resources. Solving problems related to the use of cosmetics in skin care products, September 28, 2003. American Academy of Dermatology. Produced by NetOn-Line Services.
3. Rules and regulations sunscreen drug products for over the counter human use. Final Monograph, Federal Register/Vol. 64, No. 98/Friday May 21, 1999.
4. Pinnell SR, et al. Dermatol Surg 2000; 26(4):309–314.

5. DeBuys HV, et al. Dermatol Clin 2000; 18(4):577–590.
6. Opinion concerning zinc oxide, COLIPA no. S 76. The Scientific Committee on Cosmetic Products and Non-Food Products Intended for Consumers, SCCNFP/0649/03, final.
7. Steinberg DC. Sunscreen regulations update. Florida Chapter Society of Cosmetic Chemists Sunscreen Symposium, Orlando, FL, September 2003.
8. CIBA® Tinosorb™ M CIBA Specialty Chemicals, Inc. Pub. No. Tinosorb M.TB. 0103.e.02.
9. Lloyd TB. Zinc compounds. In: Mark HF, Othmer DF, Overberger CG, Seaborf GT, eds. Kirk-Othmer. Encyclopedia of Chemical Technology. 3rd ed. Vol. 24. New York: John Wiley and Sons, 1984:854–863.
10. Merck and Co. The Merck Index. 11th ed. 1989, 1599.
11. Weast RC, ed. Handbook of Chemistry and Physics. 70th ed.
12. Kobayashi M, Kalriess W. Photocatalytic activity of titanium dioxide and zinc oxide. Cosmet Toilet 1997; 112:83.
13. Ultrafine zinc oxide, SF-20 SF-20LP, Technical Bulletin, Sakai Chemical Industry.
14. Ishii N, Wada K, Takama M, Ogawa K, Joichi K, Ohno K. Development of thin-layer silica-coated zinc oxide and superior sunscreens. Proceedings of the 21st IFSCC International Congress, Berlin, 2000.
15. Micro titanium dioxide—MT series, Technical Bulletin, Tayca Corporation.
16. Kerker M. The Scattering of Light. New York: Academic Press, 1969.
17. Mie G. Phys Lpz 1908; 25:377.
18. Balfour JG. Back to basics, durability and titanium dioxide pigments. J Oil Color Chem Assoc 1990; 78:478.
19. Innes B, Tsuzuki T, Dawkins H, Dunlop J, Trotter G, Nearn M, McCormick PG. Nanotechnology and the cosmetic chemist. Technical Bulletin, Advanced Nano Technologies Pty Ltd.
20. Yoffe AD. Adv Phys 1993; 42:173–266.
21. Solomon DH, Hawthorne DG. Chemistry of Pigments and Fillers. 2nd ed. Krieger, FL: Wiley, 1991.
22. Transparent titanium dioxide for ultraviolet protection. Technical Bulletin, Sachtleben Chemie.
23. Cowie AG (Tioxide Group PLC). US Patent 4,927,464, 1998.
24. Cowie AG (Tioxide Group PLC). US Patent 5,599,529, 1997.
25. STT-490. Technical Bulletin, Titan Kogyo Kabushiki Kaisha.
26. Showa Denka, Technical Bulletin.
27. Functional materials of titanium dioxide. Technical Bulletin, Ishihara Sangyo Kaishi, Ltd, April 1999.
28. NST-B1. Technical Bulletin, ISK.
29. Härkönen R, Kujansivu L. Ultrafine titanium dioxide—effects on UV protection. Technical Bulletin, Kemira Pigments Oy, Finland.
30. Mirasun™ Technology. Invisible high protection. Technical Bulletin, Rhodia.
31. Zinclear, the nanofine zinc oxide for cosmetic clarity and broad spectrum UV protection. Technical Bulletin, Advanced Nano Technologies Pty Ltd.
32. New developments in nanoparticle titanium dioxide, dispersions with ultra low whitening effect and improved SPF. Technical Bulletin, Rhône-Poulenc.
33. Tsuzuki T. Photocatalytic behaviour of ZnO nanoparticle produced by mechnochemical processing. Technical Bulletin, Advanced Nano Technologies Pty Ltd.

34. Tayca Corporation, Okayama Research Laboratory. Technical Bulletin, December 1, 1996.
35. Micro titanium dioxide, Technical Bulletin, Tayca Corporation.
36. Schlossman D, Shao Y. Silicone dispersants and physical sunscreen dispersions: recent developments. SCC Florida Chapter Sun Screen Symposium, Orlando, FL, 2003.
37. Corcoran C, Zecchino J, Mesin S, Chung K (Estee Lauder, Inc.). US Patent 5,468,471, 1994.
38. Schlossman D, et al. High Solids® dispersions. Technical Bulletin, Kobo Products, Inc.
39. Nguyen U, Schlossman D. Stability study of avobenzone with inorganic sunscreens. SCC Annual Meeting, 2001.
40. Schlossman D, Shao Y. Super dispersible pigments for color cosmetics. Color Cosmetics Summit 2003, Montréal, Québec, October 20–22, 2003.
41. Stamatakis P, Palmer BR, Salzman GC, Bohren CF, Allen TB. Optimum particle size of titanium dioxide and zinc oxide for attenuation of ultraviolet radiation. J Coating Technol 1990; 62(789):95.
42. Sakamoto M, Okuda H, Futamata H, Sakai A, Iida M. J Jpn Soc Mater (Shikizai) 1995; 68(4):203–210.
43. Solarshields T. Micro titanium dioxide dispersion. Technical Bulletin, New Paradgim Technologies, Inc.
44. Hewitt JP, Woodruff J. IFSCC Mag 2000; 3(1):18.
45. Flairhurst D, Mitchnick MA. Particulate sun blocks, general principles. In: Lowe NJ, Shaath NA, Pathak MA. Sunscreens: Development, Evaluation and Regulatory Aspects. 2nd ed. New York: Marcel Dekker, 1997:313–352.
46. Oyarzún JM. Pigment Processing: Physico-chemical Principles. Hannover, Germany: Vincentz Verlag, 2000.
47. Schlossman D, Shao Y. Silicone dispersants and physical sunscreen dispersions, recent developments. The European Sunfilters Conference, Paris, 2003.
48. Dispersion process of UV-Titan. Things to remember about pre-dispersions. Technical Bulletin, Kemira Pigments Oy, Finland.
49. Cowie AG (Tioxide Group PLC). Dispersions, US Patent 5,599,529, 1997.
50. Shao Y, Schlossman D. Silicone dispersants and physical sunscreen dispersions, recent developments. IV Colloque Unipex-ADF, Paris, March 6, 2003.
51. Hewitt J. Formulating with an aqueous TiO_2 dispersion. European Sunfilters Conference, Paris, 2004.
52. Howe A. Formulating hydrophobic pigments via the water phase: a new aqueous titanium dioxide dispersion. Florida Chapter Society of Cosmetic Chemists, Orlando, FL, 2003.
53. Tapley C, Allyson M, Lyth PL, Harper IM. Zinc oxide dispersion. US Patent 5,914,101, 1999.
54. Tapley C. Method of preparing sunscreens. US Patent 5,605,562, 1997.
55. Nearn MR, Redshaw SJ, Burgess G. Titanium dioxide based sunscreen compositions. US Patent 5,498,406, 1996.
56. Silicones for personal care-emulsifier series. Technical Bulletin, Shinetsu 2002.2/2003.5(1).
57. KP series. Acrylic silicones for personal care. Technical Bulletin, Shinetsu 1999.4/2001.4 (1) BP.
58. Anderson MW, Hewitt JP, Spruce SR. Broad spectrum physical sunscreens, titanium dioxide and zinc oxide. In: Lowe NJ, Shaath NA, Pathak MA, eds. Sunscreens:

Development, Evaluation and Regulatory Aspects. 2nd ed. New York: Marcel Dekker, 1997:353–397.
59. Nearn MR, Redshaw SJ, Burgess G. Titanium dioxide based sunscreen compositions. US Patent 5,498,406, 1996.
60. Allard D, Ascione J-M, Hansenne I (Société L'Oréal S.A.). Nanopigmented sunscreen compositions. US Patent 5,616,331, 1995.
61. Allard D, Ascione J-M, Hansenne I (Societe L'Oreal S.A.). Storage-stable ultrafine oil-in-water emulsion nanopigmented sunscreen compositions. US Patent 5,730,993, 1996.
62. Nicoll GA, Ojo-Osagle AC, Scott IR (Chesebrough-Pond's USA Co.). US patent 5,188,831, 1993.
63. Dahms GH (Tioxide Specialties Ltd.). US Patent 5,443,759, August 22, 1995.
64. Dahms GH (Tioxide Specialties Ltd.). US Patent 5,543,135, August 6, 1996.
65. Dahms GH (Tioxide Specialties Ltd.). US Patent 5,516,457, May 14, 1995.
66. Eusolex®, the inorganic range for modular sun protection. Technical Bulletin, Merck, KGaA, Darmstadt, Germany.
67. Schlossman D. Sunscreen technologies for foundations and lipsticks. Intertech, Color Cosmetics Summit, Nice, France, 1998.
68. Mitchell K, Mitchnick M (SunSmart). US Patent 5,587,148, 1996.
69. Fukuda H, Naito N (Kose Cosmetics Co., Ltd.). JP 60-231607, 1985.
70. Tanner PR, Irwin C, O-Donoghue MA (The Procter & Gamble Company). US Patent 5,989,528, November 23, 1999.
71. Cole CA, Lindemann MK, Lukenbach ER, Strutzman RC (Johnson and Johnson Consumer Products, Inc.). US Patent 5,340,567, 1994.
72. Boots EP 463030.
73. Titanium dioxide, USP 24: 25, 4, August 1999.
74. Opinion concerning titanium dioxide COLIPA no. S 75. The Scientific Committee on Cosmetic Products and Non-Food Products Intended for Consumers, SCCNFP, October 24, 2000. (French Government work).
75. Lansdown ABG, Taylor A. Zinc and titanium oxide: promising UV-absorbers but what influence do they have on the intact skin ? Int J Cosmet Sci 1997; 19:167–172.

15

Inorganic Particulate Ultraviolet Filters in Commerce

Nadim A. Shaath
Alpha Research & Development, Ltd., White Plains, New York, USA
Ismail I. Walele
Finetex, Elmwood Park, New Jersey, USA

INTRODUCTION

Responding to the recent medical advances and expanded demands of both the industry and the consumers ultimately using these products, the need for new and improved sunscreen agents is well documented (1). The more than 1.5 million new cases of skin cancer reported each year in the USA alone, along with the new emerging evidence of the damaging effects of UV-A rays and the depletion of the ozone layer through the use of chlorofluorohydrocarbons, as well as the demographic considerations and the popularity of modern leisure outdoor lifestyles, are but a few of the reasons for the need for photoprotection (2). The production of new, safe, more selective, specific, and effective ultraviolet (UV) filters is paramount.

The heart of any sunscreen cosmetic formulation is the UV active ingredient. Formulations with organic UV absorbers and the new organic particulates are dealt with in other chapters in this manuscript (3,4). Inorganic particulates have witnessed a major boost in their use in cosmetic preparations especially in sunscreen products for children, in products for sensitive areas of the body, such as lips and eyes, and other products for both daily wear and recreational protection.

INORGANIC PARTICULATES: BACKGROUND

Inorganic particulates, zinc oxide and titanium dioxide, have become an indispensable tool in the UV protection of cosmetic and toiletry preparations (5).

Titanium dioxide has been on the FDA's monograph since the introduction of the Advance Notice of Proposed Rulemaking (ANPRM) in 1978 (6). The approved level of use of 25% is still valid today, however, with major modifications in the physical and chemical properties of the particulates. No longer are the pigment-like ingredients used, rather micronized particulates that are coated with hydrophilic and/or hydrophobic ingredients and predispersed in a variety of organic emulsions are available today.

Zinc oxide has only been recently approved for use as a Category I ingredient (October 1998) despite the fact that millions of pounds have been used in cosmetic applications annually. Microfine zinc oxide particulates (below 50 nm) that are coated and predispersed have also been introduced to the cosmetic industry and have received wide acceptance as UV-A and broad-spectrum UV protectors.

There are many reasons for this increase in the use of the inorganic particulates, chief of which is their UV-A protection as well as their chemical and photochemical stability in cosmetic applications. They absorb, scatter, and repel a broad range of UV radiation. They have been perceived as being more natural and benign than the organic UV filters despite the fact that they are not used as the raw mineral itself, rather they now contain a wide array of coatings, additives, predispersants, and dispersion enhancers. Their attenuation of the sun protection factor (SPF) of cosmetic formulations has been exceptional, covering both the UV-A and the UV-B spectrum when used in combinations. The disadvantages of using the inorganic particulates include the higher cost when compared to the current traditional organic UV absorbers approved in the USA and more importantly, the difficulty in formulations. Due to the variations in particle size, particle distribution, coatings, dispersants, and other additives in the inorganic particulates, the cosmetic chemist must be a real expert to decipher all these variations in form and activity. The inorganic particulates may be either hydrophilic or hydrophobic and thus the appropriate phase, aqueous or oil, to add to the particulates needs to be experimented with for optimal use. When the particle size of the particulates is not sufficiently small (>100 nm), the so-called "whitening" phenomenon upon application is observed leading to undesirable esthetic and efficacy considerations.

FORMULATING WITH ZINC OXIDE AND TITANIUM DIOXIDE

Hewitt, in a recent article (7), has listed three fundamental requirements for achieving optimum efficacy when formulating with inorganic particulates, namely:

1. Select material with the optimum particles size and particle size distribution. As mentioned earlier, a particle size >100 nm or thereabouts may cause skin whitening and render reemulsification after application on the skin difficult. The supplier should provide this information and the cosmetic chemist should run a UV/visible spectrum and verify that no problem occurs in the formulation. It should also be noted that in *microfine* titanium dioxide ingredients in particular, a "graying" of the formulation when the particle size is well below 50 nm might be observed.
2. Insure that the particles are dispersed homogeneously throughout the emulsion. This of course depends primarily on the type of predispersion and coating of the inorganic particulate (hydrophilic or hydrophobic), the type of emulsion (o/w or w/o) and the many other ingredients present in the formulation.
3. Insure an even distribution of the particles on the skin when the cosmetic product is applied to the skin. The reader is referred to the excellent discussions on rheology found in the chapters of Hewitt (8) and also that of Dahms (9).

The cosmetic chemist should pay particular attention to the pH of the formulation, especially for those involving zinc oxide. At pH values <6, the solubility of zinc oxide increases and migration from the oil phase to the water phase is observed. Another consideration is the adequate dispersion of the inorganic particulates into the formulation. If they are not predispersed with organic emollients, the proper addition of sufficient quantities of emollients may be required. Finally, care should be taken to insure that these high specific gravity particulates remain in the suspension especially after storage and higher temperatures are encountered. Note that carbomers in particular are incompatible with zinc oxide and should be avoided.

Stability testing of the cosmetic formulation and quality control procedures for both the inorganic particulates and the finished product should be implemented. The reader is referred to the many chapters dealing with these two issues, in particular Klein and Palefski (10) for stability and the chapters by Kalinoski (11), and Shaath and Flores for quality control and analytical procedures (12).

Finally, the formulator of cosmetic products utilizing inorganic particulates should be aware of the intellectual property and the many patents issued that limit and restrict the use of a particular ingredient in their cosmetic formulation. Also, regulatory issues should be monitored closely. For example, the inorganic particulates are restricted in the USA when used in combination with avobenzone. Also zinc oxide's use in Europe is not yet approved. Both issues are currently under review by the FDA and COLIPA, respectively.

INORGANIC PARTICULATE SUPPLIERS IN THE USA

The number of suppliers of inorganic particulates to the cosmetic industry has quadrupled in the last 10 years. This is in response to the dramatic increase in the use of inorganic filters in particular and the increase in the number of products on the market that contain UV filters in general.

Micronized inorganic particulates (titanium dioxide and zinc oxide) are commercially sold in several forms:

1. In powder form with or without surface treatments
2. In predispersions.

Each variety may be supplied in different particle sizes and particle size distributions. A partial listing of current suppliers is as follows.

Suppliers of inorganic particulates in powder form with or without surface treatments:

1. Advanced Nano Technologies (ZnO)	10. Rhodia (TiO_2)
2. BASF Z-Cote (ZnO)	11. Sachtleben (TiO_2)
3. Degussa (TiO_2)	12. Sakai LP (ZnO)
4. Elementis (ZnO)	13. Showa Danka (TiO_2)
5. EMD Eusolex (TiO_2)	14. Sumitomo (ZnO)
6. Ishihara ISK TTO (TiO_2)	15. Symrise (ZnO)
7. Kemira (TiO_2)	16. Tayca MT/MZ (TiO_2 and ZnO)
8. Nanophase (ZnO)	17. Titan Kogyo ST (TiO_2)
9. Particle Sciences T-Cote (TiO_2)	18. Uniquema (TiO_2 and ZnO)

Suppliers of predispersions of inorganic particulates

1. BASF Z-Cote HP-1	9. Kemira (TiO_2)
2. Collaborative Labs TioSperse and Z-Sperse	10. Kobo (ZnO and TiO_2)
3. Degussa Tego Sun (TiO_2)	11. Rhodia Mirasun (TiO_2)
4. EMD Eusolex (TiO_2)	12. Sachtleben (TiO_2)
5. Finetex (Natrlfine ZnO and TiO_2)	13. Sakai (ZnO)
6. Granula (ZnO and TiO_2)	14. Showa Denka (TiO_2 and ZnO)
7. Ishihara (TiO_2)	15. Tri-K Industries
8. ISP Escalol (ZnO and TiO_2)	16. Uniquema Tioveil TiO_2 and Solaveil ZnO

The coatings and surface treatments that have been used in TiO_2 and ZnO include:

1. Alginic acid	13. PEG-10
2. Alumina	14. Polyglyceryl-6-polyricinoleate
3. Aluminum hydroxide	15. Polyhydroxystearic acid
4. Aluminum laurate	16. Silica
5. Aluminum stearate	17. Silicone
6. Dimethicone	18. Simethicone
7. Ferric hydroxide	19. Sodium metaphosphate
8. Ferric stearate	20. Stearic acid
9. Glycerine	21. Triethoxy capryl silane
10. Isopropyl titanium triisostearate	22. Trimethoxy capryl silane
11. Methicone	23. Zirconia
12. Organopolysiloxane	

The emollients that have been used as dispersants in the inorganic particulates include:

1. Apricot kernel oil	15. Hexyl laurate
2. Behenyl benzoate	16. Hydrogenated decene oligomers
3. C_{12}–C_{15} alkyl benzoate	17. Isohexadecane
4. Caprylic capric diglyceride	18. Isononyl nonanoate
5. Caprylic capric monoglyceride	19. Isopropyl myristate
6. Caprylic capric triglyceride	20. Isopropyl palmitate
7. Cetearyl alcohol	21. Isostearyl benzoate
8. Cetearyl glucoside	22. Mineral oil
9. Cetyl dimethicone	23. Octinoxate
10. Copolyol	24. Octyl dodecanol
11. Cyclomethicone	25. PEG-40 esters
12. Cyclopenta siloxane	26. Polyglyceryl-4-isostearate
13. Ethyl hexyl hydroxy stearate benzoate	27. Stearyl benzoate
	28. Trioctyl dodecyl citrate
14. Ethyl hexyl palmitate	29. Water

It should be noted that in predispersions, the percentage of active may vary from 25% to 60%. Request detailed information from your supplier on the particle size, the particle size distribution, the coatings, surface treatments, dispersants, predispersant enhancers, and above all, the percentage of active in their formulation of the inorganic particulate.

US CONSUMER PRODUCTS WITH INORGANIC PARTICULATES

One of the first daily wear cosmetics with SPF that incorporated only inorganic particulates was Clinique's Citiblock Oil Free Daily Face Protector launched in 1991 (13). It had an SPF of 13, claimed both UV-A and UV-B protection, and used only micronized titanium dioxide. Unfortunately, they claimed that the product did not contain any "chemical UV filters." This misnomer had encouraged others to label their product as having an "All Natural" claim that was unsupported. Titanium dioxide is a chemical and the current commercial forms undergo a number of chemical reactions and may include other synthetic chemical coatings or dispersants that render all current titanium dioxide UV ingredients not truly "natural."

Inorganic particulates are incorporated mainly into two types of consumer products, namely, children/baby sunscreen products and daily wear long-term protective products, in particular, for individuals with sensitive skin. It should be noted that both zinc oxide and titanium dioxide particulates are also being rapidly incorporated into other general recreational sunscreen products.

Following is a review of the types of sunscreen products that include inorganic particulates in their formulations. This review is not intended to serve as an exhaustive review of all sunscreen products on the market rather it is presented to illustrate the categories and type of products only. The listings are reported alphabetically, not in any order of importance or commercial rankings. The products have not been analyzed and the information relies totally on the data available on the internet and the product label.

Children/Baby Product

Formulations with Combination of Organic/Inorganic UV Filters

Schering-Plough's new sunscreen line Spectra 3 highlights in their advertisement campaign that their products have three modes of action, a clear reference to the presence of the inorganic particulate ZnO with other organic UV absorbers, namely that they scatter, absorb, and reflect the harmful rays of the sun. Products that have both inorganic particulates and organic UV absorbers combined include:

- Banana Boat (Playtex) Baby Magic Block Spray SPF 48 has 2.14% TiO_2 plus four other organic UV filters.
- Banana Boat Kids (Playtex) SPF 30 has TiO_2 plus three other organic UV filters.
- Coppertone Kids Spectra 3 Block SPF 50 has ZnO and five organic UV filters.
- Coppertone Water Babies Spectra 3 SPF 50 has ZnO as well.

- Hawaiian Tropic Baby Faces SPF 50 has TiO_2 and two other organic UV filters.

Formulations with Inorganic Particulates "Only"

A number of baby products have recently appeared on the market with only inorganic particulates. These include:

- California Baby SPF 30+ with micronized TiO_2 (fragrance free).
- Mustela Bebe High Protection Lotion SPF 50 with 14.4% TiO_2 and 7% ZnO.
- Playschool Baby Blanket SPF 50+ with TiO_2.
- Playschool Baby Blanket SPF 45+ with ZnO.

It should be noted that most micronized forms contain about 50% load of the inorganic particulate in a dispersant. Thus 5% ZnO or TiO_2 reflects the addition of about 10% of the inorganic particulate predispersion.

Daily Wear Long-Term Protective Products

Formulations with Combination of Organic/Inorganic UV Filters

Synergistic effects have been observed when combining inorganic and organic UV filters. The reasons given include:

- Increased skin coverage
- Improved spectral coverage
- Increasing the optical path length of the UV light passing through the sunscreen film (8).

Examples of products with the popular combination of octinoxate for UV-B protection and ZnO/TiO_2 for UV-A protection include:

- California North Titanium SPF 15 and 30 with TiO_2 and octinoxate.
- M.D. Forte Total Daily Protector SPF 15 has 5% ZnO and 7.5% octinoxate.
- Olay (P&G) Provital Day Lotion SPF 15.
- Olay (P&G) Complete All day SPF 15.
- Ti Silc Sheer Waterproof Sunblock SPF 45 contains octinoxate and ZnO.
- Vanicream SPF 35 has 8% Z-Cote HP1 and 7.5% octinoxate.
- Vaseline Removal Protection SPF 15 (Cheeseborough Ponds) has TiO_2 and an organic UV absorber.

Examples of other products with multiple organic UV of absorbers and ZnO/TiO_2 include:

- Bristol Myers Squibb SPF 20 has two organic UV absorbers and ZnO.
- Celex-C Sunscreen SPF 30+ with 3% ZnO, 2%TiO_2, octinoxate, and octisalate.
- Eucerin (Beiersdorf) SPF 30 has four organic UV absorbers and ZnO.
- Guthy-Renker Natural Advantage Moisturizer SPF 15 has TiO_2 and three organic UV absorbers.

- Neova Z-Silc Sunblock SPF 30 contains ZnO with octinoxate and octisalate.
- Neutrogena Healthy Defense Moisturizer SPF 30 has three organic UV absorbers and ZnO.
- Purpose One Treatment with SPF 15 has octinoxate, meradimate, and TiO_2.

Several lip balms contain titanium dioxide in combination with other organic UV absorbers. Examples include Blistex Berry lip with TiO_2 and two other UV absorbers. Chapstick lip balm regular has TiO_2 and Padimate-O and NO-AD lip balm SPF 30 has TiO_2 and three other organic UV absorbers.

Formulations with Inorganic Particulates "Only"

Recently, a number of consumer products with inorganic particulates only and some with significantly high SPF labels have appeared on the US market. They include:

- Celex-C Sunscreen SPF has 2% TiO_2 and 2% ZnO.
- Neostrata Sun Block Lotion SPF 30 has only TiO_2.
- Neutrogena Sun Block Lotion for Sensitive Skin SPF 30 has only TiO_2.
- Peter Thomas Roth SPF 30 with TiO_2 and ZnO.
- Skin Ceuticals Physical UV Defence SPF 30 contains 10% TiO_2 and 5% ZnO.

Titanium dioxide has been an approved Category I ingredient long before zinc oxide, hence there are currently many more formulations with it than those with zinc oxide. This is likely to change in the future since zinc oxide offers better UV-A protection.

Recreational Products

The use of titanium dioxide particulates in recreational products appeared on the US market in the 1990s mostly in products with very high SPF products (SPF 30 and above) due to the ability of these ingredients to substantially boost the SPF. Recently, zinc oxide has been added to the regimen for SPF boosting and more importantly for UV-A and broad-spectrum protection claims. Once the UV-A claims and testing procedures by the FDA are finalized, a surge in the use of zinc oxide will be witnessed. Also, if combinations of the particulates with avobenzone are approved in the USA, an increase in their use will also be seen. Finally, if COLIPA in Europe approves zinc oxide as an active ingredient, this will qualify that ingredient to be used interchangeably in all formulations that are manufactured worldwide.

Formulations with Combination of Organic/Inorganic UV Filters

Examples of the many formulations of recreational products that have an inorganic particulate in combination with an organic UV filter include:

- Coppertone Spectra 3 SPF 30 and 50 contains ZnO and four other organic UV filters.

- Hawaiian Tropic Ozone SPF 70 has TiO_2 and five other organic UV filters.
- Sea & Ski Faces Sensitive Skin Sun Block SPF 50 has ZnO and three organic UV filters.
- Blue Wizard Australian Sunscreen SPF 30 has 5.7% ZnO plus three organic UV filters.
- Banana Boat (Playtex) Ultra Sun Block Lotion SPF 15 has 1.2% TiO_2 and three other organic UV filters.

Inorganic Particulates "Only" Products

Examples of the formulations that contain only inorganic particulates include:

- Cotz Total Block SPF 58 has both TiO_2 and ZnO.
- Glyderm Super Sun Block SPF 25 has 2.5% TiO_2.
- OBAGI Nu-Derm Sun Block 24AM has 9% TiO_2 and 6% ZnO.
- Vanicream SPF 15 with 3% T-Cote and 8% Z-Cote.

It should be noted that with few exceptions, the products on the market that include the inorganic particulates are doing so to increase both the SPF and the UV-A claims of their formulations. They are rarely added in recreational products only for their perceived safety, photostability, or inertness.

Finally, we have found no "sunless" tanning products that list inorganic particulates in their label. We have also noted that very few "generic" or drugstore chain brands such as Eckerd, Rite Aid, Stop and Shop, Target and Wal-Mart have products with only inorganic particulates in their formulations. This obviously will rapidly change in the future since most of these brands generally formulate products that follow the lead of the top-selling brands on the market.

CONCLUSIONS

Inorganic particulates have come of age. The micronized forms of titanium dioxide and zinc oxide have made a significant contribution to the growth and credibility of the sunscreen industry. Though they have been used primarily to formulate products for children and for individuals with sensitive skin, they are rapidly finding their way into daily wear sunscreen products and traditional recreational products.

With the finalization of all the pending regulatory issues concerning the inorganic particulates, purveyors of these ingredients will enjoy a wave of unprecedented growth as new and more innovative products appear in the market place. These issues include the UV-A and broad-spectrum claims that may be allowed pending the finalization of the standardized UV-A testing procedures. They also include the adoption of zinc oxide in Europe and the permission by the FDA to allow for the combinations of inorganic particulates and avobenzone.

The proliferation of the inorganic particulates in the sunscreen industry has increased the burden on the cosmetic chemist to decipher between the hundreds of variations of particulates in commerce today. Issues of photo-reactivity needs to be resolved by the suppliers by providing more conclusive data on their safety and improving the coatings, dispersants and additives to insure their lack of photo-reactivity. New simplified and advanced analytical procedures to insure quality and consistency have to be developed and adopted by the instrumentation, research and quality control chemists. Standardization of the many variations of inorganic particulates by the suppliers and by the United States Pharmacopoeia will only make the task of the cosmetic chemist easier. All of the above considerations bode extremely well in facilitating immensely their incorporation into more preparations, thereby providing better products to protect the consumer from the wrath of the harmful UV rays and allow for a major expansion of the sunscreen industry in the future.

REFERENCES

1. Diffey BL. Dosimetry of ultraviolet radiation. In: Shaath NA, ed. Sunscreens: Regulations and Commercial Development. 3rd ed. New York: Marcel Dekker, 2005:827–841.
2. Nelson C. Photoprotection. In: Shaath NA, ed. Sunscreens: Regulations and Commercial Development. 3rd ed. New York: Marcel Dekker, 2005:19–43.
3. Shaath NA. The chemistry of ultraviolet filters. In: Shaath NA, ed. Sunscreens: Regulations and Commercial Development. 3rd ed. New York: Marcel Dekker, 2005:217–238.
4. Herzog B, Hueglin D, Osterwalder U. New sunscreen actives. In: Shaath NA, ed. Sunscreens: Regulations and Commercial Development. 3rd ed. New York: Marcel Dekker, 2005:291–320.
5. Schlossman D, Shao Y. Inorganic sunscreens. In: Shaath NA, ed. Sunscreens: Regulations and Commercial Development. 3rd ed. New York: Marcel Dekker, 2005:239–279.
6. Holman MR, Shetty D. The role of FDA in sunscreen regulation. In: Shaath NA, ed. Sunscreens: Regulations and Commercial Development. 3rd ed. New York: Marcel Dekker, 2005:85–94.
7. Hewitt JP. Formulating water-resistant TiO_2 sunscreens. Cosmet Toilet 1999; 114(a):59–63.
8. Hewitt JP. SPF modulation: optimizing the efficacy of sunscreens. In: Shaath NA, ed. Sunscreens: Regulations and Commercial Development. 3rd ed. New York: Marcel Dekker, 2005:385–412.
9. Dahms, G. The role of surfactants in sunscreen formulations. In: Shaath NA, ed. Sunscreens: Regulations and Commercial Development. 3rd ed. New York: Marcel Dekker, 2005:413–448.
10. Klein K, Palefsky I. Formulating sunscreen products. In: Shaath NA, ed. Sunscreens: Regulations and Commercial Development. 3rd ed. New York: Marcel Dekker, 2005:353–383.
11. Kalinoski HT. Quality control of finished sunscreen products. In: Shaath NA, ed. Sunscreens: Regulations and Commercial Development. 3rd ed. New York: Marcel Dekker, 2005:719–733.
12. Shaath NA, Flores F. Modern analytical techniques in the sunscreen industry. In: Shaath NA, ed. Sunscreens: Regulations and Commercial Development. 3rd ed. New York: Marcel Dekker, 2005:751–766.
13. Lentini PJ. Daily use sunscreens. In: Shaath NA, ed. Sunscreens: Regulations and Commercial Development. 3rd ed. New York: Marcel Dekker, 2005:535–540.

16

New Sunscreen Actives

Bernd Herzog
Ciba Specialty Chemicals Inc., Grenzach-Wyhlen, Germany

Dietmar Hueglin and Uli Osterwalder
Ciba Specialty Chemicals Inc., Basel, Switzerland

INTRODUCTION

Sunscreens should protect not only against sunburn, which is mainly caused by UV-B radiation, but also against the damaging effects of the more deeply penetrating UV-A radiation (1). This new expectation from consumers and the medical community has triggered the development of new UV absorbers and led to the approval of seven new, organic UV absorbers in Europe over the last decade (2). The US Food and Drug Administration has approved none of them so far. In this chapter, the new development of UV filters will be presented and the significant progress over the last few years, mainly in UV-A protection will be discussed.

Trends in the Sunscreen Market

There are three major product categories that use UV absorbers for skin protection. The classical sunscreen or so-called "beach product," the daily skin care formulation "with sun protection factor" designed to avoid photoaging such as wrinkles, and the tanning prevention or whitening products that are very popular in Asia. Besides these three major categories, there are differences from country to country in terms of formulation, for example, Australians prefer water-in-oil type formulation for the beach, whereas Europeans prefer oil-in-water type emulsions in lotion or spray form. Depending on the country and the region, there is also more or less cost pressure on the established mass market brands due to tough competition from other brands and the low-cost private label copies. These developments have to be taken into account in the design of new sunscreen actives. In spite of the variations in the market, there are many common factors that allow us to treat the requirements for UV absorbers very generally. From an economical point of view, UV absorber manufacturers would like to satisfy these criteria and categories with as few ingredients as possible.

Since sun protection is a health issue, there are controversies regularly brought up in the media about the safety of the sunscreens and particularly their actives, the UV absorbers. A recent sunscreen issue is the compliance and misuse to extend sun exposure excessively (3). The reasonable value of the sun protection factor (SPF), and if there should be a cap, are also discussed in this context. Most people do not realize that the actual SPF in use corresponds only to about one-third of the value as declared on the product (4). In contrast to the SPF value, which addresses mainly the UV-B radiation, there is still no common standard for protection against UV-A. Other issues related to UV absorbers are their skin penetration and sensitization potential (5), and also the potential for endocrine disrupter activity (6).

Objectives—Requirements

Sunscreen manufacturers have four basic requirements on sunscreen actives, which all must be fulfilled by the existing and new ingredients before they can be incorporated in a final product.

Efficacy
Safety
Registration
Patent freedom

Efficacy

An efficient sunscreen active must, first of all, show good absorption at least in parts in the relevant UV range between 290 and 400 nm. Efficacy also means that the UV absorber must be easily incorporated in any kind of formulation. If not, it may become difficult to achieve formulations that are also cosmetically acceptable. This, in turn, would negatively influence the compliance of the sunscreen user. The second requirement is thus the solubility of an UV absorber in different emollients relevant to cosmetics. The third major characteristic influencing efficacy is the photostability of the UV absorber, which can be determined by irradiating a sunscreen sample in the laboratory (7). Unstable sunscreen actives lose efficacy and may lead to safety concerns upon irradiation.

Furthermore, the UV absorber substance must be compatible with all other ingredients in a formulation; there should be no discoloration of skin and hair, no staining of textiles, and no odor. For claims of water resistance, the UV absorber should be insoluble in water and, last but not least, the UV filter should be economical in its use.

Safety

Sunscreen actives should have no adverse effect on humans and environment. Although direct comparison with a new pharmaceutical drug is not appropriate, the development of a new sunscreen active for global use is highly demanding.

Table 16.1 Typical International Safety Dossier of a New Sunscreen

Acute oral and dermal toxicity
Dermal, ocular irritation, skin sensitization
Photo-irritation, photo-sensitization
Subchronic oral and topical toxicity
Chronic toxicity
Fertility, early embryonic development
Embryofetal toxicity and peri-/post-natal toxicity
In vitro and in vivo percutaneous absorption
Topical and oral pharmacokinetic and metabolism
In vitro and in vivo genetic toxicity
Carcinogenicity
Photo-carcinogenicity
Safety and efficacy in humans

Source: Ref. (8).

The toxicological studies required for a global registration are listed in Table 16.1 (8).

Registration

In order to exploit the full economic potential of a UV filter, UV absorber manufacturers are aiming for global registration. In Europe, South America, Asia, and Africa, where sunscreens are considered as cosmetics, approval is possible within 1–2 years of filing. In Australia, Japan, and the USA, it takes longer. Only recently was a new procedure (TEA: material time and material extend application) introduced in the USA. After a minimum of 5 years foreign marketing experience in five countries, a new sunscreen active can be registered in an accelerated procedure (9). In a second step, data on efficacy and safety have to be submitted. So far, three UV-B filters that are widely used outside the USA have received the status of "eligibility to enter the Sunscreen Monograph" (10):

- Isoamyl *p*-methoxycinnamate (IMC), Amiloxate (US drug name)
- 4-Methylbenzylidene camphor (MBC), Enzacamene (US drug name)
- Ethylhexyl triazone (EHT), octyl triazone.

More recent filters as discussed here in this chapter will have to fulfill the 5-year marketing experience first before they can apply for eligibility considerations.

Patent Freedom

Patenting of sunscreen actives and their applications deserve special attention in this chapter. Patent freedom means the free use of sunscreen actives by any sunscreen manufacturer, that is, without any uncertainty about whether any third party patent rights are infringed by the use of a particular ingredient.

Until about 10 years ago, UV absorber manufacturers protected their inventions by simple substance patents that included the basic applications, for example, "invention of a novel UV absorber for the incorporation in personal care formulations for the protection of skin and hair." The innovative cosmetics manufacturers would then file their own patents on specific applications and technologies that they had invented and were using in order to differentiate themselves from their competitors. This system allowed both the supplier and the manufacturer of sunscreens to create new business by protecting their respective inventions. In the mid-1990s, important cosmetics manufacturers started to patent not only their specific technologies but also generic combinations of different ingredients without the intention for use. This "blocking strategy" is aimed to keep competitors from using new technology that emerged on the market (11). But this strategy not only limits the potential of the competitors, which is part of business, but is also detrimental for the suppliers who suddenly see the potential of their new sunscreen active shrinking due to patent restrictions.

As a consequence, the suppliers had to react and rethink their patenting strategy and the whole innovation process, especially in the realization phase and the market introduction. Patenting a substance together with its major applications and sampling customers with new ingredients only under Confidential Disclosure Agreement is not sufficient anymore. As soon as the identity of a new ingredient becomes known, "all" applications have to be disclosed in detail and explicitly as well, for example, combinations of the novel ingredient with other sunscreen actives and other compounds such as emollients, emulsifiers, or thickeners, otherwise such a new ingredient faces the threat of being blocked from major applications.

A recent example is the combination of the two newly approved UV filters, bis-ethylhexyloxyphenol methoxyphenyltriazine (BEMT) and disodium phenyl dibenzimidazole tetrasulfonate (DPDT). The combination of these two UV filters is mutually blocked by the two leading sunscreen manufacturers in Europe and for everybody else in countries where the patent applications were filed (12). A strategy to avoid such situations in the future is to publish all sorts of combinations of ingredients and claims that may ever become relevant before the identity of the new ingredient becomes publicly known. Institutions to publish quickly, now exist on the Internet, for example, www.ip.com. IP.com enables innovative companies to quickly and easily protect their inventions by offering security services for many aspects of the invention process: from the safeguarding of sensitive information such as R&D lab notebooks, to the rapid publication and creation of prior art in the form of technical disclosures.

NEW TRENDS IN THE DEVELOPMENT OF UV ABSORBERS FOR SUNSCREENS

During the last few years, the focus in R&D of several UV filter producers has been in the development of new UV-A filters because of the necessity to cover that part of the spectrum and because of the gap in the availability of such filters. On the other hand, development of new UV-B filters is driven by need to replace traditional filters mainly because of growing safety concerns, for example, skin penetration of some of the lower molecular weight filters. Since higher efficacy in terms of "less chemicals on the skin" is desirable, the class of UV broad-spectrum filters is emerging, covering the UV-A and UV-B ranges with one chemical entity.

To date, the two "workhorses" in UV-B and UV-A protection, ethylhexyl methoxycinnamate (EHMC) and butyl methoxydibenzoylmethane (BMBM), dominate the ranking of market shares in most countries. Exactly this combination is incompatible due to mutual amplification of photoinstability. Such systems can also not be stabilized. As an alternative to organic UV filters, and for better SPF and UV-A protection, the microfine inorganic pigments TiO_2 and ZnO are gaining importance. They account for about 20% of the total value of sunscreen actives, although a well-accepted cosmetic formulation is still not easy to achieve.

Three trends to improve efficacy and/or safety of UV filters could be observed in recent years:

- New developments with respect to conventional UV absorbers
  - Stabilizing agents for BMBM
  - SPF boosters (use of non-absorbing materials that increase SPF)
- New product forms
  - Encapsulation of conventional UV absorbers
  - Organic particles
- New Molecules
  - Chromophore grafted onto polymer backbone
  - Extending or multiplying the chromophore.

New Developments with Respect to Conventional UV Absorbers

As an example, the photostability problem of the widely used UV-A filter BMBM can be overcome to a certain extent by stabilizing it with other UV filters such as octocrylene or 4-methylbenzylidene camphor (MBC), or with non-UV-absorbing compounds such as diethylhexyl-2,6-naphthalate (DEHN) (13).

A new way of boosting the efficacy of current filter systems was suggested by incorporation of nonabsorbing particles that scatter the UV radiation and thus lead to a longer pathway through the sunscreen film on the skin (e.g. Sun-Spheres®) (14).

New Product Forms

The efficacy and safety aspect of UV absorbers has been addressed by reducing skin penetration via encapsulation of UV absorbers, for example, EHMC in glass particles (UV Pearls®) (15). The UV filter is thus kept on the outermost layer of the skin, reducing the dermal uptake as compared to free UV filters. The UV Pearls prevent the chemical interaction of EHMC with BMBM, leading to a significantly improved photostability of the combination.

Another new product form of UV filters is the use of insoluble organic UV absorbers as pigment-like fine particles, which are held in a stable dispersion. This concept will be pointed out in more detail in case study 1.

Case Study 1: Dispersions of Particulate Organic UV Absorbers

In their search for a new UV absorber, which has a good solubility in most cosmetic solvents, researchers at Ciba got a bit frustrated, because the large molecules they were looking at showed mostly low solubility. One day they came up with a really creative idea. Making a virtue of necessity, molecules with weakest solubility were identified in order to create organic UV absorbers in microfine pigment form as already known from the inorganic filters. This led to a new class of UV filters (16).

Methylene bis-benzotriazolyl tetramethylbutylphenol (MBBT) is the first representative of this new class of UV absorber. The commercial form Tinosorb® M is produced as a 50% aqueous dispersion of colorless organic microfine particles with a size <200 nm ($d_{0.5}$). These small particles are stabilized in their size by a surfactant (17).

Composition of the dispersion of MBBT (Tinosorb® M):

Organic micropigment (MBBT)	50%
Surfactant (decyl glucoside)	7.5%
Thickener (xanthan gum)	0.2%
Propylene glycol	0.4%
Water	to 100%

The structure of MBBT is shown in Fig. 16.1(a). Figure 16.1(b) shows the UV spectra of MBBT dissolved in dioxane and in aqueous dispersion. Due to scattering and an intermolecular interaction of the UV chromophores, the spectrum of the particles is changed in comparison to that in solution. The most striking difference is that the extinction maximum in the UVA range is shifted from about 350 to 360 nm (16).

Figure 16.1(c) shows the specific extinction $E_{1,1}$ at 360 nm as function of particle size. There is a strong dependence on particle size. It is obvious from Fig. 16.1(c) that one has to create particles of sizes significantly below 1 μm in order to obtain a satisfactory efficacy.

Photostability of MBBT

The absorption spectrum of MBBT shows a double band structure (Fig. 16.1b). The longer wavelength band occurring between 340 and 350 nm in organic solvents can be attributed to a $\pi\pi^*$ charge transfer (CT) state. This is favored by the planar orientation enforced by the intramolecular hydrogen bond, made possible by the hydroxy group in the *ortho* position. The shorter wavelength

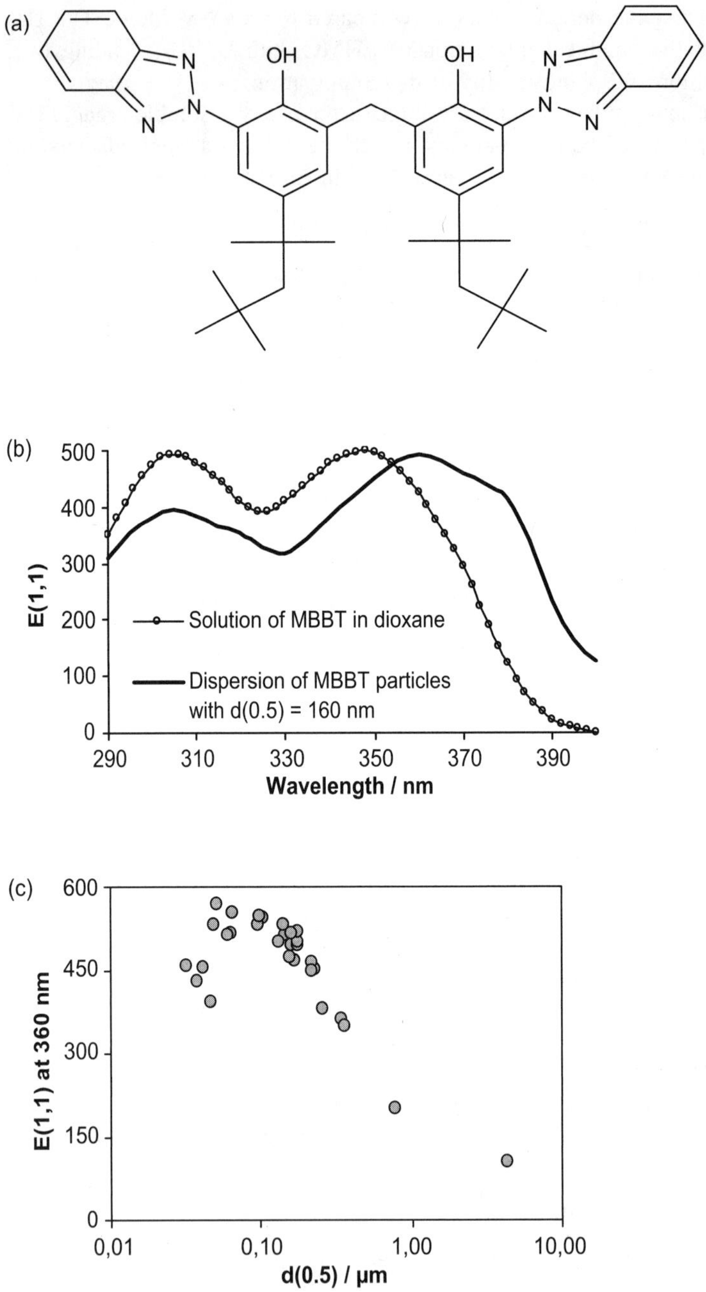

Figure 16.1 (a) Structure of MBBT. (b) Spectra of MBBT in solution and dispersion. (c) $E_{1,1}$ of micronized MBBT at 360 nm in aqueous dispersion as function of particle size (16).

band at about 305 nm arises from a local transition within the benzotriazole moiety (18).

Excitation of the molecule by a photon increases the energy of the molecule, which switches from the electronic S_0 ground state to the first electronic excited state S_1. After excitation different processes are possible (Fig. 16.2a) (19). Fluorescence can occur, or, after intersystem crossing (ISC, a radiationless pathway from S_1 to T_1) phosphorescence can also occur. There may be photoreactions ongoing from S_1 or T_1. Internal conversion (IC), another radiationless pathway, is a redistribution of the absorbed energy from electronic excitation to vibrational excitation. In contrast to the electronically excited molecule, the vibrationally excited one can be deactivated by collisions with surrounding molecules, dissipating the energy into harmless heat. Therefore, the faster the rate of internal conversion, the higher the photostability (20).

The energy gap law (19) states that the rate of IC becomes faster as the energy gap between the ground state and the excited state decreases. This, for instance, is the case with molecules where an excited state proton transfer (also called phototautomerism) occurs, such as MBBT (Fig. 16.1a). The state S_1', which is reached after isomerization, has less energy than S_1. After IC the

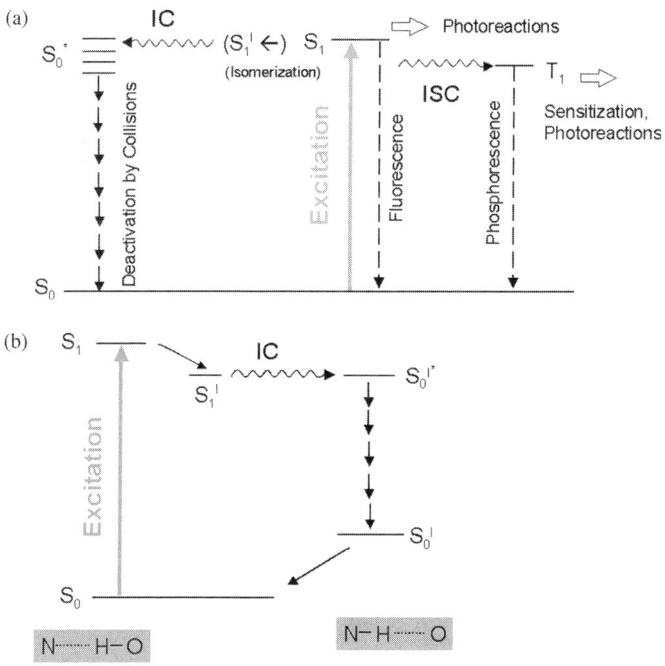

Figure 16.2 (a) Processes that may occur after photon absorption (Jablonski diagram). (b) Reduction of the energy gap between ground and excited state after excited state intramolecular hydrogen transfer.

molecule relaxes from $S_0'^* \rightarrow S_0'$. Since the ground state S_0' of the isomer is energetically higher than the ground state S_0, the deactivated isomer reacts back immediately to the original ground state S_0 (Fig. 16.2b). The whole proton transfer cycle lasts less than 1 ps (10^{-12} s). Since it is much faster than the other processes, which may occur after excitation, it is a very efficient deactivation mechanism.

Benzotriazole chemistry has been utilized for decades in technical applications. MBBT and drometrizole trisiloxane (DTS) are the first examples used in sunscreens.

Synthesis of New Molecules

There is a comprehensive patent literature describing many new structures and substances that can, in principle, be used as sunscreen actives. Most substances that were once identified will, however, never make it to a commercial product. A strategy for the development of UV filters, combining theoretical aspects with practical synthesis within the quinoxaline chemistry has been published recently (21), but there is no indication that this class of UV absorbers will ever be used in sunscreens. In the following case study, the molecular design of bis-ethylhexyloxyphenol methoxyphenyl triazine (BEMT), which is already in use in Europe and South America, will be demonstrated.

Case Study 2: BEMT—A New Filter Designed for Application in Sunscreens

In the year 2000, the first UV filter based on hydroxyphenyltriazine (HPT) technology was added to the positive list of European cosmetic UV filters (INCI: bis-ethylhexyloxyphenol methoxyphenyl triazine, BEMT; trade name: Tinosorb®S, Ciba Specialty Chemicals). BEMT is a new oil-soluble filter with strong broad-spectrum protection in the UV-A and UV-B regions. Due to its outstanding filter efficacy, combined with its inherent photostability and compatibility with all types of cosmetic filters as well as other cosmetic ingredients, BEMT represents a new generation of cosmetic UV filters. Its structure and UV-spectrum are depicted in Fig. 16.3 (case D).

The strong absorption of tri-phenyl-triazines shown in the UV-B range (see Fig. 16.3, case A) has $\pi\pi^*$ character. An $n\pi^*$ transition may also contribute to this band (22). As an *ortho*-hydroxy group is introduced (Fig. 16.3, case B), a UV-A band emerges, which is due to an intramolecular charge transfer ($\pi\pi^*$-CT). With two *ortho*-hydroxy groups at different phenyl moieties, this UV-A absorption increases (Fig. 16.3, case D) and with three, even more so (Fig. 16.3, case C). The optimized broad-spectrum structure was obtained with case D (Fig. 16.3) referring to BEMT, which shows absorption maxima at 310 and 343 nm with $\varepsilon_{max} = 46{,}800$ and $51{,}900\ M^{-1}\ cm^{-1}$, respectively, measured in ethanol.

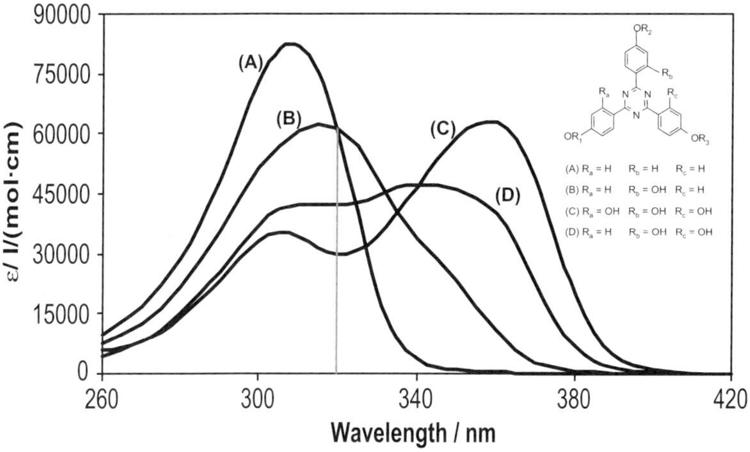

Figure 16.3 HPT structure and spectral performance.

BEMT contains two intramolecular hydrogen bridges that enable an excited-state intramolecular proton transfer (phototautomerism) after photoexcitation. This is followed by internal conversion and rapid energy dissipation, resulting in inherent photostability. Thus, the presence of *ortho*-hydroxy groups not only influences the shape of the absorption spectrum, but also the photostability. The respective mechanism has been already discussed in detail in case study 1 with MBBT. The photostabilizing effect of an *ortho*-hydroxy group is also discussed by Shaath (23).

The molecular design was directed toward broad-spectrum characteristics with high molecular extinction in the UV-A and the UV-B ranges, good solubility in cosmetic solvents, and inherent photostability (Fig. 16.4) (24).

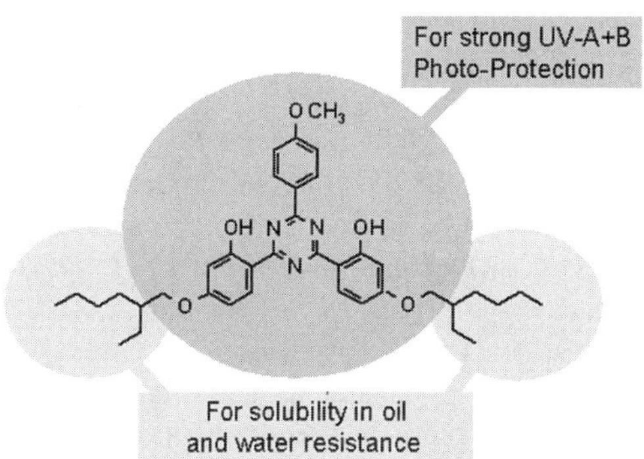

Figure 16.4 Molecular design for absorption efficacy, solubility, and water resistance.

OVERVIEW OF NEW SUNSCREEN ACTIVES

The Most Important Properties of UV Absorbers for Sunscreens

The most important properties of UV absorbers for use in sunscreens are

- the UV-spectroscopic performance
- the solubility in media used in sunscreen formulations
- the photostability.

UV-Spectroscopic Performance

There are two features which are important for the UV-spectroscopic performance:

1. The wavelength at which the extinction is at maximum, thus defining whether the substance is a UV-A, a UV-B, or a UV-broad-spectrum absorber.
2. The extinction efficiency, which is best expressed as the $E_{1,1}$ value, referring to the theoretical extinction of a 1% solution of the substance, measured at an optical pathlength of 1 cm.

The $E_{1,1}$ value can be calculated using Lambert–Beer's law with the molar decadic extinction coefficient ε and the molar mass M via Eq. (16.1):

$$E_{1,1} = \varepsilon[\mathrm{L/(mol\ cm)}] \cdot \frac{10[\mathrm{g/L}]}{\mathrm{M[g/mol]}} \cdot 1[\mathrm{cm}] \tag{16.1}$$

Thus, the $E_{1,1}$ value has the meaning of extinction per mass of the UV absorber. A further important quantity is the mean value of the specific extinction over the spectral range from 290 to 400 nm, $\langle E_{1,1}\rangle_{\mathrm{mean}}$, characterizing the area under the UV extinction curve.

Solubility

Most UV absorbers for use in sunscreens are more or less hydrophobic, which means that the solubility in oils is better than that in water. In most cases it is desirable to be able of achieving a concentration of an individual filter in the order of 5%. Most formulations on the market are o/w emulsions with an oil content of may be 30%. Thus the solubility of hydrophobic UV absorbers in oils should be at least 15% in order to achieve the overall concentration of 5%. With water-soluble filters the solubility should be in a comparable range.

Solubility of the oil-soluble filters is given for a limited number of typical solvents (isopropylmyristate, caprylic/capric triglyceride, and dimethicone—see Tables 16.3–16.5). The solubility was measured by stirring an excess of the active ingredient in the respective oil for 7 days at 25°C. After this time the nondissolved material was separated by centrifugation and filtration. The concentration of the UV absorber in the clear saturated solution was determined via UV spectroscopy.

Photostability

There are two advantages of photostable filter systems:

1. There is no loss of extinction upon irradiation and filter efficiency is constant. Thus, the amount of filter used for a certain effect is less compared to an unstable system.
2. There is no need to worry about the toxicology of possible photoproducts.

Photostability was tested according to the method suggested by Berset et al. (25) and modified by Herzog and Sommer (26).

Discussion of the New UV Filters for Sunscreens

In Table 16.2, the new filters are listed using their names according to the International Nomenclature for Cosmetic Ingredients (INCI) and the numbers of the European Cosmetic and Toiletry and Perfumery Association (COLIPA). Supplier and trademark are given as well as the maximum extinction coefficient, the wavelength at the extinction maximum, an information whether the filter goes to the oil or the aqueous phase, molecular mass, synthesis strategy, and status of approval. Although photostability data are available, they will not be presented in detail, since all new filters, with one exception, showed good photostability Recovery of the parent substance [2% in formulation, applied on rough quartz substrates as described in Refs. (25,26)] after irradiation with 10 minimal erythemal doses (MED) was >90%.

UV-B Filters

Ethylhexyl triazone (EHT) (27): With EHT, the chromophore of para-amino benzoic acid (PABA) was trebled by linking it to a triazine ring. Doubling or trebling a chromophore is a strategy to optimize the specific extinction $E_{1,1}$ and to create filters with higher molecular mass (>500 Da). The chemical name of EHT is 2,4,6-trinanilin-(*p*-carbo-2′-ethyl-1′-oxi)-1,3,5-triazine. The structure and the UV spectrum (in ethanol) of this efficient UV-B absorber are shown in Fig. 16.5.

The solubility of EHT is listed for three typical emollients in Table 16.3. Although its solubility is limited, EHT can be incorporated in sunscreen formulations in substantial amounts. The low solubility can be understood as a consequence of the high symmetry of the molecule. In terms of synthetic feasibility the symmetric structure is of advantage.

Dioctyl butamido triazone (DBT) (28): DBT can be regarded as an improved version of EHT. The chromophore system is nearly the same, but considering the side groups the molecule is no longer symmetric and the solubility is thus much increased in comparison to EHT (Table 16.3).

Table 16.2 Overview of New Actives for Sunscreens (Not Yet Approved in the USA)

Type	Sunscreen Active COLIPA #, INCI name	Trademark (supplier)	Ext. coeff. ($mol^{-1} cm^{-1}$)	Spectrum max (nm) (O/W soluble)	Mol. Mass (Da) (synthesis strategy)	Approval (status)
UV-B	S69 EHT Ethylhexyl Triazone	Uvinul T150 (BASF)	119,500	314 (oil)	823 (triple chromophore)	Europe USA (TEA[a])
	S78 DBT Dioctyl Butamido Triazone	Uvasorb HEB (3V Sigma)	111,700	312 (oil)	766 (triple chromophore)	Europe
	S74 BMP Benzylidene Malonate Polysiloxane	Parsol SLX (Roche/DSM)	~108,000	312 (oil)	~6000 (polymer backbone)	Europe
UV-A	S71 TDSA Terephthalylidene Dicamphor Sulfonic Acid	Mexoryl SX (L'OREAL)	47,100	345 (water)	607 (extended chromophore)	Europe, Japan, USA (NDA[b])
	S 80 DPDT Disodium Phenyl Dibenz-imidazole Tetrasulfonate	Neo Heliopan AP (Symrise)	52,400	334 (water)	675 (extended chromophore)	Europe
	DHHB Diethylamino Hydroxy-benzoyl Hexyl Benzoate	Uvinul A Plus (BASF)	35,900	354 (oil)	398 (extended chromophore)	Europe (in progress)
	BDHB (tentative) "Bis diethylamino hydroxybenzoyl benzoate"	None (Ciba SC)	66,200	354 (oil)	679 (double chromophore)	No application so far
	BBET (tentative) "Bis benzoxazoylphenyl ethylhexylimino triazine"	Uvasorb K2A (3V Sigma)	105,000	338 (oil)	760 (double chromophore)	No application so far
UV-B/ UV-A	S73 DTS Drometrizole trisiloxane	Mexoryl XL (L'OREAL)	15,900 and 15,500	303, 341 (oil)	501 (extended molecule)	Europe, Japan
	S79 MBBT Methylene bis-benzotriazolyl tetramethylbutylphenol (Bisoctrizole[c])	Tinosorb M (Ciba SC)	26,600 and 33,000	305, 360 (water dispersible)	659 (double chromophore; microfine particles)	Europe, Australia, USA (TEA[a])
	S81 BEMT Bis-ethylhexyloxyphenol methoxyphenyltriazine (Bemotrizinol[c])	Tinosorb S (Ciba SC)	46,800 and 51,900	310, 343 (oil)	629 (extended chromophore)	Europe, USA (TEA[a])

[a]TEA: Material Time and Extend Application with foreign marketing data.
[b]NDA: New Drug Application.
[c]Generic drug name (United States Adopted Name).

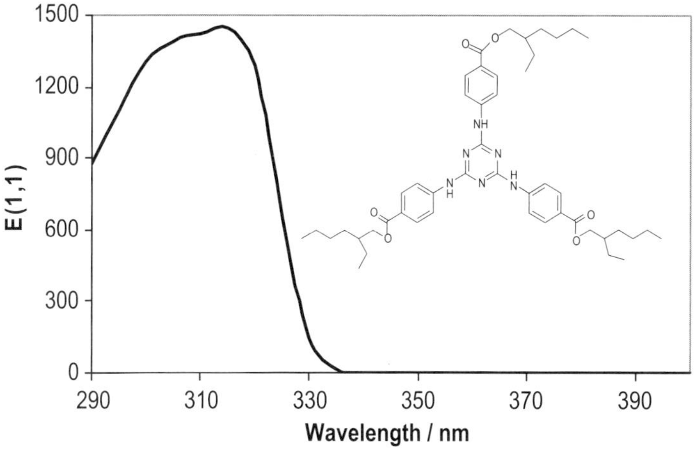

Figure 16.5 UV spectrum and structure of ethylhexyl triazone $E_{1,1}(314) = 1450$, $\langle E_{1,1}\rangle_{\text{mean}} = 420$.

The chemical name of DBT is benzoic acid, 4,4′-[[6-[[4-[[1,1-(dimethylethyl)amino]carbonyl]phenyl]amino]1,3,5-triazine-2,4-diyl]diimino]bis-,bis(2-ethylhexyl) ester. The structure and the UV spectrum (in ethanol) of this efficient UV-B absorber are shown in Fig. 16.6.

Benzylidene malonate polysiloxane (BMP) (29): BMP is a polymeric UV absorber with the chromophores in the side chains. The molecular weight of the molecule is about 6000 Da. There is an improvement of safety since skin penetration is practically excluded at this molecular size. The polymer also shows some film-forming properties (30). However, since the fraction of UV absorbing moieties in the overall mass of the molecule is small, the efficiency in terms of $E_{1,1}$ is quite low.

The chemical name of BMP is α-(trimethylsilyl)-ω-(trimethyl-silyloxy) poly[oxy(dimethyl)silylene]-*co*-[oxy(methyl)(2-{*p*-[2,2-bis(ethoxycarbonyl) vinyl]phenoxy}-1-methyleneethyl)silylene]-*co*-[oxy(methyl)(2-{*p*-[2,2-bis(eth oxycarbonyl)vinyl]phenoxy}prop-1-enyl)silylene]. The structure and the UV

Table 16.3 Solubility of New UV-B Absorbers in Few Selected Cosmetic Solvents

UV-B absorber	Isopropyl myristate	Caprylic/capric triglyceride	Dimethicone
Ethylhexyl triazone	2%	6%	<1%
Dioctyl butamido triazone	>50%	47%	<1%
Benzylidene malonate polysiloxane	>50%	>50%	1%

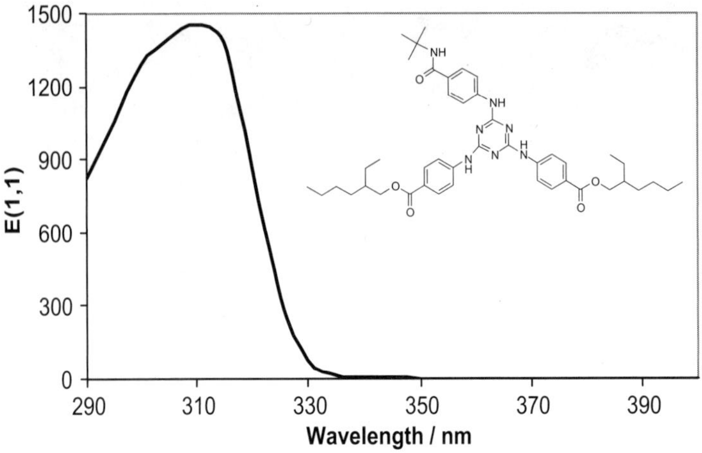

Figure 16.6 UV spectrum and structure of diethylhexyl butamido triazine $E_{1,1}(312) = 1460$, $\langle E_{1,1}\rangle_{mean} = 380$.

spectrum (in ethanol) of this polymeric UV-B absorber are shown in Fig. 16.7.

The solubility of BMP in three typical emollients is listed in Table 16.3.

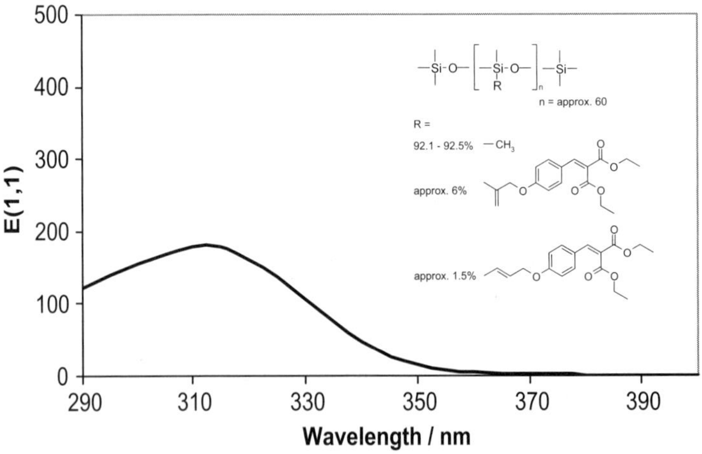

Figure 16.7 UV spectrum and structure of benzylidene malonate polysiloxane $E_{1,1}(312) = 180$, $\langle E_{1,1}\rangle_{mean} = 67$.

UV-A Filters

Terephthalylidene dicamphor sulfonic acid (TDSA) (31): TDSA was the first development of an organic UV-A filter after BMBM. It is water soluble, and therefore less efficient in terms of water resistance. The photostability of TDSA, though still limited (60% recovery after 10 MED), is better than that of BMBM.

The chemical name of TDSA is 3,3′-(1,4-phenylendimetylene)-bis-(7,7-dimethyl-2-oxo-bicyclo-[2.2.1]heptane-1-methane sulfonic acid. The structure and the UV spectrum (in water) are shown in Fig. 16.8. TDSA is captively used by L'Oreal.

Disodium phenyl dibenzimidazole tetrasulfonate (DPDT) (32–34): Another water-soluble UV-A filter, which in contrast to TDSA is freely available, is DPDT.

The chemical name of DPDT is 1H-benzimidazole-4,6-disulfonic acid, 2,2′-(1,4-phenylene)bis-, disodium salt. The structure and the UV spectrum (in water) are shown in Fig. 16.9.

Diethylamino hydroxybenzoyl hexyl benzoate (DHHB) (35,36): DHHB was launched as a successor of BMBM. The UV-spectral properties are similar to BMBM, but the photostablility of DHHB, designed on classic benzophenone chemistry, is superior.

The chemical name of DHHB is 2-(4-diethylamino-2-hydroxybenzoyl)-benzoic acid hexylester. The structure and the UV spectrum (in ethanol) of this UV-A absorber are shown in Fig. 16.10. The solubilities of DHHB in three typical emollients are listed in Table 16.4.

Bis-diethylamino hydroxybenzoyl benzoate (BDHB, tentative INCI name) (37): This UV-A absorber is made by doubling the chromophore of DHHB, leading to a molecular weight >500 Da. The solubility of these types of duplicated benzophenones depends on the characteristics of the bridge between the chromophores.

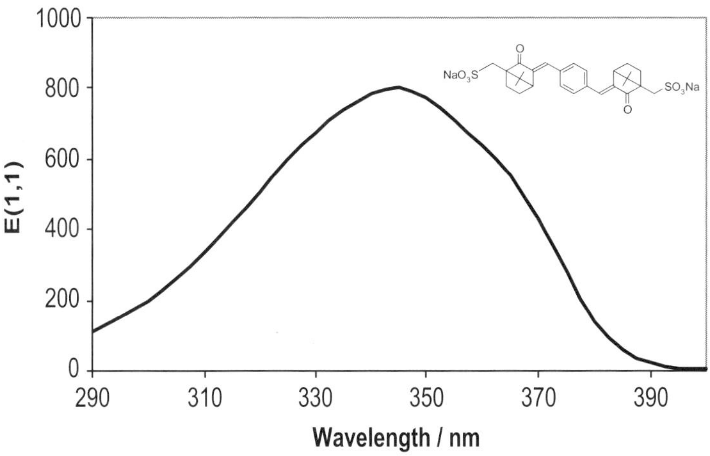

Figure 16.8 UV spectrum and structure of terephthalylidene dicamphor sulfonic acid $E_{1,1}(345) = 775$, $\langle E_{1,1}\rangle_{\text{mean}} = 400$.

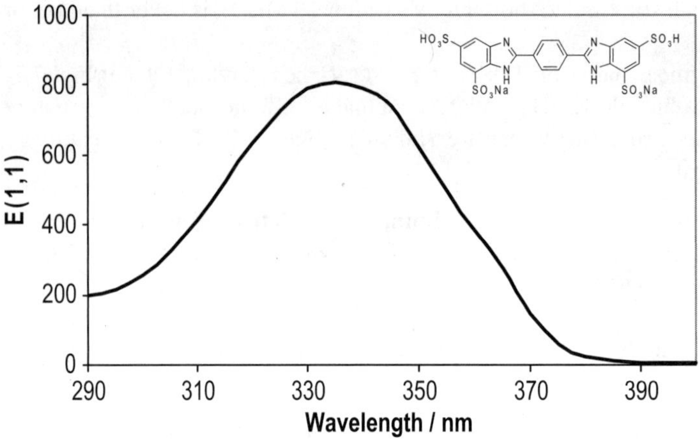

Figure 16.9 UV spectrum and structure of disodium phenyl dibenzimidazole tetrasulfonate $E_{1,1}(334) = 775$, $\langle E_{1,1}\rangle_{\text{mean}} = 367$.

The structure and the UV spectrum (in ethanol) of BDHB are shown in Fig. 16.11.

Bis-benzoxazoylphenyl ethylhexylimino triazine (BBET, tentative INCI name) (38): The chemical name of BBET is 2,4-bis-(5-1(dimethylpropyl)-benzoxazo-2-yl-4-phenyl)-imino(-6-(2-ethylhexyl)-imino-1,3,5-triazine. The structure and the UV spectrum of this UV-A absorber are shown in Fig. 16.12.

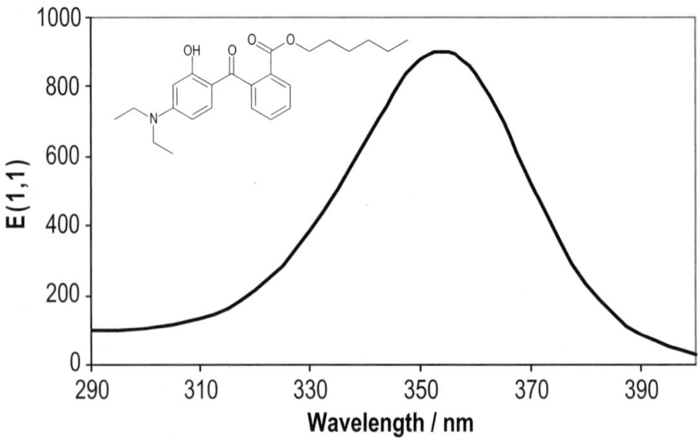

Figure 16.10 UV spectrum and structure of diethylamino hydroxybenzoyl hexyl-benzoate $E_{1,1}(354) = 900$, $\langle E_{1,1}\rangle_{\text{mean}} = 359$.

Table 16.4 Solubilities of New UV-A Absorbers

UV-A absorber	Isopropyl myristate	Caprylic/capric triglyceride	Dimethicone
Terephthalylidene dicamphor sulfonic acid		Water soluble	
Disodium phenyl dibenzimidazole tetrasulfonate		Water soluble	
Diethylamino hydroxybenzoyl hexyl benzoate	12%	15%	1%

Again, the strategy of doubling a chromophore was employed in this case, and a high molecular weight has been achieved. Since the triazine ring is substituted asymmetrically, several synthesis steps are necessary for preparing this substance. Patents have been filed not only by the inventor 3V Sigma, but also by the sunscreen manufacturer Beiersdorf, see application patents (39).

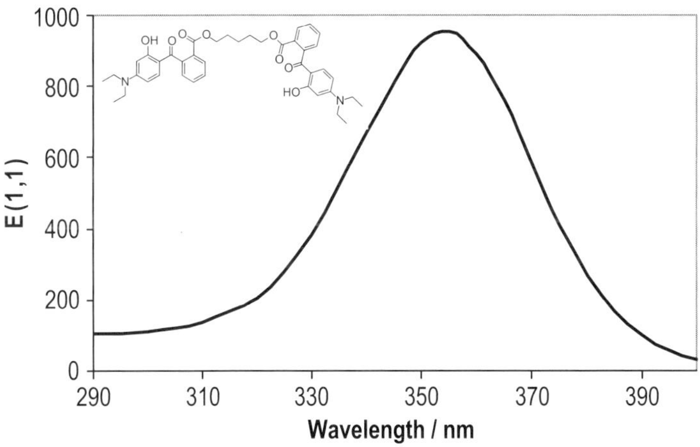

Figure 16.11 UV spectrum and structure of bis diethylamino hydroxybenzoyl benzoate (BDHB) $E_{1,1}(354) = 975$, $\langle E_{1,1} \rangle_{mean} = 380$.

UV Broad-Spectrum Filters

Drometrizole trisiloxane (DTS) (31): DTS is a pioneer in the category of oil-soluble broad-spectrum filters. The siloxane rest gives rise to good oil solubility and a high molecular weight (>500 Da), but at the cost of a lower specific extinction ($E_{1,1}$).

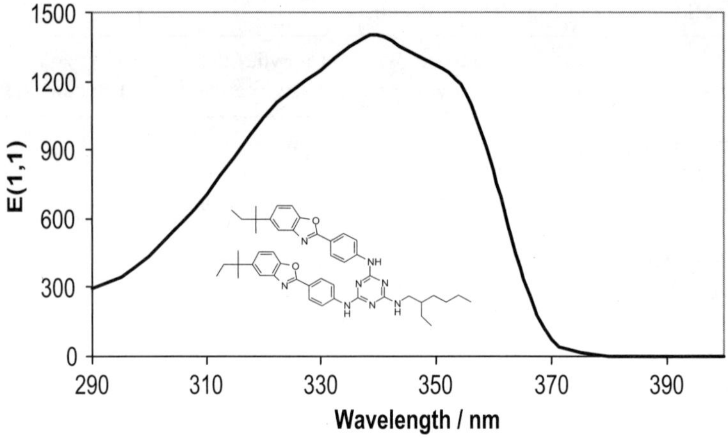

Figure 16.12 Structure and UV spectrum of bis benzoxazolylphenyl ethylhexylamino triazine (BBET) $E_{1,1}(338) = 1405$, $\langle E_{1,1}\rangle_{\text{mean}} = 626$.

The chemical name of DTS is 2-(2H-benzotriazol-2-yl)-4-methyl-6-[2-methyl-3-[1,3,3,3-tetramethyl-1-[(trimethylsilyl)oxy]disiloxanyl]propyl]-phenol. The structure and the UV spectrum (in ethanol) of this UV broad-spectrum absorber are shown in Fig. 16.13.

The solubilities of DTS in three typical emollients are listed in Table 16.5. DTS is captively used by L'Oreal.

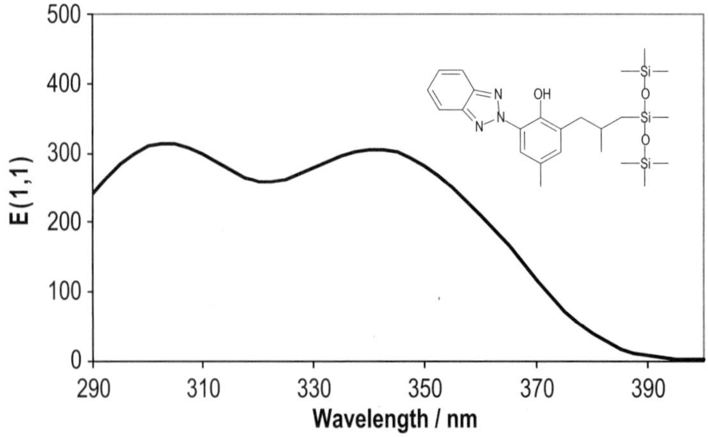

Figure 16.13 UV spectrum and structure of drometrizole trisiloxane $E_{1,1}(303) = 309$, $E_{1,1}(341) = 317$, $\langle E_{1,1}\rangle_{\text{mean}} = 200$.

Table 16.5 Solubilities of New UV Broad-Spectrum Absorbers

UV broad-spectrum absorber	Isopropyl myristate	Caprylic/capric triglyceride	Dimethicone
Drometrizole trisiloxane	>50%	>50%	6%
Methylene bis-benzotriazolyl tetramethylbutylphenol		Water dispersable	
Bis-ethylhexyloxyphenol methoxyphenyltriazine	6%	5%	<1%

Methylene bis-benzotriazolyl tetramethylbuty!phenol (MBBT, Bisoctrizole) (40–42): MBBT is the organic UV filter that comes as microfine organic particles (see case study 1).

The chemical name of MBBT is 2,2′-methylen-bis-[6-(2H-benzotriazol-2-yl)-4-(1,1,3,3-tetramethylbutyl)]-phenol. The structure and the UV spectrum (dispersion in water) of this UV broad-spectrum absorber are shown in Fig. 16.14.

Bis-ethylhexyloxyphenol methoxyphenyltriazine (BEMT, Bemotrizinol) (40,41,43): BEMT was specially designed as a broad-spectrum UV filter and up to now it is the most effective representative of this category.

The chemical name of BEMT is 2,4-bis-{[4-(2-ethyl-hexyloxy)-2-hydroxy]-phenyl}-6-(4-methoxyphenyl)-1,3,5-triazine. The structure and the

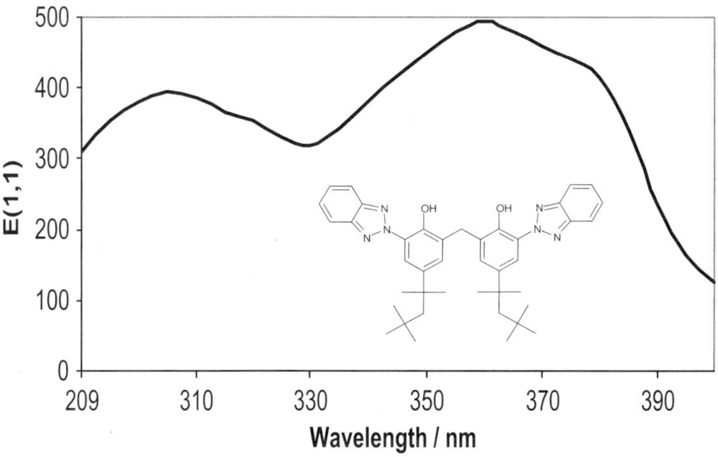

Figure 16.14 UV spectrum and structure of methylene bis-benzotriazolyl tetramethylbutylphenol $E_{1,1}(305) = 404$, $E_{1,1}(360) = 495$, $\langle E_{1,1}\rangle_{mean} = 373$.

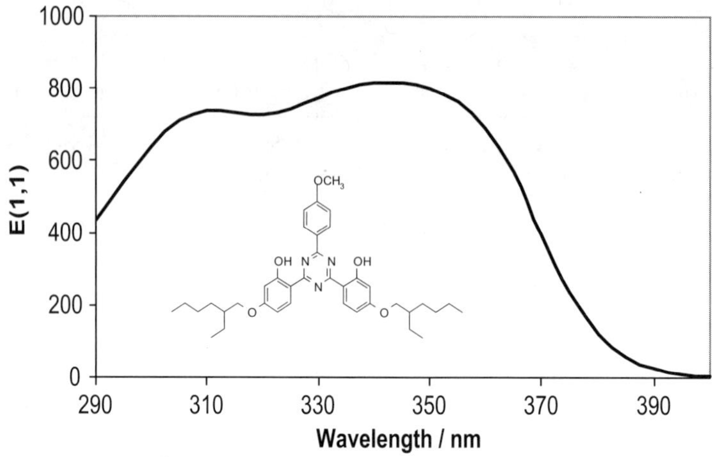

Figure 16.15 UV spectrum and structure of bis-ethylhexyloxyphenol methoxyphenyl-triazine $E_{1,1}(310) = 745$, $E_{1,1}(343) = 820$, $\langle E_{1,1}\rangle_{mean} = 529$.

UV spectrum (in ethanol) of this UV broad-spectrum absorber are shown in Fig. 16.15. The solubility of BEMT in three typical emollients is listed in Table 16.5.

IMPROVED UV-A PROTECTION WITH NEW UV-A AND BROAD-SPECTRUM UV ABSORBERS

In countries where the new UV filters are approved, there are more possibilities than ever before to achieve good coverage of the UV-A region. The question as to what this exactly means in terms of actual protection of the sunscreen user still remains. There are several *in vivo* and *in vitro* methods to assess UV-A protection. Except for Japan where an *in vivo* method based on persistent pigment darkening (PPD) is used (44,45) and Australia where an *in vitro* method based on transmission measurement is applied (46), there are no official standards yet. The chances for a harmonization as it has been achieved with the SPF seem to be rather remote at the moment. To agree on a common UV-A assessment method will be a substantial challenge in the future.

Figure 16.16 shows the results of PPD measurements according to the Japanese standard. The meaning of the UV-A protection factor (PFA) is analogous to the SPF, but referring to the UV-A range only and based on PPD measurements. The formulations investigated contain various concentrations of the photostable, broad-spectrum UV filter BEMT with and without the presence of EHMC. All three Japanese categories of UVA protection PA+ ($2 < \text{PFA} < 4$), PA++ ($4 < \text{PFA} < 8$) and PA+++ ($\text{PFA} > 8$) can easily be achieved with this new system, whereas the reference sample of the Japanese Standard that

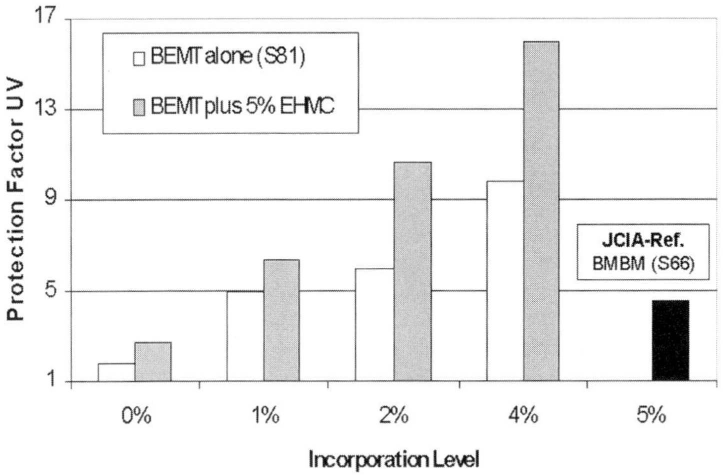

Figure 16.16 Concentration dependence of the UV-A protection in terms of PFA of formulations containing BEMT with and without 5% of EHMC.

contains 5% BMBM and 3% EHMC does not get beyond a PFA of 4.5, since its combination of filters is not photostable.

In Australia, a pragmatic approach was taken resulting in the UV-A Standard 2604, since in this continent the rate of skin cancer is high and no delay can be justified. Without waiting for all details of a scientific proof about how damaging UV-A radiation may be, it was defined that a broad-spectrum sunscreen has to reduce the UV-A radiation at least 10-fold between 320 and 360 nm (Australian Standard).

If we assess the available UV-A and broad-spectrum UV absorbers we can determine the following ranking in terms of meeting the Australian Standard (Table 16.6). This ranking is just one way to show the efficacy of these filters. In real sunscreen formulations, they will of course be used in combination with UV-B filters, which also contribute to fulfilling the Australian Standard. Nonetheless, this comparison gives the formulator an upper limit about how much UV-A filter is required to meet the Australian Standard. The performance of these filters in commercial products also depends on the formulation.

There is a correlation between the Australian UV-A standard and the Japanese *in vivo* standard. Achieving the Australian standard corresponds to an *in vivo* PFA of about 4, that is, the minimum requirement to qualify for protection class PA++ (47).

From the new broad-spectrum UV absorbers we expect better UV-A coverage when incorporated into a sunscreen or day cream (48). To illustrate and quantify the improvement some calculations were carried out with different formulations using the Ciba® Sunscreen Simulator (49) (www.cibasc.com/personalcare).

Table 16.6 Efficacy of Available UV-A and Broadband Filters in Terms of Fulfilling the Australian Standard on Its Own (Transmission <10%, 320–360 nm, Without Taking into Account Photostability)

Efficacy	Filter COLIPA #		Amount required (%)
1.	S 81	BEMT	1.8
2.	S 80	DPDT	2.1
3.	S 71	TDSA	2.5
4.	S 66	BMBM	2.9
5.	S 79	MBBT	3.7
6.	S 73	TDS	4.9
7.	S 76	ZnO	7–14[a]

[a]Depends on size of microfine particles.

Figure 16.17 shows the UV transmission of three formulations with similar SPFs, that is, UV-B protection, but different degree of UV-A protection. In spite of great differences, all these formulations could make "UV-A" or "broad-spectrum" claims.

Formula	Composition	SPF (calc.)	UV-A transmission (%)
A1	8% EHMC, 2.5% BP-3	14.8	100
A2	5% EHMC, 3% BEMT	15.5	55
A3	1.5% EHT, 2.5% BEMT, 3% MBBT	15.1	25

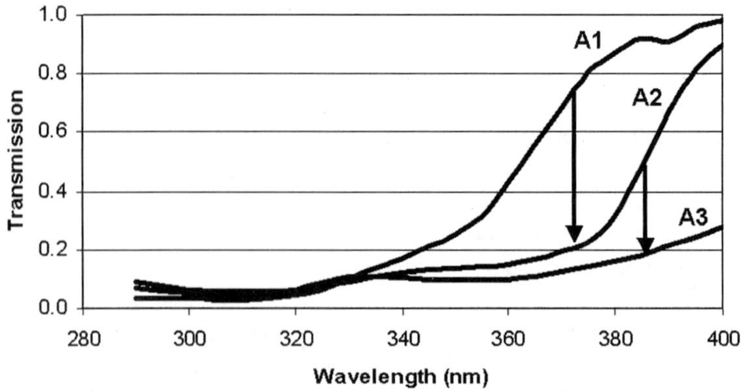

Figure 16.17 Progress in UV-A protection.

The transmission spectrum was calculated using a two-step film model (50). The area below the sunscreen with the highest UV-A transmission (320–400 nm), A1 with benzophenone-3 has arbitrarily been set as 100%. Formula A2 with BEMT reduces this UV-A exposure already to 55%. With formula A3, using BEMT and another new UV-A filter such as MBBT, the UV-A exposure is reduced down to 25% of the value achieved with the conventional formulation.

SAFETY OF THE NEW UV ABSORBERS

The approval procedure in Europe is demonstrated in Table 16.7 with the first broad-spectrum filter on the market, DTS. A margin of safety (MOS) is calculated as the ratio between the no-observable adverse effect level (NOAEL) and the systemic exposure determined via the percutaneous absorption data. The European authorities require an MOS of >100-fold. Modern filters have values >1000-fold. Table 16.7 lists the requirements for the assessment of human safety (8).

What is the contribution of the new filters to the safety of sunscreens? A major concern with the conventional UV absorbers has always been skin penetration. Even if a substance is supposed to be "inert" it should not enter the body. In order to penetrate the skin, a substance has to be lipophilic. In other words, there should be practically no penetration of water-soluble substances. Highly lipophilic substances tend to stay in the upper layer of stratum corneum and are thus also useful for water-resistant formulations.

The skin penetration of filters can be influenced by the formulation, some ingredients may act as enhancer (as desired in transdermal drug delivery) and some do the opposite (51). Another very important factor is the molecular weight (MW) of the UV absorber. Figure 16.18 shows the increase in the MW

Table 16.7 Assessment of Human Safety: EU 2001 (8)

Parameter	Example Mexoryl XL (DTS, S73)
Amount of formulation applied (mg)	18,000
Concentration of UV filter (%)	10
Amount of filter applied (mg)	1,800
Percutaneous absorption (%)	0.5
Total absorbed amount (mg)	9
Typical human body weight (kg)	60
Systemic exposure dose (SED, mg/kg per day)	0.15
NOAEL = no observable adverse effect level (mg/kg per day, toxicology studies)	1,000
Margin of safety (MOS)[a]	6000-fold

[a]MOS must be >100-fold, but modern sunscreens have MOS values >1000-fold.

Classic		New	
S1	PABA	S69	Ethylhexyl triazone
S13	Ethylhexyl salicylate	S73	Drometrizole trisiloxane
S28	Ethylhexyl methoxycinnamate	S78	Diethylhexylbutamido triazone
S38	Benzophenone 3	S81	Bis-ethylhexyloxyphenol methoxyphenyl triazine
S60	4-Methylbenzylidene camphor	XA	Diethylamino hydroxybenzoyl hexyl benzoate
S66	Butyl methoxydibenzoylmethane	XB	Bis-diethylamino hydroxybenzoyl benzoate
		XC	Bis-benzoxazoylphenyl ethylhexylimino triazine

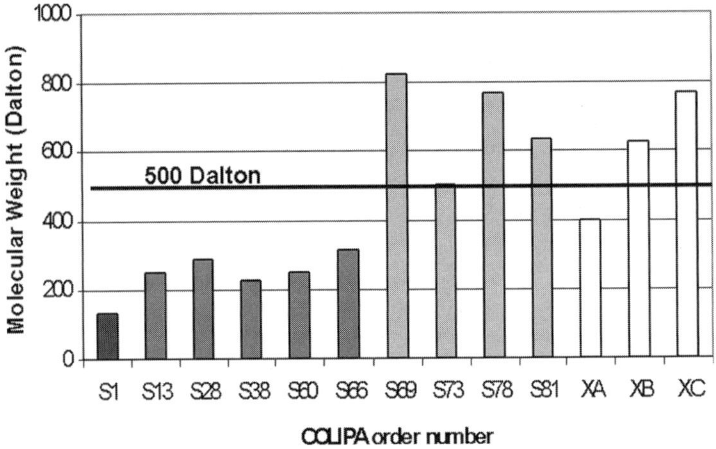

Figure 16.18 Molecular weight of classic and modern lipophilic sunscreen actives.

of the oil-soluble, lipophilic UV filters starting with PABA (COLIPA # S1) at a MW of 137 Da and the other classic UV filters with MWs between 228 (benzophenone-3) and 310 Da (buthylmethoxydibenzoyl methane). The turning point in the development of sunscreen actives came with the introduction of ethylhexyl triazone (EHT, S69). EHT is the first filter based on chromophore multiplication, and may thus be called the first modern UV filter. In EHT, three moieties of PABA (ethylhexylester) are attached to a triazine core. Since then all newly approved UV filters have had MW >500 Da.

The "500-Da rule for the skin penetration of chemical compounds and drugs" has recently been proposed for the development of drugs to describe the limit beyond which larger molecules cannot pass the corneal layer (52). Arguments for the 500-Da rules are: (1) virtually all common contact allergens are under 500 Da, larger molecules are not known as contact sensitizers. They cannot penetrate and thus cannot act as allergens in man; (2) the most commonly used pharmacological agents applied in topical dermatotherapy are all under 500 Da; and (3) all known topical drugs used in transdermal drug-delivery systems are under 500 Da. As it seems logical to restrict the development of new innovative compounds, to MW of $<$500 Da, when topical dermatological therapy or percutaneous systemic therapy or vaccination is the objective, we may conclude that it makes sense to restrict the search for new sunscreen actives to MW $>$500 Da. Figure 16.18 shows that this principle has been utilized in the development of new sunscreen actives. In any case, all new sunscreen actives have to undergo the scrutiny of safety testing as described in Table 16.1 (8).

CONCLUSIONS

Triggered by new requirements towards better UV protection, seven new UV absorbers have been developed and approved in Europe over the last few years. These new filters give the formulators new possibilities to cover the whole UV range from 290 to 400 nm, and also to use less filter due to the superior efficacy of some of the new UV-A and broadband filters. With the considerably higher molecular weight, leading to lower skin penetration, and the good photostability of most of these new filters, additional safety of sun protection products for adults and children can be gained.

REFERENCES

1. Pathak MA. Photoprotection against harmful effects of solar UVB and UVA radiation: an update. In: Lowe NJ, Shaath NA, Pathak MA, eds. Sunscreens: Development, Evaluation, and Regulatory Aspects. 2nd ed. New York: Marcel Dekker, 1997:59–79.
2. World Health Organization, International Agency for Research on Cancer. Sunscreens. IARC Handbooks of Cancer Prevention. Vol. 5. Lyon, France: IARC, 2001.
3. Autier P, Doré JF, Négrier S, Liénard D, Panizzon R, Lejeune FJ, Guggisberg D, Eggermont AM. Sunscreen use and duration of sun exposure: a double-blind, randomized trial. J Natl Cancer Inst 1999; 91:1304.
4. Diffey BL. Sunscreens: use and misuse. In: Giacomini PU, ed. Sun Protection in Man, Amsterdam: Elsevier Science BV, 2001:521–534.
5. Funk JO, Dromgoole SH, Maibach HI. Contact sensitization and photocontact sensitization of sunscreen agents. In: Lowe NJ, Shaath NA, Pathak MA, eds. Sunscreens: Development, Evaluation, and Regulatory Aspects. 2nd ed. New York: Marcel Dekker, 1997:631–651.
6. Schlumpf M, Cotton B, Conscience M, Haller V, Steinmann B, Lichtensteiger W. In vitro and in vivo estrogenicity of UV screens. Environ Health Perspect 2001; 109:239–244.
7. Sayre RM, Dowdy JC. Photostability testing of avobenzone. Cosmet Toilet 1999; 114(5):85–91.

8. Nohynek G, Schaefer H. Benefit and risk of organic ultraviolet filters. Regul Toxicol Pharmacol 2001; 33:1–15.
9. Food and Drug Administration. Additional Criteria and Procedures for, Classifying Over-the-Counter Drugs as, Generally Recognized as Safe and, Effective and Not Misbranded, 21 CFR Part 330, [Docket No. 96N–0277], RIN 0910–AA01, Federal Register/Vol. 67, No. 15/Wednesday, January 23, 2002/Rules and Regulations, 3060–3076.
10. Food and Drug Administration, Over-the-Counter Drug Products; Safety and Efficacy Review; Additional Sunscreen Ingredients, [Docket No. 2003N–0233], Federal Register/Vol. 68, No. 133/Friday, July 11, 2003/Notices, 41386–41387.
11. Rudolph M. Specific UV filter combinations and their impact on sunscreen efficacy. International Sun Protection Conference, Commonwealth Institute, London, Mar 9–10, 1999.
12. DE 198 17 296, Beiersdorf, EP 1027 881 A1, L'Oreal.
13. Bonda C, Steinberg DC. A new photostabilizer for full spectrum sunscreens. Cosmet Toilet 2000; 115(6):37–45.
14. Pohl VT. Sunspheres—NovaTechnologia para Incremento Substancial do Fator de Protecao Solar. Proceedings, Congresso Nacional de Cosmetologia, Sao Paulo, Brasil, July 5–7, 2000:93–103.
15. Pflücker F, Guinard H, Lapidot N, Chaudhuri R, Marchio F, Driller H. Sunglasses for the skin: reduction of dermal UV filter uptake by encapsulation. SÖFW-J 2002; 128(6):24–28.
16. Herzog B, Quass K, Schmidt E, Mueller S, Luther H. Physical properties of organic particulate UV absorbers used in sunscreens. II. UV-attenuating efficiency as function of particle size. J Colloid Interface Sci 2004; 276:354–363.
17. Osterwalder U, Luther H, Herzog B. UV-A protection with a new class of UV absorber. Proceedings, 47th SEPAWA Kongress, Proceedings, 2000:153–164.
18. Rieker J, Lemmert-Schmidt E, Goeller G, Roessler M, Stueber GJ, Schettler H, Kramer HEA, Stezowski JJ, Hoier H, Henkel S, Schmidt A, Port H, Wiechmann M, Rody J, Rytz G, Slongo M, Birbaum JL. Ultraviolet stabilizers of the 2-(hydroxyphenyl)benzotriazole class. Influence of substituents on structure and spectra. J Phys Chem 1992; 96:10225–10234.
19. Baltrop JA, Coyle JD. Excited States in Organic Chemistry. Chapter 3. London: Wiley & Sons Ltd., 1975.
20. Otterstedt JE. Photostability and molecular structure. J Phys Chem 1973; 58:5716–5725.
21. Scholz V, Neunhoeffer H, Driller H, Witte G, Pflücker F. A strategy for the development of UV-filters and control of their absorption properties. SÖFW-J 2001; 127(4):3–11.
22. Stueber GJ, Kieninger M, Schettler H, Busch W, Goeller B, Franke J, Kramer HEA, Hoier H, Henkel S, Fischer P, Port H, Rytz G, Birbaum JL. Ultraviolet stabilizers of the 2-(2′-hydroxyphenyl)-1,3,5-triazine class: structural and spectroscopic characterization. J Phys Chem 1995; 99:10097–10109.
23. Shaath NA. Evolution of modern sunscreen chemicals. In: Lowe NJ, Shaath NA, Pathak MA, eds. Sunscreens: Development, Evaluation, and Regulatory Aspects. 2nd ed. New York: Marcel Dekker, 1997:17.
24. Hueglin D, Herzog B, Mongiat S. Hydroxyphenyltriazines: a new generation of cosmetic UV filters with superior photoprotection. Oral presentation. 22nd IFSCC, Edinburgh, Sep 23–26, 2002.

25. Berset G, Gonzenbach H, Christ R, Martin R, Deflandre A, Mascotto RE, Jolley JDR, Lowell W, Pelzer R, Stiehm T. Int J Cosmet Sci 1996; 18:167–177.
26. Herzog B, Sommer K. Investigations on photostability of UV-absorbers for cosmetic sunscreens. Poster presentation (P60, CD-ROM). 21st IFSCC, Berlin, 2000.
27. Sunscreen Enyclopedia—Regulatory Update. Cosmet Toilet 1996; 111:78–86.
28. Malpede A, Fumagalli S. Diethylhexyl butamido triazone—nuovo filtro per la protezione cutanea. Cosmet Technol 2000; 3:33–38.
29. Roche Vitamins, PARSOL SLX, Product Brochure, 2001.
30. Schwarzenbach R, Huber U. Optimization of sunscreen efficacy. SÖFW-J 2002; 128(6):20.
31. Vichy/La Roche-Posay, Capital Soleil & Anthélios au Mexoryl XL, Information Professionell sur la campage "Peau et Soleil" de la ligue contre le cancer, Switzerland, 2000.
32. Haarmann and Reimer, Neo Heliopan AP, Product Brochure, 2002.
33. EP 0669323, Haarmann & Reimer GmbH.
34. Johncock W, Langner R. Advances in UVA photoprotection via a novel water soluble UVA absorbing bis-phenylimidazole derivative. Proceedings: 21st IFSCC Congress, Berlin, Sep 11–14, 2000:372–377.
35. BASF, UVINUL A Plus, Product Brochure, 2002.
36. Wuensch T, End L. Synergistic effects with high performance UV filters. Conference Proceedings "Personal Care Ingredients Asia." Shanghai, China, Mar 19–21, 2002: 437–444.
37. Amino substituted hydroxyphenyl derivatives, IPCOM000018721D, www.ip.com.
38. EP 1300137, 3V Sigma.
39. WO 0353389, WO 0353390, WO 0353391, WO 0353393, WO 0353395, Beiersdorf AG.
40. Opinion of the EU Scientific Committee on Cosmetic Products and Non-Food Products Intended for Consumers, February 17, 1999. http//europa.eu.int/comm/dg24/health/sc/sccp/out53-en.html.
41. Twenty Fourth Commission Directive 2000/6/EC of 29 February 2000. Council Directive 76/768/EC. Official Journal of the European Communities L56/42, 1.3.2000.
42. EP 0746305, Ciba Specialty Chemicals Inc.
43. EP 07756981, Ciba Specialty Chemicals Inc.
44. Chardon A, Moyal D, Hourseau C. Persistent pigment-darkening response as a method for evaluation of ultraviolet A protection assays. In: Lowe NJ, Shaath NA, Pathak MA, eds. Sunscreens: Development, Evaluation, and Regulatory Aspects, 2nd ed. New York: Marcel Dekker, 1997:559–582.
45. JCIA Measurement Standard for UVA Protection Efficacy. Japan Cosmetic Industry Association—JCIA, 9-14, Toranomon 2-Chome, Minato-Ku Tokyo, 1995:105.
46. AS/NZS (1998) Australian/New Zealand Standard. AS/NZS, 2604.
47. Herzog B, Mongiat S, Deshayes C, Neuhaus M, Sommer K, Mantler A. In vivo and in vitro assessment of UVA-protection by sunscreen formulations containing either butyl methoxy dibenzoyl methane, methylene bis-benzotriazolyl tetramethylbutylphenol, or microfine ZnO. Oral presentation. 22nd IFSCC, Edinburgh, Sep 23–26, 2002.
48. Mongiat S, Herzog B, Deshayes C, König P, Osterwalder U. BEMT: an efficient broad-spectrum UV filter. Cosmet Toilet 2003; 118(2).
49. Herzog B. Prediction of sun protection factors by calculation of transmissions with a calibrated step film model. J Cosmet Sci 2002; 53(1):11–26.

50. O'Neill JJ. Effect of film irregularities on sunscreen efficacy. J Pharm Sci 1984; 73:888–891.
51. Walters A, Gettings SD, Roberts MA. Percutaneous absorption of sunscreens. In: Bronaugh RL, Maibach HI, eds. Percutaneous Absorption Drugs—Cosmetics—Mechanisms—Methodology. New York: Marcel Dekker, 1999: 861–877.
52. Bos JD, Meinardi MM. The 500 Dalton rule for the skin penetration of chemical compounds and drugs. Exp Dermatol 2000; 9(3):165–169.

17

The Photostability of Organic Sunscreen Actives: A Review

Craig A. Bonda
CPH Innovations (an affiliate of the C.P. Hall Company), Chicago, Illinois, USA

INTRODUCTION

Organic ultraviolet (UV) filters, such as those used in sunscreens, convert the energy in UV radiation into electronic excitation energy (1). At a molecular level, the physical reality of this conversion is a sudden expansion of an area of the electron cloud surrounding the molecule (2,3). This happens so rapidly (on the order of 10^{-15} s) (1: p.6) that the nuclei of the molecule at first remain in their original positions. In effect, an electronic isomer of the original molecule has been created. If we were to isolate and observe the molecule, we might in one common scenario see the distorted electron cloud collapse almost immediately to its original shape. Simultaneously, we might see a flash of light emerge from the molecule. Close examination would reveal that the molecule is now indistinguishable from its preabsorbance condition. In another common scenario, we might see that the distortion of the electron cloud persists and exerts a force that causes bonds to stretch and nuclei to move to accommodate the new shape. We might see that the bond stretching and nuclear motion dissipates the electronic excitation energy until the electron cloud returns to its preabsorbance shape and the nuclei return to their previous positions relative to each other. Again, the molecule would be indistinguishable from its preabsorbance condition. Therefore, it can repeat the cycle of absorbance, electronic isomerization, and energy dissipation. It is, in effect, photostable.

If somewhere between absorbance and energy dissipation something happens to the molecule that prevents it from returning to its preabsorbance state, we say the molecule is photounstable or photolabile. We may apply other terms such as "photodegraded," "photoinactivated," or "photodecayed." If enough of the UV filter molecules in a sunscreen undergo photodecay, the sunscreen loses absorbance and its protective properties are reduced below those expected from the level of active ingredients it contains. At the least, this is wasteful and inefficient.

Which UV filters are prone to photodecay? Under what circumstances are they most likely to decay? What can be done to improve photostability of those chemicals and the sunscreens that contain them? Which UV filters are photostable? And what steps can be taken to design new photostable UV filters? In this chapter we will address these questions and others. To find the answers, we will begin with a review of basic photochemistry. Following that, we will draw on the published findings of numerous investigators around the world, as well as data and commentary from research my colleagues and I conducted in the laboratories of CPH Innovations.

PHOTOSTABILITY AS A SUNSCREEN INDUSTRY CONCERN

Interest in sunscreen photostability has grown as use of the UV-A* filter, avobenzone, in sunscreens has grown.† Spurred on by consumer demand for greater protection against solar UV-A radiation, which many believe causes a number of damaging effects to skin including premature aging (4,5), avobenzone has become the most widely used UV-A filter in the world. However, as discussed below, under certain experimental conditions avobenzone is photolabile; that is, under these conditions exposure to solar UV radiation causes its absorbance of UV radiation to decline.

Several researchers have reported on avobenzone's behavior in dilute solutions, and in emulsions and commercial sunscreen products. Other researchers have measured the photostability of other UV-B and UV-A filters. Photostability of sunscreen preparations has become an important basis for predicting their performance (6–9). Researchers have sought with some success to find or develop ways to ameliorate avobenzone's photolability (10–12).

Over the past 10 years or so, the effect of this research and development has been a greater appreciation and understanding among major sunscreen manufacturers and their chemical suppliers of the photophysics and photochemistry underlying these important consumer products. Many (though not all) sunscreen products in the USA today reflect this new understanding with improved efficacy against UV-A radiation. In Europe, new active ingredients are available that have to some degree the advantage of avobenzone's excellent UV-A absorbance, without the disadvantage of its photolability.

PHOTOCHEMISTRY REVIEW

Background

As we shall see, a UV filter's fate is best understood as a competition between the many pathways the molecule can take between its elevation to an excited state and its return to the ground state. All of the pathways result in the dissipation of excited state energy. Some of the pathways are destructive to the molecule (e.g., fragmentation, some types of isomerization, bimolecular reaction); others are nondestructive (e.g., fluorescence, phosphorescence, some types of isomerization, energy transfer to another molecule). Each pathway is associated with its own rate constant. If nondestructive pathways predominate, then, relatively

*Throughout this chapter, the term "UV-A" is used to represent radiation from 320 to 400 nm, and "UV-B" is used to represent the radiation from 290 to 320 nm. UV-C is the portion of the spectrum between 200 and 290 nm.

†Avobenzone is the USAN name for the chemical butyl methoxydibenzoylmethane (BMDM), and is the name that appears in the United States Pharmacopoeia. The main body of the text will use nomenclature that I consider the most recognized for each of the chemicals discussed. In Fig. 17.5, alternative nomenclature for each chemical is shown.

speaking, the molecule will be photostable. Conversely, if destructive pathways predominate, then the molecule will be unstable.

The Nature of Photon Absorption

To begin at the beginning: a photon is a quantum or "packet" of electromagnetic energy with an energy equal to Planck's constant (h) times its frequency (ν). The absorption of a photon by an organic molecule causes the excitation of one of a pair of electrons in a low energy orbital to a higher energy unoccupied orbital (1) (Fig. 17.1).

Before absorption, the orbital configuration of the electrons is the "ground" state. Upon absorption, two electronic states are possible. In one, the spins of the two electrons remain paired and, as in the ground state, the net spin of the pair is zero. This is called the "singlet" excited state. In the other, the spins of the two electrons are unpaired, and there is a net spin. This is called a "triplet" excited state because three variations can be resolved in a magnetic field (1: p. 23). The energy of both excited states is eventually dissipated as heat (vibration, including both bond stretching and nuclear motion), or heat and light (emission of a photon of lower energy/longer wavelength). Emission of a photon from the singlet state is called "fluorescence." Photon emission from the triplet state is called "phosphorescence." The singlet state may return to the ground state directly, or it may decay to the triplet state (1: pp. 4–6) (Fig. 17.2).

Photochemical Reactions

The singlet state is often short-lived, typically 10^{-9}–10^{-8} s. Therefore, reactions that proceed from it must be quite rapid. Of more importance are reactions that

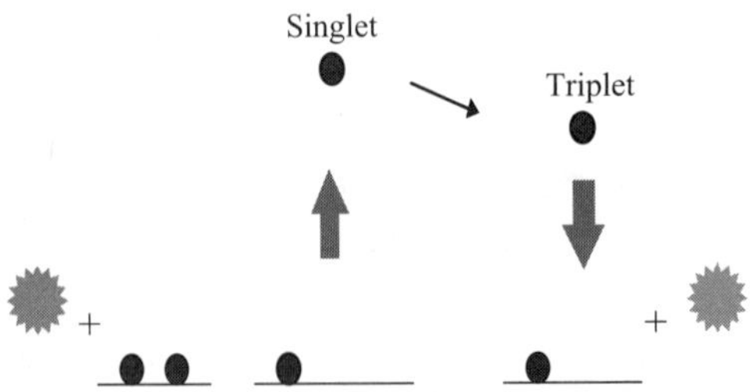

Figure 17.1 Schematic representation of photon absorption resulting in the excitation of an electron to the singlet state, the decay to the triplet state, and the emission of a photon before returning to the ground state.

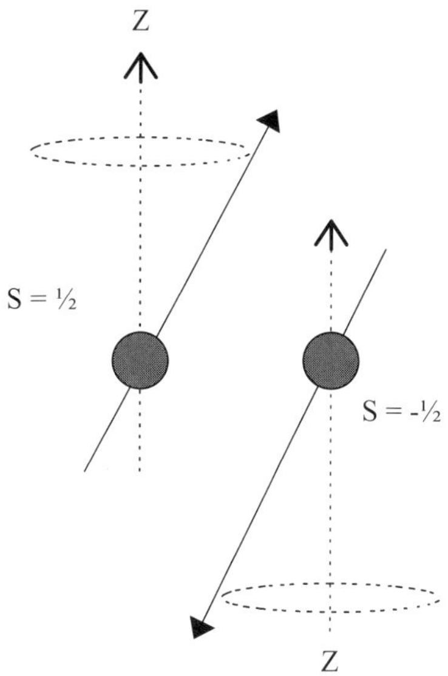

Figure 17.2 Vectoral model of an electron pair. Each electron may be viewed as spinning about a vector that is precessing about an axis (Z). In the ground and singlet states, the spins are paired, as indicated above. Net spin, therefore, is 0. In the triplet state, the spins are unpaired and the net spin is 1.

proceed from the (usually) much longer-lived triplet state, which may last 10^{-4} s or longer (1: p. 90, 105, 352). During the triplet state lifetime, the excited molecule looks and behaves as a diradical (1: p. 364–365) from which many chemical reactions are possible. In general, these reactions can be grouped into four categories: photoaddition/substitution; cycloaddition; isomerization; and photofragmentation (1: Chaps. 10–13). Of particular importance to the sunscreen formulator are reactions between like or different UV filter molecules, those between UV filter molecules and sunscreen excipients, and isomerizations or fragmentations of the UV filter molecules, any one of which may alter or destroy the UV absorption capacity of the sunscreen formulation (Fig. 17.3).

Energy Transfer

The excited molecule may react (to produce isomers or new products), or return to the ground state in its original form. Clearly, the latter is the preferred outcome because the UV filter molecule is again available to absorb a photon. Many factors determine the pathway an excited molecule will take including the

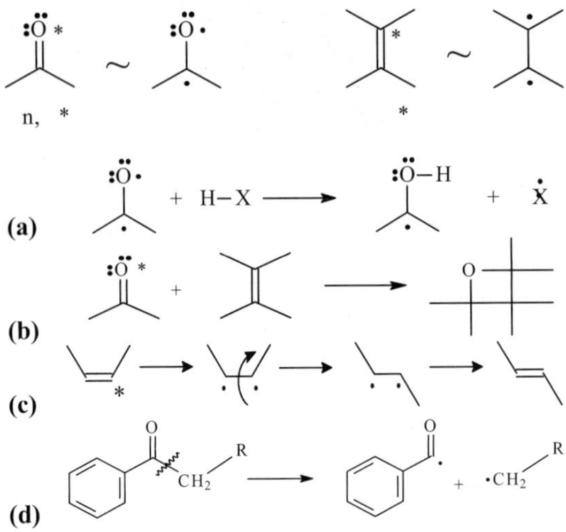

Figure 17.3 Top: carbonyl and ethylene models show the diradical nature of the excited triplet state. Bottom: (a) abstraction of a hydrogen; (b) 2+2 cycloaddition; (c) *cis–trans* isomerization; (d) photofragmentation.

triplet energy, the triplet lifetime, the identity and concentration of the reactants, and the rates and activation energies of each competing reaction. Under certain conditions, the excited molecule may return to the ground state (and its original form) by transferring its energy to a nearby molecule. The excited molecule becomes a "donor" (D*) and the nearby molecule becomes an "acceptor" (A). Upon the transfer of energy, the donor returns to its ground state (D) and the acceptor becomes elevated to its excited state (A*). Generally, triplet energy transfer takes place when the triplet energy of the acceptor is equal to or lower than the triplet energy of the donor (1: Chap. 9). The triplet energies of several UV filters may be found in Table 17.1 (13).

Table 17.1 Triplet Energies of Some Common Sunscreen Actives

PABA	75 kcal/mol
Oxybenzone	66 kcal/mol
Avobenzone	59.5 kcal/mol
Octocrylene	55–60 kcal/mol
OMC	57 kcal/mol
MBC	55 kcal/mol

Optimizing sunscreen performance depends in part on encouraging a photolabile UV filter such as avobenzone to dissipate its excited state energy through nondestructive pathways. One strategy to accomplish this is to include in the formulation an acceptor that will "quench" the excited state energy of avobenzone. Chemicals useful as acceptors for this purpose are diethylhexyl 2,6-naphthalate, octocrylene, and methylbenzylidene camphor. Patent and regulatory considerations sometimes affect the ability of formulators to use these chemicals in their formulations. The uses of photostabilizers in formulation are discussed later in the chapter.

Solvent Polarity and Electron Transfer Theory

Excited state quenching and its opposite phenomenon, sensitization, represent the intermolecular transfer of excited state energy and, for organic chromophores, it relies primarily on charge transfer; that is, the movement of an electron from one molecule to another (1: p. 329).

The rapid expansion and contraction of a molecule's electron cloud following absorbance and relaxation cause dislocation and rearrangement of the solvent molecules in the immediate vicinity. The energy required for the solvent molecules to accommodate these changes in dimension and charge distribution has a direct relationship to the rate at which electron transfer takes place (2,3). The rules governing electron transfer processes were first elucidated by Rudolph Marcus, now of the California Institute of Technology. In a series of papers published between 1956 and 1965 and in numerous subsequent publications, Marcus introduced simple equations that proved to be highly predictive of electron transfer reactions in chemistry and biology. In part, his theory proposed that the solvent mediates electron transfer reactions and the rate of electron transfer is related to the driving force by a quadratic expression that is descriptive of a parabola (14–16). In 1992, Marcus was awarded the Nobel Prize in Chemistry for his discovery.

Studies conducted at CPH Innovations documented a parabolic relationship between the dielectric constant of the oil phase and the photostability of several avobenzone-containing sunscreens that is reminiscent of the Marcus theory (17). Briefly, we determined that in many sunscreens, the photodecay rate, k_{pd}, is related to the polarity of the sunscreen oil phase by the expression, $a\varepsilon^2 + b\varepsilon + c$, where ε is the dielectric constant of the oil phase (comprising the solvents, emollients, and UV filters), and a, b, and c are empirically derived values for a given filter combination. The expression describes a parabola, the vertex of which identifies the dielectric constant at which photodecay will be minimized and, therefore, sunscreen performance may be optimized. The similarity of our findings to Marcus theory is perhaps not surprising given the prominent role played by charge transfer in the causation and amelioration of photodecay (Fig. 17.4).

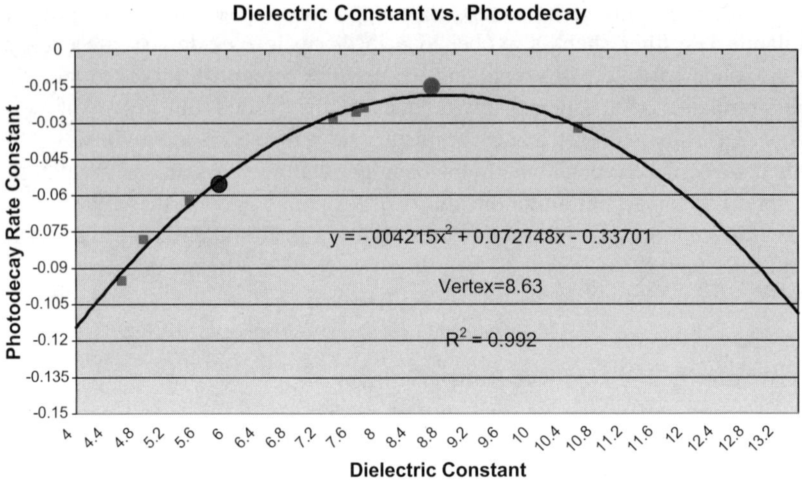

Figure 17.4 Data compiled on nine sunscreens prepared with identical UV filters (5% octyl salicylate, 3% oxybenzone, and 2% avobenzone) but different solvents and emollients. Results show steady improvement in photostability as the dielectric constant of the oil phase approaches the vertex, 8.63, then declining as the dielectric constant exceeds the vertex value. The formulation represented by the large dot to the left achieved SPF 17.14 *in vivo*. The formulation represented by the large dot at the vertex, or peak, achieved SPF 25.0 *in vivo*, a 46% improvement.

PHOTOSTABILITY OF INDIVIDUAL SUNSCREEN ACTIVE INGREDIENTS*

Studies of individual UV filters are often carried out in dilute solutions of various laboratory solvents. These studies are valuable for what they reveal about the photochemistry of these chemicals, and instructive to the issue of what *could* happen to them under actual conditions of use. However, a note of caution is

---

*Photostability studies involve irradiating samples with UV radiation. People in the sunscreen industry often express UV radiation in MED units. MED is an acronym for minimum erythemal dose. Theoretically, 1 MED is the amount of solar UV radiation from 290 to 400 nm that, in the average person with light skin, will result in a slight reddening (erythema). In 1987, McKinlay and Diffey published an erythemal action spectrum that assigned to each wavelength of solar UV radiation an erythemal effectiveness value or weight (see chapter titled "Dosimetry of UV Radiation" elsewhere in this volume). This led to the development of radiometers that are filtered to "see" (and, therefore, measure) erythemally effective radiation with greater sensitivity than other wavelengths. Sunscreen researchers often employ these biologically weighted radiometers to measure the UV doses they deliver to their sunscreen samples. When measured thusly, 1 MED is equivalent to 21 mJ/cm^2. When all the UV radiation is measured without giving special weight to some wavelengths over others, 1 MED is equivalent to 2.7 J/cm^2.

in order. In the real world, UV filters are never used in isolation; they are always combined with other UV filters and, indeed, with numerous excipients. Their concentrations in sunscreen formulations are above those used in most photochemical research by several orders of magnitude. Unquestionably, UV filters are affected by the nature of the solvent. However, sunscreen formulations never employ laboratory solvents (with the exception of ethanol, which is used specifically for its volatility). Importantly, sunscreens are designed to "set up" as films on the skin (6), and therefore may behave more as solid state systems and less as solutions. As any chemist will tell you, chemical behavior is very different for solids, liquids, and gases. Consequently, the data generated by studies of individual UV filters in dilute solutions may not be predictive of the behavior of the same UV filters in sunscreen formulations and under actual conditions of use. Please keep these "caveats" in mind as we review what is known about the photostability of individual UV filters.

The molecular structures of the more common sunscreen UV filters and schemes for the photoinduced isomerization of each are presented in Fig. 17.5. Frequent reference to these graphic depictions may be helpful to the reader as the findings of various researchers are discussed in the following text. Recall earlier when discussing photochemical reactions, that isomerization was identified as one of the four photoinduced pathways a molecule can take following photon absorption. Isomerization is an important pathway for dissipation of excited state energy. Not all molecules can isomerize, and not all isomerizations are nondestructive to the molecule. But in cases where the isomerization is reversible, or where it has little effect on spectral attenuation, it often represents an energy dissipation pathway that contributes to photostability.

Avobenzone (Butyl Methoxydibenzoylmethane)

Deflandre and Lang (18) incorporated avobenzone into an emulsion at 2% (w/w), and then spread the emulsion in a very thin film (1.35 μm) between two finely roughened quartz plates. Then they irradiated the sample with a solar simulator filtered to deliver radiation between 290 and 400 nm, measuring UV absorbance before and after irradiation. The researchers processed the data to produce an estimate of photodegradation under standardized conditions: a 10-μm film exposed to 1 h of sunlight. Based on their data, Deflandre and Lang projected that avobenzone will degrade by 36%. Deflandre and Lang also investigated the photostability of other dibenzoylmethane derivatives including two that, unlike avobenzone, featured hydroxyphenyl groups *ortho* to one of the carbonyls. Both of these derivatives proved to be relatively photostable. In contrast to avobenzone's 36% loss, one was projected to degrade by 5%, and the other by only 3.6%.

Andrae et al. (19) employed steady state irradiation using various UV-B and UV-A radiation sources and flash laser photolysis (excitation at 355 nm) to induce changes in avobenzone's absorbance spectra. The solvent used was acetonitrile and the avobenzone concentration was $10^{-5}-10^{-10}$ M. Before irradiation, avobenzone

Sunscreen UV filter	Isomerization or resonance scheme
Avobenzone[u] Butyl methoxydibenzoylmethane[i]	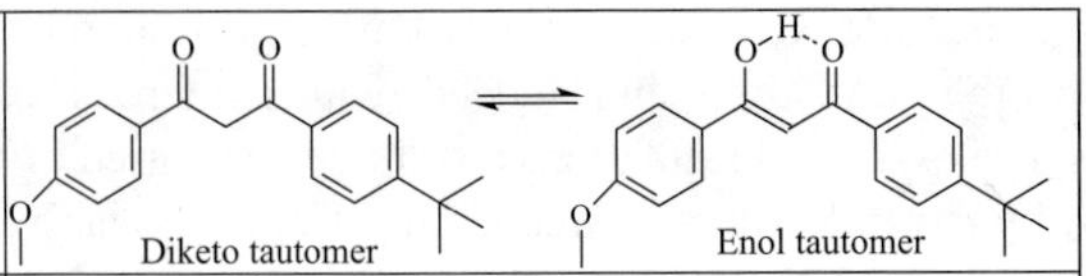
Octyl methoxycinnamate[c] **(OMC)** Ethylhexyl methoxycinnamate[i] Octinoxate[u]	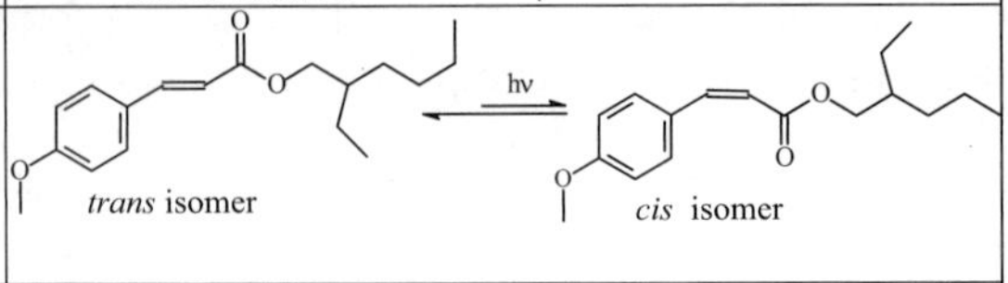
Oxybenzone[u] Benzophenone-3[i] 2-Hydroxy-4-methoxybenzophenone[c,r]	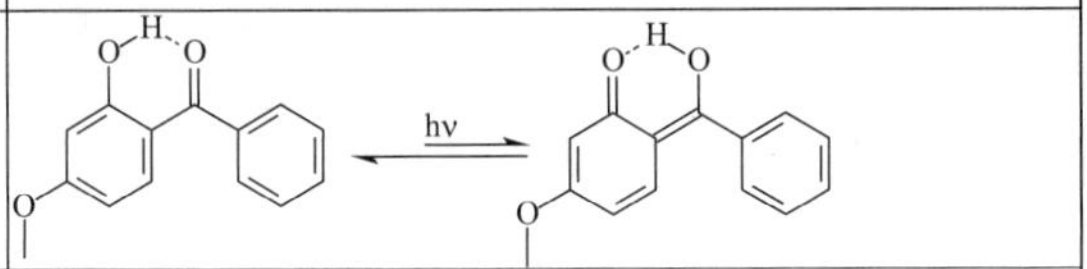
Octyl salicylate[c] Ethylhexyl salicylate[i] Octisalate[u]	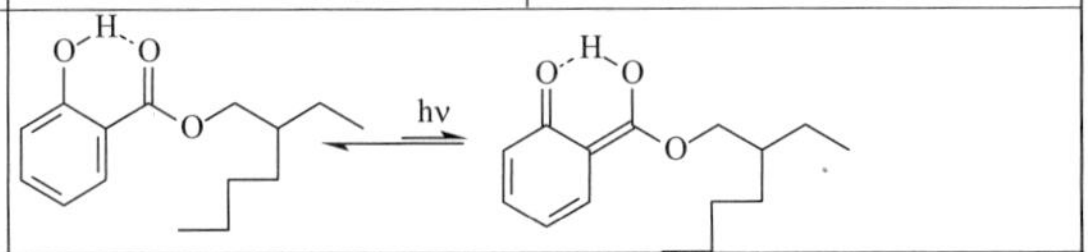
Homosalate[u] Homomenthyl salicylate[c]	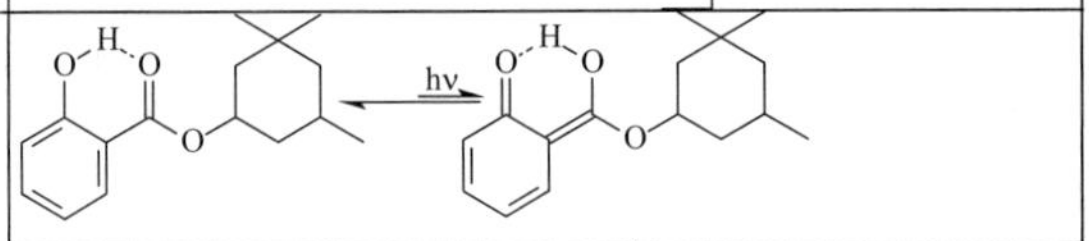
4-Methylbenzylidene camphor[i] **(MBC)** Enacamene[u]	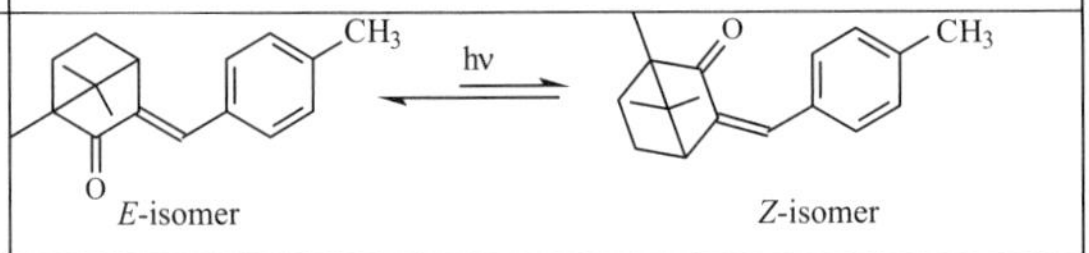
Octocrylene[u,i] 2-Ethylhexyl-2-cyano-3,3-diphenyl-2-propenoate[r]	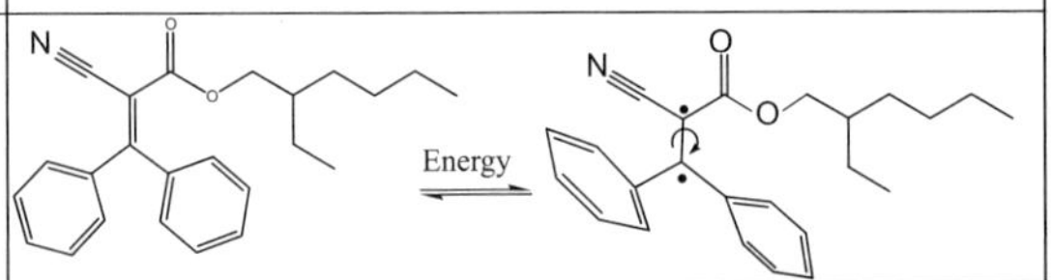
Phenyl-benzimidazole sulfonic acid[i] Ensulizole[u]	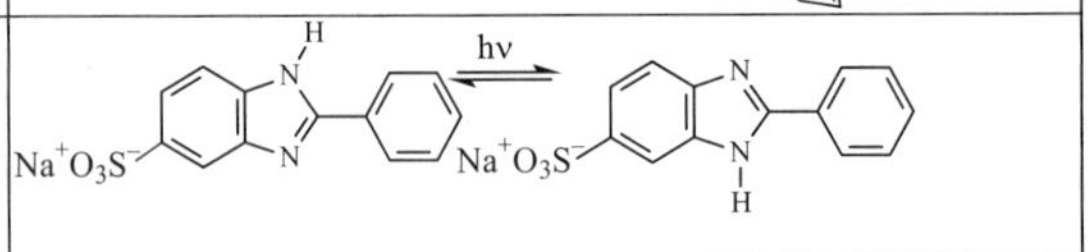
Octyl dimethyl PABA[i] Padimate O[u]	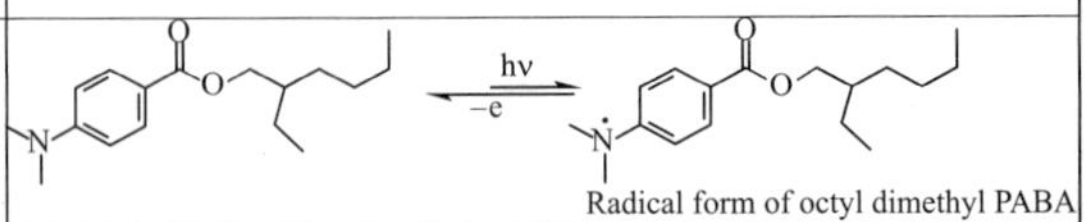
Methylene bis-benzotriazolyl tetramethyl-butylphenol[i] **(MBBT)**	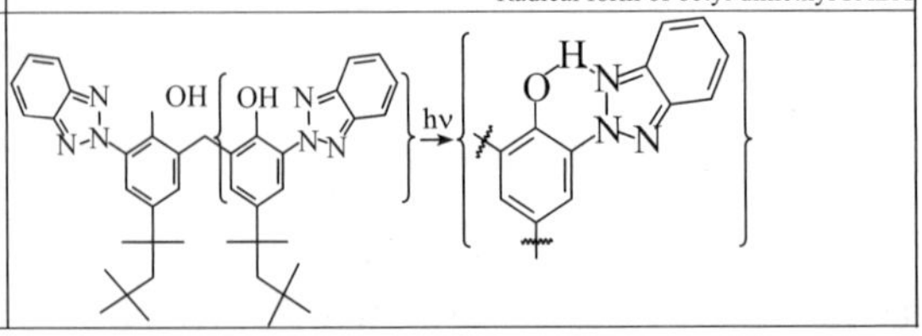

[u]USAN name (United States Adopted Name); [i]INCI name (International Nomenclature Cosmetic Ingredients); [c]Common name; [r]CAS Registry Name

Figure 17.5 Sunscreen UV filters and their isomerization or resonance schemes.

Terephthalylidine dicamphor sulfonic acid[i] (TDSA)	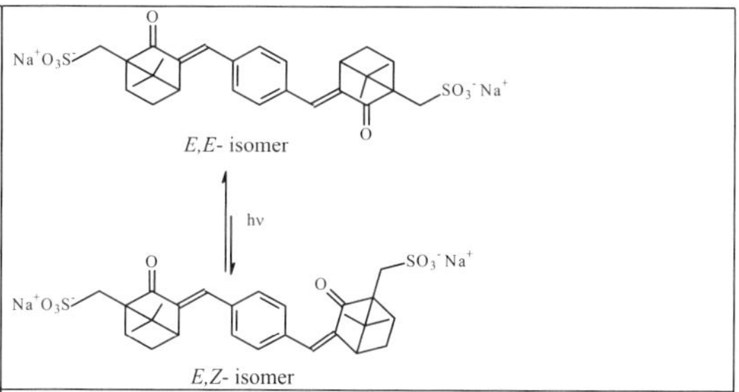
Disodium phenyl dibenzimidazole tetrasulfonate[i] (DPDT)	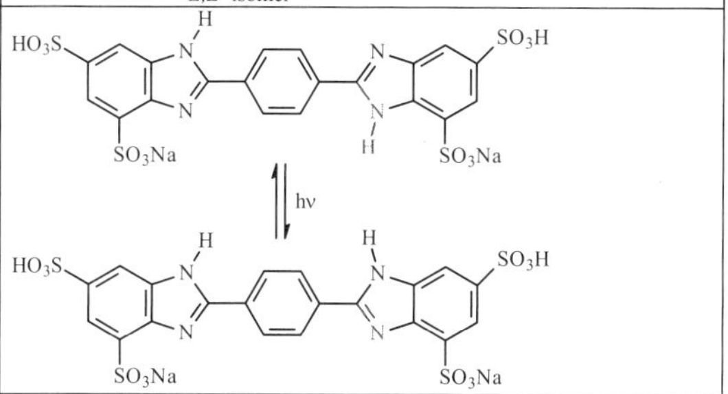
Bis-ethylhexyloxyphenol methoxyphenyltriazine[i] ((BEMT)	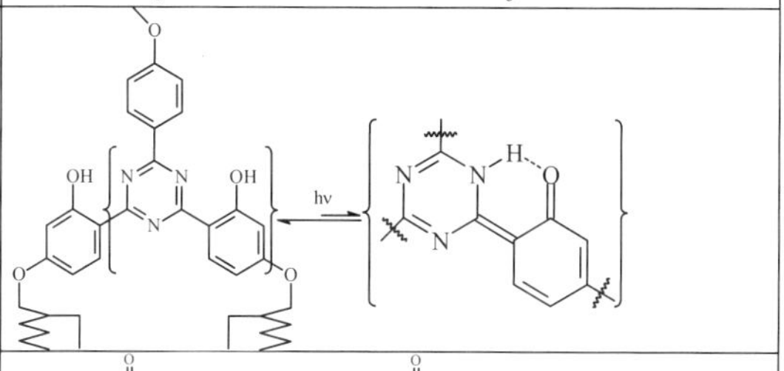
Octyl triazone[i]	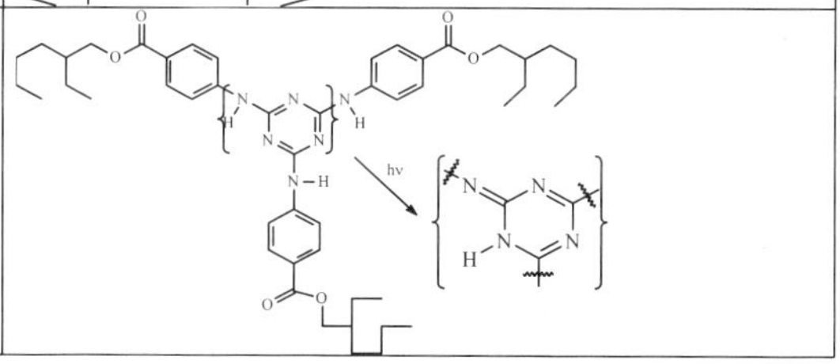

Figure 17.5 Continued

exhibited its characteristically broad UV-A peak ($\lambda_{max} = 350$ nm). After irradiation, the UV-A peak virtually disappeared and was replaced by a similarly broad UV-C peak ($\lambda_{max} = 260$ nm). Flash laser photolysis, also done in acetonitrile, revealed a short-lived peak in the UV-B region ($\lambda_{max} = 300$ nm). The authors of this study attributed the broad UV-A peak to absorbance by the enol tautomer of avobenzone, the UV-C peak to absorbance by the diketo tautomer of avobenzone (see Fig. 17.6), and the UV-B peak to a transient species that they speculated is an isomer, possibly a rotamer, of the enol tautomer.

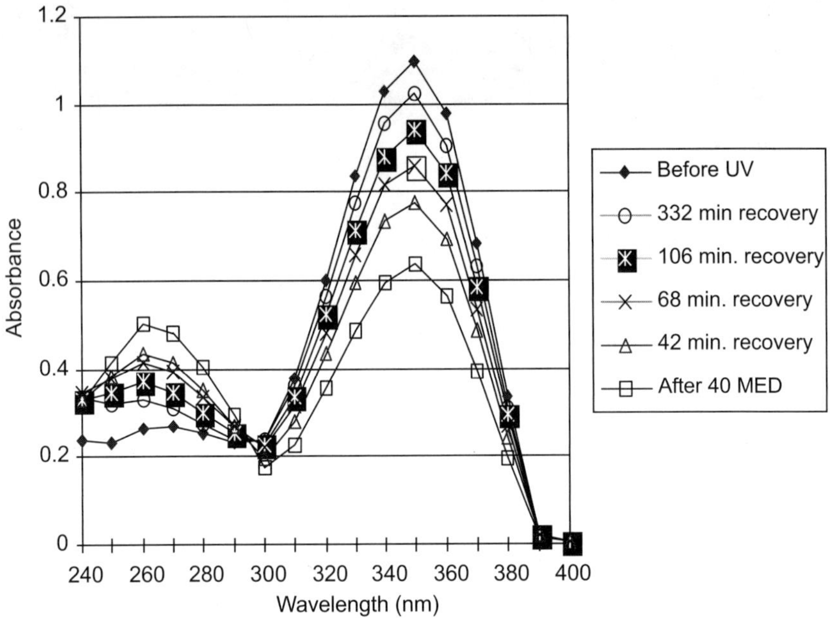

Figure 17.6 Enol recovery. Graph shows absorbance measurements of a dilute solution of avobenzone in cyclohexane taken before UV irradiation, immediately after, and over a 6.5-h span.

Schwack and Rudolph (20) irradiated dilute solutions of avobenzone with a solar simulator in the polar solvents isopropanol and methanol, and in the nonpolar solvents cyclohexane and isooctane. They monitored the photodegradation and isolated the resulting photoproducts by high performance liquid chromatography (HPLC), and characterized them using gas chromoatography–mass spectrometry (GC–MS). They conducted two sets of experiments: one with the light source filtered to exclude radiation <320 nm; the other filtered to exclude radiation below <260 nm. Surprisingly, they found that in the polar solvents, avobenzone was photostable. In the nonpolar solvents, however, photodegradation grew exponentially with increasing time of irradiation. Irradiation with shorter wavelengths (and therefore, higher frequencies and energies) (i.e., 260–320 nm) produced higher rates of photodegradation. They classified seven groups of photoproducts, all originating from two radical precursors—a benzoyl radical and a phenacyl radical, indicating that the avobenzone had fragmented on one side of the central methane. To find out why avobenzone was photostable in the polar solvents, and photolabile in the nonpolar solvents, the researchers took nuclear magnetic resonance (^{1}H NMR) measurements on solutions of avobenzone in deuterated solvents. They found that in the nonpolar solvent cyclohexane-d_{12}, both enol and diketo tautomers of avobenzone exist in equilibrium, with the enol form predominating, 96.5% to 3.5%, over the diketo form. In the polar solvent isopropanol-d_8, NMR detected no diketo resonances. They concluded that photodegradation probably proceeds through the diketo tautomer and that in the absence of the specie avobenzone is photostable.

Shaath et al. (21) studied dilute solutions (200 ppm) of avobenzone in mineral oil, isopropyl myristate, and a 70/30 mixture of ethanol and water. Samples were placed in quartz cells and irradiated with a solar simulator equipped with filters to eliminate radiation <290 nm and >400 nm. Measurements were made on a spectrophotometer before and after irradiation. After 5 MED, avobenzone absorbance declined 20.6% in mineral oil, 2.9% in isopropyl myristate, and 4.8% in the ethanol and water mixture.

Roscher et al. (22) investigated photolysis reactions of avobenzone by irradiating a solution in cyclohexane for 70–140 h using a mercury vapor lamp. Photolysis products from avobenzone included *tert*-butylbenzene, *p*-*tert*-butylbenzoic acid, and *p*-methoxybenzoic acid. Products obtained from the cyclohexane included cyclohexanol, cyclohexanone, and dicyclohexyl ether. Also identified were esters formed from the products of avobenzone and cyclohexane.

A 1997 study (23) also irradiated dilute solutions (10 ppm) of avobenzone in isopropanol and cyclohexane, using optical filters to exclude radiation <290 nm and >400 nm. This study confirmed the Schwack and Rudolph finding that avobenzone is photostable in isopropanol and not in cyclohexane. As Andrae et al. (19) had, the investigators observed a decline in absorbance attributed to the enol tautomer, and a corresponding increase in absorbance attributed to the diketo tautomer. However, continued observation revealed that within a few hours following irradiation, in the nonpolar solutions, absorbance returned almost to pre-irradiation levels, indicating that the enol–diketo tautomerization was reversible and that there was virtually no permanent loss of avobenzone concentration. This finding, shown in Fig. 17.6, was contrary to Schwack and Rudolph's finding of significant photodegradation by fragmentation that may have resulted from the higher frequency, more energetic radiation and longer exposures used in the Schwack and Rudolph study (>260 nm and 8 h) compared to the 1997 study (>290 nm and <30 min). It should be noted that the radiation used in the newer study (24) more closely resembles the UV irradiance from sunlight, which does not include radiation <290 nm, and that the exposure times used were calculated to approximate realistic exposure times of several hours on the beach.

The newer study also looked at the photostabilizing effects of protic solvents of lower polarity such as longer chain alcohols and salicylates. The purpose here was to test the hypothesis that it may be the protic nature of isopropanol and methanol that is responsible for the much higher photostability observed in these solvents. The data appeared to support the hypothesis, demonstrating that protic solvents have, to a point, a concentration-related effect on avobenzone's photostability.

Tarras-Wahlberg et al. (25) blended avobenzone in petrolatum in a concentration intended to approximate commercial use levels (exact concentration not reported). The group then applied the mixture to a quartz slide, placed another quartz slide on top, and squeezed the two slides to achieve a uniform thickness. They irradiated the sample with two radiation sources: one for UV-A; another for UV-B. The UV-A dose was 100 J/cm^2. The UV-B dose was 20 MED. In addition to monitoring changes in UV absorbance during and after irradiation, the Tarras-Wahlberg group also employed GC–MS to isolate and identify the resulting photoproducts, if any. They found avobenzone to be relatively photostable upon irradiation with UV-B, and photounstable upon irradiation with UV-A. They reported a well-defined photoproduct with absorbance in the UV-B, but provide no further details.

Octinoxate (Octyl Methoxycinnamate)

Octinoxate, better known as octyl methoxycinnamate (OMC), is the most widely used UV filter in sunscreens in the world and is well known for its low potential to behave as a sensitizer or as a photoallergen (26). Therefore, its photostability is of great interest to sunscreen formulators.

Deflandre and Lang (18) studied the photostability of OMC using the same procedure they used for avobenzone, described above. Based on their data, they projected that OMC would degrade by 4.5% after 1 h in sunlight. Deflandre and Lang note that cinnamates isomerize when submitted to UV radiation, reaching a photostationary equilibrium shortly after exposure begins. Before equilibrium is reached, degradation occurs rapidly. After equilibrium is reached, degradation occurs more slowly.

Shaath et al. (21) irradiated dilute solutions (200 ppm) of OMC in mineral oil, isopropyl myristate, and a 70/30 mixture of ethanol and water, using the same protocol as described for avobenzone previously. They reported declines in OMC absorbance in the three solvents of 18.7%, 18.7%, and 39.1%, respectively.

Serpone et al. (27) irradiated dilute solutions (8 mg/L) of OMC in water, methanol, acetonitrile, and *n*-hexane with UV radiation. Radiation was provided by a 1000 W Hg/Xe lamp that was optically filtered to remove wavelengths >400 nm and <290 nm. Absorbance of the OMC was measured over time. Irradiance was not given. Contrary to previous reports (28,29), the Serpone study documented rapid and significant photodegradation of OMC. After 30 min of UV exposure, the amount of OMC lost was reported as 90% in water, 40% in methanol, 45% in acetonitrile, and 40% in *n*-hexane.

At CPH Innovations, we qualitatively confirmed the Serpone study result by irradiating a 10 ppm solution of OMC in isopropanol with 35 MED. OMC absorbance declined by approximately 50% (unpublished results).

Tarras-Wahlberg et al. (25) also investigated the photostability of OMC, employing the same protocol as described for their investigation of avobenzone. They reported slight decomposition after 20 MED of UV-B irradiation, and slightly greater decomposition following irradiation with UV-A. GC revealed an additional peak; however, its mass spectrum was similar to the original substance assigned as the *cis*-isomer.

Schrader et al. (30) isolated and identified eight photoproducts following irradiation of isoamyl methoxycinnamate, a close chemical cousin of OMC that is used in European sunscreens. Schrader irradiated a 10% isopropanol solution with 16.4 J/cm^2 radiation from a xenon light source that was filtered to approximate solar UV radiation. Schrader's report does not indicate how much of the isoamyl methoxycinnamate remained after irradiation, but seemed to indicate that the photoproducts appeared in low concentrations. The report proposed that the main reaction products resulted from a cycloaddition between the *trans* double bond of one molecule and the 3,4 double bond of the aromatic ring of a second molecule.

Another study prepared and tested a sunscreen emulsion containing 7.5% OMC as the sole UV filter (unpublished data). A thin film of the sunscreen was prepared on a substrate designed for *in vitro* sunscreen analysis,* and this was irradiated by a solar simulator† in increments of 5 MED doses to a total of 25 MED. The total exposure approximates the exposure during 5–6 h of direct sunlight. As shown in Fig. 17.7, the OMC experienced rapid photodegradation (approximately 10%) after the initial 5-MED exposure, then declined more gradually with subsequent 5-MED radiation doses. After 25 MED, the sample had lost ~17% of its UV-B attenuation. This reinforces the earlier statement that UV filters often behave very differently in formulation than they do in dilute solutions. It also provides qualitative support for the finding and observation of Deflandre and Lang (18) as mentioned earlier. An interesting result of this study was the increase in absorbance at wavelengths >375 nm, possibly indicating the appearance of photoproducts that absorb in the visible range, though none were visible to the eye, and any result such as this could be unique to the particular formulation tested.

Other UV Filters

Deflandre and Lang (18) applied the protocol described above to photostability studies of methylbenzylidene camphor, phenylbenzimidazole sulfonic acid (as the sodium salt), octyl dimethyl PABA (Padimate-O), and oxybenzone. They found all but Padimate-O to have good photostability. Their results are summarized in Table 17.2.

Shaath et al. (21) used the same protocol as described in their study of avobenzone and OMC to study dilute solutions of oxybenzone, octocrylene, Padimate-O, homosalate, and octyl salicylate. Their results are summarized in Table 17.3.

Serpone et al. (27) also determined the photostabilities of PABA, Padimate-O, oxybenzone, and phenylbenzimidazole sulfonic acid in dilute solutions using the same protocol they used for OMC outlined above. The results are summarized in Table 17.4.

---

*The thin film was prepared on the substrate, Vitro-skin, available from IMS Inc., Milford, CT.

†Model 16S Solar UV Simulator equipped with PMA 2105 biologically weighted UV-B detector with beam splitter adapter and controlled by a PMA2100 dose controller, Solar Light Company.

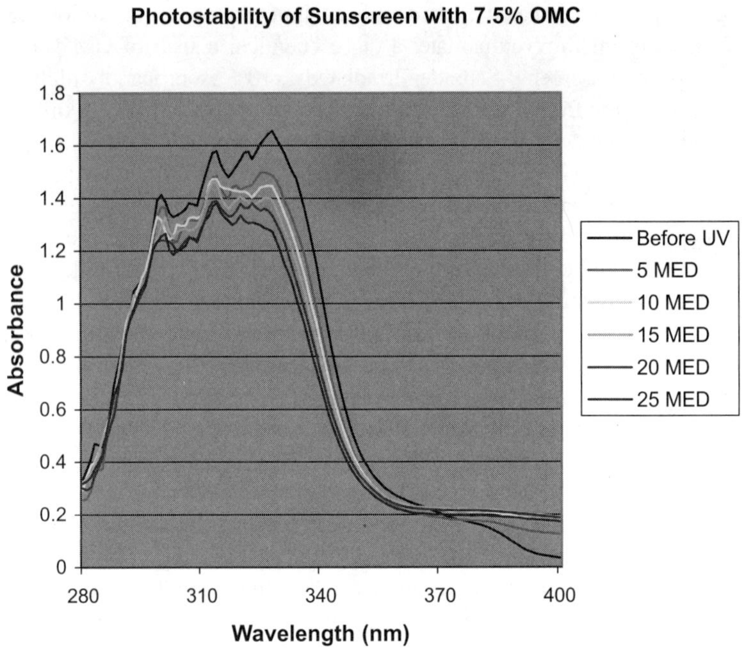

Figure 17.7 Absorbance of a sunscreen containing 7.5% OMC as the sole UV filter before and after irradiation with 25 MED in 5 MED increments. This dose is approximately equivalent to 5–6 h of direct sunlight. Note the rapid decline after 5 MED (about 10%), followed by the more gradual decline with repeated radiation doses.

A previously unpublished study tested the photostability of the organic UV filters octocrylene, octyl salicylate, homosalate, and octyl triazone in dilute solutions (approximately 10–90 ppm) of isopropanol and cyclohexane. Results are expressed as absorbance lost at the λ_{max}. The results of these studies are summarized in Table 17.5.

Table 17.2 Results of Study by Deflandre and Lang (18)

UV filter	% (w/w) in formulation	% Loss
Methylbenzylidene camphor	4	<1
Padimate-O	4	15.5
Oxybenzone	2	>1
Phenylbenzimidazole sulfonic acid	4	<1

Table 17.3 Results of Study by Shaath et al. (21)

UV filter	Concentration (ppm)	Radiation (MED)	% of degradation by solvent		
			Mineral oil	IPM	Ethanol/water
Oxybenzone	200	5	0	1.8	Not soluble
Octocrylene	200	5	2.8	1.1	0
Padimate-O	200	5	31.2	52.8	3.9
Homosalate	200	5	4.0	4.7	1.6
Octyl salicylate	200	5	0	9.8	1.5

Tarras-Wahlberg et al. (25) tested the photostability of Padimate-O, methylbenzylidene camphor (MBC), and oxybenzone. The study found Padimate-O to be the least stable of the three. Analysis of the sample by gas chromatography following irradiation revealed two peaks in addition to the one for the parent compound. They tentatively identified these as octyl 4-methylaminobenzoate (representing the loss in the parent compound of a methyl group) and octyl 4-(formylmethylamino) benzoate (presumed to represent oxidation of the amine part). For MBC, they observed an initial decline in the absorbance after 20 MED. They reported that the observed spectrum was indicative of a *cis–trans* photoisomerization. In a finding similar to Deflandre and Lang's for OMC (see preceding text), the Tarras-Wahlberg group noted the establishment of a photostable equilibrium that changed very little after irradiation with an additional 100 J/cm^2 of UV-A. Oxybenzone, in their study, declined in absorbance very slightly after 20 MED of UV-B, and no further after the additional UV-A dose of 100 J/cm^2.

Roscher et al. (22) irradiated oxybenzone in cyclohexane for 70–140 h using a mercury vapor lamp. The oxybenzone was recovered unchanged, and no detectable products were produced. Irradiation of Padimate-O in cyclohexane yielded the ethylhexyl esters of *p*-aminobenzoic acid, *p*-mono-methylaminobenzoic acid, and *p*-dimethylamino(*o*/*m*)-methylbenzoic acid.

Table 17.4 Results of the Serpone et al. Study (27)

UV filter	Exposure time (min)	% degradation by solvent			
		Water	Methanol	Acetonitrile	*n*-Hexane
PABA	60	65	60	45	87
Padimate-O	20	75	15	94	97
Oxybenzone	120	20	90	5–10	15
Phenyl benzimidazole sulfonic acid	10 (*20*)	90	N/A	(*50*)	N/A

Table 17.5 Results of a Previously Unpublished Study

UV filter	Radiation dose (MED)	% Loss in isopropanol	% Loss in cyclohexane
Octocrylene	35	11	0
Octyl salicylate	35	1	<1
Homosalate	35	2	<1
Octyl triazone	35	31	13

Terephthalylidine dicamphor sulfonic acid (TDSA) used as a salt is a water-soluble UV filter that is proprietary to one company. It is photostable (18,31). Its photostability is attributed to its ability to dissipate its excited state energy through a nondestructive E–Z isomerization (see Fig. 17.5).

Three relatively new European UV filters are also reported to be photostable, as noted in the following text.

The sodium salt of disodium phenyl dibenzimidazole tetrasulfonate (DPDT) is soluble in water at 12% (w/w). Johncock and Schuricht (32) prepared 1% and 3% solutions of DPDT, which they irradiated with 13.5, 27, 40.5, and 54 J/cm^2, (equivalent to 5, 10, 15, and 20 MED, respectively). As determined by HPLC, the 1% DPDT solution showed loss of 1%, 4%, 4%, and 8%, respectively, and the 3% DPDT solution showed losses of 1%, 2%, 3%, and 3%, respectively. Johncock and Schuricht reported similar results when DPDT was incorporated into an oil in water emulsion, of which 2 mg/cm^2 was applied to quartz plates. They observed 2%, 5%, 7%, and 8% loss after irradiating the 1% DPDT emulsion with 5, 10, 15, and 20 MED, and 1%, 1%, 3%, and 3% loss, respectively, for the emulsion with 3% DPDT.

Methylene bis-benzotriazolyl tetramethylbutylphenol (MBBT) is an organic microparticle that is employed in sunscreen formulations much as microfine metal oxides are. The photostability of MBBT was tested according to the method of Berset et al. (33). Herzog et al. (34,35) report that 99% of MBBT was recovered after irradiation with 10 MED, and 98% was recovered after irradiation with 50 MED.

Bis-ethylhexyloxyphenol methoxyphenyltriazine (BEMT) is an oil-soluble crystalline solid. In a study comparing the photostability of BEMT with OMC, avobenzone, and MBBT, BEMT was reported to be photostable; recovery of BEMT was higher than 95% after irradiation with 50 MED (36,37).

UV Filter Combinations

Serpone et al. (27) combined the two organic UV filters, OMC and oxybenzone, at 8 mg/L in air-equilibrated aqueous media and irradiated the solution with UV-A/UV-B radiation. They reported significant photodegradation of the OMC after only 15 min. Oxybenzone degraded by 60% after 260 min.

The Serpone group (27) also irradiated oxybenzone and titanium dioxide at 8 and 300 mg/L, respectively, in aerobic aqueous media, using what they call an "ultrafine sunscreen-grade TiO_2." They report that about 70% of the oxybenzone degraded after 20 min of UV exposure. This was much faster degradation than observed in the solution containing oxybenzone alone, where it took 260 min of UV irradiation to achieve 50% degradation. The Serpone report concluded that oxybenzone degradation was photocatalyzed by the titanium dioxide. As the mechanism, they note that "UV illumination of TiO_2 yields conduction band electrons and valence band holes, which interact with surface-adsorbed molecular oxygen to yield superoxide radical anions, O_2^{-}, and with water to produce the highly reactive $^{\cdot}OH$ radicals," which then may react destructively with oxybenzone.

The photostability of a sunscreen emulsion (oil in water, O/W) that contained OMC and oxybenzone at 5% and 3%, respectively was tested (unpublished data). The emulsion contained no other UV filters. The investigator prepared a thin film of the emulsion and allowed it to dry before irradiating it with 20 MED from a solar simulator. Scans of the thin film performed on a Labsphere UV-1000 Ultraviolet Transmittance Analyzer before and after irradiation showed a 13.5% reduction in UV-B attenuation and no loss of UV-A attenuation.

PHOTOSTABILITY OF SUNSCREEN FORMULATIONS

Diffey et al. (7) tested nine commercial sunscreens available on the market in Europe during 1997. Briefly, the researchers dispensed each sunscreen on a quartz plate such that the sunscreen coated the quartz to 1 mg/cm^2. The quartz plates were dried in an oven set at 30°C for 15 min, then exposed to radiation provided by a Xe lamp that was filtered to remove wavelengths $<$290 nm and $>$400 nm. The UV transmittance of the quartz plates was measured at intervals of continuous irradiation of 60, 120, and 180 min. The cumulative dose of UV radiation received by each slide at each time interval corresponded to 18, 36, and 54 J/cm^2, respectively. A theoretical sun protection factor (SPF) was calculated from the transmission data.

Of the nine products tested, five were photostable, one showed minor photodegradation, and three exhibited marked increases in transmittance and were therefore judged to be photounstable. The photostable products lost no more than 10% of their calculated SPF after 3 h of irradiation. The UV filter systems in four of the five photostable products included the combination of avobenzone and methylbenzylidene camphor (MBC) (see section on photostabilizers). Three of the five photostable products also contained terephthalylidine dicamphor sulfonic acid (TDSA) and TiO_2. A fourth photostable sunscreen, in addition to the avobenzone and MBC, also contained octyl triazone, octyl salicylate, homosalate, and TiO_2. The fifth contained no avobenzone, containing instead OMC, octyl salicylate, and oxybenzone.

The three photounstable products in the Diffey study all combined avobenzone with either OMC or isoamyl methoxycinnamate. Cinnamate derivatives and avobenzone have been widely reported to be photounstable in combination (6,32). The sunscreen that showed minor degradation contained OMC and TiO_2. It lost about 33% of its calculated SPF after 3 h.

Stokes and Diffey (6) also tested the photostability of four commercial sunscreen products by applying them to roughened quartz plates and to *ex vivo* human skin excised during breast reduction surgery. The study tested the effect of application thickness (1 vs. 2 mg/cm^2) and radiation source (Xe lamp vs. sunlight) on photostability assessment. Of the four sunscreens tested, one combined avobenzone and octocrylene in its UV filter system and also contained TDSA and TiO_2. Octocrylene is widely known to photostabilize avobenzone (see section on photostabilizers). Not surprisingly, this product proved to be photostable on both the roughened quartz and *ex vivo* human skin substrates, and under all test conditions. The other three sunscreens combined OMC and avobenzone, a combination known to be unstable. In addition to OMC/avobenzone, one also contained oxybenzone, another contained methylbenzylidene camphor and TiO_2, and the third contained only TiO_2. All three sunscreens proved to be photounstable when tested on roughened quartz. Surprisingly, however, the sunscreen that combined OMC, avobenzone, and oxybenzone proved to be photostable when tested on *ex vivo* human skin. By way of explanation, Stokes and Diffey speculated that an epidermal substrate may provide the excited sunscreen molecules with alternative pathways to dissipate their energy than they would have on a roughened quartz plate, adding that these alternative pathways may affect sunscreen efficiency in a beneficial way.

In 2001, Maier et al. (38) tested the photostability of 16 sunscreens commercially available in Europe. They spread measured amounts of each sunscreen to a quartz slide to make a uniform film. The slides were dried for 30 min, then irradiated with a solar simulator at a rate of 12.75 SED (standard erythemal dose) per hour. Spectral absorbance of each slide was measured in both the UV-A range (320–400 nm) and UV-B range (280–320 nm) using a spectrophotometer.

In reporting their results, the Maier group distinguished between UV-B and UV-A photostability. Basically, they found all 16 products to be photostable in the UV-B range; one product showed inactivation of 5.1% after a 25 SED exposure; all others showed inactivation of less than 1% in the UV-B range.

In contrast, Maier et al. found seven of the 16 products to be photounstable in the UV-A range. Photoinactivation in these products after 25 SED ranged from a low of 12.3% to a high of 48.4%. All seven of the photounstable products contained avobenzone as one of the filters, as did most of the photostable products. All seven of the unstable products combined OMC (and/or isoamyl methoxycinnamate) with avobenzone in their filter systems. Surprisingly, three of the photostable products also combined OMC with avobenzone. Methylbenzylidene camphor was used in six of the seven photounstable products, and in the three photostable products that also contained OMC and avobenzone. In apparent frustration, the Maier report concluded "that the behavior of suncare products was not predictable from its individual ingredients." It continued, "The inclusion of a single photounstable filter did not mean photoinstability of the complete suncare product."

Research at CPH Innovations into the relationship between solvent polarity and sunscreen photostability may offer a partial answer to the Maier group's dilemma. The CPH Innovations study (17) included an experiment in which a matched pair of sunscreens was tested *in vivo* for SPF. Both sunscreens contained 5% octyl salicylate, 3% oxybenzone, and 2% avobenzone. One sunscreen was made with the relatively nonpolar solvents, C12–15 alkyl benzoates and octyldodecyl neopentanoate, while the other was made with the relatively polar solvents, diisoamyl malate, dibutyloctyl malate, and dimethyl capramide. The measured dielectric constants of the sunscreen oil phases were 5.48 and 8.71, respectively. The sunscreen with the nonpolar solvents achieved SPF 17.1; the sunscreen with the relatively polar solvents achieved SPF 25, a 46% improvement.

The photostability of an SPF 30 sunscreen, commercially available in the USA in 2003, was tested (unpublished data; test peformed on Coppertone SPF 30 Sunblock Lotion). The sunscreen's filter system included octyl salicylate, homosalate, oxybenzone, avobenzone, and octocrylene determined by GC to be present at 2% (w/w) in the formulation. A measured amount of the sunscreen was spread on an artificial skin-like substrate, allowed to dry, and then irradiated with 35 MED. Absorbance across the solar UV spectrum was measured before and after irradiation. The sunscreen proved to be quite photostable, losing none of its UV-B attenuation, and only about 4% of its UV-A attenuation. The results of this test can be seen in Fig. 17.8.

Sayre and Dowdy (39) tested six commercial sunscreen preparations available in the USA in 1999. They used an apparatus that simultaneously irradiated a film and monitored the UV transmittance of the film in real time. Of the products tested, four contained OMC and avobenzone, one contained Padimate-O and avobenzone, and one contained OMC, homosalate, and oxybenzone (and not avobenzone). Results were reported in terms of "monochromatic protection factor" (MPF), which was calculated as the reciprocal of transmittance. Sayre and Dowdy reported that only the sunscreen that contained no avobenzone was photostable; it lost none of its MPF after irradiation with 10 MED. The sunscreen with Padimate-O and avobenzone was the most unstable, retaining only 20% of its MPF after 2 MED, and <10% after 10 MED. The other avobenzone-containing sunscreens showed various degrees of instability, retaining from about 60% MPF to 30% MPF after 10 MED.

PHOTOSTABILIZATION STRATEGIES

Formulation Strategies

By one count, 126 US patents were granted between 1984 and 2003 that are concerned in some way with photostabilizing avobenzone, the latest being granted

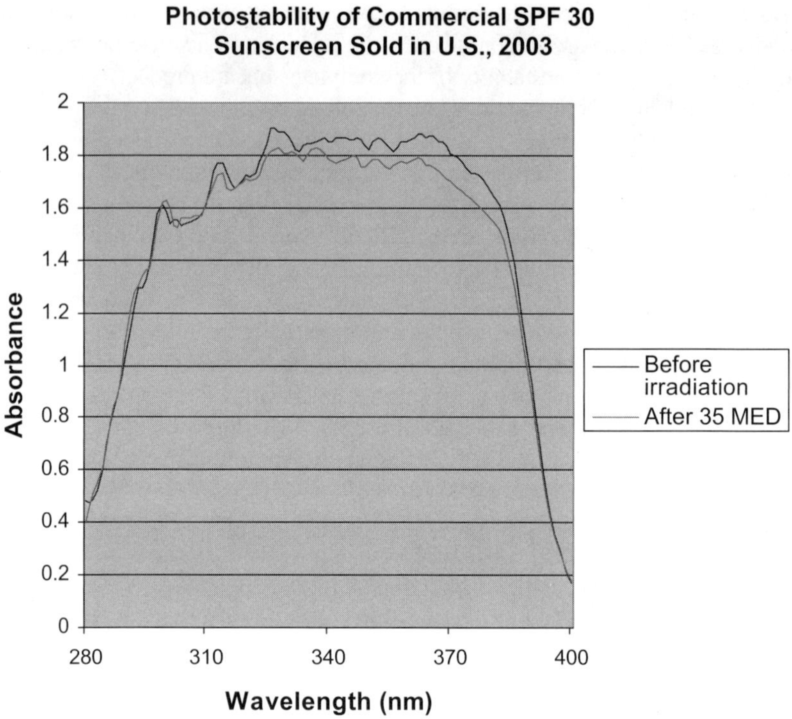

Figure 17.8 The good photostability of an SPF 30 sunscreen sold in the USA in 2003 after a 35-MED exposure. The filter system of this sunscreen includes octyl salicylate, homosalate, oxybenzone, avobenzone, and octocrylene at 2% (w/w) by GC.

two days before this search was undertaken.* Clearly, the task of photostabilizing avobenzone has been, and remains, a primary focus of sunscreen formulators and chemical suppliers worldwide.

The ideal formulation strategy removes ingredients known to be deleterious to avobenzone photostability, and includes ingredients that are known to improve photostability. A survey of the sunscreen products tested by investigators whose work has been cited in the chapter reveals that few appear to meet this ideal. Many, for example, combine avobenzone with OMC. Exceptions notwithstanding (see the Maier study referenced earlier), the OMC/avobenzone combination is well known to be photounstable and not amenable

*Search by author of United States Patent and Trademark Office website (www.USPTO.gov) conducted August 21, 2003. Search terms used were (avobenzone AND photostability) OR (dibenzoylmethane AND photostability) OR (dibenzoylmethane AND photostable).

to photostabilization unless segregated by some means such as encapsulation (40,41).

Certain UV filters and chemical additives are known to exert a photostabilizing effect on avobenzone. These chemicals share two things in common: they "quench" the triplet state of the avobenzone by an energy transfer mechanism, and they dissipate the excited state energy harmlessly.

One of these photostabilizers is methylbenzylidene camphor (MBC), a UV filter permitted in Europe, though not in the USA. Berset et al. (42) reported that even low concentrations of MBC (0.5–3%) in formulation are sufficient to preserve 80–90% of the avobenzone from photodegradation.

Octocrylene, a UV-B filter used worldwide, is well known to be an effective photostabilizer for avobenzone. Patents exclude most formulators from using octocrylene for this purpose when the mole ratio of octocrylene to avobenzone is $\geq$0.8 (12). Translated, this means, for example, that when the avobenzone concentration is 3%, the octocrylene concentration cannot exceed about 2.5%. Berset et al. (42) reported that low levels of octocrylene (0.5–2.5%) in formulation will preserve 80–90% of the avobenzone from photodegradation. Use of these low levels of octocrylene to photostabilize avobenzone is also the subject of a patent from one of the manufacturers of avobenzone and is, therefore, available to license (43).

A relatively new addition to the list of photostabilizers is diethylhexyl 2,6-naphthalate (DEHN). According to Bonda and Steinberg, use of DEHN at 4% can preserve over 90% of avobenzone's UV-A and UV-B attenuation after irradiation with 10 MED of UV radiation from 290 to 400 nm (10). In another example, a formulation containing 5% octisalate, 4% oxybenzone, 3% avobenzone, and 5% DEHN, lost virtually none of its absorbance across the UV spectrum after irradiation with 25 MED. The same formulation was tested *in vivo* and achieved an average SPF of 32. Figure 17.9 shows the high photostability of a formulation stabilized by diethylhexyl 2,6-naphthalate that contains in its filter system 8% homosalate, 5% octyl salicylate, 5% oxybenzone, and 3% avobenzone. After 35 MED, this sunscreen lost none of its UV-B attenuation, and only 3.5% of its UV-A attenuation (unpublished data).

Derivatives of benzophenone such as oxybenzone and others that share the basic 2-hydroxybenzophenone structure help to photostabilize avobenzone. According to one patent, adding a 2-hydroxybenzophenone moiety can increase avobenzone photostability by a factor of 10, though the avobenzone still loses >60% of its absorbance (44).

A study by Chatelain and Gabard (37) showed that bis-ethylhexyloxyphenol methoxyphenyl triazine (BEMT) improves the photostability of avobenzone, and the combination of avobenzone and OMC. The researchers employed the method of Diffey et al. (7) and Sayre to compare UV filter recovery as measured by HPLC on irradiated quartz slides and nonirradiated quartz slides. They used a standard dose of 30 MED of UV radiation, 290–400 nm. They report that formulations containing avobenzone alone lost between 56% and 70% of the starting material after irradiation. With BEMT added, only 5% to 15% of the

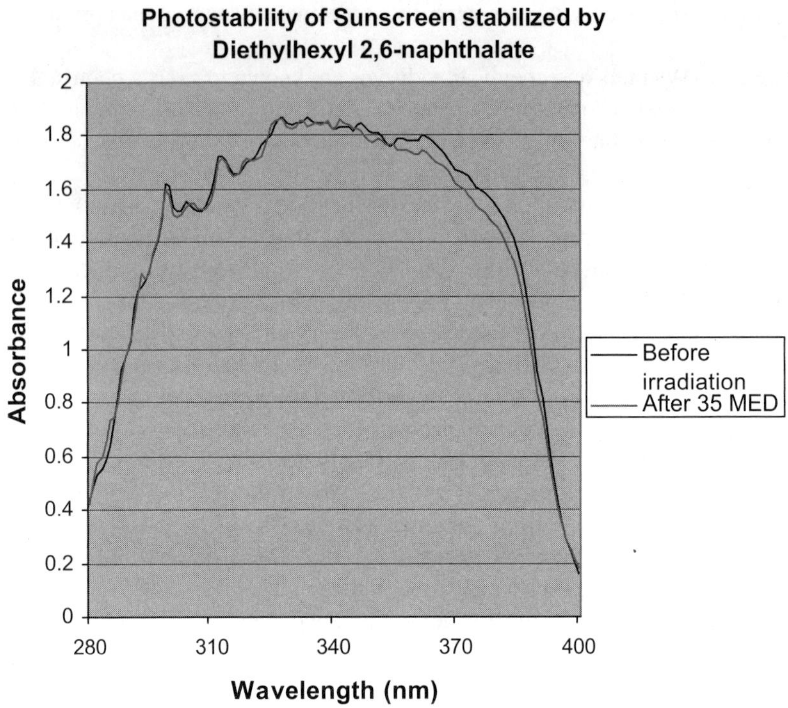

Figure 17.9 After irradiation with 35 MED, this SPF 30 sunscreen lost no UVB absorbance and only 3.5% UVA absorbance. Its filter system is comprised of 8% homosalate, 5% octyl salicylate, 5% oxybenzone, and 3% avobenzone. It is stabilized with 5% diethylhexyl 2,6-naphthalate.

original avobenzone was lost. In a formulation containing 5% avobenzone and 5% OMC and no BEMT, 65% of the OMC and 45% of the avobenzone were lost. With BEMT, the comparative loss was 35% of the OMC and 17% of the avobenzone. Chatelain and Gabard report that the optimal photoprotective amount of BEMT for OMC and avobenzone is 5%.

Methylene bis-benzotriazolyl tetramethylbutylphenol (MBBT) is reported to improve the photostability of OMC (45). Without MBBT, 27% of OMC was lost after irradiation with 10 MED. In the presence of MBBT, the loss was only 8%.

Molecular Strategies

Earlier, we discussed some of the many pathways a molecule may take between absorbance of a photon and dissipation of its excited state energy. Each pathway is associated with a rate constant, and each is associated with its own timescale. To illustrate, laser flash photolysis studies of terephthalylidine dicamphor sulfonic acid (TDSA) revealed that, following UV-A excitation, $<10\%$ of the initially excited molecules decay to the triplet state, and that they remain in the triplet excited state about 100 ns (100×10^{-9} s) (33). This information tells us that, at most, 10% of the TDSA can engage in reactions that proceed from the triplet state, and further, that TDSA is likely to engage in reactions that take place in 100 ns or faster. We know that even fast chemical reactions between two molecules require timescales more on the order of 1000 ns (1: p. 7). So we can conclude that TDSA is not likely to undergo much photodegradation as a result of bimolecular reactions, though photodegradation by other pathways is still theoretically possible.

The process by which an excited molecule shifts from one spin-paired state to another (e.g., from the singlet excited state to the ground state) is called *internal conversion.* The transition from a spin-paired state to an unpaired state (e.g., a singlet excited state to a triplet excited state) is called *intersystem crossing.* Since intersystem crossing leads to the triplet excited state, and since most chemical reactions proceed from the triplet state, a sound molecular strategy to encourage photostability will promote internal conversion to the exclusion of intersystem crossing. Isomerization and intramolecular hydrogen transfer can facilitate rapid internal conversion (46). We have seen that some isomerizations such as those presumed for MBC and octocrylene, are associated with relatively high photostability, and with the ability to photostabilize avobenzone. We have also seen that molecules that contain a hydroxyphenyl group ortho to a carbonyl or a ring-bound nitrogen, such as octyl salicylate, homosalate, oxybenzone, MBBT, and BEMT are all very photostable. This structural feature permits a very rapid excited-state intramolecular proton transfer (ESIPT) that, in turn, promotes rapid internal conversion. Residual energy can then be dissipated harmlessly in collisions with surrounding molecules (47).

CONCLUSIONS

The organic UV filters used in sunscreens are powerful photochemicals whose behavior is closely related to their molecular structure and their immediate environment. Individually, they exhibit varying degrees of photoinstability depending in part on the experimental model used to measure them. In general, they can be divided into a relatively photostable group and a relatively photounstable group. Into the first group may be placed octyl salicylate, homosalate, oxybenzone, methylbenzylidene camphor, TDSA, octocrylene, DPDT, MBBT, and BEMT. Into the second group may be placed octyl dimethyl PABA, octyl methoxycinnamate, octyl triazone, and avobenzone. Of the photounstable UV filters, avobenzone has attracted the greatest attention because of its preeminent role as the UV-A absorber of choice, and therefore, its greater potential impact on overall sunscreen performance.

For reasons that are not always clear, UV filters often behave differently in sunscreen formulations and under conditions of use than they do in some laboratory experiments. Some of their behavior in formulation may be explained by solvent considerations. In particular, the photostability of avobenzone may be influenced by the protic and polar natures of other chemicals in the formulation. As a practical matter, avobenzone may be rendered photostable in formulation by using photostabilizers such as octocrylene, methylbenzylidene camphor, diethylhexyl 2,6-naphthalate, and BEMT, and by avoiding chemicals that are destabilizing such as octyl methoxycinnamate and octyl dimethyl PABA.

Photostability bears a direct relationship to molecular structure. Molecules with vinylic moieties (octyl methoxycinnamate) or amine substituents (octyl dimethyl PABA) exhibit lower photostability, though it must be emphasized that formulations containing OMC without avobenzone generally exhibit high photostability. Molecules that undergo rapid isomerization upon excitation (octocrylene, methylbenzylidene camphor, TDSA) dissipate their excited state energy efficiently and show good photostability. Molecules that are capable of extremely fast intramolecular proton transfer (octyl salicylate, homosalate, oxybenzone, MBBT, and BEMT) are all very photostable. At first glance, it may appear that avobenzone should be one of these since in its enol form it appears equipped to undergo rapid intramolecular proton transfer. However, photodegradation takes place through the diketo form and the drive to maintain the enol–diketo equilibrium likely paves the way for further degradation.

Designers of new UV filters would be wise to heed these lessons in their efforts to develop the next generation of sunscreen active ingredients.

ACKNOWLEDGMENTS

I gratefully acknowledge the invaluable contributions of Gary Wentworth, PhD, and Anna Pavlovic, PhD of CPH Innovations, Gary Neudahl of RTD*Hallstar, and Tom Meyer, PhD, of Schering-Plough Healthcare, to the preparation of this chapter.

REFERENCES

1. Turro NJ. Modern Molecular Photochemistry. Menlo Park, CA: Benjamin/Cummings, 1978.
2. Schwartz BJ, Rossky PJ. The interplay of dielectric and mechanical relaxation in solvation dynamics. J Mol Liq 1995; 65/66:23–30.
3. Barthel ER, Martini IB, Schwartz BJ. How does the solvent control electron transfer? Experimental and theoretical studies of the simplest charge transfer reaction. J Phys Chem B 2001; 105:12230–12241.
4. Pinnell SR. Cutaneous photodamage, oxidative stress, and topical antioxidant protection. J Am Acad Dermatol 2003; 48:1–22.

5. Hansen KM, Simon JD. Epidermal *trans*-urocanic acid and the UV-A-induced photoaging of the skin. Proc Natl Acad Sci USA 1998; 95:10576–10578.
6. Stokes R, Diffey B. In vitro assessment of sunscreen photostability: the effect of radiation source, sunscreen application thickness and substrate. Int J Cosmet Sci 1999; 21:341–351.
7. Diffey B, Stokes RP, Forestier S, Mazilier C, Rougier A. Suncare product photostability: a key parameter for a more realistic in vitro efficacy evaluation. Eur J Dermatol 1997; 7:226–228.
8. Cambom M, Issachar N, Castelli D, Robert C. An in vivo method to assess the photostability of UV filters in a sunscreen. J Cosmet Sci 2001; 52:1–11.
9. DGK (German Society for Scientific and Applied Cosmetics) Task Force "Sun Protection". The reproducibility of an in-vitro determination of the UVA index describing the relative UVA protection of sun care products. IFSCC Mag 2002; 5:161–166.
10. Bonda CA, Steinberg DC. A new photostabilizer for full spectrum sunscreens. Cosmet Toilet 2000; 115(6):37–45.
11. Bonda CA, Marinelli PJ, Hessefort YZ, Trivedi J, Wentworth G. Photostable sunscreen compositions containing dibenzoylmethane derivative, e.g. Parsol® 1789, and diesters or polyesters of naphthalene dicarboxylic acid photostabilizers and enhancers of the sun protection factor (SPF). US Patent No. 5,993,789.
12. Deflandre A, Dubois M, Forestier S, Richard H. Photostable cosmetic screening composition containing a UV-A screening agent and an alkyl β,β-diphenylacrylate or α-cyano-β,β-diphenylacrylate. US Patent No. 5,576,354.
13. Gonzenbach H, Hill TJ, Truscott TG. The triplet energy levels of UVA and UVB sunscreens, J Photochem Photobiol B: Biol 1992; 16:377–379.
14. Marcus RA. J Chem Phys 1956; 24:966.
15. Marcus RA. Annu Rev Phys Chem 1964; 15:155.
16. Marcus RA, Sutin N. Electron transfers in chemistry and biology. Biochim Biophys Acta 1985; 811:265–322.
17. Bonda CA. Solvent polarity and sunscreen photostability. Presentation made to the Society of Cosmetic Chemists Annual Scientific Meeting, New York, December 2002.
18. Deflandre A, Lang G. Photostability assessment of sunscreens: benzylidene camphor and dibenzoylmethane derivatives. Int J Cosmet Sci 1988; 10:53–62.
19. Andrae I, Bringhen A, Bohm F, Gonzenbach H, Hill T, Mulroy L, Truscott TG. A UVA filter (4-*tert*-butyl-4′-methoxydibenzoylmethane): photoprotection reflects photophysical properties. J Photochem Photobiol B 1997; 37:147–150.
20. Schwack W, Rudolph T. Photochemistry of dibenzoyl methane UVA filters Part I. J Photochem Photobiol B 1995; 28:229–234.
21. Shaath NA, Fares HM, Klein K. Photodegradation of sunscreen chemicals: solvent considerations. Cosmet Toilet 1990; 105:41–44.
22. Roscher NM, Lindemann MKO, Kong SB, Cho CG, Jiang P. Photodecomposition of several compounds commonly used as sunscreen agents. J Photochem Photobiol A 1994; 80:417–421.
23. Bonda CA, Marinelli PM, Trivedi J, Hopper S, Wentworth G. Avobenzone photostability in simple polar and non-polar solvent systems. Presentation made to the Society of Cosmetic Chemists Annual Scientific Seminar, Seattle, WA, May, 1997.
24. Bonda CA, Marinelli PJ. The photochemistry of sunscreen photostability. TechnoScienze Agro-Food-Ind. Hi-Tech, 2000; 11(1):29–31.

25. Tarras-Wahlberg N, Stennhagen G, Larko O, Rosen A, Wennberg A, Wennerstrom O. Changes in ultraviolet absorption of sunscreens after ultraviolet irradiation. J Invest Dermatol 1999; 113:547–553.
26. Marks JG, Elsner P, Deleo VA. Contact & Occupational Dermatology. St. Louis, MO: Mosby, 2002.
27. Serpone N, Salinaro A, Emeline AV, Holrikoshi S, Hidaka H, Zhao J. An in vitro systematic spectroscopic examination of the photostabilities of a random set of commercial sunscreen lotions and their chemical UVB/UVA active agents. Photochem Photobiol Sci 2002; I:970–981.
28. Vanquerp V, Rodriguez C, Coiffard C, Coiffard LJM, De Roeck-Holtzhauer Y. High-performance liquid chromatographic method for the comparison of the photostability of five sunscreen agents. J Chromatogr A 1999; 832:273–277.
29. Stenberg C, Mellstrand T, Larko O. Stability of PABA after UV irradiation in vivo and in vitro. Photodermatology 1987; 4:201–204.
30. Schrader A, Jakupovic J, Baltes W. Photochemical studies on trans-3-methylbutyl 4-methoxycinnamate. J Cosmet Sci 1994; 45:43–52.
31. Cantrell A, McGarvey DJ, Mulroy L, Truscott TG. Laser flash photolysis studies of the UVA sunscreen Mexoryl® SX. Photochem Photobiol 1999; 70:292–297.
32. Johncock W, Schuricht M. Advances in broad spectrum UVA/UVB photoprotection. Cosmetics and Toiletries Manuf. Worldwide, 2002.
33. Berset G, Gonzenbach H, Christ R, Martin R, Deflandre A, Mascotte RE, Jolley JDR, Lowell W, Pelzer R, Stiehm T. Int J Cosmet Sci 1996; 18:167–177.
34. Herzog B, Mongiat S, Dehayes C, Neuhaus M, Sommer K, Mantler A. In vivo and in vitro assessment of UVA protection by sunscreen formulations containing either butyl methoxy dibenzoyl methane, methylene bis-benzotriazolyl tetramethylbutylphenol, or microfine ZnO. Int J Cosmet Sci 2002; 24:170–185.
35. Ciba® TINOSORB™ M. Product brochure from Ciba Specialty Chemicals.
36. Herzog B. Investigations of photostability of UV-absorbers for cosmetic sunscreens. Proceedings: 21st IFSCC Congress, Berlin, Sep. 11–14, 2000.
37. Chatelain E, Gabard B. Photostabilization of butyl methoxy dibenzoylmethane (avobenzone) and ethylhexyl methoxycinnamate by bis-ethylhexyloxyphenol methoxyphenyl triazone (Tinosorb S), a new UV broadband filter. Photochem Photobiol 2001; 74:401.
38. Maier H, Schauberger B, Brunnhofer K, Honigsmann H. Change of ultraviolet absorbance of sunscreens by exposure to solar-simulated radiation. J Invest Derm 2001; 117:256–262.
39. Sayre RM, Dowdy JC. Photostability testing of avobenzone. Cosmet Toilet 1999; 114:85–91.
40. Schwack W, Rudolph T. Photoreactions of chemical UVA filters in Cosmetics. GIT Lab J 1997; 1:17–20.
41. Chadorowski S, Quinn FX, Sanchez C. Assignee: L'Oreal. Method for improving UV radiation stability of photosensitive sunscreen filters. US Patent No. 6,607,713, issued August 19, 2003.
42. Berset G, Bringhen A, Gonzenbach J. Photostable UV-filter combinations containing butyl methoxy dibenzoylmethane. Poster presentation at SCC Scientific Meeting, New York, 1996.
43. Gonzenbach HU, Pittet G. Assignee: Roche Vitamins Inc. Light screening agents. US Patent No. 6,033,649. March 7, 2000.

44. Forestier S, Richard H. Assignee: L'Oreal. Photostable sunscreen compositions comprising dibenzoylmethane compounds and 2-hydroxybenzophenone-substituted silanes/organosiloxanes. US Patent No. 6,071,502. June 6, 2000.
45. Ciba® Tinosorb™ M, A microfine UV-A absorber with triple action, product brochure, Ciba Specialty Chemicals, Inc., Pub. No. Tinosorb M. TB. 0103.e.02.
46. Otterstedt J-E, Photostability and molecular structure. J Chem Phys 1973; 58:5716–5725.
47. Picket JE. Review and kinetic analysis of the photodegradation of UV absorbers. Macromol Symp 1997; 115:127–141.

Cosmetic Formulations

18

Formulating Sunscreen Products

Kenneth Klein and Irwin Palefsky
Cosmetech Laboratories, Inc., Fairfield, New Jersey, USA

INTRODUCTION

With the publication of the Final Sunscreen Monograph on May 21, 1999, the "playing field" for marketers of finish goods became more complex and now offered some new opportunities for "marketing handles." Although some claims could no longer be made, such as those relating to aging and wrinkling, we now see the appearance of strong claims dealing with ultraviolet-A (UV-A) radiation. In fact, the US Food and Drug Administration (FDA) has even published a list of those sunscreens for which usage permits UV-A reference. Some additional claims have begun to appear deal with protection against infrared (IR) radiation. The FDA Tentative Final Monograph (TFM) does not deal with IR in any way. Thus, IR claims are cosmetic and not drug claims. They must be substantiated for the Federal Trade Commission (FTC), but not the FDA. Marketersalso have made claims for "all-day" waterproof protection. The FDA no longer allows a waterproof claim. They feel that the term suggests an absolute—waterproof—which is not borne out by the currently available test methods. The sweat proof claim can now be made, if the product meets the requirements for a very water-resistant claim. Additionally, extended claims such as "all day" are not permitted.

The last several years have seen the appearance of products on the shelf that make the claim "chemical-free" sunscreens. Marketers are trying to take advantage of the public's general erroneous belief that "chemicals" are "bad." This claim is silly and has no basis in reality. All sunscreen actives whether they are organic or inorganic are "chemicals." Products that make this claim generally are formulated with particulate sunscreens (zinc oxide or titanium dioxide). In the minds of some consumers "chemicals" are bad things to put on their skin, so marketers try to take advantage of this. This is a questionable approach, at best, and quite misleading. The FDA has not looked kindly at this "claim."

The cosmetic chemist has at his or her disposal many vehicles from which to choose; these include, but are not limited to, emulsions, oils, gels, sticks, mousses, aerosols, and ointments. There are many factors, some technical and some not, that determine which will be the vehicle of choice. Each of the vehicles has strengths and weaknesses that can have a significant influence on the cosmetic chemist's choice. To make a wise choice, relevant factors and questions must be addressed:

What is the target sun protection factor (SPF)? This is a market- and marketing-driven question. The trend toward higher SPFs seen from the mid-1980s through the 1990s has not yet leveled off. Although there have been products introduced with an SPF as high as 70 by major marketers, almost all sunscreen products have SPFs of 45 or less. One should question the real need for a product with this degree of protection. If the average minimum erythemal dose (MED) is taken as 20 min (for a person with type II skin in New Jersey exposed to noonday sun), then a SPF 50 product would permit exposure to noonday sun for 1000 min (16.67 h). Where can one get this type of exposure? Certainly not in New Jersey! Although it is true that other latitudes do indeed yield much shorter MED times, an SPF of 50 would seldom, if ever, be required by most of the population at large. With this in mind, the FDA has limited the maximum that can be claimed to "30+." It is likely that when the monograph becomes the "law of the land" products making SPF claims beyond "30+" will be seized and forced off the market by the FDA.

Who is the target group? If it is persons with very sensitive skin then maybe "aminobenzoic acid (PABA) free" should be the approach of choice. The FDA feels that a PABA-free statement should not appear on the label. First, the drug name for PABA is aminobenzoic acid. Second, by making the statement that this product is PABA free you are implying that PABA is either unsafe, or is ineffective. Because it has been judged safe and effective by the FDA, they feel that such a statement should not be made. Although it is true that more people are sensitive to PABA than some of the other approved materials, the PABA-free statement implies a degree of safety that may not be present. With this in mind, the FDA will permit marketers to say "aminobenzoic acid (PABA) free." Certainly, there have been ample questions raised concerning the safety profile of several sunscreens including oxybenzone, yet in this country; there has been no major push to market products that are "oxybenzone free." From this situation one could conclude that marketers and raw material suppliers, at least occasionally, put economic considerations before technical and safety ones.

What is the cost of materials limitations? The sunscreen business, as with all mass merchandise efforts, is extremely sensitive to pricing. While the cost of the popular approved organic sunscreen active agents has dramatically dropped throughout the 1990s into 2003, their cost contribution to the overall formulation is still quite high compared with other typically employed cosmetic raw materials. This reflected in the high selling price of finished goods in this category. It is most notable because of the increasing popularity of high SPF products.

How important are water-resistant or very water-resistant claims? This claim is most important for those sunscreen products designed for use at the "beach." Consumers now expect the products they purchase, that have an SPF of 15 or higher to be very water resistant.

How will the formula be packaged? Because sunscreens are very good solvents, particular care must be paid to this factor. Use of low-density polyethylene should be avoided since the sunscreen will possibly collapse the package. Additionally, do not forget that often the sunscreens will be stored in a very warm environment such as the glove compartment of your car where the temperature may, for short time periods, exceed 50°C! With this in mind, be sure your package (and product) can stand up to this temperature extreme.

How important are esthetic considerations? Although sunscreens are drugs, the consumers who purchase them have become accustomed to elegant vehicles, such as those that deliver their cosmetics. If the sunscreen gives a greasy, occlusive feel, or leaves an opaque residue, then the purchaser will probably look elsewhere. In recent years, formulators have become more sophisticated, and successful, in developing products that are quite elegant and yet deliver a very high level of sunscreen protection. As dermatologists have found, the more the patient (or consumer) wants to use the product the greater the likelihood of "patient compliance."

FORMULA TYPES

Emulsions

By far the most popular of all vehicles used for sunscreens, the emulsion offers almost unlimited versatility. Lotions are more popular than creams owing to their easier spreadability on the skin and dispensability from bottles. An emulsion is termed a cream or lotion on the basis of its viscosity (resistance to flow). It is difficult to determine the exact point at which a lotion becomes a cream and, sometimes, the designation may be quite arbitrary. Lotions typically have viscosities <50,000 centipoise (cP) and will flow when the container is tilted or squeezed. The viscosity of creams can run into the millions of centipoises, but usually is in the 150,000–500,000 cP range. Although emulsions are the most popular vehicle, they are also the most difficult to stabilize. We will discuss methods of stabilizing emulsions later in this chapter. If the highest SPF possible, at the lowest possible cost, is the goal, then the emulsion vehicle must be strongly considered. To appreciate why emulsions are so effective one must understand the factors (1) that lead to consistently high SPFs:

Uniform sunscreen film
Thick sunscreen film
Nontransparent sunscreen film
Minimum ingredient interaction with the sunscreen's active agent.

In each of these important areas, emulsions exhibit good performance. Emulsions allow easy incorporation of sunscreen active agents, which are typically oils that can be readily emulsified. Emulsions can be prepared that contain a large percentage of water; thus, they can be, and are, a most cost-effective vehicle. From an esthetic viewpoint, emulsions are an elegant medium that can give the skin a smooth silky feel without being greasy. They can accommodate an almost infinite variety of raw materials; thus, you can tailor the formulation to suit your needs. On the negative side, emulsions are quite difficult to stabilize, particularly at elevated temperatures. Cosmetic emulsions are thermodynamically unstable (with the exception of spontaneously forming microemulsions). Thus, they will always eventually separate. Hopefully, the sunscreen emulsion will be purchased and used before the separation occurs! Additionally, emulsions present a perfect medium for microbial contamination and eventual product breakdown. As more and more consumers seek the protection of very high SPF products (30 and higher) that are water resistant or very water resistant, the cosmetic chemist finds it increasingly difficult to achieve these goals with an emulsion vehicle. Emulsions can be broadly placed into two categories: oil-in-water (O/W) and water-in-oil (W/O). By far, the O/W emulsions are more popular vehicles. This is, at first glance, a bit surprising since W/O emulsions are inherently better sunscreen vehicles. W/O emulsions are by their very nature very water resistant and they will consistently yield a higher SPF for the same concentration of sunscreen actives when compared to O/W emulsions. One explanation for this better sunscreen performance rests with the notion that since (most) sunscreens are soluble in the oil phase, in W/O emulsions the oil phase is continuous and thus when they are applied to the skin there is no need for agglomeration to occur (as there is with O/W emulsions) and so a very uniform sunscreen film results along with a high SPF. Additionally, W/O emulsifiers (low hydrophilic–lipophilic balance) do not have a "large head group" and thus they will not upset the lipid bilayer between the skin cells. Thus, they do not promote the penetration of sunscreens or other materials in the emulsion which may have a negative effect on the skin.

Another formula approach to consider is the use of emulsifiers that promote the formation of liquid crystals as emulsifiers. It has been known for many years that emulsions are often stabilized by liquid crystals. Generally, these liquid crystals are lamellar in structure and either form a gel network in the external phase or surround the oil droplets as layers (onion skin effect). In both cases the liquid crystals act as a barrier to coalescence (due to the high viscosity of the lamellar structure) and thus promote emulsion stability. This emulsion approach is a very good one for sunscreen formulators to consider for several reasons:

1. Emulsifiers that form liquid crystals are not very hydrophilic and thus do not promote sunscreen wash-off. Thus, they are excellent in formulations where water resistance is an important factor. It has been suggested that the lipophilic sunscreen migrates to a place between the fatty tails of the liquid crystal emulsifiers and thus can be delivered in a most uniform film to the skin surface. This insures a most efficient sunscreen system!

2. Liquid crystal emulsions are nonirritating. Since the skin lipids and skin cell membranes are of liquid crystalline structure, it is not surprising that emulsions that utilize these structures as a stabilization mechanism are less likely to upset the cell membranes or mobilize the interstitial lipids. With this in mind, emulsions based on liquid crystal emulsifiers will not upset the lipid bilayer and will not increase the trans epidermal water loss (TEWL). Additionally, they will not promote penetration of emulsion ingredients such as sunscreens (2).

As can be readily seen, emulsions present great opportunities for the creative, experienced formulators and great difficulties for the novice. Without doubt they will remain the vehicle of choice for the foreseeable future.

Oils

Oils are one of the oldest and most easily formulated sunscreen vehicles. There is only one phase, so excellent product stability is readily achievable. Because most sunscreen active agents are lipophilic, they are soluble in sunscreen oils; thus, manufacturing processes are greatly simplified (most can even be prepared at room temperature); certainly when compared with the manufacture of emulsions. Oils are easily applied to the skin, spreading rapidly to cover a wide surface area. Unfortunately, there are numerous negatives associated with sunscreen oils. Their excellent spreadability results in a very thin, transparent sunscreen film, and thus lowered SPF. Sunscreen oils exhibit the poorest SPF performance of any vehicle. This poor performance is further explained by the interaction between the most popular sunscreen (nonpolar esters) and the very nonpolar oils vehicles. Nonpolar oils, such as mineral oil, cause the position of the UV curves to shift to shorter wavelengths (3). Thus, part of the curve is moved into the area of wavelength <290 nm where it is wasted (from an erythemal perspective). The result is a poorer-performing sunscreen; that is, a lowered SPF rating (4). This shift to the shorter wavelengths is due to stabilization of the ground state by the nonpolar vehicle. Another factor to consider is the spreading ability of the emollients, which can play a major role in determining the SPF of the finished formula (5). Lastly, the solubility parameter (a measure of molecular stickiness/cohesiveness) will influence how the sunscreen is oriented within the oil (or oil phase of an emulsion) (6). An additional negative for oils relates to packaging. Sunscreen esters are excellent solvents. When they are combined with other esters in sunscreen oils, the resulting product can attack the plastic packaging typically used. Certainly, low-density polyethylene is a poor choice, unless expensive internal coatings are employed. Another obstacle to their use relates to cost of goods. Since this in an anhydrous system, there is no water to lower the cost of expensive raw materials. Sunscreen oils are one of the most expensive systems found.

Gels

The crystal clarity of cosmetic sunscreen gels projects an aura of purity and elegance. On initial consideration, they would seem to present, from an esthetic perspective, the ideal sunscreen vehicle. Unfortunately, this perception is quiet premature. There are four major formula categories of sunscreen gels: (1) aqueous, (2) hydro-alcoholic, (3) microemulsion, and (4) gelled oleaginous (oily anhydrous). All of these present the cosmetic formulator with an abundant supply of formulating difficulties.

The aqueous gel must use water-soluble sunscreens or employ solubilizers (usually nonionic surfactants), which may be ethoxylated fatty moieties or phosphate esters at sufficiently high levels to ensure that the gel will remain clear at all temperature extremes. Neither of these approaches provides good answers, for the resultant product is very prone to wash-off when exposed to water or perspiration. The high level of surfactant can often make the finished formula both expensive, and more importantly, quite irritating. Add to all of this the great batch-to-batch variation these gels exhibit, owing to the very delicate raw material balance required to achieve clarity. Manufacturing these gels presents a rather unique problem in itself. Aeration must be avoided, because deaeration can be time-consuming, expensive, and sometimes impossible. The gel formation is often accomplished through the incorporation of an appropriate "gum." Although cellulose-based materials can be used, they must be incorporated at very high levels (2–3%) to obtain the desired gel structure. At these use levels, they can be quite sticky on application. The carbomers, synthetic carboxyvinyl polymers, first introduced by the B. F. Goodrich Company (now Noveon), are by far the most popular thickeners used in this category, allowing the cosmetic formulator to achieve crystal clarity at reasonable use levels (0.5–1.0%). Unfortunately, the carbomers have compatibility, esthetic, and performance problems. Because they are anionic when neutralized, care must be taken not to include any cationic ingredients, as gel breakdown will probably result. The carbomers can impart a transient tackiness that is most evident during rubout. This is very apparent in gels for which use of emollient esters must be minimized or eliminated to ensure optimum clarity. In addition to these difficulties, the carbomers are quite sensitive to electrolytes found on the skin. Thus, when applied, the carbomer gel "breaks," and the product exhibits very poor application characteristics. This effect is exacerbated by swimming in salty water or by heavy sweating. Lastly, it is very difficult to obtain high SPFs in this vehicle because the clarity issue rules out the use of high levels of the best sunscreen active molecules, such as octinoxate, oxybenzone, or octocrylene. Many of the comments concerning the aqueous gel also apply to the hydro-alcoholic gel. A real benefit that is afforded by this vehicle is the desirable cooling effect as it is applied to the skin. This is particularly refreshing on a hot summer day. As its name implies, this gel employs the use of alcohol (usually ethanol) in conjunction with water (which frequently comes from the alcohol being used), as the main carrier components. The use of alcohol greatly reduces the need for additional solubilizers because most of the lipophilic sunscreens are readily miscible in ethanol. Some of the problems associated with the hydro-alcoholic gels are the following:

1. Water resistance: By incorporating resins and other film formers, water resistance can be improved, but the inherent nature of this vehicle limits its effectiveness.
2. Facial or eye sting: The high levels of alcohol tend to cause facial and eye stinging on certain individuals. Use of humectants can ameliorate this but not eliminate it entirely.
3. Packaging: The high volatility of alcohol gives it a great tendency to evaporate. This is most evident at high temperatures, such as those encountered at the beach in the summer. Packaging must use barrier coatings to retard this, which further increases costs. Closures should be tight-fitting and easily resealable.
4. Efficacy: It is in this key area that hydro-alcoholic gels exhibit their poorest performance. As mentioned earlier, to realize high SPFs, one must lay down a uniform sunscreen film on the skin. On exposure to heat and sunlight, the alcohol flashes off rapidly, leaving a porous or discontinuous film. Thus, there are areas where there is no coverage, and a lowered SPF is the result. Use of film formers can help, but in the end the level of sunscreen must be increased to overcome this effect; in reality, it is never completely conquered.

In microemulsion gels, the particle size is so small ($<0.25\ \mu m$) that light seems to pass right through the emulsion and a clear gel is the result. These gels can have an elegant skin feel and can lay down a smooth, thick, and uniform film on the skin, thus optimizing the SPF. Unfortunately, as with the previous gels, there are numerous negative factors to contend with:

1. Cost: To achieve clear microemulsions, it is necessary to employ very high levels of emulsifiers. Levels as high as 15–25% are not uncommon. This results in a very costly product.
2. Safety: In many emulsion systems the emulsifier is often one of the most irritating ingredients in the formula. At use these levels one must indeed be aware of this factor.
3. Water resistancy: The high emulsifier levels make the sunscreen easily removed by swimming or perspiring.
4. Manufacturing problems: Slight variations in raw materials can, and often do, lead to hazy or cloudy products. A slight change in the ethoxylation distribution may be all that is needed for disaster.

The microemulsion route is certainly a precarious one at best.

The oleaginous gels share many attributes with the ointments (addressed later), but they are clear, whereas the ointments are translucent or opaque.

There are no popular products of this type on the market, as they are difficult to manufacture and are quite expensive. They are generally produced by gelling a combination of mineral oil and sunscreen with fumed silica or other gellants.

Sticks

A relatively new form of sunscreen vehicle, the stick, brings with it a real convenience of usage. Sticks are mostly used on the lip or nose. Because they cover very small surface area on each application it is not practical to use them on large areas of the body. The vast majority of sticks are composed of oils and oil-soluble sunscreens, which in turn are thickened through the incorporation of waxes and petrolatum. They tend to have an oily or greasy skin feel and are probably the most water resistant of any product form. With the addition of a particulate sunscreen, such as titanium dioxide or zinc oxide, the resultant product is often seen on the noses of lifeguards—not very esthetic, but quite functional. Clear sticks can be made (using organic sunscreens), with the use of alkanolamides as gellants, but stability and cost considerations have not allowed marketing of these products. Recent work, modeled on the technology of antiperspirant sticks (W/O microemulsions), has led to some niche clear gel sunscreens, but the high cost of goods and difficult formulation issues will keep this a very minor entry.

Mousses

The sunscreen mousse was first introduced several years ago. It has not attained much consumer acceptance, and remains a niche product at best. A mousse is typically an emulsion lotion to which some propellant has been added. When the product is exposed to the lower pressure of the atmosphere (as compared with the inside of the container), the propellant flashes off and a foam is formed. These foams have more in common with shave creams than with other product types. Most use anionic (triethanolamine stearate) emulsifier systems, often coupled with a lesser amount of nonionic (ethoxylates). The sunscreen active agents can be readily incorporated into the internal phase of these O/W emulsions. They mimic most of the functional and esthetic characteristics of the non aerosol emulsions. Their primary functional reason for being lies in their ease of use. Great care must be taken to ensure that the cans are able to withstand the temperature extremes encountered at the beach that give rise to a significant increase in internal pressure and could potentially present a safety hazard. Nonaerosol mousses have begun to appear on the market. They employ a foaming surfactant and use high pressure (mechanical) to force the product through a mesh to produce the form. The highly hydrophilic surfactant will make it very difficult to keep this sunscreen from washing off.

Aerosols

The sunscreen aerosols have not enjoyed the same popularity as have the other sunscreen vehicles for several reasons. Typically, they are oil-based, which makes them rather expensive and often reduces their effectiveness (see foregoing discussion). Additionally, it is difficult to see where you have applied the sunscreen, and unless you are careful the sunscreen could be sprayed accidentally into the eyes. Aerosols also put down a discontinuous film onto the skin; this to, reduces their effectiveness. They can be either mechanical (pump spray) or propellant-base, at this time neither has made any significant market penetration.

Ointments

These oily products closely mirror the composition and function of the stick products. They are generally based on mineral oil and esters that have been thickened by the addition of petrolatum and some waxes. Their main benefit is that they are very difficult to remove with water; thus, they are used by people who must have a sunscreen that stays on the skin no matter how much swimming or physical activity is done. They are, however, not very esthetic to use because they are oily and greasy.

FORMULATING BASICS

Because the vast majority of all sunscreen products are creams or lotions, it is important to understand the intricacies of formulating this most challenging product category.

Principles of Emulsification

Although it is clear that it is extraordinarily difficult to produce emulsions that meet the primary market objectives of efficacy, esthetics, and cost parameters. An ever-present, but underlying, requirement is product integrity; or stated another way: emulsion stability. At times it may seem that obtaining emulsion stability is quite an elusive goal, in fact, perhaps unattainable. But by understanding underlying principles of emulsification, coupled with a healthy mix of experience gained through many failures, we can make real inroads in this quest.

Even though emulsions come in two basic varieties, O/W and W/O, and two basic "styles," creams and lotions, the ideas presented in this chapter are quite universal; thus, they can be successfully applied to all.

It is good to start with a healthy appreciation for the problem at hand; improving emulsion stability. That which you are trying to do (make a stable emulsion) is quite impossible (from a thermodynamic viewpoint) (7). An emulsion is a dispersion (the internal phase) of one immiscible liquid in another (the external phase) in the form of tiny droplets. These droplets are constantly trying to come back together, coalesce, to form a single large droplet phase. This is the continuing battle of the cosmetic formulator against the laws of thermodynamics. Can the battle ever be won, or is the only hope to put off the inevitable for a long enough period to successfully market the product? Sometimes this emulsion breakdown can be put off for several years. Some very viscous creams have remained "stable" for more than 10 years through rather harsh temperature fluctuations. The basic goal of all cosmetic chemists who formulate emulsions must be to prevent, or more realistically, minimize particle interaction. If this can be accomplished, the formulator is well along the road to success. There is an equation that describes this interaction: Stokes law (8)

$$V = \frac{[d^2(p_1 - p_2)g]}{18\eta}$$

where V is the velocity of sedimentation (interaction) of spherical particles, d is the diameter of the particles of the dispersed phase, p_1 is the specific gravity of the dispersed (internal) phase, p_2 is the specific gravity of the continuous (external) phase, g is the acceleration due to gravity, and η is the viscosity of the external phase.

After studying this simple equation it becomes apparent that our goal is to minimize the value of V, the velocity of sedimentation (coalescence). This can be done in only two ways.

1. Reduce the value of the numerator
2. Increase the value of the denominator.

Let us first deal with the numerator, d: reducing the size of the dispersed droplets is indeed a very good approach that may be accomplished in several ways. Choice and level of emulsifier (see discussion later) is certainly of primary importance. Choice of optimum manufacturing procedure is also most important. Generally, it is advisable to add the external phase to the internal phase. In this way, the emulsion can go through a definite phase inversion. This occurs because of the predominance of the internal phase relative to the external phase. The phase volume ratio does not permit the formation of the expected emulsion type. As more of the external phase is added, the phase volume ratio permits the formation of the predicted emulsion type and, thus, a phase inversion is seen. The result will be a reduced particle size and, just as important, a narrow distribution of particle sizes. Unfortunately, this type of phasing is seldom available during production, as usually the phase volume ratio between the internal and external phases is such that there is not enough internal phase to reach the mixing blade; thus, one cannot use this method. The particle size can also be reduced by employing the method of Lin (9). An emulsion concentrate is formed, composed of all of the internal phase (oil, emulsifier, sunscreen, and other components) and a part (approximately 30%) of the external phase (water, emulsifier, or such). The water phase can be added to the oil phase to go through a phase inversion. The percentage of emulsifier is higher in the concentrate than it will be after all of the water is added; thus, you have effectively increased the level of emulsifier, without adding more emulsifier. Very often a smaller particle size will be the result. The remainder of the water (at room temperature) can be added to the emulsion concentrate. It will cool the emulsion and dilute the external phase. This addition of water will not have a detrimental effect on the particle size. Lin's technique can dramatically reduce production cost and produce better emulsions.

The particle size can also be reduced through mechanical means. If the finished emulsion is subjected to high shearing forces, the large particles will be reduced in size. Numerous devices have been designed to accomplish this feat, which are categorized broadly as homogenizers or (colloid) mills. Although they often do an excellent job in reducing the particle size, great care must be taken with their use, as they can degrade certain emulsion components, such as gums, with their high shear. Another benefit of using homogenizers is that they give a more uniform particle size distribution. Very often this is even more important than reducing the average particle size. If the range of particle size is quite narrow, there will be lower probability of coalescence when two particles of similar masses collide, as the collisions tend to be more elastic (less transfer of energy) under these conditions. Thus, the emulsion will exhibit better stability. Another way to decrease the numerator is to make the factor $(p_1 - p_2)$ as small as possible. In other words, make the specific gravities of the internal and external phases as close as possible to each other. Since the external phase primarily composed of water (O/W emulsion) the *specific gravity* (SG) (ratio of the density of a substance relative to the density of water) (10) is approximately 1. The internal phase is mostly composed of oil, which has an SG of 0.80–0.95. Therefore, to make these two phases close to each other in density we must either lower the SG of the water phase. The obvious way to accomplish this is by adding alcohol to the water phase. At first glance this seems to work quite well. But the emulsion rapidly breaks down because of the alcohol's excellent solvency with various emulsifiers; hence, because of partition coefficient considerations, it extracts the emulsifier from the oil–water interface and the emulsion breaks. Adding alcohol to the water phase is thus not a worthwhile approach.

The last factor in the numerator is g, the acceleration due to gravity. This cannot be altered by even the most creative cosmetic chemist.

The denominator has only one factor that we can work with, η (the viscosity of the external phase). If we could increase this, it would decrease (velocity of sedimentation coalescence), and a more stable emulsion would be the result. Here, we have the most often used technique (successfully) by cosmetic chemists. There are many ways to increase the viscosity of the external phase.

1. Add more internal phase: This can effectively be used in both O/W and W/O emulsions. It will certainly increase the viscosity of the emulsion at room temperature, but at elevated temperatures, the emulsion will thin out and instability may very well result.

2. Reduce the particle size, so that the same amount of internal phase will seem to occupy a greater volume, and the viscosity will increase.
3. Add a fatty moiety to form liquid crystals in the external phase. The following phenomenon has been observed by many cosmetic chemists: When a small amount of fatty alcohol is added to an O/W emulsion the viscosity is seen to dramatically increase. According to Suzuki et al. (11) "The self-bodying action of fatty alcohols was caused by the formation of a network structure of liquid crystalline phase in the emulsion system." In addition, the fatty alcohol will complex with emulsifiers at the O/W interface to strengthen it and improve emulsion stability.
4. Add a thickener ("gum") to the external phase. Indeed this is a simple and very effective approach. There are a bewildering number of gums available to serve this purpose. Cellulosics are often used and can be very successful. Unfortunately, they do not improve the high-temperature stability to any great extent. There are several gums that can do this: the carbomers and xanthan are the most popular. Both of these allow the emulsion to retain a real measure of viscosity at elevated temperatures. Consequently, the emulsion is much less likely to show signs of instability. One must, however, be careful to only use these last two thickeners in nonionic (the emulsifiers are unchanged) systems because they are anionic in character themselves.

Selecting Key Ingredients

To formulate successfully you must have a thorough understanding of the principles and rules by which we choose the appropriate ingredients for each formula. Nowhere is this truer than in the formulation of sunscreen emulsions, which are drug vehicles. One must appreciate the potential for ingredient interaction and keep in mind the formula requirements laid down by the various interested internal groups: marketing, R&D, packaging, claim substantiation, and safety. Certainly, all ingredients selected must be cosmetically acceptable (color, odor, skin feel, have good safety parameters, be stable to chemical and UV exposure, and must not interfere with the efficacy of the sunscreen active agent in any way. The following are some comments on how to select ingredients with these thoughts in mind.

Emulsifiers

The oldest and most widely used method of selecting emulsifiers is the hydrophilic–lipophilic balance (HLB) system. This system, invented by Griffin (12) in 1949, was the first attempt to put a scientific basis behind the choosing of emulsifiers. The HLB was determined for each emulsifier: that is, the relative percentage by weight of the molecule that is water-loving vs. the oil-loving part. If a greater weight percentage was water-loving, the emulsifier would be assigned a high

HLB number and this would be judged to be an O/W emulsifier. The oil phase components are assigned a required HLB; thus, by choosing emulsifiers that match the HLB requirements of our oil phase, a fairly good emulsion can be formed. Experience has shown that this system works better for nonionic than for ionic emulsifiers. Although the HLB system has great usefulness for choosing a starting point for emulsions, there are several major concerns about the use of this system that must be addressed.

Temperature effect on nonionics (ethoxylates): As the temperature increases, the apparent HLB of emulsifiers decreases. Because ethoxylates (emulsifiers that employ ethylene oxide to increase their polarity and, hence, water solubility) are soluble as a consequence of hydrogen bonding to water, they become less soluble as increased kinetic energy (heat) causes a breakage in the hydrogen bonds. This is often referred to as the inverse solubility of nonionics. As the temperature increases they become less soluble. This is not what we typically see dealing with chemicals. Thus, an emulsifier that orients toward O/W emulsions at one temperature may indeed orient toward W/O at some higher temperature. The temperature at manufacture will play a significant role in the quality (type and particle size) of the emulsion. This is one of the reasons that many nonionic emulsions are not so easily scaled-up from the bench top to the 5000 gal kettle.

Ingredient interaction: Anionic and cationic emulsifiers will interact to produce a precipitate and break the emulsion, but the HLB system does not take this into account.

Fatty alcohol: According to the HLB system fatty alcohols are oils that have a required HLB. However, experience has shown us that indeed fatty alcohols are effective emulsion stabilizers and can be considered to be secondary emulsifiers.

Phase/volume relations: The HLB system ignores the relative sizes of the internal and external phases. As we know, this factor can and does have a profound effect on the emulsion. Yet, while all of these drawbacks to the HLB system exist, it should not be abandoned by cosmetic chemists. Rather, it should be used in conjunction with sound experience and other systems to choose emulsifiers.

The phase inversion method of choosing emulsifiers was proposed by Shinoda (13). This system takes into account many of the drawbacks of the HLB system, yet its underlying principles are closely linked to it. The inverse solubility phenomenon can be used to choose emulsifiers. After the oil and water phases have been combined, the cooling process begins. During this cooling, the effective HLB of the emulsifiers becomes higher. There is a temperature, the phase inversion temperature (PIT), at which the hydrophilic and lipophilic tendencies of the emulsifiers balance. At this temperature, a phase inversion can be observed as a dramatic change in viscosity. Additionally, one can notice a stable pH below the PIT. If the PIT is at least 20°C above the highest storage temperature, you can be fairly confident that the emulsion will be a stable one. You thus choose the level and type of emulsifier to achieve this PIT temperature.

Lin et al. (14) have proposed a rather unique method of selecting emulsifiers. All of the oil phase components are combined (esters, waxes, emulsifiers, sunscreens) and heated until liquid. Then water is slowly added (titrated in) while stirring. As the first drop of water hits the oil mixture, turbidity is formed that slowly disappears. According to Lin et al. the more water that can be solubilized into the oil phase, the smaller the emulsion droplets; hence, the better the emulsion will be. You can modify the emulsifier types and concentrations to increase the water solubilization capacity of the oil phase. There is ample experience to show that this method does indeed work. There is an inverse correlation between the amount of water soluble in the oil phase and the particle size of the final emulsion.

Up to this point, I have addressed mainly nonionic emulsifiers. Perhaps the most widely used emulsifier is, however, anionic: soap; to be specific, triethanolamine (TEA) stearate. This emulsifier, prepared *in situ*, is one of the most powerful and inexpensive of the O/W emulsifiers known. This accounts for its unmatched popularity. Other monovalent soaps can be used (sodium and potassium), but the interfacial film they form is not as flexible as that of TEA stearate. Emulsion stability will be further enhanced if combinations of emulsifiers are employed. Thus, use of several types of emulsifiers (anionic and nonionic) is recommended. The variety of emulsifiers is almost unlimited; by using one or more of the foregoing systems you can minimize the trial-and-error approach, and maximize your chances for success.

Emollients

Emollients represent one of the most important classes of emulsion components. Although there are both oil-soluble and water-soluble emollients, by far the oily materials predominate. They provide a silky skin feel on application, while acting as the vehicle in which the oil-soluble sunscreen is delivered. There are several categories of fatty emollients: esters (liquid and solid), waxes, fatty alcohols, mineral oils, and silicone materials.

Esters are a very widely used class of compounds in sunscreen emulsions. Quite simply, they are the condensation product of an alcohol and an acid. By varying the fatty moiety of each, an almost endless variety of esters can be produced, each with slightly different properties from the next. Some general rules can be made that should provide guidance in choosing the best ester for your requirements.

1. Chain length increase: As the chain length increases, the ester becomes more viscous, eventually becoming solid; it becomes more difficult to emulsify; it becomes less irritating to the skin; it acquires an oilier skin

feel and becomes less polar (this has an effect on the position of the UV curve that may influence the effectiveness of the sunscreen actives).

2. Branching: As the ester becomes more branched it produces a drier skin feel; it becomes less polar.
3. Unsaturation: As the ester becomes more unsaturated it becomes less polar; it becomes harder to emulsify; and it seems to disappear into the skin during rubout.
4. One area that should be considered when choosing an emollient for use in formulating a sunscreen product is the solubility of one or more of the sunscreens (i.e., oxybenzone, avobenzone) in the particular emollient system. Poor solubility will have an adverse affect on sunscreen performance and possibly product stability.

Waxes are not used to any great extent in sunscreen emulsions. Certainly, carnauba, ceresin, beeswax, and many others are available to us, but they tend to give a rather "draggy" feel to the skin and, thus, their use is held to a minimum.

Fatty alcohols provide a skin-smoothing during rubout, a matte, nongreasy feel that is quite desirable. They can, however, if used at too high a level (2% maximum), become "draggy" on the skin, certainly not a desirable feature. As would be expected, as the chain length increases the melting point increases. Thus, stearyl alcohol (18 carbon atoms) has a higher melting point than cetyl alcohol (16 carbon atoms) and has a slightly heavier feel on the skin.

Mineral oil is one of the main constituents of many emulsions. Its widespread use can be easily understood when one considers its low cost, broad chemical compatibility, and safety. There are several grades of viscosity to consider, depending on the skin feel and emulsion viscosity desired (minor effect). One must remember that mineral oil can have a rather oily skin feel, which can be reduced by combining it with esters. Because it is so nonpolar, it usually has a detrimental effect on the sunscreen efficacy.

Silicone-based "oils" have enjoyed an almost explosive increase in popularity in recent years. Dimethicone (polydimethylsiloxane) is the most widely used material of this type. It provides a smooth initial skin feel, reduces skin whitening (soaping), and minimizes tacky afterfeel. The cyclomethicones, also called volatile silicone, greatly improve initial skin feel without contributing to final greasiness. Questions have been raised regarding the safety of cyclomethicones in recent years and thus their popularity is diminishing. Additionally, use of volatile low molecular weight hydrocarbons and poly-alpha-olefins can effectively reduce sticky afterfeel.

Film Formers

In recent years, there has been a noticeable trend toward increased efficacy in sunscreen products. This could be manifested in a higher SPF or a product that maintains its SPF after exposure to water. Film formers play a key role in both of these endeavors. One of the primary factors that influence the ability of a sunscreen product to achieve a high SPF is the uniformity of the sunscreen film on the skin. It is absolutely crucial that this film be thick and uniform. Several materials have been used to develop this type of film. Cellulosic gums lay down a rather even film and can be readily incorporated into almost any emulsion. Polyvinylpyrrolidone (PVP) also serves this purpose. Unfortunately, none of these ingredients imparts any measure of water resistancy to the formulation. There are, fortunately, materials that can function as film formers that impart wash-off resistance. The two that are used most are based on acrylic–acrylate copolymer or PVP-hexadecene copolymer. Recently, polyethylene has also been used. This material can act to increase the film thickness and additionally can improve both the SPF and the water resistancy.

Stabilizers/Protectants

Emulsions are very delicate and are subject to attack from many directions. If any of these attacks are successful, the emulsion will exhibit instability and will not be sellable. We have previously discussed the thickeners (gums) as stabilizers and will not do so again. Antioxidants represent a most useful and functional class of materials. When oil-phase components are used that are unsaturated (contain one or more double bonds), it is advisable to employ an antioxidant to prevent oxidation of the double bond, with its associated rancidity and discoloration. BHA, BHT, propyl gallate, and tocopheryl (acetate) are frequently used. Antioxidants can also act as free radical scavengers and, thereby, reduce chances of skin damage by these highly reactive moieties. It has been suggested that use of antioxidants can actually increase the SPF. It is likely that this effect is due to a reduction in erythema, rather than any increase in UV absorbance. Chelating agents find use in many cosmetic formulations, ranging from emulsions to hair products (shampoos). They can improve the preservative efficacy of conventional preservatives and can tie up unwanted metal ions that can cause discoloration and viscosity of the emulsion. Preservatives must be considered one of the most important parts of the emulsion. No emulsion is complete or safe without them. As with emulsifiers, they seem to work best when several are combined at the same time. The subject of preservation is so important and complex that the reader is urged to study it in some depth using the many excellent texts available. This is no area for the novice. Some suggestions that should be kept in mind when formulating emulsions include:

When using gums or proteins, enhance the preservative system. When using ethoxylated nonionic emulsifiers, paraben use levels should be increased (the *para-hydroxyl* group of the parabens can hydrogen bond to the ethylene oxide chains and thus effectively inhibit it from acting as a preservative).

Always place the preservative in the water phase (this is the phase that must be protected).

Organic Sunscreens

We are now ready to choose the primary functional ingredient in the sunscreen formulation—the sunscreen. At the present time (in the USA) our choice is limited to 16 sunscreen chemicals (15). Although the list of chemicals may seem to be extensive, in reality only very few are seen in finished products. Most of the materials have serious drawbacks associated with them.

Aminobenzoic acid: One of the oldest sunscreens, *p*-aminobenzoic acid, commonly known as PABA has many drawbacks. Its UV curve peaks at the low end of the UVB spectrum; it is too water-soluble (owing to high polarity at both ends of the molecule); a segment of the population exhibits some sensitivity to it; and it can stain clothing and skin.

Avobenzone (butylmethoxy dibenzoylmethane): A UVA absorber, this sunscreen has enjoyed wide usage in the European Union (EU), Australia, and Japan for a number of years. When approved by the FDA in its final monograph it began to see acceptance in the USA. Issues exist regarding its photostability and compatibility with commonly used cosmetic ingredients (formaldehyde donating preservatives and transition metals). It cannot be used (at the time of this writing) with either titanium dioxide or zinc oxide in sunscreen products in the USA. Additionally, there are several sunscreen combinations that are not permitted when using avobenzone (see Final Sunscreen Monograph) such as ensulizole. Avobenzone is sold as an off-white crystalline powder that must be solubilized into the oil phase of emulsion. Care must be taken to insure its complete solubility. A number of materials have been proposed for use with avobenzone to reduce the photo instability seen when used in many formulations. The reader is urged to fully explore this area since there are several patents issued (L'Oreal, P&G, C.P. Hall).

Oxybenzone and dioxybenzone: The best known of the UV-A absorbers (they are actually primarily UV-B absorbers with a slight peak in the short UV-A); they are seldom if ever used alone, but are combined with UV-B screens to give high SPFs. They have poor solubility and moderate extinction coefficients. The benzophenones are all ketones and thus can show discoloration when used in the presence of primary or secondary amines (Schiff base formation). Since they are *ortho* (and *para*) they do not exhibit a solvent shift often seen with the para disubstituted sunscreens.

Cinoxate: A UVB absorber that is no longer in use.

Octocrylene (2-ethylhexyl-2-cyano-3, 3 diphenylacrylate): This had not seen wide acceptance owing to its high cost, stickiness, off-yellow color, and moderate extinction coefficient. In recent years, however, its usage has dramatically increased. This is probably due to its ability to boost the SPF and also improve the water-resistancy of many formulations. It also has the ability to help stabilize avobenzone through triplet–triplet quenching (16).

Octisalate (octyl salicylate) and homosalate (homomenthyl salicylate): Both of these compounds have a long history of use. Both were supplanted by the more efficient PABA and cinnamate derivatives. With the trend toward high SPFs, a significant increase in the use of octyl salicylate has been observed. This has been accelerated by another marketing trend: PABA-free. Octyl salicylate, like all salicylates, is *ortho*-disubstituted and, thus, exhibits a rather low extinction coefficient. It has the ability to solubilize oxybenzone.

Octinoxate (octyl methoxycinnamate): This *para*-disubstituted sunscreen is, by far, the most popular sunscreen in the world. It is principally a UV-B absorber. Since it contains a conjugated double bond, its UV curve is broader than one would typically expect. Another consequence of the conjugated double bond is that this sunscreen can (and does) exist in two isomeric forms (*cis* and *trans*). As would be expected the *trans* form has a higher extinction coefficient and is the primary form. When used alone, SPFs of 6–8 can be achieved. It exhibits very strong absorbance in the middle of the UV-B range (310 nm) and has the attributes most sought after in a sunscreen chemical. It is not water soluble (will not wash off easily); will not stain the skin or clothing; are very safe, chemically inert, and UV stable; stay on the skin (minimal percutaneous absorption); have minimal odor; will not color the emulsion; and are relatively inexpensive. It seems like the ideal sunscreen and, in fact, it comes very close to that goal.

Padimate-O (octyldimethyl PABA): Padimate-O was for many years the most widely used sunscreen agent throughout the world. It has the highest extinction of any UV-B organic sunscreen filter permitted in the USA. Companies have moved away from it since "PABA free" has become a marketing approach, and thus it is now very rarely used.

Ensulizole (phenylbenzimidazole sulfonic acid): This material becomes water soluble when neutralized by an appropriate base (triethanolamine, NaOH, AMP, trisamino, or others). It has found use in clear gels owing to its water solubility. It also exhibits a very high efficiency. This is probably due to its ability to partition into the upper layers of the stratum corneum; thereby providing a very uniform film on the skin. Additionally, its high polarity does not allow it to be adversely affected by the nonpolar skin lipids. Some formulators have neutralized it with fatty amines and thus (to some extent) made it useful in water-resistant products. It has also been used in W/O emulsions where it resides in the internal phase and thus is somewhat resistant to wash-off.

Trolamine salicylate: A weak UV-B absorber, it has poor oil solubility (good water solubility).

Sulisobenzone: This sulfonated version of oxybenzone is water soluble and thus, is not used in water-resistant formulations. As with oxybenzone, it is a rather reactive molecule; thus, care must be taken when formulating with these materials from a stability and safety viewpoint.

Meradimate (menthyl anthranilate): This UV-A screen is not widely used because of its low absorptivity (*ortho*-disubstituted). This screen may see increased acceptance as the trend toward higher SPFs and UV-A claims continues. It should be combined with other screens to achieve this end.

Inorganic/Particulate Sunscreens

We should discuss how solid opaque (high index of refraction) particles like titanium dioxide and zinc oxide can be used in sunscreen formulations and still appear transparent on the skin. If a particle is one-fourth or less of the wavelength of light then it will be invisible. Let us assume the average wavelength of light is 600 nm. This means those particles 150 nm or less will be invisible. The average wavelength of UV radiation is 300 nm, thus particles between 75 nm (1/4 of 300 nm) and 150 nm will be invisible to visible light but scatter/block UV radiation. In reality, both titanium dioxide and zinc oxide are sold as microfine particles with an average primary particle size of less than 40 nm! This is because there is always some agglomeration and the size of the agglomerates must be less than 75 nm as discussed. When smaller particles are present in significant quantities we will often see the "blue/white" appearance seen on the skin during application of these products. Formulators sometimes incorporate colorants (iron oxide) or natural antioxidants (melanin) to mask this effect.

When incorporating these sunscreens into a formulation great care must be taken to insure that good dispersion has been achieved. Formulators are urged to predisperse the particulate into a portion of the oil phase (if the particulate has been treated with a hydrophobic coating, as they typically are) using high shear agitation. The dispersion should be checked for dispersion quality by using a Hegman gauge to check for large particles (agglomerates) and then by examining the dispersion under a light microscope at 200–400 magnification. There has been a movement away from the usage of particulate powders given the difficulty of adequately dispersing them and towards predispersed systems. Several companies now offer predispersed titanium dioxide and zinc oxide in various "oils" such as C12–15 alkyl benzoate, caprylic/capric triglygerides, ethylhexyl palmitate, cyclomethicone, poly-alpha-olefins, etc. Often a dispersing agent is employed to minimize dispersion and reagglomeration. Phosphate esters have been widely used for this purpose.

Another factor to consider when using particulates is suspension! The relatively high SG of these materials will cause them to fall out of suspension. This is most evident at elevated temperature conditions (40°C and higher) when most emulsions thin out. With this in mind it is strongly suggested that the formulator employ a suspension aid. When using titanium dioxide the choice is quite wide since it is very compatible with practically all thickeners/suspension aids. Use of carbomer, xanthan gum, sodium polyacrylates, and many other materials is commonly seen. However, when using zinc oxide the choice is much narrower due to the solubility (even though small) of zinc ion in water. The polyvalent zinc will react with the acrylic acid in carbomer and all suspension will be lost! A similar thing is seen when using zinc oxide with fatty acids. Polyvalent soaps are W/O emulsifiers and thus zinc stearate (or laurate) will destabilize O/W emulsions. It is suggested that the reader consider using W/O emulsions when employing particulate sunscreens. When the consumer applies a W/O sunscreen and goes swimming (or perspires) no rewhitening is observed. Quite the opposite is seen with particulate based O/W emulsions. Another consideration using particulates is to combine them with organics into what is referred to as a hybrid system. In this case the consumer gets the best of all worlds! The organics provide excellent UV absorbance and the SPF is dramatically boosted through the UV absorption and increase in optical path length afforded by the particulates.

Titanium dioxide: This physical blocker had not gained acceptance for many years owing to its poor esthetics (skin whitening). Usage has skyrocketed with the appearance of microfine grades of this material that substantially address this problem. Additionally, titanium dioxide comes in two crystalline varieties (anatase and rutile). While both have UV blocking/absorption abilities, the use of rutile is preferred since it is far more photostable. If too much anatase titanium dioxide is present, then a graying will be noticed upon exposure to UV radiation.

Zinc oxide: This material has been used for many years in both cosmetic and toiletry products. It was not on the original list of 21 sunscreens approved by the FDA. With the publication of the TFM it was placed into category III (needs more data). Data submitted to the FDA illustrating its efficacy caused the agency to move it into Category I status with the publication of the final monograph. It now enjoys wide usage. The reader is urged to review the patent literature when using this material for sunscreen applications, since patents have been issued dealing with particle size and surface coatings.

Fragrances

The choice of a proper fragrance can enhance the esthetics of any sunscreen product. Because these materials can be quite irritating, their use level must be kept as low as possible. A typical use level is 0.2–0.4%. Additionally, their breakdown products can be photosensitizers; hence, great care must be taken in choosing them (the reader is referred to the chapter on fragrancing of sunscreens).

ACHIEVING FORMULA GOALS

To Achieve High SPFs

a. Avoid "bad" ingredients. Use of ethanol at high levels can reduce the SPF of the finished formulation. It is likely that ethanol (very volatile) flashes off and leaves a porous film on the skin. This discontinuous (17) film is not conducive to high SPFs. The use of very nonpolar materials, such as mineral oil, petrolatum, and highly branched esters, results in a shift of the λ_{max} (wavelength of maximum absorption), of nonpolar sunscreens, to a shorter wavelength. This is very detrimental to the efficiency of these sunscreens.

b. Use the correct vehicle. Emulsions in general, and creams in particular, can achieve the highest SPFs attainable. They put down a very uniform film on the skin. This is most true with W/O emulsions.
c. Combine sunscreens. Use sunscreens that absorb into the short UVB area (320–340 nm), as well as sunscreens that show good absorbance in the erythemal range (290–320 nm). Although these wavelengths are much less effective at producing erythema than the 290–320 nm wavelengths, they must be blocked *if* very high SPFs are to be realized.
d. Obtain uniform film on skin: use *of* film formers (see foregoing) can optimize the SPF.

To Achieve Water Resistance

a. Use water-resistant sunscreens (18).
b. Use high-level oil phases in O/W emulsions.
c. Use water-resistant resins.
d. Use minimum levels *of* hydrophilic emulsifiers. This will minimize the reemulsification of films left on the skin when exposed to water.
e. Have the O/W emulsion break on the skin during rubout. This leaves an oily (water-resistant) film on the skin. This can be accomplished by making an O/W emulsion using weak O/W emulsifiers and add in low levels of W/O emulsifiers. As the emulsion is rubbed onto the skin and water begins to evaporate, the phase volume ratio now favors a W/O emulsion. Given the presence of W/O emulsifiers, the emulsion now inverts. The sunscreens are now in the continuous external phase and a high SPF results with excellent water resistancy!
f. Use W/O emulsions.
g. Use liquid crystal based emulsions.

To Obtain Mild Formulations

a. Use minimum emulsifier levels, particularly soaps.
b. Minimize use of fragrances.
c. Minimize use of preservatives, making sure, however, to use adequate levels.
d. Use the minimum level of sunscreen to achieve the target SPF.

e. Use long-chain esters, which are less irritating than their short-chain analogs.

Patent Issues

Before selecting the sunscreens to be used it would be advisable to understand the patent environment. As of this writing there are several patents that have been issued that involve the use of combinations of sunscreens in particular the use of avobenzone with octocrylene for the purposes of stabilizing avobenzone/octinoxate combinations (19,20).

Stability Evaluation

The stability evaluation of sunscreen products is not unlike that required for other cosmetic or toiletry products. The finished formulation, in the production package, must be subjected to both high- and low-temperature extremes. A typical minimal program should include the following:

25°C for 6 months
37°C for 3 months
45°C for 2 months
50°C for 1 month
4°C for 6 months
−20°C for 6 months
Freeze–thaw (45°–25°C) for five cycles
UV exposure
High-humidity exposure.

The following parameters must be monitored:

Particle size and distribution (for emulsions)
Color
Odor
Preservative efficacy
Weight loss
Viscosity
pH
UV profile (curve)
Closure torque.

While it is generally believed that storage at 45°C for 90 days will predict room temperature storage for 2 years, many times this is not the case. This is most often seen with W/O emulsions where, typically we observe better high-temperature stability than that seen at room temperature! When using particulates (titanium dioxide and zinc oxide) it is suggested that the formulator subject the formula to centrifuge testing (3000 rpm and 60°C for 15 min) to insure that adequate suspension has been achieved.

Organoleptic Considerations

Although consumers purchase sunscreen products for protection from the damaging rays of the sun, they will not buy them a second time if they do not possess the cosmetic attributes they have come to expect from all toiletries. Use of fragrance to provide a pleasant note on application and hide the unpleasant odor of some needed ingredient is a must. Use of silicones or other emollients will reduce the dragginess on rub out often found in high glyceryl monostearate (GMS), stearic acid, or fatty alcohol-containing emulsions. The formulation should exhibit easy spreadability on the skin, without any dragginess. When particulate materials (TiO_2 and zinc oxide) are used, great care must be taken to ensure that minimum skin whitening is seen. Additionally, these formulations have a tendency to rewhiten when one goes into the water or sweats profusely. The cosmetic chemist's assignment is not complete until the formula for efficacy, safety, stability, and last, but not least, organoleptic considerations is optimized. A successful formula has all of these areas addressed.

The Use of Antioxidants in Sunscreen Formulations

As was mentioned previously, antioxidants are frequently used in formulations to help protect product integrity and can help reduce skin damage. In addition to these erythemal effects of excessive, unprotected UV exposure there is also evidence that there is oxidative damage that may result in DNA damage, immunological responses and the possibility of potentiating UV carcinogenesis (21). As a result there is much interest in using antioxidants in sunscreen formulations. These antioxidants can be vitamins, botanicals, or synthetic materials and there has been much published information about the use of antioxidants in topical formulations (22,23) and there have been patents issued that cover the use of antioxidant ingredients, that is, green tea (24).

The use of antioxidants in combination with sunscreens is not currently regulated any more than the use of any other non-OTC regulated ingredient by the FDA. It is, however, an area of interest to regulatory agencies in the USA and other major markets. Their use currently falls under the area of "cosmetic" claims.

FORMULATIONS

Following is a compilation of formulations that serves to illustrate the diversity of formula types currently available in the marketplace. By no means, is this collection of formulations complete; but it is representative of the state of art and science (as of this moment).

Formula type: Cream
Comments: Emollient skin feel
Expected SPF: 45

Ingredients	%w/w
Phase A	
Octocrylene	8.0
Oxybenzone	4.0
Octinoxate	7.5
Cyclomethicone	10.0
Glyceryl stearate SE	5.0
Phenyldimethicone	2.0
Cetearyl alcohol (and) ceteareth-20	2.0
Cetyl alcohol	1.0
Ethylhexyl palmitate	10.0
Phase B	
Water	qs
Preservative	qs
Glycerin	5.0
Titanium dioxide (water dispersible, hydrophilic coating)	5.0
Xanthan gum	0.2
Hydroxyethylcellulose	0.1
Phase C	
Fragrance	0.3

Comments: This O/W emulsion uses three organic sunscreens in combination with titanium dioxide to achieve a very high SPF. Xanthan gum is used to suspend the titanium dioxide. Note the use of ethylhexyl palmitate to assist in solubilizing the oxybenzone. This formula would not be water resistant due to the inclusion of the rather hydrophilic emulsifiers (glyceryl stearate SE, cetearyl alcohol, and ceteareth-20). If we wanted to make this more water resistant we might consider incorporating a good film forming resin as well as reducing the concentration of the emulsifiers.

Formula type: Daily use lotion
Comments: Inexpensive lotion with outstanding high-temperature stability
Expected SPF: 8

Ingredients	%w/w
Phase A	
Octinoxate	6.0
Oxybenzone	2.0
Stearic acid XXX (triple pressed)	4.0
Isopropyl Palmitate	7.5
Myreth-3 myristate	4.0
Glyceryl dilaurate	1.5

Ingredients	%w/w
Phase B	
Water	qs
Preservative	qs
Carbomer 1342	0.2
Propylene glycol	2.5
Phase C	
Triethanolamine 99%	0.7
Phase D	
Fragrance	0.3

Comments: This light lotion is designed to be used under make up without being greasy/oily. Note the use of glyceryl dilaurate to make this inexpensive lotion feel much richer with more cushion.

Formula type: Cationic lotion
Comments: Cationic lotion offers excellent skin feel
Expected SPF: 4–6

Ingredients	%w/w
Phase A	
Glycol stearate	5.0
C12–15 alcohol benzoate	3.5
Octinoxate	5.0
PEG-40 stearate	1.5
Phase B	
Water	
Preservative	qs
Stearamidopropyl PG-dimonium chloride	qs
Phosphate	3.5
Glycerin	4.0
Phase C	
Fragrance	0.3

Comments: Cationic lotions are substantive to the skin and provide wonderful skin feel! The cationic emulsifier used here is stearamidopropyl PG-dimonium chloride. We have added an nonionic emulsifier (PEG-40 stearate) to insure good stability with a small uniform particle size.

Formula type: Water-resistant lotion
Expected SPF: 15

Ingredients	%w/w
Phase A	
Mineral oil	5.0
Sorbitan sesquioleate	1.0
Octinoxate	7.5

Ingredients	%w/w
Oxybenzone	4.0
Octyl salicylate	3.0
Laureth-23	1.0
Stearic acid XXX (triple pressed)	2.0
PVP/eicosene copolymer	2.5
Phase B	
Water	qs
Sorbitol 70%	5.0
Acrylates C10–30 alkyl acrylates cross polymer	0.2
Preservative	qs
Phase C	
Triethanolamine 99%	0.3
Phase D	
Fragrance	0.5

Comments: This lotion uses very low emulsifier level to insure that this sunscreen will be very water resistant. Additionally, we have added a low HLB emulsifier (sorbitan sesquioleate) to counteract any high HLB emulsifier left behind on the skin further inhibit washoff. Lastly, note the inclusion of a film former (PVP/Eicosene copolymer) to thicken the sunscreen film on the skin and improve water resistancy.

Formula type: Sunscreen oil
Expected SPF: 4–6

Ingredients	%w/w
Octisalate	5.0
Meradimate	3.5
Jojoba oil	2.0
Cocoa butter solid	2.0
Isocetyl alcohol	15.0
Fragrance	1.0
Octyl palmitate	qs
Vitamin E acetate	0.1
Mineral oil	40.0

Comments: Meradimate provides absorbance into the short UVA in this simple sunscreen oil. Isocetyl alcohol acts as an emollient and as a coupling agent to insure excellent compatibility of the materials with varying polarities.

Formula type: Sunscreen cream (very water resistant)
Expected SPF: 30+

Ingredients	%w/w
Phase A	
Water	27.65

Ingredients	%w/w
Xanthan gum	0.3
Propylene glycol	2.0
Phase B	
Octinoxate	7.50
Dihydroxycetyl phosphate	1.50
Cyclomethicone	1.00
Tridecyl neopentanoate	7.50
Octisalate	5.00
Cetearyl alcohol	2.00
Octocrylene	10.00
Tocopheryl acetate	0.25
Ceteareth-20	0.50
Tricontanyl PVP	3.00
Phase C	
Zinc oxide (microfine)	7.00
Phase D	
Preservative	1.00

Comments: A sunscreen cream that provides a very high level of SPF protection! The combination of the particulate zinc oxide with the organics (octinoxate, octisalate, and octocrylene) gives broad spectrum UV absorbance. Tricontanyl PVP improves water resistancy. The emulsifier level is quite low and this too improves water resistancy. During manufacture the zinc oxide should be added to the oil phase (phase B) using high shear to insure good dispersion and reduce agglomeration.

Formula Type: W/O cream
Expected SPF: 25+

Ingredient	%w/w
Water (aqua), deionized	qs
Preservative	qs
Disodium EDTA	0.05
NaCl	1.00
PEG-30 dipolyhydroxystearate	3.00
Cyclomethicone (pentamer)	10.00
Zinc oxide (microfine)	7.00
Titanium dioxide (microfine)	7.00
Ethylhexyl palmitate	5.00
Octyldodecanol	4.00
Hydrogenated castor oil	0.75
Polyethylene	2.00

Comments: This W/O cream uses PEG-30 dipolyhydroxystearate as the W/O emulsifier. We use NaCl to enhance the stability of this cream. Hydrogenated castor oil and polyethylene act as external phase thickeners to further improve high temperature stability. This cream would exhibit excellent broad spectrum absorbance!

Formula Type: Lip balm
Expected SPF: 25+

Ingredient	%w/w
Octinoxate	7.50
Oxybenzone	5.00
Octisalate	4.00
Zinc oxide (micronized)	7.50
Castor (*Ricinus communis*) oil	qs
Octyldodecanol	10.00
Beeswax (cera alba)	6.00
Ozokerite	4.00
Candililla (euphorbia cerifera) wax	6.00
Myristyl lactate	4.00
Petrolatum	5.00

Comments: This lip balm provides excellent protection. Octyldodecanol improves spreadability and dispersion of the zinc oxide. Thus we do not get the white residue often seen with products of this type.

Formula Type: Lotion with UV-B/UV-A absorbers
Expected SPF: 20

Ingredient	%w/w
Water (aqua), deionized	qs 100.00
Disodium EDTA	0.05
Methylpropanediol	2.00
Carbomer	0.20
Ethylhexyl naphthalate	8.00
Dihydroxycetyl phosphate	1.25
Octinoxate	7.50
Oxybenzone	5.00
Avobenzone	3.00
Cetearyl alcohol (and) ceteareth-20	0.50
PVP/eicosene copolymer	2.00
NaOH, 10% soln	2.50
Phenoxyethanol (and) methylparaben (and) propylparaben	1.00

Comments: This O/W lotion provides excellent broad spectrum performance. The oxybenzone helps to stabilize the avobenzone in the presence of octinoxate. Ethylhexyl naphthalate also improves the photostability of this lotion. We have taken care not to employ a preservative that may liberate formaldehyde which would play havoc with the avobenzone. Additionally, we use disodium EDTA to insure that no excess metals are available to react with avobenzone.

Formula type: Water-resistant spray
Expected SPF: 15+

Ingredient	%w/w
Water (aqua), deionized	qs 100.00
Disodium EDTA	0.1
Methylpropanediol	2.50
Acrylates C10–30 alkyl acrylates crosspolymer	0.25
Octinoxate	7.5
Octisalate	5.0
Oxybenzone	2.0
Castor isostearate succinate (and) PEG-8 ricinoleate	1.5
Castor isostearate beeswax succinate	2.5
Triethanolamine (99%)	0.20
Phenoxyethanol (and) methylparaben (and) propylparaben	1.00

Comments: This O/W spray is very water resistant and has elegant skin feel. The primary emulsion stabilizer is acrylates C10–30 alkyl acrylates crosspolymer neutralized by the triethanolamine. Castor isostearate succinate (and) PEG-8 ricinoleate improve film spreadability and reduce oiliness.

REFERENCES

1. Stockdale M. Sun protection factor. Int J Cosmet Sci 1985; 7:235–246.
2. Gao T, Tien J, Choi Y. Sunscreen formulas with multilayer lamella structure 2003; 118(October):41–52.
3. Agrapidis-Paloympis L, Nash RA, Shaath N. The effects of solvents on the ultraviolet absorbance of sunscreens. J Soc Cosmet Chem 1987; 38(July/Aug):209–221.
4. Klein K, Doshi I. Sunscreen solvent interactions: an in-vitro evaluation. 14th IFSCC Congress, Barcelona, Spain, Sep 1986.
5. Dahms G. Choosing emollients and emulsifiers for sunscreen products. Cosmet Toilet 1994; 109(11):45–52.
6. Vaughan CD. Using solubility parameters in cosmetic formulation. J Soc Cosmet Chem 1985; 36(5):319–333.
7. Klein K. Improving emulsion stability. J Cosmet Toilet 1984; 99(March):121–126.
8. Stokes GG. Philos Mag 1851; 1:337.
9. Lin TJ. Low energy emulsification, principles and applications. J Cosmet Chem 1978; 29(March):117–125.
10. Martin A, et al. Phys Pharm 1969; 2:4–5.
11. Suzuki T, Tsumi H, Ishida A. Secondary droplet emulsion: Mechanism and effects of liquid crystal formation in o/w emulsions. Dispers Sci Technol 1984; 5(2):119–141.
12. Griffin WC. Classification of surface active agents by "HLB." J Soc Cosmet Chem 1940; 1:311–326.

13. Shinoda K. Comparison between phase inversion system and the hydrophilic lipophilic balance value system for emulsifier selection. Nippon Kagaku Zashi 1968; 89:1–8.
14. Lin TJ, et al. Prediction of optimum o/w emulsification via solubilization measurements. J Soc Cosmet Chem 1977; 28(August):457–479.
15. Docket No. 78N-0038, Sunscreen Drug Products for over the counter human use; final monograph, 21CFR Parts 310, 352, 700 and 740, May 21, 1999; 64:98.
16. Bonda C. Avobenzone Photostability in Simple Polar and Non-Polar Solvent Systems. C.P Hall Publication.
17. Eierman H. US Patent 3,342,419, 1967.
18. Formulating vehicles for sunscreens. Norda Shimmel Briefs, 935, Feb. 1966.
19. Tanner, et al. US Patent 5,935,556, August 10, 1999.
20. Kaplan. US Patent 6,048,517, August 11, 2000
21. Ichihashi M, et al. UV-induced skin damage. Toxicology 2003; 189(1–2):21–39
22. Vayalil PK, Elmets CA, Katiyar SK. Treatment of green tea polyphenols in hydrophilic cream prevents UVB-induced oxidation of lipids and proteins. Carcinogenesis 2003; 24(5):927–936.
23. Afaq F, Adhami VM, Ahmad N. Prevention of short-term ultraviolet B radiation-mediated damage by resveratrol in SKH-1 hairless mouse. Toxicol Appl Pharmacol 2003; 186(1):28–37.
24. McCook, et al. US Patent 5,306,486, April 26, 1994.

19

SPF Modulation: Optimizing the Efficacy of Sunscreens

Julian P. Hewitt
Uniqema Health & Personal Care, Wilton, Redcar, UK

OUTLINE

Formulators of modern sunscreen products are required to meet ever-increasing demands in terms of product efficacy, both for SPF claims and for broad-spectrum (UV-A) protection. While it is well known (and intuitively understood) that SPF is dependent on the type and concentration of UV filters incorporated in a formulation, what is sometimes overlooked is the vital role played by the formulation itself. This chapter discusses the influence of various aspects of the formulation on product efficacy, and aims to provide the formulator with the some guiding principles to optimize the effectiveness of UV filters in finished products.

The topics covered include

- Fundamental requirements for achieving high SPF
- Formulating with organic sunscreens
- Formulating with inorganic sunscreens
- Combining sunscreens
- Modulation of SPF by external factors—water resistance

INTRODUCTION

In recent years, SPF claims for sunscreen products have increased rapidly. Less than 20 years ago, the vast majority of sunscreen creams and lotions provided SPFs of less than 10, and SPF 15 was considered very high. Nowadays, most experts would regard SPF 15 as the minimum required to provide effective protection, while SPF 30 has become the norm and claims of SPF 50 and above are not uncommon. Whether it is meaningful or useful for such high claims to be used is still a subject of debate (1,2), and indeed in some countries such claims are not permitted [at the time of writing, the US FDA's Final Monograph on Sunscreens (3) proposes a maximum SPF claim of 30+]. Nevertheless, the sunscreen formulator is often presented with the task of creating formulations which will achieve these high SPF values.

Increasing SPF values is not simply a matter of adding more and more active ingredients (UV filters) into the formulation; many other factors influence the efficacy of products, and the formulator must be aware of these factors and how to optimize them in order to achieve high SPF in a cost-effective, elegant formulation. This chapter discusses the various parameters which affect SPF and aims to provide some practical guidance on how to optimize the SPF efficacy of both organic and inorganic UV filters.

FUNDAMENTAL REQUIREMENTS

Ideally, for maximum efficacy of actives, what is required is for the product to deposit a film on skin which is of even thickness, following the contours of the skin and containing a homogenous distribution of the UV filter(s) (dissolved molecules of organic sunscreen or dispersed particles of physical sunscreen). This is illustrated in Fig. 19.1. However, this is never achieved in the real world [Sottery (4) showed that if this could be achieved, then at an application rate of 2 mg/cm^2, a concentration of only 2.8% octyl dimethyl PABA would be sufficient to achieve a monochromatic protection factor of 1,000,000 at 310 nm]. The true situation is probably more like that depicted in Fig. 19.2, with the product film partially "pooled" in the wrinkles of the skin, while the peaks have only thin coverage or even no coverage at all. O'Neill's "Step Film Model" (5) showed how uneven distribution of sunscreen could account for the discrepancy between the measured SPF results and theoretical expectations based on simple spectrographic data. Other workers (4,6–8) have expanded upon this model, demonstrating that it is the areas where film is either very thin or nonexistent which have the biggest influence on SPF. A simple example will serve to illustrate this.

Suppose we have a sunscreen product which deposits an incomplete film on skin, such that 5% of the skin area has no coverage. In this situation, no matter how much active is incorporated into the product, *at least* 5% of the incident

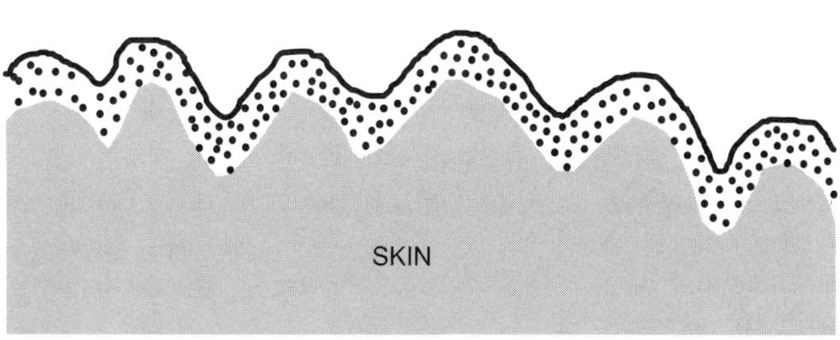

Figure 19.1 Idealized distribution of sunscreen on skin.

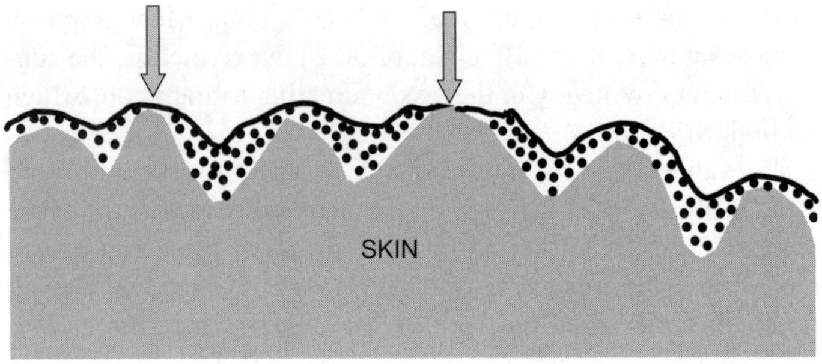

Figure 19.2 Uneven distribution of sunscreen on skin; arrows indicate where film is thin or broken and UV light is most likely to penetrate through to skin.

UV radiation will reach the skin. Therefore, it will be impossible for the product to achieve an SPF of greater than 20. However, if the formulation is modified such that film-forming is improved and only 2% of the skin is left uncovered, then the absolute maximum achievable SPF increases to 50.

So we see that good film-forming is a fundamental requirement for achieving high SPF efficacy. The second fundamental requirement is a homogenous distribution of the sunscreen active(s) throughout the film. The factors which influence the latter are dependent on the type of sunscreen active used, and are dealt with in the next two sections. However, the factors influencing film-forming are applicable generally, whatever type of active is used. These can be discussed under the general headings of rheology and de-emulsification behavior.

Rheology

In order to achieve even coverage of the skin, the product must initially spread well over the skin surface to form a film, but this film must have a degree of structure in order to maintain coverage over the peaks and valleys of the skin. Therefore, the rheological behavior of the product critically influences the SPF efficacy (9).

Spreading of a personal care product on skin is a high-shear process, with shear rates typically of the order of $10^3-10^4\ s^{-1}$. Therefore, it is the behavior of the product under such high-shear conditions, and then immediately after the shear is removed, which affects film-forming and hence SPF. It has been demonstrated (10,11) that the main requirements for high SPF efficacy, in terms of rheological behavior, are

- Low viscosity under high-shear conditions
- Short recovery time after spreading, that is, rapid recovery of structure and viscosity once shear is removed
- Low but finite thixotropy

These can be intuitively understood. To start with, the product must spread easily to achieve good coverage of the skin. Note that this does not mean that the viscosity of the product at rest must be low; for example, a high-viscosity cream can still achieve good spreading if it is very shear-thinning. Once even coverage has been achieved, however, it is not desirable for viscosity to remain low because this would result in the product continuing to flow and pooling in the skin wrinkles, hence the requirement for rapid recovery. Thixotropy is more complex because it in turn depends on other rheological parameters: viscosity at rest (the so-called "zero-shear" or residual viscosity), viscosity under shear, and recovery time. Measured values of thixotropy are dependent on the conditions under which the rheological measurement is carried out and hence such values cannot be compared unless they are measured under identical conditions.

Sunscreen products can take a variety of different physical forms (12). Sunscreen oils usually resemble Newtonian fluids in their rheological behavior, that is, viscosity does not vary with shear. They also usually are of low viscosity. As a result, while initial spreading is very efficient with such products, film-forming tends to be poor because the product has no structure; therefore, sunscreen oils tend to be limited to low SPFs only. Most other product forms (gels, sticks, foams/mousses, emulsions) exhibit—to varying degrees—viscoelastic behavior. In other words, their flow behavior includes elements of both viscous (liquid-like) and elastic (solid-like) behavior. Therefore, it is possible to design such products so that they exhibit the required rheology outlined here, that is, predominantly liquid-like at high shear (to facilitate spreading) and predominantly solid-like at very low shear (to maintain film structure).

Emulsion Rheology

The vast majority of sunscreen products are emulsions, so the remainder of this discussion concentrates on these. As well as the traditional creams and lotions, a strong recent trend has been the growth in sunscreen sprays based on emulsions, and wipes impregnated with sunscreen emulsions. Both these approaches usually require a very low-viscosity emulsion, and one might intuitively expect that such emulsions would suffer from similar drawbacks as the sunscreen oils (plus the inherent difficulty of stabilizing such low-viscosity emulsions). However, technology is now available which allows formulation of emulsions which are thin enough to be sprayable (at least when subjected to the shear of a spray nozzle) but have sufficient structure to be stable and give good film-forming on skin (13).

Obviously, the strategies to be adopted in order to optimize rheology depend on whether the emulsion is of the oil-in-water (o/w) or the water-in-oil (w/o) type. W/O emulsions are the simpler case to discuss and to study, because the evaporation of water from the emulsion is relatively slow. This means that rheological measurements on the emulsion itself represent a close approximation to the behavior of the product in actual use.

Waxes and other rheological additives have been found to boost SPF in W/O sunscreen formulations (11,14–16) and this has been correlated with shorter recovery times after shear (11). The rheology of W/O emulsions can also be modified by altering the phase volume fraction; because cosmetic W/O emulsions typically have a high internal phase (usually >50% water), the water droplets are crowded close together. In this situation an increase in the proportion of internal water phase results in an even more crowded system, causing viscosity to increase.

The combined effects of wax concentration and phase volume fraction have been investigated in the following frame formula:

	%w/w
PEG-30 dipolyhydroxystearate	2.5
Mineral oil	4.0–8.0
Hybrid sunflower oil	2.0–4.0
Isopropyl myristate	4.0–8.0
Beeswax	0–3.0
TiO_2 dispersion	5.0
Demineralized water	To 100%
Magnesium sulfate	0.7
Propylene glycol	5.0
Preservative	qs

Note: The TiO_2 dispersion was a 50% solids dispersion of coated TiO_2 in a 50:50 blend of mineral oil and caprylic/capric triglyceride.

The content of beeswax was varied from zero to 3%, and the total content of added oils was varied from 10% to 20%, with the relative proportions of the three oils kept constant. The SPF data obtained from these formulations are shown in Fig. 19.3.

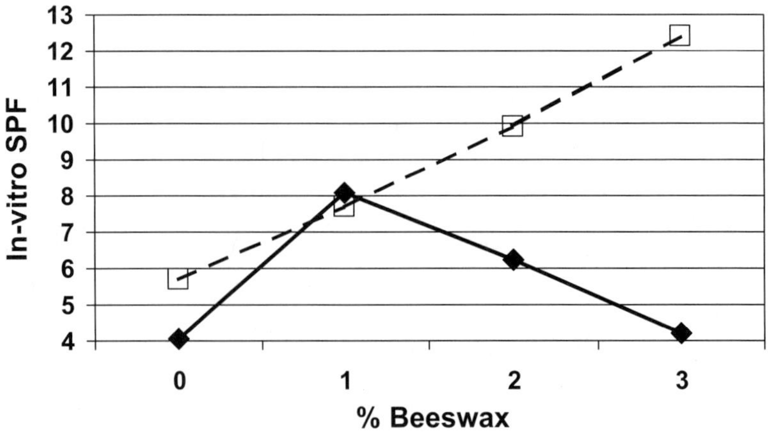

Figure 19.3 Effect of waxes on SPF in W/O emulsions at different phase volume fractions (◆: 10% oil; □: 20% oil).

As can be seen from this data, the optimum level of wax (in terms of SPF) depends on the phase volume fraction. At 5% dispersion (2.5% solids), with only 10% of added oils, the phase volume fraction is such that the formulation is already quite viscous with no addition of wax. Therefore, while adding 1% wax increases the SPF, any further addition means that the formulation becomes too viscous to spread easily (i.e., high-shear viscosity is now too high), and SPF decreases. When we increase the amount of oil phase, the viscosity of the base emulsion is lower, and the beneficial effect of the wax (shorter recovery time) continues to outweigh the negative effect (increase in high-shear viscosity) even at higher wax loadings. At 20% added oils, we see that the SPF continues to increase up to 3% wax, where the SPF is over 12 (from the same level of active).

O/W emulsions represent a more complex case, because evaporation of water is more rapid and occurs already to a significant extent during rub-in of the product. Therefore, the composition of the emulsion (and hence its rheology) is constantly changing while the product is being applied. Laboratory measurements of rheology are conducted on the complete emulsion, without any evaporation taking place, and hence do not replicate the real situation. Nevertheless, some correlations between SPF and rheological parameters have been observed (17).

The rheological behavior of O/W systems is influenced by many formulation components, including emulsifiers, hydrocolloids, and "lipid thickeners" such as fatty alcohols or fatty acids. Many O/W cosmetic emulsions incorporate liquid crystalline structures (18–21), and these also have a significant influence on rheology.

De-Emulsification Behavior

With O/W emulsions, film-forming is also affected by the breakdown of the emulsion during application. As the water phase evaporates, the oil droplets coalesce to form a film. In a sunscreen product, for optimum efficacy, this film needs to be as homogenous as possible, with the active(s) dispersed evenly within it. Dahms (22) discussed how the coalescence and spreading of the oil phase is affected by the properties of the oil/air and oil/skin interfaces, and derived a relationship between SPF, the surface tension of the oil phase, and the interfacial tension between oil phase and water phase. In a separate paper, the same author showed how efficient and rapid de-emulsification is aided by the small droplet size in the emulsion (23).

FORMULATING WITH ORGANIC SUNSCREENS

Most organic UV filters are oil-soluble; however, a few are designed to be incorporated into the water phase. The latter are usually molecules with an acid group and are only rendered soluble in water when this group is neutralized by addition of a base. Another recent innovation is the development of an organic UV filter which is an insoluble particulate, and is incorporated into the finished formulation as a water-based dispersion (24). Organic UV filters are usually also classified as either UV-B or UV-A filters, since most only absorb over a relatively narrow wavelength range (although there are examples with broader absorption spectra). This means that in the vast majority of formulations, more than one filter is used, as it is necessary to protect against both UV-B and UV-A in order to achieve high SPF values.

Detailed practical advice on formulating with organic sunscreens is given elsewhere in this book. The following discussion concentrates on how to achieve a homogenous distribution of the active in the product film that is deposited on skin; as indicated in the previous section, this is key to achieving high SPF efficacy. With organic sunscreens, how this is done depends on whether the active is oil-soluble or water-soluble.

Oil-Soluble Organic UV Filters

Effect of Emulsion Type

Oil-soluble organic sunscreens generally exhibit greater efficacy in W/O than in O/W emulsions, as evidenced by the data shown in Fig. 19.4 (25). In this work, various UV filters were individually incorporated into W/O and O/W emulsions, with different carrier emollients. Each data bar in Fig. 19.4 therefore represents an average over 12 formulations. In most cases, it is apparent that the W/O system gives higher SPF efficacy than the O/W one. This is to be expected since the active is in the external phase in a W/O system and achievement of an even distribution of sunscreen is not dependent on the de-emulsification of the emulsion on skin.

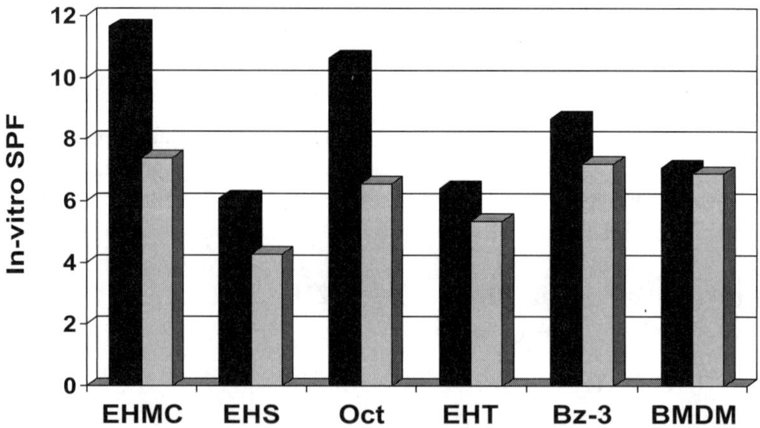

Figure 19.4 Effect of emulsion type on efficacy of organic UV filters. (■: W/O emulsions; □: O/W emulsions. EHMC = ethylhexyl methoxycinnamate; EHS = ethylhexyl salicylate; Oct = octocrylene; EHT = ethylhexyl triazone; Bz-3 = benzophenone-3; BMDM = butyl methoxydibenzoylmethane.)

Effect of Added Emollients

Some oil-soluble organics [e.g., octocrylene, ethylhexyl methoxycinnamate (EHMC)] are liquids and are readily mixed with the oil phase of the formulations. One might think, therefore, that a homogenous distribution of the active is virtually automatic and good efficacy is assured. However, even in these cases, one must ensure that the actives are compatible with the oil phase; the materials may be visibly miscible but, on a molecular level, flocculation can occur which will have an adverse effect on SPF (4). Also, as is well known (26,27), the solvents within which the actives are dispersed can affect the absorption spectrum, either by shifting the peak of absorption to a different wavelength or by affecting the amplitude of the peak.

Many organic UV filters are crystalline solids, and for these materials the solubility of the active in the oil phase is a critical factor. The oils or esters used must be capable of dissolving the UV filters and maintaining them in solution over the lifetime of the product; if the active crystallizes to any degree, it's efficacy can be significantly reduced. Polar oils tend to be the best solvents; suppliers of organic UV filters typically include in their literature data on the solubility of their products in various cosmetic emollients. Use of liquid UV filters (e.g., ethylhexyl methoxycinnamate) in combination with the solid filters can be a useful tactic, as the liquid UV filters are themselves good solvents for the solid actives.

Figure 19.5 [data from Ref. (25)] shows *in vitro* SPF data for various solid actives, in different carrier emollients, in W/O systems. There is a clear correlation between SPF and solubility in the carrier emollient.

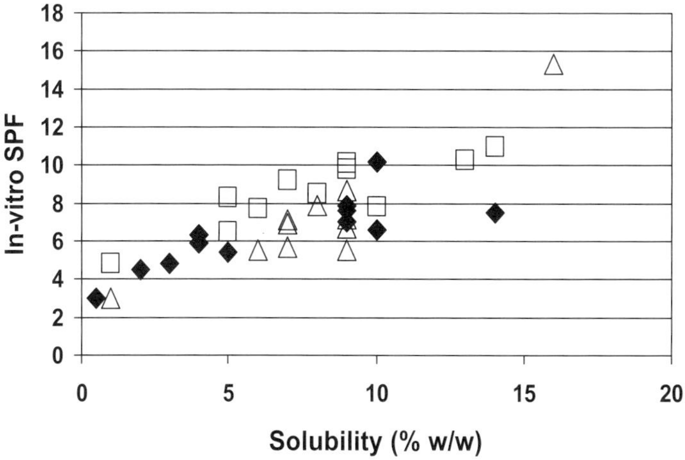

Figure 19.5 SPF vs. solubility for solid organic UV filters in various solvents (◆: ethylhexyl triazone; □: benzophenone-3; Δ: butyl methoxydibenzoylmethane).

The nature of the emollients can also, of course, affect the rheology of the emulsion or the de-emulsification behavior, as discussed in the previous section.

Water-Soluble Organic UV Filters

Effect of Emulsion Type

While it is intuitive that oil-soluble organics should be more effective in W/O than in O/W emulsions, what is perhaps more surprising is that the same applies to water-soluble sunscreens. Experiments with phenylbenzimidazole sulfonic acid (S. Housley, personal communication, 1998) show that this active gave a higher SPF in a W/O emulsion than in an O/W system.

This can be understood by once again considering what happens to the emulsion during and after application on skin. In an O/W emulsion, as the water evaporates, a water-soluble active may partially crystallize on the skin surface if it cannot disperse into the oil film deposited on skin, whereas in a W/O emulsion, the water phase is encapsulated within the product film, so the active can remain dissolved. Provided that the droplets are small and homogeneously dispersed (which, for a stable W/O emulsion, would normally be the case), a good dispersion of the active within the product film can be achieved.

Effect of Emulsifiers

In truth, with most O/W emulsions, the product film on skin is not entirely homogenous, since in addition to oils it may contain liquid crystalline phases, silicones, etc. The nature and type of liquid crystalline phases formed depends on the emulsifiers used (18,19), and will often include both lipophilic and hydrophilic parts, including entrapped water. In such cases, the efficacy of water-soluble organic UV filters can be maintained if the hydrophilic structures are sufficiently well dispersed. This requires therefore that the structures be delocalised, for example of a lamellar gel network type (21).

FORMULATING WITH INORGANIC SUNSCREENS

Basic Principles

By far the most commonly used inorganic (or "physical") sunscreens are titanium dioxide (TiO_2) and zinc oxide (ZnO). TiO_2 provides mainly UV-B protection but is also effective in the UV-A, while ZnO is principally used for UV-A protection, its efficacy in the UV-B being relatively low. A list of the principal suppliers of inorganic sunscreens and their products is given in Tables 19.1 and 19.2 (note that this is not intended to be an exhaustive list).

It is well known that the efficacy of inorganic sunscreens depends on particle size and size distribution (15,28–30). Ultimately, if we think again about the general principles discussed in the second section, what is required is a homogenous dispersion of the particles on skin after the product has been applied.

Table 19.1 Inorganic Sunscreens Supplied in Powder Form

Supplier	Type	Product name	Surface treatment
Tayca	TiO_2	MT-100S	Aluminum laurate/aluminum hydroxide
		MT-100T	Aluminum stearate/aluminum hydroxide
		MT-100Z	Aluminum stearate/aluminum hydroxide
		MT-100F	Ferric stearate/ferric hydroxide
		MT-150W	None
		MT-100AQ	Alumina/silica/alginic acid
		MT-100SA	Alumina/silica
		MT-100HD	Alumina/zirconia
		MT-100SAS	Alumina/silica/silicone
	ZnO	MZ-300	None
		MZ-300S	Methicone
		MZ-300M	Dimethicone
Ishihara	TiO_2	TTO-S-3	Alumina
		TTO-S-4	Alumina/stearic acid
		TTO-V-3	Alumina
		TTO-V-4	Alumina/stearic acid
Kemira	TiO_2	M160	Stearic acid/alumina
		M170	Alumina/dimethicone
		M212	Glycerin/alumina
		M262	Alumina/dimethicone
Degussa	TiO_2	T805	Trimethoxycaprylylsilane
BASF	TiO_2	Uvinul TiO_2	Trimethoxycaprylylsilane
	ZnO	Z-Cote	None
		Z-Cote HP1	Dimethicone
Titan Kogyo	TiO_2	ST-452	Alumina/stearic acid
		ST-455	Alumina/stearic acid
		ST-485SA15	Alumina/stearic acid
		ST-485DS	Alumina/silicone
Merck	TiO_2	Eusolex T-2000	Alumina/simethicone
Particle Sciences	TiO_2	T-Cote 031	Dimethicone
Elementis	ZnO	Nanox 200	None
Symrise	ZnO	Zinc oxide neutral H&R	None
Sakai	ZnO	50LP	Organopolysiloxane

Therefore, there are three fundamental requirements for achieving optimum efficacy with inorganic sunscreens (31):

1. Select material with the optimum particle size and particle size distribution
2. Ensure that the particles are dispersed homogeneously throughout the emulsion
3. Ensure an even distribution of the particles on skin when the product is applied

Table 19.2 Inorganic Sunscreen Predispersions

Supplier	Type	Product name	Surface treatment	Carrier medium	%Solids
Uniqema	TiO_2	Tioveil FIN	Alumina/silica	C_{12-15} alkyl benzoate	40
		Tioveil IPM	Alumina/silica	Isopropyl myristate	40
		Tioveil MOTG	Alumina/silica	Mineral oil/caprylic-capric triglyceride	40
		Tioveil OP	Alumina/silica	Ethylhexyl palmitate	40
		Tioveil TG	Alumina/silica	Caprylic-capric triglyceride	40
		Tioveil AQ-G	Alumina/silica	Water	40
		Tioveil AQ-N	Alumina/silica	Water	40
		Tioveil 50 FCM	Aluminum stearate/alumina	C_{12-15} alkyl benzoate/cyclomethicone	50
		Tioveil 50 FIN	Aluminum stearate/alumina	C_{12-15} alkyl benzoate	50
		Tioveil 50 GCM	Aluminum stearate/alumina	Octyldodecanol/cyclomethicone	50
		Tioveil 50 IPM	Aluminum stearate/alumina	Isopropyl myristate	50
		Tioveil 50 MOTG	Aluminum stearate/alumina	Mineral oil/caprylic-capric triglyceride	50
		Tioveil 50 OP	Aluminum stearate/alumina	Ethylhexyl palmitate	50
		Tioveil 50 TG	Aluminum stearate/alumina	Caprylic-capric triglyceride	50
		Tioveil CM	Aluminum stearate/alumina	Cyclomethicone	40
		Solaveil CT-100	Aluminum stearate/alumina	C_{12-15} alkyl benzoate	45
		Solaveil CT-10W	Aluminum stearate/alumina	Water	40
	ZnO	Spectraveil FIN	None	C_{12-15} alkyl benzoate	60
		Spectraveil IPM	None	Isopropyl myristate	60
		Spectraveil MOTG	None	Mineral oil/caprylic-capric triglyceride	60
		Spectraveil OP	None	Ethylhexyl palmitate	60
		Spectraveil TG	None	Caprylic-capric triglyceride	60

Kobo	TiO_2	GC40VS	Aluminum hydroxide/stearic acid	Caprylic-capric triglyceride	40
		IN60S4	Aluminum hydroxide/stearic acid	Isononyl isononanoate	60
		TNP055S4	Aluminum hydroxide/stearic acid	C_{12-15} alkyl benzoate	55
		CM3K25VM	Alumina/methicone	Cyclopentasiloxane	25
		CM3K40T4	Alumina/methicone	Cyclopentasiloxane	40
		CMKP25VM	Alumina/methicone	Cyclopentasiloxane	25
		CMKP60M262	Alumina/silica/methicone	Cyclopentasiloxane	60
		INP45M170	Alumina/dimethicone	Isononyl isononanoate	45
		TNP40VTTS	Alumina/Isopropyl titanium triisostearate/ Triethoxycaprylylsilane cross-polymer	C_{12-15} alkyl benzoate	40
	ZnO	GC55XZ4	Methicone	Caprylic-capric triglyceride	55
		INH73MZ	Isopropyl titanium triisostearate	Isononyl isononanoate	73
		CE50ZCI	Triethoxy caprylylsilane	Trioctyldodecyl citrate	50
		CM3K50XZ4	Methicone	Cyclopentasiloxane	50
		CM3K50HP1	Dimethicone	Cyclomethicone	50
		CMKP50XZ4	Methicone	Cyclopentasiloxane	50
		TNP50ZSI	Triethoxycaprylylsilane	C_{12-15} alkyl benzoate	50
Granula	TiO_2	Granlux CCT-40	DNA[a]	Caprylic-capric mono/ diglycerides	40
		Granlux MSN-50	DNA	Apricot kernel oil PEG-40 esters/cetearyl glucoside/ cetearyl alcohol/hydrogenated decene oligomers	50
		Granlux EM-50	DNA	Cetearyl glucoside/cetearyl alcohol	50

(continued)

Table 19.2 *Continued*

Supplier	Type	Product name	Surface treatment	Carrier medium	%Solids
		Granlux TEM-45	DNA	Caprylic-capric triglyceride/cetearyl glucoside/cetearyl alcohol	45
		Granlux AB-50	DNA	C_{12-15} alkyl benzoate	50
		Granlux TG-50	DNA	Caprylic-capric triglyceride	50
		Granlux TG2-50M1	DNA	Caprylic-capric triglyceride	50
		Granlux GAW-45	Alumina/dimethicone	Polyglyceryl-4-isostearate/cetyl dimethicone copolyol/hexyl laurate	45
		Granlux GAI-45	Alumina/stearic acid	Polyglyceryl-4-isostearate/cetyl dimethicone copolyol/hexyl laurate/isononyl isononanoate	45
		Granlux NA-50M1	Alumina/dimethicone	Hydrogenated decene oligomers/cetyl dimethicone copolyol	50
	ZnO	Granlux EM-45Z	DNA	Cetearyl glucoside/cetearyl alcohol	45
		Granlux TEM-45Z	DNA	Caprylic-capric triglyceride/cetearyl glucoside/cetearyl alcohol	45
		Granlux AB-55Z	DNA	C_{12-15} alkyl benzoate	55
	TiO_2/ZnO	Granlux EM-45TZ	DNA	Cetearyl glucoside/cetearyl alcohol	45
		Granlux TEM-45TZ	DNA	Caprylic-capric triglyceride/cetearyl glucoside/cetearyl alcohol	45

		Granlux GAW-45TZ	Alumina/dimethicone	Polyglyceryl-4-isostearate/cetyl dimethicone copolyol/hexyl laurate	45
		Granlux GAI-45TZ	Alumina/stearic acid	Polyglyceryl-4-isostearate/cetyl dimethicone copolyol/hexyl laurate/isononyl isononanoate	45
		Granlux GAC-45TZ	Alumina/dimethicone	Polyglyceryl-4-isostearate/cetyl dimethicone copolyol/hexyl laurate/cyclopentasiloxane	45
		Granlux NA-50TZ	Alumina/dimethicone	Hydrogenated decene oligomers/cetyl dimethicone copolyol	50
Collaborative Labs	TiO_2	TioSperse Ultra	Stearic acid/dimethicone/aluminum hydroxide	Ethylhexylhydroxystearate benzoate/cyclopentasiloxane	50
	ZnO	Z-Sperse Ultra	Dimethicone/triethoxycaprylylsilane	Ethylhexylhydroxystearate benzoate/cyclopentasiloxane	60
	TiO_2/ZnO	TZ-Sperse Ultra	Stearic acid/dimethicone/aluminum hydroxide/dimethicone/triethoxycaprylylsilane	Ethylhexylhydroxystearate benzoate/cyclopentasiloxane	DNA
Degussa	TiO_2	Tego Sun TAQ40	Trimethoxycaprylylsilane	Water	40
Rhodia	TiO_2	Mirasun TiW60	Silica/alumina	Water	40
Merck	TiO_2	Eusolex T-Aqua	Alumina	Water	30
ISP	TiO_2	Escalol T-100	Alumina/dimethicone	Ethylhexyl methoxycinnamate	50
	ZnO	Escalol Z-100	Methicone	Ethylhexyl methoxycinnamate	DNA

[a]DNA = data not available.

The first requirement is primarily the responsibility of the raw material supplier. Most suppliers of inorganic sunscreens will provide particle size data for their products; unfortunately, it is difficult or impossible to compare data provided by different suppliers in any meaningful way, because measured particle size data vary enormously depending on the technique used for the measurement and how the samples are prepared. (It is for this reason that particle size data are omitted from Tables 19.1 and 19.2.) In selecting a particular product, it is more meaningful and informative to look at the UV/visible absorption spectra of the materials being considered, as this bears a closer relationship to the properties of the active in the final formulation.

The tasks for the formulator, then, are to fulfill requirements 2 and 3. Keeping a homogenous dispersion of the particles within the emulsion requires that there must be sufficient repulsive force between the particles to prevent them from agglomerating if they approach each other. This is achieved by means of either electrostatic or steric repulsion (29). Within the formulation, these repulsive forces need to be maintained in order to keep the particles well dispersed.

Physical sunscreen particles used in sunscreens are almost always coated (surface-treated); these coatings can be either hydrophilic or hydrophobic. Hydrophilic coatings typically consist of other inorganic oxides, such as silica or alumina. Electrostatic repulsion is normally used to maintain dispersion of such particles in water, either by making use of the inherent surface charge on the particles or by including a dispersing agent which itself carries a charge. In either case, a key parameter in maintaining the dispersion is the point of net zero charge, or isoelectric point.

All inorganic particles carry charges on their surface. When such particles are dispersed in water, the surface charges can play a major role in the interparticle forces. Both positive and negative charges are present; at high pH there is a net negative charge, while at low pH the net charge is positive. In between, there is a certain pH at which the positive and negative charges exactly balance each other and there is no net charge; this is the isoelectric point (see Fig. 19.6). The isoelectric point is characteristic of the surface of the particles, and therefore depends on the coatings applied and also on the dispersing agent used.

In formulation, the isoelectric point must be avoided, since the lack of electrostatic repulsion at this point means that the particles can agglomerate. These agglomerates are difficult to break up again once formed. Therefore, control of emulsion pH is an important aspect of formulating with hydrophilic particles in the aqueous phase.

One might intuitively expect that hydrophilic coating is a prerequisite for dispersion of TiO_2 particles in water; however, recently, there have been two aqueous dispersions launched on the market (32,33) which are based on hydrophobically coated particles. In these cases, surfactants or polymers are used to provide steric repulsion between the particles and hence maintain the dispersion. The molecular architecture of these dispersing agents is critical; the molecule must have an anchor group, which associates or binds with the particle surface, and a stabilizer part which extends out into, and is solvated by, the carrier

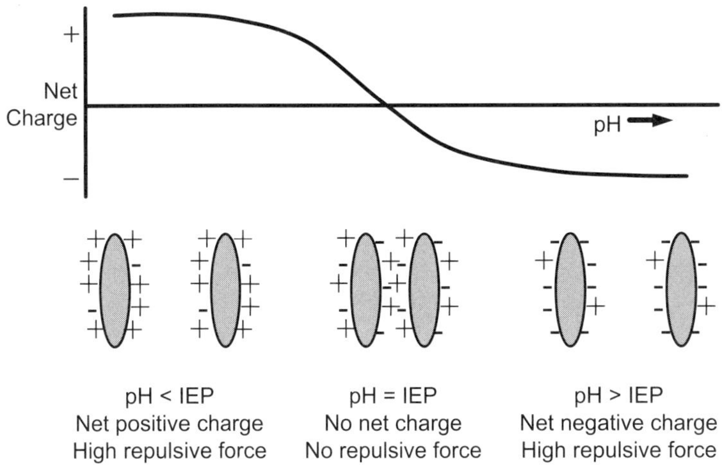

Figure 19.6 Effect of pH on the net charge on particle surfaces.

medium. In the case of hydrophobic particles in a water dispersion, the anchor should be hydrophobic and the stabilizer hydrophilic, so that it is effectively solvated by water in order to provide the steric repulsion. An advantage with such dispersions is that the repulsive forces are not pH dependent; therefore, they do not exhibit an isoelectric point, and so can be used over a wide range of pH.

When physical sunscreens are incorporated into the oil phase, the surface charges are insulated and electrostatic repulsive forces are small; in this case, steric repulsion once again plays the major role in keeping the particles dispersed. This is achieved either by coating the particles with organic or silicone species, or by use of a suitable dispersing agent which associates with the particle surfaces.

In either case—oil-dispersed or water-dispersed particles—the best results are normally achieved by use of a stabilized predispersion of the physical sunscreen, formed by milling the particles in the carrier medium in the presence of a suitable dispersing agent. Fine powders tend to agglomerate in the dry state, and these agglomerates cannot be broken down by the mixing energies normally found in the production of cosmetic emulsions. As a result, the dispersion of the particles is not ideal, and SPF is adversely affected. Published data indicate that predispersions give higher SPF efficacy than dry powders (34).

Assuming that an optimized predispersion is used, the factors further affecting SPF with physical sunscreens depend on whether the particles are dispersed in the water phase or the oil phase.

Formulating with Water-Dispersed TiO_2

As discussed earlier in this chapter, optimum SPF efficacy requires that the active(s) be well dispersed throughout the film that is deposited on skin. In the case of an O/W emulsion (Fig. 19.7), this film consists predominantly of lipophilic materials (the oil phase of the emulsion), so one might logically expect that water-dispersed TiO_2 would have poor efficacy in such systems, as it would be excluded from the oil film (Fig. 19.7b). And yet there are numerous examples of formulations containing aqueous TiO_2 dispersions which display good efficacy (both in the literature and on the market). This suggests that there must be a mechanism by which the TiO_2 particles are incorporated into the oil film (Fig. 19.7c).

With hydrophilic TiO_2 particles, the most likely explanation for this is liquid crystals. Liquid crystalline structures are present in many cosmetic O/W emulsions (18–21), and studies using freeze–fracture electron microscopy have shown that, with a suitable dispersing agent, TiO_2 particles from an aqueous dispersion tend to locate within these structures (35). Previous formulation studies (36) have indicated that gel networks formed from lamellar liquid crystalline structures are advantageous for achieving optimum efficacy with such dispersions. A logical explanation for this is that the TiO_2 is preferentially located within the lamellar structures, which are in turn incorporated into the oil film during de-emulsification. In other words the liquid crystalline

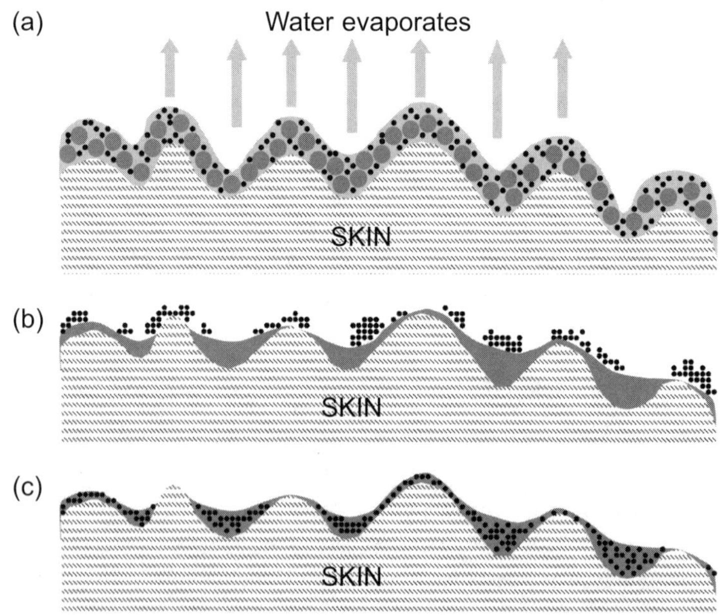

Figure 19.7 (a) Schematic representation of O/W emulsion, containing TiO_2 particles in the water phase, on skin immediately after spreading. (b) Emulsion after dry-down; if TiO_2 is hydrophilic and cannot migrate into oil film, coverage is discontinuous leading to low SPF. (c) If TiO_2 can migrate into the oil film, much better coverage is achieved (see text).

structures provide a vehicle to ensure the transfer of the TiO_2 into the oil film. A variety of different types of surfactants can form these structures, including glyceryl stearate, sorbitan esters, sucrose esters, and polyglyceryl esters. As a result, many familiar and commonly used emulsifier systems can be used to formulate effective products with these aqueous TiO_2 dispersions. However, recognition of the potential of lamellar gel networks (in other applications as well as this one) has led to the development of emulsifier systems designed specifically for this purpose. An additional advantage of such emulsifiers is that they can be used with a wide range of different oils, including silicone oils (20,21).

With hydrophobic TiO_2, the mechanism is simpler. In this case it is unlikely that the particles will be located within the lamellar structures, but the hydrophobic coating means that, as the water evaporates, the particles have a natural tendency to migrate into the oil phase. So lamellar structures are not required to ensure homogenous distribution of the particles in the oil film.

In the subsection on the effect of emulsion type, we discussed how water-soluble organic UV filters have often been found to be more effective in W/O emulsions than in O/W systems. And yet the same has not been found to be the case with water-dispersed TiO_2 (15). This is because, historically, all aqueous dispersions used hydrophilic TiO_2; as discussed in the subsection on basic principles, such dispersions rely principally on electrostatic repulsion to keep the particles well dispersed. It is common practice in W/O emulsions to incorporate an electrolyte, which aids stability by preventing dissolution of the emulsifier in the water phase. This electrolyte content is sufficient to destabilize an aqueous TiO_2 dispersion based on hydrophilic particles, resulting in poor efficacy. However, the advent of aqueous dispersions containing hydrophobic TiO_2 opens up new possibilities, since such dispersions are not expected to be sensitive to electrolytes.

Formulating with Oil-Dispersed TiO_2

By using appropriate dispersing agents, either hydrophilic or hydrophobic TiO_2 can be used to make a stable oil-based dispersion, and either can be used effectively in both O/W and W/O emulsions. Evidence indicates that hydrophobic TiO_2 is more versatile in formulation (16) and that such a coating, together with optimized particle size distribution, gives improved cosmetic elegance as well as high efficacy (30).

Other ingredients included in the formulation can affect the SPF provided by physical sunscreens via two principal mechanisms:

1. Altering the degree of dispersion of the particles
2. Altering the extent to which the product effectively covers the skin

Each of these mechanisms can be subdivided into different effects. For example, consider the use of oil-dispersed TiO_2 in an O/W emulsion. In this case, the degree of dispersion can be improved by optimizing the dispersion of the particles within the oil phase by selection of suitable emollients (16), or by altering the droplet size of the oil phase. Effective coverage of skin can be achieved by optimizing the rheology of the emulsion (as discussed in the subsection on emulsion rheology), altering droplet size (23), and using film-forming polymers (37), for example.

Formulating with Zinc Oxide

The primary purpose of ZnO in sunscreen formulations is UV-A protection, rather than SPF; nevertheless, UV-A filters do make a significant contribution to SPF, and the same principles apply to optimization of UV-A efficacy.

Many of the principles of formulating with TiO_2 also apply with ZnO, because they are based on the characteristics of inorganic particulates rather than of TiO_2 specifically. However, there are additional challenges presented by ZnO (15,38–40). ZnO tends to form alkaline complexes when dispersed in water, causing pH values which are too high for products which are to be left on the skin. For this reason, ZnO is usually incorporated into the oil phase of the formulation. However, ZnO is highly hydrophilic, and tends to migrate from the oil phase to the water phase. This process is promoted if the pH of the water phase is less than 6, as the solubility of ZnO in water increases significantly below this pH (39). This migration/solubilization causes pH to drift upward, and can also decrease the efficacy of the ZnO, if measures are not taken to maintain a good dispersion of the particles in the aqueous phase.

These problems can be minimized or eliminated by various means. Use of an optimized predispersion maintains the ZnO in a finely dispersed form in the oil phase. In W/O emulsions, such dispersion techniques are sufficient to eliminate migration and maintain the efficacy of ZnO. ZnO can also be coated with hydrophobic materials in order to reduce migration. However, in either case further formulation measures are necessary in order to completely eliminate migration, or to mitigate its effects, in O/W systems (15).

COMBINING SUNSCREENS

Of course, it is unusual nowadays for sunscreen products to contain only a single UV filter, the possible exception being products formulated with only an inorganic filter and targeted at young children or individuals with sensitive skin. This is because it is virtually impossible to achieve the high SPFs demanded by today's market by using a single organic filter, and while such high SPFs are achievable by use of TiO_2 alone, it is often necessary to use a high concentration of the active, resulting in poor aesthetic properties (whitening on skin).

The difficulty in achieving high SPF with a single organic filter is due to two main reasons: the narrow spectrum of most organics and the fact that product films deposited on skin rarely are completely homogenous oil films.

Consideration of the erythemal action spectrum and the solar spectrum (41) shows that SPF is dependent primarily on UV-B protection, but that UV-A also plays a part, in particular the short-wavelength UVA region sometimes referred to as "UV-A-II" (320–340 nm). Products must provide effective protection at these wavelengths in order to reach a high SPF, and most UV-B filters fail to do this, while UV-A filters tend to have poor efficacy in the UV-B. Also, since product films often contain both hydrophilic and lipophilic regions, a product which contains, say, only an oil-soluble filter will not adequately protect the whole surface and this also limits efficacy. Combination of these two factors leads to a "Law of Diminishing Returns", illustrated in Fig. 19.8 for EHMC. This shows SPF values for a series of formulations containing increasing levels of EHMC as the sole active. As the active level is increased, SPF increases, but the overall efficacy (in terms of SPF per %active) decreases.

Combining Organic Sunscreens

It is common practice, then, to combine UV filters. In designing a filter system, the formulator should take account of the principles discussed in this chapter and elsewhere in this book, and choose filters which complement one another in some way. This usually means combining UV-B filters with UV-A filters to achieve better spectral coverage, or combining oil-soluble and water-soluble filters to achieve better skin coverage. The formulator must also be mindful of intellectual property, however, as there are numerous patents covering such combinations.

Certain combinations have other advantages, for example, ethylhexyl methoxycinnamate is a very good solvent for solid organic UV filters, and

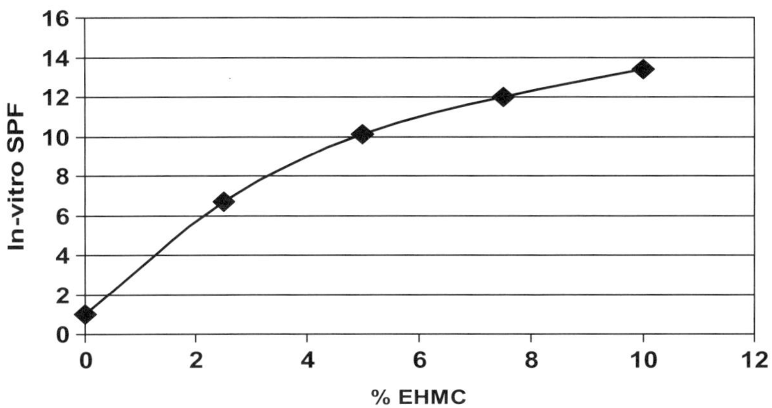

Figure 19.8 SPF vs. %active for a series of formulations containing ethylhexyl methoxycinnamate.

therefore can help to optimize the efficacy of such filters. Another consideration might be photostability; it is well known that certain organics, for example, avobenzone, decay on exposure to UV (42,43), but it is also well known that this decay is automatically taken into account by *in vivo* SPF testing since this is a time-resolved measurement. However, the *in vivo* efficacy of such materials can be improved by combining them with other filters which photostabilize them; it has been established that, for example, octocrylene achieves this with avobenzone (44).

Combining Inorganic Sunscreens

TiO_2 alone is effective enough in both UV-B and UV-A to generate high SPF values when used as a sole active. However "broad-spectrum" coverage can still be improved by combining it with ZnO (39). Another "combination" strategy is to use oil-dispersed and water-dispersed TiO_2 in the same formulation, thereby achieving more efficient overall skin coverage (45).

Combining Organic and Inorganic Sunscreens

A very common strategy is to combine both organic and inorganic filters, not the least because substantial "synergistic effects" have been observed when organic and inorganic sunscreens are combined; the SPF data measured on the combinations are substantially higher than would be expected from adding together the SPFs from the individual actives (46–51). There are three reasons for these synergistic effects:

- Improved skin coverage—incorporation of one active in the oil phase and one in the water phase of an emulsion results in improved overall coverage of the skin, as explained earlier.
- Improved spectral coverage—for example, addition of ZnO to a formula containing an organic UV-B sunscreen can dramatically improve the SPF, in the same way as can be achieved with a UV-A organic.
- Increased path length—the scattering of UV light by the inorganic sunscreen means that light does not pass through the sunscreen film in a straight line (see Fig. 19.9); therefore, the optical path length is increased. As a result, the efficacy of the organic is improved.

SPF MODULATION BY EXTERNAL FACTORS: WATER RESISTANCE

The bulk of this chapter has discussed how different aspects of the formulation affect SPF. However, the true SPF in use is also affected by external factors, relating to the type of activity in which the user is engaged. Most commonly, sunscreen products are used during leisure time, since this is when most people receive the majority of their sun exposure. For example, the average British

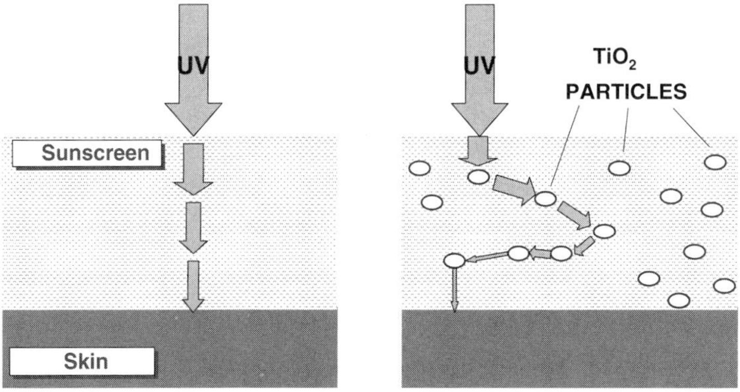

Figure 19.9 Increase of optical path length due to scattering by TiO_2 particles.

consumer receives 70% of his annual UV dose during summer vacations and summer weekends (2). Typical activities during these times would include outdoor sports, sunbathing, and swimming. As a result of these activities, SPF can be affected by sweating, water immersion, towelling, and other external agents such as sand. Claims for "sand resistance" or "rub resistance" are somewhat unusual, probably because there are no universally recognized methods for substantiating such claims, although methods have been proposed (52). On the other hand, tests for water resistance are well established (3,53), and water-resistant claims are now the norm for "beach" suncare products. So how can the formulator make his product water resistant? To answer this we need to once again go back to first principles.

Fundamental Requirements for Water Resistance

Once a product has been applied and has dried down on skin, there are three processes by which UV filters may be removed on contact with water:

1. Re-emulsification of the product film
2. Removal of the product film by mechanical action of water moving over the skin surface
3. Removal of active UV filters which are excluded from the product film

The first of these occurs where a significant concentration of hydrophilic emulsifiers is present in the product film. This facilitates easy re-emulsification of the oils, etc., by the water moving over the skin.

Mechanical removal can occur where the product film is discontinuous or has poor adhesion to the skin. This allows water to penetrate under the product film and "lift" it from the skin surface. This can be observed in a simple *in vitro* experiment. A film of an emulsion is applied onto a glass slide, left to dry, and then placed in a beaker of water which is gently agitated. If the product re-emulsifies, the water becomes turbid or cloudy; such products are unlikely to be water resistant. However, some products do not re-emulsify but peel away from the slide in one piece.

An example of exclusion of active from the film was illustrated earlier in Fig. 19.7b. If hydrophilic TiO_2 is incorporated into an O/W emulsion, and has no means of migrating into the oil film on dry-down, then even if the film itself is water resistant, the TiO_2 is readily redispersed and removed by water.

The fundamental requirements for water resistance are therefore

1. A low concentration of hydrophilic emulsifiers, to avoid re-emulsification
2. A continuous, coherent product film after application and dry-down
3. Actives effectively dispersed within the product film

Strategies for Water Resistance

Several different formulating strategies have been employed to provide water resistance. Each of these approaches addresses one or more of the fundamental requirements mentioned earlier.

W/O Emulsions

The film deposited on skin by a W/O emulsion can be expected to be resistant to re-emulsification, since oil is the external phase of the emulsion, and such emulsions employ predominantly hydrophobic emulsifiers. There are guide formulations available in the literature (54,55) demonstrating the use of this strategy for water resistance.

Silicones

Silicone oils aid water resistance in two ways: the oils themselves are inherently hydrophobic and they also have very good spreading properties, which assist in formation of a coherent, continuous film. Certain specialty silicone ingredients have also been shown to give improvements in water resistance (14,56).

Specialized Emulsifiers

Several specialized emulsifiers are now available which use different technologies to impart water resistance. For example, phosphate-based emulsifiers such as potassium cetyl phosphate, have a similar chemical structure as that of skin lipids, and it is claimed that this facilitates increased water resistance. Phosphate emulsifiers have been developed which are targeted specifically at this application (57).

Another material, acrylates/C10–30 alkyl acrylate cross-polymer, stabilizes emulsions by electrostatic means, forming an aqueous gel structure within which the oil droplets are suspended. By use of such technology, surfactant-free (so-called "emulsifier-free") emulsions can be made. With no surfactant present, re-emulsification is prevented. Sunscreen formulations based on this material have been published (54,55).

Liquid Crystal Gel Networks

Lamellar gel network systems are based on hydrophobic, lipid emulsifiers, making them difficult to re-emulsify after dry-down. Additionally, as far as physical sunscreens are concerned, such liquid crystalline systems have been found to be especially suitable for use with aqueous TiO_2 dispersions (36), providing a means of incorporating the water-dispersed TiO_2 in the oil film, as illustrated earlier in Fig. 19.7c.

Film-Forming Polymers

Perhaps the most common approach is to incorporate a "waterproofing agent". These materials are typically film-forming polymers, which can be used to make the product film more coherent and hence more substantive. The efficacy of these polymers in promoting water resistance has been demonstrated (58,59) and specific example formulations can be found in the literature (54,55).

The "Dual-Strategy" Approach

While all of the above strategies have been used successfully, none provides a guarantee of success. With each strategy, examples can be found in which the strategy failed to yield a water-resistant formula. For example, Angelinetta and Barzaghi (37) observed significant increases in SPF when film-forming polymers were incorporated into TiO_2 formulations. However, the formulations used by were based on high-HLB (hydrophile–lipophile balance), hydrophilic emulsifier systems, which are readily re-emulsified. Despite the improvement in static SPF, subsequent *in vivo* SPF tests demonstrated that the formulations were not water resistant.

In order to build a more reliable approach for creating water-resistant products, we must consider all of the fundamental requirements. This means invoking at least two of the basic strategies in the same formula. The two chosen strategies should complement each other, that is, one should address the re-emulsification issue, while the other should take care of forming a homogenous film. This "dual-strategy" approach (60) can be applied in different ways, for example:

- W/O emulsions with high silicone content
- Film-forming polymers in a liquid crystal gel network system
- Phosphate emulsifiers formulated to give a multilayer lamellar structure (61)

Test data indicate that considering the fundamental requirements in this way significantly increases the chances of achieving a water-resistant formulation.

SUMMARY

The demands of the modern sun care market mean that the formulator must be able to achieve high efficacy from the actives used in order to meet ever-increasing SPF targets. However, by a judicious choice of filters, and by considering how other aspects of the formulation influence SPF, the need for numerous and time-consuming "trial-and-error" experiments can be substantially reduced.

REFERENCES

1. Finkel P. Protection categories in place of numbers? COSSMA 2000; 1(3/2000):20–22.
2. Diffey BL. How much sun protection do we need? In: Sun Protection. Augsburg, Germany: Verlag fur Chemische Industrie, H Ziolkowsky GmbH, 2003:9–18.
3. Food and Drug Administration. Sunscreen drug products for over-the-counter human use; final monograph. Fed Reg 1999; 64:27666–27693.
4. Sottery JP. Modelling the human experiment. Educational Seminar, SCC Sunscreen Symposium, Miami, FL, 1997.
5. O'Neill JJ. Effect of skin irregularities on sunscreen efficiency. J Pharm Sci 1984; 73:888–891.
6. Brown S, Diffey BL. The effect of applied thickness on sunscreen protection: *in-vivo* and *in-vitro* studies. Chem Photobiol 1986; 44:509–513.
7. Ferrero L, Pissavini M, Zastrow L. Spectroscopy of sunscreen products: how to use basic absorbance data. Proceedings of the European UV Sunfilters Conference, Paris, 1999:52–64.
8. Tunstall DF. A mathematical approach for the analysis of *in vitro* sun protection factor measurements. J Cosmet Sci 2000; 51:303–315.
9. Laba D. Rheological Properties of Cosmetics and Toiletries. New York: Marcel Dekker, 1993.
10. Dahms GH. Influence of thixotropy on the UV absorption of sun protection emulsions. Parf Kosmet 1994; 75:675–679
11. Hewitt JP, Dahms GH. The influence of rheology on efficacy of physical sunscreens. Proceedings of the IFSCC Between-Congress Conference, Montreux, 1995:313–323.
12. Klein K. Sunscreen products: formulation and regulatory considerations. In: Lowe NJ, Shaath NA, Pathak MA, eds. Sunscreens: Development, Evaluation, and Regulatory Aspects. 2nd ed. New York: Marcel Dekker, 1997:287–292.
13. Tadros Th, Taelman M-C, Leonard S. Principles of formulation of sprayable emulsions. International Conference on Sun Protection: A Time of Change, Summit Events Ltd, London, 2003.
14. Floyd DT, Macpherson BA, Bungard A, Jenni KR. Formulation of sun protection emulsions with enhanced SPF response. Cosmet Toil 1997; 112(6):55–64.
15. Anderson MW, Hewitt JP, Spruce SR. Broad spectrum physical sunscreens. In: Lowe NJ, Shaath NA, Pathak MA, eds. Sunscreens: Development, Evaluation, and Regulatory Aspects. 2nd ed. New York: Marcel Dekker, 1997:377–379.
16. Hewitt JP, Woodruff J. Factors influencing efficacy of oil-dispersed physical sunscreens. IFSCC Mag 2000; 3(1):18–23.
17. Woodruff J. Rheology modifiers and inorganic sunscreens. Proceedings of the In-Cosmetics Conference, Dusseldorf, 1997:297–317.
18. Junginger HE. Crystalline gel structures in O/W creams. Skin Care Forum Nr. 5 Dusseldorf: Henkel KGaA, February 1993.

19. Dahms GH. Properties of oil-in-water emulsions with anisotropic lamellar phases. Cosmet Toil 1986; 101(11):113–115.
20. Dahms GH. Optimised formulations for skin-care products 1990. SÖFW 1990; 10:388–392.
21. Loll P. Liquid Crystals in Cosmetic Emulsions. Cosmetics & Toiletries Manufacture Worldwide, Aston Publishing Group, 1994:108–120.
22. Dahms GH. Choosing emollients and emulsifiers for sunscreen products. Cosmet Toil 1994; 109(11):45–52.
23. Dahms GH. Recent and future advances in sun product formulations and actives. International Conference on Broad Spectrum Sun Protection: The Issues and Status, London: Summit Events Ltd, 1997.
24. Mongiat S, Deshayes C, Konig P, Osterwalder U. Microfine organic particles UV absorber. In-Cosmetics Conference, Dusseldorf, 2001.
25. Wright C. Effects of Emollients on Efficacy of UV Filters. MChem Report. York University, 2002.
26. Agrapidis-Paloympis LE, Nash RA, Shaath NA. The effect of solvents on the ultraviolet absorbance of sunscreens. J Soc Cosmet Chem 1987; 38:209–221.
27. Shaath NA. The chemistry of sunscreens. In: Lowe NJ, Shaath NA, Pathak MA, eds. Sunscreens: Development, Evaluation, and Regulatory Aspects, 2nd ed. New York: Marcel Dekker, 1997:276–279.
28. Robb JL, Simpson LA, Tunstall DF. Scattering and absorption of UV radiation by sunscreens containing fine particle and pigmentary titanium dioxide. Drug Cosmet Ind 1994; 154(3):32–39.
29. Fairhurst D, Mitchnick MA. Particulate sun blocks: general principles. In: Lowe NJ, Shaath NA, Pathak MA, eds. Sunscreens: Development, Evaluation, and Regulatory Aspects. 2nd ed. New York: Marcel Dekker, 1997:313–352.
30. Dransfield GP, Hewitt JP, Lyth PL. Advances in titanium dioxide technology. Proceedings of the SCS Spring Conference Session on Sunscreens, London, 1998:7–18.
31. Hewitt JP. Effective use of physical sunscreens—recent advances. International conference on Broad Spectrum Sun Protection: The Issues and Status, London: Summit Events Ltd, 1997.
32. Howe AM. Formulating hydrophobic pigments via the water phase. SCC Florida Sunscreen Symposium, Orlando, 2003.
33. Hewitt JP. Formulating with aqueous TiO_2 dispersions. European Sunfilters Conference, Paris: Step Exhibitions Ltd, 2003.
34. Woodruff J. Formulating Sun Care Products with Micronised Oxides. Cosmetics & Toiletries Manufacture Worldwide, Aston Publishing Group, 1994:179–185.
35. Catlow B. Formulating with ultrafine TiO_2. SOFW J 1993; 119:497–500.
36. Dahms GH. Formulating with a physical sun block. Cosmet Toil 1992; 107(10):87–92.
37. Angelinetta C, Barzaghi G. Influence of oil polarity on SPF in liquid crystal emulsions with ultrafine TiO_2 pre-dispersed in oil, and cross-linking polymers. Cosmet News (Italy) 1995; 100:20–24.
38. Catlow B. In search of ultimate protection. SPC 1993; 66(3):29–30.
39. Spruce SR. Formulation efficacy of zinc oxide. Proceedings of the In-Cosmetics Conference, Barcelona, 1994:275–292.
40. Tapley C. Broad spectrum protection. SOFW J 1994; 120:518.

41. Diffey BL. Dosimetry of UV radiation. In: Lowe NJ, Shaath NA, Pathak MA, eds. Sunscreens: Development, Evaluation, and Regulatory Aspects. 2nd ed. New York: Marcel Dekker, 1997:178.
42. Rieger MM. Photostability of cosmetic ingredients on the skin. Cosmet Toil 1997; 112(6):65–72.
43. Marginean Lazar G, Fructus AE, Baillet A, Bocquet JL, Thomas P, Marty JP. Sunscreens' photochemical behaviour: in vivo evaluation by the stripping method. Int J Cosmet Sci 1997; 19:87–101.
44. European patent 0 514 491.
45. European patent 0 456 460 A2.
46. UK patent 2 279 007.
47. UK patent 2 278 055.
48. European patent 0 456 458 A2.
49. US patent 5 417 961.
50. International patent WO 94/04131.
51. Spruce SR. 5th Florida SCC Sunscreen Symposium, Orlando, 1995.
52. Stokes RP, Diffey BL. A novel *ex vivo* technique to assess the sand/rub resistance of sunscreen products. Int J Cosmet Sci 2000; 22:329–334.
53. Ferguson J. Evaluation of the effectiveness of UV sunscreens—water resistance. Proceedings of the 24th Symposium of the Belgian Association of Dermato-Cosmetic Sciences, September 2001:F1–F7.
54. Sun Products Formulary. Cosmet Toil 1994; 109(11):71–94.
55. Sun Products Formulary. Cosmet Toil 1996; 111(12):131–160.
56. Van Reeth I, Blakely J. Use of current and new test methods to demonstrate the benefits of alkylmethylsiloxanes in suncare products. Proceedings of the European UV Sunfilters Conference, Paris, 1999:65–74.
57. Gallagher KF. A new phosphate emulsifier for sunscreens. Cosmet Toil 1998; 113(2):73–80.
58. Gupta VK, Zatz JL. *In vitro* method for modelling water resistance of sunscreen formulations. J Cosmet Sci 1999; 50:79–90.
59. Markovic B, Laura D, Rerek M. A laboratory method for measuring the water resistance of sunscreens. Cosmet Toil 2001; 116(9):61–68.
60. Hewitt JP. Formulating water-resistant TiO_2 sunscreens. Cosmet Toil 1999; 114(9):59–63.
61. Gao T, Tien J-M, Choi Y-H. Sunscreen formulas with multilayer lamella structure. Cosmet Toil 2003; 118(10):41–52.

20

The Role of Surfactants in Sunscreen Formulations

Gerd Dahms
Institüt für Angewandte Colloidtechnologie, Duisberg, Germany

Although the formulation of emulsions is not all that easy, they are the most frequently used vehicle for UV filters. Here, as in all emulsions, the most important structural element is the emulsifier system used; this system is primarily responsible for the stability of the sunscreen emulsion. In addition to ensuring emulsion stability across a broad temperature range, the emulsifier system used contributes to many other quality characteristics of a sunscreen product, for example, easy spreadability on the skin, the waterproofness of the formulation, the film formation during and after application, the stability of the degree of dispersion of micropigments, and product safety—to name only a few examples.

Even today a suitable emulsifier system is selected for sun protection products on a purely empirical basis in most cases. However, this approach results in an optimum selection of emulsifiers in only a few cases—and even less frequently when the formulating chemist has to choose from among an overwhelming assortment of emulsifiers.

For this reason, this chapter intends to explore the role of the emulsifier in sunscreen products more closely and thus facilitate a targeted and product-specific selection of emulsifiers for sun protection products.

THE ROLE OF EMULSIFIERS IN GENERAL

The relationships between the chemical structure of surfactants and their emulsifying effect are quite complicated because, in general, the oil and the aqueous phase are of variable composition. It is not possible, therefore, to classify individual surfactants as general emulsifiers. Nevertheless, we can set down several general guidelines which can be useful for selecting surfactants as emulsifiers.

To be effective, an emulsifier must possess the following qualities:

1. It must generate a sufficiently low interfacial tension at the oil–water interface to make the emulsification process possible at all. It must be possible, therefore, for the emulsifier to migrate to the oil–water interface and be firmly fixed there instead of remaining in the bulk phase. Hence, there must be a balance between the hydrophilic and lipophilic groups in the emulsifier.
2. At the oil–water interface, the emulsifier, acting on its own or together with other molecules, must form a resilient, elastic, and condensed film. On the basis of our present knowledge, such films occurring in cosmetic products such as sunscreen emulsions consist of liquid crystalline surfactant structures.
3. It must be available at the oil–water interface quickly enough to ensure that the interfacial tension is reduced to a sufficient degree during the emulsification process.
4. It must be adapted to the polarity of the oil phase. Very polar oils require emulsifiers that are more hydrophilic than do oils with low polarity.

The reduction of the interfacial tension between oil and water is only one criterion for the dispersion of droplets during the emulsification process proper; however, it is of secondary importance for the stability of the emulsion.

Whether an oil-in-water (o/w) or a water-in-oil (w/o) emulsion will be formed depends primarily on the selection of the emulsifier. Which of the two emulsion types is formed depends on the solubility of the emulsifier in the phases. According to Bancroft's rule, the phase in which the emulsifier is most soluble will constitute the external continuous phase. However, this maxim should be viewed with caution. In particular, solid lipophilic coemulsifiers, which are by nature soluble in oil, can migrate at temperatures above their melting point to the water phase, thereby forming with small amounts of a hydrophilic surfactant mixed micelles. As a result, such systems form oil-in-water emulsions. Since the interfacial film has two surfaces, we can apply the Windsor principle which says that a film will bend on the side with the higher interfacial tension. In other words, the curvature will enclose the dispersed phase (1–4).

In addition to Bancroft's rule and the Windsor principle, the "oriented wedge theory" can also be used to derive the type of emulsion. According to this theory, the part of the surfactant with the larger cross-section will also always project into the continuous phase. Thus, a typical W/O emulsifier always has a hydrophobic part exhibiting a larger cross-section than its hydrophilic part.

In addition to the criteria stated above, which depend on the solubility, the interfacial tension behavior, or the molecular geometry of the emulsifier, there is also the phase–volume theory, which states that above the densest sphere packing, a breakdown of the emulsion or phase inversion will occur.

Depending on the structure and concentration of the emulsifier, however, this limit can be exceeded without the emulsion breaking down or inverting. In such cases, the emulsion structure will change and be converted into a single-phase microemulsion after the critical phase–volume ratio has been exceeded. Such systems are used in sunscreens only very rarely even though they have a high potential for incorporation in highly efficient sunscreen products, especially with regard to film formation.

FILM FORMATION

We do not know what actually happens to an emulsion on the skin during and after application. The analytical methods at our disposal determining film-forming properties are either unsatisfactory or too complicated. In a first approximation, however, we can look at the spreading equilibrium of liquids on solids in combination with the rheological properties of the emulsion and its oil phase in order to achieve a better understanding of film formation.

When a droplet of liquid or, in our case, a droplet of emulsion is placed on the surface of a solid body, it can either spread over the solid body or remain there in the form of a droplet with a defined contact angle θ. Figure 20.1 shows various contact angles.

Assuming that various surface forces are represented by interfacial tensions, we see that they can act in the direction of the surfaces. For the three phases, that is, air (A), liquid (L) and solid surface (S), that are found at one point, we obtain Young's equation by vector addition (Fig. 20.2):

$$\gamma_{SA} = \gamma_{SL} + \gamma_{LA} \cos \theta \qquad (20.1)$$

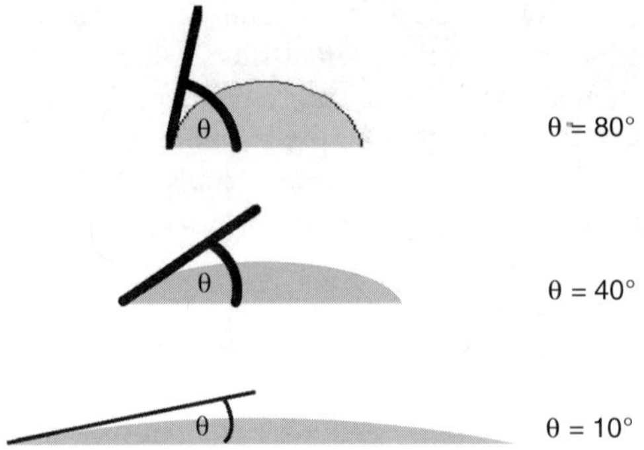

Figure 20.1 Contact angles between liquids and solids.

where γ_{SA} is the solid–air interfacial tension, γ_{SL} is the solid–liquid interfacial tension, γ_{LA} is the liquid–air interfacial tension, θ is the liquid–solid contact angle.

Generally, $\theta \leq 90^\circ$ is correlated with wetting and $\theta > 90^\circ$ with nonwetting. By combining Eq. (20.1) with Dupré's equation,

$$W_{SL} = \gamma_{SA} - \gamma_{SL} + \gamma_{LA} \tag{20.2}$$

we obtain the Young–Dupré equation:

$$W_{SL} = \gamma_{LA}(1 + \cos\theta) \tag{20.3}$$

According to this equation, a reduction of γ_{LA} by means of a wetting agent always causes a reduction of the contact angle θ and thus improved spreading (Fig. 20.3). This has been proven by *in vivo* testing on the human forearm (5).

However, the wetting process taking place on a nonsmooth surface containing capillaries, that is, a surface similar to the skin, is even more complex than that described here since the penetration of the liquid into the capillaries, that is, the folds of the skin, also has to be taken into account. The following applies to penetration by a liquid (Fig. 20.4)

$$P = \frac{2\gamma_{LA}\cos\theta}{r} \tag{20.4}$$

where P is the capillary pressure and r is the capillary radius.

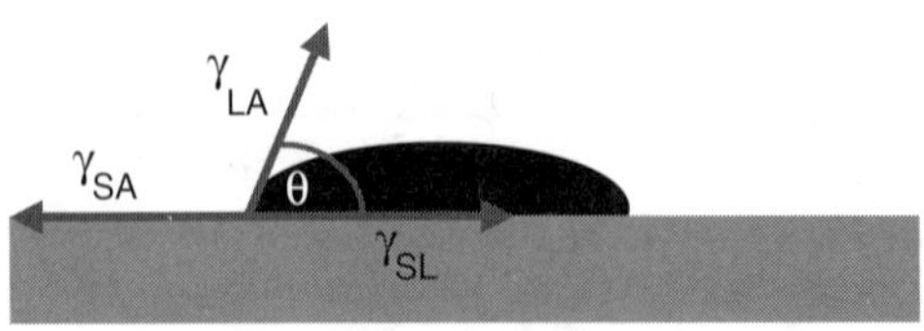

Figure 20.2 Spreading equilibrium according to Young.

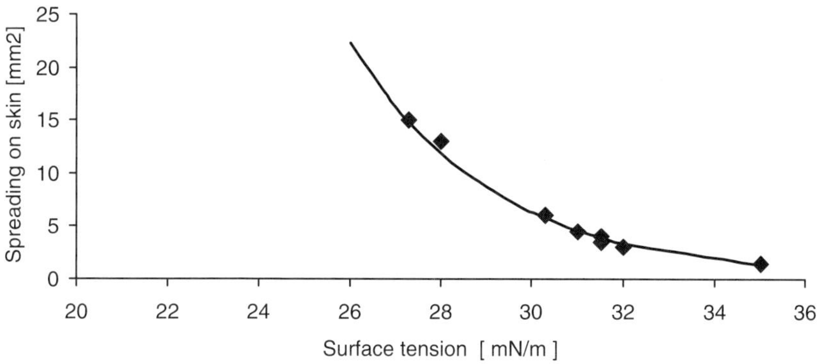

Figure 20.3 Impact of surface tension γ_{LA} of oils on spreading on skin according to Kaymer (5).

According to Washburn, the wetting of a rough surface containing capillaries over time can be described by the following equation:

$$\frac{dl}{dt} = \frac{r\gamma_{LA} \cos\theta}{4^* \eta^* l} \tag{20.5}$$

where l is the depth of penetration, t is the time of wetting, and η is the viscosity of the liquid.

It is important for the wetting process that the contact angle θ is $<90^\circ$ and that the rate of penetration into the capillaries is relatively high.

According to the Washburn equation, quick penetration occurs at a high value of $\gamma_{LA} \cos\theta$, a small contact angle θ, a low viscosity η, and a large diameter of the folds of the skin. A high value for γ_{LA} and a low contact angle θ are mutually exclusive.

According to Young's equation, however, the following applies:

$$\gamma_{LA} \cos\theta = \frac{\gamma_{SA}}{\gamma_{SL}} - 1 \tag{20.6}$$

Thus, as soon as the interfacial tension between the solid body and the liquid approaches zero, $\gamma_{LA} \cos\theta$ takes on high values. The interfacial tension between a solid body and a liquid cannot be determined with sufficient accuracy. Moreover, it is difficult to find reliable values in the literature. Nevertheless, the

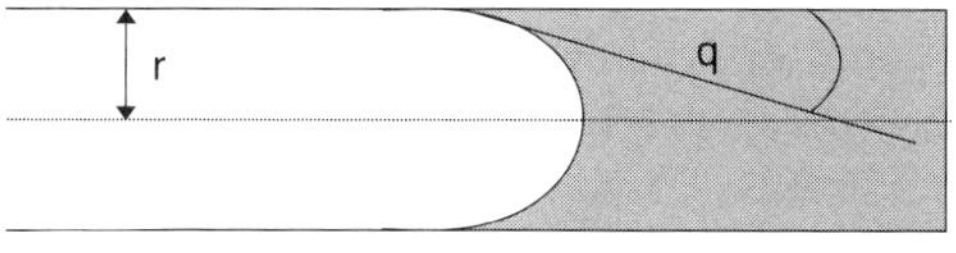

Figure 20.4 Penetration of a liquid into a capillary.

old rule that polar solids are wetted well by polar liquids is very useful here. In other words, the higher the affinity of a liquid to the surface of a solid body, the better the liquid will spread.

The spreading of liquids on the skin can be simulated quite well on filter paper because both skin and filter paper represent porous and absorbing surfaces. In this context, however, we must point out that it is not possible to use filter paper as a general skin model. It is suitable, however, for performing the first investigations, using the technique of approximation, on the spreadability of oils on the skin. For comparative spreading studies a defined quantity of oil dispersion is trickled onto filter paper and the spreading radius determined in defined time intervals. The spreading speed of the pure oils and of the oil–pigment dispersions can be determined quite easily in this manner.

The independent spreading of pigment-in-oil dispersions, which was measured without additional rubbing, is indeed an important indicator of spreading on the skin. However, it cannot completely reflect the spreading process taking place during rubbing-in under the effect of shear forces since, under the influence of shear forces, the viscosity η of structured dispersions can be reduced or, alternately, flocculation of the pigments on the skin can be induced. The risk of migropigments flocculating on the skin when rubbed in increases with pigment concentration. In most cases, flocculation of the micropigments manifests itself as a whitening of the micropigments during rubbing. In the area of the hair follicles, in particular, this is a constant danger. If there are good spreading conditions for the oil in which the pigments have been dispersed and the average particle diameter is larger than the pores on the hair follicles, only the pure oil will penetrate the pores. As a result, the concentration of the pigment will increase in the oil phase above the pores. If, during this process, the pigment in the oil phase is enriched up to concentrations close to the critical phase–volume range, during application irreversible flocculation will occur in insufficiently stabilized pigment dispersions, that is, the aggregates generated cannot be redispersed by further rubbing. As flocculation increases, and the average diameter of the particles becomes larger, wetting decreases.

In order to form the required uniform film, micropigments must be dispersed in a manner resistant to the effect of shear forces. The dispersing agent must, on the one hand, be well anchored in the pigment surface and, on the other hand, display a good skin affinity in order to form, by means of an anchoring mechanism, a homogenous layer on the skin which almost completely absorbs and reflects the UV light hitting the skin. PVP and their alkyl-substituted derivatives are good dispersing agents satisfying these requirements.

Although the spreading of the oil phase is the basic prerequisite for film formation, the rheology of the oil phase plays a decisive role in the creation of a film with a sufficient layer thickness on the skin (6). The rule of thumb for a high photoprotection effect is that the film must have a corresponding thickness. It is obvious that a film can only achieve a high layer thickness when the viscosity of the film-forming substance is high. High viscosity, however, is in conflict with spreadability. Viscoelastic behavior represents a compromise here.

In a resting state, substances with viscoelastic behavior display very high viscosities. Under the effect of shear forces, however, such as those that occur when an emulsion is rubbed into the skin, the viscosity can take on a low value in comparison with the value in the resting state. The viscosity values for a viscoelastic oil phase under the effect of shear forces are usually 10 times higher than that of an oil phase with Newtonian flow. In accordance with the Washburn equation, the spreading of such viscoelastic systems depends primarily on the value of $\gamma_{LA} \cos \theta$, which is directly connected to the interfacial tension γ_{SL} existing between the viscoelastic liquid and the solid surface of the skin. As discussed above, this value can be sufficiently reduced only by the affinity of the emulsifier and coemulsifier to the skin during film formation by sunscreen lotions. Thus, for achieving the required viscoelasticity of the photoprotection film, γ_{SL} is the only variable available to guarantee sufficient spreading. Hence, the selection of the emulsifier system to be used plays a key role.

After having discussed the fundamental principles of spreading and the penetration of the skin by emulsions and oils so far, we will now explore the practical application of these principles to show the role played by the emulsifiers used in sunscreen formulations.

Films are formed on the skin by sunscreen emulsions in two steps. In the first step the emulsion is spread over the skin; a pure emulsion film is formed. In the second step, during which the emulsion is rubbed further into the skin, the aqueous phase is caused to evaporate and the oil film is massaged into the skin. However, the underlying mechanism is quite different for W/O and O/W emulsions.

When a W/O emulsion is applied, it is the continuous external oil phase which first comes into contact with the skin. Consequently, for this type of emulsion, it is primarily the spreading and penetration capability of the oil phase which is decisive for film formation. With the exception of silicone emulsifiers, W/O emulsifiers are not capable of significantly reducing the interfacial tension γ_{LA}. Accordingly, spreading and penetration by the oil phase can only take place to a significant extent as a result of the interfacial tension between the oil phase and the skin. According to the rule that the high affinity of the liquid phase to a solid body leads to high spreadability, only emulsifiers exhibiting a high affinity to the skin can be employed to reduce γ_{SL} to a sufficient degree. For this purpose, all emulsifiers with hydrophilic amino-functional head groups can naturally be used. Especially, alkyl modified PVP derivatives and hydrophobic amino-functional silicones seem to work best. By bridging these groups with the skin, the interfacial tension γ_{SL} can then be reduced to a sufficient degree, resulting in spreading of the film.

The required viscoelastic behavior of the oil phase is achieved by adding waxes. In order to obtain a favorable viscoelasticity achieving sufficiently low values during shearing and permitting extremely high viscosity values in the resting state, a favorable wax structure and an optimum concentration must be found for the selected oil phase. Figure 20.5 demonstrates the influence of wax structure and concentration in a simple W/O sunscreen formulation.

The process of film formation by an O/W emulsion is much more complex in comparison with the same process for a W/O emulsion. It is true that during application, in this case as well, the pure emulsion is spread over the skin during the first step. In the case of an O/W emulsion, however, there is no film formation by the oily photoprotection phase at this stage. Spreading of the emulsion provides only the basis for such formation. Only in the second step, when the aqueous phase evaporates and the critical phase volume is exceeded, does film formation start after the emulsion has been rubbed in further. After the critical phase–volume ratio has been exceeded, there are two possible scenarios. Either the emulsion breaks and the oil droplets quickly coalesce to create a homogenous film when rubbed in further or the emulsion is converted into a single-phase microemulsion in which the remaining amount of water is present in stored form. If the microemulsion is distributed further, it will display a behavior similar to that of a W/O emulsion.

When an O/W emulsion comes into contact with the skin, the spreading that occurs during the primary distribution initially depends on the interfacial tension γ_{SA} of the aqueous phase to the skin and the viscosity of the emulsion when the emulsion is rubbed in. It is doubtful, however, whether these conditions suffice to cover all inner folds of the skin and pores with the emulsion. Distribution of the emulsion is important mainly as preparation for the eventual spreading of the oil film. During distribution, only the rheological properties of the emulsion appear to be important. If these have been favorably designed, it creates a good basis for the decisive film formation phase.

During distribution of the O/W emulsion, the water phase, in particular, is distributed. Depending on the interfacial tension γ_{LA} and the viscosity η_{Ext} of the

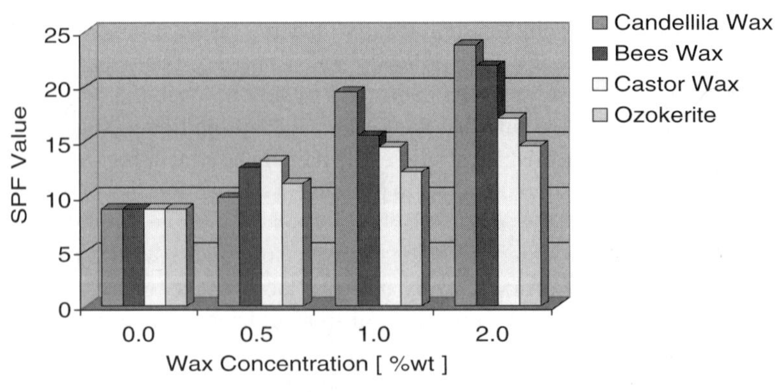

Figure 20.5 Impact of wax concentration and structure on SPF value.

external aqueous phase, the water also reaches the pores and the folds of the skin. The more the pores and folds of skin that get into contact with the aqueous phase, the more the skin is hydrated. Sufficient hydration of the skin leads often to a higher SPF efficiency (7).

Actual spreading of the sunscreen film starts only when most of the water has evaporated and the concentration of the oil phase has exceeded the critical phase–volume fraction. At this point, it depends on the emulsifier system used whether a coherent microemulsion film is formed or the emulsion breaks down and only the pure oil phase is spread.

If a microemulsion is formed during dry-down of the emulsion on skin, during this transition state the system takes on a slightly higher viscosity which, however, breaks down upon being rubbed in further and thus achieves the required lower values. From the point of view of the Washburn equation, this means that independent spreading without further rubbing is nearly excluded due to the high viscosity. As the water is more strongly bound in the microemulsion than in a normal emulsion, the evaporation process is delayed. At this stage, spreading of the emulsion is determined by the liquid crystalline structure. We can proceed on the assumption that the interfacial tension γ_{SL} of the microemulsion to the skin drops to nearly zero and good spreading and penetration are guaranteed at this stage. We do not know how long this intermediate condition of the microemulsion is maintained. In many cases, however, we can expect that the microemulsion will survive the period of normal rubbing in and that film formation will start relatively late. This process probably plays a decisive role in the delayed occurrence of the maximum SPF value which is described in the literature (8).

Proceeding on the assumption that the microemulsion changes over time by losing the stored water into a pure oil phase, we see that at this point spreading and penetration display the behavior already described for the W/O emulsion. The emulsifier mixture, which has to generate the low interfacial tension γ_{SL} required for spreading, is now responsible for this phenomenon.

If the stage of microemulsion formation is not attained during the rubbing-in of an emulsion, de-emulsification will occur when the critical phase–volume ratio φ_c is exceeded in the emulsion. Subsequently, rubbing will only lead to spreading of the oil phase.

Whereas in W/O emulsions the required viscoelasticity of the oil phase is controlled by waxes, in most O/W sunscreen emulsions the viscosity is regulated by means of the mixed emulsifier system used. As a result, modifications of the viscoelastic behavior can only be achieved in such cases via the emulsifier composition and its concentration ratio compared with the oil phase. Achieving this type of optimization is not all that simple, however, because both changes in emulsifier concentration and variations in emulsifier composition can exert a detrimental effect on emulsion stability.

It should be noted, moreover, that, in contrast to an oil–wax film, the emulsifier–oil film can absorb water from the skin and store it. When the storage space for the bound water is larger than one photon, light can pass through it without being filtered. The possibility of such gaps in the photoprotection film occurring for O/W emulsions is demonstrated by the fact that the addition of water-soluble UV filters often creates synergistic effects with regard to the photoprotection effect. On the basis of the small amount of data available, we are at the moment not in a position to make a useful prediction as to which emulsifier system can store larger amounts of water in which oil phase. Further investigations need to be conducted on this subject.

O/W SUNSCREEN FORMULATIONS

The majority of sun protection formulations are based on complex mixed emulsifier systems. Mixed emulsifiers of this kind are built up from micelle-forming hydrophilic emulsifiers and lipophilic coemulsifiers. Depending on their composition, mixed emulsifiers may be capable of creating membrane-like multilamellar liquid-crystalline structures in aqueous phases; in emulsions these structures can envelop the dispersed phase in a multilamellar membrane as well as create gel networks in the continuous water phase.

Mixed emulsifiers exhibit a multifunctional behavior in emulsion structures. The lamellar gel network structure running, in the form of a gel structure, through the continuous water phase is responsible for the flow behavior of an emulsion and its stability against creaming (Fig. 20.6). The viscosity η of an emulsion with a lamellar gel network running through the water phase rises

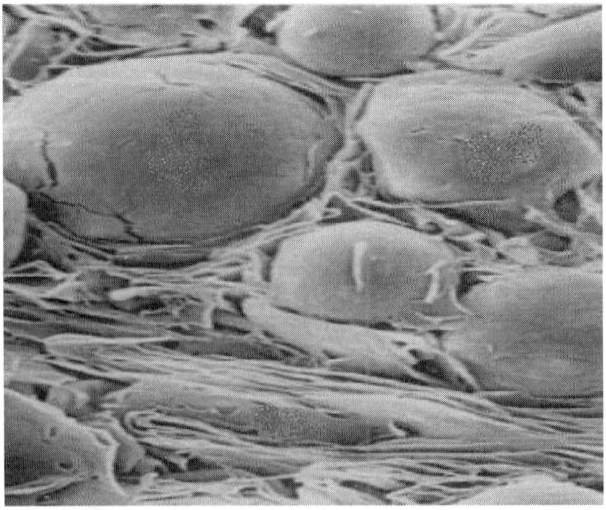

Figure 20.6 TEM of an O/W emulsion containing gel network structures.

exponentially as the liquid-crystalline gel structure increases:

$$\eta = A\mathrm{e}^{(BC_{\mathrm{G}})} \tag{20.7}$$

where η is the emulsion viscosity, C_{G} is the gel network concentration, and A and B are constants. If the concentration of the gel network phase in an O/W emulsion is low, flowable liquid emulsions will be formed. At higher concentrations, the viscosity increases and emulsions with a creamy to solid consistency are created.

According to Stoke's Law, the creaming behavior or sedimentation of the dispersed phase is described by the following equation:

$$V = \frac{2R^2 \Delta\rho g}{9\eta} \tag{20.8}$$

where V is the creaming/sedimentation velocity, R is the particle radius, $\Delta\rho$ is the density difference between the oil and water phases, η is the emulsion viscosity, and g is the gravity constant.

It is evident, from the Eq. (20.8), that the rate of creaming and sedimentation drops sharply at increasing gel network concentrations, that is, as the viscosity η rises. It is thus possible to stabilize an O/W emulsion by boosting the concentration of the mixed emulsifier. If micropigments are worked into the emulsion as sunscreen filters, the difference in density $\Delta\rho$ will quite naturally rise appreciably. Here again this tendency can be counteracted by raising the concentration of mixed emulsifier.

The gel network structure only exists, however, within a certain temperature range. Above a critical temperature, the gel network phase will collapse and the viscosity of the emulsion will consequently decrease to the same extent. In the temperature range in which the gel network is completely dissolved, the viscosity of the emulsion will conform to the expanded Einstein equation:

$$\eta = \eta_{\mathrm{k}} \left[\frac{1 + (1 + 2.5\eta_{\mathrm{dk}})\varphi}{1 + \eta_{\mathrm{dk}}} \right] \tag{20.9}$$

where $\eta_{\mathrm{dk}} = \eta_{\mathrm{d}}/\eta_{\mathrm{k}}$, η_{d} is the viscosity of the dispersed phase, η_{k} is the viscosity of the continuous phase, and φ is the phase volume fraction.

The critical temperature range in which the structure-forming gel network is broken down depends primarily on the melting point of the mixed emulsifier. The lower the melting point, the lower the critical temperature at which the gel network breaks down. This process is reversible, that is, when the temperature falls below this critical temperature, the gel network will be built up again. The critical temperature range can be determined relatively easily analytically by rheological measurements or conductivity determination.

The critical temperature spectrum can be reliably identified by determining the complex shear modulus G^* by rheological oscillation measurements (Fig. 20.7). If we plot ln G^* vs. temperature, we see that G^* remains relatively

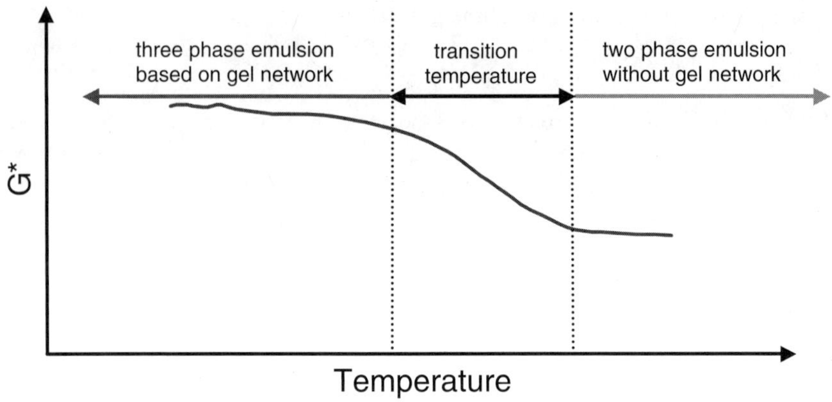

Figure 20.7 Determination of temperature-dependent states in three-phase O/W emulsions by complex shear modulus G^*.

constant in the temperature range in which the gel network is stable. In the temperature range in which the gel network breaks down, however, G^* drops sharply; it does not take on constant values again until the gel network has dissolved completely.

With the commonly used mixed emulsifiers, we can achieve a critical temperature range of about 40–45°C in sunscreen formulations. Since sunscreen emulsions are often exposed to temperatures above this critical range, however, hydrocolloids have to be added to ensure that the emulsion will have sufficient stability even in higher temperature ranges. Taking film formation and the compatibility of the emulsion with micropigments into account, we see that only a limited number of hydrocolloids are suitable for this purpose. To promote film formation, the selected hydrocolloids, which first come into contact with the skin when an emulsion is rubbed in, must form a compatible intermediate layer between the skin and the sunscreen film. Hydrocolloids with amino-functional groups appear to be advantageous in this context. Quite frequently, the commonly used cross-polymers of the carbomer or Permulen® type display very poor compatibility with micropigments. If cross-polymers are mixed with linear polymers such as xanthan gum or PVP, however, incompatibility with micropigments can no longer be detected.

As already mentioned, mixed emulsifiers are not only responsible for the creation of gel networks in O/W emulsions, but they also cover the interface of the dispersed oil phase with multilamellar liquid-crystalline layers. Below the critical gel network temperature, these layers form a solid mechanical barrier which prevents the droplets from coalescing when they come too close to each other. Above the critical temperature, the viscosity of this barrier declines markedly. If two droplets collide in this state, the lamellar layers may merge. A fusion process of this kind may lead to coalescence, depending on the size of the droplets and the thickness of the lamellar layer. Large droplets with a thin lamellar layer coalesce more readily than small droplets with a relatively thick lamellar layer. If the outer shell of the droplets is covered by linear polymers, fusion and coalescence can be prevented by steric repulsion. At the very most, aggregation caused by the entanglement of polymer layers will then occur.

The lamellar layer built up by the mixed emulsifiers displays favorable properties with respect to the emulsification process as well. It is known that liquid-crystalline lamellar structures reduce the interfacial tension between oil and water to extremely low values. Nature also makes use of this phenomenon in the production of milk. During the milk production process, oil droplets come into contact with a liquid-crystalline membrane; the droplets are stably emulsified by this membrane with practically no input of energy. The emulsification process for O/W emulsions can proceed in a similar low-energy fashion on the basis of mixed emulsifiers. If new emulsification techniques (9) are employed in a laminar and viscous flow field, even nanoemulsions may result. If the emulsification process is carried out with conventional methods, care should be taken that a turbulent flow field prevails during the mixing process.

It is advantageous in any case to place the mixed emulsifier in the oil phase; care should be taken, however, to always add the oil phase to the water phase. Placing the emulsifier in the oil phase during the emulsification process leads to the "stranding" phenomenon. When the mixed emulsifiers diffuse out of the oil phase into the water phase during mixing, they tear oil droplets from the phase interface of the bulk oil phase. These oil droplets then strand finely dispersed in the water phase. The "stranding" process is thus very close to the process found in self-emulsifying systems.

The most favorable emulsification temperature lies in the range just above the melting point of the mixed emulsifiers (Fig. 20.8). If a homogenization

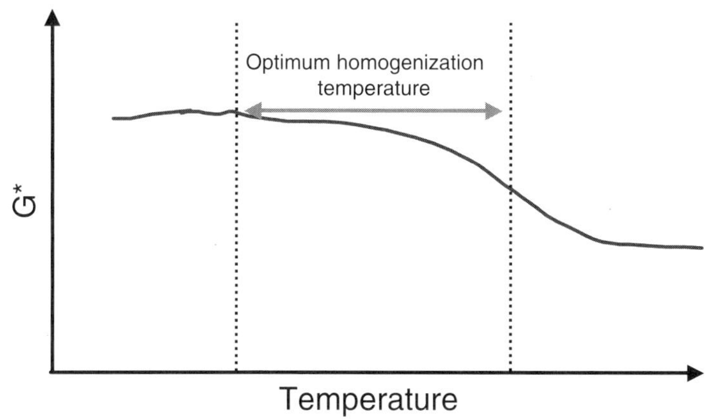

Figure 20.8 Determination of optimum emulsification temperature of O/W emulsions by complex shear modulus G^*.

process is necessary, it should always be carried out slightly below the melting point of the mixed emulsifiers since the interfacial tension reaches its minimum value here.

The favorable dermatological characteristics of the mixed emulsifiers are among their multifunctional properties. Multilamellar gel networks have a positive effect on transepidermal water loss (TEWL). This effect appears to be of interest for the formulation of sun protection products since it is general knowledge that longer exposure to UV radiation dries out the skin. In predamaged skin as well, however, the addition of an aqueous gel network dispersion results in much quicker regulation of the TEWL value than can be achieved by the skin's natural healing process (Fig. 20.9).

In addition to the properties discussed so far, gel networks can also incorporate amphiphilic sunscreen filters into their membrane structure. All molecules with a structure including a free hydrophilic group can be classified as amphiphilic sunscreen filters. Two examples are octyl salicylate and avobenzone.

The admittance of amphiphilic sunscreen filters into the gel network structure can have both positive and negative repercussions. The process leading to these inclusions will be discussed later in this chapter on emulsifier optimization.

Among the positive qualities of the gel networks is the protective effect they exert against changes in the structure of the sunscreen filters. Inside the gel networks the molecules placed firmly in the lamella are protected for the most part against attack from the outside. A good example of how sensitive sunscreen filters can be protected by being incorporated into the gel network lamella is provided by avobenzone. In oily media avobenzone forms crystalline complexes together with microcrystalline titanium dioxide, for example; the nature of these complexes remains largely unexplored. After only a few days,

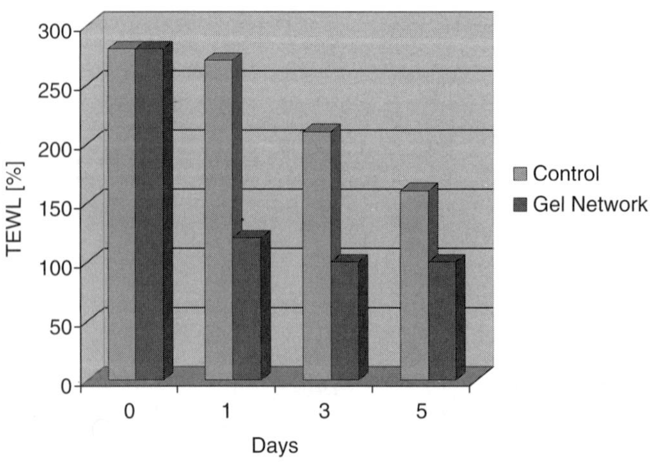

Figure 20.9 Impact of gel networks on TEWL.

submarine-shaped crystal structures are formed in oily titanium dioxide dispersions containing dissolved avobenzone; the concentration of these crystal structures rises quickly with storage time. In O/W emulsions in which avobenzone has been firmly incorporated in the liquid-crystalline lamella of the gel network, incompatibility with microcrystalline titanium dioxide is not created.

If avobenzone is incorporated in gel network lamella, it can be assumed, moreover, that the undesirable keto-enol tautomerism does not take place or at least occurs with a noticeable time delay.

The changed rheological behavior of the emulsion testifies to the fact that avobenzone has actually been taken up by the mixed micelles since any change in the viscosity behavior of an O/W emulsion built up from gel networks must be attributable solely to changes within the gel network structure. Increasing the avobenzone concentration in a defined emulsion causes the viscosity of the emulsion to rise exponentially along with the avobenzone concentration, that is, as the avobenzone concentration rises, the gel network concentration will go up as well (Fig. 20.10).

Like avobenzone, octyl salicylate is incorporated at least partially into gel networks. As a liquid component, octyl salicylate, when incorporated into the lamella of a gel network, exerts an effect on the critical gel network temperature and thus on the thermal stability of the emulsion. The critical gel network temperature drops steadily as the concentration of octyl salicylate rises.

If sunscreen filters are built into gel network lamella, disturbances may occur in the film formation process. If the gel network is not completely broken down during the drying phase on the skin so that all of its components are fused homogenously with the oil phase, homogenous spreading of the amphiphilic sunscreen filters will not be possible either. As a result, the efficiency of this UV filter as a sunscreen will be reduced. Care should be taken during emulsion formation, therefore, to ensure that the emulsion goes through a critical phase during drying in which the existence of the gel network comes to an end.

So far we have discussed only the multifunctional properties of mixed emulsifiers in O/W emulsions. In the following we will be looking into the

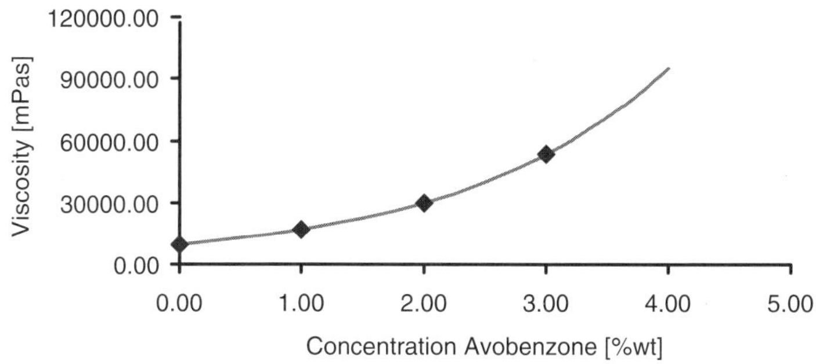

Figure 20.10 Impact of avobenzone concentration on three-phase O/W emulsion viscosity.

question of how to find the right combination of single emulsifiers for a mixed emulsifier composition.

A basic observation to be made about an O/W emulsion consisting of an oily phase, an aqueous phase, and an emulsifier is that it will always be unstable when the emulsifier system consists solely of either hydrophilic micelle-forming emulsifiers or lipophilic coemulsifiers. Only a combination of hydrophilic emulsifiers and lipophilic coemulsifiers results in stable systems. Emulsifier combinations of this kind are referred to as mixed emulsifiers.

Before going into the details of the actual combination technique used to manufacture mixed emulsifiers, we will first discuss the mechanism by which liquid-crystalline lamellar structures are formed from mixed emulsifiers. The formation of micelles, which are present in the aqueous phase in spherical or disk form, constitutes the basis for the formation of liquid-crystalline lamellar structures. If the number of micelles in an aqueous system exceeds the critical concentration, the micelles will be converted to the rod form. A further increase in the rod micelle concentration causes the formation of lamellar liquid-crystalline structures superimposed on the micelles (10). Accordingly, a sufficient concentration of emulsifier micelles serves as the basis for the formation of lamellar structures. If the lamellar structures are cooled below the melting point of the emulsifiers they contain, solid gel networks may be formed.

The role played by the hydrophilic emulsifier becomes clear at this point. A useful rule of thumb when drawing up the definition of a hydrophilic emulsifier is that such emulsifiers have an hydrophilic lipophilic balance (HLB) value >6. Emulsifiers with an HLB value <5 can be defined as coemulsifiers. Coemulsifiers can be taken up by the micelles of a hydrophilic emulsifier, thereby creating mixed micelles.

The concentration of a coemulsifier in a mixed micelle may be several times the concentration of the hydrophilic emulsifier present at that location. The ratio between the concentration of the hydrophilic emulsifier and the concentration of the lipophilic coemulsifier depends, in the first approximation, on the HLB value of the latter. The higher the HLB value of the coemulsifier, the higher is the proportion of the mixed micelle it accounts for.

During the formation of mixed micelles, the geometric properties of the participating emulsifier molecules naturally also play a role. Thus, not every micelle is capable of taking up every coemulsifier in sufficient amounts to create the critical concentration of mixed micelles leading to the formation of liquid-crystalline lamellar structures.

It is fairly easy to select hydrophilic emulsifiers. Regardless of their structure, nearly all emulsifiers or surfactants which form micelles in aqueous systems can serve as building blocks for mixed emulsifiers. Selecting a suitable coemulsifier is admittedly somewhat more difficult.

Initially, only emulsifiers that exist in solid form at room temperature are potential coemulsifiers since only solid emulsifiers can give the gel network the necessary mechanical strength.

Microscopic examination is the best method of determining whether a selected coemulsifier builds up the necessary lamellar structure with a hydrophilic emulsifier. To perform this examination, first coat part of a microscopic slide with the selected solid coemulsifier. Then, using a dropper, deposit an ~10 wt.% of aqueous solution of the hydrophilic emulsifier at the interface with the coemulsifier.

Next, heat the slide slowly to the melting temperature of the coemulsifier. Using polarized light, observe the interface. If the formation of lamellar liquid-crystalline structures can be observed at the phase interface after a certain time, you can assume that the emulsifier and the coemulsifier will form the desired lamellar structure if they are mixed in the correct proportions (Fig. 20.11). Table 20.1 provides an overview of several classes of hydrophilic emulsifiers and the matching coemulsifiers.

From the discussion so far, it is very evident that, in addition to the coemulsifiers, there are other molecules which also have an amphiphilic structure and can thus be easily incorporated into mixed micelles which can be inserted into liquid-crystalline lamellar structures. The substances which can be included in sunscreen formulations for this purpose include, in particular, sunscreen filters, film-forming agents, and certain active agents.

The process of optimizing a mixed emulsifier system is based on the following assumption. Lamellar gel networks are always formed from mixed micelles containing a maximum concentration of coemulsifier; geometrical considerations are also taken into account here. Below the maximum coemulsifier concentration, the curvature displayed by the lamellar sandwich structure of the gel network increases, owing to the growing number of voluminous head groups in the hydrophilic emulsifier. Since not all of the micelles in a mixed micelle system have the same composition and number of aggregates, an

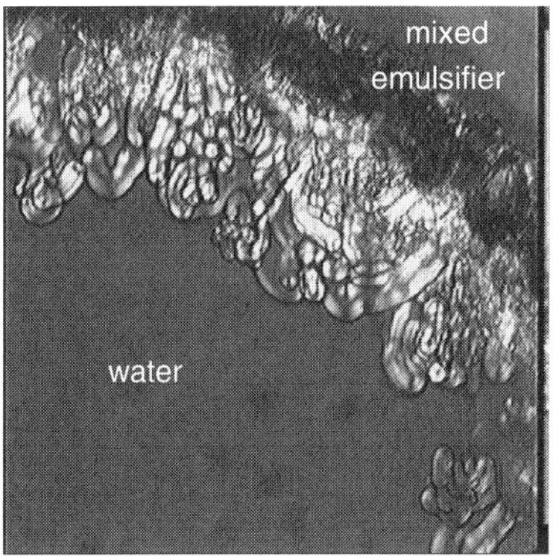

Figure 20.11 Lamellar liquid crystalline myelin structures formed at the mixed emulsifier–water interface.

Table 20.1 Examples of Hydrophilic Surfactants and Coemulsifiers That Form in Combination Gel Networks

Hydrophilic surfactants	Coemulsifiers
Lecithin	Solid fatty acids (myristic, palmitic, stearic, etc.)
Acyl lactylates	Solid fatty alcohols (myristyl, cetyl, stearyl, etc.)
Cetyl sulfates and phosphates	Glycerol monostearates
Alkyl polyglucosides	Solid sorbitane esters
PEG surfactants (HLB >7)	Solid polyglycerine esters
Sugar ester	Solid methyl glucoside esters
Cationic surfactants	Cholesterol, ceramides, etc.

equilibrium is established between the lamellar sandwich structure and the spherical vesicular structure (Fig 20.12).

Whereas the micelles saturated with coemulsifier form the gel network structure, the micelles with surplus hydrophilic emulsifier form vesicles. As the concentration of coemulsifier drops further, the equilibrium between the vesicular and the sandwich structures will increasingly shift toward the vesicular structure. If the coemulsifier concentration falls below a critical concentration, there will now be only a micelle structure and micelle concentration which do not permit the formation of liquid-crystalline structures.

If there is a high surplus concentration of coemulsifier, mixed micelles will be formed with the maximum coemulsifier concentration until the hydrophilic

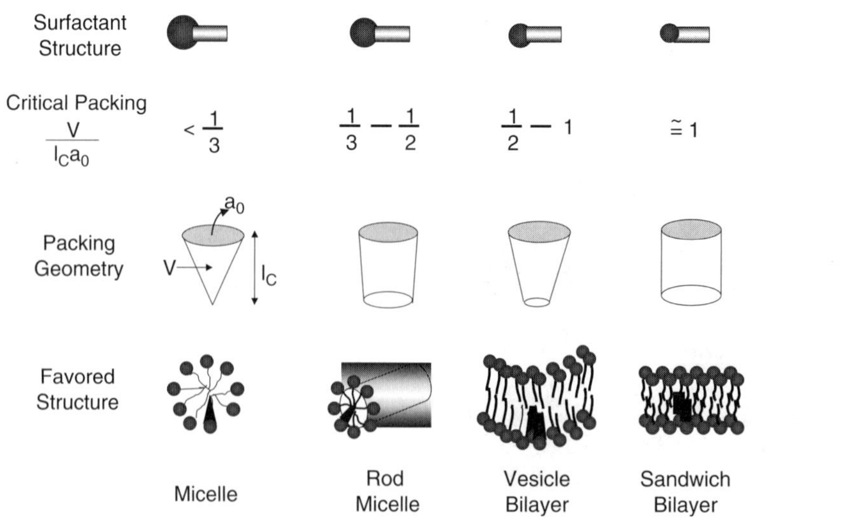

Figure 20.12 Impact of surfactant structure on micelle and bilayer formation.

emulsifier is consumed. The mixed micelles with maximum coemulsifier concentration are converted to a lamellar gel network structure, whereas the surplus coemulsifier remains behind in the water phase in the form of incompletely swelled crystals. If the concentration of coemulsifier continues to rise, the concentration of incompletely swelled crystals will also increase and the gel network concentration will decrease to the same degree.

Since the lamellar gel network structure, the vesicles, and the incompletely swelled coemulsifier crystals take on different viscosities in an aqueous medium, the optimal mixed emulsifier composition can be determined by viscosity measurements. The lamellar gel network sandwich structure is the structure that determines the viscosity. The mathematical relationship between the concentration of gel network structure (C_G) and the viscosity behavior in aqueous media is described by the following equation:

$$\eta = A e^{BC_G} \tag{20.10}$$

where η is the emulsion viscosity, C_G is the gel network concentration, and A and B are constants.

Since both vesicular structures and incompletely swelled coemulsifier crystals display nearly Newtonian flow behavior at a correspondingly low concentration in aqueous media, a viscosity maximum is attained once the gel network structure has been established on the basis of optimal proportions of coemulsifier and hydrophilic emulsifier (Fig. 20.13). Below this maximum we find either incompletely swelled crystals or mixtures of gel networks with vesicles. Mixtures of this kind display a lower viscosity than a pure gel network.

Just how pronounced the viscosity maximum is depends on the structure of the hydrophilic emulsifier used. Extremely hydrophilic emulsifiers with

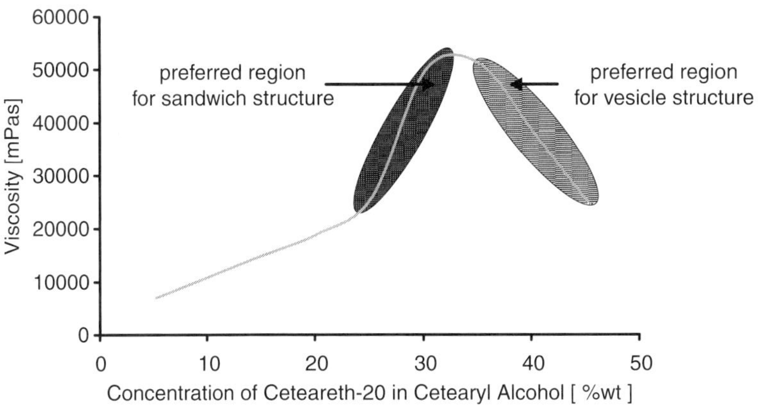

Figure 20.13 Impact of ceteareth-20–cetearyl alcohol ratio on the formation of lamellar sandwich and vesicle structures.

voluminous head groups bring about curvatures in the sandwich structure of the gel network and thus display a lower viscosity at the gel network point than do emulsifiers with a lower HLB value. The lower the critical micelle concentration of a hydrophilic emulsifier, the earlier the viscosity maximum is achieved, that is, the concentration of the hydrophilic emulsifier in the mixed emulsifier system is relatively low. In keeping with the rule that the maximum concentration of the coemulsifiers in mixed emulsifiers increases as the HLB of the coemulsifier rises, the required concentration of hydrophilic emulsifier will, of course, decrease (Fig. 20.14). The following mathematical relationship has been derived from the results of numerous experiments carried out to determine the optimal proportion of the hydrophilic emulsifier C_S:

$$C_S = 87e^{-0.54\mathrm{HLB}_{co}} \tag{20.11}$$

where C_S is the required concentration of hydrophilic surfactant and HLB_{CO} is the HLB value of the coemulsifier.

It is now relatively simple to determine the optimal concentration ratio for the hydrophilic emulsifiers and the coemulsifiers. In actual practice the following procedure can be followed. The first step is to select the individual emulsifiers which will later be used to make up the mixed emulsifier, that is, a hydrophilic emulsifier and a coemulsifier system. The selected coemulsifier system usually consists of several single coemulsifiers. In cosmetic emulsions mixtures of cetyl alcohol and glyceryl stearate are frequently employed for this purpose. The second step is to calculate the correct proportions of the coemulsifiers to be missed and their respective HLB values. On the basis of Eq. (20.11), we can now calculate the approximate composition of the mixed emulsifier. To be sure that the calculated composition is optimal for the mixed emulsifier as well, we can perform practical tests to check this ratio. For this purpose, 10 parts of the emulsifier mixture determined by calculation are heated to ≈75°C

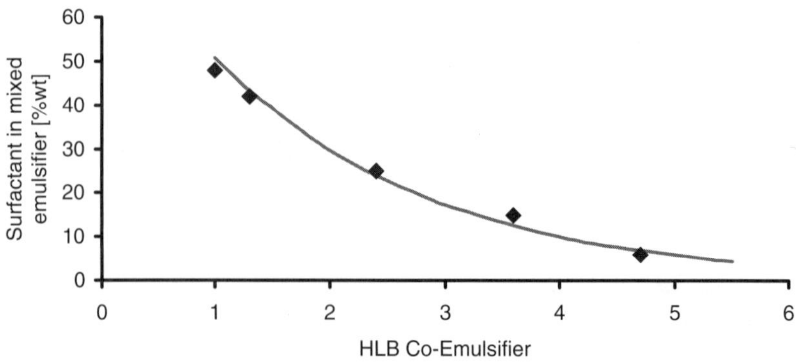

Figure 20.14 Impact of HLB value of coemulsifier on required hydrophilic surfactant concentration in mixed emulsifiers.

and then emulsified into 90 parts of the water phase foreseen for the sunscreen formulation, whereby the water phase has also been heated to $\approx 75^\circ C$. After the emulsifier mixture has been added, the entire mixture is homogenized for ≈ 1 min and subsequently cooled. Afterward, two experiments with a similar configuration are carried out in which the calculated composition of the mixed emulsifier is shifted slightly in the direction of the hydrophilic emulsifier in one experiment and slightly in the direction of the coemulsifier in another. The emulsifier mixture which has exhibited the highest viscosity in the water phase during the three experiments represents the optimum.

Optimal mixed emulsifiers are relatively resistant to variations in oil phase polarity: both nonpolar oils, for example, isoparaffins and silicone oils, and polar oils such as sunscreen filters can be emulsified without any difficulty to form a stable emulsion with a fine droplet distribution.

O/W sunscreen formulations based on mixed emulsifiers may react sensitively to the addition of micropigments. Owing to their enormous polar surface, micropigments are able to adsorb substantial amounts of hydrophilic emulsifiers and thus disturb the equilibrium of the mixed emulsifier. The concentration of hydrophilic mixed emulsifiers adsorbed by micropigments is strongly dependent on the surface modification and degree of dispersion of the micropigment used in the particular case. For this reason, it is not possible to carry out exact calculations showing the percentage by which the concentration of the hydrophilic emulsifier is to be raised by a given micropigment dispersion.

It is always beneficial, however, to predisperse the micropigments to be employed. Alkyl-substituted PVP derivatives, silicone polyoils, and mixtures of these are suitable dispersants for this purpose. Dispersants of this kind are able to cover large parts of the pigment surface, thereby reducing the free interface on which the hydrophilic emulsifiers can be adsorbed.

Pigment dispersions are ideally added to an emulsion below the critical gel network temperature. The reason for this is that the hydrophilic emulsifier is already firmly bound into the gel network matrix in this temperature range and is thus still available to only a limited degree for adsorption onto free pigment surfaces. Since gel networks are relatively resistant to the impact of shear forces, the homogenization energy required to finely distribute the pigment dispersion can be introduced without any difficulty and without any notable disturbance of the gel network occurring as a result. If micropigments are employed, care should always be taken, when determining the composition of the mixed emulsifier, to select a concentration of hydrophilic emulsifier above the optimal gel network concentration.

QUICK-BREAKING O/W SUNSCREEN EMULSIONS

Most sunscreen emulsions in cream or lotion form are stabilized by the use of mixed emulsifiers, which results in the buildup of a liquid-crystalline gel network and the formation of a multilamellar interfacial membrane.

Nevertheless, we would like to discuss the quick-breaking type of O/W emulsion here since this type of emulsion exhibits a film-forming mechanism quite different from that displayed by conventional emulsions. When these emulsions are rubbed into the skin, and the water phase allowed to evaporate, they break when the critical phase–volume ratio is exceeded. Continuing to rub these products into the skin after this point results in further distribution of the coalesced oil film. The literature does not shed any light on the question of whether the films formed by these emulsions are superior, with respect to SPF efficiency, to the films formed by emulsions based on mixed emulsifier systems.

The task of stabilizing a quick-breaking emulsion and thus preventing possible sedimentation or creaming is carried out by hydrocolloids. These build up a gel structure in the aqueous phase which counteracts the movement of particles due to the effect of gravity. Much like the gel networks formed from mixed emulsifiers, organic hydrocolloids, for example, carbomers, sodium alginate, and cellulose, display a certain skin protection effect (11).

The role played by the emulsifier in a quick-breaking O/W emulsion system is fairly simple to describe. The emulsifier is responsible for creating droplets of sufficient size and for protecting the droplets created during the emulsification process against coalescence.

The maximum input of mechanical energy during an emulsification process can be varied to only a small degree. On the basis of the emulsification tools available, it can be viewed as practically constant. If we study the mathematical relationship described by La Place's equation, namely,

$$\Delta P = \frac{2\sigma}{r} \tag{20.12}$$

where ΔP is the pressure difference, σ is the interfacial tension, and r is the droplet radius. It becomes evident that the only way to actually produce an emulsion with a sufficiently fine droplet distribution is to lower the interfacial tension by adding an appropriate amount of a suitable emulsifier. The most favorable characteristics in this context are displayed by nonionic emulsifiers with an HLB of 7–14. However, a number of anion-active emulsifiers, for example, sodium cetearyl sulfate, sodium lauroyl lactylate, and potassium cetearyl phosphate, also display good values to lower the interfacial tension here. The selected emulsion should be soluble in the oil phase in any case; otherwise, disturbances may occur during film formation which impair the SPF efficiency. In the event that the chosen emulsifier is insoluble in the selected oil phase, it must be mixed with an emulsifier displaying a lower HLB value in proportions ensuring sufficient solubility.

The necessary concentration of emulsifier is based primarily on the selected phase–volume ratio. The higher the concentration of the selected oil phase, the higher the concentration of the chosen emulsifier. Since the thickness of the emulsifier layer at the water–oil interface is not known, it is impossible to set down an equation that calculates the correct emulsifier concentration for the particular oil phases to be emulsified. The correct emulsifier concentration can thus only be determined empirically. After conducting numerous studies of our own on this subject, however, we have found that the necessary emulsifier concentration is located in the range between 0.2 and 0.6 wt.% (of the total formulation), depending on the selected phase–volume ratio.

La Place's equation does not provide sufficient information, however, on the optimal droplet size to be achieved in emulsions. Favorable flow conditions must be present before droplets pull out of the bulk oil phase. The Weber number is an important parameter in this context (12). It is defined as follows:

$$\mathrm{We} = \frac{\tau}{p} \tag{20.13}$$

where We is the Weber number, τ is the emulsion yield stress, and p is the emulsification pressure.

$$\tau = \gamma\eta \tag{20.14}$$

where γ is the shear rate and η is the viscosity.

$$\Delta P = \frac{2\sigma}{r} \tag{20.15}$$

where ΔP is the pressure difference, σ is the interfacial tension, and r is the droplet radius.

Inserting the parameters τ and p, we obtain

$$\mathrm{We} = \frac{\gamma\eta r}{2\sigma} \tag{20.16}$$

Solving Eq. (20.16) for the droplet radius r, we see that we can expect to obtain very small droplets in the presence of the prevailing high values for viscosity η and low values for interfacial tension σ:

$$r = \frac{2\mathrm{We}\sigma}{\gamma\eta} \tag{20.17}$$

The high viscosity required during the emulsification process for a quick-breaking O/W emulsion cannot be generated solely by the polymer used since a polymer solution usually takes on low viscosity values under the effect of the shear forces occurring during emulsification.

To attain the viscosity needed to produce the required droplet size, it is necessary to resort to a small trick (6), namely, to simply divide the emulsification process into two phases. During the first phase a concentrated emulsion is produced in which the dispersed phase accounts for a large volume fraction;

this is because the viscosity η increases exponentially as the phase–volume ratio rises:

$$\eta = Ae^{B\varphi_i} \tag{20.18}$$

The decrease in viscosity η observed under the effect of shear forces is lower in emulsions with a high phase–volume fraction than in polymer solutions.

From Eq. (20.17) we see that the droplets become smaller and smaller as the phase–volume ratio rises. It is not necessary to increase the input of mechanical energy in this context. In the range shortly before the critical phase–volume ratio, nanoemulsions will be produced.

After a concentrated O/W emulsion has been produced, it is diluted by means of the remaining water phase down to the stipulated phase–volume ratio, a process accompanied by mild agitation.

The two-stage process can be simplified into a continuous process via continuous process guidance. Continuous processes carried out in a microreactor with a suitable mixing unit result in time, space, and energy savings. The droplet sizes which can be achieved here lie in the nanometer range, that is, they are considerably smaller than the droplet size found in conventional emulsions.

As has been mentioned at the beginning of this chapter, the emulsifier suitable for use in a quick-breaking O/W emulsion determines droplet size in several ways and not just by reducing the interfacial tension. In addition, this emulsifier should envelop the emulsified droplets so well that they are protected against coalescence during storage. As discussed above, emulsifiers which are able to build up liquid-crystalline interfaces provide the best protection here. Several anionic emulsifiers, as well as several nonionic polyglycerine esters, satisfy this requirement without the addition of coemulsifiers. Prominent examples include polyglycerine-10 dicaprylate, sodium lauroyl lactylate, and sodium cetearyl sulfate.

If film-forming agents from the class of solid alkyl-substituted PVP derivatives are used in the formulation, they can act as coemulsifiers and, in combination with the selected hydrophilic emulsifier, also build up lamellar liquid-crystalline structures at the oil–water interface. The concentration of solid alkyl-substituted PVP derivatives must be determined with extreme caution. If high concentrations are used, lamellar liquid-crystalline gel networks will be formed automatically. In such cases, we are no longer working in the range of quick-breaking emulsions since the film-forming mechanism now at work is similar to that observed in emulsions based on mixed emulsifiers.

Here again it is important to note, when adding micropigments, that they can bind nondefined amounts of the particular emulsifier system used. This can result in a critical disturbance of the emulsifier concentration equilibrium, which is already on a shaky footing in quick-breaking emulsions. When adding micropigments, the only course of action available is to determine the required emulsifier concentration empirically. As we have already discussed in the section on mixed emulsifiers, predispersed micropigment dispersions, in which hydrophobic dispersants are used to cover the pigment surface, are the most suitable dispersants for this purpose.

At the end of this discussion on quick-breaking O/W emulsions, it should be pointed out that—in contrast to O/W emulsions based on mixed emulsifiers—the former type of emulsion does not build up an oil film possessing the required viscoelasticity on the basis of the particular emulsifiers used. For this reason, it is advisable to compensate for this deficit in quick-breaking O/W sunscreen emulsions by adding wax-like emollients. The group of wax-like emollients that can be used here include, in particular, hydrogenated cocotriglyceride, bethenyl triglyceride, cetyl palmitate, or myristyl myristate. The concentration of solid emollient should be about 5–10 wt.% of the oil phase used.

SPRAYABLE O/W EMULSIONS

The sprayability of an emulsion depends primarily on its rheological behavior. Emulsion viscosity plays an especially important role in this context as can be demonstrated by the example of sprayable Newtonian liquids. The spray cone generated by a given pump spray head decreases exponentially as the viscosity increases. This can be illustrated by using silicone oils of different viscosities:

$$\alpha = Ae^{B\eta} \tag{20.19}$$

where α is the spray cone and η is the viscosity.

It is easy to see from Fig. 20.15 that only an emulsion with a fairly low viscosity will be able to generate a decent spray cone. According to Stoke's Law, emulsions with a low viscosity are only stable against creaming if the droplets

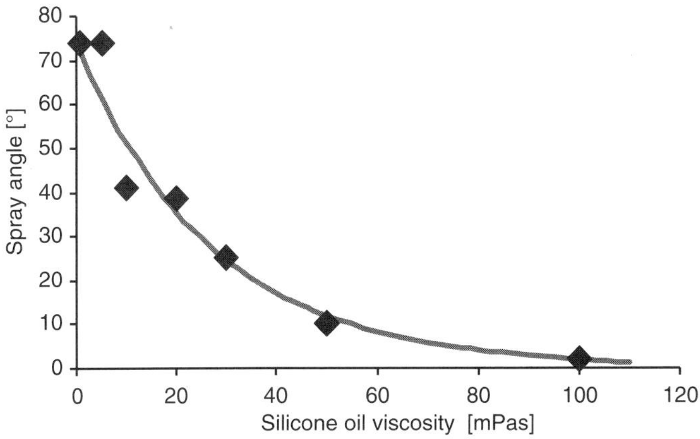

Figure 20.15 Impact of oil viscosity on spray angle by the use of a hair spray nozzle.

are correspondingly small. As already discussed in the foregoing chapter on quick-breaking emulsions, small droplets can only be generated if the interfacial tension is low and the rheological conditions are favorable for the droplet break up.

The phase inversion temperature (PIT) method, which uses ethoxylated niosurfactants, is frequently employed to manufacture emulsions (13). The mechanism of action of the PIT method can be explained quite well by describing the cloud point phenomenon observed in conjunction with alkoxylated surfactants.

Below a critical temperature, ethoxylates with an HLB >10 usually form a clear solution when dissolved in water. If aqueous emulsifier solutions of this kind are heated to a critical temperature, however, they become turbid instantaneously. This turbidity is caused by a sudden enlargement of the micelles. In this temperature range, the micelles attain a mean diameter above the critical wavelength of light. Above the cloud point the emulsifier experiences an almost complete loss of its previous solubility in water. If we repeat the experiment, and this time oil is placed on the water phase and then interfacial tension is measured as a function of temperature, we see that the interfacial tension approaches zero at the cloud point. Above the cloud point, however, it increases markedly again. What has happened here? Below the cloud point temperature, the emulsifier is present in the water phase in micellar form. As we approach the cloud point, the micelles grow. At the cloud point, also known as the demicellation point, the micelles fuse to form liquid-crystalline lamella. Above the cloud point the liquid-crystalline structures collapse again and the emulsifier migrates into the oil phase, where it forms inverse micelles.

In the field of emulsion technology, the cloud point phenomenon is also known as the PIT. The observations made with emulsions at the PIT suggest that it might be possible to produce emulsions with nanofine droplets in this temperature range, owing to the low interfacial tension produced by the liquid crystalline phases. This is in fact possible. Unfortunately, however, there are still numerous obstacles to the technical production of such emulsions on a large scale. First, it is very difficult to stay within the stipulated narrow temperature window, especially when energy is constantly introduced into the emulsion structure by vigorous homogenizing. Second, the cloud point of the emulsifiers used quite naturally fluctuates from batch to batch, causing the PIT to change as well, of course. Third, detailed investigations have not yet been carried out to determine how stable the liquid-crystalline phases are once the entire mixture has cooled down after emulsification. For all of the above reasons, colloid chemists currently resort to the addition of hydrophobic solid coemulsifiers, which are known to stabilize liquid-crystalline lamellar structures, to stabilize such emulsions.

Despite the use of such stabilization techniques, it has been our experience that nanoemulsions produced via the PIT often display a very strong tendency toward coalescence; this tendency is especially pronounced in the temperature range containing the melting point of the coemulsifier.

To illustrate this statement, we performed somewhat more extensive tests on a commercially available low-viscosity spray emulsion formulated according to the PIT method. Applying laser light scattering analysis to investigate the droplet size distribution, we did, in fact, detect a very fine droplet distribution which should actually suffice to trigger Brownian motion (Fig. 20.16)

However, if we then–parallel to this test–analyze the creaming behavior of the same emulsion with the very sensitive method of conductivity analysis, during which the conductivity is measured simultaneously at the bottom of the vessel and at the fill height, we observe that the conductivity at the bottom of the vessel has already increased after about 2 h. This process can be speeded up by heating the sample. During these measurements, a sudden difference in conductivity can be clearly observed at ~32°C (Fig. 20.17).

After a longer storage period at room temperature, there is an increase in both particle size and the critical time within which the first detectable instability occurs.

A second method that can be employed to manufacture sprayable O/W emulsions is the three-phase emulsification method already described in the chapter on quick-breaking emulsions. When selecting emulsifiers which will result in an extremely low viscosity, particular care should be taken to select substances which (a) lower the interfacial tension sufficiently to ensure the production of extremely small droplets during the emulsification process and (b) permit the formation of a robust interfacial layer to protect the droplets against coalescence despite the high-energy Brownian motion.

As explained above, lamellar liquid-crystalline mixed emulsifiers are best suited for this task since they lower interfacial tension to an extreme degree (14) and, at the same time, build up a sturdy interfacial layer. In the case of low-viscosity emulsions, however, mixed emulsifiers of this kind should presumably not build up any gel networks. To prevent the formation of sandwich-type gel

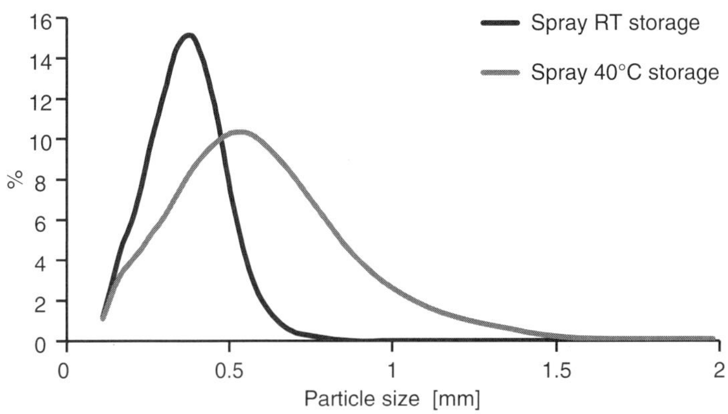

Figure 20.16 Impact of 4 weeks' storage of PIT emulsion on particle size.

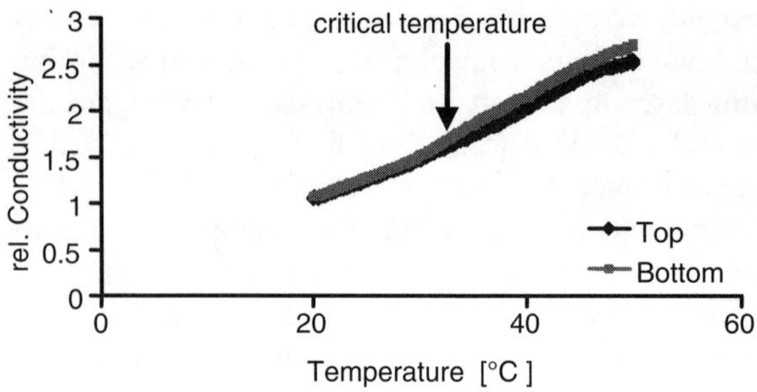

Figure 20.17 Determination of critical temperature stability by relative conductivity measurement.

network structures the composition of the mixed emulsifier must provide for a surplus of hydrophilic emulsifier. This surplus of hydrophilic emulsifier suppresses the formation of the sandwich structure for geometric reasons and leads to the formation of spherical multilamellar protective layers instead. The approach taken to formulate a mixed emulsifier is similar to that followed during the selection, described above, of an O/W mixed emulsifier. In this case, however, the descending viscosity curve is selected.

To prevent a possible superimposition of the liquid-crystalline structures which envelop the dispersed droplets, polymer hydrocolloids are employed. These have the characteristic of attaching themselves to the outer boundary layer of the membranes (15), thus creating a steric barrier which prevents the membranes from coming too close to each other and merging. Highly branched polymers, for example, gum arabic, are most suitable for this purpose. When they are in equilibrium with the external water phase, polymers of this kind preserve the sprayability of the emulsion since they do not create any viscosity in this phase. However, highly thixotropic polymers such as microcrystalline cellulose can also be used successfully for this purpose.

To permit optimal film formation, a wax-like emollient should be added to the oil phase at an optimal concentration in any case.

W/O EMULSIONS

In the original sense of the word, W/O emulsions are pure two-phase systems. In these emulsions the emulsifiers serve the sole function of protecting the dispersed water phase against coalescence. The viscosity required to counteract the force of gravity is attained by regulating the phase–volume ratio or raising the viscosity of the external phase by the addition of waxes.

In cosmetic W/O emulsions, the selected concentration is usually above 50 vol.%. In concentrated emulsions of this kind, the droplets lie close together and are subject to different forces (Fig. 20.18).

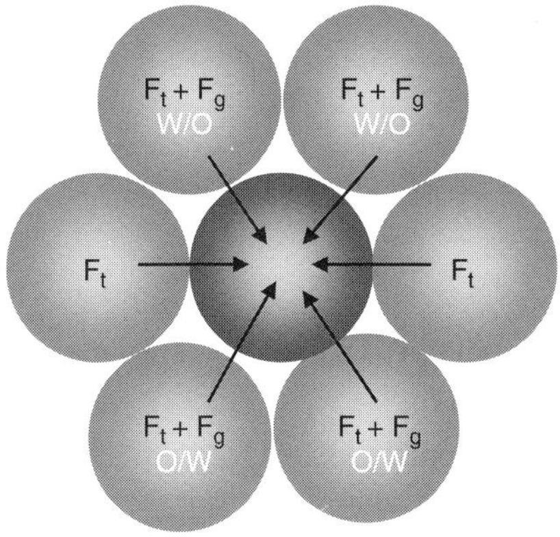

$$F_t = F_h + F_s + F_{vw}$$

F_h = hydrodynamic force causing the flow of the continuous oil phase between the water droplets.

F_s = the steric repulsion

F_{vw} = van der Waal's attraction forces

F_g = gravity force

Figure 20.18 Forces which have an impact on droplets in concentrated emulsions.

To successfully counteract forces of this kind and thus avert the threat of coalescence, the water–oil interface formed via the emulsifiers must possess a high mechanical strength. In the case of W/O emulsions, this strength is achieved via the inverse liquid-crystalline hexagonal phase formed by means of the emulsifiers. Moreover, part of the oil phase is embedded in these phases. The oil structure in the external phase plays a decisive role in the creation of these inverse hexagonal phases. The anchoring with the dispersed water phase is carried out by means of the hydrophilic groups of the emulsifier system.

Because of the necessity for the oil phase to be compatible with the inverse hexagonal structure created via the emulsifier, the emulsifier is selected according to the polarity of the oil phase.

To find the right emulsifier for the oil phase selected, the droplet retention method (16) can be used. This method is based on the development of highly viscoelastic interfacial films between the oil and water phases. With this method, an oil phase containing a selected emulsifier system at a concentration of about 10 wt.% is layered over a given water phase. A highly viscous film will invariably form at the interface if the emulsifier is capable of forming inverse liquid-crystalline structures together with the water and oil phases.

The viscosity of the interfacial film drops drastically if inverse liquid-crystalline structures are not formed.

If we place a water droplet on the oil side of the oil–water phase interface, the retention of the droplet at this location will be depend on the interfacial viscosity η_{Int}, the film thickness b, and the film elasticity G:

$$t = \eta\left[\frac{3C}{Ab^2} - \frac{1}{G} - \varphi^t\right] \tag{20.20}$$

where t is the droplet retention time, η the interface viscosity, C is the critical deformation factor of droplet, G is the droplet elasticity, b is the thickness of the interface, and $\varphi^{(\mathrm{t})}$ is the elastic deformation per unit stress.

If the interfacial viscosity η is high, and the film thickness b and film elasticity G assume high values as well, the retention time for a droplet placed on the interface may be several days. If no high-viscosity inverse liquid-crystalline layer is formed at the phase interface, however, the maximum droplet retention time will be several minutes. After the selected oil phase has been layered over the water phase, and before the water droplet is placed on the interface, an equilibrium time of about 30 min should be maintained. This amount of time is required for the necessary liquid-crystalline interfacial film to be completely formed.

The method described above is relatively simple to carry out and yields excellent values for predicting whether a selected W/O emulsifier system will be suitable for the intended oil and water phases. At retention times longer than 8 h, we can assume that sufficiently stable interfacial films will be formed; in this case the selected emulsifier can be considered suitable.

The usefulness of the droplet retention method for making predictions concerning the suitability of a W/O emulsifier for a stipulated oil–water system can be tested impressively by the following experiments.

Sorbitan monooleate is very suitable as a W/O emulsifier in paraffin-based systems; however, it is completely unsuited for the task of stabilizing water droplets in a polar oil medium, for example, capric/caprylic triglyceride. It is also known that silicone copolyoils exhibit excellent emulsification properties in cyclomethicone. The droplet retention times found in this case verify this quite clearly. If we employ silicone copolyoils in polar oil phases, for example, isopropyl myristate or capric/caprylic triglyceride, we can observe that films of sufficient viscosity are still formed at the phase interface; however, much higher concentrations of silicone copolyoils are needed to accomplish this.

As in all liquid-crystalline phases, the formation of the inverse hexagonal structure is a function of the temperature. If, for example, we measure the interfacial tension of an isoparaffin–water interface stabilized by sorbitane oleate as a function of temperature, we observe that the interfacial tension rises steadily at

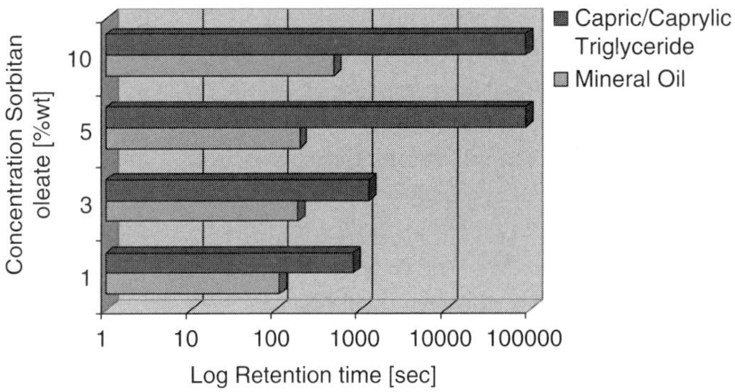

Figure 20.19 Impact of oil structure on droplet retention time.

temperatures above 60°C. Below this temperature range, the interfacial tension remains nearly constant. It does not matter at all in this context whether we measure the interfacial tension from the lower temperature range into the higher or the other way round. We can proceed on the assumption, therefore, that the inverse hexagonal layer required for the formation of stable W/O emulsions is formed within a temperature range below 60°C.

Since this temperature range is similar for most W/O emulsifiers, we can assume that the stability of W/O emulsions is guaranteed up to this temperature range—provided that the right emulsifier system has been chosen. The information that inverse hexagonal structures are only formed at temperatures below 60°C is also important for the conduct of the emulsification process. The homogenization of a W/O emulsion at temperatures above 60°C is very inefficient, therefore, since the relatively high interfacial tension at high temperatures permits only a coarse droplet distribution. It should thus be taken into account, during the manufacture of W/O emulsions, that the actual homogenization process should take place distinctly below this temperature. Just how far we have to go below the critical temperature of 60°C depends on the energy performance of the particular emulsifier used. The higher the energy input, the larger the energy portion dissipated as heat and the more the emulsion is heated up during homogenization. By carrying out homogenization at temperatures around 45°C, we can be confident of being on the safe side in most cases.

The simplest way to manufacture a W/O emulsion is the hot–cold method. When this method is used, the cold water phase is added to the oil phase during vigorous homogenization. With this approach, any waxes present in the oil phase will not crystallize.

Since most W/O emulsifiers are mixtures of polymer homologs, they also generally contain hydrophilic portions. The hydrophilic molecules can migrate out of the oil phase into the aqueous phase. At this location they are able to extract large fractions of hydrophobic emulsifier molecules out of the oil phase during the formation of mixed micelles. Consequently, the emulsifier concentration can rise steadily in the water phase and be simultaneously depleted in the oil phase. If the concentration of the emulsifier fraction in the water phase exceeds the concentration of the fraction remaining in the oil phase, phase inversion will occur according to Bancroft's rule. Depletion of the emulsifier in the oil phase can also result in not enough emulsifier molecules being still available to build up a sufficiently thick layer of the required inverse hexagonal structure at the phase interface. This phenomenon can be counteracted by adding an electrolyte to the aqueous phase.

By means of a "salting out" effect, the electrolyte added to the water phase causes the suppression of micelle formation by the hydrophilic polymer homologs in the water phase. The type of electrolyte added is irrelevant in this context. The only thing that matters is the correct concentration. This concentration can be determined empirically and is different for every formulation.

A concentration that is "too high" is impossible. The results of numerous experiments have shown, however, that a concentration of 0.5–1.0 wt.% of sodium chloride is sufficient.

Classic W/O emulsions are stable only up to the critical phase–volume ratio. If the water phase is increased above this ratio, the surplus water will separate out during storage or sometimes even during manufacturing. The critical phase–volume ratio depends on droplet size and on the layer thickness of the inverse hexagonal structure present at the interface. The explanation for this phenomenon is that part of the oil phase is incorporated firmly into the phase interface of the inverse hexagonal structure. For a given emulsifier system, the layer thickness can be viewed as constant. If the dispersed water phase is broken down further to form smaller and smaller droplets, new interfaces are continually created which are covered by the inverse liquid-crystalline hexagonal structure consisting of emulsifier, water, and oil phase. Since the water droplets and the hexagonal structure bound to them constitute a single unit, the inverse hexagonal structure must also be considered part of the dispersed phase.

It is easy to understand, therefore, that, as the degree of dispersion rises, the critical phase–volume ratio must decline. Since the layer thickness of the inverse hexagonal phase depends on the concentration of the incorporated oil phase as well as on the emulsifier system, no precise prediction can be made with respect to the critical phase–volume ratio in the particular case.

The breakdown of an emulsion due to overhomogenization is a frequently observed phenomenon caused by the exceeding of the critical phase–volume ratio when a critical small-droplet diameter is reached. Overhomogenization can be easily brought under control, however, by adding oil phase to the collapsed emulsion again. In such a case, a small amount of emulsifier must often be added as well.

Not all W/O emulsions secrete water when the critical phase–volume ratio is exceeded. If the size of the droplets in the water phase lies in the nanometer range, W/O microemulsions can also be formed if the emulsifier composition is favorable. A transition of this kind is thoroughly plausible in connection with the formation of bicontinuous structures (17). The concept of a microemulsion structure containing bicontinuous phases was developed on the basis of photographs made with an electron microscope. According to this theoretical model, a mixture containing both a spongy structure and a pure droplet structure is present at the critical phase–volume ratio. If the critical phase–volume ratio is exceeded, the emulsion structure will shift increasingly toward the spongy microstructure. This process has been observed, in particular, when silicone polymers are used.

At a critical concentration of polyols in the water phase, clear microemulsions can also be formed when the critical phase–volume ratio is exceeded. Several experiments performed to explore this question have shown clearly that the transparency of the emulsion is not attributable to an equalization of the index of refraction of the two phases. If we assume that the transparent mixed emulsions are also formed from bicontinuous phases with a spongy structure, we see that the continuous bilayer structures are probably cubic in nature.

In W/O sunscreen formulations, the critical phase–volume ratio is also affected by the addition of micropigments. In W/O emulsions, micropigments are considered part of the dispersed phase, as are the emulsified water droplets. Consequently, as the micropigment concentration rises, the emulsion moves closer and closer to the critical phase–volume ratio. If the critical phase–volume ratio is exceeded, owing to the addition of micropigments, the result–depending on the type of emulsion structure created–is either the breakdown of the emulsion accompanied by separation of water or the formation of microemulsions. Adding micropigments to the emulsion in nonpredispersed form results, in most cases, in adsorption of the emulsifier onto the surface of the micropigments. Since substantial amounts of the W/O emulsifier are adsorbed on the pigment surface at higher pigment concentrations, emulsifier will be depleted in the actual W/O emulsion. If the emulsifier concentration falls below the critical concentration required to stabilize the W/O emulsion, the equilibrium of the W/O emulsion will become instable. In many W/O sunscreen formulations, it has proven advantageous to raise the emulsifier concentration when micropigments are added. The micropigments should be predispersed before being added in any case.

In W/O sunscreen formulations micropigments can also be predispersed in the water phase in the first step. Since the water phase usually constitutes the largest fraction by volume in a W/O emulsion, an undesired crowding effect can be avoided via a higher pigment concentration. Ideally, pigments that are readily dispersed in water should be used for this purpose. After the pigments have been ground in the water phase, they should be emulsified in the oil phase. During the emulsification process the micropigments undergo a "flushing process" during which they are transported from the water phase into the inverse liquid-crystalline hexagonal structure consisting of the emulsifier and the oil phase.

As a result of being embedded in the hydrophobic hexagonal structure, the pigment surface takes on a lipophilic character. This guarantees that the final formulation will be sufficiently waterproof even though a hydrophilic micropigment has been used. The degree of dispersion of the micropigments dispersed via a "flushing process" is usually considerably higher than that achieved in W/O emulsions with conventional dispersing techniques. Using a "flushing process" of this kind, it is possible to produce waterproof W/O sunscreen formulations containing micropigments as the sole UV filter with *in vivo* sun protection effects equal to an SPF >40. Owing to the extremely good pigment dispersion, only a slight whitening effect is noticeable even at high micropigment concentrations.

In W/O emulsions undesirable interactions have been observed in numerous cases between the preservatives used and the liquid-crystalline protective layer protecting the dispersed water droplets against coalescence. Preservatives, like emulsifiers, are amphiphilic molecules. The same amphiphilic molecular configuration which allows the preservative to attack microbial cells via a membrane-active mechanism also allows them to penetrate the liquid-crystalline emulsifier membrane. As lipophilic amphiphilic substances, preservatives are able to penetrate—and eventually break down—the inverse hexagonal structure.

The kinetics governing the penetration of preservatives into the hexagonal structure are very slow; for this reason, the incompatibility and destabilization of the interface are not evident immediately after emulsion manufacture. Analytical methods suitable for detecting instabilities attributable to the preservative used include both droplet size analysis and rheological studies. Owing to the low-grade kinetics, however, only small changes can be detected over a short period of time. For particle size analysis, therefore, we have to resort to measuring the change in specific surface over the storage time instead of the usual particle size determination. Since the kinetics for the migration of the preserving agent increase at rising temperatures, samples stored at around 50°C are best suited for these tests. Tests performed at 2-day intervals reveal constant changes in the specific surface if the preserving agent used causes instabilities in the W/O system.

Any change in droplet size occurring during storage also causes changes in the rheological parameters of the emulsion (18). The larger the droplets become during storage, the lower is the resulting viscosity of the emulsion.

AUTOXIDATION OF EMULSIFIERS

"Mallorca acne", or acne aestevalis, is a special form of sun allergy which occurs frequently during summer vacations in southern countries. Typical dermatological symptoms are red keratinous papules on the upper arms, back, and face. Mallorca acne is presumably caused by the application of especially greasy and oily sunscreen products in combination with intensive exposure to solar radiation. In persons with a predisposition to Mallorca acne, moreover, the eruptions can be triggered by the application of peroxide simultaneously with exposure to UV radiation (phototoxic–chemotoxic skin reaction). In $\approx$90% of individuals with this predisposition, cutaneous manifestations can be prevented by using sunscreens and after-sun products containing no peroxide-forming ingredients.

One of the main causes for the formation of radicals is the autoxidation of emulsifiers. In particular, emulsifiers with a molecular structure containing ether bonds oxidize very readily when exposed to light and oxygen. The nonionic polyethylene glycol (PEG) emulsifiers are a classic example of this phenomenon. The degradation of the PEG chain takes place via the following mechanism:

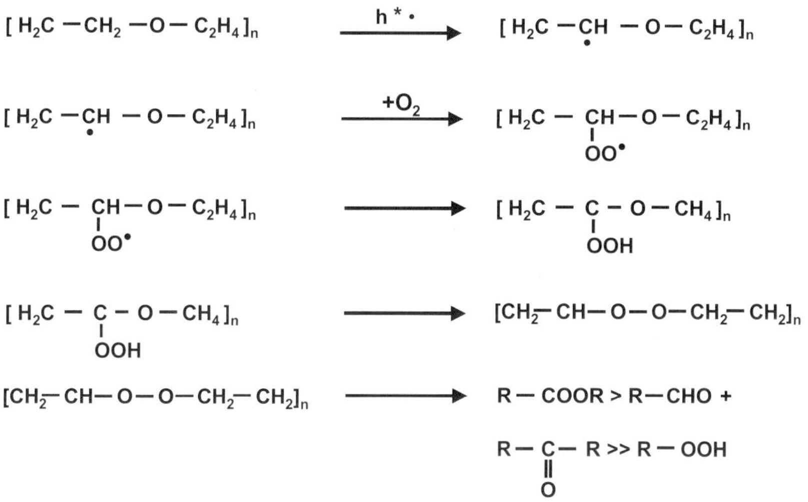

A number of secondary products, for example, aldehydes, ketones, and carbonic acids, are formed in addition to the radicals. The oxidative degradation of nonionogenic PEG emulsifiers can be detected via IR analysis or wet analytical methods such as the determination of the acid or saponification number.

The oxidative degradation of a PEG emulsifier starts at the end of the PEG chain. The results of recent studies indicate that closed PEG chains are degraded via oxidation to a far lesser extent than are open chains.

However, the oxidative degradation of emulsifiers containing ether bonds does not take place only on the skin following exposure to light. Progressive oxidative degradation can also be observed during the storage of emulsions. The oxidative degradation occurring during the storage of O/W emulsions can be demonstrated analytically, for example, by measuring the change in pH. During the storage of O/W emulsions containing PEG emulsifiers, an increasing number of water-soluble short-chain carboxyl acids are formed by the process described above. This process is naturally accompanied by a steady drop in pH.

Antioxidants cannot stop the autoxidative process either on the skin or in emulsions; at best they can slow it down. Furthermore, antioxidants can ensure optimal protection against oxidative reactions only if the starting materials for these reactions are protected against light, heat, and oxygen (19). In the presence of excess oxygen—like that observed on the skin after the application of a sun protection emulsion—the process of resonance stabilization will not be sufficient to bind all the radicals which are formed.

This kind of situation is totally beyond the ability of antioxidants to cope since even suberythematogenic doses of UV radiation induce the formation of free radicals—in addition to the radicals created by other processes, for example, the autoxidation of PEG emulsifiers. If antioxidants are to have any effect at all in sunscreen emulsions, the use of emulsifiers or other substances susceptible to oxidation should be avoided when formulating sun protection products.

Since the process of autoxidation induced by PEG emulsifiers takes place during the storage of sunscreen emulsions—and not just after the application of sunscreen products to the skin in combination with direct exposure to solar radiation—we must assume that other ingredients of sunscreen emulsions, such as the sensitive sunscreen filters, are also vulnerable to oxidative attack.

REFERENCES

1. Winsor PA. Trans Faraday Soc 1948; 44:351.
2. Winsor PA. Trans Faraday Soc 1950; 46:762.
3. Gray GW, Winsor PA. Liquid Crystals and Plastic Crystals. New York: John Wiley and Sons, 1975:100.
4. Winsor PA. Chem Rev 1968; 68:1.
5. Kaymer R. Pharm Ind 1970; 32:577.
6. O'Neill IJ. J Pharm Sci 1983; 7:888.
7. Charlet E, Finkel P. Arztl Kosmetol 1979; 9:368.
8. Tsutsumi H, Utsugi T, Hayashi S. I Soc Cosmet Chem 1979; 30:345.
9. Patent pending PCT/EP03/02996.
10. Hoffmann H. Ber Bunsenges Phys Chem 1984; 88:1078.
11. Laba D. Rheological Properties of Cosmetics and Toiletries. New York: Marcel Dekker, 1993:403.
12. Asche, Essig, Schmidt. Technologie von Salben, Suspensionen und Emulsionen. Stuttgart: Wissenschaftliche Vertriebsgesellschaft, 1984:71.
13. Shinoda KJ. Colloid Interface Sci 1969; 24:4.
14. Benton I, Miller C, Fort T. J Dispersion Sci Techol 1982; 3:1.
15. Ringsdorf H, Schlarb B, Venzmer I. Angew Chem 1988; 100:117.
16. Biswas B, Haydon DA. Proc Royal Soc 1963; 271:296.
17. Strey R. Chem Tech Lab 1992; 40:213.
18. Sherman P. Encyclopedia of Emulsion Technology. Vol. 1. Becher P, ed. New York: Marcel Dekker, 1983:425.
19. Essig D. Stabilisierungstechnologie. Tuebingen:Gulde Druck, 1986:69.

21

Role of Emollients and Emulsifiers in Sunscreen Formulations

Utilizing Synergies in the Formulation of Cosmetic Sunscreen Products

Stefan Bruening and Mark Leonard
Cognis Corporation, Ambler, Pennsylvania, USA

Rolf Kawa and Ulrich Issberner
Cognis Deutschland GmbH & Co. KG, Duesseldorf, Germany

Andrea Tomlinson
Cognis UK, Waltham Cross, UK

INTRODUCTION

In recent years innovative products with high sun protection factors (SPFs) have shaped the global sun care market.

Consumer education has resulted in the growing use of higher SPF products. In 2002, 41% of sun protection products purchased in Germany and 28% of those in the UK had SPFs higher than 15 (1). Consumers are also becoming increasingly educated on the need for UV-A protection with many products claiming to protect them from high levels of UV-A and UV-B radiation or to offer "broad-spectrum" cover. Mass market products with SPFs of up to 60 are widely available across the USA, Europe, and Asia.

Application properties and skin feel are becoming ever more important with many sun care brands matching the aesthetics of everyday face and body care products and offering a range of physical forms from creams and lotions to sprays and gels. Markets are increasingly fragmented with products targeted at those with sensitive skin, children, babies and different activities such as sports or swimming.

It is not only dermatological and sensory factors that are responsible for influencing the efficiency of the formulation matrix of sunscreen products. Synergies between cosmetic raw materials and UV filters must be utilized to create cost-efficient products with high SPFs.

The authors describe modern formulation technologies, technical performance profiles, and synergistic effects of innovative cosmetic emollients and emulsifiers for formulating contemporary cosmetic sunscreen products.

WHAT ARE THE FUNCTIONS OF COSMETIC EMOLLIENTS IN SUNSCREEN EMULSIONS?

The cosmetic emollients used to formulate sunscreen products must contribute more than just sun care properties. They must also be good solvents and dispersants for UV filters and pigments and they must significantly boost the SPF. In addition, they must exert a positive influence on the overall sensory properties of the formulation.

Solvent Properties

If sunscreen products are to be stable and effective, it is essential that crystalline UV filters dissolve fully and remain dissolved in the cosmetic emollients of

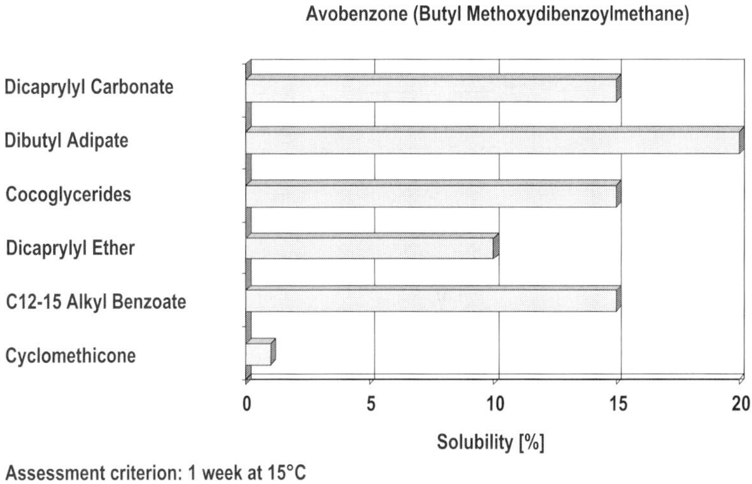

Figure 21.1 Solubility of Avobenzone.

the oil phase. The performance of various emollients as solvents for three common crystalline UV filters was tested. It was found that the UV-A filter Butyl Methoxydibenzoylmethane, the UV-B/UV-A filter Benzophenone-3, and the UV-B filter 4-Methylbenzylidene Camphor can be dissolved especially in Dibutyl Adipate[1] in high concentrations. There is, therefore, no danger that the filters will crystallize over time, causing the formulation to become unstable and the SPF to decrease (Figs. 21.1–21.3).

Pigment-Dispersing Properties

Inorganic micropigments, for example, microfine Titanium Dioxide and Zinc Oxide, are gaining in importance in the field of cosmetic sun protection. The particles of these materials usually measure between 10 and 100 nm, so they reflect almost no visible light. Formulations containing these substances appear almost transparent when applied to the skin and do not tend to whiten. The correct blending of micropigments, however, makes considerable demands on developers' skills. The micropigments must not agglomerate during preparation or storage, otherwise the product will provide less protection against UV, the pigment particles will tend to separate, and an undesirable whitening will occur on application. Detailed knowledge of the dispersing properties of the emollients is,

[1]Dibutyl Adipate—Cetiol® B (Cognis Corporation, Care Chemicals).

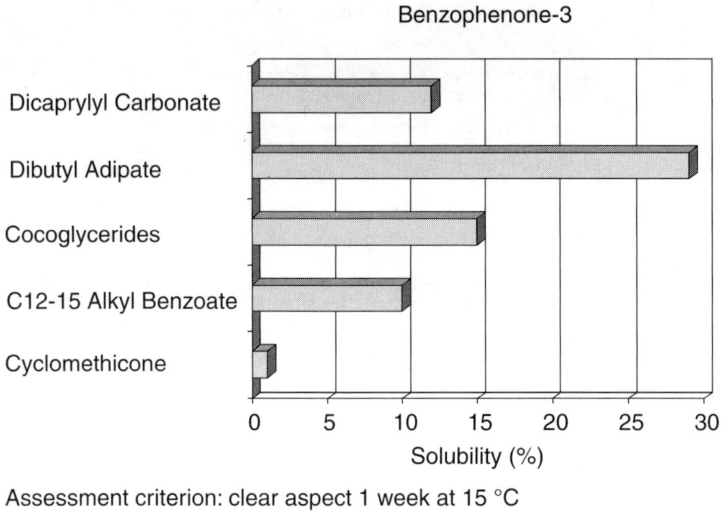

Figure 21.2 Solubility of Benzophenone-3.

therefore, essential if uniform distribution of the pigment particles is to be achieved and their agglomeration prevented.

Comparisons of the ability of emollients with different structures and polarity to disperse microfine Titanium Dioxide showed that polar

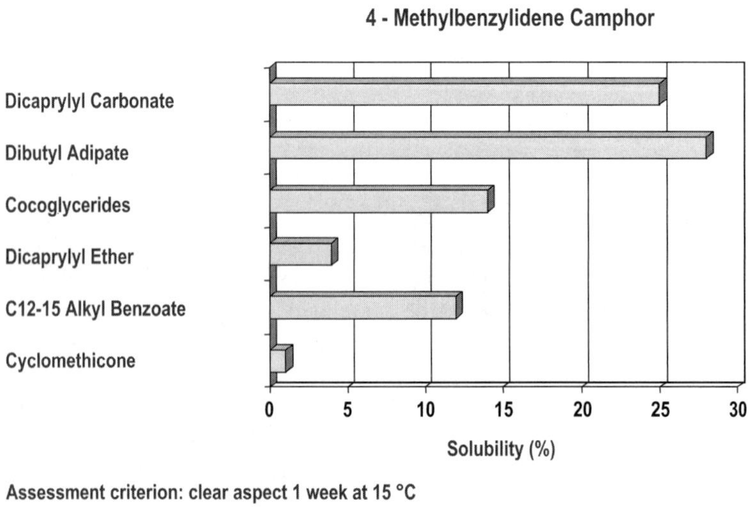

Figure 21.3 Solubility of 4-Methylbenzylidene Camphor.

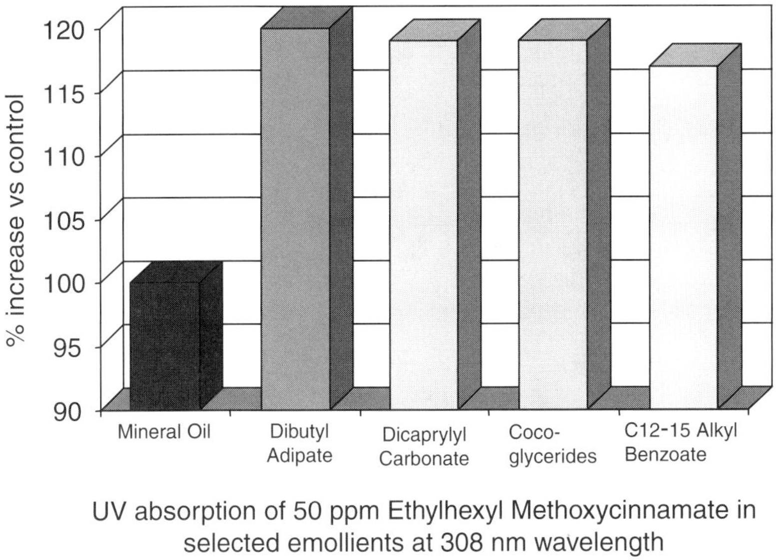

Figure 21.4 Influence of emollients for UV absorption.

Cocoglycerides[2] and emollients with medium polarity, for example, Dibutyl Adipate and Dicaprylyl Carbonate[3] influence pigment distribution very favorably and also have a positive effect on the viscosity of the dispersion. They can therefore contribute considerably to the stability of the emulsion whereas nonpolar emollients influence the homogeneity of pigments unfavorably. Therefore, their use should be avoided in pigment containing sunscreen formulations.

Increased UV Absorption

In addition, it has been found that the efficiency with which organic UV protection filters absorb UV light increases significantly as a function of the polarity of the emollients. Figure 21.4 shows a comparison of the increases in absorption associated with emollients of different polarity.

The absolute absorption in mineral oil was used as a reference value. The results were subsequently checked *in vivo* and *in vitro* with a model formulation (Fig. 21.5).

It was shown that an increase in UV absorption results in a considerable increase in the SPF if, for example, the polar Cocoglycerides or Dicaprylyl Carbonate are used instead of the nonpolar Paraffin Oil (Table 21.1).

---

[2]Cocoglycerides—Myritol® 331 (Cognis Corporation, Care Chemicals).

[3]Dicaprylyl Carbonate—Cetiol® CC (Cognis Corporation, Care Chemicals).

INCI / CTFA	weight %
Emollient	16.0
Isoamyl Methoxycinnamate	6.4
Benzophenone-3	1.6
Tocopherol	1.0
Carbomer	0.3
Lauryl Glucoside, Polyglyceryl-2 Dipolyhydroxystearate, Glycerin[5]	3.5
Glycerin	3.0
Aqua	67.5
KOH (20%)	0.7
Perfume, Preservatives	qs

Figure 21.5 *In vivo/in vitro* SPF evaluation/test formulation.

Spreading Properties

The spreading ability of an oil component is an important and objective criterion for the sensory properties of a sunscreen emulsion (2). The emulsion must spread evenly if the UV filters are to be distributed uniformly and homogenously on the skin. Only in this way reproducible sun protection can be guaranteed.

As described by Zeidler (2), cosmetic emollients were classified as slow-, medium-, and fast-spreading emollients. If a cosmetic emulsion is formulated solely on the basis of fast-spreading emollients, the desired smooth sensation is imparted to the skin very quickly. However, it does not last long and the original situation is soon restored (3). At the same time there is a wax-like sensation on the skin, that is, a higher frictional resistance, which is related to the amount of nonspreading substances, for example, consistency factors or emulsifiers, that are present. In contrast, slow-spreading oil-soluble UV filters, for example, Ethylhexyl Methoxycinnamate, give a less marked sensation of smoothness, which

Table 21.1 *In Vivo/In Vitro* SPF Evaluation for Various Emollients

Emollients	SPF *in vivo*, COLIPA	SPF *in vitro*, Labsphere UV 1000 S
Cocoglycerides	11	15
Dicaprylyl Carbonate	—	15
Paraffinum liquidum	8	6

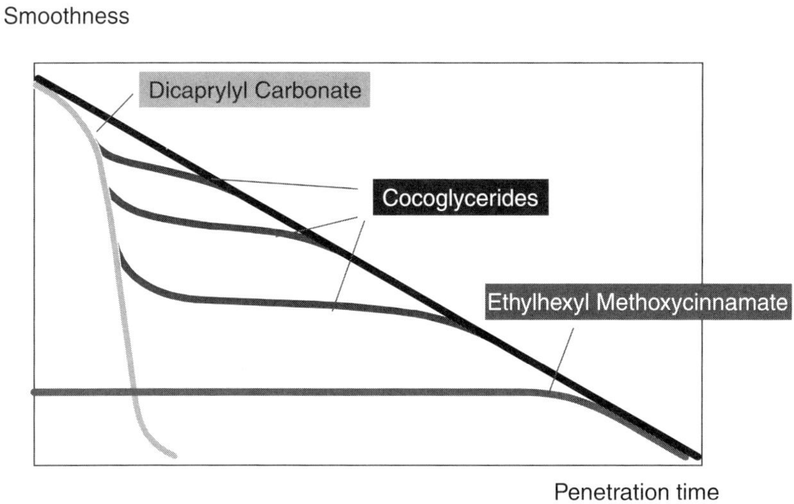

Figure 21.6 Spreading cascade of emollients.

remains virtually unchanged over a very long period of time. Ideally, slow-spreading UV filters are now brought together with fast and medium-spreading emollients, for example, a combination of Dicaprylyl Carbonate or Dibutyl Adipate with Cocoglycerides, to give a spreading cascade, avoiding any gaps in the imparted sensation of smoothness (Fig. 21.6).

Figure 21.7 describes a sun milk formulated in this way, which can be prepared by cold processing.

Knowledge of the spreading properties are especially useful if the sensory properties of a range of sun protection products with increasing SPFs are to be harmonized. To compensate for the negative sensory properties of the UV filters as the SPF increases, it is necessary to increase the proportion of fast-spreading emollients, for example, Dicaprylyl Carbonate or Dibutyl Adipate, and to combine them in a balanced relationship with medium-spreading emollients, for example, Cocoglycerides or Hexyldecanol and Hexyldecyl Laurate.[4] In this way it is possible to obtain a constant sensory profile across a complete product range despite the variation in the SPF.

WHAT ARE THE FUNCTIONS OF EMULSIFIERS IN SUNSCREEN EMULSIONS?

In normal use, sunscreen emulsions are often exposed to high temperatures. They therefore need emulsifiers with excellent interfacial stabilizing characteristics,

[4]Hexyldecanol and Hexyldecyl Laurate—Cetiol® PGL (Cognis Corporation, Care Chemicals).

INCI Name (DE02/096/77)	weight %
Lauryl Glucoside (and) Polyglyceryl-2 Dipolyhydroxystearate (and) Glycerin[5]	0.5
Cocoglycerides[2]	10.0
Dicaprylyl Carbonate[3]	6.0
Tocopherol	1.0
Ethylhexyl Methoxycinnamate	7.5
Butyl Methoxydibenzoylmethane	2.0
Sodium Polyacrylate	0.3
Glycerin	5.0
Aqua	67.7
Preservative	q.s.

Figure 21.7 O/W sun fluid cold processed, with harmonized spreading properties—SPF 16 acc. COLIPA.

even at high temperatures, irrespective of the polarity of the components used in the formulation.

O/W Emulsifiers

In the light of these considerations, tests were carried out on a new vegetable-based O/W emulsifier compound. It is a mixture of a hydrophilic part and a hydrophobic, stabilizing synergist with the nomenclature Lauryl Glucoside, Polyglyceryl-2 Dipolyhydroxystearate, Glycerin.[5] This synergistic blend exhibits good dermatological compatibility, and the fact that it is pumpable makes it suitable for the production of emulsions by either an energy saving cold process or (in combination with hydrophilic waxes, e.g., glycerides) by a conventional hot processing method. Its emulsification performance in a test formulation based on 4.5% emulsifier and 16% emollient was systematically studied in relationship to the structure of cosmetic emollients. The emollients were emulsified by cold processing, in the way that the water phase was blended into the oil phase at room temperature. No additional homogenization was carried out. The viscosity was adjusted with a polymer, as is usual in cold processes. The size of the droplets, evaluated under the microscope, was used as the assessment criterion,

[5]Lauryl Glucoside, Polyglyceryl-2 Dipolyhydroxystearate, Glycerin—Eumulgin® VL 75 (Cognis Corporation, Care Chemicals).

because this parameter is a significant indicator of the stability of an emulsion and can also influence the magnitude of the SPF.

The results show that the tested emulsifier exhibits very good emulsification potential for different emollient structures. Emulsions with Cocoglycerides in particular were very finely distributed. This is important as Cocoglycerides are of considerable importance for sun protection, due to their good solubilizing, dispersing, and booster properties. It was also clearly demonstrated that polar UV filters, such as Ethylhexyl Methoxycinnamate, and medium and nonpolar emollients are emulsified very finely. Only Cyclomethicone showed unacceptable particle distributions.

The new emulsifier enables sunscreen emulsions to be produced by the ecologically and economically superior cold emulsification concept, as shown with an example in Fig. 21.7. In this context the authors wish to point out that emulsions based on the new vegetable emulsifier exhibit especially favorable stabilization properties if polymers like Sodium Polyacrylate or the Carbomer types are dispersed in the oil phase.

W/O Emulsifiers

Alongside their good protection and care properties, W/O emulsions have the advantage of being water resistant. Moreover, the use of Polyglyceryl-2 Dipolyhydroxystearate[6–8] as a W/O emulsifier enables lighter emulsion concepts with superior sensory properties to be achieved, irrespective of the polarity of the formulation components (4). Figure 21.8 shows the formulation of an elegant W/O baby sunscreen cream.

TECHNOLOGY FOR NEW SUNSCREEN APPLICATIONS: PHASE INVERSION TEMPERATURE EMULSIONS

One of the trends in the sun protection market are O/W emulsions with the viscosity of water, which can be sprayed. These emulsions can be formulated with the help of phase inversion temperature (P.I.T.) technology. This technology is based on the knowledge that O/W emulsions with nonionic ethoxylated emulsifiers exhibit different phase behavior, depending on the composition, structure, and concentration of the emulsifiers (Fig. 21.9). The temperature level determines the phase in which the emulsifier accumulates (water or oil). In the transition range, at the P.I.T., the interfacial tension is at a minimum. As a consequence, microemulsions form spontaneously and without any special input of mechanical energy (5). O/W emulsions produced in this way contain

---

[6]Polyglyceryl-2 Dipolyhydroxystearate—Dehymuls® PGPH (Cognis Corporation, Care Chemicals).

[7]Polyglyceryl-3 Diisostearate—Emerest® 2452 (Cognis Corporation, Care Chemicals).

[8]Titanium Dioxide, Alumina, and Simethicone—Eusolex® T 2000 (EMD Chemicals Inc.—Rona Business Unit).

INCI Names (DE99/095/14)	weight %
Polyglyceryl-2 Dipolyhydroxystearate[6]	4.0
Polyglyceryl-3 Diisostearate[7]	2.0
Zinc Stearate	1.0
Beeswax	3.0
Dicaprylyl Carbonate[3]	11.0
Cocoglycerides[2]	10.0
Titanium Dioxide, Alumina, Simethicone[8]	15.0
Isostearic Acid	1.0
Tocopherol	2.0
Glycerin	5.0
Magnesium Sulfate	1.0
Aqua	44.5
Bisabolol	0.5
Perfume, Preservative	q.s.

Figure 21.8 Elegant W/O baby sunscreen cream—SPF 30 acc. COLIPA.

very fine droplets in the range of, on average, 100–300 nm even after cooling to room temperature; they have the viscosity of water and exhibit excellent phase stability due to their very small-sized inner phase.

A clear understanding of the structure-based relationships between nonionic ethoxylated emulsifiers and cosmetic emollients allows the optimal

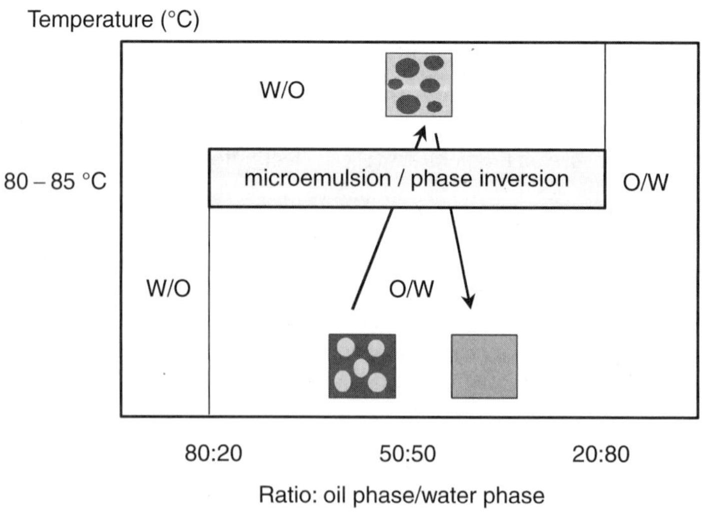

Figure 21.9 Phase behavior of O/W emulsions.

INCI/CTFA (DE99/240/2)	weight %
Glyceryl Stearate, Ceteareth-20, Ceteareth-12, Cetearyl Alcohol, Cetyl Palmitate[9]	7.8
Ceteareth-30	5.2
Dicaprylyl Ether	2.0
Cetearyl Isononanoate	2.0
Benzophenone-3	4.0
Ethylhexyl Methoxycinnamate	7.5
Homomenthyl Salicylate	7.0
Octyl Salicylate	5.0
Glycerin	5.0
Aqua	54.5
Perfume, Preservatives	qs

Figure 21.10 Sprayable O/W sun fluid—SPF 30 acc. FDA.

composition of a P.I.T. emulsion to be calculated. It is then not necessary to carry out a time-consuming empirical test series. Fine-particle O/W emulsions can therefore be produced by a time and money saving method that requires no homogenization or special equipment. As a result of applied research studies a tailor-made compound based on a balanced composition[9] of hydrophilic and hydrophobic ingredients has been proven to be the best material for phase inversion formulations. The only technical production steps needed are heating, simple stirring, and cooling. Figure 21.10 describes a sprayable sunscreen emulsion as an example of this marketing concept.

CONCLUSIONS

New emulsion technologies as well as innovative emulsifiers and emollients with polyfunctional and synergetic performance profiles are described. The authors demonstrate that balanced sensory effects in sun care formulations require accurate knowledge of the spreading behavior of the emollients used and can best be formulated on the basis of the concept of cascading spreading values. Furthermore, it is shown that the emulsifying and pigment dispersal properties, the suitability as solvents for UV filters, and the dermatological compatibility govern the choice of emulsifiers and emollients. Ways of increasing the SPF by targeted use of raw materials are explained.

---

[9]Glyceryl Stearate, Ceteareth-20, Ceteareth-12, Cetearyl Alcohol, and Cetyl Palmitate—Emulgade® SE (Cognis Corporation, Care Chemicals).

ACKNOWLEDGMENTS

The authors wish to thank Helga Gondek and Susan Lang for the care taken in carrying out the experiments.

REFERENCES

1. The market report, sun care: summer loving. ECM April 2003; 125–142.
2. Zeidler U. Fette Seifen Anstrichmittel 1984; 87:403.
3. Ansmann A, Kawa R, Prat E, Wadle A. Seifen Öle Fette Wachse J 1994; 120:160.
4. Ansmann A, Kawa R, von Kries R, Strauß G. Seifen Öle Fette Wachse J 1996; 122:653.
5. Förster Th, Schambil F, von Rybinski W. J Dispersion Sci Technol 1992; 13(2):183.

22

Surfactant-Free Sun Care

James M. Wilmott
Ridgefield Drive, Shoreham, New York, USA

INTRODUCTION

The sun may be considered one of life's ultimate enigmas. On the one hand, it is critical for the support of life on earth. From photosynthesis in plants to vitamin D production in mammals, the sun plays an integral role in sustaining our existence. On the other hand, studies during the past half-century have clearly demonstrated that too much sun can give rise to physiological complications that can lead to the premature appearance of aging, the development of uneven pigmentation, the formation of cancer, and even death in some cases. In fact, incidents of skin cancer are one of the fastest growing problems in the field of dermatology. Why is this trend occurring when the knowledge of the damage done by the sun is so well recognized?

Ironically, the rise in skin pathologies associated with sun exposure exists at the same time that the use of sunscreens is increasing dramatically. The Skin Cancer Foundation, the American Academy of Dermatology, and other medical organizations have done a very effective job in promoting the use of sunscreens with higher sun protection factors (SPFs) to counter the detrimental physiological effects of ultraviolet (UV) light. They have recruited celebrities and have published extensively in professional journals and in the popular press. However, their effort is countered by society's desire to be outdoors more often. More people want to have a tanned appearance, which represents an image of health and success.

To some extent the use of sunscreens has encouraged people to be in the sun for a longer duration, but, unfortunately, with a false sense of security. Recent studies have determined that most people apply far less sunscreen than is necessary to achieve the claimed SPF value. Why is this the case? The cosmetic and over-the-counter (OTC) drug industries have developed a seemingly infinite variety of creams, lotions, gels, sticks, and sprays to appeal to the user's every need and aesthetic preference. Further, the Food and Drug Administration (FDA) has identified in its final OTC Sunscreen monograph the ultraviolet A (UV-A) and ultraviolet B (UV-B) absorbers that are considered "safe and effective" for use in successful sunscreen products. With all this available, one might think that everything that can be done with sunscreens has been done already. But this is not the case!

Most current sunscreens are prepared by combining a hydrophobic phase with a hydrophilic phase in the presence of a surface-active agent called an emulsifier. This approach to formulating sunscreen products has many deficiencies, which will be outlined later. There is clearly a need for an alternative approach to the formulation of sunscreens. This chapter will present a new method of compounding sunscreen products that does not utilize traditional emulsifying agents. This approach offers many advantages over the current art.

BACKGROUND

Issues with the Current Sunscreen Products

Perhaps the single greatest reason that sunscreens are applied inadequately by the user is the typically poor aesthetic characteristics of most products. Many forms of sunscreens leave a heavy, greasy residue on the skin due to the physical properties of the chemical UV absorbers employed and the high concentrations required to achieve maximal SPF values. Sunscreens containing physical UV absorbers, such as titanium dioxide (TiO_2) or zinc oxide (ZnO), can be sticky because of the dispersing fluids used to homogenously suspend the particles of physical absorber. Further, these products can leave an undesirable white cast to the skin especially as the particle size gets larger. The use of alcohol or other volatile solvents to prepare spray sunscreens can pose a respiratory concern and may leave the skin looking and feeling dry and damaged.

Another potential issue with current sunscreens is the effect that sunlight has on the chemical and physical UV absorbers. Chemical filters can absorb a photon of light. Typically, they will dissipate this energy by exchanging it with another molecule in the vicinity, by releasing the energy at much lower dosages, or by re-emitting it as quanta of much lower, less damaging energy such as heat. However, occasionally conditions occur whereby the UV filter absorbs UV light and then goes through an irreversible molecular rearrangement or a reaction with a neighboring compound to produce a new entity that has different properties from the original UV absorber. These by-products may provoke unwanted irritation, sensitization, or other physiologically damaging reactions. Similarly, it has been shown that certain physical UV absorbers, such as TiO_2, can induce the generation of physiologically damaging free radicals in response to UV exposure if they are not surface treated properly and used in well-conceived sunscreen formulations.

The trend to market products with extremely high SPFs and the desire of marketing departments in many companies to produce even higher values has led to the incorporation of large quantities of multiple UV absorbers. As indicated earlier, this trend creates aesthetic problems. Ironically, some of these problems may be unnecessary. The latest version of the FDA monograph has focused more extensively on the generation of a sunburn rather than on total UV damage. The sunburn process concentrates exclusively on the development of erythema from the exposure of skin to UV-B radiation and, to a lesser extent, UV-A radiation. Historically, this has been evaluated by measuring the minimum dosage of incident UV light that can produce an erythemal effect or minimal erythemal dose (MED). SPF values are calculated from the multiple MEDs that the UV protected skin can withstand vs. unprotected skin. From a realistic point of view, a product containing SPFs approaching 30 should effectively prevent up to 99.9% of the erythemal response to UV radiation if applied correctly. Products with SPF values much higher than 30 really have no appreciably greater value in preventing the onset of the sunburn response than those with an SPF of 30. That is not to say that products with very high concentrations of UV absorbers do not have any value. They are just not as relevant for the reduction of erythema. Since sunburn development appears to be the main focus of the FDA's final OTC Sunscreen monograph, a cap may be put on the maximum SPF value that a product can claim. This would reduce the amount of UV absorbers used and improve the aesthetic properties of the marketed sunscreens.

Products with high concentrations of UV filters may still be critically important to reduce or eliminate UV radiation that can lead to other deleterious physiological effects such as cancer and uneven pigment development, which were alluded to earlier. However, high UV absorber levels generally maximize the aesthetic concerns of the product.

Another issue with the current approach to sun care formulation is that the SPF value can change enormously from composition to composition even with the same level of UV absorbers added. One reason for this effect is that the change in the solvent character of the oils used for aesthetic purposes can modify the absorbance properties of the UV filters, thus making them less effective. Another, perhaps more compelling, reason for this effect is that the nature of the film that is deposited on the skin is changed by the addition or substitution of formula components. Generally, new marketing concepts will necessitate a change in composition from the prior art. Also, different aesthetic properties are frequently requested by Marketing in order to generate new products with compelling claims. This is particularly true for cream and lotion products that presently constitute the vast majority of product forms on the market. Clearly, the preferred cosmetic and personal care vehicle for topical application contains both aqueous and anhydrous phases. Such products have a variety of aesthetic properties and can be applied in many forms such as serums, lotions, and creams. However, these components are generally incompatible with one another unless an agent is added that more significantly reduces the interfacial tension between the oil and the water phases. This phenomenon allows the formation of a two-phase system in which one of the phases (e.g., the oil) is suspended in the other (e.g., the water). Such ingredients are called surface-active agents (surfactants). A special subcategory of surfactants is called an emulsifier. These materials not only lower the interfacial tension at the oil/water interface but, with the input of shearing energy, they enable the formation of droplets of one phase within the other. Such emulsifiers have a wide range of surface-active properties. When carefully selected, they can stabilize the incorporation of oil into a water phase or water into an oil phase. The resulting product is called an emulsion. In many cases such emulsions are prepared by heating the oil and water phases to a temperature of 70°C or greater before combining the two phases. The purpose of heating the phases is to insure that all waxes used are melted, and that the two phases have a low enough viscosity so the two phases can mix freely. The oil and water phases are typically mixed together until they achieve a homogenous appearance. Thereafter, they are slowly cooled to insure the formation of appropriately small-sized droplets. It is essential that the droplets be very small in order to insure the stability of the emulsion since, in these cases, Brownian motion will retard sedimentation. Such emulsions typically have a homogenous, opaque, white appearance. They provide a smooth, pleasant feel upon application to the skin, hair, or other epithelial surfaces.

Issues with Emulsions

The introduction of surfactants in the cosmetic industry has provided a "double-edged sword" for formulators. Although the many different types of surfactants have yielded a vast array of cosmetics with very desirable aesthetic properties, they have also generated undesirable issues associated with their use. These issues can produce thermodynamically unstable, nonreproducible, and difficult-to-scale emulsion systems that have limited aesthetic properties. Further, the development of emulsion-based sunscreens is a time-consuming event because of the complexity of the process used to prepare them.

When changes to either the aqueous or the oil phase are made, the emulsifer blend, which was effective in previous systems, generally must be altered. The stability of the sunscreen composition is often compromised as a result, and the SPF performance may be radically altered. This behavior may indicate a potential problem with the long-term shelf life of the product, and it is insidious since it requires either rebalancing of the emulsifier ratios or a change in the emulsifiers selected. Such modifications may result in a change in one or more aesthetic, safety, or performance properties. Often the SPF value of the product will vary significantly with seemingly minor changes to the oils, emulsifiers, or other formula components. This is typically due to the change in the thickness and uniformity of the sunscreen film on the surface of the skin. If the emulsifier blend permits greater and nonuniform penetration of the sunscreen into the skin, then either gaps in the film occur or the concentration of the sunscreen is decreased. Since by the Beer–Lambert law the absorbance of the UV filter is proportional to its concentration, the absorbance will decrease and the SPF value will be reduced.

Compounding this issue is the effect that processing can have on the outcome of a batch. Emulsion stability is dependent on a variety of parameters such as the zeta potential, particle size, crystal formation, and water binding activity of the ingredients employed to achieve the desired rheological properties of the product. These parameters are dependent on the temperature to which the oil and water phases are heated, the rate of heating, the method and rate of mixing of the phases when combined at elevated temperatures, and the rate of cooling. Most emulsions require heating to insure that all higher melting point materials, such as waxes and butters, are completely melted, dissolved, or dispersed in the appropriate phase. Further, if the rate of mixing is high, there is a chance that air can be entrapped in the emulsion. This phenomenon causes an undesirable decrease in the specific gravity of the product and an increase in product viscosity. Any variability in processing can lead to a range of undesirable rheological and textural properties. This issue can occur even if the formulation is not modified! Often, if two or more formulators prepare the same product, the resulting compositions may vary considerably. This surprising variation can occur even though each person utilizes the same lots of raw ingredients. This unsettling phenomenon occurs because it may be very difficult to exactly reproduce all of the processing parameters used to make an emulsion. If any of the processing variables is modified, unexpected particle size variations may occur or the crystalline properties of the emulsion can be compromised.

Since there is so much uncertainty at the "bench" level in the laboratory, there is often concern that a typical 500 to 2000 g laboratory preparation of a sunscreen will not translate directly to a manufacturing environment. This concern is often well founded. Compounding this scale-up problem is the fact that the equipment used in the laboratory generally does not correlate with that used in the plant. There is usually a need for an intermediate phase during scale-up that facilitates this transition. Some equipment is engineered to mimic plant conditions but at a fraction of the size. Even so, scale-up issues abound. To deal with the vagaries of scale-up, the product may be subjected to a wide range of processing variations in order to optimize the conditions of manufacture. Since sunscreens are OTC drugs, the reproducibility of the properties of the product and the concentrations of the active ingredients must be validated every time a new piece of equipment is used. Products made at each level of scale-up must be subjected to accelerated stability testing in order to insure the integrity of the product for its anticipated shelf life. When one adds the processing variability and the need for scale-up to the uncertainty of the selection of the emulsifier system, it is almost a wonder that any product ever makes it to the market on time!

Beyond the problems already cited, there are other issues with sunscreen emulsions. The presence of a surface-active agent, coupled with the need for high-temperature water or steam to heat the phases, can damage many of the unique delivery systems that are being used to enhance the SPF. Wax-based particles will melt. Vessicular delivery systems, such as liposomes, will be destroyed. The contents of polymeric encapsulates will partition into the aqueous phase. They can also damage the properties of adjuvants, such as antioxidants and anti-inflammatories, which are being added to sunscreens to boost their performance properties. Finally, prolonged heating of certain sunscreens, such as avobenzone (butyl methoxydibenzoylmethane), can accelerate the reaction of the UV absorber with other components in the emulsion. This is particularly noticeable if iron, copper, or some other metals are present since an undesirable color change may result.

Traditional emulsion systems also create difficulties in manufacturing. The need for heating and cooling systems, specialized high- and low-shear mixing, and assorted additional processing devices makes the manufacture of emulsion systems very capital intensive. Further, equipment specifications and energy requirements will vary from country to country. This situation will cause a modification in the processing variables, thereby making it almost impossible to have a truly "global" manufacturing protocol. The energy needed to process such products can be significant and undoubtedly will add to the final cost of the finished unit. This is especially true in Europe and Asia where the cost of energy is very high. Similarly, there is the long duration of time required to prepare a batch.

It can take from 5 to 24 h, or more, to complete the processing of emulsions depending on the batch size and number of subphases required. This reality makes the production of sunscreens labor intensive, adds to the cost, and reduces the gross margin of the final product.

As indicated above, the complexity of the manufacturing procedure for personal care emulsions, and its dependence on many processing variables, leads to frequent quality issues. This is especially true with respect to the product's final textural and rheological properties. If any factors such as the heating, cooling, or mixing rates are not carefully duplicated, the material prepared may have different properties from the preceding batches of the same product! As a result, the stability of the emulsion may vary from batch to batch.

Often, the difference of a single parameter is significant enough to cause the product to be outside the established optimum specifications. Inevitably, batches have to be either discarded or reworked. The lack of reproducibility is especially problematic for a sunscreen product, which is a drug and contains an "active" ingredient. Lack of reproducibility, due to manufacturing variations, can affect the SPF performance and decrease consumer satisfaction. It also results in products having undesirable aesthetic properties that the user may perceive as a lack of quality. This will ultimately lead to consumer dissatisfaction or reduced compliance in product use. This may result in a lower SPF protection than that which is claimed for the product.

Perhaps most importantly, the presence of a significant amount of surfactant in an emulsion can strip the lipid barrier of the skin. It can also disrupt the lipid bilayer of epithelial cell membranes, thereby leaving the tissue vulnerable. The surfactants themselves may evoke an irritation. Furthermore, the resulting damaged skin barrier then can permit the passage of other materials that can cause irritation, or increase skin sensitivity.

Figure 22.1 illustrates the migration of auxiliary emulsion components into the skin. These components include the preservative, chelating agent, fragrance, buffers, and other actives. Migration of these components is sufficient to allow penetration deep enough into the lower layers of the skin and evoke an irritation reaction. The literature is replete with clinical evidence of the damaging consequences that can occur with the use, or overuse, of such surfactants. Effendy and Maibach (1) state that "many surfactants elicit irritant reactions when applied to the skin, partially due to their relative ability to solubilize lipid membranes" Barany et al. (2) claim that "the majority of adverse skin reactions to personal care products are presumed to be caused by substances like surfactants". In view of their surface-active nature, surfactants and emulsifiers can alter membrane fluidity, disorganize lipid structure, denature both proteins and nucleic acids, disrupt barrier function, and release inflammatory mediators. The results of these actions on the skin can lead to a variety of undesirable conditions. These include redness, dryness, scaliness, swelling, and tightness. Other conditions that can occur include itching, fissuring, stinging, roughness, and even clinical conditions such as contact dermatitis (3–9).

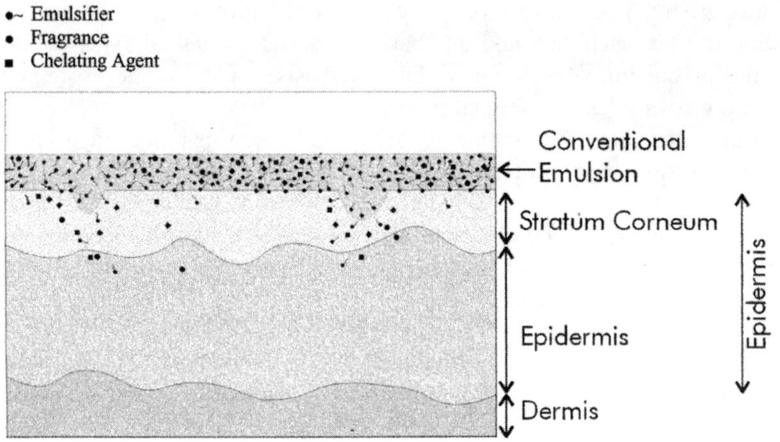

Figure 22.1 Penetration of emulsion content into the skin.

As discussed earlier in the chapter, the presence of surface-active agents in sunscreen emulsions can reduce the SPF efficacy of the product due to the uneven penetration of the UV absorbers into the skin. Further, the surfactants remain in the film once the aqueous phase is absorbed or evaporated. However, because of their amphiphilic nature, surfactants will try to recreate micelles of the hydrophobic UV absorbers when they again come in contact with water. This property reduces the interfacial tension between the hydrophobic sunscreen and the surrounding water and promotes the transfer of the UV absorber from the skin into the water. This water can come from swimming in a pool, a lake, or the ocean. It can also be produced internally due to increased perspiration. Thus, surfactants facilitate the removal of the sunscreen from the surface of the skin when it comes in contact with water. Therefore, emulsion-based sunscreen formulations often include waterproofing agents, such as high-molecular weight polymers or high-molecular weight silicone derivatives, to improve the water-resistant properties of the sunscreen. Unfortunately, the addition of waterproofing agents increases the cost of the formulation and may cause a deterioration of the product's aesthetic properties.

USE OF SURFACTANT-FREE DISPERSIONS IN SUN CARE

It is, therefore, easy to understand the need and desirability of finding an alternative approach to the manufacture and formulation of conventional emulsion-based sunscreen systems. Ideally, the resulting formulation would have the same, or improved, aesthetic properties and would be prepared without the use of traditional surfactants and emulsifiers. But where can such a system be found? What means can be employed that will allow two immiscible substances to mix? The answer to these questions appears to lie more in the realm of physics than chemistry. Another approach does, indeed, exist.

Properties of Lamellar Phase Dispersions

It has been found that familiar hydrophobic materials (i.e., oils, waxes, silicones, etc.) can be formed into stable aqueous dispersions by the application of an extraordinary high-pressure, high-shear process that utilizes unique blends of alkylated phosphatidyl choline. Molecules of phosphatidyl choline and certain other phospholipids will form assemblies with one another in water at extremely low concentrations with a low input of energy. These assemblies are typically bilayers with the polar head group of the molecule interacting with the external and internal aqueous phases. Concurrently, the nonpolar, aliphatic portions of several molecules interact with one another or with a nonpolar fluid to form the bilayer.

Phosphatidyl choline can form up to 11 different stereochemical assemblies in water depending on the alkyl groups present, the phase transition temperature of the molecule, the concentration of phosphatidyl choline present, the temperature at the time of formation, and the shearing energy applied during formation. Some of these assemblies are more thermodynamically stable. Typically, assemblies formed above the temperature at which the molecule changes the structural character of the phospholipid (i.e., transition temperature) are more stable because of the lower entropy present. However, assemblies often transition to a less stable assembly as the system is cooled. Blends of phospholipids generally form more stable assemblies probably due to the synergistic packing of the phospholipids. Ideally, if one could introduce energy without the use of heat, then it would be possible to form more stable assemblies. One type of more stable assembly is known as the lamellar phase (L_α).

A solution to this problem is the introduction of high energy input at low temperatures. This can be achieved by exposing phospholipids to extremely high shear rates under extreme pressure. Such shear is achieved by having the fluid physically diverted into two channels that impinge upon each another in a chamber at velocities that can approach 500 m/s. Further, the shearing action resulting from this geometry takes place under extremely high pressures ranging from 10,000 to almost 50,000 $\mathrm{lb/in.}^2$ (psi). Upon exiting the chamber, the fluid expands as it returns to atmospheric pressure, and this causes an ultraefficient breakup of the hydrophobic material. Under the right combination of shear and pressure, enough energy can be imparted to allow almost instantaneous formation of extremely small droplets of the hydrophobic fluid which are stabilized by the concomitant formation of L_α phospholipid assemblies. Since the formation process is almost instantaneous, the amount of time that the process media needs to be exposed to high shear rates and extremely high pressures can be very short indeed! This time duration is so short, in fact, that the phospholipid assemblies formed do not have time to disassemble before they are no longer exposed to the shear and pressure conditions used to form them. Remarkably, by employing this procedure, lipophilic materials can be successfully incorporated into an otherwise all-water-based product.

The most important state in which the phospholipid assembly can exist for generating stable oil-in-water dispersions is the fluid lamellar or L_α phase, also known as the liquid crystalline phase. The liquid crystal phase exists as a transition between the solid and liquid states. The existence of this phase is only possible above the gel-to-liquid crystalline transition temperature (i.e., the required energy level) of the phospholipid or mixture of phospholipids used. The gel-to-liquid crystalline transition temperature is defined by the amount of work input needed to change the structural character of the native phosphatidyl choline molecule that exists as a less stable L_β phase (also known as a gel phase) to a more stable L_α phase. The L_α phase has two phopholipid assemblies that can form. The first type is the usual unilamellar or multilamellar phospholipid bilayer. This bilayer has large regions of water between the bilayers. Figure 22.2 is an illustration of a unilamellar liposome containing an encapsulated aqueous phase.

The second type of assembly that can form is the result of a conversion that occurs in the presence of relatively large amounts of hydrophobic materials and water. Here, the phospholipids rest at the surface of the hydrophobe droplet. The lipophilic tails of the phospholipids extend into the hydrophobe while the more polar heads of the phospholipids interact with the surrounding water to produce a micelle-like structure. Unlike many emulsions prepared by conventional means, the amount of hydrophobe that can be accommodated into a stable, water miscible dispersion can be greater than 50% by weight. Different

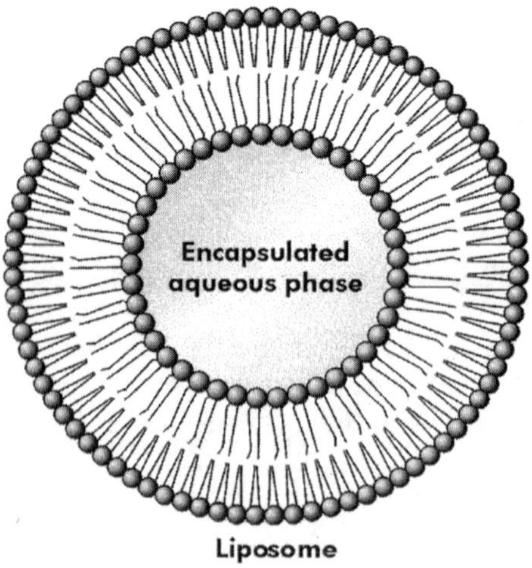

Figure 22.2 Liposome bilayer.

hydrophobes vary in their ability to be incorporated into the stable L_α phase configuration. Generally, nonpolar hydrophobes can be incorporated much more easily than more polar ones. Higher-purity hydrophobes will usually be capable of incorporation at higher levels than those of lower purity. Most silicone derivatives can be incorporated at very high levels. Figure 22.3 is an illustration of a particle containing a high level of an oil whose surface is stabilized by the presence of phospolipid molecules.

The critical aspect of the production of stable L_α phase dispersions is processing at low temperatures and using high energy input. The process used must exceed the energy level requirements needed for the transition from the gel phase to the liquid crystalline phase without actually heating the system to the transition temperature. The L_α phase assembly must be formed in a fraction of a second, and the conditions that allowed the assembly to form must then be removed immediately after the assembly formation is complete. The result of this process is a stable dispersion of highly concentrated hydrophobes that can, thereafter, be freely dispersed in water or water-based products. Typically, the particle size of the micellar structures created during the process will be from 100 to 500 nm in diameter. This size is about 1/10 to 1/50 the size of particles produced by standard emulsification techniques. Further, the high-pressure, high-shear processing described earlier is so efficient that the distribution of particle sizes for the micelles is extremely narrow.

While a small amount of phospholipid is required for the formation of L_α dispersions, the resulting product can clearly be considered to be surfactant free. The phospholipid molecules contained in the L_α dispersions have the tendency to self assemble into micelles even in the absence of a hydrophobe. This happens even when the concentration of phospholipid is extremely small (less than

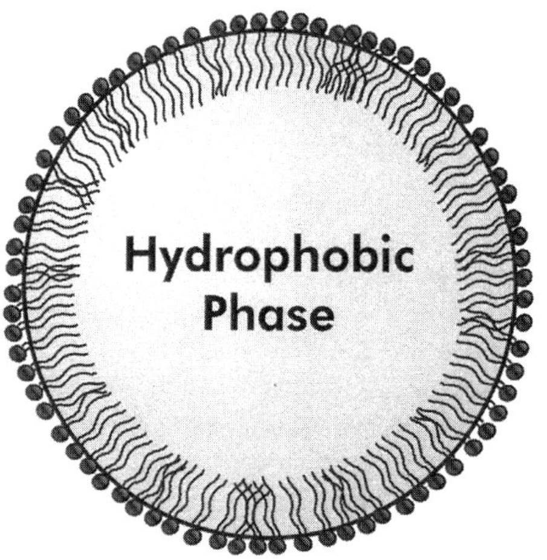

Figure 22.3 Micelle-like phospholipid assembly of an oil.

10^{-10} mM). As a result of this behavior, the phospholipids produce essentially no irritation when applied to the skin. Further, they do not promote skin barrier damage, but rather promote its repair since phospholipids constitute a critical component of the cellular membrane. Oil dispersions made by the high-pressure/high-shear process, using these phospholipids, have a surface tension that is essentially the same as that of water. Figure 22.4 illustrates a comparison of the surface tension of pure water (73 dyn/cm), an L_α dispersion (71 dyn/cm), and a conventional oil-in-water emulsion (25 dyn). Figure 22.5 depicts the contact angle of a droplet of water on skin treated with an L_α dispersion (61°), a cationic emulsion (37°), an anionic emulsion (13°), and a conventional nonionic emulsion (15°). These data suggest that L_α dispersions are truly different from surfactant-based emulsions and, in fact, may be considered surfactant free.

One of the most interesting aspects of the L_α phase dispersions made by the high-shear/high-pressure process is the viscosity of the final dispersion. Typically, any stable emulsion containing 25% or higher concentration of petrolatum will have a Brookfield LVT viscosity measuring over 100,000 cP. By contrast, a high-shear, high-pressure processed dispersion of 25% petrolatum in water will have a much lower apparent viscosity in the range of less than about 400 cP as recorded by a Brookfield LVT viscometer. As a result of this low viscosity, such dispersions can be readily sprayed by means of a finger-actuated pump sprayer. This astonishing difference is entirely due to the type of dispersion produced by the high-shear, high-pressure process. A formula containing 50% petrolatum, processed by the high-shear, high-pressure process described, is a stable, elegant lotion with an apparent Brookfield viscosity of approximately 4000 cP. The same formula made by conventional homogenization has an

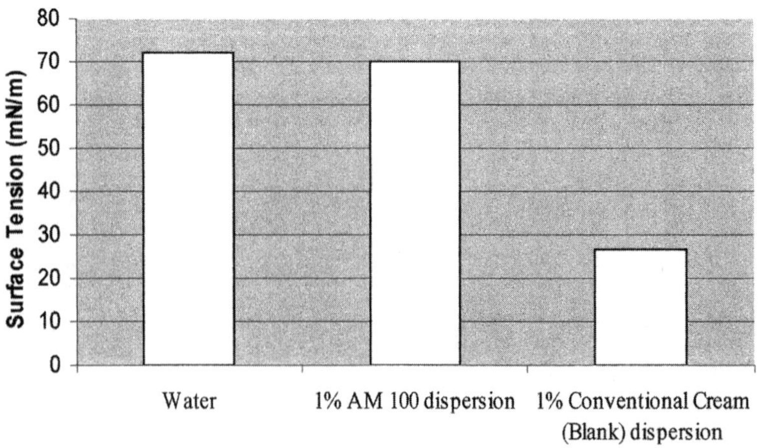

Figure 22.4 Surface tension of L_α dispersions and a conventional emulsion.

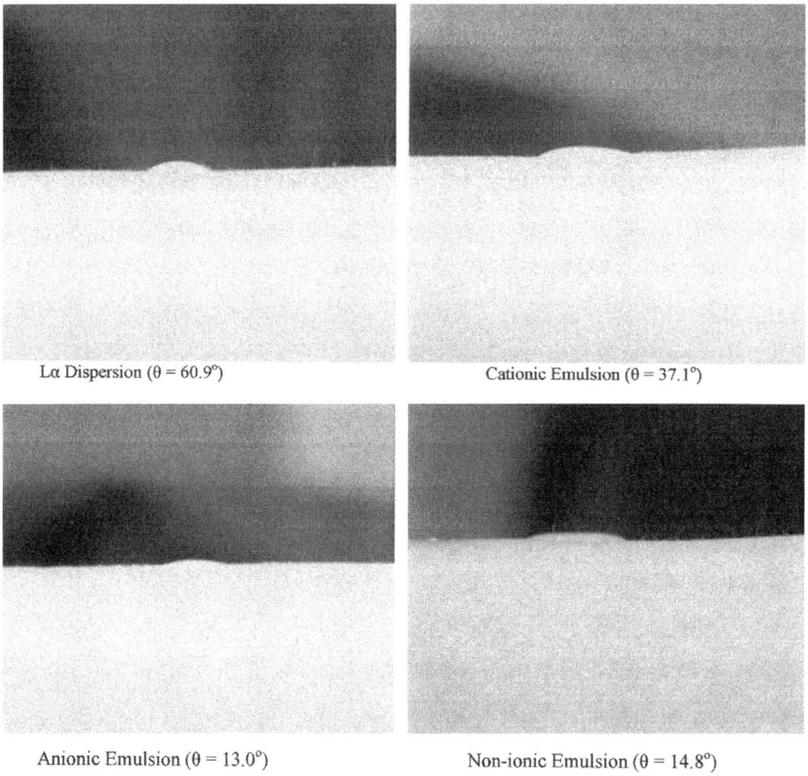

Figure 22.5 Contact angle of water on skin after treatment with L_α dispersion, cationic emulsion, nonionic emulsion, and anionic emulsions.

initial viscosity of 360,000 cP, is extremely inelegant, and is not stable at room temperature for more than 7 days. Further, the high-pressure, high-shear process imparts a negative charge or zeta potential on the surface of the micelle that repels it from neighboring micelles. Therefore, the hydrophobic micelles are free to move past one another, thereby creating a low-viscosity, fluid environment.

L_α dispersions can sometimes provide a method to incorporate ingredients that do not lend themselves to processing by any conventional emulsification system. For example, it is possible to make stable 30–50% L_α phase dispersions of fluorinated materials such as polytetrafluoroethylene and perfluoropolymethylisopropyl ether. These dispersions can be further diluted in water to achieve the desired aesthetic or performance property.

L_α dispersions can be made with virtually any hydrophobic material by carefully controlling the selection of phospholipids and the processing conditions during manufacture. One interesting property of these dispersions is that can alter the aesthetic properties of virtually all materials. This feature results in the opportunity to create new sensations with familiar materials. Conventional materials such as petrolatum, lanolin, waxes, and natural oils are given a new "life" and purpose. Since the micelles of each hydrophobic material are made the same way, they are all independent of any surfactant, and because they have approximately the same particle size and negative surface charge, there is no tendency for the micelles to coalesce. High-pressure, high-shear manufactured dispersions of various low-polarity lipophilic agents (lipophiles) mix together readily, without issue. The practice of balancing the hydrophilic and lipophilic emulsifiers (HLB) depending on the composition of the lipophilic phase that is used so commonly in the preparation of standard emulsion systems is now obsoleted by L_α systems. Thus, a virtually infinite array of lipophilic dispersions can be mixed, in any proportions, without creating any instability in the final blend.

L_α Dispersions of Ultraviolet Absorbers

The principle of forming L_α dispersions can be applied to most nonpolar compounds. Because of their properties, L_α dispersions are particularly useful in sunscreens.

Dispersions of Organic UV Absorbers

It is relatively straightforward to prepare homogenous dispersions containing 30–50% of the UV absorbers ethylhexyl methoxycinnamate, octacrylene, octyl salicylate, homosalate, and other fluids. Because these dispersions are prepared without the use of surface-active agents, they produce a uniform, continuous film on the skin. This property typically results in SPF values that are considerably higher than in conventional emulsions containing an equivalent amount of the same UV absorber(s). An example of such a homogenous dispersion is Solarease™ OMC-50, which contains 50% ethylhexyl methoxycinnamate in an aqueous base.

Heterogenous dispersions containing mixtures of fluid, nonpolar UV absorbers can also be readily formed. Octocrylene, homosalate, octyl salicylate, and ethylhexyl methoxycinnamate can be mixed in virtually any ratio to form a homogenous solution. This system can then be subjected to the high-pressure, high-shear conditions described earlier to create the L_α dispersion. As will be seen later in the chapter, the heterogenous dispersions formed by mixing two or more nonpolar, fluid UV absorbers typically result in higher SPF values than the mixing of homogenous dispersions of the individual UV absorbers.

Dispersions of the solid UV filters, such as benzophenone-3 and avobenzone (butyl methoxydibenzoylmethane), can also be prepared. First, the UV absorber is dissolved in a suitable solvent and then the solution is subjected to the high-pressure, high-shear conditions needed to produce the L_α dispersion. Serendipitously, the fluid, nonpolar UV absorbers are excellent solvents for the solid UV absorbers. This is particularly true for ethylhexyl methoxycinnamate and octacrylene. For example, one part of benzophenone-3 can be dissolved in three parts of ethylhexyl methoxycinnamate. This solution can then be dispersed in a water phase at a 40% level via high-pressure, high-shear mixing. Silmilarly, 1 part of avobenzone can be dissolved in 3.75 parts of ethylhexyl methoxycinnamate. This solution can then be dispersed in an aqueous phase at a 47.5% level. In the final example, a solution is prepared by dissolving 3 parts of avobenzone and 4 parts of benzophenone-3 with 12.5 parts of ethylhexyl methoxycinnamate. This solution is dispersed in an aqueouse base at a 39% level using high-pressure, high-shear mixing. These examples are commercially available from Collaborative Laboratories as Solarease OMC/B3, Solarease II, and Solarease Plus, respectively.

As can be readily observed, a wide variety of homogenous and heterogenous L_α dispersions can be made that contain organic, hydrophobic UV absorbers. A summary of some of the dispersions that will be considered further is found in Table 22.1.

Physical Sunscreen Suspensions

It is interesting to note that the high-pressure, high-shear processing conditions that produce L_α dispersions of hydrophobic fluids in water can also be used to disperse very fine particulate matter in a suspending fluid. Coated, ultrafine TiO_2 and ZnO are examples of particulates of interest in the formation of effective sunscreen products. The thorough breakup of any aggregates of these materials or blends thereof will permit the addition of 50% or greater loading of the coated or uncoated particulates into a suitable suspending fluid such as a benzoate ester. The turbulent mixing conditions will create stable particulate aggregates of less than 75 nm in size, which optimizes the UV-A and UV-B absorbance of the TiO_2 and ZnO. This enhances the SPF value of the final sunscreen product into which they are incorporated. Further, it also minimizes the white cast often associated with the use of TiO_2 and ZnO. Some of the suspensions prepared using high-shear mixing that will be considered further in this chapter are summarized in Table 22.2.

These products are commercially available from Collaborative Laboratories as TiO-Sperse Ultra, Z-Sperse Ultra, and TZ-Sperse Ultra. However, suspension of coated ultrafine TiO_2 and ZnO in a variety of suspending fluids is available from many suppliers to the cosmetic and OTC drug industries.

FORMULATING WITH DISPERSIONS

Defining a Semiquantitiative Aesthetic Scale

A series of L_α dispersions can be prepared that have a range of aesthetic properties from "very light" with no residual feel to "very emollient" with a noticeable and prolonged residual feel. This range of properties permits the generation of a

Table 22.1 Homogenous and Heterogenous Sunscreen Dispersions

	Dispersions (%UV absorbers)					
UV absorber	1	2	3	4	5	6
Ethylhexyl methoxycinnamate	50.0	37.5	30.0	25.0	21.5	30.0
Octacrylene					28.5	
Octyl salicylate						
Benzophenone-3			10.0	8.0		
Butyl methoxydibenzoylmethane		10.0		6.0		12.0
Total UV absorber	50.0	47.5	40.0	39.0	50.0	42.0
Trade name	Solarease™ OMC	Solarease™ II	Solarease™ OMC/B3	Solarease™ Plus	Solarease™ OMC/OS	Solarease™

Note: Dispersions are sold by Collaborative Laboratories, Stony Brook, NY.

Table 22.2 ZnO and TiO_2 Suspensions

	Suspensions (%UV absorbers)		
UV absorber	1	2	3
Ultrafine TiO_2	60.0		
Micronized ZnO		50.0	
Total UV absorber	60.0	50.0	
Trade name	TioSperse Ultra	Z-Sperse Ultra	TZ-Sperse Ultra

Note: Suspensions are sold by Collaborative Laboratories, Stony Brook, NY. The inorganic UV absorbers are suspended in Finsolv TN.

spectrum of tactile sensations that can be combined to create virtually any aesthetic experience. An arbitrary aesthetic scale of 1–1000 can be established to describe the aesthetic properties of a given dispersion. Those having a light, rapidly absorbing property would be on the low end of the scale. Dispersions having a more unctuous, long-lasting effect would be designated with a value at the higher end of the scale. Other lipophilic dispersions could then be assigned intermediate values depending on the degree of tactile properties they demonstrate. For example, a low-viscosity, hydrogenated polyisobutene dispersion is assigned the number 100 for its light tactile impression and fleeting after feel. By contrast, a cetearyl alcohol dispersion is assigned a value of 900 because of its pronounced emolliency and noticeable, prolonged "waxy" after feel. Similarly, cylcomethicone, phenyl trimethicone, a higher-viscosity hydrogenated polyisobutene, petrolatum, gelled silicone, and gelled hydrogenated polyisobutene have been assigned numbers of 200, 300, 400, 500, 600, and 700, respectively. Recently, dispersions of grape seed oil, cotton seed oil, olive oil, mineral oil, and cocoa butter have been developed. These have been assigned numbers of 250, 450, 650, 750, and 850, respectively.

Mixing these dispersions creates a virtually limitless range of tactile properties. Statistically speaking, the mixing of the simple 15 aesthetic-modifying dispersions described, can produce 15 factorial combinations (i.e., 1.307×10^{12}) when the concentration of each active modifier is constant! Table 22.3 is a chart that illustrates the effect of various aesthetic-modifying dispersions on the properties of a final product. When the concentrations are varied, almost limitless numbers of combinations of aesthetic behavior are possible. This effect is analogous to that obtained in the color field, where the blending of three primary colors (red, blue, and yellow) can create virtually any shade of color that exists simply by varying the ratio of each of these primary colors. History shows that with these three agents, artists have been able to produce countless great masterpieces that possess myriad shades of color.

L_α dispersions of lipophilic performance materials (i.e., actives) can also be readily prepared. These materials provide auxiliary functionality to the finished

Table 22.3 Properties of Aesthetic Modifying Dispersions

Aesthetic modifier[a]	Initial feel	Absorbancy/ playtime	Residual	Comments
AM 100	Very light	Short	Low, smooth	Increases opacity of final product; oil free
AM 200	Very light	Short	Emollient with smooth afterfeel	Helps to reduce any tackiness in finished product; imparts a matte finish
AM 300	Light	Medium	Light, silky afterfeel	Helps to minimize tackiness in finished product; provides "dry" emolliency to the end feel
AM 400	Light but with richer texture	Medium	Emollient with slight tackiness	Use in products for normal–oily skin; consider using AM 200 or AM 300 to eliminate any tack; increases opacity of final product
AM 500	Rich	Medium	Slightly unctuous rub in with rich, slightly tacky afterfeel	Tackiness can be reduced with AM 200 or AM 300; provides good residual feel
AM 600	Elegant texture	Short	Emollient, silky afterfeel	Good moisture barrier; ideal for sunscreens and waterproofing; reduces tack and drag
AM 700	Rich	Long	Unctuous, slighty tacky emollient afterfeel	Excellent waterproofing agent for sunscreens
AM 800	Rich, heavy	Long	Unctuous, waxy afterfeel	Tackiness can be reduced with AM 200 or AM 300; increases viscosity
AM 900	Very rich	Very Long	Waxy	Increases opacity of final product; adds body with elegant waxy afterfeel; reduces tackiness

[a]Asthetic modifiers are oil-in-water dispersions manufactured by Collaborative Laboratories.

sunscreen product. Materials such as retinoids, vitamin E (α-tocopherol), α-bisabolol, polydimethylsiloxane, essential fatty acids, and petrolatum can be made into stable dispersions in order to provide the finished sunscreen with a range of useful properties. These include antiaging, skin whitening, antioxidant, anti-inflammatory, moisturization, and skin protectant features. In recent years the practice of combining UV absorbers and additional functional agents has become common. Many, if not most, of the moisturizers and other treatment products currently being marketed contain UV absorbers. This trend clearly reinforces the recognition that the protection of the skin from damaging radiation is very important. Dispersions of UV absorbers and dispersions of other hydrophobic actives are completely compatible with the L_α dispersions used to modify the aesthetic properties.

Since all of the dispersions discussed thus far are made essentially devoid of traditional surfactants, they offer a powerful new degree of flexibility since they are compatible with the sophisticated delivery systems being created for pharmaceutical and personal care applications. Liposomes, nanospheres, encapsulates, and many other types of delivery systems maintain their integrity when mixed with L_α dispersions. By contrast, emulsifiers and other surfactants rapidly disrupt such systems, which makes them valueless in the formulated product.

Preparing the Final Formulation

Since the L_α dispersions are freely miscible with water, they can be infinitely diluted if desired. The dilution process simply reduces their viscosity. However, if the water is first thickened with a natural or synthetic rheologically modifiying agent, then the addition of the L_α dispersions creates a product that looks and feels like a traditional emulsion system. Accordingly, the preparation of surfactant-free, L_α-dispersion sunscreen formulas requires three components: a thickened water phase, a selection of L_α dispersions to produce the desired aesthetic properties, and one or more approved UV absorbers. The UV absorber is preferably incorporated as an L_α dispersion (see the section on L_α dispersions of UV absorbers). This combination of components provides the final product with its aesthetic and functional properties. They may be combined concurrently or sequentially. Since the particle size of the lipophilic dispersions is already pre-established by the high-pressure, high-shear processing, they can be simply mixed into the thickened water phase with gentle agitation at room temperature. The rheological properties demonstrated are primarily due to the presence of the thickening agents employed. Examples of such rheological modifying agents include carbohydrate polymers such as xanthan gum or acrylate-based polymers like carbomer. Depending on the amount of the thickening agent or agents used, the final form of the formulated product can be designed to be a thick cream, a soft cream, a lotion, a serum, or even a low-viscosity fluid. Virtually every aqueous thickening agent is compatible with the L_α dispersions. However, materials such as xanthan gum, methacrylate polymers or copolymers, starches, and silicates that introduce thixotropy (i.e., viscosity decreases with time at a constant shear rate) permit the formulation of elegant finished goods. Other potentially useful polymeric thickening materials can be found in Table 22.4.

These thickened water phases should contain little, and preferably no, surfactant. The presence of surfactant can perturb the stability of the surfactant-free dispersions.

Surfactant-free sunscreen preparations are completely independent of the complex processing conditions required to make conventional emulsions. No heat or extraordinary processing conditions are required. More remarkably, these systems are far more stable than their emulsifier-based counterparts. The hydrated thickening agent(s) provide a matrix into which the L_{α} aesthetic and performance dispersions are embedded. As long as the thickening agent retains its integrity at various temperatures, the product will maintain its stablility. Thus, unlike ordinary emulsions, these dispersions have the potential to be thermodynamically stable indefinitely! Products can be made that are indistinguishable from standard emulsion systems. More importantly, formulations with unique aesthetic and performance properties can be prepared that enhance the enjoyment of the customer during use. Formulas 1–3 represent different forms of sunscreen prepared using a surfactant-free approach.

THE ADVANTAGES OF SURFACTANT-FREE SUNSCREENS

Surfactant-free formulating of sunscreens has many advantages. The time of development, from concept to the market place, is dramatically reduced. There is no longer a need for the preparation of multiple, redundant formulations. Laboratory efficiency can be increased dramatically. Typically, surfactant-free formulations can be prepared in 10–15 min. This allows a formulator to prepare 30 or more prototypes daily. This acceleration in the speed of formulation variation is amenable to the effective use of statistically designed experiments. The aesthetic and rheological properties of the product can be evaluated immediately. There is no need to wait overnight to determine the properties of the product, as is often the case with standard emulsions. Greater flexibility and rapid formulation changes are possible. Since the products are devoid of traditional surfactants, they are less irritating to the skin. A much wider range of aesthetic product types can be made. The compounding of surfactant-free formulations is a cold process that readily scales to manufacturing conditions. The need for multiple pilot batches to optimize the processing conditions is virtually eliminated.

Surfactant-free formulations have distinct advantages in manufacturing as well. They are significantly less expensive to produce. The process conditions are uncomplicated. Labor, overhead, and processing time can be reduced from 50% to 75%. This improvement in production efficiency results in plant capacity increases without any additional capital investment. If capital equipment is needed, it will generate savings of about 70–80% as compared to the processing equipment needed for the manufacture of conventional emulsions. Since no

Table 22.4 Rheological Modifiers

Type	Thickening agent	
A. Carbohydrate	1. Algin	19. Gellan gum
	2. Calcium alginate	20. Guar gum
	3. Propylene glycol alginate	21. Hydroxypropyl quar
	4. Carrageenan	22. Guar hydroxypropyltrimonium chloride
	5. Calcium carrageenan	23. Hyaluronic acid
	6. Sodium carrageenan	24. Dextran
	7. Agar	25. Dextrin
	8. Cellulose gum	26. Locust bean gum
	9. Carboxymethyl hydroxyethylcellulose	27. Mannan
	10. Hydroxyethylcellulose	28. C1-5 aklylgalactomannan
	11. Hydroxypropylcellulose	29. Starch
	12. Hydroxypropylmethylcellulose	30. Hydroxyethyl starch phosphate
	13. Methylcellulose	31. Hydroxyethyl distarch phosphate
	14. Ethylcellulose	32. Pectin
	15. Chitosan	33. Sclerotium gum
	16. Hydroxypropyl chitosan	34. Gum tragacanth
	17. Carboxymethyl chitosan	35. Xanthan gum
	18. Chitin	
B. Polymeric	1. Carbomer	7. Polyacrylic acid
	2. Sodium carbomer	8. PVM/MA decadiene cross-polymer
	3. Acrylate/C10-C30 alkyl acrylate cross-polymer	9. Sodium acrylate/vinyl isodecanoate cross-polymer
	4. Acrylic acid/acrylonitrogen copolymers	10. Ethylene acrylic acid copolymer
	5. Ammonium acrylate/acrylonitrogen copolymer	11. Ethylene/VA copolymer
	6. Glyceryl polymethacrylate	12. Acrylate/acrylamide copolymer

(*continued*)

Table 22.4 *Continued*

Type	Thickening agent	
	13. Acrylate copolymer	18. Ethyl ester of PVA/MA copolymer
	14. Acrylate/hydroxyester acrylate copolymer	19. Isopropyl ester of PVP/MA copolymer
	15. Acrylate/octylarylamide copolymer	20. Polyvinyl pyrrolidone (PVP)
	16. Acrylate/PVP copolymer	21. Sodium polyacrylate
	17. AMP/acrylate copolymer	
C. Inorganic	1. Bentonite	6. Sodium maganesium silicate
	2. Quaternium-18 bentonite	7. Lithium magnesium silicate
	3. Hectorite	8. Silica
	4. Quaternium-18 hectorite	9. Hydrophobic silica
	5. Magnesium aluminum silicate	
D. Protein/Peptide	1. Albumin	5. Milk protein
	2. Gelatin	6. Wheat protein
	3. Keratin	7. Soy protein
	4. Fish protein	8. Silk protein

heating and cooling is required, energy savings can be greater than 90%. There are fewer materials to compound, and no subphases are required. Quality is dramatically improved since it is much easier to insure batch-to-batch reproducibility. There is little waste, and virtually no "rework" of a batch is required. Kettle dwell time is greatly reduced, and the product can be transferred directly to the filling line once ingredient additions are completed. In fact, continuous processing is possible. Finally, the ease of manufacturing enables the product made with $L\alpha$ dispersions to be exactly the same regardless of the manufacturing location anywhere in the world.

Perhaps most importantly, the consumer benefits from the use of surfactant-free sunscreen formulations. The L_α-based systems are potentially more efficacious and less irritating. They will therefore have much greater consumer appeal. The use of L_α dispersions to produce surfactant-free sunscreens results in dramatically higher SPF values for the same amount of UV-A and UV-B absorbers. As stated previously, since no surfactant is present, the vehicle has a surface tension essentially the same as water. When applied to a surface like hair or skin, the lipid barrier of the substrate is not compromised. Penetration of the UV absorber is then controlled by the nature of the delivery system and not by the properties of the vehicle. The use of a surfactant-free base typically provides lower penetration of the vehicle components into the skin and, consequently, irritation potential is reduced as compared to standard emulsion. Because of the low penetration, the uniformity of the resulting layer of product on the skin allows for an even distribution of the active or the delivery system at the skin surface. This property is readily confirmed when 20.0% of an L_α dispersion containing 37.5% ethylhexyl methoxycinnamate and 10.0% butyl methoxydibenzoylmethane is added to a surfactant-free vehicle so that the concentration in the final product is 7.5% and 2%, respectively. The SPF performance of this formula is compared with a conventional surfactant-based emulsion containing the same level of sunscreen (see Table 22.5). In this example there is essentially a doubling of the SPF value when the surfactant-free vehicle is employed. Another added advantage observed is that the surfactant-free formula is essentially waterproof whereas the conventional emulsion vehicle is not. In fact, the conventional emulsion vehicle would require the addition of supplemental waterproofing agents to achieve this effect. Table 22.6 illustrates sunscreen formulas that have a variety of SPF values. All of these products have an SPF value that is higher than expected for the amount of UV absorbers present!

It has been observed that the SPF efficacy of sunscreens made with L_α dispersions that contain a combination of UV absorbers, is generally much higher than that of sunscreens that contain combinations of dispersions containing only one absorber in each dispersion. This is probably due to the synergistic effect that occurs when different UV absorbers are in close proximity to one another. This effect is even more readily observed in Table 22.7, which lists a series of sunscreen formulations that were tested by an *in vitro* SPF method using the SPF 290S from Optometrics, Inc. with software from Lab Sphere.

Table 22.5 SPF Efficacy of Surfactant-Free vs. Traditional

Ingredients	A	B
Moisturizing base	35.25	
Deionized water	18.25	63.50
Pemulen TR-1		0.20
Keltrol		0.20
AMC	1.00	
AM 200	9.50	
AM 300	4.50	
AM 400	11.50	
AM 400	11.50	
Solarease II	20.00	
Micromerol		5.00
Hampene Na-2		0.05
Glycerin		1.00
Germazide MPB		1.25
Seamollient CL		0.75
DC 345 Fluid		5.00
Isopropyl Palmitate		7.00
Stearic Acid		3.00
Soybean Oil		2.00
Amphisol K		0.80
Polyprepolymer 2		0.30
Escalol 557 (OMC)		7.50
Parsol 1789		2.00
Triethanolamine (99%)		0.45
Totals	100.00	100.00
In vivo SPF value	16.85	8.18

The mixing of L_α multicomponent dispersions, with free UV absorbers and inorganic TiO_2 suspensions can produce SPF values that are incredibly high! This phenomenon permits products with very high protection with lower UV absorber levels. Similarly, SPF values of 30 or less can be generated with a very low level of UV absorber. This permits the formulation of products with elegant aesthetics.

Unlike standard emulsion-based sunscreens, which demonstrate large variances in SPF efficacy with changes in composition, the surfactant-free formulas do not! The SPF values for a given concentration of UV absorbers are remarkably consistent regardless of the type or amount of "oils" added to modify the aesthetics. This effect is valid provided the oils are added as L_α dispersions. Table 22.8 illustrates a series of sunscreen lotion and cream products made with a variety of predispersed oils to modify the aesthetic properties. The static and water-resistant SPF values of these formulas vary by less than two units.

Table 22.6 Sunscreen Composition vs. SPF Efficacy

Ingredients	A	B	C	D	E	F
Moisturizing base	35.25	35.25	35.25	35.25	35.25	35.25
Deionized water	9.25	0.00	0.00	4.25	23.25	18.25
AMC	1.00	1.00	1.00	1.00	1.00	1.00
AM 200	9.50	9.50	9.50	9.50	9.50	9.50
AM 300	4.50	4.50	4.50	4.50	4.50	4.50
AM 400	11.50	10.75	9.75	11.50	11.50	11.50
AM 400	11.50	10.75	9.75	11.50	11.50	11.50
Octacrylene	4.00	4.00		4.00		
Solarease	25.00	25.00				
Tiosperse ultra		10.00	10.00			
SS OMC/Octacrylene			30.00			
Solarease plus				30.00		
Solarease OMC					15.00	
Solarease II						20.00
Totals	100.00	100.00	100.00	100.00	100.00	100.00
In vivo SPF value	21.40	35.90	34.39	46.89	15.54	16.85/ 16.65 WR.
In vitro SPF value	32.76	33.97	33.30	49.99	22.10	

BEYOND CONVENTIONAL SUNSCREENS

The use of UV-B and UV-A absorbers in consumer products has expanded dramatically in recent years. Originally, they were added to minimize the production of sunburn in traditional sunscreen products. Initially, they were used at low levels to minimally reduce erythema while still permitting the development of a luxurious tan. As research revealed the negative physiological consequences of sun exposure, the amount of UV absorber added to sunscreens increased. Ultimately, levels of UV absorbers were incorporated to produce extraordinarily high SPF values. Marketers realized that the need for UV protection had to be expanded to every day use. This became particularly important because some of the more aggressive skin treatment products and various dermatological procedures thinned the stratum corneum leaving the underlying tissue more vulnerable to UV damage. As a result, UV absorbers were added to moisturizers, lipsticks, foundations, and eye creams. They were even added to hair care products to minimize the negative effect of UV radiation on the structure of the hair and to protect its natural or artificial color. The ubiquitous use of UV absorbers is likely to continue as more sophisticated treatment products are developed.

Surfactant-free formulating is likely to be the vehicle of choice for the next generation of physiologically active materials. As mentioned earlier, many of these actives are denatured or otherwise destabilized by the presence of surface-active agents. Further, the integrity of liposomes and other delivery

Table 22.7 Sunscreen Composition vs. *In Vitro* SPF

Ingredients	1	2	3	4	5	6	7	8	9
Cationic/acid stable base	30.0		30.0	30.0				19.3	
Lotion base		37.0			37.0	37.0	34.3		37.0
Germazide MPB	0.7	0.7	0.7	0.7	0.7	0.7	0.7	0.7	0.7
Deionized water	14.3	17.3	9.3	2.3	12.3	5.3			10.3
AM-100		5.0			5.0	5.0	5.0		5.0
AM-200	5.0	5.0	5.0	5.0	5.0	5.0	5.0		5.0
AM-400	5.0		5.0	5.0					
TioSperse Ultra	25.0		25.0	25.0				25.0	
Solarease OMC-50	15.0								
Solarease OMC/B3			25.0	25.0				25.0	
Solarease Plus		30.0			30.0	30.0	30.0		30.0
Solarease OC/OS							25.0	25.0	
Octacrylene				7.0	10.0	7.0			7.0
Octyl salicylate	5.0	5.0				5.0			5.0
Homosalate						5.0		5.0	
Total	100.0	100.0	100.0	100.0	100.0	100.0	100.0	100.0	100.0
In vitro SPF value	51.5	61.3	48.1	57.8	66.3	71.5	75.6	80.3	73.5

Table 22.8 Base Composition vs. SPF Level

Ingredients	Moist cream, very dry	Moist lotion, very oily	Moist cream, dry	Moist cream, very dry	Moist lotion, very dry
Moisturizing base	44.00		48.40		32.55
Lotion base		35.00		37.00	4.75
Deionized water	q.s.	q.s.	q.s.	q.s.	q.s.
AMC	4.75	5.00	4.75	4.25	
AM 900	13.00		10.00	7.90	
AM 100		5.00		4.13	
AM 200		5.00		7.13	
AM 300				7.13	
AM 400	6.50		6.50		
AM 500					10.00
AM 600	2.75		2.75		10.00
AM 700					10.00
Solarease II	20.00	20.00	20.00	20.00	20.00
Totals	100.00	100.00	100.00	100.00	100.00
Performance					
Static SPF	20.28	20.00	20.56	20.28	20.28
Water-resistant SPF	19.72	19.48	20.00	18.92	18.68

systems is maintained using an L_α-based formulation system. This permits the optimal penetration of the desired physiologically active ingredients, while retarding the penetration of unwanted materials. Figure 22.6 shows the long-term stability achieved by means of an L_α-based system when it contains liposomes compared with the stability of liposomes in a conventional emulsifier-based

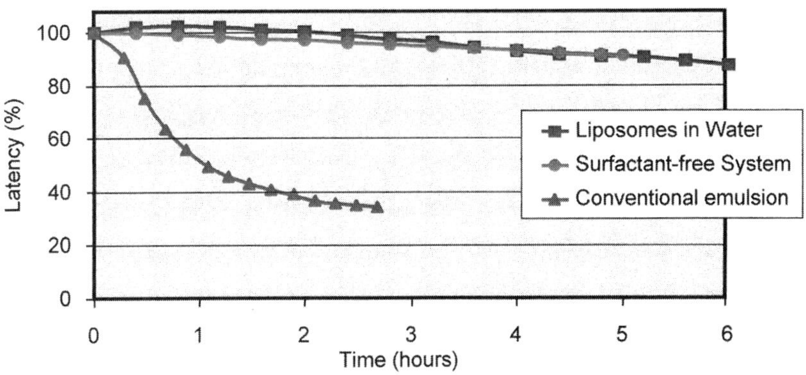

Figure 22.6 Compatibility of liposomes in a surfactant-free system vs. a conventional emulsion.

emulsion. Essentially, there is no loss of liposome integrity with the surfactant-free approach! As a result, new products can be developed that significantly repair various skin disorders. When UV absorbers are added to these products they provide the protection from UV radiation that can compromise these improvements. Such products are likely to be the future of cosmetic and dermatological skin care.

CONCLUSION

Sunscreen products prepared using L_α-based dispersions in a surfactant-free formulating system offer many advantages vs. the conventional emulsifier-based methods. This approach results in greater SPF potency that is water resistant. It offers unlimited aesthetic and form versatility in a vehicle that elicits virtually no irritation. It is also compatible with delivery systems and the next generation of therapeutic agents.

When one combines this with the myriad manufacturing benefits, it makes surfactant-free formulating the method of choice for future sunscreen products. New, unique aesthetic properties can be imparted to the formulated product, thereby creating more elegant systems that heighten the enjoyment of using the preparation. Since the quality of the product can be maintained so tightly, the consumer will experience the same benefits and enjoyment from purchase to purchase and from application to application. Brand loyalty will increase with greater compliance with the usage directions. This will provide the incentive to use the sunscreen correctly, which will enable to consumer to get the maximum SPF protection offered by the product.

REFERENCES

1. Effendy I, Maibach HI. Surfactants and experimental irritant contact dermatitis. Contact Dermatitis 1995; 33(4):217–225.
2. Barany E, Lindberg M, Loden M. Biophysical characterization of skin damage and recovery after exposure to different surfactants. Contact Dermatitis 1999; 40(2):98–103.
3. Rhein LD. Review of properties of surfactants that determine their interactions with stratum corneum. J Soc Cosmet Chem 1997; (5):253–274.
4. Rieger M. Surfactant interaction with skin. Cosmet Toilet 1995; 110(4):31–50.
5. Kawasaki Y, Quan D, Sakamoto K, Maibach H. New technique for the determination of skin lipid structure: ESR studies on the influence of anionic surfactants on human skin. 18th International IFSCC Congress, 1994:37–50.
6. Casterton PL, Potts LF, Klein BD. Use of in vitro methods to rank surfactants for irritation potential in support of new product development. Toxicol In Vitr 1994; 8(4):835–836.
7. Bielfeldt S. A comparison of dermatophysiological methods to detect the influence of surfactants on the human skin. Parfuem Kosmet 1990; 71(5):312–318.
8. Walters KA. Methods for predicting the effect of surfactants on skin. Seminar at In Cosmetics, Birmingham, UK, 1990.
9. Zeidler U. Physico-chemical in vitro methods for determination of the skin compatibility of surfactants, J Soc Cosmet Chem Jpn 1986; 20(1):17–26.

APPENDIX 1

Sunscreen Formulations

Formulation 1
Suncare: SPF 15 Lotion

Formulation

Phase	*Ingredient*	*Function*	*Wt.%*
A	Moisturizing base	Viscosity control	35.25
	Deionized water		16.75
	Advanced moisture complex	Moisturization	1.00
	Aesthetic modifier-200	Emollient	9.50
	Aesthetic modifier-300	Emollient	4.50
	Aesthetic modifier-400	Emollient	11.50
	Solarease II	Sunscreen	20.00
	Germazide MPB	Preservative	0.50
	Liposomes C and E	Antioxidant	1.00
	Total		100.00

Mixing Procedure

1. Weigh the moisturizing base into a vessel large enough for the entire batch.
2. With propeller and sweep agitation add deionized water and mix until a smooth, uniform lotion results.
3. With continued mixing, sequentially add the remaining ingredients ensuring that the product is smooth and uniform before adding the next ingredient.

This formula is offered for informational purposes to represent a particular product concept. There is no expressed or implied warrantee regarding its use in commerce. The authors are not responsible and should be held harmless for any regulatory, legal, performance, or safety liabilities that that may result from its use. Each individual or company is encouraged to conduct the appropriate due diligence to insure that the formula meets internal corporate standards.

Formulation 2
Suncare: SPF 50 Plus Cream—Mixed Chemical and Physical Sunscreens

Formulation

Phase	*Ingredient*	*Function*	*Wt.%*
A	Cationic/acid stable base	Viscosity control	18.30
	Germazide MPB	Preservative	0.70
B	TioSperse Ultra TN	Sunscreen	25.00
	Solarease OMC/B3	Sunscreen	25.00
	SanSurf OC/OS	Sunscreen	25.00
	Eusolex HMS	Sunscreen	5.00
	Liposomes C and E	Antioxidant	1.00
	Total:		100.00

Mixing Procedure

1. Weigh cationic/acid stable base into a vessel large enough for the entire batch.
2. Add Germazide MPB with propeller or sweep agitation.
3. Sequentially add ingredients in B to the main batch.
4. Mix entire batch until it is smooth and uniform. Use homogenizer to increase smoothness and gloss.

This formula is offered for informational purposes to represent a particular product concept. There is no expressed or implied warrantee regarding its use in commerce. The authors are not responsible and should be held harmless for any regulatory, legal, performance, or safety liabilities that that may result from its use. Each individual or company is encouraged to conduct the appropriate due diligence to insure that the formula meets internal corporate standards.

Formulation 3
Suncare: SPF 50 Plus Cream—Chemical Sunscreen

Formulation

Phase	*Ingredient*	*Function*	*Wt.%*
A	Lotion base	Viscosity control	37.00
	Deionized water		11.30
B	Germazide MPB	Preservative	0.70
	Aesthetic modifier-100	Emollient	5.00
	Aesthetic modifier-200	Emollient	5.00
	Solarease Plus	Sunscreen	30.00
	Uvinul N-539-SG (octocrylene)	Sunscreen	10.00
	Liposomes C and E	Antioxidant	1.00
	Total:		100.00

Mixing Procedure

1. Weigh lotion base into a vessel large enough for the entire batch.
2. Slowly add deionized water to the main batch and mix with propeller or sweep agitation until the system is smooth.
3. Sequentially add ingredients in B and mix until smooth.
4. Mix entire batch until completely uniform. Use a homogenizer to achieve a smooth, glossy appearance.

23

Fragrancing of Sun Care Products

Felix Buccellato
Custom Essence Incorporated, Somerset, New Jersey, USA

Generations ago, people realized that the sun is not particularly good for the skin. We probably became "Cave Man" to escape the elements, one of which was the relentless rays of the sun.

The sun is also the reason why we developed melanin in our skin—to help protect us from the damaging rays. After some time man sought to control his environment, fashioning clothing, head gear, hats or cloth all with the same purpose, to protect his skin from the sun. As society became more sophisticated, we began to learn as a collective and share resources. We used clothing, parasols and then science and chemistry in the early 1900s. It is always a source of wonder and amazement how we can adapt and change our lives.

I always have a reservation when using the term "first" when it comes to any use or discovery. Experience has told me over and over that the first in anything is an elusive term which usually means "first recorded history." It is nearly impossible to say who was first, but a good bet is that Nature is usually first and a great teacher when it comes to absorbing ultraviolet (UV) rays. Some of the first ointments, developed in the early 1900s, contained natural sunscreens or UV absorbers like quinine from South American cinchona trees, and cinnamates from cinnamon bark (1).

It appears that the first commercial availability and use of sunscreen was developed in 1928 for the military during World War II (2). It was a chemical mixture of salicylates and cinnamates. The US Army was using red veterinary petrolatum ("red vet pet") prior to that time. The need to protect men who are required to spend time in the sun drove the development of new sun protection agents such as para amino benzoic acid (PABA) as well as various salicylates and cinnamates.

Things have changed slightly since that time. The largest share of the market is still dominated by sunscreens that use a combination of salicylates or cinnamates. What has changed is our understanding of the nature of sunlight, the various UV rays and wavelengths being generated by nuclear fusion, and the protective layer of ozone in our atmosphere, which thankfully filters out wavelengths less than 290 nm (1 nm = 1 billionth of a meter). We have come to understand that the types of UV rays that cause skin damage have ranges of 320–400 nm (UV-A) and 290–320 nm (UV-B). We have also learned that UV-B, while constituting about 1% of the total UV radiation that reaches the surface of the earth, causes 98–99% of the erythema (skin redness) and is the major source of skin cancer. UV-A does not cause sunburn but intensifies the effect of UV-B and inflicts its own type of damage (2). Currently one in five Americans develop skin cancer at some point in their lives (1).

We have discovered that certain chemicals have the ability to absorb specific wavelengths and as a result act as "sunscreens." These various types of chemicals, many salicylates and cinnamates along with some others, are the components used in sunscreen lotions that have allowed us expose ourselves to UV rays and minimize the cumulative damage that is caused by the sun's rays.

There are 17 sunscreens approved by the Food & Drug Administration for use in the USA and 25 being used in Europe.

I have listed below some synonyms (Table 23.1) to help minimize confusion and help understand the table of products listed below.

Products using sunscreens: almost every product (several hundred available) uses a combination of sunscreens for providing a specific sun protection factor (SPF). In the suntan area, the most commonly used are octinoxate,

Table 23.1 Synonym Chart

Name	Synonyms
Octinoxate	Ethyl hexyl p methoxy cinnamate
Octisalate	Octyl salicylate, 2 ethyl hexyl salicylate
Avobenzone	Parsol 1789 (trademark), Giv-Roure, butyl methoxy dibenzoylmethane
Ensulazole	Phenyl benzimidazole sulfonic acid
Oxybenzone	Benzophenone-3

octisalate, oxybenzone, and octocrylene or homosalate, used ubiquitously in the Coppertone line.

SUNTAN LOTIONS, CREAMS, AND SPRAYS

There are hundreds of products (SKUs) of various types of suntan lotion or cream products that are specifically designed to protect the skin from sunburn. They provide from SPF 2 to SPF 70 for the extreme Ozone brand sunblock. They are available for adults, children, and babies.

Each product contains at least two different sunscreens, with many using four or five UV absorbers or reflectors and is normally a combination of materials.

The most frequently used sunscreens are homosalate, octyl methoxy cinnamate, octyl salicylate and oxybenzone. Note that inorganic sunscreens like titanium and zinc oxides reflect and scatter sunlight. [TiO_2 absorbs short wavelengths and reflects longer wavelength light rays (3).]

I have tabulated the sunscreen products in alphabetical order by manufacturer for comparison purposes.

They are presented in the product table (Table 23.2) under the following headings.

As can be seen from Table 23.3, the variety of fragrances used is quite small for the number of products used.

Bain de Soleil—a red gel (similar to red veterinary petrolatum?)—is truly unique in the sun protection market. It is the only one with a spicy oriental fragrance and is arguably more popular in Europe than in the USA. The color and the packaging are appropriate (packaging that blocks out light and prevents discoloration from light induced fragrance/base reactions) for that type of

Table 23.2 Guide to Sections I–III of Table 23.3

Section	Products	Number of products
I	Suntan products	53
II	Skin treatment products	31
III	Lip balm products	24

Table 23.3 Product Table by Manufacturer

Products	SPF	Sunscreen agents used	Fragrance type
		Section I—sun protection	
Bain de Soleil			
Orange Gelee	4	Octinoxate, octisalate	spice, oriental
Banana Boat (Sun Pharmaceuticals)			
Baby Magic Sun Block Spray	48	Homosalate, octinoxate, octisalate, oxybenzone, TiO_2	tropical fruit, coconut
Suntannicals	8	Octinoxate, octisalate	Melon, fruity
Faces Plus	23	Octinoxate, octisalate, oxybenzone,	No fragrance
Sports Block	50	Octinoxate, octisalate, oxybenzone, octocrylene	Fragrance free
Vitaskin	30	Octinoxate, octisalate, oxybenzone, avobenzone	Fragrance free
Dark Tanning Lotion	4	Octinoxate, padimate O	Coconut, banana
Ultra Sun Block	30	Octinoxate, octisalate, oxybenzone, TiO_2	Fragrance free
Protective Tanning Oil	8	Octinoxate, octisalate, Padimate O	Coco banana
Protective Tanning Oil	4	Octisalate, padimate O	Coco banana
Kids	30	Octinoxate, octisalate, oxybenzone, TiO_2	Fragrance free
Protective Tanning Oil	15	Octinoxate, oxybenzone, octocrylene, padimate O	Coco banana
Hair & Scalp Protector	15	Octinoxate, octisalate, oxybenzone	Orange flower
Bath & Body Works			
Sunscreen	15	Octinoxate, avobenzone	Coconut, tropical
Blue Lizard			
Sun Cream	30+	Octinoxate, oxybenzone, ocotcrylene, zinc oxide	Fruity floral
Dermatologic Cosmetic Labs			
Essential Skin Protection	30	Homosalate, octinoxate, octisalate, butyl methoxy dibenzoyl methane, benzo phenone 3	No fragrance
Eckerd Drug			
Eckerd Baby	45	Octinoxate, octisalate, oxybenzone, octocrylene	Baby powder
Eckerds	30	Homosalate, octinoxate, octisalate, oxybenzone, avobenzone, octocrylene	Orange flower
Eckerds	15	Octinoxate, oxybenzone,	Orange flower
Eckerds (note: same as SPF 30)	45	Homosalate, octinoxate, octisalate, oxybenzone, avobenzone, octocrylene	Orange flower

(continued)

Table 23.3 *Continued*

Products	SPF	Sunscreen agents used	Fragrance type
Eckerd Baby Spray	45	Octinoxate, octisalate, oxybenzone, octocrylene	Baby powder
Eckerds	8	Homosalate, oxybenzone	Orange flower
Faulding Products			
Sea & Ski Faces	50	Octinoxate, octisalate, oxybenzone, zinc oxide	Fragrance free
Hawaiian Tropic			
Golden Tan	6	Octinoxate, octisalate,	Coconut
Barbie	30	Octinoxate, octisalate, oxybenzone, octocrylene	Strawberry
Dark Tan Gel	2	Ensulizole	Coco banana
Baby Faces	50	Octinoxate, octisalate, TiO_2	Fragrance free
Ozone (Note SPF 100 from Bioderma)	70	Homosalate, octinoxate, octisalate, oxybenzone, TiO_2, octyl dimethyl PABA	Coconut
Kids Splash	30	Homosalate, octinoxate, octisalate, octocrylene	Lime kiwi (strawberry)
L'Oreal			
Ombrelle Anti Aging	15	Octisalate, avobenzone, octocrylene	Fragrance free
Age Perfect Anti Wrinkle	15	Octinoxate, ensulazole	Rose floral
Revitalift Complete	18	Octinoxate, ensulazole	Mild floral rose
Neutrogena			
Healthy Defense	30+	Homosalate, octinoxate, octisalate, avobenzone	Creamsicle
Ultra Sheer Day Dry Touch	30	Homosalate, octinoxate, octisalate, oxybenzone, avobenzone	Herbal floral
Schering-Plough			
Coppertone Oil Free	30	Homosalate, octisalate, oxybenzone, avobenzone, octocrylene	Fragrance free
Coppertone Ultra Sweat Proof	30	Homosalate, octinoxate, octisalate, oxybenzone	Orange flower
Coppertone Sun Block Lotion	15	Octinoxate, oxybenzone	Orange flower
Coppertone Ultra Sweat Proof	30	Homosalate, octinoxate, oxybenzone	Orange flower
Kids Trigger Spray	30	Homosalate, octinoxate, octisalate, oxybenzone	Orange flower
Lotion & Splash Coppertone	30	Homosalate, octinoxate, octisalate, oxybenzone	Orange flower
Dry Oil Coppertone	4	Homosalate, oxybenzone	No fragrance, SDA 40
Spectra Coppertone	30	Homosalate, octinoxate, octisalate, octocrylene, zinc oxide	No fragrance
Oil Free Coppertone	30	Octinoxate, octisalate, oxybenzone, avobenzone	No fragrance

(*continued*)

Table 23.3 *Continued*

Products	SPF	Sunscreen agents used	Fragrance type
Kids Coppertone Sun Block	50	Homosalate, octinoxate, octisalate, oxybenzone, octocrylene, zinc oxide	Fragrance free
Dry Oil Coppertone	15	Homosalate, octinoxate, octisalate, oxybenzone	No fragrance
Kids Coppertone	30	Homosalate, octinoxate, octisalate, oxybenzone, avobenzone	Orange flower
Sports Gel Coppertone	30	Octisalate, oxybenzone, Parasol 1789, octocrylene	Orange flower
Kids Coppertone	40	Homosalate, octinoxate, octisalate, oxybenzone	Orange flower
Kids Spray Coppertone	30	Homosalate, octinoxate, octisalate, oxybenzone	Orange flower
Lotion Coppertone	4	Octinoxate, avobenzone	Orange flower
Water Babies Coppertone	45	Homosalate, octinoxate, octisalate, oxybenzone	Floral fresh
Faces Coppertone	30	Homosalate, octisalate, oxybenzone, svobenzone, octocrylene	No fragrance
Coppertone Spectra Triple	50	Homosalate, octinoxate, octisalate, oxybenzone	Orange flower
Stop & Shop	30	Homosalate, octinoxate, oxybenzone, octisalate	Orange flower
		Section II—skin treatments	
Products other than suntan lotion (products by company) 31 products out of 200 products (about 15.5%) containing sunscreens of some type			
Almay Incorporated			
Age Decelerating Cream	15	Octinoxate, octisalate, oxybenzone, avobenzone	Fragrance free
Avon Incorporated			
Biologique +	15	Octinoxate, oxybenzone	No fragrance
Retroactiv	None	Benzophenone 4	No fragrance
Antibac. Moisturizing Gel	None	Benzophenone 2	No fragrance
Beieresdorf			
Eucerin	30	Octinoxate, avobenzone, octocrylene, zinc oxide, ensulizole	No fragrance
Nivea Q 10	4	Octinoxate	Soft floral
Nivea Visage Anti Wrinkle Lotion	15	Octinoxate, octisalate, oxybenzone	Soft floral
Bristol Meyers Squibb	20	Octinoxate, octisalate, Zinc oxide	
Keri Moisturizing Lotion	15	Octinoxate, oxybenzone	Rose floral
Keri Revitalizing	15	Ocitnoxate, benzophenone 3	Soft floral

(*continued*)

Table 23.3 *Continued*

Products	SPF	Sunscreen agents used	Fragrance type
Banana Boat Max Sun Block	50	Octinoxate, octisalate, oxybenzone, octocrylene	No fragrance
CHANEL Age Delay	15	Octinoxate, oxybenzone, avobenzone	Mild floral, sophisticated
Cheesborough Ponds			
Vaseline Renewal Protection	5	Octinoxate, TiO_2	Light herbal
Guthy-Renker			
Natural Advantage Moisturizer	15	Octinoxate, oxybenzone, octisalate, TiO_2	Thea sinensis/ Matricaria oil
Galderma Labs			
Cetaphil Facial Moisturizer	15	Avobenzone, octocrylene	No fragrance
Johnson & Johnson			
Retinol Actif Pur	15	Octinoxate, avobenzone	No fragrance
Ocean Potion	15	Octinoxate, octisalate, avobenzone	Creamsicle, orange, vanilla
Ocean Potion Baby	50	Octinoxate, octisalate, oxybenzone, Parasol 1789, octocrylene	Fragrance free
L'Oreal			
Age Protection	15	Octinoxate, ensulizole	Rose floral
Futur - e Moisturizer	15	Octocrylene, ensulizole	Floral
Revitalift Complete	18	Octinoxate, ensulazole	No fragrance
Age Perfect Cream	15	Octinoxate, ensulazole	No fragrance
Visible Results	15	Octinoxate, TiO_2	No fragrance
Neutrogena	20		
Visibly Younger Hand Cream	20	Octinoxate, avobenzone	No fragrance
Visibly Younger Hand Cream	15	Octinoxate, octisalate	No fragrance
Healthy Defense Moisturizer	30	Octinoxate, octocrylene, zinc oxide, ensulizole	No fragrance
Face Lotion	20	Oxtinoxate, octisalate	No fragrance
Olay–Proctor & Gamble			
Protective Renewal Lotion	15	Octinoxate, octisalate	No fragrance
Provital, Day Lotion	15	Octinoxate, zinc oxide	Fresh floral
Complete All Day	15	Octinoxate, zinc oxide	Fragrance free
Complete Moisturizer Lotion	15	Octinoxate, octocrylene	No fragrance
Wakefern			
Lotion Shop Rite	4	Octinoxate, oxybenzone	Orange flower

(*continued*)

Table 23.3 *Continued*

Products	SPF	Sunscreen agents used	Fragrance type
Section III—lip balms: 34 units on market shelf, 24 using sunscreens (65%)			
Sport Sunblock	30	Homosalate, octinoxate, oxybenzone, padimate O	No flavor
Blistex			
Ultra	30	Homosalate, octinoxate, oxybenzone, menthyl anthranilate 4.8%	No flavor
Clear Advance	30	Homosalate, octinoxate, octisalate, avobenzone	No flavor
Complete Moisture	15	Octinoxate, oxybenzone	Flavored
Lip Balm	15	Oxybenzone, padimate o	Flavored
Medicated Lip Balm	15	Oxybenzone, padimate O	Menthol, camphor, flavor
Herbal Answer	15	Octinoxate, octisalate	Chamomile, *Helianthus annus*
Lip Tone	15	Octinoxate, menthyl anthranilate	No flavor
Berry Lip Balm	15	Oxybenzone, TiO_2, padimate O	Berry flavor
Silk & Shine	15	Octinoxate	Flavored
Chapstick			
Fruit Smoothies	15	Octinoxate, oxybenzone	Natural fruit, flavors, vitamins
Lip Balm	15	Octinoxate, oxybenzone	Tropical
Lip Balm	15	Octinoxate, octisalate	Strawberry, kiwi
Lip Balm	15	Octinoxate, oxybenzone	Wild crazeberry
Lip Balm Ultra	30	Octinoxate, octisalate, oxybenzone, octocrylene	Flavored
Lip Balm	15	Octinoxate, oxybenzone	No flavor
Lip Balm Moisturizer Stick	15	Octinoxate, oxybenzone	Vanilla, mint
Lip Balm Moisturizer Squeeze	15	Octinoxate, oxybenzone	Aloe, No flavor
Lip Balm Regular	4	TiO_2, padimate O	Fragrance
Lip Balm Regular	4	Padimate O	Cherry fragrance
Hawaiian Tropic			
Lip Balm Sun Block	45	Homosalate, octinoxate, octisalate, oxybenzone, octocrylene	Herbal
Lip Balm Sun Block	45	Homosalate, octinoxate, octisalate, oxybenzone	Orange
Lip Balm Sun Block	45	Homosalate, octinoxate, octisalate, oxybenzone, octrocrylene	Coconut
NO AD			
Lip Balm	30	Octinoxate, octisalate, oxybenzone, TiO_2	Berry, tropical

fragrance. This oriental fragrance type is very good but may not be color stable in a white lotion or cream like many of the usual sun tan products sold in the USA. The *Coppertone* brand appears to have used the same floral jasmine (though closer to orange blossom) fragrance for almost all their products. This seems appropriate, knowing that Benjamin Green, the pharmacist who developed the Coppertone line in 1944, was from Florida. It is a mixture of cocoa butter and jasmine and it has served the manufacturers well, establishing their brand identity (4). The *Hawaiian Tropic* brand has always been characterized by a tropical coconut. Overall, the US market is saturated with coconuts. The notable exception is the strawberry fragrance added to the Barbie brand for children. Seventeen out of 50 products are fragrance free. These are for sensitive skin, baby products, or for facial use.

FRAGRANCING SUNSCREENS

The wide variety of sunscreen bases and materials used does not pose a significant problem with regard to fragrance. When we examine the structures of the sunscreen molecules we see that many of them have bifunctionality, both ketones and phenols, along with various points of unsaturation. One might suspect that these groups would be reactive or unstable. One might also suspect that the sunscreens could react with the various functional groups or materials used in fragrances. The fragrance molecules cover a wide range of functional groups themselves. They include, but are not limited to, terpenes (unsaturated hydrocarbons), alcohols of all types, primary, secondary, and tertiary, as well as diols, ketones, aldehydes, amines, esters, lactones, and a variety of bifunctional or multifunctional groups. The full range can occur in a single fragrance, and often all these functional groups and more are present in a single natural product. One might anticipate that the sunscreens would react with many or at least some of the fragrance ingredients. This in fact does not appear to be the case. Most fragrance ingredients and indeed a variety of blends seem to be stable, with a few notable exceptions that are common to many creams and lotions as will be noted later. This may be more a function of the medium than the materials. It has been my experience that the environment or the medium of the product is more determinate than the materials. It seems that the same materials which are reactive in a water based system react more readily and frequently than in a system where a minimum amount of water is used. This appears to be the case with suntan lotions or creams.

The base odors and the odors of the sunscreens themselves are quite mild and easily mixed or masked with the use of low levels of fragrance. They may range from 0.1% to 1.0% on the high end. They are actually very easy media to work with. The base odors are generally very mild, they are not very reactive, application to the skin provides a broad surface from which fragrance can emanate, and a wide variety of types could be employed. This, however, does not appear to be the case. Almost all the sun care fragrances on the market have followed a market leader and are of either the floral orange blossom type like Coppertone or the coconut type like the Hawaiian Tropic brand. This does not appear to be caused by stability requirements or for any other reason than following the lead of a successful product. The changes in the market are not due to a shift in this thinking, rather it is due to the introduction of fragrance products marketed for young children and infants. The fragrances have followed suit to accommodate the image of kids, Strawberry for Barbie from Hawaiian Tropic and powder florals for Baby Magic.

The skin treatment products which are made for adults employ milder floral fresh and clean aromas that are more appropriate for the market.

FRAGRANCE SAFETY AND PHOTOSENSITIZATION

It has long been established that fragrances add a measure of acceptability to a wide variety of products, and sunscreen products are no exception. However, when the objective is to prevent skin damage and provide protection from the sun, fragrances are not always necessary or desirable. The modern bases used in sunscreen and their lack of background or base odor permits perfectly acceptable products to be designed and marketed without any fragrance whatsoever. The elimination of fragrance also removes another factor or potential source of skin irritation and a variety of reactions that may take place in the presence of UV rays.

There are a few items that have a potential to be photosensitizers or cause skin irritation after being exposed to UV rays. They are usually citrus products like lemon, lime, or bergamot which contain a class of chemicals called psoralenes or bergaptenes. The fragrance industry has guidelines regarding their use or nonuse in skin applications. The fragrance industry follows the guidelines of the Research Institute for Fragrance Materials (RIFM) and the International Fragrance Association (IFRA). When the citrus products mentioned above are used, they are employed at 10 times below their no-effect level, providing a large margin of safety.

STABILITY OF FRAGRANCES IN SUNSCREEN PRODUCTS

Most fragrance ingredients are stable in the fairly mild sunscreen and moisturizer bases and as a result do not pose a severe restriction on the types of fragrance that could be used. Having said that, it is somewhat puzzling that a greater variety of fragrances has not appeared in the suntan product market. Are we all coconuts? There are a few basic considerations such as color stability (not fragrance or odor stability) that can arise with fragrance/fragrance or fragrance/base or light induced color changes that can seriously affect the color and appearance of a product but not have much olfactory or performance effect.

A review from Custom Harley Davidson Motorcycle Parts & Accessories appeared in April 2000. Paul (in sales department), comments on his experience trying dozens of sunblockers over the years and succinctly says, "I've trashed a lot of them. Some burned my eyes and some were so greasy they caused my hands to slip off the grips. My bike smelled like the beach for months." He winds up recommending Coppertone to go with SD-40 alcohol. This is an unlikely source for an on-target evaluation of the sunscreen market. I have personally received many comments about the odor and greasiness of creams and lotions and the difficulties in using these products.

Application by pump spray is easier and more evenly distributed, and does not leave streak marks as creams do when you try to apply them on yourself. The odor is in fact milder, perhaps because you tend to use less, thereby delivering less fragrance as well as less salicylates that contribute to the odor profile. Why do not these sprays out sell the creams and lotions?

It could be price, but as our biker friend points, out he has used a small pump spray for months and it is waterproof and does not run and burn his eyes when perspiring! The buying public does respond negatively to higher priced items as their perceived value is less. They very rarely have the time or inclination to do a cost/use study on a product. It appears that there could be an opportunity for some clever and focused marketer to gain a niche and develop a part of the market for people who desire the attributes of a pump spray (5).

COLOR STABILITY: ENSULAZOLE (INCI NAME PHENYLBENZIMIDAZOLE SULFONIC ACID)

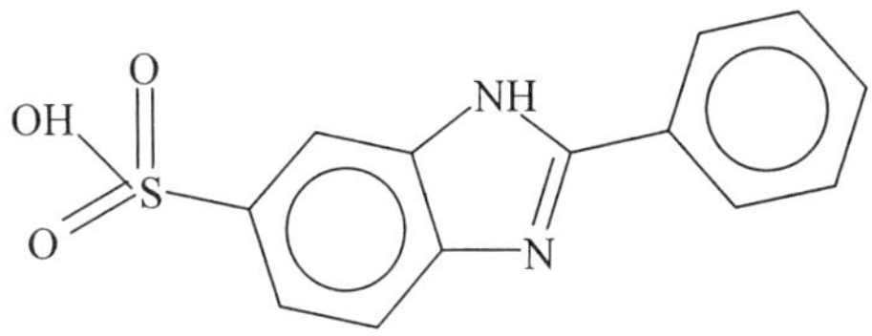

Reactive Acid and Amine Groups

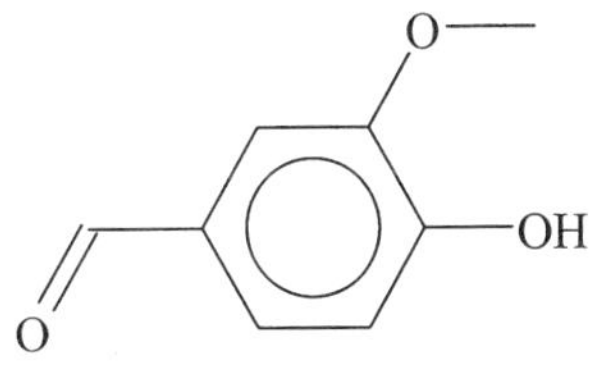

Vanillin, a multifunctional aroma chemical (3 methoxy, 4 hydroxy benzaldehyde), has two reactive groups, the aldehyde group and the hydroxyl group, that can either form Schiff's bases or react with trace metals or other fragrance ingredients. They have a tendency to turn the base from any shade of pink or red to dark brown. While the odor and performance do not suffer, the appearance has been degraded enough to cause consumers and, as a result, marketers to want to avoid this condition.

There are other materials like phenols, hydroxy cyclopenteneones, and unsaturated phenols, often multifunctional, that should be avoided because they cause the same type of problems.

Normally unstable fragrances would be true vanilla, spices, orientals, and berry fragrances of any type which can cause color problems. Many of these effects can be mitigated to some degree but the character of the fragrance usually suffers to some degree.

Fragrances that are good for color are generally fresh clean, floral, or lightly herbal fragrances or use expensive decolorized versions of raw materials or natural products. Rose, a perennial favorite, is a widely acceptable cosmetic aroma that exhibits very good stability in a wide variety of applications. Rose is often the base accord or floral base upon which many floral fragrances or twists, including herbals, are constructed.

ODOR STABILITY

From an olfactory viewpoint, all natural citrus products in general should not be used in these types of products. All citrus products are constituted of mostly limonene, a cyclic unsaturated terpene, and many other unsaturated terpene hydrocarbons that react with oxygen and develop an off-odor similar to turpentine. In addition, the unsaturated terpenes react with oxygen and will create a vacuum in the package, causing it to warp and bend. This is commonly referred to as "paneling" and produces an unsightly package, usually within 60 days or less. The odor change begins immediately and is quite noticeable within 30 days. Additionally, the more odor-active components of citrus oils are aldehydes, both saturated and unsaturated, that also oxidize readily, eventually altering the odor significantly, and in many cases the odor will seem to have vanished. This is due to the active odor components, often aldehydes, that have been oxidized to the corresponding acids, which have a much lower odor impact. When citrus is used, it is usually in smaller amounts in conjunction with another type of aroma like cream or vanilla to make a creamsicle. This is one of the types currently being used.

Some of the effects of color and odor instability can be reduced using antioxidants and, ironically, different and specialized UV absorbers which help prevent light induced oxidation or cross fragrance and base reactions.

FUTURE DEVELOPMENTS

There are some concerns that current UV absorbers form free radicals on the skin following absorption of UV radiation. Antioxidants are used to try and neutralize the free radicals formed. A novel material called Optisol, a patented product which modifies the structure of titanium and zinc oxides, is promising to eliminate the problem of formation of free radicals and additionally extending the life of other active ingredients.

More recently, researchers are studying coral reefs which have developed mycosporine-like amino acids (MAAs). As a result of this discovery and research, new synthetic ingredients related to MAAs may soon become available. They will be highly efficient at capturing, absorbing, and dissipating the UV energy. Additionally, they promise to cause less allergic reactions than commercial sunscreens and exhibit greater stability (1). Combination functional products like anti-aging creams, face lotions, creams, and lip glosses with sunscreens are already on the market. Pediatricians warn parents that the West Nile Virus rarely makes people sick but using an insect repellent with more than 10% diethyl-*m*-toluamide (DEET) can be deadly for small children as it is a neurotoxin. The combination product incorporating a sunscreen may help DEET be absorbed more into the skin, thereby putting small children at greater risk (6). These new materials may all benefit from a fragrance which can be tailor-made to suit the image and utility of each product. It would certainly be beneficial to market a new product with new claims of efficacy and safety and have a unique corresponding fragrance to enhance the image and branding of the new product. There are few technical reasons limiting the types of fragrances that could be used in a sunscreen product other than some of the stability guidelines mentioned above. It usually requires the imagination of a courageous marketer or the naiveté of an entrepreneur with a different vision and desire to do something independent and new to the market.

Fragrance Appropriateness

As mentioned above, it is somewhat surprising that the number of fragrances used in most of the suntan products are so few. I realize that once a market and product is established and is well known as in the case of the Coppertone and Hawaiian Tropic brands, it is extremely difficult to replace or to add a competing product with a different aroma. The fragrance identifies a successful brand name and any decision to replace or modify the aroma requires careful consideration. It appears that both Schering Plough (Coppertone) and Tanning Research (Hawaiian Tropic) have found the appropriate fragrance for their respective products. The Coppertone brand is a jasmine/orange blossom aroma that ties in to Florida's Sunshine State, and the Orange Groves and Hawaiian Tropic brands are very closely associated with the coconut/pina colada Hawaiian Vacation theme. The new skin treatment products coming out the cosmetic section of the market have a free reign to utilize new and different fragrances that are more appropriate for their image or brand. This is clearly seen in the case of Chanel's Age Delay cream, which uses a sophisticated and light modern floral aroma. In the case of Procter & Gamble's Olay brand they have used a very pretty rose floral which has always been regarded as the single most important floral aroma in the cosmetic world. This dates back to ancient Egyptian and Roman times, when rose petals were used to add fragrance to baths. The rose aroma has been a basic in cosmetics since that time, and little has changed over the millennia. Modern perfumery still uses rose but with new nature identical synthetics that are available for enhancing nature. These materials, like damascenone, and a variety of damascones as well as other specialty aroma ingredients, are synthetic but nature-identical and commercially available with the advantage of continuous supply for the cosmetic market. This philosophy of developing nature-identical materials providing a continuous, reliable supply is one of the three legs of perfumery material development. The other two, synthetic materials with unique odor properties and synthetic materials with unique functional stability, provide a wide variety of fragrance ingredients from which to build new and unique fragrances for new and unique products. I am certain the future of sunscreens and new sunscreen products will utilize the new materials. New appropriate cosmetic aromas will be developed and utilized for them as society becomes more cognizant of the danger of overexposure to our life- and energy-providing sun.

REFERENCES

1. Chen I. The biology of sunscreen. Discover 2003; 24(6).
2. Kim JJ, Lim HW. Primary Care Cancer 2000; 20(5).
3. Reisch M. Sci Techno 2002; 80(25).
4. Coppertone Solar Research Center. The History of the Solar Research Center. 1.
5. Bikers Sun Block Internet article April 11, 2000. Custom Harley Davidson Motorcycle Parts & Accessories, Paul in Sales.
6. O'Connell J. Academy of Pediatrics, Hubbard Broadcasting Inc. 2003.

24

Formulating Natural Sun Care Products

Timothy Kapsner, Peter Matravers, Ko-ichi Shiozawa, and Patricia Peterson

Aveda Corporation, Minneapolis, Minnesota, USA

INTRODUCTION

The word "natural" has evolved, over the past several years, to mean the exclusive use of plant-based ingredients to create a finished product. Consumers now seek out products that claim to be "natural" or "all-natural," even though the FDA has not issued regulations to define the term "natural" when applied to cosmetics. Just recently, C&T Magazine reported, "new ingredients—vitamin C and naturals such as aloe vera and chamomile are also finding their way into sun product formulations to make them more attractive to customers" (1). The sunscreen development process, therefore, must not stop at adding a few natural ingredients to an otherwise traditional product. It must start with a re-examination of all the components that make up a sunscreen, with an eye to maximizing the efficacy and sustainability of each. Then, and only then, can a formulator put together a sunscreen product that is truly "natural."

In a practical sense, very few products fulfill this condition but instead rely on any number of non-plant-based ingredients to perform certain functions. These ingredients are generally petroleum based. Our goal and mission has been to avoid depleting finite resources of fossil fuels by substituting renewable plant sources. There are also other advantages to using plants as a resource:

- Supports local farmers
- Diversifies and strengthens local economies
- Supports and sustains indigenous peoples
- Uses a renewable resource

We have continued to improve our product development efforts as our mission has evolved. We now find ourselves facing tough questions about the impact of our products on the fragile ecosystem of our Earth.

FORMULATION FOCUS

We have explored several new product areas in the last few years and, following a precautionary principle, the Research and Development staff is taking steps to focus on ingredient issues in the product development process. In formulating sunscreen products there are two areas of interest that have been addressed.

The first challenge is to address the health and safety questions being raised for certain widely used active ingredients and preservatives. A very active search for natural preservatives and physical sunscreens is attempting to address this issue. UV radiation contains a tremendous amount of energy, and this energy, besides causing the damage it does to the skin, can also break down the molecules that are intended to absorb or reflect it. Studies have shown that some of the organic sunscreens are photochemically unstable (2; see also this volume, Chapter 17 by Craig Bonda). A safety review that takes this into consideration would be beneficial when evaluating sunscreen ingredients and products. Mineral replacements, including titanium, zinc, and iron oxide-based compounds, are being used to avoid these concerns with organic sunscreen actives (3). Titanium dioxide is found in many minerals and is highly abundant. It is estimated that the world's mineral resources contain in excess of 1 billion tons of titanium dioxide (4). After the valuable minerals are separated, the remaining sands are returned to the deposit and the land recultivated. In the USA, titanium-rich sands are mined in Florida and Virginia. It is our goal to assure responsible mining of these materials.

The second challenge is our continuing effort to replace petroleum-based synthetic ingredients or petroleum-processed natural ingredients with plant- and mineral-based alternatives. These alternatives must provide a similar level of functionality, benefit, and elegance to the consumer without introducing additional negative environmental impacts or related hazards. For example, zinc oxide is a Category I sunscreen in the USA but not in the European Union (EU), since the EU has concerns regarding pollution at zinc oxide manufacturing sites (5).

Most important for the consumer is "wearability". The best-intentioned product will be a complete market failure if the user is not provided with an elegant, effective product. At the same time, the use of plant and mineral-based materials that may adversely affect threatened or endangered species should be strenuously avoided. This requires careful investigation of ingredient options, which often slows down the product development process. Further, renewable resources should be used wherever possible in products and packaging.

The intent, however, is to go beyond reducing the "footprint" on the environment—of just doing "less bad in the world"—to become a restorative force, where there is actually measurable benefit from "doing good". A truly sustainable business model must incorporate elements of providing for current needs without compromising the ability of future generations to provide for their needs. As difficult as this concept of sustainability is to understand and to put into daily practice, we have made some small steps in the direction we want to go and where we think others may want to go as well.

UV ABSORBING INGREDIENTS

The sunscreen final monograph, published on May 21, 1999, lists 16 Category I active ingredients (6). These 16 active ingredients vary significantly in their physical and chemical properties, and there are many considerations as to which ones to use in building a sunscreen product. The easiest, and most common, way to classify the active ingredients is in which part of the UV spectrum they are active. When considering which active ingredients should be used to formulate natural sun care products, however, another way of classifying the active ingredients may be more relevant. Titanium dioxide and zinc oxide are the two Category I actives that are inorganic pigments. All of the other actives are synthesized organic compounds. A natural sunscreen should use natural ingredients; this applies especially to the active ingredients. The FDA does not currently allow the claim "natural sunscreen" to be used in marketing a sun care product. A marketer can claim that their sunscreen contains natural ingredients. Some of these natural ingredients may, among their other functions, also increase the SPF of the product. There are, however, no active ingredients that the FDA will allow a sunscreen manufacturer to call "natural". This begs the question as to what active ingredients should be used in natural sun care products. Titanium dioxide and zinc oxide are minerals, which, according to Webster's New College Dictionary, are naturally occurring inorganic substances. The organic food industry allows mined minerals to be used in certified organic processed products. By the time titanium dioxide and zinc oxide find their way into a sunscreen, however, they have been processed in one or more ways to make them more compatible and more effective. Many different types of coatings and dispersants, sometimes natural and sometimes not, have been added.

Anyone who has ever used paints or color cosmetics knows that the main function of titanium dioxide and zinc oxide in those products is to opacify them. They do this very well in sunscreens also. Early versions of sunscreens containing only these two pigments left an unacceptable white residue on the skin, and were thus not very popular. This challenged the producers of these ingredients to improve them, and they soon responded with micronized versions, with much smaller particle sizes, which significantly reduced the whitening. Further refinements of the micronization technology resulted in the recent discovery that there is a specific particle size range that gives the lowest whitening but still reflects UV radiation (7). Other chapters of this book deal extensively with the selection and technology of the inorganic sunscreen actives.

As improved as these new pigments are, these materials are still difficult to work with, and it is not unusual for the final product to lend a significant—and undesirable—white chalky sheen to the skin, sometimes with a bluish cast. Manufacturers and formulators have found a number of ways to overcome this challenge, but it takes definite skill to avoid the "whitening" outcome. The key to success is in first keeping the solid in suspension and preventing agglomeration both in the product and on the skin, and then keeping the overall product from drying out on the skin. Specific plant-based solvents and emulsifiers have been introduced to do just that. For example, polyglyceryl-6 polyricinoleate is an emulsifer based on natural glycerin and ricinoleic acid, which is said to be particularly good at dispersing titanium dioxide. Two other emulsifiers, one a blend of coco-glucoside with coconut alcohol and the other a blend of coco-glucoside with cetearyl alcohol, will help keep the pigments dispersed in the finished emulsion. Another new ingredient, dimyristyl tartrate, helps to stablize the emulsion viscosity and improves water resistance.

Titanium dioxide pastes and slurries have been created to maintain a physical distance between the particles and therefore prevent agglomeration. One of the newest entries in this ingredient category uses alkyl benzoates to disperse the titanium dioxide or zinc oxide in a solid flake. This keeps the pigments finely dispersed until they go into the emulsion, resulting in a finer dispersion in the finished product. Another approach to the challenge of dispersing solid materials may be to formulate a water-in-oil or water-in-silicone lotion, with the solid titanium or zinc well dispersed in the internal water phase. The external silicone or oil phase then creates a nonevaporating moisture layer on the skin, thus maintaining physical distance between the particles to prevent agglomeration, while also preventing dry-out and whitening. These emulsions are also waterproof (without the need for film-forming resins) and therefore more effective for outdoor and beach products. A raw material based on natural ingredients used for this approach is a blend of cetearyl alcohol, dicetyl phosphate, and ceteth-10 phosphate. This material helps create an emulsion with good shear-thinning properties, and also improves the deposition of oils on the skin, improving water resistance.

Unusually stable and functional gel matrix emulsions are especially suited for physical sunscreens. Not only are the solid particles held tightly in the matrix, but the emulsion forms a hydrophobic film on the skin to effectively prevent agglomeration, add waterproofing, and boost overall SPF by virtue of these inherent emulsion characteristics. An emulsifier blend created for this purpose contains polyglyceryl-10 pentastearate, behenyl alcohol, and sodium stearoyl lactylate.

INCREASING SPF

A sunscreen is, of course, an OTC drug product. As such, it is subject to the requirements of the sunscreen monograph. This means that the active ingredients added to achieve the SPF must be on the Category I list and must be used in concentrations prescribed by the monograph.

There are, however, many ways to enhance the performance of a natural sunscreen. The organic sunscreens absorb UV radiation because they contain aromatic rings that are conjugated with a carbonyl group and also contain electron-donor groups in either the *ortho* or the *para* positions on the aromatic ring (8). Structures very similar to this are abundant in nature, so these natural materials should also have some UV absorption. For example, ethylhexyl methoxycinnamate is a Category I sunscreen active. Galanga extract (a rhizome in the ginger family, commonly used in Thai cooking) contains high levels of ethyl methoxycinnamate, a safe, natural material with a structure very similar to the Category I ingredient. Other cinnamic acid derivatives can be found in sage, thyme, and rosemary. Flavonoids are naturally occurring polyphenolic molecules that contribute color to many plants. Some plant extracts, such as ginko biloba, contain flavonoids which absorb UV as well as visible radiation, and thus may boost the SPF of a sunscreen (9).

Many other natural extracts have UV absorption. Annatto is a well-known food colorant; what is not so well known is that in addition to absorbing visible light, it also absorbs UV radiation. Gamma oryzanol, which is extracted from rice bran oil, also absorbs UV radiation and can boost the SPF of a natural sunscreen.

Licorice (*Glycyrrhiza glabra*) extract is reported to be as effective as ethylhexyl methoxycinnamate in absorbing UV rays. Lawsone, the functional ingredient in henna, is a known UV absorber and approved sunscreen blend ingredient. Calophylum inophylum seed oil has some UV absorption and also acts as an antioxidant, which may add a further benefit in a natural sunscreen as a free-radical scavenger (10).

Pongamol is a natural material extracted from the karanja tree, which grows in India. This material is reported to enhance the UV protection of sunscreen actives and to broaden UV absorption, especially into the UV-A region (11). Two other plant extracts that have been tested to have UV absorption are coffee extract and wild pansy extract. Other natural materials that have been, or are being, evaluated as natural UV absorbers are rutin, helichrysum italicum, lupinus albus, rhamnus frangula, naringin, neohesperidine, luteolin, and aloin (12).

Although private industry has made most of the contributions to the advancement of sunscreen chemistry, the USDA has also recently announced a significant advance. They have applied for a patent (13) on a material they are calling "soyscreen." This material is produced by reacting soybean oil with ferulic acid, which has UV absorbing properties. The result is a molecule that absorbs UV rays and is oil soluble, so it should stay on the skin. The manufacturing process is low energy and uses an enzyme that can be recycled, so this ingredient gets high marks for environmental responsibility. The finished ingredient is biodegradable, so it will not accumulate in the environment. This material will presumably be available soon for licensing.

NATURAL FRAGRANCES

In the last few years, it has become more and more popular to see the term "natural" associated with cosmetic products and fragrances. For many people, if a product contains some natural ingredients, along with synthetics, it is still considered to be natural. By all-natural fragrances, however, we mean that the fragrance contains *no* synthetic ingredients at all. Natural fragrances should be prepared with aromatic materials obtained from plant sources. Many of these aromatic plant materials, such as rosemary, rose, and jasmine, possess antioxidant activity as well.

Natural aroma ingredients include the following:

Essential oils: These are obtained through steam distillation process, for example, oils of lavender, rose, thyme, ylang ylang, etc., and also by physically extracting the rind of citrus fruits, for example, bergamot oil, lemon oil, orange oil, grapefruit oil, etc.

Absolutes: A plant is treated with a solvent to extract the oil mixed with vegetable wax. This first-phase material is called a "concrete" because of its hard texture. Then the concrete is dissolved with ethanol to produce an absolute, for example, most flowers, such as jasmine, mimosa, geranium, rose, lavender, clove, clary sage, neroli, etc.

CO_2 extraction: Supercritical CO_2 is used as a solvent to extract oils from plants such as seeds, resins, and barks. Then, lowering the pressure, the CO_2 becomes a gas and evaporates, leaving behind the extracted CO_2 absolute.

Enfleurage: Plants are steeped in fat (beef, suet, or lard) on plates, which will absorb their fragrance. It is used mainly for jasmine and tuberose. This technique, first reported by the ancient Egyptians, is hardly practiced anymore due to its high cost. Solvent extraction methods have replaced this process.

Resinoids: obtained through the application of alcohol to resins, for example, benzoin, labdanum, galbanum, opoponax, peru balsam, styrax, tolu, etc.

Isolates: These are obtained from essential oils by heating them and separating a major component of the essential oil, for example, linalool from coriander oil, geraniol from palmarosa oil, methyl salicylate from wintergreen oil, eugenol from clove bud oil, anethol from anis oil, etc.

Natural chemicals: These are obtained by treating isolates with physical processes (mixing, heating, stirring, washing, etc.), or with fermentation or enzymatic action to connect them with other natural components, for example, linalyl acetate (linalool + vinegar), geranyl acetate (geraniol + vinegar), etc.

Natural Standards

These items are natural as defined by the following standards, which are adhered to by the cosmetic and food industries:

1. The FDA definition of "natural" in the context of flavor, given by 21 C.F.R.101.22(a)(3) (14). (The FDA has not issued regulations to define the term "natural" when applied to cosmetics.)
2. The terms and definitions laid down in the Norme Francaise T 75-006 issued in October 1987 by the French standardization organization AFNOR (Association Francaise de Normalisation). [The International Fragrance Association (IFRA) General Assembly subsequently adopted this in October 1989, as the statement on Natural Fragrances. The IFRA Board of Directors then circulated this on June 14, 1991, to all members of the Association.]
3. The term "natural flavouring substance" mentioned in the Code of Practice as 88/388/EEC, article 1 for the Flavour Industry, issued in October 1989 by the International Organization of the Flavour Industry (IOFI) (15).

Points of Difference

The major differences between mainstream perfumery and natural perfumery are

1. Mainstream perfumery uses mainly synthetic sources with a palette ranging from 5000 to 30,000 materials. They have a variety of scents available that are inexpensive powerful aromas with a long shelf life.
2. Natural perfumery uses a limited number of natural essential oils and extracts. Among the 250,000 species of flowering plants (16) only about 3000 plants carry essential oils, of which only 200 or so plants yield their oil readily. They have a limited variety of scents available that are expensive and subject to change due to climatic, geographical, and political changes. They are generally weak aromas with a short shelf life.

Environmental Concern and Aromatherapy

Until 10 years ago, or so, natural fragrances were considered an alternative. Due to the recent resurgence in environmental concern and interest in aromatherapy, natural aromas are gaining in popularity and are in serious demand with the general public today. All indicators point to this trend continuing and growing in the future. Natural products are now found in every category from hair and skin care to cleaning products.

The Environmental Principle

We feel by using natural ingredients, we are doing our part to help nature to stay in good health and beauty. We avoid using materials that can eventually hurt the environment in any of the following ways:

- If used or handled improperly, they can contribute to pollution.
- They are a depletable resource.
- They are slow to degrade.

Even Mother Nature cannot reproduce petrol, which makes its use not environmentally sustainable. On the contrary, Mother Nature can produce every year all the plants that supply us with the beautiful essential oils, absolutes, and other natural materials that we need—mimosa in February, violet in May, rose and jasmine in July, etc.

Aromatherapeutic Principle

Aromatherapists believe that essential oils possess beneficial effects, from the medical and pharmaceutical points of view, such as sedating and stimulating effects, antiseptic and disinfectant effects, spasmolytic and diuretic effects, and so on. They firmly believe that essential oils have the power to cure people. From their point of view, perfumers are using only one small aspect of what these essential oils can offer. Dr. Jean Valnet and Robert Tisserand were the pioneers of this practice. Dr. Valnet's book, published in 1964, made a great impact on the world of aromatherapy; these days more and more people are studying and practicing this discipline (17). The result of this study and practice is a considerable body of knowledge regarding the beneficial effects of natural essential oils. The calming effect of natural rose oil and the stimulating effect of peppermint are well known. A talented perfumer can create natural aroma blends that complement and enhance these benefits. With this approach, the exclusive use of natural aroma materials can be perceived not as a challenge or a restriction, but as a tremendous opportunity.

Natural Aromas as they Relate to Sun Care Products

For sun care products (presun, sunscreen, and after sun) it is most important to avoid what are considered the phototoxic groups of oils. The photosensitizing components in essential oils are the furanocoumarins such as bergaptene and psoralen. Photosensitization is the process by which the skin is made more sensitive to UV radiation. The furanocoumarins absorb the UV radiation very easily and then reradiate this energy into the skin causing the skin to burn faster (as well as tan faster as bergamot was used in sun tanning preparations in the past) (18).

Phototoxicity is defined as a skin reaction that occurs after exposure to UV light. In the case of sun exposure, sunburn appears much more quickly, evidenced by the usual redness (erythema) which will disappear within 1–3 days and is followed by mild tanning. Another reaction to furanocoumarin containing compounds is a photoallergy or an allergic response. Photoallergy is also known as berloque dermatitis, and it usually occurs on areas such as the neck and chest, which are exposed to sunlight (18). The perfumer should always be careful of the phototoxic essential oil concentrations in the final product (19). Because of this risk, in the perfume industry the perfumer only uses the furanocoumarin-free bergamot. The oils listed below contain a much smaller amount (less than 0.5%) of furanocoumarin, which makes their phototoxicity negligible.

Rutaceae	Apiaceae
Bergamot (highest possibility)	Angelica root
Fig leaf	Cumin
Lemon (expressed)	Opoponax
Lime (expressed)	
Orange (bitter, expressed)	
Mandarin	
Grapefruit	
Rue	

The IFRA has also issued a list of restricted oils, which includes angelica root, cumin, and bergamot essential oils. Among the others in this list are oils such as baume de Perou, cassia, cinnamon, sassafras, verbena, anise, aspic, basil, clove, corriander, hyssop, sage, and tansy flower, which are on this list for other reasons (20). Other than these groups of essential oils to avoid, there are no known phototoxic contraindications to using the remaining oils as a part of sun care product formulations.

Natural aroma ingredients are very complex mixtures of dozens, if not hundreds, of components. As well as having subtle aromatic effects, these natural compounds have many beneficial effects on the skin. Chamomile oil contains significant amounts of bisabolol, which is a known anti-irritant. Lavender oil is also known to soothe the skin. These benefits can be put to use by formulating the aromas from natural essential oils and other natural aroma compounds in natural sun care products.

PRESERVATIVES

Preservation is probably the most difficult task for a formulator to accomplish while holding true to the mission of developing a natural sun care product. For a sunscreen product to be safe, it must be adequately preserved. Doing this with natural, or naturally derived, ingredients is a serious challenge indeed.

Through the 1970s, formaldehyde was the most common cosmetic preservative. It had several advantages, being inexpensive, highly effective, and relatively stable. With the widespread use of cosmetics, household, and industrial products, however, toxicity issues led to its downfall. It is very difficult to find an effective preservative that is also nontoxic to humans, other animals, and plants, and safe for the environment. (After all, the function of a preservative is to kill, or control the growth of, microorganisms.) As formaldehyde fell from favor, another class of preservatives was created, those that produce formaldehyde on demand (called formaldehyde donors). While much safer than pure formaldehyde, their use is also being questioned today, and they also do not have a place in natural sunscreens.

One of the most difficult aspects of marketing cosmetic products worldwide is preservation. Two major markets, the European Union and Japan, have a positive list of allowed preservatives. Japan's list is the most restrictive. Of those, a few could be considered for use in natural sunscreens: benzoic and sorbic acids and their salts, benzyl alcohol, phenethyl alcohol, and phenoxyethanol (21). While judicious use of these ingredients may adequately preserve a product, staying true to the spirit of formulating a natural sunscreen calls for a more creative approach to preservation.

There are many natural ingredients that can contribute to preservation. Many essential oils have antimicrobial properties. Some of the more effective ones are sage, thyme, and oregano (all of which have significant levels of thymol), tea tree, lemongrass, clove, and cinnamon. Any essential oil used at a high enough level to assist in preservation will, of course, have a significant impact on the aroma of the finished product. Careful selection of the essential oils used to fragrance a natural sunscreen will certainly help in its preservation.

Although foods do not have the long shelf-life requirements that cosmetics do, considerable work has been done to determine how best to preserve foods. The most useful natural ingredients from this work are the acids, citric, lactic, and sorbic. Although citric acid does not have a significant direct antimicrobial effect, it can enhance the effect of other ingredients by lowering the pH and chelating metal ions. Lactic and sorbic acids do have antibacterial and antifungal effects. In addition to the acids, saponins and flavonoids may give a boost to antimicrobial systems (22). Polyphenols are known to have an antimicrobial effect. Green tea extract is high in polyphenols and flavonoids, and can also give an antimicrobial boost (23). Grapefruit seed extract has been used in cosmetics for many years as a natural preservative. It has a significant advantage over other natural preservatives in being water soluble. Benzyl alcohol has been used in cosmetics for many years. Natural benzyl alcohol, though expensive, is available. Its use is restricted to fairly low levels in some countries.

The need in the cosmetic industry for natural preservatives has spurred considerable research and the introduction of many interesting ingredients. Hinokitiol is an exudate from a cedar tree. Although extremely expensive, it is highly effective at low levels. Asparagopsis armata extract is a seaweed extract that contains natural halogenated "macromolecules." It is water soluble, fairly expensive, and fairly effective. Olive leaf extract not only helps in preservation, but doubles as a free-radical scavenger. Malaleuca alternifolia leaf oil and leptospermum scoparium oil consist of fractions from several Australian essential oils. They have a strong essential oil aroma but can help in preservation. A plant extract blend of *Origanum vulgare* L. (Apiaceae), *Thymus vulgaris* L. (Apiaceae), *Cinnamomum zeylanicum* Nees (Lauraceae), *Rosmarinus officinalis* L. (Lamiaceae), *Lavandula officinalis* L. (Lamiaceae), and *Hydrastis canadensis* L. (Ranunculacea) also has a significant antimicrobial effect. Short-chain fatty acids, such as caprylic and capric, can have an antimicrobial effect (24). Unfortunately, however, they also tend to be fairly irritating. Creative chemists have come up with glyceryl esters of these materials, glyceryl caprate and glyceryl caprylate, which seem to retain some of the antimicrobial effect but with less irritation.

In addition to adding ingredients specifically for their antimicrobial effect, sunscreen formulas can be modified to make a more "hostile" environment for microbial growth. Lowering the water activity of a formula, by adding inorganic salts or glycerin, can help significantly. Moving the pH away from neutral (above 8 or below 5) will itself discourage microbial growth. Cationic emulsifiers such as cocamidopropyl PG-dimonium chloride phosphate can also help. Ethanol, if used at a high enough level, can preserve a product by itself. Unfortunately, it is also a very effective solvent, and can dry the skin. Judicious use of low levels of ethanol can reduce the requirement of other preservatives.

As traditional preservatives fall from favor, creative formulators have explored other, more natural ways to accomplish this important task. The many new ingredients and techniques now available ensure that a natural sunscreen need not be significantly less natural just because it is adequately preserved.

NEXT-GENERATION SUN CARE

The next-generation sun care products must address all detrimental sun damage beyond just UV shielding. Current SPF measurement addresses only UV-B erythema redness and does not account for the silent cellular damage—a time bomb for disaster on prolonged exposure.

Advanced sun care should address the following biological effects, thus providing total protection during and after sun exposure.

Biological Effects Due to Sun Exposure

1. Erythema UV-B damage on skin epidermis.
2. DNA damage by UV-A in skin dermis.
3. Photoaging process begins with the release of collagenase and elastase enzyme ultimately causing skin sagging and wrinkles. This process is regulated by matrix metalloproteinase (MMP) and tissue inhibitors of matrix proteinase (TIMP).
4. Immunocompromised.
5. Inflammatory cellular reactions.
6. Free radical generation in the skin.
7. Skin barrier protection compromised; skin dehydration.

Today we have a better understanding of the mechanisms of the above biological effects and have identified active ingredients to augment, prevent, and protect these destructive processes (25).

Sun exposure biological effects	Solution
Erythema UV-B, UV-A, and DNA damage	UV-A and UV-B protection with ZnO and TiO_2, phytothergenetic sunblock Cajolone, and isoamyl salicylate from potatoes and oil of wintergreen
DNA damage	DNA repair by liposomes from biofermentation of *Micrococcus lutenus*; it contains endonuclease, which recognizes UV damage and repairs UV-DNA damage
Photoaging	Collagenase and elastase inhibition by wheat cerasomes
	TIMP enrichment by white lupin flower peptides

Sun exposure biological effects	Solution
Immunocompromised	Plankton have evolved to protect themselves from sun exposure as they need UV light to manufacture energy; they contain photolyase which clears and reverses damage caused by shorter-wavelength UV; this ingredient is available as photosomes
Inflammatory reaction to the sun	A complex from algae, blue chamomile, and sucrose; licorice extract
Free radical	Free radical quenching by antioxidants from rosemary, astaxanthin, grapefruit seed extract, and jasmine absolute (hexane free)
Skin barrier compromised	Skin barrier replenishment by organic ingredients jojoba oil, almond oil, quinoa protein, and Aloe Vera

We should look well beyond simply treating the skin's surface for prevention of sun damage. Sun protection can—and should—focus on integral skin metabolism and immunological processes for true sun protection. This next-generation sun care should also improve skin health for future sun exposure as well as with continual skin integrity enhancement (e.g., reverse photoaging).

The ingredients listed in the table all speak to strengthening specific skin mechanisms, instead of simply "grabbing" damaging UV rays with resonance structures. Instead, this approach assumes that the skin itself can act as its own effective barrier to sun damage. It may also be possible to take a step beyond even this approach and use nutrition and other internal processes to further aid in overall sun protection. It is our approach, then, to see skin processes as a whole, working together in preventive and repair processes, rather than rely on a few ingredients to play such a vital role in sun protection.

CONCLUSIONS

Formulating natural sun care products is no easy task. It demands a vast knowledge of plant sources and functions as well as excellence in formulation. Development times are likely to be long; the final product is likely to be more expensive and perhaps less versatile than its synthetic counterparts. As mentioned earlier in this chapter, current FDA regulations do not allow a sunscreen product to be labeled and marketed as totally natural. As seen in this discussion, however, significant advances are being made in all categories of natural ingredients needed to build a sunscreen: emulsifiers, UV absorbers, aromas, and preservatives. As these frontiers continue to advance, there may come a time when the sunscreen monograph process will be required to re-examine the claim of a natural sunscreen.

The effort of attempting to create natural sun care products, if done with conscience, is worth the outcome. It is our desire to make a positive impact on the world, from the perspective of maintaining consumers' health as well as initiating positive environmental policies with measurable outcomes. Above all, we recognize that we are only on this earth for an instant; we are guardians for our children's children.

REFERENCES

1. Rasmussen R. Cosmet Toilet Mag 2003; 118(2):5.
2. Shaath NA, Fares H, Klein K. Photodegradation of sunscreen chemicals. Cosmet Toilet 1990; 105:41–44.
3. Pinell SR. Dermatol Surg 2000; 26:309–314.
4. Fairhurst D, Mitchnick M. Particulate sunblocks. In: Lowe NJ, Shaath NA, Pathak MA, eds. Sunscreens: Development, Evaluation, and Regulatory Aspects. 2nd ed. New York: Marcel Dekker, 1997.
5. Steinberg DC. Regulations of sunscreens worldwide. In: Shaath NA, ed. Sunscreens: Regulations and Commercial Development. 3rd ed. New York: Marcel Dekker, 2005:173–198.
6. Food and Drug Administration. Final rule for sunscreen drug products. Fed Reg 1999; 27666.
7. Presperse Incorporated. Product Literature, Ti-Sphere, 2003.
8. Shaath N. Chemistry of sunscreens. In: Lowe NJ, Shaath NA, Pathak MA, eds. Sunscreens: Development, Evaluation, and Regulatory Aspects. 2nd ed. New York: Marcel Dekker, 1997.
9. Lee KT. Preliminary studies on natural plant extracts as sunscreen agents. IFSCC Congress: Science and Beauty at the Dawn of the Third Millennium, Cannes, France, Sept. 14–18, 1998:1–8.
10. Plant Sun International. Product Literature, Scaveng Oil, 2003.
11. Quest International. Product Literature, Pongamia Extract, 2003.
12. Proserpio G. Cosmet Toilet 1976; 91:34–46.
13. US Patent No. 6,346,236.
14. Food and Drug Administration. Code of Federal Regulations. Washington, DC: FDA, Title 21, Section 101.22(a)(3).
15. International Organization of the Flavor Industry. 88/388 EEC Article 1, October 1989.
16. Pelt JM. Les Plantes: Amours et civilisations vegetal. Librarie Artheme Fayard, 1980–1981.
17. Valnet J. The Practice of Aromatherapy. Rochester, VT: Destiny Books, 1980.
18. Guba R. Specification Sheets. The Center for Aromatic Medicine, 1995.
19. Tisserand R, Balacs T. Essential Oil Safety: A Guide for Health Care Professionals. Churchill Livingstone, 1995.
20. Ryman D. Aromatherapy: Complete Guide to Plant and Flower Essences for Health and Beauty. Bantam Books, 1993.
21. Steinberg DC. Preservatives for Cosmetics. Cosmet Toilet, 1996; 111:42.

22. Otshudi AL, Foriers A, et al. In vitro antimicrobial activity of six medicinal plants traditionally used for the treatment of dysentery and diarrhoea in Democratic Republic of Congo (DRC). Phytomedicine 2000; 7(2):167–172.
23. Elmets CA, Katiyar SK, Yusuf N. Photoprotection by green tea polyphenols. Shaath NA, ed. Sunscreens: Regulations and Commercial Development. 3rd ed. New York: Marcel Dekker, 2005:639–656.
24. Kabara JJ, Orth DS, eds. Preservative-Free and Self-Preserving Cosmetics and Drugs: Principles and Practice. New York: Marcel Dekker, 1997:120–123.
25. Pinnell FR. Cutaneous photodamage, oxidative stress and topical protection. J Am Acad Dermatol 2003; 48(11):1–19.

Consumer Products with Ultraviolet Filters

25

Recreational Sunscreens

James P. SaNogueira
Playtex Products, Inc., Allendale, New Jersey, USA

INTRODUCTION

What are recreational sunscreens and what sets them apart from other types of products that attenuate UV rays? Is the term "recreational sunscreen" an oversimplification? After all, it includes many types of products whose performance and benefits vary widely. Other terminology such as "beach products," for example, can be even more misleading as descriptors of products used under demanding conditions and in a wide variety of situations. Often, sunscreen products that offer the type of performance attributes and benefits of recreational sunscreens are required as an important part of a daily photoprotection regime. This is especially important for those who are frequently exposed to UV radiation, perhaps for long periods because of their occupation (not recreation) outdoors.

Perhaps a good definition of recreational sunscreens is, those products which provide UV attenuation as the primary benefit, with other benefits being added to segment performance and appeal to consumers who have specific secondary benefit needs. Thus, recreational sunscreens are differentiated from products whose primary purpose is the delivery of other skin care benefits and which are designed to also offer the additional benefit of UV protection.

In all, this chapter is dedicated to the discussion of products that must go beyond the addition of UV attenuation to moisturizers, makeup, and other skin care products whose users require benefits different from and even beyond those afforded by products offering UV protection as a secondary benefit.

SUNSCREEN HISTORY

The use of sunscreens predates the discovery and use of our "modern" ingredients and products used to attenuate UV radiation. Beauty, social status, and even health and comfort drove the ancients to find ways to help protect their skin. As they worked in the fields and began traveling and resettling around the world in areas where the incidence of UV radiation outmatched their genetic code, effective compositions were developed over time to protect their skin. Some of these ingredients are still used today. While this is the topic of a previous chapter (1), it is mentioned here to help demonstrate that the use of "recreational" sunscreens predates the modern area of vacations in the sun.

MARKET SHARE AND TRENDS

In terms of market growth, recreational sunscreens have enjoyed steady growth over the last 20 years as people have become more aware and concerned with protecting themselves from UV rays. Today, the recreational sunscreen market stands at over $450 million in the USA alone. The chart below illustrates the growth in sales over time (2).

Growth in Recreational Sunscreen Sales

Year	1997	1998	1999	2000	2001	2002	2003, YTD (Sept)
Sales in millions ($)	458	499	551	572	634	470[a]	451[a]
% Increase		2.8	10.4	3.9	10.4	0.9	−6.0

[a]Excludes Walmart sales figures.

Source: AC Nielsen Scantrack data, total USA, provided by Playtex Products Inc.

Major US Manufacturers/Marketers Dollar Sales

	2002	2003, YTD (Sept)
Banana Boat	21.7	21.9
Coppertone	30.5	31.1
Neutrogena	12.8	14.4
Hawaiian Tropic	8.7	9.8

Source: AC Nielsen Scantrack data, total USA, provided by Playtex Products Inc.

Microbrands and store brands also exist, with the former shrinking as a whole over time while store brands have shown growth. Recreational sunscreens are largely seasonal products in most areas of the USA and in countries with similar climates. Sales of recreational sunscreens are highly dependent on the weather, particularly in the time frame of major summer holidays and vacation periods. This translates into a challenge for marketers and retailers alike in terms of forecasting, manufacturing, and stocking sunscreen products.

FORMULATIONS

To the formulator, the structure of the sunscreen business provides both challenges and opportunities. Approximately 20% of annual sales of sunscreen products come from new product introductions year in and year out. Consequently, there is a constant challenge to develop new products that offer benefits and features that will help to capture incremental sales volume and profit as well. Sunscreen formulators have to respond very quickly to meet the timing of this seasonal business while insuring that the products delight consumers, are economically and technically feasible, and can be executed on time. In the USA, as all products with an SPF are OTC drugs by definition, formulators must also meet regulatory requirements that are a moving target at present.

The market trend over time has been toward higher SPF products and an increasing number of products that offer meaningful levels of UV-A protection through the addition of avobenzone, or titanium dioxide and zinc oxide. More modern formulas use ingredients that help to boost or maintain the photostability of the sunscreen active ingredients. Recent market trends include a focus on improved aesthetics, convenient application/usage, and specialized applications or subsegments.

CONSUMER BENEFITS AND PERFORMANCE NEEDS

As noted earlier, recreational sunscreens cover a wide spectrum in terms of performance requirements and the consumer benefits that they need to deliver to insure efficacy and provide consumer satisfaction. Some consumers desire products that help to make sunbathing a more enjoyable experience by providing a luxurious or oily skin feel, a high degree of shine, and tropical scent with minimal protection while others seek fast absorbing fragrance-free products with high protection that stays on in water and after perspiration. Over time the number of product forms, methods of delivery, and varying product aesthetics/sensory characteristics have continually expanded. Of course this extends to everything in between, additional benefits and an abundance of product forms, that is, lotions, creams, oils, sprays, sticks, gels, pastes, and mousses. Sunscreens combined with skin protectants are classified as "dual drugs" because they cross two monographs. Sunscreen products with insect repellants such as DEET help to provide dual protection against the sun and mosquitoes in one product.

Visual signals have been added to products; these include indicators represented by the addition of color to the entire product or to colored microcapsules to help consumers see where the product has been applied and where they have missed. Shine enhancers have been added to give the skin more gloss when sunbathing, glitter has been added to give the skin a shimmering appearance.

Recreational sunscreen products also cover a wide range of other skin care benefits. The emulsions used to deliver sunscreen actives also have the capability to effectively deliver all the skin care benefits of more cosmetic products. Moisturization, antiaging, antioxidants, vitamins, botanicals, skin protectants, alpha and beta hydroxy acids, pigments, etc, can and are delivered effectively by recreational sunscreens. Recreational sunscreens provide robust protection to the skin against UV damage, outperforming the so-called daily photoprotection products, while enhancing the appearance and condition of the skin as effectively as cosmetic products without UV protection.

USAGE AND PERFORMANCE NEEDS DURING UV EXPOSURE

Formulators approach the design of sunscreen formulas based on the particular application and intended product concept and positioning in the marketplace. Although there is often some overlap of product benefits across segments, there are normally one or more differentiating attributes offered by a particular positioning that must be accounted for in the product design.

Recreational sunscreens are designed to deliver product performance that will meet a variety of consumer needs as dictated by their personal preference for aesthetics, activity, and amount of protection. Differences in the level and type of physical activity can influence the need for product substantivity (water resistance/sweat resistance, resistance to rub-off/toweling. Over the years specialized products based on increased levels of substantivity marketed to people who take part in surfing, water skiing, snorkeling, etc., have led to marketplace successes. The point of usage and the environmental conditions for recreational products are generally more diverse and must also be accounted for in the product design. As such this presents both a challenge and an opportunity to formulators, package engineers, and marketers alike.

WATER/SWEAT RESISTANCE

Sunscreen formulations can be made water resistant by using one or more formulation techniques to help form a film that will keep sunscreens on the skin upon immersion in water or exposure to perspiration. Some product forms such as water-in-oil or water-in-silicone emulsions are inherently more waterproof than their counterpart oil-in-water emulsions and can sometimes be formulated with little or even no additional "waterproofing" ingredients. Water-in-oil emulsions have the added advantage of providing instant waterproofing and SPF efficacy as they more readily form a continuous film of sunscreen in an inherently waterproof layer. Emulsions of this type can also offer "instant" efficacy as illustrated in patent art (3) and by recent launches of products offering instant waterproofing and SPF efficacy.

An example of a high-SPF water-in-oil sunscreen formulation is given. A crystalline organic sunscreen (bisethylhexyloxphenol methoxyphenol triazine, tinasorb S), a sunscreen ester in the oil phase, and titanium dioxide powder that is dispersed in the water phase are featured in this formula. Glycerin is added to help with skin moisturization. This type of formula lends itself to being instantly effective and resistant to both fresh-and saltwater (4).

Sun Protection Lotion with High SPF

Phase A	
Cetyl PEG/PPG—10-1 dimethicone	2.5
Cetyl dimethicone	1.0
Diethylhexyl carbonate	6.5
C12–C15 alkyl benzoate	4.0
Macadamia nut oil	2.0
Tocopherol acetate	0.5
Tinasorb S	3.0
Octinoxate	6.5
Phase B	
Allantion	0.5
Sodium carboxymethyl betaglucam	
Glycerin	2.0
Sodium chloride	0.5
Tegosun 40 (TiO_2 and glycerin and isolaureth—4-phosphate and vinyl buteth-25 and sodium maleate)	12.2
Copolymer	
Water	52.0
Preservative	q.s.

Any number of optional ingredients such as fragrance, color, additional antioxidants, or aesthetic modifiers could be added or substituted. Various levels and combinations of sunscreen actives as found in the various versions of the proposed FDA, TFM, and FM dating back to 1978 and or other internationally available sunscreens could also be added or substituted (see section on sunscreen actives).

Oil-in-water emulsions normally require one or more waterproofing ingredients in order to retain sunscreen actives on the skin. Careful choice of the type and amount of emulsifier used in emulsions can limit the need for waterproofing agents by avoiding or reducing the tendency of the product to re-emulsify when exposed to water. Generally speaking, oil-in-water emulsions require longer to set up a fully effective continuous film on the skin than water-in-oil emulsions and being composed of a water-soluble continuous phase, are more likely to mix readily with water and require a set time before becoming waterproof. Depending on the thickeners and emulsifiers used, this type of emulsion may also be more or less sensitive to salts.

Product forms such as certain types of gels and sprays are solutions that rely on volatile components as carrying agents that flash off or evaporate upon application leaving behind a film of sunscreen ingredients, solubilizers, and excipients. Waterproofing ingredients are useful not only in keeping the sunscreen on the skin, but also in helping the sunscreen form an effective layer as it is rubbed onto the skin and the volatile components evaporate or "flash off" from the skin.

Waterproofing agents work via two basic mechanisms. The most traditional approach is the use of film forming ingredients that help the sunscreen to stay on the skin after the waterproofing agents form a hydrophobic film that binds or anchors at least temporarily to the skin. A second mechanism works by increasing the viscosity of the oil phase ingredients, in turn helping to reduce the mobility of the sunscreen and causing them to deposit onto the skin from the emulsion upon application and dry-down of the product film. A poster presented by Rerek (5) discusses the mechanism of waterproofing via thickening of lipids.

Some of the commonly used waterproofing ingredients are listed in the following table. This is not a complete listing but does serve to illustrate some of the different types of waterproofing chemistries that are used. The choice of waterproofing ingredients can be dependent on the overall formulation type, the oil phase load, the desired skin feel, and the particular application. Combinations of different waterproofing ingredients are often helpful in achieving the desired results.

Waterproofing Ingredients

Trade name	INCI name	Typical usage range (%)
Ganex V-220	PVP/eicosene copolymer	(1–3)
Lexorez 100	Adipic acid/diethylene glycol/glycerin cross-polymer	(1–4)

Trade name	INCI name	Typical usage range (%)
Allianz OPT	Acrylates/C12–22 akylmethylacrylate copolymer	(1–3)
Performa V1608	C30–38 olefin/isopropyl maleate/MA copolymer	(0.5–3)
PA-18 Resin	Octadecene/MA copolymer	(0.5–2)
Panalene 300	Hydrogenated polyisobutane	(1–5)
Lexorez 200	Trimethylpentadiol/adipic acid/ glycerin cross-polymer	(1–4)
Performalene 400	Polyethylene	(0.5–3.0)
Fomblin HC/PC-1000	Polyperfluroethoxymethoxy difluroethyl PEG phosphate	(0.5–3)

An example of a typical waterproof water-in-oil sunscreen follows. This formula features the use of TiO_2 as the sole sunscreen ingredient, approximate SPF 15.

	%w/w
Phase A	
Stearyl alcohol	2.00
Estol 1543	5.00
Prisorene 3631	5.00
Tween 60	2.00
Solaveil CT-100	11.11
Phase B	
Demineralized water	56.49
Arlatone 2121	2.50
Rewoderm S1333	0.20
Phase C	
Veegum Ultra	0.80
Sodium lactate (50%)	0.40
Germaben II	1.00
Propylene glycol	4.0

Source: Formula courtesy of Uniquemia, formula reference 5468*1.

SUNBATHING/SUNTANNING PRODUCTS

Sunscreen products designed for "sunbathing" are less concerned with duration and even waterproofing in many cases. The users of these products are more interested in relaxing in the sun and are usually intent on tanning, although there are a number of these types of products that offer a higher SPF reflecting the consumers desire to protect their skin while sunbathing. There is a general belief among some sunbathers that oils and a shiny appearance attract the sun and help to facilitate tanning. Others simply enjoy the look, feel, and fragrance as they relax and bask in the sun.

The predominant form of these products is tanning oils, which includes "dry oils" and tanning sprays. Tanning gels, butters, and lotions are also common forms used to deliver a combination of UV protection, shiny appearance, and tropical fragrance.

Spray forms in various configurations have become more popular, with both lotions and alcohol-based formulas being delivered in a mist from a number of packaging options such as finger pumps, trigger sprays, and bladder sprays. This form provided the benefit of fast and easy application for consumers and in some cases could allow application without rubbing the product in.

A number of new products have been launched into the sports segment offering benefits of fast drying formulas that tend to be dryer in feel and have less of a tendency to leave skin feeling oily or slippery.

Fast Drying Sunscreen Gel

This oil-free quick drying SPF 23 sunblock formula demonstrates a product designed to evaporate quickly leaving behind an effective water and sweat resistant layer of sunscreen. The fast drying and relatively nongreasy skin feel is particularly attractive for use in sport applications.

This formula demonstrates an alcohol-based sunscreen that dries quickly. The amount of alcohol can be increased to give a drier feel. The octocrylene in the formula not only provides UV protection, but also helps to photostabilize the octinoxate and aids waterproofing due to its affinity for skin.

Phase A	
Deionized water	50.40
Propylene glycol	5.00
Sodium polyacrylate (Rapthix TM A-100)	1.00
Phase B	
Ocitnoxate	7.50
Oxybenzone	4.00
Octisalate	5.00
Octocrylene	7.00
Phase C	
Alcohol	20.00
Butylated PVP (Ganex R P-904LC)	0.10

Source: Formula courtesy of ISP.

ADDITIONAL CONSIDERATIONS

Patents

Those who formulate sunscreen products will find that the patent art presents difficult challenges as they construct their products. Published patent applications also present problems during the course of product development. Therefore, it is necessary for the formulator not only to be an expert in product design, but also to be conversant in the patent art and, importantly, the prior art that may help them to add perspective to the relevance or importance of published patents and applications. Unfortunately, some patents have become more about business strategy and less about true discovery and science. Nonetheless, there are important patents in the sunscreen area, that deal with photostabilization. In particular, the use of naphthalates, maleates, and glycoside dioleate esters are among the more recent patents issued. Other important patents include the use of coatings to increase the compatibility of inorganic sunscreens with avobenzone, thereby preventing degradation or crystallization of the organic sunscreen.

Photostability

Photostability is an important concern for recreational sunscreens and other products that have an SPF. This concern has been slower to develop in the USA than in Europe where photostability has become a market claim as well as a scientific issue. Achievement of efficient formulas and high levels of UV-A protection require the formulator to take photostability into account in the product design. This issue may in some ways have a greater impact on recreational sunscreens because of the duration of sun exposure vs. incidental or intermittent UV exposure for other products. The chemistry of sunscreen photostability is well covered elsewhere in this book, but deserves mention here as an important and emerging issue.

CONCLUSIONS

Recreational sunscreens are a diverse category of products that offer robust UV protection as the primary benefit under a variety of consumer habits and practices and use conditions. Water and sweat resistance, resistance to rub-off, and duration and amount of UV energy exposure are the primary areas of differences between recreational and other types of sunscreens, both of which can and do deliver a multitude of other skin care benefits.

REFERENCES

1. Giacomoni PU. Sun protection: historical perspective. In: Shaath NA, ed. Sunscreens: Regulations and Commercial Development. 3rd ed. New York: Marcel Dekker, 2005:71–81.
2. AC Neilsen Scantrak data, supplied by Playtex Products, Inc.
3. Stewart, E. US Patent 6,197,281, Amon-Re.
4. Degussa/Goldschmidt AG, Happi, March 2003:22.
5. Rerek M. SCC Meeting, Proceedings, December 2001:27.

26

Daily Use Sunscreens

Peter J. Lentini

The Estee Lauder Companies, Melville, New York, USA

INTRODUCTION

For the majority of their history, sunscreen preparations were relegated to the realm of overexposure, for those who spent an inordinate amount of time in the sun, such as lifeguards, athletes, etc. Little or no consideration was given to the average person, who can accumulate a tremendous amount of sun damage through intermittent or incidental exposure. Sunscreens were the product one took on vacation or to the beach. Rarely, except for those with hypersensitivities, were they used on a daily or regular basis, until recently. Marketers of skincare products have capitalized on the need for daily protection, and it is the intent of the author to discuss the need, implications, engineering, marketing, and positioning that goes behind this growing area of skin care.

BIOLOGY

Numerous studies conducted over the past few decades indicate a strong correlation between UV exposure and photoaging, accumulation of lines and wrinkles, and various lesions and cancers. While large doses (long-term exposure) produce the fastest deleterious effects, it has been purported that intermittent suberythmal doses can elicit similar responses. English et al. (1) report on site specific exposure to UV during childhood correlating to squamous cell carcinoma, more strongly associate this form of UV-dependent carcinogenesis to historical exposure than to adult exposure, and describe it as the more classic model of photodamage (gross dose dependence). Koh (2), reporting on melanoma, another UV induced carcinogenesis, and far more deadly and controversial, states that this particular diseased skin state is far more dependent on intermittent exposure to the sun, especially earlier in life, and more influential on long-term skin health than simple cumulative exposure. Darlington et al. (3) report on yet another exposure marker, solar keratoses, and conclude that this precancerous state is reduced by about 25% with the introduction of a daily use (discretionary) sunscreen. What this points to is a variety of exposure patterns resulting in sun damage. Classic dose-dependent damage from UV may no longer be the primary modality.

Take into consideration something like driving to work every day. Walking to and from your car, home, office, mall/shopping center, wherever, can lead to something like a $\frac{1}{2}$ h of "exposure" per day. Adding this up over the course of a working year, assuming 50 weeks of work, one accrues about 125 h of UV exposure. While this may not all be in direct sunlight at noon in Arizona, it shows clearly how this intermittent/incidental exposure can add up and add up quickly, and actually amounts to more than one would get on a typical Caribbean vacation. Further to this, recent research from a variety of sources demonstrates the insidious accumulated damage from suberythemal exposure. Ishitsuka et al. (4) report a greater reduction in the number of viable Langerhans cells subjected to intermittent suberythemal UV exposure than to a single high dose, and researchers at The University of Pennsylvania School of Medicine found similar results at $\frac{1}{2}$ MED for a variety of markers, including Langerhans cells reduction, stratum cornea thickening, dermal inflammatory infiltrates, and deposition of lysozyme on elastin fibers, while a single large dose of UV did not elicit these responses (5). The bottom line is that one will accumulate sun damage from a variety of exposure modalities, both early and throughout adult life, and this intermittent and incidental exposure may be as damaging as a sunburn.

ENGINEERING

Traditionally, one would apply a sun protection product to alleviate daily exposure. Unfortunately, the form does not lend itself to daily use. Sun protection products come primarily in two forms: beachwear and dailywear. An understanding of the forms and their differences seems appropriate. Beachwear products are generally higher-SPF products (domestically >15), wear and water resistant, and provide little else aside from sun protection. They can be emulsions or anhydrous products, and are generally "heavier" in feel than most other skin care products, due to the sunscreen content and various emulsifiers and resins used to impart stability and wear/water resistance. Some are intentionally made to be very shiny in appearance on skin, to enhance the look of a sun-kissed body. They may also contain large amounts of film-forming agents used to thicken the film of sunscreens as the product dries on the skin, to increase path-length and the efficiency of the screening system. The claims one can make on the said product are restricted by the FDA, and refer specifically to verbage approved in the sunscreen monograph (same as for daily wear). Base selection for daily wear thus becomes a very important consideration, as it will dictate overall performance and product acceptance, and ultimately, use compliance. Dailywear needs to be lightweight by comparison to the beach product, and generally carries an SPF of 15 or less. The lighter texture lends to layering, which is an important consideration for dailywear, as one will have to accommodate items such as makeup on top of the daily protection product if one is to expect use compliance. Furthermore, the selection of the sunscreen system becomes very important. As opposed to what one would do for a high-SPF beachwear product, where the SPF number usually drives the development, safety and texture become primary considerations, as it is well known in the literature that certain combinations of sunscreens can cause adverse reactions and sensitivities (6). During the early 1990s, when the popularity of dailywear facial sunscreen products rose, the first entries were basically beachwear modifications, and suffered from many of the weight- and shine-related drawbacks described earlier. Over time, these early entries paid the price in the marketplace, and were eventually replaced by more elegantly engineered products based on well-tolerated combinations of category items, such as micronized TiO_2 and octylmethoxycinnamate, in relatively lighter-textured bases. Both category items benefit from wide consumer acceptance from an irritation and allergy perspective, and depending on the base selection, can be quite transparent and matte, so layering with makeup, for example, can be achieved with little or no deleterious effects to the makeup wear or appearance. Furthermore, the consumer receives the ever-important immediate gratification, that feeling of being moisturized or smoothed to the touch, and will, most likely, continue to obtain the appropriate photoprotection on a regular basis because the product makes the consumer's skin feel and look "better".

MARKETING

Translating this to a marketing opportunity requires the development of yet another need, as prevention and protection are difficult concepts to market on their own. As opposed to a beachwear product, where one is selling the prevention of sunburn, dailywear, from a sun protection perspective, sells better skin health 10–20 years down the road. As such, there remains a strong possibility of noncompliance, and one needs to "hook" the consumer to the product in order to gain the purported long-term benefit (Table 26.1). By positioning the product as a moisturizer used every day, for example, that happens to provide SPF 15 protection, one can depend more on the likelihood of compliance to daily application. Marketers have covered a wide range of "needs" for daily use, inclusive of, but not limited to, moisturization, antioxidant protection, vitamins/minerals, humectancy, myriad botanical extracts, and essential lipids. These daily requirements are positioned almost as a daily dietary supplement for the skin and the more successful entries truly hone in on these needs, and the protection seems almost ancillary.

HISTORY

A historical perspective seems appropriate here. The prestige entries of the early to mid 1990s encompass the most appropriate examples of this positioning. Three particular entries come to mind. Clinique's City Block, Estee Lauder's Daywear, and Lancôme's Bienfait Total. All three entries appeared in the early to mid 1990s, and were reasonably successful sellers for their marketers. The first two entries actually grew to become branded franchises within their lines, an indication of their continued success.

City Block Oil-Free Daily Face Protector SPF-13 debuted in the spring of 1991 featuring UV-A and UV-B protection, no "chemical" sunscreens, and no fragrance. Targeting city dwellers, this fairly lightweight inorganic susncreening system provided a matte finish and good compatibility with makeup. According to the manufacturer, "even in the city, most days allow for a little sun on your face" (7). Backed by the dermatological support mentioned earlier, the consumer

Table 26.1 Beachwear vs. Dailywear: General Trends

	Beachwear	Dailywear
Sunscreening system	Multiple screens, high percentage; organic with filmogens	One to two materials only; organic/inorganic hybrid
Product form	Heavy lotion, cream, or anhydrous spray/gel	Light oil-in-water emulsion
Emulsifier type/content	Soap or high HLB nonionic	Gentler, polymeric or biomimetic
Ancillary items	Humectants, high-fragrance load, shine-enhancing esters	Moisturizers, antioxidants; lipids, treatment items, optics for matte finish
Claims	Protection and prevention	Myriad positioning, but with an eye toward the FDA monograph verbage

Note: HLB is hydrophilic–lipophilic balance.

was hooked into daily use by the sheerness of the formula, and the linkage of daily exposure to UV and premature wrinkling. This is more the exception than the rule so far as positioning is concerned, although even here, the SPF claim was sublined. Bienfait Total debuted to mixed reviews in the spring of 1994, including an investigation of claims by the National Advertising Board of the Better Business Bureau. The product faired well in support of the "physico-conversion" of a glyceryl phosphate into a moisturizing entity by the skin's own enzymatic processes, and the product sold well, especially in the EEC. Once again, the protection of SPF 15 was secondary to the alpha-hydroxy acid claims of smoother skin, moisturization benefits, and "total well-being" (8).

Finally, in the spring of 1995, Lauder introduced Daywear Super Antioxidant Complex, "a cucumber-scented, protective morning moisturizer for skin showing premature signs of aging caused by indoor and outdoor pollution" (9), with little or no mention of the SPF 15 protection afforded by the formula. The antioxidant cocktail featured in the formula addressed a number of consumer concerns, including radical scavenging, traditional vitamins, and state-of-the-art delivery of ingredients. Lauder's marketers hailed this product as "a one-step environmental plan" for skin care (10). While the protection was subverted in positioning for many years, the introduction of a retinol repair product in the late 1990s by Lauder allowed for the product's repositioning and reintroduction as a powerful UV protector for those needing it when using retinoid therapies. The product line continues to sell very well at the time of publication.

CURRENT MARKET

A recent review of skin care introductions, both domestically and internationally, shows an increase in the number of skin care products providing UV protection. Looking at two mass marketers, P&G (Olay) and Biersdorf (Nivea), one of every two moisturizers they offer for facial care carries UV protection. Similar trends are seen among the prestige marketers as well, running about one out of four facial moisturizer entries providing protection (11). Both marketers have captured the essence of daily-use protection in creating a need for application. In the case of the Nivea Visage entries, the "need" is for CoQ10, an antioxidant requiring application on a daily basis to be effective. The sunscreening systems rely heavily on octyl methoxycinnamate and the oxides of Zn and Ti, a "hybrid" system maximizing transparency, efficiency, and safety at the SPF 15 level. The emulsion systems used in these products are polymeric in nature, similar in approach to that of the prestige marketers, conveying inherent safety in a daily-use setting via the stratification of the sunscreening agents on the surface of the skin, significantly reducing the likelihood of penetration and a neurosensory event or allergic reaction. The more successful entries will follow this prescription: surface-attenuated sunscreens (particles or otherwise), light skin feel with a matte finish, and a daily need/requirement in the form of a botanical extract or nutrient, to ensure daily application.

CONCLUSIONS

While the form has been around for over a decade, the daily-use sunscreen remains an underutilized product form. While all indications are that this category continues to grow in volume (12,13), the message seems to fall on some deaf ears. The Sun Safety Alliance reported earlier this year that skin cancer continues to rise at a rate of over 6% per year. They have, however, pushed through legislation in several states, including California, providing funding for sun education, targeting school children, and providing at least a baseline education in sun protection. The Alliance has also provided for children to self-apply sunscreen during the school day without the need for a physician's note or prescription (14). Hopefully, the education and application will change habits and significantly reduce the childhood exposure so closely related to the more serious intermittent-or-casual-exposure-related diseases, and the next generation of sun worshippers will grow up healthier and more aware of the potential damage caused by this mode of exposure.

REFERENCES

1. English DR, Armstrong BK, et al. Case-control study of sun exposure and squamous cell carcinoma of the skin. Int J Cancer 1998; 77:347–353.
2. Koh HK. Cutaneous melanoma. New Engl J Med 1991; 325(3):171–182.
3. Darlington S, et al. A randomized controlled trial to assess sunscreen application and beta carotene supplementation in the prevention of solar keratoses. Arch Dermatol 2003; 139:451–455.
4. Ishitsuka Y, et al. Repeated irradiation with suberythemal UVB reduces the number of epidermal Langerhans cells. Arch Dermatol Res 2003; 295(4):155–159.
5. Lavker RM, et al. Cumulative effects from repeated exposures to suberythmal doses of UVR in human skin. J Am Acad Dermatol 1995; 32(1):53–62.
6. Foley P, et al. The frequency of reactions to sunscreens: results of a longitudinal population-based study on the regular use of sunscreens in Australia. Br J Dermatol 1993; 128(5):512–518.
7. Clinique City Block Oil-Free Daily Face Protector—SPF-13. Product Alert, June 24, 1991. Marketing Intelligence Service, 1991.
8. Lancome Bienfait Total claims substantiated, NAD concludes. The Rose Sheet, Jan 16, 1995; 16(3).
9. Lauder attracts moisture. Soap, Perfumery & Cosmetics, Oct 1995; 68(10):12.
10. Lauder's DayWear: health food for skin. Women's Wear Daily, May 26, 1995:4.
11. New Coalition Launches Crusade against Skin Cancer Caused by Sun Exposure. New York: PR Newswire, Apr 22, 2003.
12. The sun's out: what's driving the suncare category. Beauty Fashion, May 2003:33. Kline and Company.
13. Halliday S. New technology: when skincare met suncare. World Global Style Network, Apr 4, 2003.
14. Mathews I, Marcoulet N. Suncare trends review. Int Cosmet News 2003:37.

27

Valuable Properties for Baby and Kids Segments

Dennis L. Lott, Kelly Lewellen, and Glenn Wiener
Tanning Research Laboratories, Inc., Ormond Beach, Florida, USA

INTRODUCTION

It has been shown that sun damage sustained early in life is a precursor to skin damage later in life. Specifically, recent studies revealed that severe sunburn before age 18 is a positive risk factor in developing melanoma (1,2). Additionally, it has been noted that almost 80% of total lifetime exposure is obtained by 18 years of age (3). Due to the great importance of sun protection during these early years, this chapter will address the characteristics of Baby and Kids segment products.

Several organizations have Baby and Kid specific programs to educate and promote UV protection. Use of sunscreens as well as sun avoidance and proper clothing are integral parts of these programs. A quick review of some of the organizations follows:

- The Cancer Council Victoria was one of the leaders in developing programs to encourage UV protection for children. In 1980 a cartooned seagull singing "Slip! Slap! Slop!" helped spread the message of the importance of UV protection to the young people of Australia. The name SunSmart was adopted by the program in 1988. The program is credited with slowing down the rate of skin cancer for Australians (4).
- The US Department of Health and Human Service's Center for Disease Control and Prevention developed Guidelines for School Programs to Prevent Skin Cancer (5).
- The Skin Cancer Foundation has a "Children's Sun Protection Program" that reaches out to schools, camps, and day care centers throughout the USA (6).

The overall US mass sun care market is estimated at about $600 million in factory sales to traditional food, drug, and discount stores. At retail, sun care items are often grouped together by segments, not brands. The Baby and Kids segments are part of the overall sun care category, and represent the only segments within the category based on age. Sun care is typically divided into 12 segments as follows:

Tanning: These are low SPFs, 4 and below. There are items in this category that have no protective sunscreens that are referred to as "0 SPF" (the correct terminology should be "1 SPF").

Indoor: Products designed for tanning bed parlors or home tanning bed use. They are usually limited to moisturizers and products containing "accelerators" such as riboflavin or tyrosine.

Sunless: These are products containing artificial tanning agents and/or bronzers. Typically, dihydroxyacetone and caramel are the ingredients of choice.

Protection: SPF products of 15 and higher. The higher-SPF products appear to be growing faster.

Sun lip care: Lip balms with sunscreen, almost all are SPF 15 or higher.

Sport: Products designed for active users. Almost all are SPF 15 or higher, and are characterized by light texture and nongreasy feel.

Baby: High-protection products with SPFs of 30 or higher. They almost always have a "Baby" type fragrance.

Kids: High-protection products with SPFs of 30 or higher, with additional claims that address the active lifestyle of children.

Skin: This segment includes "oil free" and "faces" type products.

Moderate: SPF 5–14 products. While this segment provides some protection, the consumer's goal is probably tanning.

After sun: Products that do not offer any SPF and are sold in the sun care section specifically for after sun exposure use. Moisturization is a key attribute.

Burn relief: May or may not contain actives from other monographs. Actives might include materials such as lidocaine or camphor, both of which are listed in the External Analgesic Drug Products for Over-The-Counter Human Use Monograph (7). Aloe type gels are very popular in this category.

Table 27.1 illustrates the approximate percent product sold by segment. The data are an estimate for all outlets based on data supplied by permission from A.C. Nielsen.

REVIEW OF BABY SEGMENT

The Baby segment was born in 1986 with the launch of Tanning Research Labs, Inc., Hawaiian Tropic® Baby Faces and Tender Places product. It was the first sun care product to break the 15 SPF barrier with an SPF of 22. In the following year, the Baby segment was in the forefront again when Schering-Plough, Inc. broke another barrier with the introduction of Coppertone Water Babies®, a product line designed specifically for babies that carried an 80 min waterproof

Table 27.1 Approximate Percent Product Sold by Segment

Segment	Approximate percentage of market
Indoor	2–2.5
Sunless	15–20
Protection	18–22
Sun lip care	1–2
Sport	10–15
Baby	5–8
Kids	5–8
Skin	9–13
Tanning	12–15
Moderate	3–6
After sun	1–3
Burn relief	6–8

claim. In August 2003, the US baby sun care segment exceeded 7% of the total sun care category in dollar sales according to A.C. Nielsen.

Today the Baby segment is dominated by a handful of products. There are approximately 10 products that account for 80% of the sales in this segment. Over 95% of the sales come from products made by Schering Plough's Coppertone®, Playtex's Banana Boat®, Tanning Research's Hawaiian Tropic®, and various Private Label brands. Generally speaking, Baby products focus on the age group from 6 months up to 6 years. The sunscreen monograph (8) mandates that products carry a warning stating that sun care products are not intended for infants under 6 months of age without physician advice. Common product attributes within the Baby segment are

Fragrance: It is a characteristic baby powder type.
SPF: Baby products are SPF 30 and above.
Packaging: Typically pink.

REVIEW OF KIDS SEGMENT

Introduction of a Kid's segment was a natural progression after the success of the Baby segment. In 1994 the first Kids products were introduced under the Coppertone® Brand. While there is no set age range for the Kids segment, it normally encompasses children up to 10 or 11 years of age. A review of the Kids segment reveals differences and commonalities when compared with the Baby segment. Unlike the Baby segment, the Kids segment is not dominated by as small a number of products; approximately 15 products account for 80% of sales. Over 92% of the sales come from products made by Schering Plough's

Coppertone®, Playtex's Banana Boat®, Tanning Research's Hawaiian Tropic®, and various Private Label brands. Additionally, the product mix is varied with no one fragrance type that dominates this segment. Products range from non-fragranced, to fruity, to indistinguishable from the main stream product line. Product appearance ranges from colored, to disappearing color to indicate coverage, to glittered, to plain white lotion. Product claims are perhaps more extensive in this segment than any other, due to the nature of the end user, children. Claims go from expounding on being gentle to being durable and therein lies difficulty for the sun care chemist. Probably, the area with the most variety is the packaging. The Kids segment encompasses all package forms and the artwork is definitely not sedate. There is one consistent theme throughout the Kids as in the Baby segment, high SPFs. A majority of the products offered are SPF 30 and above. According to A.C. Nielsen, the kids segment represented over 6% of the US suncare market in dollar sales as of early August 2003.

SUNSCREEN ACTIVES

Sunscreen products in the USA are regulated as drugs. Presently, the current regulation is the 1999 Final Monograph (8). The active ingredient list is a relatively short one and those commonly found in Baby and Kids products are even fewer. Before formulation work begins the ingredients should be reviewed keeping the formulation type and what is to be accomplished in mind, and being cognizant that the monograph does not allow all combinations. The following is a list and brief description of actives that are routinely found in Baby and Kids products.

Titanium Dioxide

This is a particulate mineral sunscreen that is primarily a physical block but also performs as an absorber. The material blocks both in the UV-B and in the UV-A range, but is usually referred to as a UV-A blocker. However, due to the cosmetic disadvantage that at high concentrations it can produce opaque whitening products, it is frequently supplied as very small nano particulates. Once it has been reduced to this size, the material performs primarily as a UV-B sunscreen. Nano particles have recently come under a great deal of criticism as being environmentally unacceptable (9). Also, it is believed that titanium dioxide serves as a semiconductor on the skin and can catalyze photolability in organic sunscreens (10,11). Titanium dioxide is reported to induce photooxidation of lipids (12). Unlike organic sunscreen actives, incorporation of titanium dioxide requires the formulator to consider particulate surface properties to ensure system compatibility and efficacy. Fortunately, advances in surface treatments allow titanium dioxide's obstacles to be effectively addressed and overcome. Inorganic treatments such as aluminum hydroxide are capable of controlling photocatalytic activity by capturing hydroxyl radicals and improving photostability by preventing the reduction of Ti(IV) to Ti(III) (13). Numerous other treatments, both inorganic as well as organic, are commercially available today.

Zinc Oxide

Another particulate sunscreen, zinc oxide, is also an approved skin protectant active as well as a sunscreen active. However when used as a sunscreen, many of the same observations as those for titanium dioxide are appropriate with the exception that it is a more recognized UV-A protectant.

Octinoxate

This is a powerful UV-B sunscreen that also shows absorbance in the short-wavelength UV-A region. It is easy to formulate with as it is a good solvent. The problem with octinoxate is its photolability, especially in conjunction with avobenzone.

Homosalate

Homosalate is a relatively weak sunscreen that has a narrow UV-B absorption band. Commercially available homosalate has two isomers. Homosalate is not difficult to formulate with.

Octisalate

The same observations as for homosalate although *cis/trans* isomerism is not possible. It is recognized as a solubilizer for the solid sunscreens avobenzone and oxybenzone.

Oxybenzone

This sunscreen is a UV-B and short-wavelength UV-A screen. It is a good sunscreen to use in combination with other actives. It has been reported to cause irritation, but this is more likely the case of not being properly formulated. Oxybenzone is relatively difficult to solubilize. Many products on the market start out with oxybenzone in a saturated solution in the emulsion's oil phase. As the product ages the oxybenzone falls out of the solution resulting in gritty, needle-like crystals. These crystals can not only be irritating, but may cause the product to be subpotent. Oxybenzone is very photostable in most formulations.

Octocrylene

A strong UV-B sunscreen with a relatively broad absorbance band. It is a good sunscreen to use in combinations and is photostable.

Avobenzone

This is a long-wavelength UV-A absorber. It is used in combination with UV-B absorbers to provide broad-spectrum products. It is not a photostable sunscreen in many formulations. The formulator must be very careful when using this ingredient. It probably should not be used with octinoxate, and the preservative system is critical.

BABY PRODUCT SPECIFIC STRATEGIES

When formulating a product for the Baby segment, sun care chemists must take into consideration important factors in order to satisfy both parent and baby. Baby skin has a higher moisture content than an adult's skin, which is ordinarily thought of in a positive manner. However, due to baby skin being thinner and the stratum corneum having a looser structure when compared to typical adult skin, baby skin barrier function is weaker. A weak barrier function could promote high transepidermal water loss and greater exposure to external stimuli (14). The good elements are not readily locked in and the bad elements are not readily locked out. To accommodate for these differences, Baby products should therefore possess the following properties:

- Must deliver a high SPF, capable of absorbing a large amount of UV-A/UV-B irradiation.
- Must be gentle to the underdeveloped baby skin, minimizing risk of irritation and sensitization.
- Must minimize levels of any defatting surfactants which can further weaken barrier function.
- Must possess a high level of occlusivity to reduce entrance of external elements and escape of internal moisture.
- Must be highly moisturizing to continually hydrate skin.

Products formulated to properly fit (both physically as well as functionally) into the aforementioned pink bottles are nearly all emulsions. Emulsions give the sun care chemist the opportunity to effectively deliver a combination of lipophilic and hydrophilic ingredients to baby skin. If formulated correctly, these emulsions can possess most, if not all of the properties listed above. To translate successful completion of these tasks, Baby product marketers present their products with claims including hypoallergenecity, nonstinging, nonirritating, fragrance free, PABA free, waterproof, nonmigrating, and pediatrician tested.

Selection of Sunscreens/Carrier System

To provide a high SPF with broad-spectrum protection, a combination of UV-A and UV-B sunscreens should be formulated into the composition in such a manner that all crystalline sunscreens avobenzone, oxybenzone, methylbenzylidene camphor, and ethylhexyl triazone (methylbenzylidene camphor and ethylhexyl triazone are not currently approved for use in the USA) are completely and permanently dissolved. Recrystallization of one or more of these filters is likely to result in a reduced absorbance profile, increased risk of emulsion instability, undesirable product application, and aesthetics as well as a heightened potential for irritation. Esters of salicylic acid (15) and cinnamic acid are good solubilizers. Numerous other esters, ethers, alcohols, alkanes, and other classes of compounds offer good solubilizing strength and should be considered based on their compatibility with the system at hand. Perhaps some of the strongest sunscreen solvents come from the amide and imide classes of compounds. Highly polar dimethyl capramide and the eutectic mixture of butylphthalimide and isopropylphthalimide are both capable of solubilizing large amounts of crystalline sunscreens. However, levels should be kept at a minimum due to the possibility of irritation associated with certain members of these respective classes.

When formulating Baby sunscreens, one school of thought is to achieve high SPF, broad-spectrum protection utilizing solely inorganic micronized titanium dioxide or zinc oxide. A number of sunscreen marketers believe that consumers associate irritation and eye stinging with Baby sun care products formulated with one or more organic filters. High-SPF products have been developed using inorganic filters, and numerous formulation challenges exist. Methods and materials have been introduced to minimize whitening upon application. Some may view this as a positive although the creative marketer might look to the traditional whitening associated with particulate sunscreens as a way to let Mom or Dad know that Baby does indeed have a thick, even layer of lotion providing protection from UV induced damage. Other formulation challenges include maintaining an even particulate dispersion in the finished product, preventing the reaction of zinc with any free fatty acids, emulsion separation, and preventing particulate photostability catalytic activity. Such problems are appropriately addressed elsewhere and are beyond the scope of this chapter.

Sunscreen Optimization

Baby skin, in its underdeveloped state, can be more prone to external irritants and allergens. Formulating Baby sun care products requires minimizing of potential irritants and allergens. Certain UV absorbers have the ability to cause contact sensitization or photosensitization and therefore should be avoided or kept to a minimum. This presents a challenge—Moms and Dads want higher-SPF products to protect their baby, but traditionally to achieve a high SPF, high levels of UV absorbers have been necessary. This rationale should be dismissed and considered old fashioned. To achieve high-SPF Baby products, formulators must seek ways to increase SPF, utilizing carefully thought out and unique methods. Absorbance curves for individual as well as blends of UV absorbers should provide insight to help in optimizing a sunscreen blend, resulting in a high-SPF, low-sunscreen-level product. The days of increasing every sunscreen in a particular system in an attempt to raise SPF are over. Using the Beer–Lambert relationship (16) (Eq. 27.1) in conjunction with sunscreen absorbance curves as well as the erythemal action and appropriate solar spectra, it can easily be shown that dilute sunscreen solutions are ideally capable of providing extremely high SPF values.

$$\varepsilon = \frac{AM}{bc} \tag{27.1}$$

In this equation, ε is the molar absorptivity, A is the absorption of radiant energy, b is the cell width, c is the concentration of the solute, and M is the molecular weight of the solute. Unfortunately, applying a sunscreen emulsion to human skin, irradiating it, and evaluating its ability to prevent an erythemal response is not necessarily closely mimicked by shooting a UV beam through a quartz cuvette and measuring how much and which parts of this beam are being absorbed by the contents inside the cuvette. Formulating techniques are quickly improving, but there still remains a large gap between the maximum UV absorbance and the maximum attainable SPF. Properties including emulsion quality, evenness of application, film formation, film uniformity, product migration, continued solubilization of sunscreens, polarity of oil phase, and others dictate how well a sunscreen chemist can succeed in optimizing a sunscreen's effectiveness at absorbing UV energy. Ratios of SPF to total UV absorber have gone up from less than 1 : 1 in the past years to much higher values at present. A traditional SPF 40 may contain as much as 35% sunscreen, thus about a 1 : 1 ratio. Products with ratios of 4 : 1, and perhaps even higher, exist today. The unpublished Tanning Research Laboratories, Inc., data shown in Fig. 27.1 indicate the expected SPF of an 8% homosalate emulsion and a 15% homosalate emulsion when measured with an Optometrics SPF290® monochromatic device and calculated using the 40° standard sun spectra. Increasing homosalate from 8% to 15% hardly changed the expected SPF. Note that this SPF to percent sunscreen ratio is about 1 : 1.5 for the 8% homosalate formula and 1 : 2.5 for the 15% formula. Thus, merely increasing the sunscreen concentration is not always the answer.

Particulates can be helpful in boosting SPFs. Particulates bend photons, increasing their path-length, and by the Beer–Lambert relationship, the absorbance of radiation (17). Other potentially irritating or sensitizing ingredients such as fragrance, preservatives, and emulsifiers should also be carefully selected and used at low, yet effective, levels.

Barrier Function Protection

Children and adults alike rely on relatively high levels of sebum to help control homeostasis. Baby skin does not produce nearly as much sebum, which results in inferior homeostasis. Transepidermal water loss is increased and potentially harmful xenobiotics are not repelled as readily. Adding a defatting surfactant to a Baby protection product will further weaken homeostasis. Anionic surfactants, in particular the alkylaryl sulfonates, alkyl sulfonates, alkyl sulfates, and

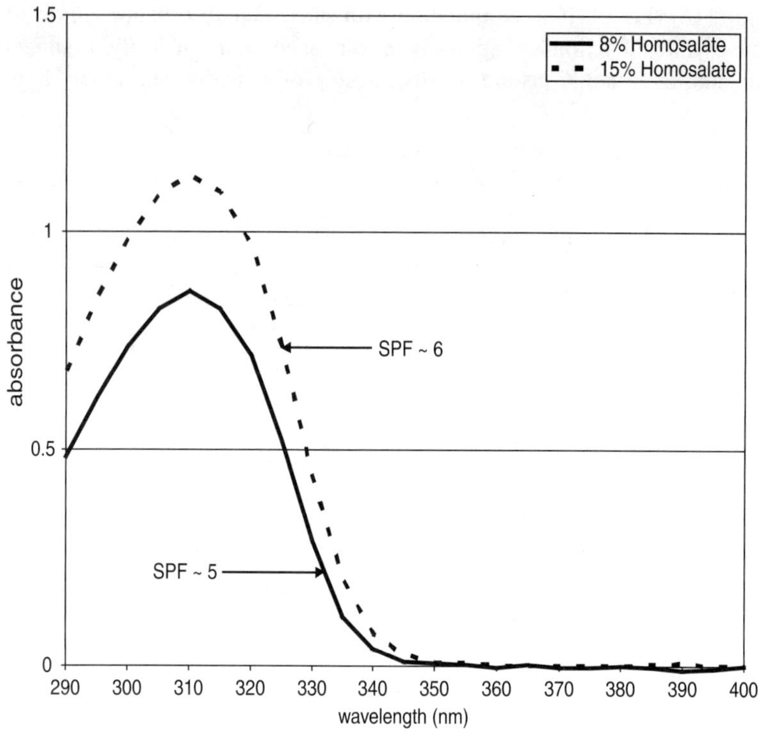

Figure 27.1 Tanning Research Laboratories, Inc. data showing the expected SPF of an 8% and a 15% homosalate emulsion.

alkyl ether sulfates, are known to strip fats from skin (18). These groups of surfactants should be avoided entirely, as they not only defat but also can be irritating and sensitizing. Baby skin should not be subjected to defatting ingredients, and taking this thought one step further, adding an occlusive agent will externally strengthen homeostatic function. After a parent bathes their infant, they are sure to coat them from head to toe with a highly occlusive lotion. Applying a protective sunscreen to their infant should provide the same occlusivity. Many such occlusive agents exist, such as dimethicone and petrolatum. Occlusive agents should be carefully chosen to minimize risk of irritation and sensitization.

Hydration of human skin, whether it be adult skin, child skin, or baby skin, is an attribute that all sun care products should carry. Although the rationale behind this statement changes from one category to the next, sun exposure, whether accompanied by some level of outdoor activity or not, continually stresses our skin. Both heat and saltwater are claimed to raise levels of transepidermal water loss. Therefore, babies brought outside into the sunlight should always have exposed areas treated with a moisturizing lotion. Technology in the field of moisturization has blossomed and as a result, many highly effective moisturizers, utilizing different modes of action, are available for use. For example, occlusive agents, such as those previously mentioned, or humectants, such as glycerine or sorbitol, can be used.

KIDS PRODUCT SPECIFIC STRATEGIES

Although no age limitations exist for this product segment, it is generally thought to include the years from when an infant becomes active up to preteen status. Marketing strategists must address the wants and needs of two divergent consumers: parents and children. Moms and dads will be influenced by gentleness, durability, and convenience. Kids want fun and minimal intrusion on their life. Successful products in this market have found unique ways to appeal to both groups.

Products are developed to meet a consumer demand. Unfortunately, one of the ways marketers become cognizant of a demand is through consumer complaints. One of the most common complaints coming from parents is eye stinging, resulting from a sun care product migrating into the child's eyes. It is not possible to formulate products that do not sting if physical eye contact is made. Sunscreens and necessary inactive ingredients will result in transient stinging and eye watering if the product gets into eyes. Therefore the goal must be to produce Baby formulations and especially formulations for more active Kids that resist migration when used on the face.

Formulations must be rugged. One only has to make a trip to the beach and observe children to understand how durable formulations must be. Kids are usually very active, constantly in and out of the water with frequent toweling, and generally playing in such a manner that could physically rub the product off. Their activity also makes it difficult for moms to corral long enough to apply sunscreen. Therefore, the product should be designed such that with even one application, a child is protected for long periods of time under extreme conditions. This means the product should be very water resistant (this is the highest claim allowable by the proposed monograph, based on 80 min of water immersion, although even longer periods of water resistance would be advantageous). The product should be nonmigratory. Kids at play, especially in and around water, are more than likely not going to be wearing head covers. Therefore, product must be applied to the face, around the eyes. A product that does not stay where applied will cause eye stinging and increased resistance by the child to further sunscreen use. The product must have rub resistance. Kids will be on the ground, playing with toys and on playground equipment and frequently toweling, making rub resistance very advantageous. The product must be photostable. Sunscreens that lose their UV absorption characteristics in the sun simply do not measure up to the standards necessary for this segment.

Adding to the dilemma for the formulators designing products for this segment is the consumer's desire for convenience. Many Kids segment leaders are sprays. It appears that many moms and dads purchase sprays for ease of application. This complicates the formulator's life in that sprays must be of a lower viscosity or more highly shear thinning than bottle or tube products to properly dispense from sprayers. Thus, the same characteristics that make for a good functional product on the skin, waterproofing, nonmigration, rub resistance, etc., are somewhat contradictory to a light sprayable product.

Summarizing, the following are the characteristics of a good Kids product:

High SPFs
Very water resistant
Nonmigrating
Rub resistant
Photostable

FORMULATION TYPES

As was discussed previously, characteristics of products designed for the Baby and Kids segments, such as high SPFs and good durability based on water resistance and nonmigration, drive the types of formulations that are most suitable for these segments. For example, oils cannot be used due to SPF limitations. The writers have no knowledge of oils having SPFs higher than about 15. Aqueous gels and aqueous spray gels are limited in that the water soluble sunscreens available to the chemist limit the SPF to about 15 and prevent the formulations from being waterproof. Therefore, the most common formulation types for these segments are as follows.

Emulsions

Emulsions are by far the most common vehicle for not only the Baby and Kids segments, but also for many other segments as well, especially protection segments. Emulsions are generally the most cosmetically elegant formula types with widespread consumer acceptance. They are generally water in oil or oil in water (the most common) types. Some mixed emulsion systems may also be found. Regardless, they share a common trait in that they contain an oil phase that delivers the active and "waterproofing" characteristics of the formula. The emulsion format can be found in a wide variety of package forms: bottles, sprays, tubes, and a variety of containers with dispensing pumps.

Since the emulsions can be so varied in form yet perform the necessary functions needed in these segments, they present the greatest challenges for the formulator. An emulsion paradoxically has several contradictions that must be solved:

1. An emulsion by definition is a mixture of oils and water—two substances that do not readily mix together and certainly do not easily stay together in a homogenous mix to produce an elegant product.
2. An emulsion in the Baby and Kids segments must be waterproof. This is somewhat strange since most of these emulsions will contain more than 50% water.

3. Most common bacteria thrive in water and require it to live and grow. Emulsions contain water. Not only can the products not have bacteria, they must also not allow bacteria to grow after contact with air, human touch, etc.

All of these contradictions provide challenges. The formulator is sometimes additionally challenged by any further desired product characteristics. It is not unusual for marketers to demand very specific fragrance, viscosity, and feel characteristics. None of the other product types discussed later offer as many challenges.

Sticks

Sticks are becoming more and more popular especially in the two subject segments discussed herein. This formula type is characterized by its wax-like structure and repel type package. The package size is almost always small, usually less than 0.5 oz. The product is generally used for small specific areas such as nose and ears. The main reason for the popularity is the ease of use that does not necessitate hand contact with the product. Since the entire formula is oleaginous it does not have many of the challenges presented by emulsion bases.

Lip Balms

Lip balms are very similar to sticks in form and function except they are specifically designed for the lips. The predominant difference is that they should contain a "flavor" that is allowable for internal use rather than a "fragrance" designed for topical use.

Alcohol Sprays

Alcohol sprays enjoy limited success in the category even though they are actually a very good dosage form for the Kids category. There is some resistance from parents to the use of a product containing alcohol, but the product type has some distinct advantages. Other than sticks and lip balms, it is probably the only formulation type that can be dispensed directly and not require further hand application to obtain a uniform coverage. It dries very quickly. It can be applied uniformly over skin that is not clean. For example, children on the beach need frequent reapplication of sunscreen. This can be difficult when rubbing is required due to the inevitable sand and salt adherence to the skin. The disadvantages associated with this formulation type are somewhat obvious: alcohol will burn abraded skin, it is drying, and it is flammable.

Formulation challenges are generally easier for alcohol bases due to good ingredient solubility in alcohol.

TESTING

One of the biggest development hurdles is how to evaluate formulas to determine if they meet the attributes desired. Brief descriptions of many of the formal tests are listed in the proceeding section, but it is up to the sun care chemist to develop "in-the-lab" means to evaluate formula attributes quickly.

SPF and Water Resistance

SPF value is the UV energy, supplied by a solar simulator, usually a xenon arc filtered with WG320, UG11, and dichroic mirrors, required to produce an MED on protected skin divided by the UV energy required to produce an MED on unprotected skin. This test is performed on Skin Types I, II, and III test subjects (highly sensitive, very sensitive, and sensitive to sun). In the USA, the labeled value is based on the average of a 20-subject test panel, adjusted down to a 95% confidence interval. A water resistant or very water resistant value is an SPF test that also includes a 40 and 80 min water immersion, respectively, before exposure to the solar simulation radiation. Some products are labeled with extended waterproof claims. These are substantiated by even longer water immersions prior to irradiation. These extended waterproof claims are beneficial to Kids, but extended waterproofing is not expected to be allowed after adoption of a final sunscreen monograph.

Migration

There is no standardized test for migration, although this test has value. One of the predominant complaint from moms concerning Kids and Baby products is eye stinging. Sunscreen products will not cause eye damage, but will sting. Therefore, the only recourse is to prevent the product from migrating into the eyes. A migration test should measure the movement potential of a topically applied product under high heat and humidity conditions that would lead to perspiring.

A typical test protocol would be similar to the following. Test product and two controls (a known migrating product and a known nonmigrating product) are applied to circular delineated test sites on a test subject's back. Under UV black light, test sites are measured and recorded. The test subject is then placed in an environmentally controlled room, with temperature at $100 \pm 2^{\circ}F$ and relative humidity 30–40%, to induce sweating. After 80 min of sweating, the test sites are measured again under UV black light conditions. Test products that move less than 10% will be considered nonmigrating and will be able to support a nonmigrating claim.

Hypoallergenicity

Hypoallergenic tests are recommended for all Baby and Kids products. This test measures the irritation and sensitization potential of products. Usually, a 100-subject test panel is used in a two-part test. Briefly, the test includes occlusive, semiocclusive, or open patches that are applied three times a week for 3 weeks on a subject and remain for 24 h after each application. A reaction indicates that the product is probably an irritant. After a 7–14 day rest period, patches are reapplied on an untreated area for 24 h. The treated sites are observed at 24 and 48 h posttreatment. A reaction indicates that the product is a sensitizer.

Moisturization

Moisturization is a popular claim for products in the Baby and Kids segment as well as in most segments. This claim is usually validated by comparing treated skin to untreated skin and a control treated area. Measurements are made with an instrument such as a Corneometer® sold by Courage + Khazaka, Cologne, Germany. The product is said to be moisturizing if the treated site displays higher moisture levels than untreated skin.

Photostability

Photostability is a subject that has received a great deal of attention, especially in regard to the UV-A filter avobenzone. Other sunscreens also exhibit photolability. Although there is no standardized method for measuring photostability, it is extremely important that sunscreen products are photostable, especially Baby and Kids products. The photostability determination test must be done on a thin film of the product that is irradiated in sunlight or with a spectrum known to mimic sunlight. A solar simulator spectrum suitable for SPF testing is not adequate to measure photostability since products do not degrade in SPF spectra as they do in sunlight. The importance of this cannot be overemphasized. If the product is not photostable, the SPF reported from solar simulator testing will result in overestimation and an improperly labeled product.

CONCLUSIONS

Ultimately, the most important aspect is creating a product that appeals to the end user, hopefully affecting adequate product usage leading to the needed protection. Inadequate usage is probably the biggest problem in protecting consumers from UV skin damage. Study after study shows that consumers do not use adequate quantities of the product to obtain the labeled SPF value. Baby and Kids products simply must be formulated and packaged to attract purchase and encourage adequate usage.

REFERENCES

1. Stern R, Weinsteirn M, Baker S. Risk reduction for nonmelanoma skin cancer with childhood sunscreen use. Arch Dermatol 1986; 122:537–545.

2. Weinstock M, Colditz G, Willett W, et al. Nonfamilial cutaneous melanoma incidence in women associated with sun exposure before 20 years of age. Pediatrics 1989; 84:199–204.
3. Sun & Skin News. A Publication of the Skin Cancer Foundation, 2001; 18(2).
4. http://www.sunsmart.com.au/s/about/about.htm.
5. http://www.cdc.gov/cancer/nscpep/index.htm.
6. http://www.skincancer.org/.
7. 21 CFR Part 348. External Analgesic Drug Products for Over-the-Counter Human Use; Tentative Final Monograph, 1983; 48(27).
8. Food and Drug Administration, Department of Health and Human Services. Sunscreen Drug Products for Over-the-Counter Human Use; Final Monograph. Federal Register: GPO, 1999:27666–27693.
9. ETC Group. No small matter II: the case for a global moratorium, size matters. Occasional Pap Ser 2003; 7(1).
10. Serpone S, Salinaro A, Emeline A, Horakashi S, Hidoka H, Zhao J. An in vitro systematic spectroscopic examination of the photostabilities of a random set of commercial sunscreen lotions and their chemical UVB/UVA active agents. Photochem Photobiol Sci 2002; 1:970–981.
11. Ricci A, Chretien M, Maretli L, Scaiano JC. TiO_2—promoted mineralization of organic sunscreens in water suspension and sodium dodecyl sulfate micelles. Photochem Photobiol Sci 2003; 2:487–492.
12. Sayre R, Dowdy J. Titanium dioxide and zinc oxide induce photooxidation of unsaturated lipids. Cosmet Toilet 2000; 115(10).
13. Judin V, Ahlnäs J. Surface chemistry of ultrafine titanium dioxide. Cosmet Toilet Manufacture Worldw 1994; 186–190.
14. Caputo R, Monti M. Children's skin and cleansing agents. Wien Med Wochenschr Suppl 1990; 108:24–25.
15. Hansenne I, van Leeuwen V. Photoprotective/cosmetic compositions comprising at least one solid organic sunscreen compound and salicylate solvents thereof. US Patent 5,667,765, September 16, 1997.
16. Ricci R, Ditzler MA, Nestor P. Discovering the Beer-Lambert law. J Chem Educ 1994; 71(11):983–985.
17. Jones CE. A new polymeric additive for sunscreens. SOFW J 1995; 21:561–565.
18. Rieger MM. Anionic Surfactants. Surfactant Encyclopedia. 1st ed. Wheaton, IL: Allured Publishing, 1993:5–14.

28

Fabrics as UV Radiation Filters

Kathryn L. Hatch
Agricultural and Biosystems Engineering, The University of Arizona, Tucson, Arizona, USA

INTRODUCTION

Engineering fabrics to increase their capability to filter solar radiation, especially the UV portion, has been of interest for a number of years (1–18). The intent is to label such fabrics and items made from them as solar (sun or UV) protective clothing. The American Society for Testing and Materials (ASTM) standard guide D6603 (19) defines UV-protective textile as "any textile whose manufacturer and/or seller claims that it protects consumers from ultraviolet (UV) light, claims the reduction of risk of skin injury associated with UV exposure, and/or uses a rating system that quantifies the amount of UV protection afforded". The purpose of this chapter is to describe the ways in which fabric can be enhanced to improve its UV-filtering capability.

FIBER DISTRIBUTION

Fabrics are manufactured assemblages of fibers or yarns that have substantial surface area in relation to thickness and sufficient mechanical strength to give this assembly inherent cohesion. The fundamental unit in all fabrics is therefore fiber, a unit of matter with an extremely small diameter and a length at least 100 times longer than its width. Most fibers are several thousand times longer than they are wide. Cotton fibers, for example, range in length from $\frac{7}{8}$ to $2\frac{1}{2}$ in. with diameters ranging from 16 to 20 μm. Fibers are usually assembled into yarns before becoming part of a fabric. Yarns, like fibers, tend to be cylindrical structures that are long in relationship to diameter. Yarns are interlaced to form fabrics in the woven fabric class, interlooped to form fabrics in the knit fabric class, and knotted and twisted to form fabrics in the class with this same name. The fabric class in which yarns seldom appear is called the nonwoven class, a class of fabrics made directly from fibers.

What is important to visualize is that this assembling of fibers into yarns and assembling of yarns into fabrics means that fiber or yarn do not fill the entire volume of the fabric. There are spaces between yarns creating holes through the fabric from its face to back. Further, there are innumerable spaces between fibers within yarns. Collectively, these "empty-of-fiber spaces" within a fabric's volume are referred to as interstices or voids.

The interstices/voids which have the major influence on the UV-filtering capability of fabric are those between yarns because they provide a direct pathway for UV directed perpendicular to the fabric surface (which is the usual case in UV transmittance testing methods) to be transmitted. Such transmitted rays are referred to as *direct transmittance*. The interstices/voids between fibers within yarns also contribute to filtering as incident radiation may be reflected from one fiber surface to another until transmitted through the fabric. Incident UV that is transmitted through the fibrous portion of the fabric is referred to as *scattered transmittance*.

The distribution of fiber/yarn within a fabric is the most important factor in determining the fabric filtering ability. Fiber distributions that result in the least surface area not containing fiber/yarn in otherwise identical fabrics (same fiber composition, thickness, chemical content, etc.) lead to the higher percent blocking values, UV protective factor (UPF) values, and SPF (sun protection factor) (SPF) values. Pailthorpe (1) called the percentage of fabric surface area containing fiber/yarn the fabric's cover factor. Assuming that the area covered with fiber/yarn completely absorbed all incident UV, the relationship between cover factor and the directly transmitted UV transmission through this ideal fabric would be expressed as % UV transmission = 100 − cover factor. This relationship is shown in Table 28.1. As is readily apparent, very small increases in fabric cover factor make a substantial change in a fabric's ability to filter UV.

FIBER COMPOSITION

The fiber composition of the fabric is a description of the class or classes of fiber used to manufacture the fabric. Fabrics may be made entirely of fibers from one fiber class, cotton, polyester, wool (laine), silk (soie), flax (linen), rayon (viscose), lyocel, acetate (cellulose acetate), nylon (polyamide), olefin (polypropylene), and acrylic (polyacrylonitrile), or from two or more fiber classes as cotton and polyester. The difficulty in directly assessing differences in fiber class filtering ability resides in finding or even engineering fabrics that are alike in all respects except for fiber composition. There is always enough difference in thickness and cover factor of fabrics of like fiber composition so that the fabric transmittance values would not reveal fiber content differences alone.

Fiber Class Differences

Excellent data on the ability of fibers from various fiber classes to filter UV is provided by Crews et al. (2). They selected 43 undyed, not optically whitened,

Table 28.1 Relationship between Cover Factor of an Ideal Fabric and Filtering Ability (1)

Cover factor	Fabric SPF/UPF
80	5
90	10
93.33	15
95	20
97.5	40
98	50
99	100
99.5	200

woven fabrics commonly found in clothing that were 100% cotton, 100% rayon, 100% nylon, 100% wool, 100% silk, or 100% polyester. Each fabric was characterized by weave class, weight, thread count, yarn number, yarn type, thickness, fabric cover, and cloth cover, and as bleached/unbleached. The percent UV transmittance of each fabric was determined using a spectrophotometer with an integrating sphere. Percent transmittance values for fabrics of like fiber composition were averaged resulting in transmittance results for fiber content groups of 25.1% (cotton fabric average), 27.3% (rayon fabric average), 24.1% (nylon fabric average), 8.6% (wool fabric average), 14.6% (silk fabric average), and 23.2% (polyester fabric average).

To determine the influence of fiber type alone on fabric percent transmittance, the fabric characterization data were used in an analysis of covariance procedure to calculate an adjusted percent transmittance for fabrics of like fiber composition. The result of this analysis gave adjusted percent transmittance values as follows: 26.9% (cotton), 26.0% (rayon), 20.6% (nylon), 18.2% (wool), 16.8% (silk), and 15.3% (polyester). Analysis using Fisher's LSD technique revealed no significant differences in the adjusted values of cotton and rayon and no significant differences in the adjusted values for nylon, wool, and silk. So cotton and rayon fibers have similar ability to filter UV radiation and nylon, wool, and silk fibers have similar ability to filter UV radiation.

The major differences between the unadjusted and adjusted fiber percent transmittance values were for wool (8.6% increased to 18.2%) and polyester (23.2% decreased to 15.3%). The change in the wool values largely reflects the fact that fabrics in the wool set were much thicker than fabrics in the other fiber sets. Once the contribution of thickness to percent fabric transmittance was accounted for in the covariate analysis, the percent transmittance due to the wool fiber composition of the fabric was evident. Adjusting the polyester values showed a decrease in UV transmittance, which makes sense because polyester fiber is the only fiber studied by Crews et al. (2) made from a polymer containing aromatic rings which are UV-absorbing entities. Because cotton and rayon fibers are both made from cellulose polymers and silk, wool, and nylon are all composed of amide polymers, the filtering abilities within these classifications would be expected to be similar. It should be noted here that these fiber values (or rankings) do not reflect SPF or UPF.

Differences Within Natural Fiber Class

Natural fibers are usually made into fabrics before the removal of naturally occurring materials within or on the surface of the fibers. These naturally occurring materials may or may not be removed from the fabric before it is worn in the sun. The question is how much difference in fabric percent transmittance occurs when the naturally occurring substances are removed. Crews et al. (2) examined this question using two pairs of fabrics.

The first pair contained a bleached and unbleached print cloth. The bleached cotton print cloth had a UV transmission of 23.7%, a value almost twice as high as that of unbleached cotton print cloth with a UV transmission of 14.4%. The reason the unbleached cotton had a lower percent transmittance is because the natural pigment and lignins on the fabric act as UV absorbers.

The second pair consisted of silk fabrics, one fabric had the coating surrounding silk fibers intact and the other fabric did not have the fiber coating because it had been removed during bleaching. A comparison of the UPF value for the crepe de chine silk fabric and the shantung silk fabric, which had similar percent cover values of approximately 92 and similar thickness, showed that the UV transmission through the bleached crepe de chine was four times higher (21.8%) than that of the similarly constructed but unbleached shantung (5.4%). They thought this difference was due to the natural pigments, lignins, and other impurities in the unbleached silk fabrics acting as UV absorbers.

Differences Within Manufactured Fiber Class

Fibers within a manufactured fiber class, such as the rayon (viscose) class, may be modified by adding titanium dioxide (TiO_2) to the fiber spinning solution or melt. TiO_2 a well-known inorganic UV-absorbing compound added to sunscreen lotions (3), attenuates UV by absorption and scattering leading to "broad-spectrum" (UV-A and UV-B) coverage. Wedler and Hirthe (4) explain the use of TiO_2 in manufactured fibers. They state that adding typical levels of white pigment grade to manufactured fibers, 0.3% to produce semidull fibers and 1.5% to produce full-dull fibers, leads to some improvement in UPF of fabric made with such fibers. High levels of sunburn protection with this grade are not possible because increasing the concentration of white pigment grade TiO_2 in the fiber creates fiber processing difficulties. However, using an ultrafine grade of TiO_2 not only eliminates the processing difficulty but also provides a much higher number of particles per portion of fiber weight. More particles means that more UV will be absorbed or reflected at the fiber level. Significant improvement in fabric UPF can be achieved when fabrics have a high cover factor.

No studies were found in the literature that demonstrated improvement in fabric UPF due to the fact that fibers in the fabric contained TiO_2. The closest indication of the effect of TiO_2 on the UPF values of fabric is provided by Gambicher and coworkers (5). In their study which focused on comparing *in vivo* and an *in vitro* testing methods, three viscose (rayon) fabrics made from TiO_2-containing fibers and four viscose fabrics without TiO_2-containing fibers were used. The TiO_2 fabrics did have higher UPF values but these fabrics also had higher fabric weights than fabrics made without TiO_2 in their fibers. Therefore, the entire increase in fabric UPF cannot be attributed to the inclusion of TiO_2.

FABRIC THICKNESS

Fabric thickness has been found to be the most useful parameter for explaining the differences in UV transmission of fabrics of like fiber composition when differences in percent cover factor of those fabrics are also accounted for (2). In this case, the incident UV has a greater distance to travel through the fabric with more opportunity for certain wavelengths to be absorbed or reflected by the fibers.

DYE COMPOSITION AND CONCENTRATION

Dyes are organic chemicals that are able to selectively absorb and reflect wavelengths of light within the visible range of the electromagnetic spectrum. A dye molecule must have a conjugated system. Dye molecules may also absorb in the UV range and those that do would be expected to contribute to the UPF value of fabrics to which they are applied. Further, dyes with UV transmittance spectra showing the strongest absorption in the UV-B region would be expected to produce fabrics with higher UPF values. As fabric is dyed to a deeper shade using the same dye, the UPF of the fabric should increase due to the greater dye concentration in the darker fabric.

Dyes may be classed by application method or by chemical type. Application classing is useful because knowing a dyes generic class reveals which fibers can be colored with it. For example, dyes in the direct and reactive classes can be used to color cotton fiber. Dyes in the acid class may be used to color nylon, silk, and wool fibers. Each dye within an application class is often identified by its color index name, a name composed of class name, dye hue (color reflected by the dye), and a unique identifying number.

Comparison of Dyed Fabrics

Srinivasan and Gatewood (6) studied the effect of dyeing a white cotton fabric with dyes of various colors (hues) but having different absorbance in the UV region. The cotton fabric selected was a bleached print cloth because (a) it had a UPF value low enough (4.0) for any improvements to UPF due to dye addition to be detected and (b) it is a fabric often dyed and finished for summer garments. Dyes from the direct classification were used because dyes from this class are most often used to color cotton fabrics. The 14 dyes selected differed in chemical classification. The hues were yellow (four dyes), red (three dyes), violet (one dye), blue (three dyes), green (one dye), brown (one dye), and black (one dye). After prescouring the print cloth, the direct dyes were applied to 5 g samples of cotton fabric at theoretical concentrations of 0.5% and 1.0% on weight of fiber (owf). The 1.0% owf represents a medium depth of shade that would be typical of summertime fabrics. A control sample was prepared by subjecting the bleached print cloth to a blank dyeing process with all ingredients except the dye to eliminate the effect of fabric shrinkage on percent transmittance and therefore on calculated UPF. Specimens of dyed fabric were submitted for UV transmittance assessment. The mean UV, UV-A, and UV-B percent transmittance values were calculated from each scan and averaged for 16 scans (four specimens × two scans × two replications). Then, the UPF values were calculated.

Analysis of variance was conducted on the UPF data to determine if the application of dyes changed the UPF values of the cotton print cloth and whether greater owf application lead to higher UPF values. The dyed fabric UPF values are shown in columns 2 and 3 of Table 28.2. These data show that increasing the concentration of the dye in the fabric leads to increased UPF values. For each dye, the fabric UPF value is higher after the 1.0 owf application of dye than after the 0.5% owf application. So, the darker fabric of each pair would afford greater sunburn protection.

To determine the specific dye effect on the UPF of the fabric, the concentration of the dyes in each fabric needed to be the same. This was not the case because the dyes had different exhaust rates. To determine the percent exhaustion from the dyebath, the absorptiometric measurements of the residual dyebath solution were compared with calibration curves prepared from dye solutions at known concentrations based on the weight of the commercial dye.

Having the dye exhaust rate data made it possible to use analysis of covariance treating concentration as a covariable. Fisher's least significant difference test was then used to determine which of the dyed fabrics differed in their UPF values. The adjusted UPF values are shown in column 4 of Table 28.2.

Table 28.2 Selected Results of the Srinivasan and Gatewood Study (6)

Direct dye used to dye fabric	Fabric UPF after 0.5% owf dyeing process	Fabric UPF after 1.0% owf dyeing process	Adjusted dyed fabric UPF
None			4.1
Yellow 12	13.1	18.6	17.8
Yellow 28	19.9	29.3	21.6
Yellow 44	18.4	28.6	25.3
Yellow 106	19.3	27.6	25.0
Red 24	27.6	37.1	31.3
Red 28	38.7	50.7	41.3
Red 80	17.3	24.7	20.3
Violet 9	20.9	28.8	23.5
Blue 1	21.5	30.2	25.5
Blue 86	16.2	18.6	24.0
Blue 218	13.1	19.0	16.6
Green 26	22.3	29.2	26.2
Brown 154	22.8	30.6	24.7
Black 38	29.8	40.2	33.7

The adjusted results show that fabric color (hue) is not a reliable indicator of the UV protection provided by dyed fabrics because dyes of the same hue produced fabrics with varying UPF values when concentration level was identical. This study also showed that black fabric does not necessarily provide the best sunburn protection as one of the red dyes produced a fabric having a higher UPF value than the fabric dyed black. Here, it is critical to remember that color seen is due to one's brain interpreting the *visible* rays that reach one's eyes. Color is not the result of "seeing" invisible UV radiation.

Comparison of Dyes in Solution

Srinivasan and Gatewood (6) also devised an equation similar to that used in calculating the UPF of fabrics for evaluating dyes in solution based on their transmittance values. This equation calculated the effective UV transmittance, which is the relative effectiveness of dyes in improving the UV protection of a fabric, based on the transmittance of dyes in solution weighted for solar spectral irradiance and relative erythemal spectral effectiveness. Because this method takes into consideration the effectiveness of both UV-A and UV-B transmittances and because the concentrations of the dyes in the solutions can be more easily controlled than in fabric, it led the researchers to conclude that determining the effective UV transmittance of dyes in solution would probably be an excellent procedure to screen dyes before going through the expense of applying them to fabrics to investigate UPF effectiveness.

UV-ABSORBENT COMPOUNDS

In this manuscript, the term UV-absorbent compound is used to indicate *colorless* compounds that have UV-absorbing capabilities. The major subclasses are optical whitening agents (OWAs), also known as fluorescent whitening agents (FWAs), and UV-cutting agents (UVCAs). The OWA compounds' main purpose is to whiten and brighten fabrics but they may also improve the UV filtering. The UVCAs' primary function is to enhance the UPF of fabrics to which they are added while also contributing to the whiteness and brightness of the fabric.

Optical Whitening (Brightening) Agents

OWAs whiten and brighten fabrics because they convert a portion of the incident UV to a visible blue wavelength and reflect this as a visible blue wavelength. In other words, OWAs cause fluorescence. More visible light reaches an observer's eye from the surface of a fabric containing OWA than from an identical fabric without OWA. More specifically, OWAs absorb UV radiation near 360 nm and re-emit it at about 430 nm. Secondarily, OWAs absorb UV, which they do better in the UV-A region than in the UV-B region, in which they absorb poorly. Additionally, they have a weakness at about 308 nm. The main thrust of work with OWAs has been to select compounds from the OWA class, some being modified to enhance UV-absorbing ability, to study how effective they are compared to each other in increasing UPF values of fabrics and in enhancing whiteness/brightness.

Mill Applied

Bleached cotton fabrics, nylon fabrics, and polyester fabrics may be enhanced in the finishing mill by the addition of OWAs. Reinehr et al. (7) finished a cotton poplin fabric (initial SPF 3.5) with three OWAs: a conventional stilbene (OWA-1), a DSBP OWA (OWA-2), a mixture of OWA-1 and -2, and a modified OWA (OWA-3), a compound similar in structure to OWA-1 but with carboxylic acid and ester groups, which results in additional UV-B absorption. At identical concentration of OWA on the fabric, the SPF values were 10 for OWA-1, 10 for the mixture, 14 for OWA-2, and 22 for OWA-3. When OWA-3 was applied by exhaust application the fabric SPF was 35 and when applied by padding it was 60+, these values being higher due to greater concentration of the OWA on the fabric. They concluded that OWAs make a positive contribution to improving the sunburn protection of cotton fabric but in many cases do not achieve the protection level usually desired (i.e., the 30+ UPF required to classify a fabric as UV protective).

Detergent Ingredient Applied

OWAs are a common additive to home laundry detergent formulations because they deposit onto fabrics of certain fiber compositions (usually cotton and cotton blends) during the wash cycle. There was interest in laundering both nonwhitened and whitened fabrics.

Nonbrightened fabric laundering: Reinehr et al. (7) laundered nonwhitened cotton poplin fabrics with a detergent containing 0.2% OWA-3 compound (an OWA with improved absorption in the UV-B) and with 0.2% of an OWA-1 compound (the traditional stilbene OWA). After five launderings, the fabric laundered with detergent containing OWA-3 had an SPF double that of the fabric laundered with the OWA-1 compound. The increase in whiteness was the same for both treatments.

Zhou and Crews (8) laundered eight white summer-weight fabrics of various fiber compositions 20 times using home laundering equipment. Some swatches were laundered with detergent containing OWAs and others with detergent without OWAs. Laundering fabric had increased UPF values due to fabric shrinkage. In laundering fabric with detergent containing an OWA the UV-blocking ability of the cotton and cotton/polyester fabrics was improved, but not that of the polyester or nylon fabrics. The cotton sheeting showed a 10-fold increase in mean UPF following 20 launderings with OWA (UPF 5.5 initially and UPF 57.1 after washing). One hundred percent cotton broadcloth showed an increase of about sixfold (ending in UPF of 22). Some of the increase was probably due to shrinkage in the fabric, but that would be small. The cotton fabrics' enhanced blocking property was attributed to the ability of cotton fiber to absorb the OWA compound, thus facilitating the buildup of OWA in the fabric. Buildup may also be due to chemical affinity of the fiber for the OWA. At 20 launderings, UPF still had not leveled off—so more laundering may lead to even greater improvement.

Pre-brighten fabric laundering: Reinehr et al. (7) laundered swatches of a prebrightened white 100% cotton poplin fabric (SPF 13) with a brightener-free detergent and with a detergent containing 0.2% OWA-1 (a conventional stilbene compound). After four to five washings in the brightener-free detergent, the prebrightened fabric had an SPF of 5. After four to five launderings in the 0.2% OWA-1 detergent formulation, the prebrightened fabric swatches had an SPF equal to or greater than the initial 13 SPF.

This research team also laundered a prebrightened blue cotton fabric (SPF 7) with a brightener-free detergent and a detergent containing 0.1% FWA-2 (conventional DSBP). After 10 washings, the swatches laundered in brightener-free detergent had an SPF of 5 while the SPF of the swatches laundered in detergent containing FWA-2 reached 15. Using a dark blue prebrightened cotton poplin fabric (initial SPF 24) showed that the SPF was reduced to 20 when the detergent contained no FWA and showed improvement with FWA in the detergent.

Rinse-Cycle Fabric Softener Ingredient Applied

Reinehr et al. (7) softened a cotton fabric with two rinse-cycle fabric-softening products: one containing a cationic OWA (OWA-4) and the other OWA-2. Two formulations were used: one had 0.3% and the other 2.7% on weight of after-rinse product of the softening compound. Whiteness of fabrics to which the cationic OWA was added was better than for those fabrics softened with OWA-2. There was little difference in the whiteness of fabrics laundered with the softening products containing different amounts of cationic OWA. However, fabric swatches laundered with the softener containing the higher concentration of cationic OWA had higher SPF values than those swatches laundered with the lower concentration of cationic OWA in the product (SPF of 30 compared to 12). The comparison treatment (OWA-2) resulted in an SPF of 5 at both concentrations.

UV-Cutting Agents

UVCAs are a classification of chemical compounds that lead to a significant improvement in the sunburn protection capability of the fabric. The main feature of UVCAs is that they have chromophore systems that absorb very effectively in the UV region, enabling them to maximize the absorption of UV radiation while *in situ* on textiles. UVCAs may be applied in the mill, added to a laundry detergent formulation, be part of a rinse-cycle fabric softener formulation, or be the main ingredient in a rinse-water additive product. UVCAs should not be confused with UV-absorbing compounds whose purpose is to slow down the solar degradation of PA (polyamide/nylon) fiber or enhance the light fastness of dyes on automotive PES (polyester/polyethylene terephthalate) fibers/fabrics.

Mill Applied

Hilfiker et al. (9) showed the effect of treating a thin (0.2 mm), slightly porous (1.5%) cotton fabric with a triazine (UVCA-1) and with a hydroxyl-triazole (UVCA-2). Theoretical values calculated using information about each compound's absorption spectra predicted that the maximum SPF of a treated cotton fabric would be 67 for UVCA-2 and 25 for UVCA-1. The authors explained that these differences are due to the fact that UVCA-1 has an upper absorption limit of about 335 nm, so it can never yield a very high SPF, while the upper absorption limit of UVCA-2 is 385. On the other hand, increases in SPF value due to increased concentration of the compound in the fabric would be expected to be greater for UVCA-1 than for UVCA-2 because the extinction coefficient of UVCA-1 at 310 nm is higher than for UVCA-2.

The authors applied UVCA-2 to a poplin cotton fabric (110 g/m^2, 0.6% porosity, SPF 3.2) and a cretonne cotton fabric (144 g/m^2, 4% porosity, SPF 6.8) so that the concentration of UVCA-2 on the fabric was in the range of 0–0.02 g/cm^3. They reported the measured SPF values of each fabric at each concentration level and the SPF values obtained using their theoretical equation. Agreement of the paired values was considered to be good in the absence of any adjustable parameters. At the lowest concentration applied, the SPF was 12 for poplin and 12 for cretonne. At the maximum concentration applied, the SPF for poplin was 103 and for the cretonne it was 19.

Reinert et al. (10) reported the results of adding different UVCAs from a dyebath to fabrics of various fiber compositions, weights, and thicknesses. The UVCA they applied to eight cotton fabrics, Cibatex UPF, was a water-soluble oxaldianilide with two reactive groups. The UVCA applied to five wool, five silk, six polyamide and polyamide elastin (spandex) blends was Cibafast W, a monosulfonated benzotriazole derivative. The UVCA applied to the five polyester and polyester blend fabrics, Cibatex APS, was a dispersion of a benzotriazole derivative. In this study, the UVCA was added to the dye bath so that the fabric was colored and UPF treated at the same time. All UVCAs were applied in the standard amount of 2% owf with the dye. A blank dyeing was done. This "dye" bath included only the UVCA at 2%.

While the exact improvement in UPF differs by specific fabric, trends are the same. The UPF increased as the depth of shade increased and especially with the addition of UVCA-2 to the dyebath. For example, the initial UPF values for two of the eight cotton fabrics were 3 (Renforce fabric) and 5 (tricot fabric). Dyeing of these fabrics with yellow dye F-4G to a pale yellow shade increased the UPF to 7 for the Renforce fabric and to 5 for the tricot fabric. Dyeing to a deep yellow shade resulted in UPFs of 7 for both. Adding 2% UVCA-2 to the dye-baths increased the UPF of the pale yellow fabrics to 20 (Renforce) and to 50+ (tricot). Adding UVCA-2 to the dyebath of the Renforce fabric containing sufficient dye to color it to a deep shade of yellow increased the UPF to 34.

Jöllenbeck (11) describes a new UV-cutting compound for mill-finishing of cotton and viscose fabrics. This UV-cutting agent, Solartex CEL (renamed Tinofast CEL), effectively absorbs in the 300–320 nm range of the electromagnetic spectrum, the range in which the erythemal effect (the product of erythemal effectiveness and spectral distribution) of UV radiation on the skin is at its highest.

UPF results are provided for cotton tricot knit fabric (UPF 5) after dyeing and finishing with Tinofast CEL. Fabrics dyed to a dark shade with Cibacron dyes blue F-GPN, red FB, and scarlet F-3G had UPF values >50 and with yellow F-4G a UPF of 44. However, the fabric dyed to a light shade with the same dyes resulted in UPFs of 10 (blue), 25 (red), 17 (scarlet), and 7 (yellow). Adding 2–4% Tinofast CEL to the dyebath resulted in UPF values for the pale dyed fabric swatches of >50.

Jöllenbeck et al. (12) compared the UV-filtering ability of cotton fabric finished with 1,3-chlor-5-(4′-sulfophenyl)-*s*-triazine to that finished with Tinofast CEL (bireactive oxalic acid derivative). The first compound, referred to herein as UVCA-1, absorbs most in the UV-C and UV-B ranges. It is usually applied to carpeting during space dyeing. The second compound, referred to herein as UVCA-2, absorbs in both UV-A and UV-B, with its maximum absorption at the maximum erythemal effectiveness.

UVCA-1 and UVCA-2 were applied to swatches of nondyed cotton tricot knit with porosity of 0.2% and initial UPF of 5. When UVCA-1 was applied at 1%, the UPF of the tricot was 31 and when applied at 4% it was 51 UPF. In contrast, with 0.5% UVCA-2, the UPF was 107 and with 1.0% it was 183.

Detergent Ingredient Applied

UV-cutting compounds may be added to a detergent formulation with the expectation that UV-cutting molecules will be deposited on fabric during the laundry wash cycle and not be rinsed out during the subsequent rinse cycles. As was the case with research involving the addition of OWAs to detergent formulations, research included laundering prewhitened and not prewhitened fabrics.

In the earliest research report, Rohwer and Eckhardt (13) laundered cotton fabric (not described) with two detergents types (powder and liquid), one formulated without the addition of Ciba Tinosorb FD and the other formulated with Tinosorb FD. They were interested in the effect of UVCA on the fabric whiteness. Results showed that fabric whiteness was not diminished and in fact was slightly increased when UVCA was included in the detergent formulation. This result was confirmed by Eckhardt and Osterwalder (14) who laundered a prewhitened cotton fabric with a UV-cutting compound incorporated into a detergent formulation. They showed that the prewhitened fabric after such laundering had increased whiteness. They also concluded that the UV-cutting agent did not quench the initial whiteness and it contributed to the whiteness of the fabric.

Eckhardt and Rohwer (15) conducted a two-part experiment. The aim of the first part was to determine whether a UV-A–UV-B absorbing compound (FD), a molecule composed of two UV-B-absorbing moieties bound to a UV-A-absorbing structure, when added to a detergent formulation at 0.1% and 0.2% would lead to greater improvement in UPF of white cotton fabrics than that achieved using the same base detergent formulation with traditional OWA added (OWA-1 and OWA-2). The aim of the second part was to explore the effect on the initial whiteness value of prewhitened fabrics as a result of laundering with a UVCA-containing detergent.

In part 1, four *not prewhitened* cotton fabrics were selected, two knit and two woven. The base detergent was AATCC (American Association of Textile Chemists and Colorists) Standard Detergent 1993 WOB (without brighteners). The UPF of the laundered not prebrightened swatches increased significantly with the use of FD in the detergent formulation at both 0.1% and 0.2%. A UPF of 15 was reached by the fifth wash with the FD-containing detergents. In contrast, it took 10 washes for the swatches laundered with OWA-1 and OWA-2 compounds at comparable percent detergent formulation to reach this UPF value. The increase in UPF value was greater for the knitted fabrics than for the woven fabrics, a result believed to be due to the greater absorption of the compound on the knit fabrics.

In part 2, the *prewhitened fabrics* laundered with the FD detergent formulation had whiteness values equal to those of the same fabric laundered for the same number of cycles in detergent containing only the FWA. This was true at 0.1% addition and 0.2% addition.

Wang et al. (16) also studied the alteration in the UPF of fabric when laundered with the Ciba FD compound. Swatches of two cotton fabrics—one a knit fabric (jersey for T-shirts) and the other a woven fabric (a mercerized print cloth)—were laundered in home laundering machines. The treatments were laundering (a) without detergent, (b) in AATCC standard detergent without OWA, and (c) in AATCC standard detergent containing a UVCA (Ciba Specialty Chemicals Tinosorb FD).

After five cycles of laundering in *water only*, the UPF of the jersey fabric increased from 4.7 to 7.1 and the UPF of the print cloth increased from 3.1 to 4.2. These increases were due to shrinkage of the fabric. After five cycles of washing in AATCC detergent with OWA, the UPF values were 6.0 for jersey fabric and 4.4 for print cloth. After washing the swatches *once* with detergent containing UVCA, the UPF for jersey was 11 and for print cloth it was 7. By the fifth wash cycle, the jersey fabric had a UPF value of 23 and the print cloth a value of about 12.

Rinse-Cycle Fabric Softener Product Applied

Rohwer and Kvita (17) report the results of using a rinse-cycle fabric softener containing a UVCA in the formulation when laundering bleached cotton fabrics, some prebrightened and some not brightened. The fabric softener formulation was 1.6 g/L of concentrated fabric conditioner containing 6% Tinosorb FR (15% active) to make an initial 1:30 active-to-liquor ratio. Bleached cotton swatches (UPF of 3.5) were laundered with 4 g/L of detergent without UVCA added. In the final rinse cycle, 2%, 4%, 6%, 8%, and 10% concentrations of the prepared 1:30 liquor ratio, UVCA-containing fabric softener were added.

The UPF of the cotton fabric increased with the number of wash/rinse cycles and was higher as the concentration of the active softener ingredient increased from 2% to 10%. At the 10% concentration, the UPF was 9 after one rinse addition, 17 after three rinse additions, and 25 after five rinse additions. Following laundering with the addition of rinse cycle fabric softener containing UVCA, the prewhitened fabrics had the same whiteness values as the fabrics not prewhitened. The absorbed energy is effectively transformed into fluorescent radiation avoiding detrimental effects on prebrightened fabrics.

Rinse Water Applied

Tinosorb FD is also available for addition during the rinse cycle in a product in which the Tinosorb FD is the major product ingredient. The sole purpose of the product is to enhance the UPF value of the fabric. This rinse-cycle added product's name as test marketed is Rit® Sunguard. Kim et al. (18) repeatedly laundered white cotton knit fabrics with this rinse-cycle product, with Rit® Whitener and Brightener, with Tide® with Bleach, or with Wisk® Liquid to determine the improvement in UPF values of two types of weft knit fabrics. Fabric swatches for the study were cut from eight polo-style shirts made with 60% cotton/40% polyester pique-stitch weft knit fabric (blended pique) and from eight undershirts made of 100% cotton jersey weft knit fabric). These swatches were laundered repeatedly in home laundry equipment.

The UPF values of both fabrics improved from initial UPF values of 14.2 and 23.4 (jersey and pique fabric, respectively) with repeated laundering in the four laundry treatments. After one laundering cycle with Sunguard®, the UPF was 81.4 ± 23.0 (jersey fabric) and 39.6 ± 8.3 (pique fabric) and with Rit® Whitener and Brightener, the UPF was 30.5 ± 6.1 (jersey) and 36.6 ± 6.1 (pique). UPF values above 30 were obtained by the conclusion of the fifth laundering with Tide® and with Wisk®. Specifically, the UPF values at this point were 43.3 ± 8.5 (jersey fabric) and 39.7 ± 10.4 (pique fabric). There were statistically significant differences in UPF values for fabric type and for laundry product used in the wash. Adding just the Rit Sunguard® product to laundry water resulted in the most rapid achievement of a 30+ UPF.

CONCLUSION

Without a doubt the most important factor controlling the degree of sunburn protection to be provided by a fabric is fiber distribution. When fiber fills a greater percentage of the fabric volume, UPF value increases. This increase is due to the reduction of directed UV radiation, radiation that passes through fabric unhindered because there is no fiber in its path to absorb any of it.

The second most important factor is concentration. This means concentration of fibers from fabric face to back (indicated often by thickness and weight per unit area), of dyes on the fibers, of OWAs on the fibers, of UVCAs on the fibers, and of TiO_2 contained in modified manufactured fibers.

The third most important factor is the fiber composition of the fabric. Polyester fiber and silk fiber have the greatest ability to filter incident UV, followed by wool fiber and nylon fiber, with rayon fiber and cotton fiber having the least filtering ability. No data were obtained to show the UPF values for various fiber classes. Such data when available may change the rank order of the fibers. The UPF value of all fabrics can be enhanced by dyeing them with dyes that absorb in the UV as well as the visible range. Using dyes that absorb strongly in the UV-B range leads to fabrics with higher UPF values than using dyes that absorb weakly in the UV-B.

For cotton fabrics, the addition of UV-cutting compounds raises the UPF value of the fabrics significantly. These compounds may be added in the mill, during the laundry wash cycle when they are included in the detergent formulation, during fabric softening in the rinse cycle when the fabric softener product contains a UV-cutting compound, and to the rinse water as a dedicated product. The UPF value of cotton fabrics can also be improved with the addition of OWAs when the compound is applied at the mill or when the optical whitener compound is included in a detergent formulation.

Fabrics (nylon, polyester, cotton, etc.) finished in the mill with OWAs will enhance the UPF over identical fabric not so finished. The durability of this finish depends on the compound selected and method of application. For prewhitened cotton fabrics, the initial UPF value can be retained or improved by laundering with detergent containing the OWA without loss of whiteness. Only cotton fabrics not prewhitened/prebrightened in the mill can be improved by laundering them in detergents and other products containing OWAs.

Another means of changing UV transmittance through textiles is fiber modification. The addition of TiO_2 to manufactured fibers increases the ability of the fiber to absorb incident UV. The increase is related to the grade of TiO_2: ultrafine grade being able to reduce transmittance to much lower levels than white pigment grade because the concentration of white pigment grade is limited by the inability to process fiber past a certain concentration of the pigment and to the fact that the smaller particle size of the ultrafine grade places pigment particles closer throughout the fiber polymer matrix.

REFERENCES

1. Pailthorpe M. Textile parameters and sun protection factors. Textiles and Sun Protection Conference Proceedings. The Society of Dyers and Colourists of Australia and New Zealand (NSW Section), 1993:32–53.

2. Crews PC, Kachman S, Beyer AG. Influences on UVR transmission of undyed woven fabrics. Text Chem Colorist 1999; 31(6):17–26.
3. Dransfield GP. Inorganic sunscreens. Radiat Prot Dosim 2000; 91(1–3):271–273.
4. Wedler M, Hirthe B. UV-absorbing micro additives for synthetic fibers. Chem Fibers Int 1999; 49:72.
5. Hoffmann K, Kasper K, Gambichler T, Altmeyer P. In vitro and in vivo determination of the UV protection factor for lightweight cotton and viscose summer fabrics: a preliminary study. J Am Acad Dermatol 2000; 43:1009–1016.
6. Srinivasan M, Gatewood BM. Relationship of dye characteristics to UV protection provided by cotton fabric. Text Chem Colorists Am Dyestuff Report 2000; 32(4):36–43.
7. Reinehr D, Eckhardt C, Kaufmann W. Skin protection against ultraviolet light by cotton textiles treated with optical brighteners. 4th World Surfactants Congress. Barcelona: Asociacion Espanola de Productores de Sustancias para Aplicaciones Tensioactivas, 1996:264–276.
8. Zhou Y, Crews PC. Effect of OBAs and repeated launderings on UVR transmission through fabrics. Text Chem Colorist 1998; 30(11):19–24.
9. Hilfiker R, Kaufmann W, Reinert G, Schmidt E. Improving sun protection factors of fabrics by applying UV-absorbers. Text Res J 1996; 66:61–70.
10. Reinert G, Fuso F, Hilfiker R, Schmidt E. UV-protecting properties of textile fabrics and their improvement. Text Chem Colorist 1997; 29(12):36–43.
11. Jöllenbeck M. New UV absorbers for sun protective fabrics. In: Altmeyer P, Hoffmann K, Stücker M, eds. Skin Cancer and UV Radiation. Berlin: Springer, 1997:382–387.
12. Jöllenbeck M, Härri H-P, Schlenker W, Osterwalder U. UV protective fabrics. Proceedings of AATCC Functional Finishes and High Performance Textiles Symposium, Charlotte, NC, January 2000:27–28.
13. Rohwer H, Eckhardt C. Laundry additive for the sun protection of the skin. SÖFW J 1998; 12(11):1–4.
14. Eckhardt C, Osterwalder U. Laundering clothes to be sun protective. In: Cahn A, ed. Proceedings 4th World Conference on Detergents: Strategies for the 21st Century, Montreux, 1998:317–322.
15. Eckhardt C, Rohwer H. UV protector for cotton fabrics. Text Chem Colorist Am Dyestuff Reporter 2000; 32(4):21–23.
16. Wang SQ, Kopf AW, Marx J, Bogdan A, Polsky D, Bart RS. Reduction of ultraviolet transmission through cotton T-shirt fabrics with low ultraviolet protection by various laundering methods and dyeing: clinical implications. J Am Acad Dermatol 2001; 44:767–774.
17. Rohwer H, Kvita P. Sun protection of the skin with a novel UV absorber for rinse cycle application. SÖFW J 1999; 125(8):1–5.
18. Kim J, Stone J, Crew P, Shelley II M, Hatch K. Improving knit fabric UPF using consumer products: a comparison of results using two instruments. Fam Cons Sci Res J 2004; 33(2):141–158.
19. ASTM International. D6603 Standard Guide for Labeling of UV-Protective Textiles. Annual Book of ASTM Standards, Volume 07.01. Philadelphia, PA: ASTM, 2002.

29

Sunless Tanning and Tanning Accelerators

Anthony D. Gonzalez and Robert E. Kalafsky
Avon Products, Inc., Suffern, New York, USA

INTRODUCTION

From the time a tan became symbolic of health and affluence in Western culture, scientists the world over have been researching ways to enhance, accelerate, and imitate the golden bronze look that consumers so deeply desire. In the dawn of the tanning industry, reflective panels redirected the suns rays to the face while mineral oil was slathered on the body to intensify the effects of basking in the sun. With the 1960's came a revolutionary new product concept, QT. This product was the first consumer product that used dihydroxyacetone (DHA) to provide a tanned appearance "in 3 to 5 hours *without* the sun". The late 1970s brought the tanning bed, a sarcophagus of fluorescent tubes that radiate UV to fuel biological tanning without the sun. The first generation of tanning beds emitted predominantly UV-A radiation. Advances in tanning beds led to quick tan bulbs, which expanded the radiation spectrum to include UV-B and produce a speedier bronze. As with many new mass recreational phenomena, the increased tan population developed its own set of health related side effects. The rise in population that tanned recreationally led to an increased population with premature photoaging and skin cancer. Nonetheless, the market demands for a healthy looking tanned appearance remain at an all-time high. While the majority of this book deals with protecting us from the detrimental effects of the sun, the authors of this chapter have chosen to investigate the science behind the consumer demand. Advances in research are taking us ever closer to that natural tan without the need for overexposure to harmful solar radiation as well as an instant bronze that looks as if you have spent a week in the Caribbean.

TANNING PRODUCTS: SUNLESS TANNING V. TANNING ACCELERATORS, A MARKET REVIEW

Tanning products have been traditionally divided into two categories, tanning accelerators and sunless tanners. Tanning accelerators rely on various technologies that enhance the body's natural tanning processes to deliver a more intense tan than exposure to the sun alone. These products typically have exotic fragrances that provide a consumer perception of a tropical environment. On the other hand, sunless tanners impart a tanned appearance to the skin using colorants that can range from pigments and dyes to compounds that react with the free amino acids on the skin to form melanin like compounds. Sunless products that deliver an intensely colored formulation to the skin are more commonly known as "bronzers." Sunless tanners come in a wide array of product forms that focus on delivering a natural looking, even tanned appearance. Regardless of the mode of action, the consumer demand for tanning products is showing steady growth.

In the 5 years since the last publication of this book, the market has seen a steady increase in the consumer demand for all types of tanning products. Both sunless tanning and tan accelerating products have outperformed the suntan lotion and oil segment in growth percentage of dollar sales in the time period from 1998 until 2002. According to IRI InfoScan Reviews data of the total US FDMX (Food, Drug and Mass excluding Walmart), the suntan lotion and oil segment total dollar sales grew by approximately 24% from 1998 to 2002. In 1998, tanning accelerators and sunless tanning products held approximately 17% of the total dollar sales in the suntan lotion and oil segment. By 2001 these two segments managed to capture 22% of the total dollar sales in the market. Dollar sales of tan accelerators and self-tanners grew by over 50% in the time period from 1998 to 2002.

Tanning accelerators reached peak sales of almost $9 million in 2000, an incredible 78% growth from the year 1998. However, by 2002 sales have declined to just under $6 million, a net gain of 14% from the 1998 selling year. As a result the three tanning product segments (sunless tanning products, tanning accelerators, and tanning bed products) captured a 21% dollar share of the total sun market in 2002. This decline may be a result of increasing public awareness of the negative effects of natural tanning. This same phenomenon may have led to the introduction of a new form of tanning accelerator, the tanning bed product. Although tanning bed products had a meager sales performance of $372,000 in 1998, they have been showing steady growth in the years since then with a peak of just over $7 million in 2002. This 18-fold dollar sales growth successfully overtook that of the traditional tanning accelerator in that year. Interestingly, on combining the sales of tanning bed/tanning accelerator products, we get total sales of $12.8 million in 2001 and $12.9 million in 2002. This modest net growth could be indicative that consumers are leaving the beach to tan in the assumed "safety" of the tanning bed (1).

Sunless tanners remain the dominant tanning products in the US market. They held around 91% of the total dollar sales of the three tanning product segments in 1998 and had just over $53 million in sales or 16% of the total dollars sold in the total suntan lotion and oil segment. Since 1998, they have shown a moderate decrease in the tanning product segment from 91% in 1998 to 85% in 2002. Nonetheless, sunless tanners have a net growth in dollar sales of 42% in the years from 1998 to 2002. Sunless tanning products had peak sales of just over $82 million in 2001. This 54% increase from the 1998 selling season secured one-fifth of the total suntan lotion and oil sales in 2001. Incredibly, 20% of the total dollars spent on sunless tanning products in the year 2001 were on Coppertone Endless Summer®.[1] With its innovative new packaging and claims of "a natural looking tan in 30 minutes", this product managed $16 million in US sales in 2001. One study, performed at Avon's Center for Consumer Sciences, showed that 58% of women who have never used a

[1]Combined Stock Keeping Unit (SKU's) 4110001623 and 4110001659.

sunless tanner are interested in trying one. This is a prime example of the unquenched consumer demand for efficacious sunless tanning products (1).[2]

In recent years it has been accepted by the consumer that the preparation of the area to be treated by sunless tanners is almost as important as the product they choose. For example, an excess of free amino acids in the skin can lead to excessively darkened spots. As a result, the majority of self-tanning products suggest some sort of special treatment in those areas. The elbows and knees are areas that should either be exfoliated prior to application or exposed to less product. The demand for a natural looking sunless tan is so great that consumers are now purchasing a wide array of pre-sunless tanning treatments. These products range from presunless moisturizers to exfoliators to application gloves. The complexity of getting the perfect artificial tan has rocketed the sunless tanning trend into the salon. Customers are relying on the skills of aestheticians to provide a solution to the potential streaky, uneven look provided by self-application of otherwise excellent products. Salon services can be as simple as a cream applied by a more experienced second party or a complex multistep preparation of the skin followed by a machine controlled application of sunless tanning concentrate. US Patent 6,468,508 (2) describes the following process for self-tanning at a salon:

> 1) Dehydration of the skin with heat and electromagnetic radiation, flowing heated air or chemically with alcohol or a ketone. 2) Applying a sprayed on self-tanning composition for 1–10 minutes and wiping off or rinsing.

Some salons now offer airbrush application of self-tanning compositions. The airbrush allows for a fine even coverage of the skin with little need for incidental contact with the palms, hair, or skin. Because this service is in its infancy stage, the equipment used for airbrush tanning is taken directly from the arts and crafts trade. The new atomized applications of self-tanning formulations lead to increased risk of exposure to the mucous membranes as well as inhalation of DHA. As a result, the FDA issued a statement regarding the approved use of DHA on the skin only. In time, the equipment used for such applications will be specialized to provide a safe and effective airbrush tanned appearance.

BIOLOGICAL TANNING

The UV Radiation Response

Although the biological tanning process has yet to be completely described, the scientific community has provided a broad understanding of this phenomenon to help in producing more efficient tanning accelerators. The most basic explanation

[2]Total dollar sales do not include private label manufactured products.

of the natural tanning process is as follows:

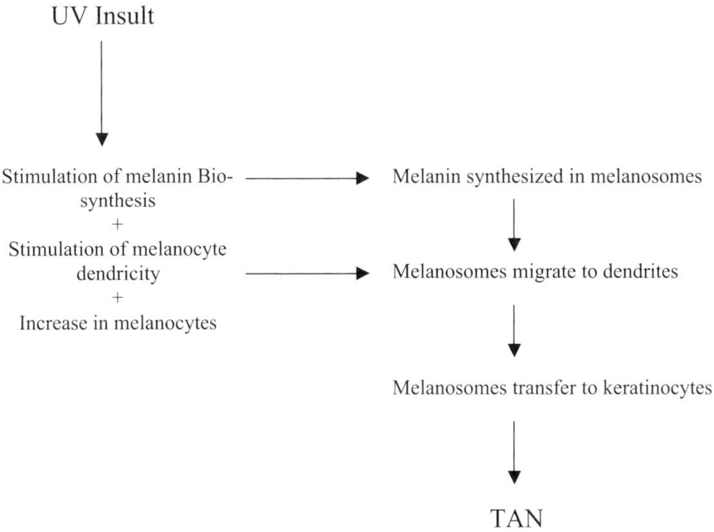

Countless hours of research have been spent in trying to understand the role of UV in the tanning process. Lavker and Kaidbey (3) demonstrated that 60 mJ/cm^2 of UV-B radiation in the spectrum of 280–320 nm was sufficient to induce tanning *in vivo*. By observing the responses of cultures of keratinocytes and melanocytes, Duval et al. (4) were able to demonstrate the independent effects of UV-A (320–400 nm) and UV-B (290–320 nm) in cell culture. A dosage of 5 mJ/cm^2 of UV-B radiation was sufficient to induce an increase in melanin synthesis in a coculture of melanocytes and keratinocytes. Increasing the UV insult by an order of magnitude was insufficient to stimulate melanogenesis in a culture of melanocytes alone. Their work also demonstrated a dose responsive increase in melanogenesis upon exposure to UV-A radiation in a monoculture of melanocytes. The authors subsequently theorized that healthy keratinocytes were necessary to elicit a tanning response to UV-B insult. However, the role of the keratinocytes may be diminished in UV-A induced melanogenesis. These results, coupled with the research of Tyrell (5) led to their hypothesis that UV-A induced tanning may be a result of oxidative stress created by UV-A radiation.

Unlike its long-wave counterpart UV-A, UV-B radiation can trigger pigmentation in the absence of oxygen (6). However, the tanning effects that are seen upon exposure to UV-B take significantly longer to manifest themselves than those observed with UV-A (7). Short-wavelength environmental UV has been shown to facilitate the release of various compounds by keratinocytes (8). The aforementioned work of Duval et al. (4) on mono- and cocultures of epidermal melanin unit cells confirms the synergistic effects of both UV-A and UV-B on the cascade of events that eventually lead to skin pigment darkening. UV-B has also been implicated in the inhibition of neprilysin, an enzyme produced on the surface of the melanocyte. This neutral endopeptidase was shown to down-regulate α-melanocyte stimulating hormone and adrenocorticotropic hormone, resulting in an inhibited production of melanin in the melanosomes (9).

UV-A induced pigmentation occurs in two steps, immediate pigment darkening and delayed tanning. The immediate tanning effect is a product of reactions on existing melanin and melanin reserves. It has been described as a combination of the darkening of endogenous melanin and the migration of existing melanosomes to the dendrites of the melanocytes (10). Delayed tanning, which requires oxygen, appears to be a systemic response to protect from repeated or impending insults with UV-A (4,6).

Seite et al. (12) were able to show that p53 protein transactivates tyrosinase related protein-1 (TRP-1) and tyrosinase promoters, which regulate the synthesis of melanin. These results suggest the following model for induction of the tanning response as a protective event (12).

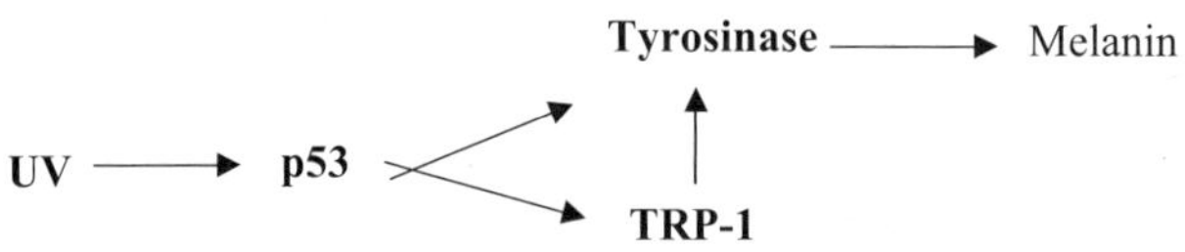

While investigating the protective effects of broad-spectrum sunscreens, Nylander et al. (13) demonstrated an induction of nuclear p53 protein with UV-A radiation from 320 to 400 nm. These data coupled with Seite's (11) work implies that p53 induced tanning is primarily a result of UV-A induced photodamage.

Several other researches have investigated the effects of UV photoproducts on the induction of tanning. Eller and Gilchrest (14) describe tanning as part of the eukaryotic response to DNA damage. By exposing melanocytes as well as intact skin to DNA fragments, they were able to demonstrate an upregulation of tyrosinase mRNA and protein levels. Their work showed a 7 fold increase in melanin content of mouse melanoma cells upon exposure to pTpT. In subsequent studies, Eller et al. (15) were able to further demonstrate the stimulation of pigmentation by using other DNA fragments. The 9-mer oligonucleotide (pGpApGpTpApTpGpApG) and 7-mer oligonucleotide (pApGpTpApTpGpA) were able to increase melanin content in mouse melanoma cells by up to 800% whereas the 5-mer oligonucleotide (pCpApTpApC) had no effect.

Melanogenesis

Once UV triggers the biological tanning process, a subsequent synthesis of melanin must occur to provide a sustained pigmentation of the skin. Two types of melanin are produced by the melanosomes, black/brown or eumelanin and red/yellow or phaeomelanin. It is the level and ratio of these melanins that lead to the plethora of phenotypes we see in the human species. A multiplicity of these pigments are synthesized within organelles of melanocytes known as melanosomes. Subsequently, various mechanisms not completely understood will lead to morphological changes in the melanocytes causing them to become dendritic. The melanosomes are then stored in these dendrites and eventually transferred to keratinocytes upon insult with UV or other pigmentation enhancing stimuli, the result of which is visible pigment darkening or tanning.

Although there have been significant accomplishments in the area of pigment cell research, the complete map of melanogenesis has yet to be charted. Prota (16) describes the Mason-Rapër pathway for melanogenesis as follows:

Tyrosine ⟶ DOPA ⟶ dopaquinone ⟶ dopachrome ⟶
⟶ leucodopachrome ⟶ dihydroxy indole (DHI) ⟶
⟶ 5,6-indolequinone ⟶ various oligomers polymerize to melanin (17)

The key enzymes to melanogenesis are tyrosinase, tyrosinase related protein-1, and dopachrome tautomerase (DCT), formerly TRP-2. Tyrosinase is responsible for the conversion of tyrosine to 3,4-dihydroxyphenylalanine (DOPA) and eventually dopaquinone. TRP-1 and DCT are primarily involved in the production of eumelanins that are derived from DOPA (18). Conversely, yellow and red phaeomelanins are produced from 5-*S*-cysteinyldopa (17).

Tanning has been described as an immune response (14). Therefore, many of the same pathways the cosmetic scientist attempts to inhibit in antiaging products are those which function to stimulate tanning. A major pathway in the irritation response of human cells is the nitric oxide (NO) pathway. It was demonstrated by Sakai et al. (19) that exposure of cells to the NO donor, 5-nitroso-*N*-acetyl-L-arginine, led to an increased expression of tyrosinase mRNA within 2 h of exposure. Subsequent increases in tyrosinase activity and protein levels were observed at 24 h. Conversely, guanosine 3′,5′-monophosphate (cGMP) inhibitors suppressed the expression of tyrosinase mRNA. The authors concluded that cGMP plays a key role in NO induced melanin synthesis. Other cyclic phosphates have been indicated in the production of melanin as well. The work of Busca and Ballotti (18) shows that the adenosine monophosphate (cAMP) pathway regulates the production of melanin. The activation of protein kinase A and cAMP response element binding protein (creb) transcription factor led to an upregulation of microphthalmia transcription factor (MITF). MITF has been shown to activate melanogenic gene promoters (12), thus increasing melanin synthesis. The same pathway ultimately leads to the phosphorylation of MITF, targeting it for degradation and eventually the downregulation of melanogenesis. Khaled et al. (20) describe the activation of glycogen synthase kinase 3B by cAMP. The phosphorylation of MITF facilitates its ability to bind to tyrosinase promoter genes. Lin et al. (21) discuss how MITF regulates pigmentation by binding to TRP-1 and DCT.

Regulatory Considerations

Because tanning accelerators are intended to affect the biological process of melanogenesis, the US FDA considers tanning accelerators to be drugs. As a result, the legal sale of such products in the USA requires the filing of a New Drug Application and approval by the FDA prior to marketing such products. Regardless of market angle or functionality, all suntan preparations that do not provide SPF must be labeled with the following warning (22):

> Warning—This product does not contain a sunscreen and does not protect against sunburn. Repeated exposure of unprotected skin while tanning may increase the risk of skin aging, skin cancer, and other harmful effects to the skin even if you do not burn. (21CFR740.19)

The FDA has issued warning letters to corporations that market tanning accelerators as unapproved drugs. As a result, many of today's products make only cosmetic claims in order to avoid further enforcement of the Food Drug and Cosmetic Act.

Enhancing Biological Tanning

Yoon et al. (23) have demonstrated that a 3-D model of reconstituted skin can be used as an effective screening tool for the investigation of pigmentation stimulators. Such *in vitro* models can significantly reduce the research time required to come up with new and novel approaches to stimulating natural pigmentation in human subjects. Other more precise *in vitro* tools enable the researcher to screen effective melanogenesis facilitators by specific mechanisms.

Tanning, being a proposed immune response (14), is most easily affected by compounds that act on the pathways involved in the response to various environmental insults. Oka et al. (24) demonstrate an increase in melanin content and tyrosinase mRNA of G 361 melanoma cells by inhibition of the phosphatidylinositol 3-kinase (P-3K) pathway. Several P-3K inhibitors, such as the fungal metabolite Wortmannin (25), have been described in the literature. Another well-known immune response that has been shown to stimulate the induction of melanogenesis is the histamine pathway. When melanocytes are treated with histamine, they undergo morphological as well as biochemical changes resulting in an increased dendricity and increase in tyrosinase activity. Additionally, the cAMP content of these cells was markedly increased with exposure to histamine and the H_2 agonist Dimaprit (26). Future investigation of H_2 agonists as additives for the induction of pigmentation by topical means may lead to new discoveries in the area of tanning accelerators. Tetradecanoylphorbol-13 acetate can also stimulate dendricity and increase melanin synthesis in neural cells as well as melanocytes (27). The compound 2-mercapto-1-(β-4-pyridethyl) benzimidazole (MPB) has been shown to increase the dendricity of B16 melanoma cells. In addition, MPB was able to increase tyrosinase mRNA without affecting cAMP levels (28).

Several neurotransmitters and modulators have been implicated in melanogenesis. The vasoconstrictive peptide endothelin-1 (ET) is secreted by melanocytes and has been shown to stimulate pigmentation. The neutral metalloproteinase endothelin-converting enzyme (ECE-1α) activates ET. The reaction is pH dependent. Several pro-inflammatory agents have been shown to increase ECE-1α (29). Koh shows that the 28-amino-acid neuropeptide, vasoactive intestinal peptide, has the ability to stimulate melanogenesis in the embryonic chick's retinal pigment epithelium by stimulation of the cAMP pathway (30). Other short amino acid chains have been shown to stimulate melanogenesis as well. Hadshiew et al. (31) found that the effectiveness of nucleotides on the stimulation of melanin synthesis was dependent on the presence of a 5′ phosphate group. Such discoveries could lead to synthetic compounds that are able to facilitate the synthesis of melanin without the negative effects of pro-inflammatory agents.

Palumbo et al. (32) have shown an increase in melanin synthesis and tyrosinase content of the ink gland of the cuttle fish, *Sepia officinalis* by L-glutamate. The authors theorize that this amino acid binds to the *N*-methyl aspartate receptor. An aqueous extract of *Astragulus membranaceus bunge* successfully upregulates MITF and tyrosinase activity in melanocytes (21). A hydroalcoholic extract of mammalian tissue rich in sphingolipids was shown to induce melanogenesis *in vitro*. The activity was compared to that of other sphingolipids and confirmed the potential for sphingolipids to stimulate melanogenesis (33). Kauser et al. (34) have shown a link between the β-endorphin/μ-opiate receptor system and the regulation of skin pigmentation. Glycyrrhizin, a triterpenoid saponin from the licorice plant, is shown to stimulate melanogenesis in B16 murine melanoma cell through increase in tyrosinase and DCT expression (35).

ARTIFICIAL TANNING

Although many technological breakthroughs have occurred in recent years, science still has no answer to the instant biological tan. Therefore, consumers have relied on basically the same sunless tanning technology for the last half of a century. DHA reacts with amino acids in the skin to form melanin-like compounds known as melanoidins. This nonenzymatic browning, known as the Maillard reaction or glycation, is most commonly observed as the browning of foods with cooking and is responsible for the "burnt sugar" odor found in commercially available self-tanning products.

Traditionally, such reactions require significant amounts of heat energy to take place. The ability of DHA to cause nonenzymatic browning under ambient conditions was discovered in the early 1900s (36). Its production from *Acetobacter* was described by Bernhauer (37) in 1928 was inefficient at best. In February 1960, Green (38) filed a patent describing an optimized process for the production of DHA. It was found surprising that by lowering what was thought of as the optimal pH for bioconversion to 5.0–5.9 and enhancing the inoculation media, Green was able to come up with a process in which DHA could be produced in mass quantities. By 1960, the first patent on DHA's use as an artificial tanning agent was filed by Andreadis and Miklean (39). US Patent 2,949,403 describes what would be the first modern self-tanning composition:

Ethyl alcohol	50.0%
Water	45.0%
DHA	4.0%
Acetone	1.0%

Shortly thereafter, Plough would market QT by Coppertone®, which claimed to impart a tan "in 3 to 5 hours *without* the sun". The product consisted of 8% homosalate and 3.5% DHA in a base of water, propylene glycol, sorbitan stearate, polyoxyethylene coconut alcohol, polysorbate-60, cetyl alcohol, lanolin, simethicone, methylparaben, citric acid, and fragrance (see Fig. 29.1).

This novel product was the first modern day self-tanner and forged a path for the subsequent generation of self-tanners. While effective in providing color to the skin, they were less than stellar in their ability to provide a natural look. Resulting artificial tans were streaky and required multiple applications to even out striations in color. The hues of these early products were closer to that of skin stained with β-carotene than skin that had been exposed to UV. Decades of advances have significantly improved the quality of the sunless active as well as the commercial products that exist today. The following paragraphs will discuss the evolution of the self-tanner as well as the potential areas for advancement in this area.

Regulatory Considerations

The US FDA considers sunless tanning actives as color additives because they impart color to the skin. According to 21CFR70, color additives are defined as:

> a dye, pigment, or other substance . . . that, when added or applied to a food, drug or cosmetic or to the human body or any part thereof, is capable (alone or through reaction with another substance) of imparting a color thereto (40).

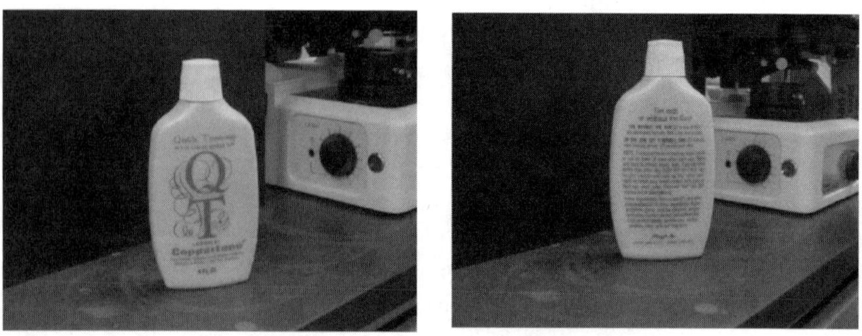

Figure 29.1 QT, the first commercial sunless tanner with DHA.

All color additives should be labeled, without respect to concentration, following noncolor additives present at a concentration of less than 1%. The actives allowed in sunless products in the USA are limited to those approved for use as such. The following color additives are described in the Code of Federal Regulations.

Color Additives Exempt from Certification per 21CFR73 2003 (41)

Annatto	Henna	Titanium dioxide
Caramel	Iron oxides	Aluminum powder
Carmine	Ferric ammonium ferrocyanide	Bronze powder
β-Carotene	Ferric ferrocyanide	Copper powder
Bismuth citrate	Chromium oxide greens	Ultramarines
Disodium EDTA copper	Guanine	Manganese violet
Potassium sodium copper Chlorophyllin	Lead acetate	Zinc oxide
Dihydroxyacetone	Pyrophyllite	Luminescent zinc Sulfide
Bismuth oxychloride	Mica	
Guaiazulene	Silver	

Color Additives per 21CFR74 2003 (42)

Citrus Red No. 2	D&C Red No. 22	D&C Yellow No. 10
D&C Blue No. 4	FD&C Blue No. 1	D&C Yellow No. 11
D&C Blue No. 6	FD&C Blue No. 2	D&C Yellow No. 7
D&C Blue No. 9	D&C Red No. 27	D&C Yellow No. 8
D&C Brown No. 1	D&C Red No. 28	Ext. D&C Violet No. 2
D&C Green No. 5	D&C Red No. 30	Ext. D&C Yellow No. 7
D&C Green No. 6	D&C Red No. 31	FD&C Red No. 3
D&C Green No. 8	D&C Red No. 33	FD&C Red No. 4
D&C Orange No. 10	D&C Red No. 34	FD&C Red No. 40
D&C Orange No. 11	D&C Red No. 36	FD&C Yellow No. 5
D&C Orange No. 4	D&C Red No. 39	FD&C Yellow No. 6
D&C Orange No. 5	D&C Red No. 6	Orange B
D&C Red No. 17	D&C Red No. 7	Phthalocyaninato 2-Copper
D&C Red No. 21	D&C Violet No. 2	

Dihydroxyacetone

The formulator is limited to the aforementioned compounds to provide coloration to the skin. Products that stain the skin (bronzers) have been marketed in the past. However, the variable solubilities of the cosmetic dyes listed in the tables lead to an unnatural appearance of skin when fading. Needless to say, today's sunless tanning products rely predominantly on one active ingredient to impart a tan

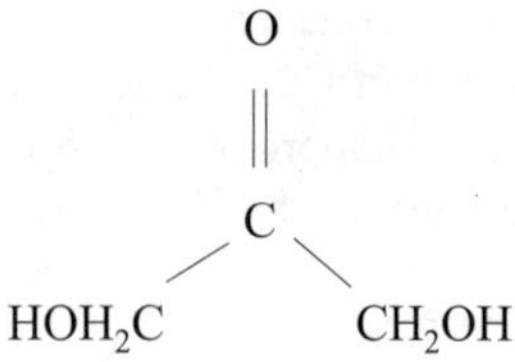

Dihydroxyacetone

Figure 29.2 Dihydroxyacetone—the reducing sugar which produces artificial tanning of the skin at ambient temperature.

color to the skin, DHA. Unlike tanning accelerators, the science of sunless tanners relies on optimizing the performance of this active (Fig. 29.2).

DHA is a three-carbon reducing sugar produced from glycerin by the bacteria *Acetobacter suboxydans.* The nonenzymatic reaction, although not completely understood, is ubiquitous to a certain point. The initial reaction, on the skin, involves the condensation of an amino group, usually from an amino acid, with the keto group on the DHA molecule. The resulting compound then undergoes dehydration to result in a Schiff base followed by a rearrangement to form a Heyns product. This cycle then is repeated with additional amine compounds to form high-molecular-weight chromophores. At Avon, our research indicates that this reaction results in a consumer perceivable darkening usually within 1–2 h of application (Fig. 29.3).

Photoacoustic spectroscopy has shown that the tanning effect takes place between the stratum corneum and stratum granulosum. Penetration of DHA into the skin results in an increased darkening of the skin (43). The structure of the resulting melanoidins has not yet been completely described. Schneider and Sprenger (44) describe the use of transaldose β to trap Schiff base intermediates for determination of their structure. Similar techniques may be useful in the determination of the structure of the various melanoidins. Such information would be extremely useful in explaining the variation in tonality and intensity of sunless tanning products.

Although we do not have a complete understanding of the chemical differences between a UV induced tan and an artificial tan, some recent research has provided insight into this phenomenon. Using a Minolta chromameter, the tonality of the natural suntan was compared to that of an artificial tan by Muizzudin et al. (45). By measuring the change in reflectance as well as the increase in yellow and red discoloration, the authors were able to categorize both pigmentation phenomena in a numerical format. When comparing the sunless tan to the natural tan a clear pattern develops. DHA induced pigmentation is clearly more yellow on the skin than a UV induced tan. This phenomenon was exaggerated in those with Fitzpatrick skin types I and II. Since sunless tanners increase the yellow color of skin greater than the red color of skin it is no surprise that

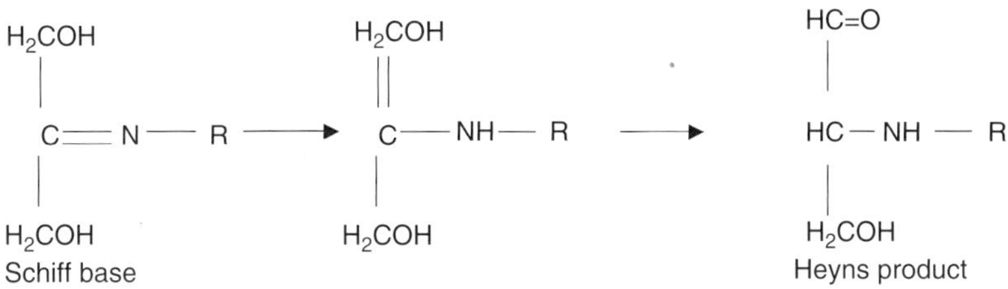

Figure 29.3 Non-enzymatic browning—initial reaction steps. Post condensation of dihydroxyacetone.

those with types I and II skin would exhibit a more orange coloration than those with skin types III and IV. The authors further describe the effects of several antioxidants on DHA induced tanning. It was observed that these antioxidant compounds were able to shift the color of DHA tanned skin more to the red. The resulting combination provided a more natural looking artificial tan than without the use of antioxidants. The authors hypothesize that the addition of antioxidant compounds alters the polymerization pattern of the DHA–amino complex to form more reddish compounds than yellow.

Even the most inexperienced of formulators is aware of the fact that self-tanning formulations require a minimum amount of water to be effective. The influence of water on the pigmentation reaction of DHA is more complex than expected. Extreme hydration has been shown to inhibit DHA induced tanning in skin. By incubating skin exposed to DHA in varying relative humidities (RHs), Nguyen and Kochevar (46) were able to shed some light on the effects of moisture in self-tanning systems. Minimal pigmentation was observed in samples kept at 0% and 100% RH while a maximum effect was shown at 84% RH. Initially, the authors expected the proteolysis of filagrin, which shows a similar response to RH, to be the main factor in their results. However, the authors were able to rule this out by incubating samples under optimal humidity conditions for proteolysis to occur prior to treatment with DHA. The optimal performance of DHA was shown to be independent of the presence of free amino acids resulting from the breakdown of filagrin. Additional work with free amino acids led them to the hypothesis that DHA induced pigmentation is a function of hydration of the skin and RH.

The utility of DHA is more than just for the sake of vanity. Dermatology is adopting its use for treatment of various skin ailments. Suga et al. (47) have acceptably treated vitiligo and piebald regions with a 5% solution of DHA. The melanoidins resulting from artificial tanners have also been shown to absorb the long-wavelength UV-A and visible light that cause photosensitivity in patients with variegate porphyria (48). DHA induced skin coloration was able to allow for higher doses of UV-A to be tolerated in patients receiving PUVA treatments by protecting unaffected skin areas (49).

Formulating with DHA

Quality Control

As with any highly functional active, the formulator must take into account the quality and chemistry of DHA when formulating. DHA exists as both a monomer and a dimer in the crystalline state. The dimer form is not considered effective for artificial tanning of the skin. It has been generally accepted that the dimer readily converts to monomer when put in aqueous solution (50). However, it was demonstrated by Forest et al. (51) that solutions made from the DHA dimer were unable to produce a visual browning of the skin. Use of fluorescence demonstrated that some minimal reaction did occur between amino acids and the DHA dimer solution. The dimer of DHA can be identified by melting point or IR analysis. The melting point of DHA varies from 60°C to 90°C depending on the monomer/dimer content. A melting point in the lower end of this range is indicative of impurities. The more accurate way to assess the quality of DHA is by infrared spectroscopy. The carbonyl function of DHA shows a peak at 1744 cm^{-1}, indicating the presence of monomer. The dimer form will present a peak at 1273 cm^{-1} due to its ether functionality. Evaluation of the ratio of monomer to dimer will allow the formulator to accurately differentiate the quality of DHA (36).

Formulation

Our studies show that both spray and lotion forms are deemed equally acceptable to current sunless tanning product users. These same studies indicate that this consumer is quite sensitive to the odor of the products they choose. This information would lead one to believe that maintaining the functional integrity of DHA is central to developing a successful product. Therefore, the formulator should take every step necessary to assure that the formulation provides functional levels of DHA for its suggested shelf life. Although DHA is known to impart color to the skin at levels of $<1\%$ to $>10\%$, the recommended use level for sunless tanning formulations is typically from 3% to 5% by weight. DHA is most easily incorporated as a concentrated aqueous solution at temperatures less than 40°C. When developing a vehicle for DHA, the most obvious components to avoid are amine compounds. However, amine compounds such as EDTA do not react as strongly to DHA and may be used if necessary. The neat raw material should be stored free from humidity at 4°C to prevent breakdown of the active. Very low pH leads to the polymerization of DHA and could result in dimer formation in finished formulations. Phosphates can facilitate the degradation of DHA in formulation, therefore buffers containing them should be avoided. Calcium ions complex with DHA and inhibit its ability to react with amine compounds. Anionic emulsifiers also facilitate the breakdown of DHA during storage. DHA is incompatible with the inorganic compounds TiO_2, ZnO, as well as iron oxides. DHA is degraded by reducing agents such as ascorbic acid. Excessively high pH can lead to the formation of hydroxyacetone and methylglyoxal (36,50).

Recognizing the potential of new discoveries in the sunless tanning market, cosmetic scientists are protecting their intellectual property in the form of patents. The filing and enforcing of patents has become a major tool in securing market share in the sunless tanning industry. Following is a list of granted US Patents that claim to enhance the color and/or intensity of sunless tanning compositions.

US Patents for Enhancing Sunless Tanning Color and Intensity

6,171,605	DHA with propolis extract (caffeic acid phenylethyl ester) to enhance sunless tan
5,827,506	Amino acids with DHA in a two-component package
5,662,890	Self-tanning spray with DHA, water, and a penetration enhancer without ethanol or oil
5,663,923	DHA in combination with amino acid and pH less than 4
5,503,824	Two-component self tanner with DHA in one component and an amino silicone in the second component
6,537,528	Self-tanning composition with a flavylium salt and radical from a hydroxy or alkoxy group
6,468,508	Conditioning skin for self-tanning by dehydration
6,406,682	Saxifragia extract and DHA for a faster, more natural tan
6,344,185	DHA with a thickener and oil-soluble polyester
6,231,837	Polyethoxyglycol with DHA, sorbitol, and polyols at pH between 3.5 and 4.5
5,801,169	5,6-dihydroxyindole polymer in combination with DHA
5,750,092	Two-component system with DHA in one component and 2^0 polyamines in the other
5,705,145	DHA in combination with azole compounds to decrease coloration time
5,302,378	DHA in combination with dimethicone copolyol phosphate
4,708,865	DHA with cutch, logwood, and walnut powder
5,700,452	DHA with a cationic polymer and cationic emulsifier
5,569,460	DHA or methylglyoxal with eosin compounds

Although US federal regulations only allow for DHA as a sunless tanning active, alternative technologies exist with the capability to impart an artificial tan to the skin. US Patent 6,344,185 describe a skin coloring powder that consists of formaldehyde, formic acid, and a source of sulfite ions. Uchida et al. (52) describe the formation of advanced glycation end products via the Maillard reaction mediated by methylglyoxal. Subsequent investigation into this compound shows that it is patented under US 5,569,460 as a skin colorant. Reducing sugars other than DHA can act as Maillard reaction intermediates, thus having the potential for use as a sunless tanning agent as well. As a general rule, reducing sugars have a free ketone or aldehyde functional group where the initial condensation reaction of nonenzymatic browning will occur. The most commonly known reducing sugar is glucose. Unfortunately, a large amount of heat energy is required to trigger the glycation reaction between glucose and free amines. Such properties render most reducing sugars useless for a self-tanning product.

As seen with methylglyoxal, corporations are aggressively pursuing new sunless tanning technologies to remain competitive in the marketplace. The key to uncovering new self-tanning actives is the screening of compounds that meet the known criteria for creating glycation end products. The reducing sugar erythrulose, which is found predominantly in the red raspberry *Rubus idaeus*, has been marketed as a self-tanning enhancer for years. Potential new sugars for use in sunless products are easily screened for their ability to act as reducing sugars. The determination of whether or not a carbohydrate is a reducing sugar must first be made. Suspect molecules may be combined with various reagents that expose the sugar to metallic ions. The reduction of these ions to form a colored precipitate is indicative of a reducing sugar. Subsequent *in vitro* experimentation with successful candidates can determine utility in a sunless product. Golz-Berner and Zastrow describe a method for screening self-tanning compositions that can be evaluated in 5 s to 5 min (53). The compositions to be screened are exposed to a mixture of amino acids and purines to determine their self-tanning ability. Another *in vitro* screen for self-tanning activity involves the application of product onto a skin mimic with a controlled level of hydration. In these systems, color development is observed within similar timing to that of human subjects. The multitude of reducing sugars both commercially available and undiscovered can provide the potential next generation of self-tanning active. Any new actives discovered will most likely appear in Europe and undergo several years of safe use before their adoption in the USA.

TOP 10 PRODUCTS REVIEW (RANKED BY 2002 SALES)[3]

Tanning Accelerators (1)

1. Hawaiian Tropic Tan Accelerator Spray $869,882
   Tanning Research Labs, Inc., USA

A highly fragranced, mineral oil based single-phase spray with natural extracts. This product claims to improve the appearance of a tan by moisturizing and nourishing the skin with natural extracts, vitamins, and amino acids.

Ingredient copy: Mineral oil, Carthamus Tinctorius (Safflower) Seed Oil, Fragrance, Beta-Carotene, Daucus Carota Sativa (Carrot) Root Extract, Aloe Barbadensis Extract, Polybutene, Phenyl Trimethicone, Tartaric acid, L-Histidine (Amino acid), L-Arginine (Amino acid), Isocetyl Alcohol, Propylparaben, D&C Yellow #11, D&C Red #17, Plumeria Acutifolia Flower Extract (Plumeria),

[3]*Source*: IRI InfoScan Review Data of the Total US Market (Food, Drug and Mass Excluding Walmart).

Mangifera Indica Fruit Extract (Mango), Psidium Guajava (Guava), Carica Papaya Fruit Extract (Papaya), Passiflora Incarnata Fruit Extract (Passion Fruit), Colocasia Antiquorum Root Extract (Taro), Aleurites Moluccana Seed Extract (Kukui Nut).

Claims: A glistening touch of Hawaiian Tropical, exotic, natural flora, fruit and nut extracts . . . amp up with Intense Tanning Power! It is boosted with Beta-Carotene, Carrot Extract, and natural Amino acids. This moisturizing oil actually intensifies the quality and appearance of your dark "tan of the islands". Moisturizing Forever Tan® ingredients like Aloe Vera, Plumeria, Mango, Guava, Papaya, Passion Fruit, Taro, and Kukui Nut. Natural Amino acids help nourish your skin. "Helps to hold your tan for weeks longer".

2. Hawaiian Tropic Ultra Sun Formula $857,971
   Tan Accelerator Spray
   Tanning Research Labs, Inc. USA

A highly fragranced, mineral oil based single-phase spray with natural extracts. This product claims to improve the appearance of a tan by moisturizing and nourishing the skin with natural extracts and amino acids. The high refractive index silicone oil, phenyl trimethicone, imparts a glossy sheen to the skin.

Ingredient copy: Mineral Oil, Fragrance, Isocetyl Alcohol, Polybutene, Phenyl Trimethicone, Tartaric Acid, Amino acids: L-Histidine and L-Arginine, Aloe (Aloe Barbadensis) Extract, Extracts of Plumeria, Manako (Mango), Kuawa (Guava), Mikana (Papaya), Lilikoi (Passion Fruit), Taro, and Kukui.

Claims: A touch of Hawaiian Tropical, exotic, natural flora, fruit and nut extracts . . . Amp up with Intense Glistening Power! Hawaiian Tropic® holds the secret to the hottest look under the sun. Our Ultra Sun® formula actually intensifies the quality and appearance of your dark, "tan of the islands". Hot tropic fragrance. Moisturizing Forever Tan® ingredients like Aloe Vera, Plumeria, and Mango defend against peeling and "help to hold your tan for weeks longer". Natural amino acids help replace skin's vital nutrients lost during the tanning process.

3. Banana Boat Tan Accelerator Oil SPF 0 $731,793
   Sun Pharmaceuticals, USA

A basic hydrophobic tan accelerator composed of triglyceride oils rather than mineral oils. This formula utilizes essential fatty acids and vitamins A and E to maintain the skin's moisture barrier. The inclusion of cyclomethicone allows this formulation to have a less greasy aesthetic than traditional tan accelerators.

Ingredient copy: Sunflower Oil, Cyclomethicone, Sunflower Oil, Cocoa Butter, Wheat Germ Oil, Aloe Extract, Oat Extract, Evening Primrose Oil (Omega-6 Oil), Tocopherol (Vitamin E), Retinyl Palmitate (Vitamin A), Fragrance.

Claims: Tan Express by Banana Boat is a unique formula that lets you tan as fast as you can. It conditions and moisturizes your skin for the deepest, darkest tan and beautiful smooth skin. Tan Express Dark Tanning Ultimate Oil contains natural oils. Sunflower Oil, and Evening Primrose Oil to help keep your skin moist and supple. This blend of exotic oils and fragrance contains vitamin A and vitamin E. This enriched formula helps improve the skin's elasticity and helps protect the skin from free radical damage. Contains no mineral oil. Tan Express for a Fast, Beautiful Tan!

4. Hawaiian Tropic Tan Amplifier Bronzing Spray $444,679
   Tanning Research Labs, Inc., USA

A highly fragranced, water based spray with natural extracts. This product claims to improve the appearance of a tan by moisturizing and nourishing the skin with natural extracts and amino acids. Caramel is used to provide the bronzing effect. Oil components are incorporated into the base using polysorbate 20. The formulation is slightly thickened with carbomer.

Ingredient copy: Purified water, Glycerin, Polysorbate 20, Caramel, Aloe Barbadensis Gel, Triethanolamine, DMDM Hydantoin, Carbomer, Diazolidinyl Urea, Fragrance, Benzophenone-4, Polybutene, Phenyl Trimethicone, Amino acids: L-Histidine and L-Arginine, Tartaric acid, Disodium EDTA, Bertholletia Excelsa Seed Oil (Brazil Nut Oil), Phospholipids, Tocopheryl Acetate (Vitamin E Acetate), Retinyl Palmitate (Vitamin A Palmitate), Plumeria Acutifolia Flower Extract (Plumeria), Magnifera Indica Fruit Extract (Mango), Psidium Guajava (Guava), Carica Papaya Fruit Extract (Papaya), Passiflora Incarnata Fruit Extract (Passion Fruit), Colocasia Antiquorum Root Extract (Taro), Aluerites Moluccana Seed Extract (Kukui Nut).

Claims: A touch of Hawaiian Tropical, Exotic, Natural Flora, Fruit, and nut extracts . . . intensify your tan with Instant Bronzing Power! Natural looking, self-activating bronzer provides instant golden color. Our Ultra Sun® Formula actually intensifies the quality and appearance or your dark, "tan of the islands." Citrus Hot Tropic Fragrance. Moisturizing Forever Tan® ingredients like Aloe Vera, Plumeria, and Mango defend against peeling and "help to hold your tan for weeks longer". Natural amino acids help replace skin's vital nutrients lost during the tanning process.

5. Ocean Potion Australian Blend Tan Accelerator Spray Gel $421,141
   Sun and Skin Care Research, Inc., Cocoa, FL, USA

An aqueous based formulation with tyrosine and riboflavin for enhancing the tanning process. Tyrosine has been a staple active in the tanning accelerator market for many years. It is theorized to supplement the skin's reservoir of the starting compound of melanin. Riboflavin is thought to synergistically enhance the effects of tyrosine in the formula. The base is thickened with an amphiphilic acrylates copolymer. Sorbitan oleate is used to disperse the hydrophobic components within the external phase.

Ingredient copy: Deionized Water, Aloe Vera Gel, Sunflower Oil, Acrylics C10-30, Alkyl Acrylate Cross-polymer, Sorbitan Oleate, Tyrosine, Vitamin A Acetate, Ascorbic Acid (Vitamin C), Vitamin E Acetate, Riboflavin, DMDM Hydantoin, Propylparaben, Methylparaben, Disodium EDTA, Tea Tree Oil, Fragrance.

Claims: Dark tanning Xcellerator spray gel promotes instant tanning by increasing the sun's heating intensity onto the skin. This advanced gel glides easily for quick absorption into the skin providing accelerated tanning and a silky smooth feel. Enriched with numerous phyto effect polymers and plant extracts such as Aloe Vera, Tea Tree, and vitamins A, C, and E to hydrate skin cells and extend tan life.

6. Australian Gold Tan Accelerator Spray	$360,669
7. Australian Gold Tan Accelerator Lotion	$337,016
8. Australian Gold Tan Accelerator Spray Gel	$307,883
9. Australian Gold Exotic Blend Tan Accelerator Lotion	$293,398
10. Australian Gold Tan Accelerator Spray Gel SPF 4	$255,468

Sunless Tanners (1)

1. Coppertone Endless Summer — $15,669,396[4]
   Schering-Plough USA

The current market leader in sunless tanning utilizes a two-component package to deliver color in 30 min without the use of dyes. Separate W/O emulsions in the same package; keeps dihydroxyacetone separate from the amino silicone, oligomeric diaminoalkyl siloxane. When the two products combine on the skin, the DHA reacts with the oligomer to provide faster color development. This formula is patented under US 5,645,822 and US 5,750,092.

Ingredient copy: Water, Cyclopentasiloxane, Isohexadecane, Propylene Glycol, PEG/PPG 20/15 Dimethicone, Polyglyceryl-4 Isostearate, Sodium Chloride, Hexyl Laurate, Retinyl Palmitate (Vitamin A Palmitate), Avena Sativa Kernel Extract (Oat), Cetyl PEG/PPG 10/1 Dimethicone, Lactic Acid, Oligomeric Diaminoalkyl Siloxane, Phenoxyethanol, Butylene Glycol, Glycerin, Isopropylparaben, Butylparaben, Isobutylparaben, Fragrance, Diazolidinyl Urea, Dihydroxyacetone, Mica, Iron oxides.

[4]Combined SKUs 4110001623 and 4110001659.

Claims: Visibly reduces fine lines and wrinkles, natural looking color in 30 min, provides just enough color to maintain a healthy, natural looking glow.

2. Neutrogena Instant Bronze Sunless Tanner/Bronzer Foam $5,483,721
Johnson & Johnson USA

This combination sunless tanner and bronzer allow the consumer to see where the product is applied in order to avoid streaking. The natural colors caramel and carmine provide the instant bronzing effects. This formulation contains the additional reducing sugar erythrulose in combination with the solvents pentylene glycol, methylpropanediol, and PPG-5-Ceteth-20. Solvents such as these are thought to facilitate the exposure of DHA to areas where they work more efficiently. The vehicle is a nonionic O/W emulsion stabilized with PVM/MA decadiene crosspolymer. The formula is packaged in a nonaerosol foaming pump that provides a rich foam for ease of application. This formula is patented under US 6,113,888.

Ingredient copy: Water, Dihydroxyacetone, Pentylene Glycol, Caramel, PPG-5-Ceteth-20, Methyl Gluceth 20, Glycerin, PEG 100 Stearate, Erythrulose, PVM/MA Decadiene Cross-polymer, Methylpropanediol, Decyl Glucoside, Cetyl Hydroxyethylcellulose, Carmine, Sodium Citrate, Citric Acid, Sodium Hydroxide, Phenoxyethanol, Methylparaben, Ethylparaben, Butylparaben, Propylparaben, Isobutylparaben, Fragrance.

Claims: Streak Free Foam. Instant hint of bronze, plus lasting sunless tan. The sheer bronzer provides a hint of temporary, natural looking color immediately upon application and allows you to see where you have applied it to help eliminate mistakes for flawless, streak-free, even coverage. Over a few hours, the sunless tanner develops a natural looking tan that looks like a real tan and fades like a real tan. Oil-free formula absorbs quickly and dries in less than 5 minutes. Light, fresh fragrance.

3. Neutrogena Instant Bronze Sunless Tanner/Bronzer Lotion $4,195,368
Johnson & Johnson USA

The lotion counterpart to the above mentioned foam, combines sunless tanner and bronzer in one. The natural colors caramel and carmine provide the instant bronzing effects. This formulation contains a sodium citrate buffer system. The solvent Methylpropanediol is thought to facilitate the exposure of DHA to areas of the skin where they work more efficiently. The base is a non-ionic emulsion stabilized with the hydrocolloids magnesium aluminum silicate and xanthan gum.

Ingredient copy: Water, Dihydroxyacetone, Glycerin, Isopropyl Myristate, Isopropyl Palmitate, Ethylhexyl Palmitate, Caramel, Glyceryl Stearate, PEG 100 Stearate, Magnesium Aluminum Silicate, Sorbitol, Cetyl Alcohol, Methylpropanediol, BHT, Tetrasodium EDTA, Stearyl Alcohol, Xanthan Gum, Sodium Citrate, Citric Acid, Carmine, Phenoxyethanol, Methylparaben, Ethylparaben, Butylparaben, Propylparaben, Isobutylparaben, Fragrance.

Claims: Streak Free. Instant hint of bronze, plus lasting sunless tan. The sheer bronzer provides a hint of temporary, natural looking color immediately upon application and allows you to see where you have applied it to help eliminate mistakes for flawless, streak-free, even coverage. Over a few hours, the sunless tanner develops a natural looking tan that looks like a real tan and fades like a real tan. Oil-free formula absorbs quickly and dries in less than 5 minutes. Light, fresh fragrance.

4. Neutrogena Sunless Tan Nonaerosol Spray $3,606,059

This nonaerosol self-tanning spray is delivered through a pressurized bladder system with a 360° valve that allows for continuous even application. Dihydroxyacetone is delivered in an aqueous base with various solvents thought to enhance the penetration of the active. It should be duly noted that this formulation contains the incompatible amino-functional components diazolidinyl urea and sodium PCA.

Ingredient copy: Water, Witch Hazel, Ethoxydiglycol, Dihydroxyacetone, Dimethyl Isosorbide, Dipropylene Glycol, Isoceteth-20, Methyl Gluceth-20, Glycereth-7, Sodium PCA, Citric Acid, Propylene Glycol, Diazolidinyl Urea, Methylparaben, Propylparaben, Fragrance.

Claims: Natural-looking tan. Fast drying, oil free. Light, fresh fragrance. Non-comedogenic. Hypo-allergenic. Get a healthy-looking glow with this safe alternative to tanning. Oil-free formula provides a completely natural looking tan that looks like a real tan and fades like a real tan—not orange or streaky. Absorbs quickly and dries in less than 5 min. The one-touch continual spray can be applied from any angle to help cover hard-to-reach areas.

5. Neutrogena Sunless Tan Foam $3,352,018

The nonaerosol mousse, counterpart to the nonaerosol spray, provides mousse-like foam through a fine mesh pump. The foaming is provided by nonionic sugar based surfactants and stabilized with cetyl hydroxyethylcellulose. The formulation contains the reducing sugar erythrulose in combination with the solvents pentylene glycol, and methylpropanediol. Solvents such as these are thought to facilitate the exposure of DHA to areas where they work more efficiently.

Ingredient copy: Water, Dihydroxyacetone, Pentylene Glycol, Glycerin, Methyl Gluceth-20, PPG-5 Ceteth-20, Erythrulose, Decyl Polyglucose, Methylpropanediol, Cetyl Hydroxyethylcellulose, Sodium Citrate, Phenoxyethanol, Methylparaben, Ethylparaben, Propylparaben, Butylparaben, Isobutylparaben, Citric Acid, Fragrance.

Claims: Streak free. Natural-looking tan. Fast drying, oil free. Light, fresh fragrance. Non-comedogenic. Get a healthy-looking glow with this safe alternative to tanning. This light, nonsticky foam glides on smoothly to apply easily and evenly. Absorbs quickly and dries in less than 5 min ... provides a completely natural-looking tan that looks like a real tan and fades like a real tan—not orange or streaky.

6.	Neutrogena Sunless Tan Lotion	$3,236,605
7.	Bain de Soleil Radiance Eternelle Sunless Tan Cream	$2,952,754
8.	Banana Boat Sunless Tan Cream	$2,763,853
9.	Tomas Tan Perfect Sunless Tan Waterproof Lotion Kit	$2,741,219
10.	Neutrogena Sunless Tan Lotion Spray	$2,613,010

CONCLUSION

Given the continued research that demonstrates the harmful effects of sun exposure, more and more people will turn to cosmetic science for that just back from vacation look. The use of products that facilitate pigmentation of the skin has shown steady sales growth and there are no signs of slowing. Economic gains of the market seem to have exceeded its growth in technology. The potential gains of the discovery of a new technology in the self-tanning market have already been demonstrated with Plough's Endless Summer®. First-year sales in the USA of this one product beat the entire tanning accelerator market by more than 60%.

Consumer awareness of the negative effects of tanning has led to a sharp decline of tanning accelerator sales. However, the tanning bed boom seems to have saved that market for now. It is only a matter of time before the negative effects of the suberythemal doses of UV light put forth by tanning beds will have widespread consumer awareness. This will eventually lead to a cessation of sales in tanning accelerators. It is not foreseen that any major corporations will see a profitable return on investment for the research required to deliver a breakthrough tan accelerating technology. The small size of the tanning accelerator market will require true breakthroughs in technology to come from the entrepreneurial spirit of the corporations who lead the market today.

The future of the tanning industry will lie in the hands of the self-tanner. Although the quality of self-tanning formulations has significantly improved in the 40 or so years they have been on the market, they are by far less than perfect. Two major technology gaps exist to date, the speed of color development and matching the hue of a natural tan. Perhaps a greater understanding of the composition of melanoidins will allow the formulator to devise compositions that can be adjusted to accommodate the natural skin tone of the end user. Such developments could lead to a new family of products for individual skin types. They may incorporate components of the still unknown polymer that are devoid in a particular skin type or have additives to alter the final color imparted by the product. We may eventually see products designed for the spectrum of "skin that burns easily" or "for skin that rarely burns", as opposed to today's products which are marketed as light, medium, and dark.

REFERENCES

1. Information Resources Inc. IRI InfoScan Review Data of the Total US Market (Food, Drug and Mass Excluding Walmart). Chicago, IL: IRI, 1998–2002.
2. US Patent 6,468,508. Laughlin T. Method, Apparatus, and Composition for Automatically Coating the Human Body and Skin Preconditioning System for Use Therewith. Grapevine, TX: Laughlin Products, Inc.
3. Lavker RM, Kaidbey KH. Redistribution of melanosomal complexes within keratinocytes following UV-A irradiation: a possible mechanism for cutaneous darkening in man. Arch Dermatol Res 1982; 272:215–228.
4. Duval C, Regnier M, Schmidt R. Distinct melanogenic response of human melanocytes in mono-culture, in co-culture with keratinocytes and in reconstructed epidermis, to UV exposure. Pigment Cell Res 2001; 14:348–355.
5. Tyrell RM. UV-A (320–380 nm) as an oxidative stress. In: Sies H, eds. Oxidative Stress: Oxidants and Anti Oxidants. New York: Academic Press, 1991:7–78.
6. Auletta M, Gange W, Tan O, Matzinger E. Effects of cutaneous hypoxia upon erythema and pigment responses to UV-A, UV-B and PUVA (8-MOP + UV-A) in human skin. J Invest Dermatol 1986; 86:649–652.
7. Kochevar IE. Acute effects of ultraviolet radiation on skin. In: Holick MF, Kligman AM, eds. Biological Effects of Light. Berlin: Walter de Gruyter, 1992:3–10.
8. Swope VB, Abdel-Malek Z, Kassem LM, Nordlund JJ. Interleukins 1-α and 6 and tumor necrosis factor α are paracrine inhibitors of human melanocytes proliferation and melanogenesis. J Invest Dermatol 1991; 96:180–185.
9. Aberdam A, Auberger P, Ortone JP, Ballotti R. Neprilysin, a novel target for ultraviolet B regulation of melanogenesis via melanocortins. J Invest Dermatol 2000; 115:381–387.
10. McGregor JM, Hawk JLM. Acute effects of ultraviolet radiation on the skin. In: Freeberg IM, Eisen AZ, et al., eds. Dermatology in Medicine. New York: McGraw-Hill, 1999:1555–1561.
11. Seite S, Moyal D, Verdier MP, Hourseau C, Fourtanier A. Accumulated p53 protein and UV-A protection level of sunscreens. Photodermatol Photoimmunol Photomed 2000; 16:3–9.
12. Hemesath TJ, Steingrimsson E, McGill G, Hansen MJ, Vaught J, Hodgkinson CA, Arnheiter H, Copeland NG, Jenkins NA, Fisher DE. Microphthalmia, a critical factor in melanocyte development, defines a discrete transcription factor family. Genes Dev 1994; 8:2770–2780.
13. Nylander K, Bourdon JC, Bray S, Gibbs NK, Kay R, Hart I, Hall P. Transcriptional activation of tyrosinase by p53 links UV irradiation to the protective tanning response. J Pathol 2000; 190:39–46.

14. Eller M, Gilchrest B. Tannin as part of the eukaryotic SOS response. Pigment Cell Res 2000; 13:94–97.
15. Eller MS, Gasparro FP, Amato PE, Gilchrest BA. Induction of melanogenesis by DHA oligonucleotides: effects of oligo size and sequence. J Invest Dermatol 1998; 110:474.
16. Prota G. Recent advances in the chemistry of melanogenesis in mammals. J Invest Dermatol 1980; 75:122–127.
17. Nicolaus RA. Link 2-melanin 84. www.tightrope.it/nicolaus/melanin85.htm, 2001:10.
18. Busca R, Ballotti R. Cyclic AMP a key messenger in the regulation of skin pigmentation. Pigment Cell Res 2000; 13:60–69.
19. Sakai M, Horikoshi T, Uchiwa H, Miyachi Y. Up-regulation of tyrosinase gene by nitric oxide in human melanocytes. Pigment Cell Res 2000; 13:248–252.
20. Khaled M, Larribere L, Bille K, Aberdam E, Ortonne JP, Ballotti R, Bertolotto C. Glycogen synthase kinas 3β is activated by cAMP and plays an active role in the regulation of melanogenesis. J Biol Chem 2002; 227:33690–33697.
21. Lin CB, Barbiarz L, Liebel F, Price ER, Kizoulis M, Gendimenico GJ, Fisher DE, Seiberg M. Modulation of mircophthalmia-associated transcription factor gene expression alters skin pigmentation. J Invest Dermatol 2002; 119:1330–1340.
22. United States Code of Federal Regulations. 21CFR740.19, 2003.
23. Yoon TJ, Lei TC, Yamaguchi Y, Batzer J, Wolber R, Hearing V. Reconstituted 3-dimensionsl human skin of various ethnic origins as an *in vitro* model for studies of pigmentation. Anal Biochem 2003; 318:260–269.
24. Oka M, Nagai H, Ando H, Fukunaga M, Matsumura M, Araki K, Ogawa W, Miki T, Sakaue M, Tsukamoto K, Konishi H, Kikkawa U, Ichihashi M. Regulation of melanogenesis through phosphatidylinositol 3-kinase akt pathway in human G361 melanoma cells. J Invest Dermatol 2000; 115:699–703.
25. Klejman A, Rushen L, Morrione A, Slupianke A, Skorski T. Phosphatidylinositol-3 kinase inhibitors enhance the anti-leukemia effect of STI571. Oncogene 2002; 21(38):5868–5876.
26. Yoshida M, Takahashi Y, Shintaro I. Histamine induces melanogenesis and morphologic changes by protein kinase A activation via H_2 receptors in human normal melanocytes. J Invest Dermatol 2000; 114(2):334–341.
27. Prince S, Wiggins T, Hulley PA, Kidson SH. Stimulation of melanogenesis by tetradecanoylphorbol 13-1cetate (TPA) in mouse melanocytes and neural crest cells. Pigment Cell Res 2003; 16:26–34.
28. Kosano H, Kayanuma T, Nishigori H. Stimulation of melanogenesis in murine melanoma cells by 2-mercapto-1-(β-4-pyridethyl) benzimidazole (MPB). Biochim Biophys 2000; 1499:11–18.
29. Hachiya A, Kobayashi T, Takema Y, Imokawa G. Biochemical characterization of endothelin-converting enzyme 1-α in cultured skin-derived cells and its postulated role in the stimulation of melanogenesis in human epidermis. J Biol Chem 2002; 277(7):5395–5403.
30. Koh SWM. VIP enhances the differentiation of retinal pigment epithelium in culture: from cAMP an $pp60^{c\text{-}src}$ to melanogenesis and development of fluid transport capacity. Prog Retinal Eye Res 2000; 19(6):669–688.
31. Hadshiew M, Eller M, Gasparro FP, Gilchrest BA. Stimulation of melanogenesis by DHA oligonucleotides: effect of size, sequence and 5′ phosphorylation. J Dermatol Sci 2001; 25:127–138.

32. Palumbo A, Poli A, Cosmo A, d'Ischia M. N-methyl-d-aspartate receptor stimulation activates tyrosinase and promotes melanin synthesis in the ink gland of the cuttlefish Sepia officinalis through the nitric oxide/cGMP signal transduction pathway. J Biol Chem 2000; 275(22):16885–16890.
33. Mallick S, Mandal SK, Bhadra R. Human placental lipid induces mitogenesis and melanogenesis in B16F10 melanoma cells. J Biosci 2002; 27(3):243–249.
34. Kauser S, Schallreuter K, Thody AJ, Gummer C, Tobin DJ. Regulation of human epidermal melanocyte biology by β-endorphin. J Invest Dermatol 2003; 120(6):1073–1080.
35. Jung G, Yang J, Song E, Park J. Stimulation of melanogenesis by glycyrrhizin in B16 melanoma cells. Exp Mol Med 2001; 33(3):131–135.
36. Soliance ARD. Dihydroxyacetone Technical File. Soliance Pomacle Fr. 1997; 9:27–42.
37. Bernhauer, Shoeniz. Production of dihydroxyacetone by Acetobacter spp. Physiol Chem 1928; 177:107.
38. US Patent 2,948,658. Process for Producing Dihydroxyacetone. Westfield, NJ: Green S. Baxter Labs Inc.
39. US Patent 2,949,403. Andreadis J, Miklean S. Dihydroxyacetone Compositions for Tanning the Human Epidermis.
40. United States Code of Federal Regulations. 21CFR70, 2003.
41. United States Code of Federal Regulations. 21CFR73, 2003.
42. United States Code of Federal Regulations. 21CFR74, 2003.
43. Pucetti G, Leblanc RM. A sunscreen-tanning compromise: 3D visualization of the actions of titanium dioxide particles and dihydroxyacetone on human epiderm. Photochem Photobiol 2000; 71(4):426–430.
44. Schneider G, Sprenger G. Transaldolase B: trapping of Schiff base intermediate between dihydroxyacetone and ε-amino group of active-site lysine residue by borohydride reduction. Methods Enzymol 2002; 354:197–201.
45. Muizzuddin N, Marenus K, Maes D. Tonality of suntan vs. sunless tanning with dihydroxyacetone. Skin Res Tech 2000; 6:199–204.
46. Nguyen BC, Kochevar I. Influence of hydration on dihydroxyacetone-induced pigmentation of the stratum corneum. J Invest Dermatol 2003; 120(4):655–661.
47. Suga Y, Ikejima A, Matsuba S, Ogawa H. Medical Pearl: DHA application for camouflaging segmental vitiligo and piebald lesions. J Am Acad Dermatol 2002; 47:436–438.
48. Asawanonda P, Oberlender S, Taylor C. The use of dihydroxyacetone for photoprotection in variegate porphyria. Int J Dermatol 1999; 38:916–925.
49. Taylor CR, Kwangsukstith C, Wimberly J, Kollias N, Anderson R. Turbo-PUVA: dihydroxyacetone-enhanced photochemotherapy for psoriasis. Arch Dermatol 1999; 135:540–544.
50. Rona EM Industries. Dihydroxyacetone. New York: EMD Chemical Hawthorne, 1995; 1:6–10.
51. Forest S, Grothaus J, Ertel K, Rader C, Plante J. Fluorescence spectral imaging of dihydroxyacetone on skin in vivo. Photochem Photobiol 2003; 77(5):524–530.
52. Uchida K, Khor T, Oya T, Osawa T, Yasuda Y, Miyata T. Protein modification by a Maillard reaction intermediate methylglyoxal immunochemical detection of fluorescent 5-methylimidazolone derivatives in vivo. FEBS Lett 1997; 410:313–318.
53. US Patent 6,036,969. Golz-Berner K, Zastrow L. Process for Measuring Cosmetic Tanning and Test Kit Thereof. Haarlem, NL: Coty B.V.

US Patents Referenced

6,171,605	Bevacqua A, Lahanas K, Muizzudin N, Vrabe N	Color Access Inc., Melville, NY	Self-tanning compositions containing DHA and propolis extract
6,344,185	Argus L, Kambe T	Shiseido Co, Ltd., Tokyo, Japan	Self-tanning composition
6,036,969	Golz-Berner K, Zastrow L	Coty B.V., Haarlem, NL	Process for measuring cosmetic tanning and test kit therefor
5,827,506	McShane J, Kaplan C, Meyer T	Schering-Plough, Memphis, TN	Sunless tanning method and apparatus
5,662,890	Punto L, Zucchino J, Lentini P	Estee Lauder Inc., New York, NY	Self-tanning cosmetic compositions and methods of using the same
5,603,923	Robinson L, Tanner P	Procter & Gamble Co., Cincinnati, OH	Artificial tanning compositions having improved color development
5,503,824	Lentini P, Marenus K, Muizzuddin N, Pelle E, Punto L		Skin tanning compositions
6,537,528	Candau D, Forestier S	L'Oreal S.A., Paris, France	Composition comprising at least one self-tanning agent chosen from monocarbonyl and polycarbonyl compounds and a flavylium salt compound which is unsubstituted in position 3, for coloring the skin, and uses thereof
6,468,508	Laughlin T	Laughlin Products, Inc., Grapevine, TX	Method, apparatus, and composition for automatically coating the human body and skin preconditioning system for use therewith

6,406,682	Martin R, Belcour-Castro B, Galup C	Societe L'Oreal, Paris, France	Saxifraga extracts for artificially tanning human skin
6,344,185	Argus L, Kambe T	Shiseido Co. Ltd., Tokyo, Japan	Self-tanning composition
6,231,837	Stroud E, Scott J	Schering-Plough, Memphis, TN	Self-tanning DHA formulations having improved stability and providing enhanced delivery
5,801,169	Marrot L	L'Oreal S.A., Paris, France	Compounds in the form of 5,6-dihydroxyindole polymers, their process of preparation and compositions comprising them
5,750,092	Meyer T, Ando M, Powell J	Schering-Plough, Memphis, TN	Sunless tanning composition and method
5,705,145	Miklean S, Lahanas K, Vrabie N, Pelle E, Bevacqua A	E-L Management Corp., New York, NY	Skin tanning compositions and method
5,302,378	Crotty B, Ziegler P	Chesebrough Pond's USA Co., Greenwich, CT	Self-tanner cosmetic compositions
4,708,865	Turner J		Method and composition for artificially tanning the human epidermis
5,700,452	Deckner G, Pichardo F, Alban N, Sills M	Procter & Gamble Co., Cincinnati, OH	Compositions for imparting an artificial tan and protecting the skin from UV radiation
5,569,460	Kurz T, Stossel S, Spiller A	Merck Patent Gesellschaft Mit Beschrankter Haftung, Darmstadt, DE	Skin-coloring preparation
2,948,658	Green S	Baxter Labs Inc., Westfield, NJ	Process for producing DHA
2,949,403	Andreadis J, Miklean S		DHA compositions for tanning the human epidermis

Other Actives in the Sun Care Industry

30

Role of Antioxidants in Sun Care Products

Ratan K. Chaudhuri
*EMD Chemicals, Inc., Hawthorne, New York, USA**

*An affiliate of Merck KGaA, Darmstadt, Germany.

INTRODUCTION

Sun is the great initiator of photochemical reactions, which provides energy that sustains plant life and maintains human health. It warms the earth and furnishes solar energy, and in humans, activates synthesis of vitamin D for utilization by the body to help it absorb calcium and other minerals. As the outermost barrier of the body, the skin is directly exposed to a pro-oxidative environment. The effects of ultraviolet (UV) radiation from sun exposure can induce or exacerbate oxidative attack leading to the generation of reactive oxygen species (ROS) and other free radicals. The most severe consequence of photodamage is skin cancer. Less severe photoaging changes result in wrinkling, scaling, dryness, and uneven pigmentation consisting of hyper- and hypopigmentation (1–3).

Extended lifespan, more spare time, and excessive exposure to UV radiation from sunlight or tanning devices, especially in the Western population, has resulted in an ever increasing demand to protect human skin against the detrimental effects of UV exposure of the skin. Sunscreens—the current gold standard of photoprotection—are useful, but their protection is inadequate against long-wave UV-A light because UV-A is especially efficient at generating ROS (4–6). UV-A is being recognized increasingly as an important cause of photoaging and skin cancer. Photoprotective products combining sunscreens and antioxidant or antioxidant mixtures have been touted to provide increased efficacy and safety of such products (1). This chapter is intended to focus on three major areas: (A) major causes and consequences of UV-induced photodamage to skin; (B) role of endogenous antioxidant defense system; and (C) the photoprotective potential of topically applied antioxidants. A list of commercially available products containing sunscreens and antioxidants has also been included in this chapter.

UV-INDUCED CHEMICAL AND BIOCHEMICAL CHANGES: CAUSES AND CONSEQUENCES

Photosensitizer and Reactive Oxygen Species

Besides direct absorption of UV-B photons by DNA and subsequent structural changes, generation of ROS following irradiation with UV-A and UV-B requires the absorption of photons by endogenous photosensitive molecules. There are many endogeneous chromophores in human skin, which in the presence of UV-A radiation can generate ROS. Porphyrins (protoporphyrin, coproporphyrin, and uroporphyrin), flavins (riboflavin), quinone (ubiquinone), and the pyrimidine nicotinamide cofactors (nicotinamide adenine dinucleotide, NADH; and nicotinamide adenine dinucleotide phosphate, NADPH) are examples of common photosentizers in mammalian cells (7). Recently, the identification of the epidermal UV-A absorbing chromophore *trans*-urocanic acid that quantitatively accounts for the action spectrum of photo aging, has been reported (8). The excited photosensitizer subsequently reacts with oxygen resulting in the generation of ROS including superoxide anion radical and singlet oxygen. Superoxide anion radical and singlet oxygen are also produced by neutrophiles that are present in increased quantities in photodamaged skin, and contribute to the overall pro-oxidant state. Superoxide dismutase (SOD) converts superoxide anion radical to hydrogen peroxide. Hydrogen peroxide is able to cross cell membranes easily and, in conjunction with Fe^{2+}, generates highly toxic hydroxyl radicals. Both singlet oxygen and hydroxyl radical can initiate lipid peroxidation. Many organic sunscreens also act as triplet sensitizers that convert harmless triplet oxygen into the highly reactive singlet oxygen (9–12).

As a consequence of their high reactivity, ROS react nonspecifically with nearly every cellular target and may damage DNA, proteins, lipids, and carbohydrates (13). On the upper surface of the skin, ROS are also capable of inducing more complex responses such as the induction of genes (14). Both UV-A and UV-B contribute to the deleterious effects on the skin, but it appears that UV-B is more associated with autoimmune diseases than UV-A. Somewhere, there is a balance between too much sun and melanoma risk or too little sun and autoimmune disease.

Iron and Copper

In mammalian cells, the level of iron-storage protein is tightly controlled by the iron-regulatory protein-1 at the posttranscriptional level. This regulation prevents iron acting as a catalyst in reactions between ROS and biomolecules. It has been shown that both UV-B and UV-A can cause biological damage in exposed tissues via iron-catalyzed oxidative stress (15,16). The iron content is substantially elevated over basal levels in the sun-exposed skin of healthy individuals (17). The underlying mechanism appears to be the UV-B-induced formation of superoxide radical anion and its attack on ferritin, resulting in the release of free iron (18).

Furthermore, superoxide anion radical can react with hydrogen, which again enters the Fenton reaction (19). Iron, singlet oxygen, and hydrogen peroxide are presently considered to be important redox active species involved in the deleterious effects of UV-A radiation on lipids and proteins of human skin cells (20,21). Figure 30.1 summarizes the chemistry involved in the iron- and copper-induced formation of ROS.

When a general use of antioxidants is advocated, it is often disregarded that these compounds not only function as antioxidants, but (intrinsically) have pro-oxidant action as well, in the presence of transition metals. There is pro-oxidant action even in well-known antioxidants, such as, vitamin C (ascorbate), vitamin E (tocopherols), glutathione, and proanthocyanidins (from pine and grape). The pro-oxidant activity of vitamin C results from the reduction of Fe^{3+} to Fe^{2+} and its reaction with H_2O_2 to generate OH radical (22). Pro-oxidant effects are not unique to vitamin C; they can be demonstrated with many reducing agents in the presence of transition metal ions, including vitamin E, glutathione and several plant phenolics. Thus, if vitamin C's pro-oxidant effects are relevant, the pro-oxidation effects of these other reductants may also be expected to occur (23).

High concentrations of vitamin E accelerate lipid autooxidation *in vitro* (24,25). Other authors also reported pro-oxidant effects *in vitro* for α-tocopherol (26,27). It is quite possible that α-tocopherol can generate tocopheroxyl radical on skin under UV radiation and may thereby act as a pro-oxidant. Indeed, adverse biological effects of α-tocopherol are documented in skin (28). A pro-oxidant activity of carotenoids has also been reported (29).

Presence of Iron (or Copper) and H_2O_2

Fe^{2+}(or Cu^{+}) + H_2O_2 → Intermediate complex (es) → Fe^{3+}(or Cu^{2+}) + $OH^{\cdot}$ + OH^{-}
(Very fast reaction)

Fe^{3+}(or Cu^{2+}) + H_2O_2 → Intermediate complex (es) → Fe^{2+}(or Cu^{+}) + $O_2^{\cdot -}$ + $2H^{+}$
(slow reaction)

Presence of Iron- (or Copper-) chelates and H_2O_2

Fe^{3+}(or Cu^{2+})-EDTA + H_2O_2 → Fe^{2+}(or Cu^{+})-EDTA + $O_2^{\cdot -}$ + $2H^{+}$

Presence of Iron (or copper), H_2O_2 & an antioxidant

Fe^{3+}(or Cu^{2+}) + ascorbate → Fe^{2+} + ascorbate$^{\cdot}$

Fe^{2+} + H_2O_2 → [intermediate complex(es)] → Fe^{3+} + $OH^{\cdot}$ + HO^{-}

Figure 30.1 Chemistry involved in the iron- or copper-induced formation of reactive oxygen species.

The key question is the availability of catalytic amounts of iron and copper in the skin (30). UV light and sweat are the two dominant sources for iron and copper (31). Water is also a source for iron in the skin. It is also easy to see from these data how athletes following an intensive training might become anemic due to loss of iron. Iron-chelating agents have been shown as protectants against UV-radiation-induced free radical production (23,30,32).

Matrix-Degrading Metalloprotease

Matrix metalloproteases (MMPs) constitute a family of structurally similar zinc-containing metalloproteases, which are involved in the remodeling and degradation of extracellular matrix (ECM) proteins, such as collagens, elastins, fibronectin, and proteoglycans, both as part of normal physiological processes and in pathological conditions. At this time over 20 different MMPs have been identified and classified (33). Based on sequence homology and substrate specificity, MMPs can be classified in five groups (Table 30.1). This classification is somewhat arbitrary, since the true physiological substrates are a matter of debate.

The ECM is the material that forms the bulk of the dermis, excluding water and cells. Proteins and complex sugars form most of the dermal ECM and they are arranged in an orderly network fibers and ground substances. The ECM is not a homogeneous structure. It can include any of several classes of biomolecules, including structural proteins, such as collagens and elastin; adhesion proteins, including fibronectins, laminins, and entactin; proteoglycans; and glycosaminoglycans. This complex mixture does not simply surround cells and hold them together, but also provides an environment in which a number of critical biological processes occur (34).

Several studies carried out by Scharffetter-Kochanek's group using dermal fibroblast cells show that both UV-A and UV-B cause a four- to five fold increase in the production of MMP-1 and MMP-3 (15,34–36). Brennan et al. have shown by punch biopsies of human skin after UV irradiation that MMP-1 rather than MMP-13 as the major collagenolytic enzyme responsible for collagen damage in photoaging (37). In contrast, the synthesis of tissue inhibitory metalloprotease-1 (TIMP-1), the natural inhibitor of matrix metalloprotease, increases only marginally. This imbalance is one of the causes of severe connective tissue damage resulting in photoaging of the skin. Although collagen content decreases, collagen synthesis in sun-damaged skin appears to remain similar to that of sun-protected sites (38,39). Thus, evidence suggests that the decrease in collagen content in photodamaged skin results from increased collagen degradation, by matrix metalloprotease, without significant changes in collagen production (40). Recently, Fisher et al. have shown that UV irradiation increases MMP-8 in human skin *in vivo* (41). Although UV irradiation induces both MMP-1 and MMP-8, UV-induced collagen degradation is stimulated primarily by MMP-1, with little, if any, contribution by MMP-8.

Table 30.1 The Matrix Metalloprotease Enzymes Relevant to Skin Care

Group	Trivial name	No.	Principal substrate
Collagenase	Interstitial collagenase	MMP-1	Fibrillar collagen types I, II, III
	Neutrophil collagenase	MMP-8	Fibrillar collagen types I, II, III
	Collagenase-3	MMP-13	Fibrillar collagen types I, II, III
	Collagenase-4	MMP-18	
Gelatinases	Gelatinase A (72 kDa)	MMP-2	Gelatins, nonfibrillar collagen types IV, V
	Gelatinase B (92 kDa)	MMP-9	Gelatins, nonfibrillar collagen types IV, V
Stromelysins	Stromelysin-1	MMP-3	Proteoglycans, laminin, fibronectin, nonfibrillar collagens
	Stromelysin-2	MMP-10	Proteoglycans, laminin, fibronectin, nonfibrillar collagens
	Matrilysin	MMP-7	Proteoglycans, laminin, fibronectin, nonfibrillar collagens
Membrane type	MT1-MMP	MMP-14	Progelatinase A, procollagenase-3
	MT2-MMP	MMP-15	Progelatinase A
	MT3-MMP	MMP-16	Progelatinase A
	MT4-MMP	MMP-17	
	MT5-MMP	MMP-21	
Others	Stromelysin-3	MMP-11	Serine protease inhibitor
	Metalloelastase	MMP-12	Elastin, nonfibrillar collagen
	Enamelysin	MMP-20	
		MMP-19	
		MMP-23	
		MMP-24	

The damage caused by excessive MMP on the ECM proteins does not appear overnight, but results from the accumulation of successive molecular damages, especially in the case of overexposure to UV light. The skin repercussion on the degradation of the ECM proteins may then be revealed in many ways depending on age, genetic predisposition, and life-style and, of course, on the general health status of the individual (42). The causes and consequences of skin damages are summarized in Fig. 30.2.

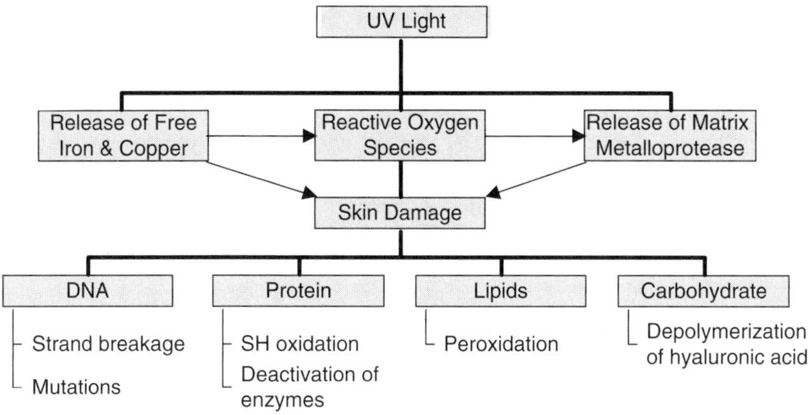

Figure 30.2 Causes and consequences of UV-induced skin damage.

ANTIOXIDANT DEFENSES OF THE SKIN

To counteract the harmful effects of ROS, the skin is equipped with antioxidant defense systems consisting of a variety of low molecular weight antioxidants and antioxidant defense enzymes forming an "antioxidant network". The antioxidant network is responsible for maintaining the equilibrium between pro-oxidants and antioxidants. However, the antioxidant defense can be overwhelmed by increased exposure to exogenous sources of ROS. Such a disturbance of the pro-oxidant/antioxidant balance may result in oxidative damage to lipids, proteins, and DNA. The skin has developed a complex system in order to protect itself from oxidative stress. This defense system consists of enzymes and nonenzymatic antioxidants.

Antioxidant Defense Enzymes

The discovery of SOD enzymes provided much of the basis for our current understanding of antioxidant defense systems, since it led to the postulation of the superoxide theory of oxygen toxicity (43). The theory gained credibility with the identification of the enzyme SOD by McCord and Fridovich in 1969 (44), which provided the first compelling evidence of *in vivo* generation of the superoxide anion radical ($O_{2^-}^{\bullet}$). Additional support came from the subsequent elucidation of elaborate antioxidant defenses (45).

SOD can be divided into three types: copper- and zinc-containing isoform (CuZn-SOD, a cytosolic enzyme), manganese-containing isoform (Mn-SOD, a mitochrondial enzyme), and extracellular SOD (EC-SOD, a tetrameric glycoprotein which contains Cu and Zn) (46). SOD catalyzes dismutation of superoxide anions to hydrogen peroxide. SODs are found in all eukaryotic cells. In human, the Cu/Zn-SOD activity seems to be five- to tenfold higher than Mn-SOD. As compared to other body tissues, SOD activity is relatively low in skin (46).

Catalase is a tetrameric enzyme that is expressed in all body organs (47). The major role of catalase is its ability to detoxify hydrogen peroxide to water and oxygen. Mates et al. (48) reported higher catalase activity in human epidermis than the human dermis.

Glutathione peroxidase (GSH-Px) is a selenoenzyme consisting of four identical subunits, each of which contains a selenocysteine residue in its active site. GSH-Px is localized mainly in the cytosol and to a lesser extent in mitochondria. They convert hydrogen peroxide to water and oxygen and reduce lipid hydroperoxides using glutathione (48). The baseline levels measured in epidermis and dermis vary considerably and therefore do not point to a clear preferential distribution in skin (49).

The ratio of reduced to oxidized glutathione (GSH/GSSH) in normal cells are high so there must be a mechanism for reducing GSHG back to GSH. This is achieved by glutathione reductase (GSH-Rx), which catalyzes the following reaction:

$$\mathrm{GSSG} + \mathrm{NADPH} + \mathrm{H}^{+} \longrightarrow 2\mathrm{GSH} + \mathrm{NADP}^{+}$$

Enzymatic antioxidant activities in human skin are higher in epidermis than in dermis; catalase is especially high (49). When skin fibroblasts were irradiated with UV-A, catalase activity was destroyed, but GSH-Px and GSH-Rx were virtually unchanged (48). Similar results were seen when murine skin was irradiated with solar irradiation (50).

Low Molecular Weight Antioxidants

Low molecular weight antioxidants can be subdivided into two groups: endogeneous (synthesized in the body) and exogeneous (derived from the diet). Human skin contains both lipophilic [vitamin E (tocopherols and tocotrienols), ubiquinones (coenzyme Q) and carotenoids], and hydrophilic [(vitamin C (ascorbate), glutathione (GSH) and uric acid (urate)] antioxidants. Vitamin E, vitamin C, and carotenoids are derived from the diet whereas the other three are synthesized *in vivo*.

On a molar basis, vitamin C is the predominant antioxidant in skin; its concentration is 15-fold higher than glutathione, 200-fold higher than vitamin E, and 1000-fold higher than ubiquinones (49). Concentrations of antioxidants are higher in epidermis than dermis; six-fold for vitamin C and glutathione, and two-fold for vitamin E and ubiquinones. Some antioxidants are also present in the stratum corneum, such as vitamin E, which is the predominant antioxidant in the human stratum corneum (51).

The antioxidants present in the stratum corneum are quite susceptible to UV radiation. For example, a single suberythemal dose of UV radiation depleted vitamin E by about 50% while dermal and epidermal vitamin E depletion required much higher doses (51). Vitamin C seems to be present in human stratum corneum at very low levels. Consequently, vitamin C is not available to recycle photo-oxidized vitamin E. Ubiquinones seem to be absent in human stratum corneum.

PHOTOPROTECTION OF HUMAN SKIN USING ANTIOXIDANTS AND OTHER PHOTOPROTECTANTS

A large number of antioxidants have been found to exhibit protective effects against the ROS-induced photoaging both on animals and human (1,52). A review of the protective effects of topical antioxidants in human has recently been published (1).

Direct application of antioxidants on to skin has the advantage over oral administration because targeting antioxidants to the area of skin needing the protection is easier to achieve. It seems desirable to add low molecular weight antioxidants to the skin reservoir by applying antioxidants topically as they protect the skin against oxidative stress.

The stratum corneum may particularly benefit from an increased antioxidant capacity to topical application because cutaneous antioxidants undergo depletion significantly under oxidative stress. To protect deeper layers of the skin, antioxidants need to be formulated in a way that delivers them into the skin. Antioxidants are inherently unstable compounds—hydrolytically and photo-chemically—that is why they function in redox reactions. This also makes it difficult to formulate a stable formulation with antioxidants. A recent study (23) has shown that antioxidants do not have adequate aqueous and heat stability (Fig. 30.3). However, exploiting multilevel approach of antioxidant

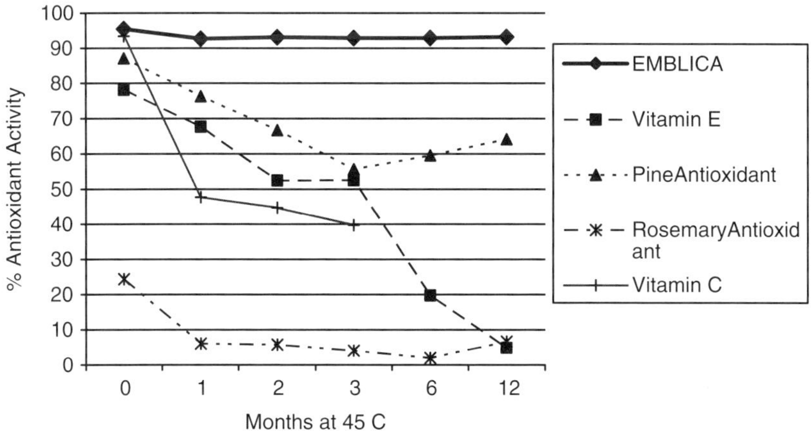

Figure 30.3 Comparative stability of Emblica and other antioxidants. All antioxidant activities were derived from optical density measurements at 517 nm in an ethanol–water mixture using diphenylpicrylhydrazide method.

activity (cascading antioxidant), one can develop stable skin care and sun care formulations having good shelf-life (53,54).

Vitamin E and Its Derivatives

The terms α-tocopherol and vitamin E are now used in the literature almost interchangeably. This is incorrect because vitamin E is a nutritional term and other tocopherols also have vitamin E activity. Tocopherols are a mixture of four lipid-soluble tocopherols (α, β, γ, and δ) and four lipid-soluble tocotrienols (α, β, γ, and δ). Tocopherols and tocotrienols differ only in their prenyl side chain. The chromanol head of each is identical with α, β, γ, and δ isomers, each containing an essential hydroxyl group necessary for antioxidant activity. Photochemically, natural tocopherols are not very stable (53). The relative antioxidant activities of tocopherols in lipid systems is $\alpha > \beta > \gamma > \delta$ isomers (55). The structures of tocopherols and tocotrienols are given in Fig. 30.4. Tocotrienols may have higher antioxidant activities than the corresponding tocopherols (56).

Vitamin E is depleted during the oxidative stress and can not be regenerated in the absence of a co-antioxidant. Vitamin E is important for protecting the lipid structures of the stratum corneum proteins from oxidation. However, topically applied α-tocopherol is rapidly depleted by UV-B radiation in a dose-dependent manner. The photo-oxidative fate of the α-tocopherol depends on the local environment of the vitamin E. α-Tocopherol quinone and α-tocopherol quinone

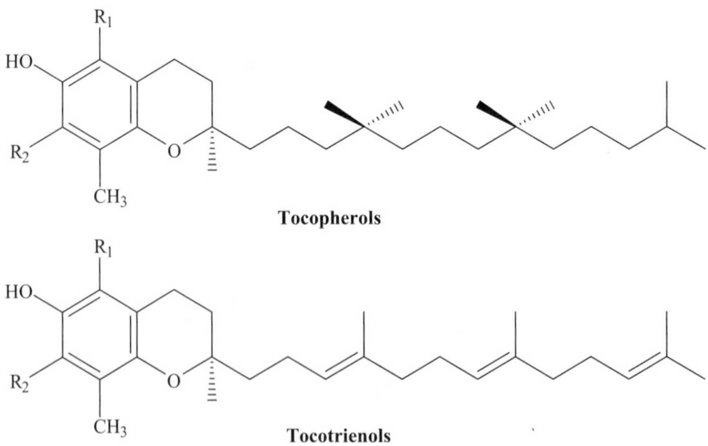

	R_1	R_2
α	CH_3	CH_3
β	CH_3	H
γ	H	CH_3
δ	H	H

Figure 30.4 Structures of tocopherols and tocotrienols.

epoxides are principal photoproducts of vitamin E that can penetrate into the epidermal layer of the skin, whereas tocopherol dimers and trimers are formed from α-tocopherol in a bulk phase at the skin surface. Dimer and trimer products may participate in the prevention of UV-induced photodamage (57,58).

The photoprotective effect of Vitamin E and its esters have been studied extensively. Topical application of vitamin E has shown significant reduction in acute responses when applied before UV-radiation exposure, such as erythema and edema (59,60), sunburn cell formation (61), lipid peroxidation (62,63), DNA adduct formation (64), and immunosuppression (62,65).

Vitamin E esters, particularly vitamin E acetate, succinate, and linoleate, were shown to be promising agents in reducing UV radiation induced skin damage (46). Their protective effects, however, are less pronounced as compared to vitamin E. This is quite understandable because vitamin E esters need to be hydrolyzed during skin absorption to show antioxidant activity. It seems that the bioconversion of vitamin E acetate to α-tocopherol is slow and occurs only to a minor extent. Table 30.2 summarizes the photoprotective effect of topically applied vitamin E and its esters on humans.

Table 30.2 Photoprotective Effects of Topically Applied Vitamin E and Its Derivatives on Humans

Compound	Endpoint	Efficacy	Remarks	References
Vitamin E	Mechanoelectrical properties of skin	Protection of UVR and PUVA-induced damage	—	66
Vitamin E and its derivatives	PUVA-induced erythema and changes in mechanoelectrical property of skin	Vitamin E acetate not protective; vitamin E and vitamin E with shorter chain protective	No protection when applied after UVR exposure	67
Vitamin E	Erythema (MED)	Protective	SPF determination	60
Vitamin E and its acetate	Erythema	Moderate protection when applied occlusively after UVR exposure	No protection when applied occlusively before UVR exposure	68
Vitamin E	Erythema (skin color and skin blood flow)	Moderate protection	No protection when applied after UVR exposure; SPF 1 (*in vitro*)	69, 70

Vitamin C and Its Derivatives

L-Ascorbic acid is involved in many biological processes such as collagen synthesis, antioxidation, intestinal absorption of iron and metabolism of some amino acids (71). An essential function of L-ascorbic acid is to act as a cofactor for the hydroxylation of proline and lysine residues in collagen, a major protein component of the body. L-Ascorbic acid also increases transcription of procollagen genes and stabilizes procollagen mRNA (72). Its ability to cure scurvy is possibly due to the stimulation of collagen synthesis in connective tissues (73). L-Ascorbic acid improves epidermal barrier function, apparently by stimulating sphingolipid production (74).

Unfortunately, L-ascorbic acid is not stable in aqueous solutions, even at neutral pH at room temperature (~25°C). Structures of ascorbic acid and its degradation products are given in Fig. 30.5. To solve this problem, a number of stable synthetic derivatives have been developed such as sodium (SAP) and magnesium ascorbyl phosphate (MAP). Ascorbic acid also acts as a pro-oxidant in the presence of transition metals (22,23). Unfortunately, SAP and MAP have to be formulated at basic pH (>7.00) due to their instability in the acidic system. A chelating agent needs to be included in the formulation to prevent degradation of MAP and SAP; most commercial products do contain EDTA as a chelating agent. Ascorbic acid has two ionizable hydroxyl groups, and consequently has two pK_a: values 4.2 (position 3) and 11.6 (position 2).

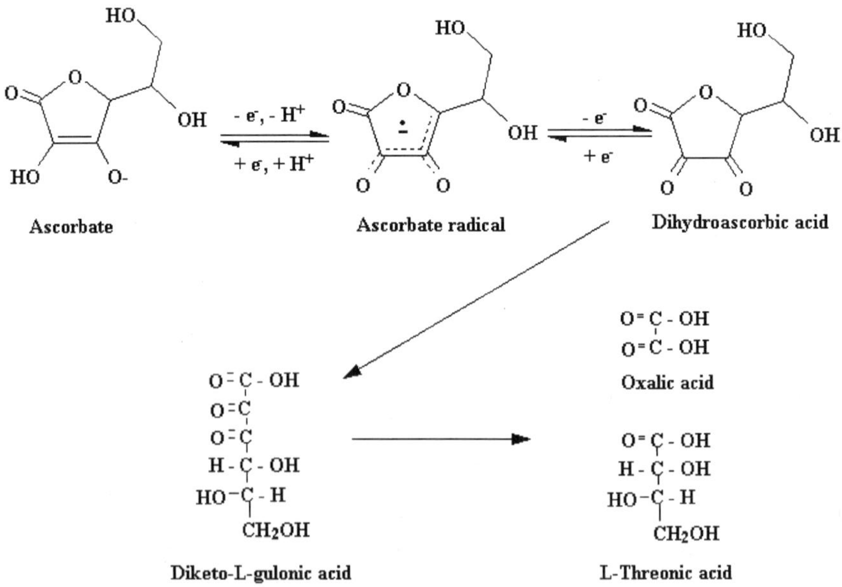

Figure 30.5 Structures of ascorbic acid and its degradation products.

Since the mono-anion form is favored at physiological pH, the name ascorbate is the right terminology for ascorbic acid in solution.

Topical L-ascorbic acid reduced UV-B-induced inflammation (75) and attenuated UV-A-induced immediate pigment response in human skin (76). Vitamin C is effective only at a high concentration in an appropriate vehicle (77). Vitamin C is highly unstable and is only poorly absorbed into the skin, possibly explaining its poor photoprotective property when applied topically. Hence, more lipophilic and more stable vitamin C esters, such as its palmityl, succinyl, or phosphoryl esters might be promising derivatives providing increased photoprotection (78). Also, a water-soluble analog of vitamin C, ascorbic acid 2-*O*-α-D-glucoside (79) has been shown to have improved stability and efficacy (80).

The stability of ascorbic acid, ascorbyl palmitate, and MAP in both standard solutions and topical formulations was investigated by Austria et al. (81). The results showed that the two vitamin C derivatives were more stable than ascorbic acid. Esterification with palmitic acid in the 6 position did not prevent hydrolysis of the molecule, either in solution or in emulsion; only a formulation with highly viscoelastic properties was able to slow down the degradation of the compound. Conversely, the introduction of the phosphoric group in the 2-position protected the molecule from the break-up of the enediol system, confirming MAP as a stable derivative of vitamin C.

Recently, several human clinical studies have been reported on the use of vitamin C at high percentage levels ($\geq$5%) and its beneficial effect on skin (82,83). Topical application of 5% vitamin C cream was an effective and well-tolerated treatment. It led to a clinically apparent improvement of the photodamaged skin and induced modifications of skin relief and ultrastructure, suggesting a positive influence of topical vitamin C on parameters characteristic for sun-induced skin aging. Table 30.3 summarizes the photoprotective effects of vitamin C and its derivatives on humans.

Carotenoids

Carotenoids are a class of lipophilic compounds of plant origin that contain an extended system of conjugated double bonds; β-carotene and lycopene are the most prominent compounds. β-Carotene, α-carotene, lycopene, β-cryptoxanthine, lutein, and zeaxanthine are major carotenoids in human skin and their levels differ between various skin areas (86). It was demonstrated that a single exposure to solar simulated UV light lowers the skin lycopene level by 31–46%, whereas the same UV dose has very little effect on the β-carotene level (87). However, repeated exposure to UV light also depletes the β-carotene level (88).

Carotenoids have been reported to react with virtually any radical species likely to be encountered in a biological system (89). Carotenoids are among the most efficient scavengers of singlet oxygen, either by physical or by chemical quenching (90). The products of such reactions are generally short-lived

Table 30.3 Photoprotective Effects of Topically Applied Vitamin C and Its Derivatives on Humans

Compound	Endpoint	Efficacy	Remarks	References
Vitamin C	Cutaneous biopsy after 3 and 6 months	Increase in the skin density and decrease in the deep furrows	Significant improvement	82
Vitamin C+ tetrahexyldecyl ascorbate	Cutaneous biopsy after 12 weeks and evaluation of overall facial improvement	Increase grenz zone collagen; improved wrinkle reduction and hydration	Statistically significant improvement	84
Vitamin C	Treatment of mild to moderate photodamage after 3 months	68.4% greater improvement vs. vehicle treated area	Statistically significant improvement shown by image analysis	85
Vitamin C	Erythema (skin color and skin blood flow)	Poor protection	SPF 1 (*in vitro*)	70
Vitamin C palmitate	Erythema (skin color)	Poor protection when applied occlusively after UVR exposure	No protection when applied occlusively before UVR exposure	68

radical species. In some cases, stable adducts can be observed, but in the majority of interactions with radicals, carotenoids break down to degradation products in a manner very similar to oxidative degradation processes (Fig. 30.6). It is only recently that the biological activity of these degradation products has begun to be investigated (89).

β-Carotene has been supplemented prior to sun exposure in order to prevent sunburn. The protective effects are related to the antioxidant properties of the carotenoid. The data obtained in different studies on this topic have been reviewed by Stahl and Sies (91,92) and appear to be conflicting (91). All the photoprotective work done on carotenoids are via oral supplementation (91). Two recently published studies provide evidence that oral supplementation with carotenoids alone or in combination with vitamin E increase the photoprotective properties of the skin and provide moderate protection against erythema formation (93,94).

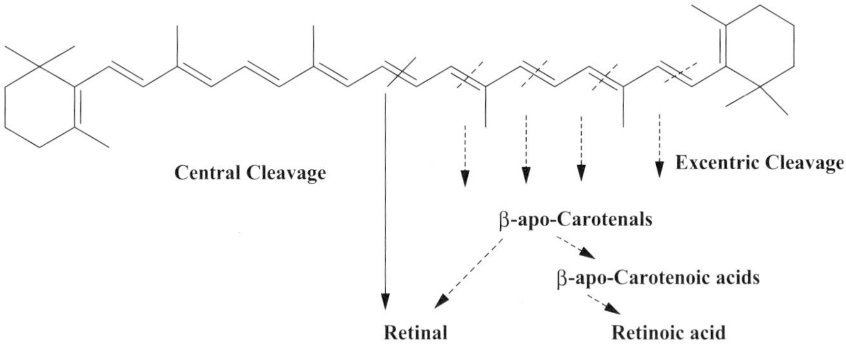

Figure 30.6 The central and excentric cleavage pathways of β-carotene.

There is some clinical evidence of increased skin cancer incidence in smokers supplemented with β-carotene (95,96). Cigarette smoke is a complex mixture of literally thousands of compounds, many of which are known or suspected human carcinogens. β-Carotene oxidation products formed by smoke may be responsible for procarcinogenic effects in human (97). It has recently been shown that 4-nitro-β-carotene is the major product of the reaction between nitrogen oxide in smoke and β-carotene (98).

Plant Polyphenolics

Polyphenolics comprise a wide variety of natural products of plant origin. Almost all of them exhibit a marked antioxidant activity. Typical examples are, oligomeric catechols, flavonoids, monomeric and oligomeric flavan-3-ols (condensed tannins), and gallo- and ellagitannins (hydrolyzable tannins). The tannins are considered superior antioxidants as their eventual oxidation may lead to oligomerization via phenolic coupling and enlargement of the number of reactive sites, a reaction which has never been observed with flavonoids themselves (53,99). Many of these plant polyphenolics are consumed in the diet and are believed to have beneficial health effect for human beings. Recently, some polyphenolics have been demonstrated to have significant photoprotective properties when used topically. Administrations of different plant extracts, particularly flavonoids, have been reported to reduce acute and chronic skin damage after UV radiation exposure (100–104). Recently, Kang et al. have shown that topical application of genistein (4′,5,7-trihydroxyisoflavone) prevent UV-light-induced signaling that leads to photoaging in human skin *in vivo* (105). Genistein blocked UV-induction of cJun-driven enzyme, collagenase. However, genistein had no effect on UV-induced erythema.

Polyphenolics are inherently unstable compounds due to aerial oxidation; this allows them to function in redox reactions. In addition, many polyphenolics are deeply colored, adding to the complexity of producing an acceptable esthetic product for topical applications.

Tea Polyphenols

Tea from the *Camellia sinensis* is consumed by more than two-thirds of the world's population. Tea is the most popular beverage next to water. Tea is a potent source of polyphenols, comprising 30–35% of the dry weight of the leaf. During processing, tea leaves are progressively fermented to produce green tea, oolong tea, or black tea. Major ingredients in green tea are epigallocatechin-3-gallate (EGCG), epigallocatechin (EGC), epicatechin (EC), gallocatechin, and catechin. Black tea contains predominantly polymeric materials (106). All these polyphenols are potent antioxidants and are capable of quenching superoxide radical, hydroxyl radical, peroxyl radical, singlet oxygen, and hydrogen peroxide. Several comprehensive reviews on tea polyphenols are available in the recent literature (1,107; this volume Chapter 31 by Elmets).

Tea polyphenols have been studied extensively for their anticarcinogenic potential (108). EGCG is the major polyphenolic constituent present in green tea that is responsible for this biological activity (109,110). In animal models, extracts from green tea have been shown to be remarkably effective at reducing the severity of adverse effects of overexposure to UV radiation (110). Topical application of green tea polyphenols reduced UV-induced erythema and sunburn cell formation in human skin (111). EGCG when applied topically reduced UVB-induced inflammatory responses and infiltration of leukocytes in human skin (112). Standardized extract of green tea polyphenols also protected against erythema, and c-Fos and p53 induction after PUVA phototoxic injury to human skin (113). Tea polyphenols protected human skin from UV-induced langerhans cell depletion (111). Topical application to skin of green tea polyphenols reduced UVB-induced pyrimidine dimmer formation in both epidermis and dermis (114).

Silymarin

Silymarin is an extract of the seeds milk thistle plant (*Silybum marianum*), which consists of a mixture of flavonolignans, namely, silybin, silidianin, silychristin, and isosylibin (115,116). A standardized extract should contain 80% silymarin. Silybin is the main component (70–80%) and is thought to have the most biological activity.

Silymarin has strong antioxidant effects. In animal models, silymarin has been shown to be remarkably effective at reducing the severity of adverse effects of overexposure to UV radiation (1,107). Topically applied silymarin was demonstrated to have a remarkable antitumor effect (117). Silymarin showed a protective effect against UV-induced oxidative damage by modulating the activation of the transcription factor NF-κB in HaCaT keratinocytes (118). In a dose-dependant manner, silymarin inhibited NF-κB activation induced by UV radiation in human keratinocytes. NF-κB is a redox sensitive transcriptional factor, which plays an important role in regulating the expression of various genes that participate in many physiological processes such as inflammation, apoptosis, and cellular proliferation.

Emblica Antioxidant

Emblica antioxidant, is a standardized extract of *Phyllanthus emblica* (syn. *Emblica officinalis)* fruits, which is isolated using a water-based process. The product is defined to the extent of well over 50% (typically, 60–75%) in terms of its key bioactive components and has acceptable color for topical application at about 1–2% level. The low molecular weight (<1000) hydrolyzable tannins, namely emblicanin A and emblicanin B, along with pedunculagin and punigluconin are the key ingredients (Fig. 30.7) in the Emblica antioxidant (53,54,119). In nature, emblicanin A and emblicanin B have only been found in *P. emblica* plants (119). Emblica is a hydrolytically as well as photochemically stable antioxidant (53,120). While most antioxidants go from an active to an inactive role, Emblica antioxidant utilizes a multilevel cascade of antioxidant compounds resulting in a prolongation of activities (120).

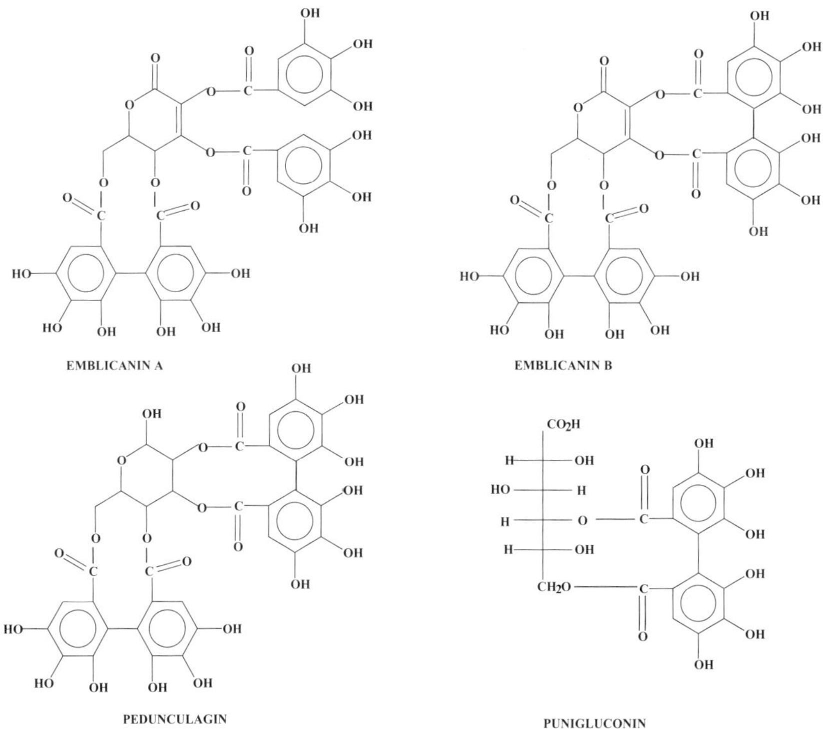

Figure 30.7 Hydrolyzable tannins of *Phyllanthus emblica*.

Emblica has an excellent free-radical and nonradical quenching ability (53,120), strong chelating ability to iron and copper (no pro-oxidative activity) (120), significant matrix metalloprotease (MMP-1 and MMP-3) inhibitory activity (53). Emblica has been shown to reduce UV-induced erythema (53) to human skin. *In vitro* study using human skin fibroblast cells, Chaudhuri et al. (53) showed that Emblica antioxidant increases the synthesis of noncollagenic proteins by about 40% over the control. An immunocolorimetric method (121) was used for quantifying collagenic and noncollagenic proteins. Interestingly, Emblica antioxidant had practically no effect on the synthesis of collagenic proteins. Characterization of the individual noncollagenic proteins has not been done. Human clinical trials have shown that Emblica has a strong skin lightening or even-toning effect (54,122), which is equal or superior to hydroquinone, magnesium ascorbyl phosphate (MAP), and kojic acid.

Recently, Morganti et al. (123) has published a randomized double-blind placebo-controlled clinical study report using Emblica as a key component. In this study, Group 1 subjects were given Emblica, melatonin, and α-lipoic acid topically (twice a day) along with a dietary supplement consisting of ascorbic acid, tocopherol, lutein, and α-lipoic acid (two capsules a day). The subjects in Group 2 received only the carrier topically (placebo, twice a day) and the dietary supplement with antioxidants (two capsules a day) and Group 3 subjects received only the carrier topically (placebo) and orally (placebo, no antioxidants). Results clearly showed statistically significant ($p < 0.005$) increase in skin hydration and skin lipids for both Groups 1 and 2 over a period of 2 months. However, Group 1 showed the highest increase both in skin hydration (55–100%) and skin lipids (55–70%) over placebo control. Moreover, oxidative stress and consequently formation of lipid peroxides in Group 1 subjects were also found to be lower by 30–40% ($p < 0.005$) over placebo control.

Possibly, Emblica antioxidant modulates UV/ROS initiated signal transduction pathways of matrix metalloprotease induction, thereby protecting the extracellular matrix proteins from degradation and providing photoprotective benefits.

Combination of Antioxidants

The antioxidant network is a complex system and is interlinked (Fig. 30.8) (1). Thus, an enhanced photoprotection can be achieved by topically applying an appropriate combination of antioxidants. The effect of topical antioxidants after UV irradiation is less obvious, whereas the photoprotective effect of topical antioxidants applied before UV exposure has been well recognized (46).

Co-application of vitamins E and C provided a much more pronounced photoprotective effect as compared to the application of a single antioxidant (46). Even further improvement in photoprotection resulted when co-application of melatonin together with vitamins E and C was topically done (69). Recently, Lin et al. (83) has shown that the combination of 15% L-ascorbic acid and 1%

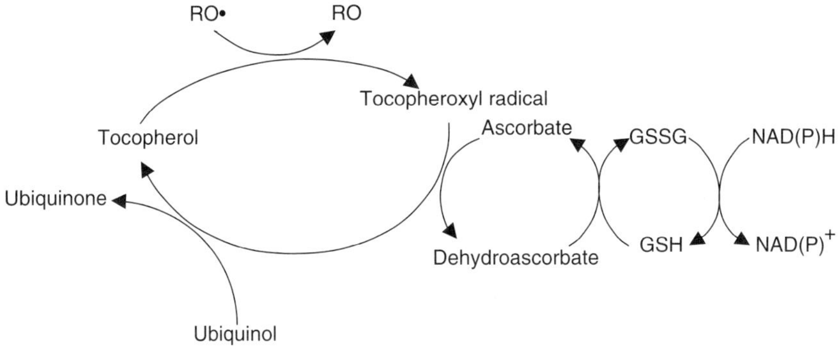

Figure 30.8 Interacting network of low molecular weight antioxidants. Abreviations: NAD(P)H, nicotinamide adenine dinucleotide phosphate reduced; GSH, glutiathione; GSSG, oxidized glutathione; NAD(P)+, nicotinamide adenine dinucleotide phosphate—oxidized form; NAD(P)H, nicotinamide adenine dinucleotide phosphate—reduced form; RO·, reactive oxygen free radical; RO, reduced reactive oxygen free radical.

α-tocopherol provided significant protection against erythema and sunburn cell formation; either L-ascorbic acid or 1% α-tocopherol alone was also protective but the combination was much superior. In addition, the combination of vitamins C and E provided protection against thymine dimer formation.

In another clinical study, Hadshiew et al. (124) have demonstrated the usefulness of applying a mixture of antioxidants in reducing the severity of experimentally induced polymorphous light eruption in humans. The antioxidant blend consists of α-glucosylrutin, ferulic acid, and tocopheryl acetate. The reduction in experimentally induced polymorphous light erruption is observed due to the reduction in UV-A-induced oxidative stress. A blend of vitamin E linoleate, magnesium ascorbyl phosphate, butyl hydroxytoluene, and nordihydroguaradinic acid provided a significant reduction in UV radiation induced erythema in humans (125). Oral supplementation with β-carotene or a similar amount of mixed carotenoids also protects humans from UV-induced erythema (92). In another clinical study, Greul et al. (126) have shown a photoprotective effect by oral supplementation of an antioxidative combination containing both lipid and water-soluble compounds: carotenoids (β-carotene and lycopene), vitamins C and E, selenium, and proanthocyanidines. The primary efficacy parameters included the reduction of UV-induced matrix metalloprotease (MMP-1 and MMP-9) expressions.

Unconventional Photoprotectants

Apart from increasing the skin's antioxidant capacity by topical or oral application of antioxidants, other substances may also boost antioxidant capacity of skin by preventing formation of reactive oxidative species, or modulating complex signal transduction pathways or inhibiting matrix metalloprotease expression and activity.

Selenium

Selenium is an essential trace mineral in the human body (127) and is an important part of antioxidant enzymes, glutathione peroxidase, and thioredoxin reductase, which protect cells against the effects of free radicals (128,129). The activity of selenoenzymes can be increased by selenium supplementation (130). Selenium is also essential for normal functioning of the immune system and thyroid gland (131). Plant foods are the major sources of selenium.

Topical L-selenomethionine protected mice against UV-induced erythema and skin cancer (132). In human beings, topical L-selenomethionine increased the minimal erythema dose in a dose-responsive manner (133).

Zinc

Zinc is an essential mineral that is found in almost every cell. It stimulates the activity of over 200 metalloenzymes, which are substances that promote biochemical reactions in the body (134). Zinc supports a healthy immune system (135), is needed for wound healing (136), helps maintain one's sense of taste and smell (137), and is needed for DNA synthesis (138). Zinc also supports normal growth and development during pregnancy, childhood, and adolescence (139,140).

Zinc has an important antioxidant effect in tissues (141). All body tissues contain zinc. In skin, it is five to six times more concentrated in the epidermis than the dermis. Topical application of zinc, in the form of divalent zinc ions, has been reported to provide photoprotection for skin (141). Topical application of zinc ions has been shown to induce synthesis of metallothionein (sulfhydryl-rich proteins), which may account for its photoprotective effect (142). Alternately, zinc may replace redox active molecules, such as iron and copper, at critical sites in cell membranes and proteins (141).

Chelating Agents

The iron content is substantially elevated over basal levels in the skin of mice exposed to UV-B irradiation and in the skin of sun-exposed body sites of healthy individuals (17,30). Iron participates as a catalyst in the formation of the highly damaging hydroxyl radical. Hence, topical application of certain iron chelators can act as photoprotectant. Thus, 2-furildioxime was shown to be an efficient photoprotectant alone (17) or in combination with sunscreens (30). Also, desferrioxamine, an iron-chelating agent, was examined as a photoprotectant against UV-radiation-induced free radical production (143). Photoprotection was demonstrated by topically applying desferrioxamine to the human skin by using electron paramagnetic resonance (EPR) examination. Desferrioxamine reduced the 5,5′-dimethylpyrroline-1-oxide (DMPO) radical signal by about 50% indicating that iron plays a major role in UV-induced oxidative

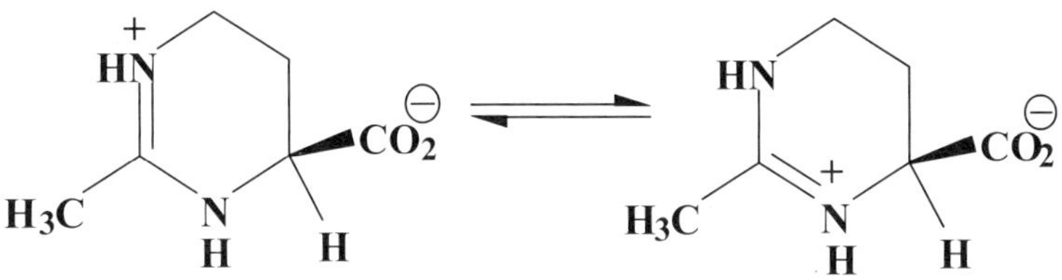

Figure 30.9 Structures of ectoin.

damage. Recently, Emblica antioxidant has also been shown to have excellent transition metal chelating ability (23,54). Application of metal chelators may be a route to prevent or reduce oxidative damage to skin.

Compatible Solutes

Compatible solutes are a group of diverse compounds; they are highly soluble in water and have either polyhydric alcohol (such as, mannosylglycerate, mannosylglyceramide diglyceryl phosphates, cyclic-2,3-bisphosphoglycerate, di-myo-inositol phosphates) or amphoteric functionalities (such as, ectoin, hydroxyectoin) (144). The term "compatible" originally coined by Brown (145), refers to the fact that these materials are compatible with the cells' metabolism, even at very high concentrations.

Recently, Bünger et al. (146,147) have shown significant photoprotective effects of one such compatible solute, namely, ectoin (Fig. 30.9). Topically applied ectoin was shown to reduce significantly sunburn cells formation and destruction of langerhans cells under UV irradiation (147). Photoprotective properties of ectoin may involve inhibition of UV-A-induced expression of intercellular adhesion molecule (ICAM-1) (148,149). Ectoin has also been found to have an excellent long-term skin moisturizing ability (146).

Retinoids

Retinoids are a class of compounds consisting of four isoprenoids units joined in a head-to-tail manner. All retinoids are derived from a monocyclic parent compound containing five carbon–carbon double bonds and a functional group at the terminus of the acyclic portion. They are vitamins, because retinol is not synthesized in the body and must be derived from the diet. Vitamin A is used as the generic descriptor encompassing retinol, retinal, and retinoic acid. The main circulating form of vitamin A in the blood is retinol, and the epidermis stores it as retinyl esters (150). The epidermis can be easily loaded with high amounts of vitamin A by topical application of either retinol or retinal. Retinol, however, is sensitive to light, oxygen, and heat and is difficult to formulate with (151).

Topical retinoids, namely retinoic acid (tretinoin), have been proven to prevent and repair clinical features of photoaging; these processes are facilitated by an ability to prevent loss of collagen from, and stimulate new collagen formation in, the papillary dermis of sun-exposed skin (152). Fisher et al. (153) have shown that pretreatment of skin with retinoic acid inhibits UV induction of matrix metalloproteases. Several good reviews on the topical application of retinoids have recently been published (151,152,154–156).

Dihydroxyacetone

Dihydroxyacetone (DHA) is a simple three-carbon sugar (157,158). It is an intermediate in carbohydrate metabolism in higher plants and animals. Specifically, this three-carbon sugar is physiological product (dihydroxyacetone monophosphate) of the body formed and utilized during glycolysis. In crystalline form, DHA is a mixture of one monomer and four dimers. The monomer is formed by heating or melting dimeric DHA or by dissolving in water.

The reaction product of DHA and the skin protein that produces the "tan" color has been shown to provide protection against UV-A in animals and humans (159–162). Experimental and clinical evidence show that skin that has been treated topically with 3% DHA solution overnight has a sun protection factor (SPF) of at least 3 in the UV-B region. Likewise, a photoprotection factor of 10 in the UV-A region has been observed with 15% solution of DHA. The advantage of this DHA-treated skin pigmentation is that it cannot be removed by perspiration, swimming, or washings. It can only be removed by desquamation. Fusaro and Lynch (161) suggest using DHA tanning in conjunction with sunscreens to reduce UV-A exposure, and thereby reduce incidence of malignant melanoma. The combination of DHA tanning and sunscreens usage has been shown to provide good protection against skin eruptions in a variegate porphyria patient (163). Petersen et al. (164) have shown that sunless skin tanning with DHA delays broad-spectrum UV photocarcinogenesis in hairless mice.

COMMERCIAL PRODUCTS

A wide range of sunscreen and skin care products containing antioxidants (with or without photoprotectants) is available commercially (Table 30.4). Information incorporated in the list is obtained mainly from the two well-known websites (www.drugstore.com and www.dermatologistrx.com) and individual company websites. This list is not an exhaustive one, but is an example to show the utility of antioxidants in sunscreen and skin care products.

CONCLUSIONS

Reactive oxygen species play a major role in photoaging and induce changes in gene expression pathways related to degradation of extracellular proteins. By now, ample evidence exists to affirm that most cutaneous cancers and many of the associated damages attributed to cutaneous aging, are results of exposure to solar radiation. In dealing with this etiology, it is almost certain that preventive modalities will continue to be the most reasonable approach to abating the

Table 30.4 Commercially Available Products Having Sunscreens and Antioxidants (and Photoprotectants): A Selected List

Brand name	Supplier	SPF	Sunscreens	Antioxidants/other photoprotectants	Selected claims
Aveeno skin brightening daily treatment	Johnson & Johnson	15	Octinoxate, avobenzone	Ascorbyl glucoside, retinol, ascorbic acid, tocopherol	Evens out skin tone and texture; brightens dull-looking skin; visibly reduces fine lines
Aveeno radiant skin daily moisturizer	Johnson & Johnson	15	Octinoxate, avobenzone, octisalate	Soya seed extract	Improving skin texture; evening out skin tone; improving skin clarity
Almay milk plus nourishing facial lotion	Revlon	15	Octinoxate, oxybenozone, avobenzone	Retinyl palmitate, tocopherol acetate, magnesium ascorbyl phosphate, green tea and other extracts	Double skin's moisture content immediately; improve skin's softness and smoothness; reduce the appearance of fine lines and wrinkles
Almay Kinetin age decelerating daily cream	Revlon	15	Octinoxate, oxybenzone, octisalate, avobenzone	Magnesium ascorbyl phosphate, tocopheryl acetate, retinyl palmitate, green tea and other plant extracts	Increase skin smoothness and clarity; diminish the appearance of fine wrinkles; significantly fade the look of brown spots and uneven skin tone
Banana boat Ultra sunblock lotion	Playtex	30	Octinoxate, oxybenzone, titanium dioxide	Tocopherol	Broad-spectrum UV-A and UV-B protection; aloe vera and vitamin E helps nourish skin
Bain de Soleil Oil-free protecteur faces sunscreen lotion	Schering-Plough	30	Avobenzone, homosalate, octocrylene, octisalate oxybenzone	Tocopherol, tetinyl palmitate	New pro-retinol formula; ultra hydrating formula for visibly smoother skin; UV-A/UV-B with avobenzone

(*continued*)

Table 30.4 *Continued*

Brand name	Supplier	SPF	Sunscreens	Antioxidants/other photoprotectants	Selected claims
Coppertone Endless summer ultrasheer sunscreen	Schering-Plough	15	Avobenzone, homosalate, octisalate, octocrylene, oxybenzone	Tocopherol, Emblica antioxidant, sodium ascorbyl phosphate, retinyl palmitate	Provides broad-spectrum UV-A/UV-B sun protection to help prevent premature skin aging, long-term skin damage and skin cancer; contains AO-7, an antioxidant complex clinically proven to combat harmful free radicals created by sun exposure
Coppertone Endless summer ultrasheer sunscreen	Schering-Plough	30	Same ingredients as above	Same ingredients as above	Same claims as above
Coppertone Endless summer ultrasheer sunscreen	Schering-Plough	45	Same ingredients as above	Same ingredients as above	Same claims as above
Coppertone Shade sunblock lotion	Schering-Plough	45	Avobenzone, homosalate, octocrylene, octisalate	Tocopherol	Broad-spectrum UV-A protection; helps protect against sunburn; reduce aging and skin cancer
Coppertone Oil-free sunblock lotion for faces	Schering-Plough	30	Avobenzone, homosalate, octocrylene, octisalate, oxybenzone	Tocopherol, retinyl palmitate	Provides powerful protection for delicate skin; Contains a special blend of antioxidant. A and E; Helps prevent the premature appearance of fine lines and wrinkles
DDF EPF moisturizer C3	DDF	15	Octinoxate, octisalate	Magnesium ascorbyl phosphate, vitamin C ester complex, tocopherol	Protect skin from environmental damage; Potent formulation that blocks free radicals most responsible for cell damage and aging of the skin

Dove Face care essential nutrients	Unilever	15	Octinoxate, octisalate, avobenzone, ensulizole	Tocopheryl acetate, Retinyl palmitate, green tea and grape seed extracts	Effectively nourish and hydrate to help make a lasting difference to the health and beauty of your skin; combines a broad-spectrum UV protection with five essential nutrients, etc.
Eucerin Daily sun defense	Beirsdorf	15	Octisalate, octctnoxate, avobenzone	Tocopheryl acetate, glucosylrutin, isoquercetin	Helps prevent sun-related irritations; advanced antioxidant complex; moisturizes as it protects
L'Oreal Dermo-expertise future-e moisturizer	L'Oreal	15	Octocrylene, ensulizole	Tocopheryl acetate, tocopherol	Softer, smoother skin today; Healthier-looking skin in 1 week
L'Oreal Dermo-expertise hydrafresh mineral-charged moisturizer	L'Oreal	15	Octinoxate, ensulizole	Tocopheryl acetate, ascorbyl glucoside	Builds healthy, strong skin with magnesium, calcium and vitamin C
Neostrata Daytime protection cream	Neostrata	15	Octinoxate, titanium dioxide	Tocopheryl acetate	A highly moisturizing cream formulated with broad spectrum SPF 15, which provides broad spectrum sunscreen protection
Neutrogena Healthy skin antiwrinkle cream	Johnson & Johnson	15	Octinoxate ensulizole	Retinol, tocopherol tocopheryl acetate green tea extract	A retinol facial treatment with multivitamins; visibly reduces the appearance of fine lines and wrinkles
Neutrogena Sunblock lotion	Johnson & Johnson	30	Titanium dioxide	Tocopherol	Broad-spectrum UV-A/UV-B protection; instant protection

(continued)

Table 30.4 *Continued*

Brand name	Supplier	SPF	Sunscreens	Antioxidants/other photoprotectants	Selected claims
Neutrogena Ultrasheer dry-touch sunblock	Johnson & Johnson	45	Avobenzone, homosalate, octinoxate, octisalate, oxybenzone	Retinyl palmitate, ascorbyl palmitate, tocopheryl acetate	UV-A/UV-B protection; waterproof, sweatproof, rubproof; enriched with antioxidant vitamins A, C, and E to help fight against environmental damage
Nivea Visage coenzyme Q10 plus wrinkle control lotion	Beirsdorf	15	Octinoxate, octisalate, oxybenzone	Ubiquinone, tocopheryl acetate,	More of skin's own wrinkle control; Proven double action wrinkle reduction
Nivea for men vitamin enriched daily protective lotion	Beirsdorf	15	Octinoxate, octisalate, oxybenzone	Tocopheryl acetate, glucosylrutin, isoquercetin	Vitamin enriched; protects every day against sun damage and moisturizes to relieve dry, wind burned skin
Olay Regenerist enhancing lotion with UV protection	Procter & Gamble	15	Octisalate, avobenzone, ensulizole, octocrylene	Tocopheryl acetate, green tea extract	Beautifully regenerates skin's appearance; broad-spectrum UV-A/UV-B sunscreen
Olay Complete UV defense moisture lotion	Procter & Gamble	15	Octinoxate, zinc oxide	Tocopheryl acetate, ascorbic acid	Gives your skin complete care, providing everything it needs most to stay younger looking and beautiful
Ombrelle lotion	L'Oreal	30	Octinoxate, oxybenzone, octisalate, avobenzone	Tocopherol	Helps prevent premature skin aging and damage
Skin Medica Daily sunprotection	Skin Medica	20	Octinoxate, zinc oxide	Tocopheryl acetate, retinyl palmitate, ascorbyl palmitate	Nonoily formula includes antioxidants and botanical extracts that provide protection from the aging effects caused by the sun, while lightly moisturizing the skin

damages resulting from actinic insult. It would seem reasonable to assume that sunscreens in combination with photoprotectants will continue to be the major weapon in this preventive campaign. In order to function as photoprotective agents, antioxidants have to be present at the right place in the right concentrations at the right time. Topical application of photoprotectants should supplement the natural antioxidant protection present in skin, and provide supplemental reserves as oxidative stress depletes antioxidant stores.

Animal studies clearly demonstrate that antioxidants have photoprotective effects. Topical application of a single antioxidant does not take into account the dynamic interplay of multiple antioxidants. Photoprotection involves the synergistic interplay of several antioxidants. Thus, topical application of a combination of antioxidants is preferred over the use of a single antioxidant.

Plant polyphenolics have been shown to have excellent photoprotective effect. As these materials are complex mixtures of many compounds, a definite need exists for standardization of these materials. Otherwise, quality, reproducibility, and effectiveness of these materials may be compromised or questioned. The technology (e.g., high-performance liquid chromatography, HPLC; high-performance thin layer chromatography, HPTLC) necessary to produce truly standardized extract exists. What is needed the standardization of these materials (at least 50% of the constituents), keeping close to the natural compositional balance.

The molecular pathways leading to the sunburn, photoimmunosupression, photoaging, and photcarcinogenesis seem to be different. However, the most studied biological end point has been the reduction of UV-induced erythema. Selection of other biological targets is important in clinical studies. Systematic published clinical studies combining true photostable broad-spectrum sunscreens along with antioxidant(s) are lacking.

Certainly, there are several promising areas of human clinical research yet to be carried out. A few examples are: (i) combination of photostable broad-spectrum sunscreens and antioxidants; (ii) combination of photostable broad-spectrum sunscreens with chelating agents and matrix metalloprotease inhibitors; (iii) combination of photostable broad-spectrm sunscreens and unconventional photoprotectants; and (iv) combination of photostable broad-spectrum sunscreens and Emblica antioxidant as it has a broad-spectrum antioxidant activity, strong chelating property, and excellent matrix metalloprotease inhibitory activity. Further long-term clinical studies are warranted before a true photoprotective composition can be proposed for skin protection against UV-induced damage.

REFERENCES

1. Pinnell SR. Cutaneous phtodamage, oxidative stress, and topical antioxidant protection. J Am Acad Dermatol 2003; 48:1–19.
2. Wenk J, Brenneisen P, Meewes C, Wlaschek M, Peters T, Blaudschwun R, Ma W, Kuhr L, Schneider L, Scharftetter-Kochanek K. UV-induced oxidative stress and

photoaging. In: Thiele J, Elsner P, eds. Oxidants and Antioxidants in Cutaneous Biology. Vol. 2. Current Prob Dermatol. Basel: Karger, 2001:83–94.

3. Berneburg M, Plettenberg H, Krutmann J. Photoaging of human skin. Photodermatol Photoimmunol Photomed 2000; 16:239–244.
4. Wlaschek M, Briviba K, Stricklin GP, Sies H, Scharfetter-Kochanek K. J Invest Dermatol 1995; 104:194–198.
5. Berneburg M, Grether-Beck S, Kurten V, Ruzicka T, Briviba K, Sies H, Krutmann J. Singlet oxygen mediates the UV-induced generation of the photoaging-associated mitochondrial common deletion. J Biol Chem 1999; 274:15345–15349.
6. Haywood R, Wardman P, Sanders R, Linge C. Sunscreens inadequately protect against ultraviolet-A-induced free radicals in skin: Implications for skin aging and melanoma. J Invest Dermatol 2003; 121:862–868.
7. Carbonare MD, Pathak MA. Skin photosensitizing agents and the role of reactive oxygen species in photoaging. J Photochem Photobiol B: Biol 1992; 14:105–124.
8. Hanson KM, Simon JD. Epidermal trans-uronic acid and the UV-A induced photoaging of the skin. Proc Natl Acad Sci USA 1998; 95:10576.
9. Cantrell A, McGarvey DJ. Photochemical studies of 4-*tert*-4′-methoxydibenzoylmethane (BM-DBM), J Photochem Photobiol B: Biol 2001; 64:117–122.
10. Stari A, Sarasin A. Ultraviolet A- and singlet oxygen-induced mutation spectra. Methods Enzymol 2000; 319:153–165.
11. Epe B. Genotoxicity of singlet oxygen Chem Biol Interact 1991;80:239–260.
12. Allen J, Gossett C. Photochemical formation of singlet molecular oxygen in illuminated aqueous solution of several commercially available sunscreen active ingredients. Chem Res Toxicol 1996; 9:605–609.
13. Kawanishi S, Hiraku Y. Sequence-specific DNA damage induced by UVA radiation in the presence of endogeneous and exogeneous photosensitizers. In: Thiele J, Elsner P, eds. Oxidants and antioxidants in Cutaneous Biology. Vol 29. Basel: Karger, 2001:74–82.
14. Rittie L, Fisher GJ. UV-light-induced cascades and skin aging. Ageing Res Rev 2002; 1:705–720.
15. Brenneisen P, Wenk J, Klotz LO, Wlaschek M, Brivia K, Krieg T, Sies H, Scharffetter-Kochanek K. Central role of ferrous-ferric iron in the ultraviolet B irradiation-mediated signaling pathway leading to increased interstitial collagenase (matrix-degrading metalloprotease (MMP)-1) and stromelysin-1 (MMP-3) mRNA levels in cultured human dermal fibroblasts. J Biol Chem 1998; 273:5279–5287.
16. Pourzand C, Watkin RD, Brown JE, Tyrell RM. Ultraviolet A radiation induces immediate release of iron in human primary skin fibroblasts: the role of ferritin. Proc Natl Acad Sci USA 1999; 96:6751–6756.
17. Bissett DL, McBride JF. Iron content of human epidermis from sun-exposed and non-exposed body sites. J Soc Cosmet Chem 1992; 43:215–217.
18. Biemond P, Swaak AJ, van Eijk HG, Koster JF. Superoxide dependent iron release from ferritin in inflammatory diseases. Free Radic Biol Med 1988; 4:185–198.
19. Masaki H, Arsumi T, Sakurai H. Detection of hydrogen peroxide and hydroxyl radicals in murine skin fibrpblasts under UVB irradiation. Biochem Biophys Res Commun 1995; 206:474–479.

20. Halliwell B, Gutteridge JM. Biologically relevant metal ion-dependant hydroxyl radical generation: an update. FEBS Lett 1992; 307:108–112.
21. Vile GF, Tyrell RM. UVA radiation-induced oxidative damage to lipids and proteins in vitro and human skin fibroblast is dependant on iron and singlet oxygen. Free Radic Biol Med 1995; 18:721–730.
22. Bast A, Haenen GRMM, Doelman CJA. Oxidants and antioxidants: state of the art. Am J Med 1991; 91(Suppl. 3C):2S–8S.
23. Chaudhuri RK, Puccetti G. Transition metal-induced oxidation: implications for skin care products. Cosmet Toilet 2002; 117:43–56.
24. Cillard J, Cillard P, Cormier M. Effect of experimental factors on the pro-oxidant behavior of α-tocopherol. J Am Chem Soc 1980; 57:255–261.
25. Hussain SR, Cillard J, Cillard P. α-Tocopherol pro-oxidant effect and malondiladehyde production, J Am Oil Chem Soc 1987; 64:109–111.
26. Khrapova NG. Kinetics, aspects of the action of tocopherols as antioxidants. Biofizica 1977; 22:436–442.
27. Hicks M, Gebicki JM. Inhibition of peroxidation in linoleic acid membranes by nitroxide radicals, butylated hydroxytoluene and α-tocopherol. Arch Biochem Biophys 1981; 210:56–63.
28. Michel REJ, McCann R. Vitamin E is a complete tumor promoter in mouse skin. Carcinogenesis 1993; 14:659–662.
29. Palozza P. Prooxidant actions of carotenoids in biologic systems. Nutr Rev 1998; 56:257–165.
30. Bissett DL, Chatterjee R, Hannon DP. Chronic ultraviolet radiation-induced increase in skin iron and the photoprotective effect of topically applied iron chelators. Photochem Photobiol 1991; 54:215–223.
31. Gutteridge JM, Rowley DA, Halliwell B, Cooper DF, Heeley D.M. Copper and iron complexes catalytic for oxygen radical reactions in sweat from human athletes. Clin Chim Acta 1985; 145:267–273.
32. Jurkiewicz Lange BA, Buettner GR. Electron paramagnetic resonance detection of free radicals in UV-irradiated human and mousse skin. In: Thiele J, Elsner P, eds. Oxidants and Antioxidants in Cutaneous Biology. Vol. 29. Current Problems in Cutaneous Biology. Basel: Karger, 2001:18–25.
33. Hoekstra R, Eskens FALM, Verweij J. Matrix metalloprotease inhibitors: current developments and future perspectives. The Oncologist 2001; 6:415–427.
34. Brenneisen P, Oh J, Wlashek M, Wenk J, Briviba K, Hommel C, Herrmann G, Sies H, Scharffetter-Kochanek K. Ultraviolet B wavelength dependence for the regulation of two major matrix-metalloproteinases and their inhibitor TIMP-1 in human dermal fibroblasts. Photochem Photobiol 1996; 64:877–885.
35. Brenneisen P, Sies H, Scharffetter-Kochanek K. Ultraviolet-B irradiation and matrix metalloproteinases: from induction via signaling to initial events. Ann N Y Acad Sci 2002; 973:31–43.
36. Hermann G, Wlaschek M, Lange TS, Prenzel K, Goerz G, Scharffetter-Kochanek K. UV-A irradiation stimulates the synthesis of various matrix-metalloproteinases (MMPs) in cultured human fibroblasts. Exp Dematol 1993; 2:92–97.
37. Brennan M, Bhatti H, Nerusu KC, Bhagavathula N, Kang S, Fisher GJ, Varani J, Voorhees JJ. Matrix metalloproteinase-1 is the major collagenolytic enzyme

responsible for collagen damage in UV-irradiated human skin. Photochem Photobiol 2003; 78:43–48.
38. Oikarinen A, Kallionen M. Biochemical and immunohistochemical study of collagen in sun-exposed and protected skin. Photodermatology 1989; 6:24–31.
39. Schwartz E, Crickshank FA, Christensen CC, Perlish JS, Lebwohl M. Collagen alterations in chronically sun-damaged human skin. Photochem Photobiol 1993; 58:841–844.
40. Bernstein EF, Uitto J. The effect of photodamage on dermal extracellular matrix. Clin Dermatol 1996; 14:143–151.
41. Fisher GJ, Choi HC, Bata-Csorgo Z, Shao Y, Datta S, Wang ZQ, Kang S, Voorhees JJ. Ultraviolet irradiation increases matrix metalloproteinase-8 protein in human skin in vivo. J Invest Dermatol 2001; 117:219–226.
42. Oikarinen A. The aging of skin: chronoaging versus photoaging. Photderm Photoimmun Photomed 1990; 43:3–4.
43. Harman D. Aging: a theory based on free radical and radiation chemistry. J Gerontol 1956; 1:298–300.
44. McCord JM, Fridovich I. Superoxide dismutase: An enzymatic function for erythrocupein (hemocuprein). J Biol Chem 1969; 244:6049–6055.
45. Yu BP. Cellular defenses against damage from reactive oxygen species. Physiol Rev 1994; 74:139–162.
46. Thiele JJ, Dreher F, Packer L. Antioxidant defense systems in skin. In: Elsner P, Maibach HI, eds. Cosmeceuticals Drugs vs. Cosmetics. New York: Marcel Dekker, 2000:145–187.
47. Kirkman HN, Gaetani GF. Catalase: a tetrameric enzyme with four tightly bound molecules of NADPH. Proc Natl Acad Sci USA 1984; 81:4343–4347.
48. Mates JM, Perez-Gomez C, De Castro IN. Antioxidant enzymes and human diseases. Clin Biochem 1999; 32:595–603.
49. Shindo Y, Witt E, Han D, Epstein W, Packer L. Enzymatic and non-enzymatic antioxidants in human skin. J Invest Dermatol 1994; 102:122–124.
50. Shindo Y, Witt E, Packer L. Antioxidant defense mechanisms in murine epidermis and dermis and their response to ultraviolet light. J Invest Dermatol 1993; 100:260–265.
51. Thiele JJ, Traber MG, Packer L. Depletion of human stratum corneum vitamin E: an early and sensitive in-vivo marker of UV-induced photooxidation. J Invest Dermatol 1998; 110:756–762.
52. Fuchs J. Potentials and limitations of the natural antioxidants RRR-alpha-tocopherol, L-ascorbic acid, and β-carotene in cutaneous photoprotection. Free Radic biol Med 1998; 25:848–873.
53. Chaudhuri RK, Puccetti G, Hwang C, Guttierez G, Serrar M. Low molecular weight tannins of *Phyllanthus emblica:* anti-aging effects. Cosmet Toilet 2004; 119:59–68.
54. Chaudhuri RK. Phyllanthus tannins. In: Elsner P, Maibach HI, eds. Cosmeceuticals: Drugs vs Cosmetics. New York: Marcel and Dekker, 2004; 26:465–488.
55. Munne-Bosch S, Alegre L. the function of tocopherols and tocotrienols in plants. Crit Rev Plant Sci 2002; 21:31–57.
56. Packer L, Weber SU, Rimbach G. Molecular aspects of alpha-tocotrienol antioxidant action and cell signaling. J Nutr 2001; 131(Suppl):369S–373S.

57. Krol ES, Kramer-Stickland KA, Liebler DC. Photoprotective actions of topically applied vitamin E. Drug Metab Rev 2000; 32:413–420.
58. Krol ES, Escalante DD, Liebler DC. Mechanisms of dimer and trimer formation from ultraviolet-irradiated alpha-tocopherol. Lipids 2001; 36:49–55.
59. Roshchupkin DI, Pistsov MY, Potapenko AY. Inhibition of ultraviolet light-induced erythema by antioxidants. Arch Dermatol Res 1979; 266:91–94.
60. Moeller H, Ansmann A, Wallat S. Wirkungen von vitamin E auf die haut bei topischer anwendung. Fat Sci Technol 1989; 91:295–305.
61. Ritter EF, Axelrod M, Minn KW, Eades E, Rudner AM, Serafin D, Klitzman B. Modulation of ultraviolet light-induced epidermal damage: beneficial effects of tocopherol. Plast Reconstr Surg 1997; 100:973–980.
62. Yuen KS, Halliday GM. Alpha tocopherol, an inhibitor of epidermal lipid peroxidation, prevents ultraviolet radiation from suppressing the skin immune system. Photochem Photobiol 1997; 65:587–592.
63. Khettab N, Amory MC, Briand G, Bousquet B, Combre A, Forlot P, Barey M. Photoprotective effect of vitamins A and E on polyamine and oxygenated free radical metabolism in hairless mouse epidermis. Biochimie 1988; 70:1709–1713.
64. McVean M, Liebler DC. Inhibition of UVB induced DNA photodamage in mouse epidermis by topically applied alpha-tocopherol. Carcinogenesis 1992; 18:1617–1622.
65. Gensler HL, Magdaleno M. Topical vitamin E inhibition of immunosuppression and tumerigenesis induced by ultraviolet radiation. Nutr Cancer 1991; 15:97–106.
66. Potapenko AJ, Abijev GA, Piszov MJ, Pliquett F. PUVA-induced erythema and changes in mechanoelectrical properties of skin. Inhibition by tocopherols. Arch Dermatol Res 1984; 276:12–16.
67. Potapenko AJ, Piszov MJ, Abijev GA, Pliquett F. l-Tokopherol, ein inhibitor von durchUV-strahlung induzierten veranderungen mechanoelektrischer hauteingenschaften. Dermatol Monatsschr 1983; 304:169.
68. Montenegro L, Bonita F, Rigano L, Giogilli S, Sirigu S. Protective effect evaluation of free radical scavengers on UVB induced human cutaneous erythema by skin reflectance spectrophotometry. Int J Cosmet Sci 1995; 17:91–103.
69. Dreher F, Gabard B, Schwindt DA, Maibach HI. Topical melatonin in combination with vitamins E and C protects skin from UV-induced erythema: a human study in vivo Br J Dermatol 1998; 139:332–339.
70. Dreher F, Denig N, Gabard B, Schwindt DA, Maibach HI. Effect of topical antioxidants on UV-induced erythema formation when administered after exposure. Dermatology 1999; 198:52–55.
71. Halliwell B, Gutteridge JMC. In: Free Radicals in Biology and Medicine. 3rd ed. Oxford: Oxford University Press, 1999:200–208.
72. Chojkier M, Houghlum K, Solis-Herruzo J, Brenner DA. Stimulation of collagen gene expression by ascorbic acid in cultured human fibroblasts. A role for lipid peroxidation. J Biol Chem 1989; 264:16957–16962.
73. Geesin JC, Hendricks LJ, Falkenstein PA, Gordon JS, Berg RA. Regulation of collagen synthesis by ascorbic acid: characterization of the role of ascorbate-stimulated lipid peroxidation. Arch Biochem Biophys 1991; 290:27–32.
74. Uchida Y, Behne M, Quiec D, Elias PM, Holleran WM. Vitamin C stimulates sphingolipid production and makers of barrier formation in submerged human keratinocyte cultures. J Invest Dermatol 2001; 117:1307–1313.

75. Murray J, Darr D, Reich J. Topical vitamin C treatment reduces ultraviolet B radiation induced erythema in human skin. J Invest Dermatol 1991; 96:587.
76. Murray J, Darr D, Reich J. Photoprotection of human skin by topical vitamin C. Clin Res 1992; 40:143A.
77. Darr D, Combs S, Duntston S, Manning T, Pinnell S. Topical vitamin C protects porcine skin from ultraviolet radiation-induced damage. Br J Dermatol 1992; 127:247–253.
78. Kobayashi S, Takehama M, Itoh S, Ogata E. Protective effect of magnesium-L-ascorbyl-2-phosphate (VC-PMG) against skin damage induced by UVB irradiation. Photochem Photobiol 1996; 64:224–228.
79. Kumano Y, Sakamoto T, Egawa M, Iwai I, Tanaka M, Yamamoto I. In vitro and in vivo prolonged biological activities of novel vitamin C derivative, 2-O-alpha-D-glucopyranosyl-L-ascorbic acid (AA-2G), in cosmetic fields. J Nutr Sci Vitaminol (Tokyo) 1998; 44:345–359.
80. Miyai E, Yanagida M, Akiyama J, Yamamoto I. Ascorbic acid 2-O-alpha-glucoside-induced redox modulation in human keratinocyte cell line, SCC: mechanism of photoprotective effect against ultraviolet light B. Biol Pharm Bull 1997; 20:632–636.
81. Austria R, Semenzato A, Bettero A. Stability of vitamin C derivatives in solution and topical formulations. J Pharm Biomed Anal 1997; 15:795–801.
82. Humbert PG, Haftek M, Creidi P, Lapiere C, Nusgens B, Richard A, Schmitt D, Rougier A, Zahouani H. Topical ascorbic acid on photodamaged skin. Clinical, topographical and ultrastructural evaluation: double blind study vs. placebo. Exp Dermatol 2003; 12:237.
83. Lin JY, Selim MA, Shea CR, Grichnik JM, Omar MM, Monteiro-Riviere NA, Pinnell SR. UV photoprotection by combination topical antioxidants vitamin C and vitamin E. J Am Acad Dermatol 2003; 48:866–874.
84. Fitzpatrick RE, Rostan EF. Double-blind, half-face study comparing vitamin C and vehicle for rejuvenation of photodamage. Dermatol Surg 2002; 28:231–236.
85. Traikovich SS. Use of topical ascorbic acid and its effects on photodamaged skin topography. Arch Otolaryngol Head Neck Surg, 1999; 125:1091–1098.
86. Stahl W, Sundquist AR, Hanusch M, Schwartz W, Sies H. Separation of β-carotene and lycopene geometrical isomers in biological samples. Clin Chem 1993; 39:810–814.
87. Ribaya-Mercado JD, Garmyn M, Gilchrest BA, Russel RM. Skin lycopene is destroyed preferentially over beta-carotene during ultraviolet irradiation in humans. J Nutr 1995; 125:1854–1859.
88. Biesalski HK, Hemmes C, Hopfenmuller W, Schmid C, Gollnick HP. Effects of controlled exposure of sunlight on plasma and skin levels of beta-carotene. Free Radic Res 1996; 24:215–224.
89. Krinsky NI, Yeum KJ. Carotenoid–radical interactions. Biochem Biophys Res Commun 2003; 305:754–760.
90. Edge R, McGarvy DJ, Truscott TG. The carotenoids as antioxidants—a review. J Photochem Photobiol B: Biol 1997; 41:189–200.
91. Stahl W, Sies H. Protection against solar radiation—protective properties of antioxidants. In: Giacomoni PU, ed. Sun Protection in Man. New York: Elsevier, 2001:561–572.
92. Stahl W, Sies H. Carotenoids and protection against solar UV radiation. Skin Pharmacol Appl Skin Physiol 2002; 15:291–296.

93. Stahl W, Heinrich U, Jungmann H, Sies H, Tronnier H. Carotenoids and carotenoids plus vitamin E protect against ultraviolet light-induced erythema in humans. Am J Clin Nutr 2000; 71:795–798.
94. Lee J, Jiang S, Levine N, Watson RR. Carotenoid supplementation reduces erythema in human skin after simulated solar radiation exposure. Proc Soc Exp Biol Med 2000; 223:170–174.
95. Greenberg ER, Baron JA, Stukel TA, Stevens MM, Mandel JS, Spencer SK, Elias PM, Lowe N, Nierenberg DW, Bayrd G, Vance JC, Freeman DH, Clendening WE, Kwan T. The alpha-tocopherol, beta carotene cancer prevention study group. A cilinical trial of beta-carotene to prevent basal-cell and squamous-cell cancer on the skin. N Engl J Med 1990; 323:789–795.
96. Heinonnen OP, Albanes D. The alpha-tocopherol, beta carotene cancer prevention study group. The effect of vitamin E and beta carotene on the incidence of lung cancer and other cancers in male smokers. N Engl J Med 1994; 330:1029–1035.
97. Wang X, Liu C, Bronson RT, Smith DE, Krinsky NI, Russell RM. Retinoid signaling and activator protein-1-expression in ferrets given β-carotene supplements and exposed to tobacco smoke. J Natl Cancer Inst 1999; 91:60–66.
98. Baker DL, Krol ES, Jacobsen N, Liebler DC. Reactions of β-carotene with smoke oxidants. Identification of carotenoid oxidation products and evaluation of the prooxidant/antioxidant effect. Chem Res Toxicol 1999; 12:535–543.
99. Bors W, and Michel C. Chemistry of the antioxidant effect of polyphenols. Ann N Y Acad Sci 2002; 957:57–69.
100. Rohdewald P. A review of the French maritime pine bark extract (Pycnogenol), a herbal medication with a diverse clinical pharmacology. Int J Clin Pharmacol Ther 2002; 40:158–168.
101. Saliou C, Rimbach G, Moini H, McLaughlin L, Hosseini S, Lee J, Watson RR, Packer L. Solar ultraviolet-induced erythema in human skin and nuclear factor-kappa-B-dependent gene expression in keratinocytes are modulated by a French maritime pine bark extract. Free Radic Biol Med 2001; 30:154–160.
102. Bagchi D, Bagchi M, Stohs SJ, Das DK, Ray SD, Kuszynski CA, Joshi SS, Pruess HG. Free radicals and grape seed proanthocyanidin extract: importance in human health and disease prevention. Toxicology 2000; 148:187–197.
103. Gonzalez S, Pathak MA, Cuevas J, Villarrubia VG, Fitzpatrick TB. Topical or oral administration with an extract of *Polypodium leucotoms* prevents acute sunburn and psoralene-induced phototoxic reactions as well as depletion of Langerhans cells in human skin. Photodermatol Photoimmunol Photomed 1997; 13:50–60.
104. S Gonzalez, Pathak MA. Inhibition of ultraviolet-induced formation of reactive oxygen species, lipid peroxidation, erythema, and skin photosensitization by *Ploypodium leucotomos*. Photodermatol Photoimmunol Photomed 1996; 12:45–56.
105. Kang S, Chung JH, Lee JH, Fisher GJ, Wan YS, Duell EA, Voorhees JJ. Topical *N*-acetyl cysteine and genistein prevent ultraviolet-light-induced signaling that leads to photoaging in human skin in vivo. J Invest Dermatol 2003; 120:835–841.
106. Harbowy ME, Balentine DA. Tea chemistry. Crit Rev Plant Sci 1997; 16:415–480.
107. Afaq F, and Mukhtar H. Photochemoprevention by botanical antioxidants. Skin Pharmacol Appl Skin Physiol 2002; 15:297–306.
108. Katiyar SK, Mukhtar H. Tea consumption and cancer. World Rev Nutr Diet 1996; 79:154–184.

109. Mukhtar H, Ahmad N. Cancer chemoprevention: future holds in multiple agents. Toxicol Appl Pharmacol 1999; 158:207–210.
110. Katiyar SK, Ahmad N, Mukhtar H. Green tea and skin. Arch Dermatol 2000; 136:989–994.
111. Elmets CA, Singh D, Tubesing K, Matsui M, S Katiyar, Mukhtar H. Cutaneous photoprotection from ultraviolet injury by green tea polyphenols. J Am Acad Dermatol 2001; 44:425–432.
112. Katiyar SK, Matsui MS, Elmets CA, Mukhtar H, Polyphenolic antioxidant (−)-epigallocatechin-3-gallate from green tea reduces UVB-induced inflammatory responses and infiltration of leucocytes in human skin. Photochem Photobiol 1999; 69:148–153.
113. Zhao JF, Zhang YJ, Jin XH, Akhtar M, Santella RM, Bickers DR, Wang ZY. Green tea protects against psoralen plus ultraviolet A-induced photochemical damage to skin. J Invest Dermatol 1999; 113:1070–1075.
114. Katiyar SK, Perez A, Mukhtar H. Green tea polyphenol treatment to human skin prevents formation of ultraviolet light-B-induced pyrimidine dimers in DNA. Clin Cancer Res 2000; 6:3864–3869.
115. Wagner VH, Diesel P, Seitz M. The chemistry and analysis of silymarin from *Silybum marianum*, Gaetern. Arzneimittelforschung 1974; 24:466–471.
116. Pepping J. Milk thistle: *Silybum marianum*. Am J Health Syst Pharm 1999; 56:1195–1197.
117. Katiyar SK, Korman NJ, Mukhtar H, Agarwal R. Protective effects of silymarin against photocarcinogenesis in a mouse skin model. J Natl Cancer Inst 1997; 89:556–566.
118. Saliou C, Kitazawa M, McLaughlin L, Yang JP, Lodge JK, Tetsuka T, Iwasaki K, Cillard J, Okamoto T, Packer L. Antioxidants modulate acute solar ultraviolet radiation-induced NF-kappa-B activation in human keratinocyte cell line. Free Radic Biol Med 1999; 26:174–183.
119. Ghosal S, Triphati VK, Chauhan S. Active constituents of *Emblica officinalis*: Part I—The chemistry and antioxidative effects of two new hydrolyzable tannins, Emblicanin A and B. Indian J Chem 1996; 35B:941–948.
120. Chaudhuri RK. Emblica cascading antioxidant: a novel natural skin care ingredient. Skin Pharmacol Appl Skin Physiol 2002; 15:374–380.
121. Guerret S, Rojkind M, Druguet M, Chevallier M, Grimaud JA. Immunohistochemical micromethods for the measurement of specific collagen types in human liver biopsies. Collagen Relat Res 1988; 8:249–259.
122. Chaudhuri RK. Low molecular weight tannins as a new class of skin-lightening agent. J Cosmet Sci 2002; 53:305–306.
123. Morganti P, Bruno C, Guarneri F, Cardillo A, Del Ciotto P, Valenzano F. Role of topical and nutritional supplement to modify the oxidative stress. Int J Cosmet Sci 2002; 24:331–339.
124. Hadshiew I, Staeb F, Untiedt S, Bohnsack K, Rippke F, Hoelzle E. Effects of topically applied antioxidants in experimentally provoked polymorphous light eruption. Dermatology 1997; 195:362–368.
125. Muizzuddin N, Shakoori AR, Marenus KD. Effect of antioxidants and free radical scavengers on protection of human skin against UVB, UVA and IR irradiation. Skin Res Technol 1999; 5:260–265.

126. Greul AK, Grundmann JU, Heinrich F, Pfitzner I, Bernhardt J, Ambach A, Biesalski HK, Gollnick H. Photoprotection of UV-irradiated human skin: an antioxidative combination of vitamins E and C, carotenoids, selenium and proanthocyanidines. Skin Pharmacol Appl Skin Physiol 2002; 15:307–315.
127. National Research Council. Food and Nutrition Board. Recommended Dietary Allowances. 10th ed. Washington, DC: National Academy Press, 1989.
128. McKenzie RC. Selenium, ultraviolet radiation and the skin. Clin Exp Dermatol 2000; 25:631–636.
129. Combs GF Jr, Gray WP. Chemopreventive agents: selenium. Pharmacol Ther 1998; 79:179–192.
130. Brown KM, Pickard K, Nicol F, Beckett GJ, Duthie GG, Arthur JR. Effects of organic and inorganic selenium supplementation on selenoenzymes. Clin Sci (Colch), 2000; 98:593–599.
131. Levander OA. Nutrition and newly emerging viral diseases: an overview. J Nutr 1997; 127:948S–950S.
132. Burke KE, Burford RG, Combs GF Jr, Bhuyan KC, Abu-libdeh H. The effects of topical and oral L-selenomethionine on pigmentation and skin cancer induced by ultraviolet irradiation. Nutr Cancer 1992; 17:123–137.
133. Burke KE, Burford RG, Combs GF Jr, French IW, Skeffington DR. The effect of topical L-selenomethionine on minimal erythema dose of ultraviolet irradiation in humans. Photodermatol Photoimmunol Photomed 1992; 9:52–57.
134. Sandstead HH. Understanding zinc: recent observations and interpretations. J Lab Clin Med 1994; 124:322–327.
135. Solomons NW. Mild human zinc deficiency produces an imbalance between cell-mediated and humoral immunity. Nutr Rev 1998; 56:27–28.
136. Andrews M, Gallagher-Allred C. The role of zinc in wound healing. Adv Wound Care 1999; 12:137–148.
137. Heyneman CA. Zinc deficiency and taste disorders. Ann Pharmacother 1996; 30:186–187.
138. Coleman JE. Zinc proteins: enzymes, storage proteins, transcription factors and replication proteins. Annu Rev Biochem 1992; 61:897–946.
139. Simmer K, Thompson RP. Zinc in the fetus and newborn. Acta Paediatr Scand Suppl 1985; 319:158–163.
140. Fabris N, Mocchegiani E. Zinc, human diseases and aging. Aging (Milano) 1995; 7:77–93.
141. Rostan E, deBuys H, Madey D, Pinnel S. Divalent zinc ion—an antioxidant for skin. Int J Dermatol 2002; 41:606–611.
142. Morgan AJ, Van Lewis GD, Akkerboom PJ. The effect of zinc in the form of erythromycin-zinc complex (Zineryt lotion) and zinc acetate on metallothionein expression and distribution in hamster skin. Br J Dermatol 1993; 129:563–570.
143. Lange Jurkiewicz BA, Buettner GR. In: Thiele J, Elsner P (ed.), Oxidants and Antioxidants in Cutaneous Biology. Vol. 29. Current Problem in Dermatology. Basel: Karger, 2001:18–25.
144. Galinski EA, Stein M, Amendt B, Kinder M. The Kosmotropic (structure-forming) effect of compensatory solutes. Com Biochem Physiol 1997; 117A:357–365.
145. Brown AD. Microbial water stress. Bacterial Rev 1976; 40:803–846.

146. Bünger J, Ectoin—added protection and care for the skin. EuroCosmetics 1999; 3:22–24.
147. Bünger J, Degwer J, Driller H-J. The protective Function of compatible solute ectoin on the skin, skin cells and its biomolecules with respect to UV-radiation, immunosupression and membrane damage. IFSCC Mag 2001; 4:127–131.
148. Bünger J, Krutmann J. Skin protection properties of compatible solutes against UVA-induced damage and skin aging. Second LOréal International Symposium on The Science and Technology of Skin Aging, Cleveland, OH, 2002.
149. Grether-Beck S, Bonizzi G, Schmitt-Brenden H, Felsner I, Timmer A, Sies H, Johnson JP, Piette J, Krutmann J. EMBO J 2000; 19:5793–5800.
150. Sorg O, Tran C, Saurat JH. Cutaneous vitamins A and E in the context of ultraviolet- or chemically-induced oxidative stress. Skin Pharmacol Appl Skin Physiol 2001; 14:363–372.
151. Chew AL, Bashir SJ, Maibach HI. Topical retinoids In: Elsner P, Maibach HI, eds. Cosmeceuticals Drugs vs. Cosmetics. New York: Marcel Dekker, 2000:107–121.
152. Griffith CE. The role of retinoids in the prevention and repair of aged and photoaged skin. Clin Exp Dermatol 2001; 26:613–618.
153. Fisher GJ, Talawar HS, Pinpin JL, McPhillips F, Wang ZQ, Li X, Wan Y, Kang S, Voorhees JJ. Retinoic acid inhibits induction of c-jun protein by ultraviolet radiation that occurs subsequent to activation of mitogen-activated protein kinase pathways in human skin in vivo. J Clin Invest 1998; 101:1432–1440.
154. Sardana K, Sehegal VN. Retinoids: facinating up-and-coming scenario. J Dermatol 2003; 30:355–380.
155. Zouboulis CC. Retinoids—which dermatological indications will benefit in the near future. Skin Pharmacol Appl Skin Physiol 2001; 14:303–315.
156. Kang S, Fisher GJ, Voorhees JJ. Photoaging: pathogenesis, prevention, and treatment. Clin Geriatr Med 2001; 17:643–659.
157. Chaudhuri RK, Hwang C. Self-tanners: formulating with dihydroxyacetone. Cosmet Toilet 2001; 116:87–96.
158. Chaudhuri RK. Dihydroxyacetone: chemistry and applications in self-tanning products. In: Schlossman ML, ed. The Chemistry and Manufacture of Cosmetics. Vol. III, Book one, 2002: pp. 383–402.
159. Fusaro RM, Johnson JA. Protection against long ultraviolet and/or visible light with topical dihydroxyacetone. Dermatologica 1975; 150:346–351.
160. Sayre RM, Torode DI, Robinson JA, Fusaro RM. Skin optics of melanoid stains versus natural melanin. In: Zeiss L, Chedekl MR, Fitzpatrick TB, eds. Overland Park. Kansas, 1995: 39–47.
161. Fusaro RM, Lynch HT, The FAMMM syndrome: epidemiology and surveillance strategies. Cancer Invest 2000; 18:670–680.
162. Levy SB. Tanning preparations. Dermatol Clin 2000; 18:591–596.
163. Asawanonda P, Oberlender S, Taylor C. The use of dihydroxyacetone for photoprotection in variegate porphyria. Int J Dermatol 1999; 38:916–925.
164. Petersen AB, Na R, Wulf HC. Sunless skin tanning with dihydroxyacetone delays broad-spectrum ultraviolet photocarcinogenesis in hairless mice. Mutat Res 2003; 542:129–138.

31

Photoprotection by Green Tea Polyphenols

Craig A. Elmets, Santosh K. Katiyar, and Nabiha Yusuf
University of Alabama at Birmingham, Birmingham, Alabama, USA

INTRODUCTION

The relationship that humans have with sun exposure is delicately balanced between the positive effects that this form of radiant energy provides and the negative aspects that overexposure engenders. The benefits of sun exposure include its positive psychological actions, the role it plays in vitamin D metabolism, and the value it has as a therapeutic agent in cutaneous and systemic disease. The adverse consequences of overexposure include acute UV-induced erythema (i.e., a sunburn), nonmelanoma skin cancer (cutaneous squamous cell and basal cell carcinoma), melanoma, photoaging of the skin, and UV-induced immunosuppression.

Lifestyle changes over the past several decades have provided individuals with much greater amounts of time for recreational activities, and much of this time has been spent outdoors. As a result, there has been an alarming increase in the incidence of sunlight-related disease. In 1999, over 30% of adults in the USA reported at least one sunburn in the prior year (1) and over 70% of youth between 11 and 18 years of age have had at least one sunburn during their life (2). Moreover, 1.3 million new cases of nonmelanoma were estimated to have been diagnosed in the USA in 2000, which is equivalent to the incidence of malignancies in all other organs combined (3). According to current projections, one in five Americans will develop at least one nonmelanoma skin cancer during their lifetime. While melanomas are not as prevalent as cutaneous squamous cell and basal cell carcinomas, they are a serious problem as well with a mortality four times that of nonmelanoma skin cancer. There were slightly more than 50,000 new cases in the USA in 2002 and over 7000 deaths (4). The incidence of melanoma is increasing more rapidly than any other type of cancer. Between 1973 and 2000 in the USA, there was >160% increase in the incidence of melanoma.

Although there are many ways in which the adverse effects of overexposure to ultraviolet (UV) radiation can be successfully treated, a much more effective method of handling this problem is through preventative measures. Physicians have a responsibility to educate their patients about the adverse effects of excessive exposure to UV radiation. They have an obligation to instruct individuals on methods by which the adverse effects of UV radiation can be prevented while at the same time allowing them to take part in the outdoor activities that they enjoy or are part of their occupation. Current methods for the prevention of acute and chronic photodamage include counseling patients about the adverse effects of sun exposure, instructing them on ways in which they can reduce their outdoor activities during peak hours of UV intensity (10 a.m. to 4 p.m.), advising them to wear hats and long-sleeved clothing, and encouraging them to apply sunscreens regularly (5).

While not denying the importance of currently available sunscreens in the prevention of UV injury, it should be noted that the efficacy of sunscreens is determined by their ability to protect against sunburn under laboratory conditions, and their value in safeguarding against photoimmunosuppression, photoaging, melanoma, and nonmelanoma skin cancer in humans has received much less attention. Fortunately, the data that are available do suggest that sunscreens are effective at preventing at least some forms of skin cancer and its precursors. With respect to nonmelanoma skin cancer, the regular use of an SPF 15 sunscreen over a 5-year period of time reduced the incidence of cutaneous squamous cell carcinomas by 35% when compared to subjects who applied them sporadically (6). The fact that regular sunscreen use did afford protection against cutaneous squamous cell carcinomas is reassuring; unfortunately, there was no reduction in the incidence of basal cell carcinomas in the same patients. This illustrates that the efficacy of currently available sunscreens, as they are used by the general public, is incomplete. In addition other issues with respect to sunscreens include the fact that large amounts of sunscreens must be applied to achieve the full SPF value as indicated on the label; most agents that are available in the USA at this time provide less protection against UV-A than UV-B, and there is increasing concern about the effects that UV-A might have; none of the currently available sunscreens has an effect on UV damage that has already occurred. Thus, there is a well-justified interest in identifying new constituents that can be incorporated into sunscreens which have mechanisms of action that complement existing formulations.

GREEN TEA POLYPHENOLS AND PHOTOPROTECTION

A particularly promising group of compounds that are being evaluated as potential sunscreen additives are polyphenolic extracts from green tea (7–10). Tea is used primarily as a beverage and is consumed worldwide. It is manufactured from the leaves and buds of the plant *Camellia sinensis*. There are three types of tea—black, oolong, and green—which differ from each other because of differences in their fermentation processes. Green tea is manufactured from fresh leaves of the plant, which are steamed and dried at elevated temperatures with care taken to avoid oxidation and polymerization of the polyphenolic compounds. Consumption rates vary among the three types, with black, oolong, and green tea having rates of 78%, 2%, and 20%, respectively (7–10).

The positive health effects of green tea have been attributed to the presence of water-soluble polyphenolic constituents termed epicatechins (7–10), although there is some evidence that caffeine present in green tea contributes as well (11–14). There are four major epicatechins in green tea: (−)-epicatechin (EC), (−)-epicatechin-3-gallate (ECG), (−)-epigallocatechin (EGC), and (−)-epigallocatechin-3-gallate (EGCG) (Fig. 31.1). EGCG is present in the greatest amount (10). Comparative studies have shown that, in general, EGCG has the greatest activity followed by ECG, EGC, and EC which are less active. The polyphenols present in green tea are also found in black tea, but in smaller amounts due to the fermentation process. Black tea also contains theaflavins and thearubugins which also have photoprotective activities (10,11,14,15).

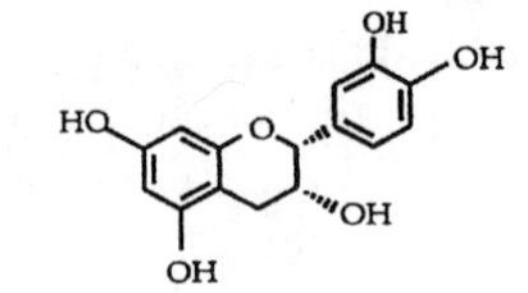

(-)-Epicatechin (EC)

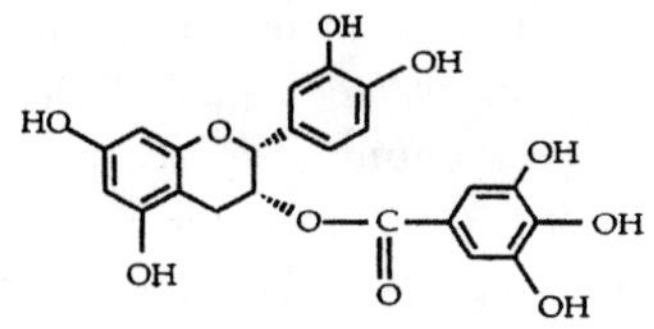

(-)-Epicatechin-3-gallate (ECG)

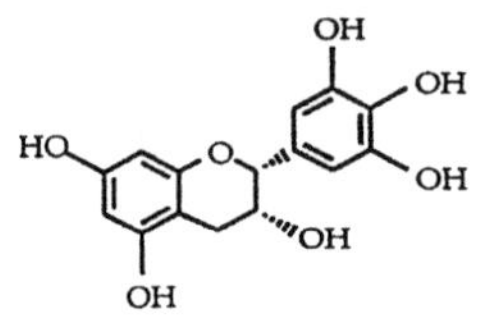

(-)-Epigallocatechin (EGC)

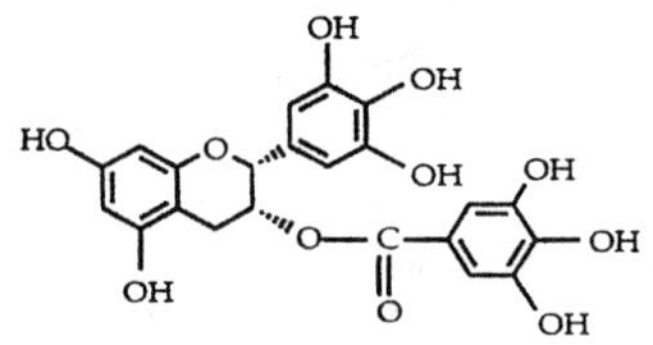

(-)-Epigallocatechin-3-gallate (EGCG)

Figure 31.1 Structure of the major green tea polyphenols.

Much of the stimulus for using green tea to protect against the adverse effects of sun exposure has come from epidemiological studies suggesting that it has chemopreventive activities in other forms of cancer (7). For example, in areas of China with the highest esophageal cancer mortality rates, tea is infrequently consumed (16). Moreover, among postmenopausal women in Iowa, daily tea consumption is associated with a >50% reduced risk of digestive tract and urinary tract cancers (17). It is important to note that, however, other epidemiologic studies have shown the opposite effect (7).

PHOTOPROTECTIVE EFFECTS OF GREEN TEA POLYPHENOLS IN SKIN CANCER

Initial studies evaluating the photoprotective effects of green tea polyphenols were conducted in animal models of skin cancer (18). When SKH-1 hairless mice are chronically exposed to UV-B radiation they develop premalignant papillomas (i.e., actinic keratoses) and cutaneous squamous cell carcinomas. When these animals were given extracts of green tea in their drinking water (0.1% w/v) or had green tea extracts applied to their skin before each UV treatment, the incidence of UV-induced tumors was reduced and the latency to tumor development was prolonged (18). The effect was dose dependent. Subsequent experimentation in mice has shown that the EGCG component of green tea is also highly effective at controlling UV-induced tumor formation (19). The vehicle in which EGCG is applied is an important factor in determining the efficacy of a given topical formulation. Incorporation of green tea polyphenols or EGCG in hydrophilic ointment appears to be significantly more effective than other vehicles (20).

GREEN TEA POLYPHENOLS AND THE DIFFERENT STAGES OF PHOTOCARCINOGENESIS

Skin tumorigenesis caused by UV light has been divided into three distinct stages (Fig. 31.2) (21). In the first stage, termed initiation, UV radiation interacts with DNA producing 6,4-photoproducts and cyclobutane pyrimidine dimers. There is an attempt by the body to correct this damage through activation of DNA repair enzymes. Patients with xeroderma pigmentosum, who are predisposed to the development of actinically induced skin cancers, have a genetic defect in the initial stages of DNA repair (22). Although the DNA repair processes are quite efficient, they are not completely effective, thus leaving a few persistent mutations. Mutations in the *p53* gene are particularly important for the development of UV-induced squamous cell carcinomas (23), whereas mutations in the *PTCH* gene are critical for basal cell carcinomas to occur (24).

The mutant cells produced during the initiation stage of photocarcinogenesis are not apparent clinically. However, with repeated UV exposure additional biochemical changes occur during the second stage of photocarcinogenesis termed promotion (21). The two key cellular events that occur during the promotion stage are amplification of the inflammatory response and increased proliferation of mutant keratinocytes. The biochemical changes that produce these events are still being worked out (Fig. 31.3). They are thought to commence, at least in part, by the generation of reactive oxygen intermediates (25–27), which then activate a variety of signal transduction pathways. This leads to the synthesis or activation of new proteins such as cyclooxygenase-2 (28) and ornithine decarboxylase (29). The end result of this stage is the development of clinically apparent premalignant actinic keratoses.

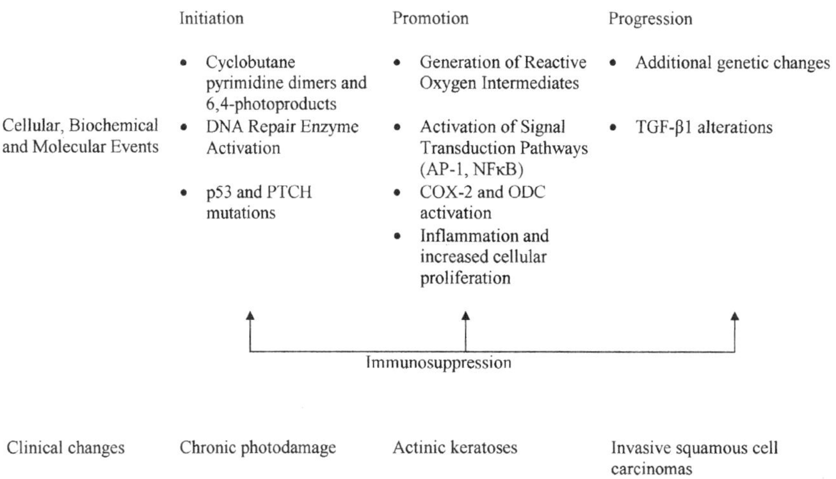

Figure 31.2 Stages of photocarcinogenesis.

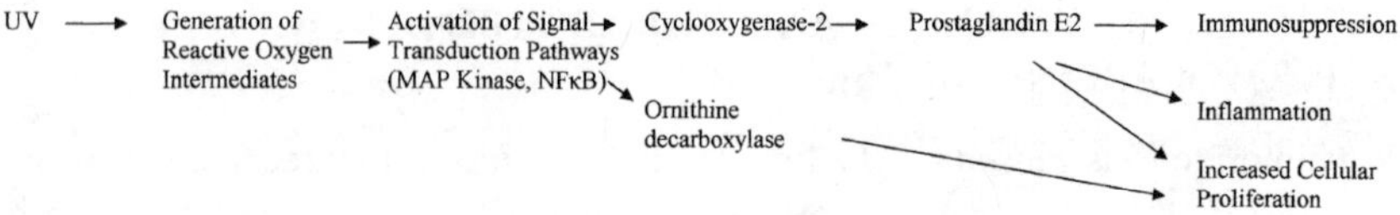

Figure 31.3 Biochemical changes occurring after UV exposure.

In the third stage, called progression, a small proportion of actinic keratoses acquire additional genetic changes that allow them to become invasive carcinomas. Alterations in TGF-β1 appear to be important during this stage (30,31).

Protocols have been developed which distinguish between the effects of UV radiation on the initiation and promotion stages of carcinogenesis. These protocols have been employed to assess at which of the stages green tea polyphenols act. When administered in drinking water, EGCG was able to reduce UV-induced tumor formation when given only during the initiation or promotion stages (32–34).

It is possible to assess the effects of green tea polyphenols on the progression stage by exposing SKH-1 hairless mice to UV radiation for 22 weeks. At that point, these mice do not have tumors but are at high risk of developing them even without further exposure to UV. When green tea was given orally in the drinking water beginning at 22 weeks and the mice were followed for tumor development, there was a significant reduction in the number of tumors that occurred over the ensuing weeks (14). Even after animals had been exposed to UV radiation for several weeks and then EGCG was applied, there was a significant reduction in tumor development and partial regression of existing tumors (13,15).

As was mentioned, because black tea has polyphenols, thearubigins, and theaflavins, it, too, has been investigated for its photoprotective properties. When black tea was given to SKH-1 mice after they had been UV irradiated for 22 weeks and had established skin tumors, subsequent tumor growth was inhibited by 70% even though UV irradiation had stopped (13). Caffeine may have contributed to this effect, because decaffeinated black tea gave inconsistent results.

The efficacy of green tea polyphenols as chemopreventive agents for actinic keratoses in human subjects at high risk of development of nonmelanoma skin cancer remains to be determined. In a small clinical trial, topical application of EGCG in an ointment base was ineffective at causing regression of existing actinic keratoses. At this point, its role in *preventing* the development of new actinic keratoses in humans has not been examined (35).

PHOTOPROTECTIVE EFFECTS OF GREEN TEA POLYPHENOLS ON THE ACUTE UV-INDUCED SUNBURN RESPONSE

In humans, acute overexposure of the skin to UV radiation causes a painful erythemal response known as the sunburn reaction (36). This is manifest as redness, pain, and swelling, which usually peaks 6–24 h after UV exposure, after which it declines. Histologically, there is an acute inflammatory response with neutrophils; within the epidermis are large numbers of dyskeratotic keratinocytes that are undergoing apoptosis and have been termed "sunburn" cells. UV-induced erythema is much more difficult to detect clinically in mice than it is in humans. In this species, the edema response, measured as an increase in ear thickness after UV compared to that prior to UV, has been employed as a quantifiable alternative (37). In this experimental system, both topical and orally administered green tea polyphenols reduce the UV-induced increase in ear swelling (37). This is associated with a concomitant reduction in the number of sunburn cells detected histologically (37) and cells in the epidermis undergoing apoptosis detected by caspase-3 immunohistochemistry (12). The effect on apoptotic cells has been corroborated *in vitro* by showing that the addition of EGCG prior to UV irradiation of cultured keratinocytes results in a significant reduction in apoptosis (38).

The effect of green tea polyphenols on the acute UV erythema response in humans is similar to that in mice (39). When graded concentrations of green tea polyphenols are applied to the skin of human volunteers prior to exposure to a 2-MED dose of solar simulated radiation, there is a dose-dependent reduction in erythema (39), which is accompanied histologically by a decrease in UV-induced keratinocyte hyperproliferation, a dramatic reduction in the number of sunburn cells, and a diminution in the inflammatory cell infiltrate (40,41). The decrease in the erythemal response is observed both in response to solar simulated radiation (in which UV-B is primarily responsible for the sunburn response) and to a UV-A radiation in which no UV-B is present (39). As with animal and *in vitro* models, EGCG is the polyphenolic constituent that is most efficient at inhibiting erythema in humans. In human volunteers, green tea polyphenols are also highly effective at decreasing the DNA damage and the number of cyclobutane pyrimidine dimers that are present in UV-irradiated skin (39,42).

PHOTOPROTECTIVE EFFECTS OF GREEN TEA POLYPHENOLS ON PHOTOAGING

Another major effect of chronic UV radiation overexposure is photoaging of the skin. This manifests as coarse and fine wrinkling, increased fragility, ecchymoses, telangiectasias, freckling and solar lentigines. Many of these clinical manifestations are caused by degradation of collagen through activation of matrix metalloproteinases and by the accumulation of abnormal elastin fibers, leading to nodular elastosis (43,44). Depletion of antioxidant enzymes, oxidative modification of proteins (25) and accumulation of lipid peroxidation and glycation products are all involved in the photoaging process (44–46). Antioxidants have been shown to reverse photoaging *in vitro* and *in vivo* in animal models (47,48). Resident cells within the skin as well as infiltrating inflammatory leukocytes are the source of these reactive oxygen intermediates

(40,41). In matrigel skin equivalents *in vitro*, EGCG alone has been shown to inhibit the expression MMP-9, MMP-2, MT1-MMP and neutrophil elastase at concentrations that can be achieved pharmacologically (49,50). With respect to UV radiation, recent studies have shown that administration of green tea polyphenols in drinking water inhibits UV-induced protein oxidation, a hallmark of photoaging (20), and activation of matrix metalloproteinases (51) presumably through its inhibitory effects on the activity of reactive oxygen intermediates.

PROTECTIVE EFFECTS OF GREEN TEA POLYPHENOLS IN UV-INDUCED IMMUNOSUPPRESSION

The extent to which green tea polyphenols and their polyphenolic constituents reverse UV-induced immune suppression has also been an active area of investigation. UV-B-induced immune suppression is considered as a risk factor for skin cancer development (52). It may also be a cause of reduced resistance to selected infectious agents and of diminished immunization rates following vaccination (53). Using murine models of contact hypersensitivity as a prototype for cutaneous cell-mediated immune responses, it has been shown that green tea polyphenol and EGCG treatment to mouse skin prevents UV-B-induced immune suppression and reverses the tolerogenic effect of this form of radiant energy (37,54). UV-induced immune suppression is mediated at least in part by an increase in the production of IL-10 and a reduction in IL-12 levels (54). Topical application of EGCG has been shown to change the balance between these two cytokines, reducing IL-10 production and increasing IL-12 (54). One of the major cellular sources of IL-10 produced in the skin following UV radiation is a CD11b+ macrophage that migrates into the epidermis following UV-B exposure (55). Application of EGCG to the skin prior to UV radiation reduces the number of CD11b+ cells that migrate into the epidermis and inhibits IL-10 production (54). Epidermal Langerhans cells, bone marrow-derived dendritic cells which are proficient at initiating cell-mediated immune responses, are a source of IL-12 in the epidermis (56). IL-12 is a mediator and adjuvant for cutaneous cell-mediated immune responses. The number of Langerhans cells is reduced in UV-irradiated epidermis as is the number of IL-12-producing cells in regional lymph nodes. Topical application of EGCG reverses the reduction in Langerhans cells in humans (39) and has been shown to greatly increase the production of IL-12 in draining lymph nodes compared to mice treated with UV-B alone (54). Evidence has been presented that prostaglandin E2 (PGE2) (57,58) and cyclobutane pyrimidine dimers (59) are responsible for the reduction in Langerhans cells. Thus, it seems reasonable to hypothesize that by reducing PGE2 and cyclobutane pyrimidine dimers, green tea polyphenols could inhibit the reduction in Langerhans cell concentrations in skin and in so doing could bring IL-12 levels back to normal.

MECHANISMS OF ACTION OF GREEN TEA POLYPHENOLS

A number of studies have been conducted to carefully define the cellular and molecular mechanisms by which green tea polyphenols protect against skin cancer. Spectrophotometric analysis has shown that these agents do not absorb wavelengths within the UV-B or UV-A and that even when administered orally they have photoprotective effects. Thus, EGCG and green tea polyphenols do not block UV radiation from reaching the skin indicating a photoprotective effect distinct from that of traditional sunscreens, which block penetration of UV radiation into the skin.

Cellular Effects

Apoptosis

The effects of EGCG on apoptosis are complex. Histologically, large numbers of apoptotic keratinocytes, known as "sunburn cells," can be found in skin following acute UV overexposure. Pretreatment with EGCG limits the number of these cells that appear both in human and in mouse skin (37,39). A very different response occurs in skin that has been chronically UV irradiated. In murine models, topical application of green tea polyphenols to skin that has already been chronically exposed to UV-B and therefore is at high risk of subsequently developing UV-induced tumors stimulates apoptosis in the malignant and premalignant tissue, but not in non-tumor bearing areas of the epidermis (12).

Proliferation of Keratinocytes

One of the major cellular events that occurs following UV radiation of the skin is increased proliferation of keratinocytes. This can be observed histologically as hyperplasia of the epidermis. The histological abnormalities revert to normal when green tea polyphenols are given prior to UV exposure. The epidermal mitotic index and BrdU incorporation into epidermal DNA after UV exposure have also been used as markers of increased epidermal proliferation. It has been shown that the UV-induced increase in BrdUrd incorporation and the epidermal mitotic index can be significantly reduced by oral administration of green tea polyphenols *in vivo* (60). Caffeine has an additive effect when given with green tea polyphenols (60).

Inflammatory Cell Infiltration

Inflammation is one of the cellular hallmarks of the sunburn response and has been implicated in the promotion stage of UV-induced skin tumorigenesis, UV-induced immunosuppression, and photoaging. Immunohistochemical techniques have been employed to show that chronic oral feeding as well as topical administration of green tea polyphenols to the skin of mice that were then exposed to UV radiation significantly reduced leukocyte infiltration into the skin (40). Similar results have been found when green tea polyphenols have been applied to the skin of human volunteers (39). These findings are of particular interest because leukocytes may be a major source of reactive nitric oxide and hydrogen peroxide, which are critical for biological changes that occur following UV exposure of the skin.

Molecular Effects

DNA Damage

Direct photochemical damage to DNA, predominantly in the form of cyclobutane pyrimidine dimers, is one of the major effects of UV radiation (21). It plays an important role in the initiation stage of photocarcinogenesis and contributes to the induction of UV-induced immunosuppression (59). By employing immunohistochemical techniques, green tea polyphenols have been shown to reduce the amount of DNA damage in UV-irradiated skin *in vivo* (39,42). One of the consequences of UV-induced DNA damage is the production of mutations in the *p53* gene (23). Given the fact that green tea polyphenols inhibited UV-induced DNA damage, it was surprising to find that green tea polyphenols augment UV-B-induced increases in wildtype *p53* gene (60). One of the major effects of *p53* is to initiate apoptosis in cells that have sustained significant DNA damage (61). It has been proposed that augmentation in *p53* is one mechanism by which green tea polyphenols exert their photoprotective effects (60).

Reactive Oxygen Intermediates

Despite the fact that the skin has a sophisticated and highly effective system to handle oxidative stress, it is not uncommon for UV radiation to overwhelm these defenses. Substantial evidence has been presented to support the concept that green tea and its polyphenolic constituents protect these antioxidant defenses (8,20,62–64). Initial studies demonstrating this effect were conducted *in vitro* on murine epidermal microsomes (64). UV exposure of these subcellular organelles enhanced lipid peroxidation, whereas the addition of green tea polyphenols reduced this effect. In *in vivo* animal models, when given orally or when applied topically prior to UV radiation, EGCG prevented UV-B-induced markers of oxidative stress (protein oxidation, lipid peroxidation), depletion of glutathione levels and the antioxidant enzymes catalase and glutathione peroxidase (20). UV augments oxidative stress through both direct effects on the skin and indirect effects through its ability to cause the recruitment of leukocytes into the skin, which then release reactive oxygen intermediates. Green tea polyphenols and EGCG reduce reactive oxygen intermediates produced by both mechanisms (40). It should be noted that nitric oxide, another mediator of inflammation in UV-irradiated skin is also inhibited by EGCG (40).

Proteasome Activation

Another molecular target for EGCG is the 20S proteasome (65). This molecule is part of the ubiquitin–proteasome pathway that is necessary for degradation of such proteins as p53, pRB, p21, $p27^{Kip1}$, IκB-α, and Bax. Protein degradation occurs through chymotrypsin-like, trypsin-like, and peptidyl–glutamyl peptide hydrolyzing activities of the 20S proteasome. The chymotrypsin-like activities of the 20S proteasome have been associated with tumor cell survival. On the basis of similarities in the chemical structure between several of the green tea polyphenols and other irreversible inhibitors of the 20S proteasome, *in vitro* studies were undertaken to determine whether the 20S proteasome might be a target for green tea polyphenols. Both ECG and EGCG, as well as (−)-catechin-3-gallate and (−)-gallocatechin-3-gallate, two other tea polyphenols, were able to inhibit the 20S proteasome in a number of different tumor cell lines, with EGCG being the most potent. Inhibition was associated with accumulation of $p27^{Kip1}$ and IκB-α and G1 growth arrest in tumor cell lines (65). Interestingly, SV40 transformed fibroblasts were much more susceptible to $p27^{Kip1}$ accumulation and G1 growth arrest than were their nontransformed counterparts. Because many of the molecules subject to degradation by this pathway regulate the cell cycle and cell death, it seems reasonable to hypothesize that irreversible inhibition of the 20S proteasome is one of the key upstream events involved in the chemopreventive actions of the green tea polyphenols (65).

Biochemical Activities

UV radiation is a potent activator of several different signal transduction pathways. Of particular interest has been its ability to upregulate MAP kinases, which in turn results in activation of the AP-1 transcription factor (Fig. 31.3). AP-1 is a nuclear transcription factor for the enzyme cyclooxygenase-2, ornithine decarboxylase, and matrix metalloproteinases.

Cyclooxygenase-2 is an inducible enzyme which is responsible for production of PGE2, a molecule implicated in many of the biological effects of UV radiation. Among other actions, PGE2 has proinflammatory activities and increases keratinocyte proliferation (66,67), it promotes angiogenesis (68,69), and it is an inductive stimulus for the immunosuppressive cytokine IL-10 (58,70). PGE2 plays an important role in the sunburn reaction (66), in photocarcinogenesis (28,66,71), and in photoimmunosuppression (57,58,72). Ornithine decarboxylase (ODC) is the rate-limiting enzyme in the polyamine biosynthetic pathway (73). Acute UV exposure increases ODC activity and chronic exposure augments basal ODC levels (74–78). The major function of MMP-1 is to degrade collagen, and therefore it plays a critical role in selected aspects of photoaging of the skin (44).

Green tea polyphenols interfere with many of the steps in this signal transduction pathway. *In vitro* studies using normal human keratinocytes have shown that EGCG interferes with UV-B-induced activation and phosphorylation of

MAP kinases (62). This effect on MAP kinases has been confirmed in *in vivo* experiments in murine skin as well (20). Experiments examining PGE2 and ODC activity in UV-irradiated skin that has been pretreated with green tea polyphenols have also been conducted, and it has been shown to be reduced (79). The first demonstration that green tea polyphenols might interfere with prostaglandin synthesis came from *in vivo* studies in which mice were fed green tea polyphenols in their drinking water. PGE2 activity following UV radiation was significantly reduced compared to controls that were UV irradiated but were not given green tea (79). Subsequent experimentation has shown that topical application of green tea suppresses COX-2 expression in UV-irradiated human and murine skin (80). In mice, suppression of COX-2 was found to occur when it was placed on the skin before or after UV irradiation (80). Mice given green tea in their drinking water fail to develop the increase in ODC activity that is normally observed in UV irradiated mice (79). This effect of green tea polyphenols on ODC induction is identical to that which is observed in mice whose skin is treated with tumor promoters such as TPA (81). With respect to matrix metalloproteinases, EGCG has been shown to inhibit MMP-3, MMP-7, and MMP-9 when given orally or topically before acute or chronic UV radiation exposure (51).

Another UV-induced signal transduction pathway that is modulated by EGCG is NF-κB (82). Exposure of cultured keratinocytes to UV-B has been shown to result in activation of the NF-κB signal transduction pathway and its translocation into the nucleus. Incorporation of EGCG into the culture medium caused a significant reduction in this process. EGCG did this by inhibiting activation of IKKα and degradation and phosphorylation of IκBα (82). Evidence has been presented to indicate that this occurs through inhibition of proteasome degradation (65). NF-κB plays a key role in the induction of UV-induced inflammatory responses and has been shown to contribute to UV-induced tumorigenesis. Thus, it is reasonable to postulate that this is one mechanism by which EGCG mediates its effect on UV-induced inflammation, cellular proliferation, and the sunburn response through its effects on the NF-κB pathway.

CONCLUSIONS

Polyphenolic extracts of green tea and the most active polyphenolic constituent EGCG show promise as new agents that can complement and enhance the photoprotective effect of currently available sunscreens. These agents, which are consumed as a beverage throughout the world, have been shown to have little, if any, irritancy or allergenicity when applied topically. In animal models and in preliminary studies in humans, they ameliorate many of the adverse effects of acute and chronic overexposure to the sun. This includes photoprotection against the sunburn response, nonmelanoma skin cancer development, photoaging, and UV-induced immunosuppression. They are potent antioxidants, are anti-inflammatory, and have a broad array of other molecular and biochemical actions. Topical formulations that include these agents are likely to lead to further improvements in the way in which humans protect themselves from overexposure to the sun.

ACKNOWLEDGMENTS

This work was supported by funds from the Department of Veterans Affairs (18-103-02), NIH grants, and contracts NO1 CN-85083, R01 CA79820, CA86172, NO1 CN1500-46, R01 CA90920, R23 ES 11421, and R23 CA94593.

REFERENCES

1. Saraiya M, Hall HI, Uhler RJ. Sunburn prevalence among adults in the United States, 1999. Am J Prev Med 2002; 23(2):91–97.
2. Davis KJ, Cokkinides VE, Weinstock MA, O'Connell MC, Wingo PA. Summer sunburn and sun exposure among US youths ages 11 to 18: national prevalence and associated factors. Pediatrics 2002; 110(1 Pt l):27–35.
3. Housman TS, Feldman SR, Williford PM, Fleischer AB Jr, Goldman ND, Acostamadiedo JM, Chen GJ. Skin cancer is among the most costly of all cancers to treat for the Medicare population. J Am Acad Dermatol 2003; 48(3):425–429.
4. American Cancer Society. Cancer Facts and Figures. Vol. 2003. American Cancer Society, 2002.
5. Elmets C. Sunscreens and photocarcinogenesis: an objective assessment. Photochem Photobiol 1996; 63:435–440.
6. Green A, Williams G, Neale R, Hart V, Leslie D, Parsons P, Marks GC, Gaffney P, Battistutta D, Frost C, Lang C, Russell A. Daily sunscreen application and beta-carotene supplementation in prevention of basal-cell and squamous-cell carcinomas of the skin: a randomized controlled trial. Lancet 1999; 354(9180):723–729.
7. Katiyar SK, Mukhtar H. Tea in chemoprevention of cancer: epidemiologic and experimental studies. Int J Oncol 1996; 8:221–238.
8. Katiyar S, Elmets C. Green tea polyphenolic antioxidants and skin protection. Int J Oncol 2001; 18:1307–1313.
9. Katiyar S, Ahmad N, Mukhtar H. Green tea and skin. Arch Dermatol 2000; 136:989–994.
10. Yang C, Maliakal P, Meng X. Inhibition of carcinogenesis by tea. Annu Rev Pharmacol Toxicol 2002; 42:25–54.
11. Huang MT, Xie JG, Wang ZY, Ho CT, Lou YR, Wang CX, Hard GC, Conney AH. Effects of tea, decaffeinated tea, and caffeine on UVB light-induced complete carcinogenesis in SKH-1 mice: demonstration of caffeine as a biologically important constituent of tea. Cancer Res 1997; 57:2623–2629.
12. Lu Y-P, Lou Y-R, Xie J-G, Peng Q-Y, Liao J, Yang C, Huang M-T, Ah C. Topical applications of caffeine or (−)-epigallocatechin gallate (EGCG) inhibit carcinogenesis and selectively increase apoptosis in UVB-induced skin tumors in mice. Proc Natl Acad Sci USA 2002; 99:12455–12460.
13. Lu Y-P, Lou Y-R, Xie J-G, Yen P, Huang M-T, Conney A. Inhibitory effect of black tea on the growth of established skin tumors in mice: effects on tumor size, apoptosis,

mitosis and bromodeoxyuridine incorporation into DNA. Carcinogenesis 1997; 18:2163–2169.
14. Lu YP, Lou YR, Lin Y, Shih WJ, Huang MT, Yang CS, Conney AH. Inhibitory effects of orally administered green tea, black tea, and caffeine on skin carcinogenesis in mice previously treated with ultraviolet B light (high-risk mice): relationshp to decreased tissue fat. Cancer Res 2001; 61(13):5002–5009.
15. Lou YR, Lu YP, Xie JG, Huang MT, Conney AH. Effects of oral administration of tea, decaffeinated tea, and caffeine on the formation and growth of tumors in high-risk SKH-1 mice previously treated with ultraviolet B light. Nutr Cancer 1999; 33(2):146–153.
16. Gao YT, McLaughlin JK, Blot WJ, Ji BT, Dai Q, Fraumeni JF Jr. Reduced risk of esophageal cancer associated with green tea consumption. J Natl Cancer Inst 1994; 86(11):855–858.
17. Zheng W, Doyle TJ, Kushi LH, Sellers TA, Hong CP, Folsom AR. Tea consumption and cancer incidence in a prospective cohort study of postmenopausal women. Am J Epidemiol 1996; 144(2):175–182.
18. Wang Z, Agarwal R, Bickers D, Mukhtar H. Protection against ultraviolet B radiation-induced photocarcinogenesis in hairless mice by green tea polyphenols. Carcinogenesis 1991; 12:1527–1530.
19. Gensler HL, Timmermann BN, Valcic S, Wachter GA, Dorr R, Dvorakova K, Alberts DS. Prevention of photocarcinogenesis by topical administration of pure epigallocatechin gallate isolated from green tea. Nutr Cancer 1996; 26(3):325–335.
20. Vayalil PK, Elmets CA, Katiyar SK. Treatment of green tea polyphenols in hydrophilic cream prevents UVB-induced oxidation of lipids and proteins, depletion of antioxidant enzymes and phosphorylation of MAPK proteins in SKH-1 hairless mouse skin. Carcinogenesis 2003; 24(5):927–936.
21. Elmets C. Cutaneous photocarcinogenesis. In: Mukhtar H, ed. Pharmacology of the Skin. Boca Raton, FL: CRC Press, 1992:389–416.
22. Cleaver J, Crowley E. UV damage, DNA repair and skin carcinogenesis. Front Biosci 2002; 7:1024–1043.
23. Ziegler A, Jonason A, Leffell D, Simon J, Sharma H, Kimmelman J, Remington L, Jacks T, Brash D. Sunburn and p53 in the onset of skin cancer. Nature 1994; 372:773–776.
24. Daya-Grosjean L, Sarasin A. UV-specific mutations of the human patched gene in basal cell carcinomas from normal individuals and xeroderma pigmentosum patients. Mutat Res/Fundam Mol Mech Mutagen 2000; 450(1–2):193–199.
25. Sander CS, Chang H, Salmann S, Muller CSL, Ekanayake-Mudiyanselage S, Elsner P, Thiele JJ. Photoaging is associated with protein oxidation in human skin *in vivo*. J Invest Dermatol 2002; 118(4):618–625.
26. Perchellet J-P, Perchellet E, Gali H, Gao X. Oxidant stress and multistage skin carcinogenesis. In: Mukhtar H, ed. Skin Cancer: Mechanisms and Human Relevance. Boca Raton, FL: CRC Press, 1995:145–180.
27. Mukhtar H, Elmets CA. Photocarcinogenesis: mechanisms, models and human health implications. Photochem Photobiol 1996; 63:355–447.
28. Buckman SY, Gresham A, Hale P, Hruza G, Anast J, Masferrer J, Pentland AP. COX-2 expression is induced by UVB exposure in human skin: implications for the development of skin cancer. Carcinogenesis 1998; 19(5):723–729.
29. Ahmad N, Gilliam AC, Katiyar SK, O'Brien TG, Mukhtar H. A definitive role of ornithine decarboxylase in photocarcinogenesis. Am J Pathol 2001; 159(3):885–892.

30. Rittie L, Fisher GJ. UV-light-induced signal cascades and skin aging. Ageing Res Rev 2003; 1(4):705–720.
31. Amendt C, Schirmacher P, Weber H, Blessing M. Expression of a dominant negative type II TGF-receptor in mouse skin results in an increase in carcinoma incidence and an acceleration of carcinoma development. Oncogene 1998; 17:25–34.
32. Conney A, Wang Z, Huang M, Ho C, Yang C. Inhibitory effect of green tea on tumorigenesis by chemicals and ultraviolet light. Prev Med 1992; 21:361–369.
33. Wang Z, Huang M, Ferraro T, Wong C, Lou Y, Reuhl K, Iatropoulos M, Yang C, Conney A. Inhibitory effect of green tea in the drinking water on tumorigenesis by ultraviolet light and 12-O-tetradecanoylphorbol-13-acetate in the skin of SKH-1 mice. Cancer Res 1992; 52:1162–1170.
34. Wang Z, Huang M-T, Lou Y-R, Xie J-G, Reuhl K, Newmark H, Ho C, Yang C. Inhibitory effects of black tea, green tea, decaffeinated black tea, and decaffeinated green tea on ultraviolet B light-induced skin carcinogenesis in 7,12-dimethylbenz[a]anthracene-initiated SKH-1 mice. Cancer Res 1994; 54:3428–3435.
35. Linden K, Carpenter P, McLaren C, Barr R, Hite P, Sun J, Li K, Viner J, Meyskens F. Chemoprevention of nonmelanoma skin cancer: experience with a polyphenol from green tea. Recent Results Cancer Res 2003; 163:165–171, 264–266.
36. Runger T. Ultraviolet light. In: Bolognia J, Jorizzo J, Rapini R, Horn T, Mascaro J, Saurat J-H, Mancini A, Salasche S, Stingl G, eds. Dermatology. Vol. 2. London: Mosby, 2003:1353–1363.
37. Katiyar SK, Elmets CA, Agarwal R, Mukhtar H. Protection against ultraviolet-B radiation-induced local and systemic suppression of contact hypersensitivity and edema responses in C3H/HeN mice by green tea polyphenols. Photochem Photobiol 1995; 62:855–861.
38. Chung J, Han J, Hwang E, Seo J, Cho K, Kim K, Youn J, Em H. Dual mechanisms of green tea extract (EGCG)-induced cell survival in human epidermal keratinocytes. FASEB J 2003; 17(13):1913–1915.
39. Elmets C, Singh D, Tubesing K, Matsui M, Katiyar S, Mukhtar H. Prevention of cutaneous photodamage by polyphenols from green tea. J Am Acad Dermatol 2001; 44:425–432.
40. Katiyar SK, Mukhtar H. Green tea polyphenol (−)-epigallocatechin-3-gallate treatment to mouse skin prevents UVB-induced infiltration of leukocytes, depletion of antigen-presenting cells, and oxidative stress. J Leukoc Biol 2001; 69(5):719–726.
41. Katiyar S, Matsui M, Elmets C, Mukhtar H. Polyphenolic antioxidant (−)-epigallocatechin-3-gallate from green tea reduces UVB-induced inflammatory responses and infiltration of leukocytes in human skin. Photochem Photobiol 1999; 69:148–153.
42. Katiyar S, Perez A, Mukhtar H. Green tea polyphenol treatment to human skin prevents formation of ultraviolet light B-induced purimidine dimers in DNA. Clin Cancer Res 2000; 6:3864–3869.
43. Brenneisen P, Sies H, Scharffetter-Kochanek K. Ultraviolet-B irradiation and matrix metalloproteinases: from induction via signaling to initial events. Ann NY Acad Sci 2002; 973:31–43.
44. Fisher G, Kang S, Varani J, Bata-Csorgo Z, Wan Y, Datta S, Voorhees J. Mechanisms of photoaging and chronological skin aging. Arch Dermatol 2002; 138:1462–1470.
45. Jeanmaire C, Danoux L, Pauly G. Glycation during human dermal intrinsic and actinic ageing: an in vivo and in vitro model study. Br J Dermatol 2001; 145:10–18.

46. Tanaka N, Tajima S, Ishibashi A, Uchida K, Shigematsu T. Immunohistochemical detection of lipid peroxidation products, protein-bound acrolein and 4-hydroxynonenal protein adducts, in actinic elastosis of photodamaged skin. Arch Dermatol Res 2001; 293:363–367.
47. Bissett D, Chatterjee R, Hannon D. Photoprotective effects of superoxide-scavenging antioxidants against ultraviolet radiation-induced chronic skin damage in the hairless mouse. Photodermatol Photoimmunol Photomed 1990; 7:56–62.
48. Bissett D, McBride J. Synergistic topical photoprotection by a combination of the iron chelator 2-furildioxime and sunscreen. J Am Acad Dermatol 1996; 35:546–549.
49. Benelli R, Vene R, Bisacchi D, Garbisa S, Albini A. Anti-invasive effects of green tea polyphenol epigallocatechin-3-gallate (EGCG), a natural inhibitor of metallo and serine proteases. Biol Chem 2002; 383:101–105.
50. Dell'Aica I, Dona M, Sartor L, Pezzato E, Garbisa S. (−)Epigallocatechin-3-gallate directly inhibits MT1-MMP activity, leading to accumulation of nonactivated MMP-2 at the cell surface. Lab Invest 2002; 82:1685–1693.
51. Vayalil PK, Mittal A, Hara Y, Elmets CA, Katiyar SK. Green tea polyphenols prevent ultraviolet light-induced oxidative damage and matrix metalloproteinase expression in mouse skin. J Invest Dermatol 2004; 122:1480–1487.
52. Yoshikawa T, Rae V, Bruins-Slot W, van der Berg J-W, Taylor JR, Streilein JW. Susceptibility to effects of UVB radiation on induction of contact hypersensitivity as a risk factor for skin cancer in man. J Invest Dermatol 1990; 95:530–536.
53. Jeevan A, Brown E, Kripke ML. UV and infectious diseases. In: Krutmann J, Elmets CA, eds. Photoimmunology. Oxford: Blackwell Science, 1995:153–163.
54. Katiyar SK, Challa A, McCormick TS, Cooper KD, Mukhtar H. Prevention of UVB-induced immunosuppression in mice by the green tea polyphenol (−)-epigallocatechin-3-gallate may be associated with alterations in IL-10 and IL-12 production. Carcinogenesis 1990; 20(11):2117–2124.
55. Kang K, Hammerberg C, Meunier L, Cooper KD. CD11b$^+$ macrophages that infiltrate human epidermis after *in vivo* ultraviolet exposure potently produce IL-10 and represent the major secretory source of epidermal IL10 protein. J Immunol 1994; 153:5256–5264.
56. Kang K, Kubin M, Cooper K, Lessin S, Trinchieri G, Rook A. IL-12 synthesis by human Langerhans cells. J Immunol 1996; 156:1402–1407.
57. Chung HT, Burnham DK, Robertson B, Roberts LK, Daynes RA. Involvement of prostaglandins in the immune alterations caused by the exposure of mice to ultraviolet radiation. J Immunol 1986; 137:2478–2484.
58. Shreedhar V, Giese T, Sung VW, Ullrich SE. A cytokine cascade including prostaglandin E2, IL-4, and IL-10 is responsible for UV-induced systemic immune suppression. J Immunol 1998; 160:3783–3789.
59. Kzipke ML, Cox PA, Alas LG, Yarosh DB. Pyrimidine dimers in DNA initiate systemic immunosuppression in UV-irradiated mice. Proc Natl Acad Sci USA 1992; 89:7516–7520.
60. Lu Y-P, Lou Y-R, Li X, Xie J-G, Brash D, Huang M-T. Stimulatory effect of oral administration of green tea or caffeine on ultraviolet light-induced increases in epidermal wild-type p53, p21(WAF1/CIPl), and apoptotic sunburn cells in SKH-1 mice. Cancer Res 2000; 60:4785–4791.
61. White E. Life, death, and the pursuit of apoptosis. Genes Dev 1996; 10:1–15.
62. Katiyar SK, Afaq F, Azizuddin K, Mukhtar H. Inhibition of UVB-induced oxidative stress-mediated phosphorylation of mitogen-activated protein kinase signaling

pathways in cultured human epidermal keratinocytes by green tea polyphenol (−)-epigallocatechin-3-gallate. Toxicol Appl Pharmacol 2001; 176(2):110–117.
63. Mittal A, Elmets C, Katiyar S. CD11b+ cells are the major source of oxidative stress in UV radiation-irradiated skin: possible role in photoaging and photocarcinogenesis. Photochem Photobiol 2003; 77:259–264.
64. Katiyar S, Agarwal R, Mukhtar H. Inhibition of spontaneous and photo-enhanced lipid peroxidation in mouse epidermal microsomes by epicatechin derivatives from green tea. Cancer Lett 1994; 79:61–66.
65. Nam S, Smith D, Dou Q. Ester bond-containing tea polyphenols potently inhibit proteasome activity *in vivo* and *in vitro*. J Biol Chem 2001; 276:13322–13330.
66. Hruza L, Pentland A. Mechanisms of UV-induced inflammation. J Invest Dermatol 1993; 100:35S–41S.
67. Pentland A, Needleman P. Modulation of keratinocyte proliferation in vitro by endogenous prostaglandin synthesis. J Clin Invest 1986; 77:246–261.
68. Salcedo R, Zhang X, Young HA, Michael N, Wasserman K, Ma W-H, Martins-Green M, Murphy WJ, Oppenheim JJ. Angiogenic effects of prostaglandin E2 are mediated by up-regulation of CXCR4 on human microvascular endothelial cells. Blood 2003; 102(6):1966–1977.
69. Form D, Auerbach R. PGE2 and angiogenesis. Proc Soc Exp Biol Med 1982; 172:214–218.
70. Stolina M, Sharma S, Lin Y, Dohadwala M, Gardner B, Luo J, Zhu L, Kronenberg M, Miller PW, Portanova J, Lee JC, Dubinett SM. Specific inhibition of cyclooxygenase 2 restores antitumor reactivity by altering the balance of IL-10 and IL-12 synthesis. J Immunol 2000; 164(1):361–370.
71. Pentland A, Schoggins J, Scott G, Khan K, Han R. Reduction of UV-induced skin tumors in hairless mice by selective COX-2 inhibition. Carcinogenesis 1999; 20:1939–1944.
72. Jun BD, Roberts LK, Cho BH, Robertson B, Daynes RA. Parallel recovery of epidermal antigen-presenting cell activity and contact hypersensitivity responses in mice exposed to ultraviolet irradiation: the role of a prostaglandin-dependent mechanism. J Invest Dermatol 1988; 90:311–316.
73. Shantz L, Pegg A. Translational regulation of ornithine decarboxylase and other enzymes of the polyamine pathway. Int J Biochem Cell Biol 1999; 31:107–122.
74. Lowe M, Verma AK, Boutwell RK. Ultraviolet light induces epidermal ornithine decarboxylase activity. J Invest Dermatol 1978; 71(6):417–418.
75. Verma AK, Lowe NJ, Boutwell RK. Induction of mouse epidermal ornithine decarboxylase activity and DNA synthesis by ultraviolet light. Cancer Res 1979; 39(3):1035–1040.
76. Hillebrand G, Window M, Benzinger M, Heitmeyer D, Bissett D. Acute and chronic ultraviolet radiation induction of epidermal ornithine decarboxylase activity in hairless mice. Cancer Res 1990; 50:1580–1584.
77. Rosen C, Gajic D, Drucker D. Ultraviolet radiation induction of ornithine decarboxylase in rat keratinocytes. Cancer Res 1990; 50:2631–2635.
78. Mizuno N, Kono T, Tanii T, Ishii M, Hamada T, Yoshida H, Matsui-Yuasa I, Otani S, Morisawa S. Increase in the expression of the ornithine decarboxylase gene in mouse skin by ultraviolet light. Arch Dermatol Res 1989; 281:514–516.
79. Agarwal R, Katiyar SK, Khan SG, Mukhtar H. Protection against ultraviolet B radiation-induced effects in the skin of SKH-1 hairless mice by a polyphenolic fraction isolated from green tea. Photochem Photobiol 1993; 58(5):695–700.

80. An KP, Athar M, Tang X, Katiyar SK, Russo J, Beech J, Aszterbaum M, Kopelovich L, Epstein EH Jr, Mukhtar H, Bickers DR. Cyclooxygenase-2 expression in murine and human nonmelanoma skin cancers: implications for therapeutic approaches. Photochem Photobiol 2002; 76(1):73–80.
81. Agarwal R, Katiyar S, Zaidi S, Mukhtar H. Inhibition of skin tumor promoter-caused induction of epidermal ornithine decarboxylase in SENCAR mice by polyphenolic fraction isolated from green tea and its individual epicatechin derivatives. Cancer Res 1992; 52:3582–3588.
82. Afaq F, Adhami VM, Ahmad N, Mukhtar H. Inhibition of ultraviolet B-mediated activation of nuclear factor kappaB in normal human epidermal keratinocytes by green tea constituent (−)-epigallocatechin-3-gallate. Oncogene 2003; 22(7):1035–1044.

32

Botanicals in Sun Care Products

Howard Epstein
Kao Brands—The Andrew Jergens Company,
Cincinnati, Ohio, USA

INTRODUCTION

Sun exposure has long been considered a healthy benefit of outdoor activity. Exposure to ultraviolet radiation (UVR) can stimulate vitamin D synthesis in the body and may promote immune tolerance toward certain antigens such as myelin autoantigens (1). Conversely, epidemiological data confirmed by research of the last 20 years have shown that exposure to UVR is a major risk factor for various skin cancers, premature aging of the skin commonly referred to as photoaging, and alteration of the skin's immune functions (2). More recently, research has shown that although sunlight and oxygen are essential for life, exposure to UVR and infrared radiation can potentially induce reactive oxygen species (ROS) in cutaneous tissue (3–5). ROS are considered to be a major factor in skin aging, cancer, and other conditions that effect the health of skin. ROS react with proteins, DNA, and unsaturated fatty acids leading to oxidative damage and immunosuppression.

Early studies of physiologic skin aging were "confounded" by the difficulty of distinguishing between extrinsic and intrinsic aging. Intrinsic aging is the natural biological progression of aging. Extrinsic aging is caused by external influences such as UVR, toxins in the environment, and other damaging environmental effects. One of the most fundamental issues for early photobiologists was to identify the molecular target for UVR in skin. UVR is arbitrarily separated into three ranges based on wavelength: UV-A (320–400 nm), UV-B (290–320 nm), and UV-C (200–290 nm). UV-C radiation is mostly absorbed by the stratosphere ozone layer, while UV-A radiation and UV-B radiation reach the earth and are considered the most "biologically relevant" wavelengths. The amount of UV-A radiation reaching the earth's surface is about 20 times greater than that of UV-B, and it can pass through the ozone layer, clouds, and glass with greater efficiency than UV-B radiation. Some investigators believe that the stratum corneum can block 90% of UV-B radiation, but only 50% of UV-A, enabling UV-A radiation to penetrate to deeper layers of the skin (6). Damage to skin from extrinsic aging serves to intensify the progression of intrinsic aging. It is now known that the sun exerts a number of effects on skin. One response of skin to UVR is tanning. Melanin in the skin is known to reduce the amount of UVR that can penetrate skin through the epidermal layers. It is a complex polymer produced by specialized cells, melanocytes located in the epidermal layer of the skin. Melanin is capable of quenching oxidative free radicals generated by exposure to UVR. The protective effect of melanin is limited and one should never assume that a tan would provide protection from the harmful effects of the sun's radiation. Skin contains two important chromophores, or photoreceptors, that can absorb UVR. One chromophore has an affinity for UV-B and the other for UV-A. Each chromophore has the potential to generate changes that may cause significant damage to skin. Nuclear DNA in the lower epidermis is the major chromophore for UV-B radiation. UVR that affects DNA can cause production of pyrimidine dimers and other damaging photoproducts directly in the DNA. If the cellular DNA does not repair the dimers, or undergoes cell death (apoptosis), cancer can develop in the cell. The other important chromophore in skin is urocanic acid. Urocanic acid can undergo photochemical reactions with DNA resulting in photoisomerization to a molecule having immunologic effects on the body and can generate singlet molecular oxygen. UV-A is believed to be much more efficient than UV-B at generating oxidative stress (7,8).

BOTANICALS OF SPECIFIC INTEREST

Botanically Derived Sunscreens and SPF Boosters

Most chemical sunscreens available to the formulator of sunscreen products provide more efficient filtering of UV-B radiation than of UV-A. Formulations containing adequate levels of chemical and physical sunscreen agents (titanium and zinc oxides) designed to achieve good UV-B and UV-A protection are frequently perceived by the consumer as being too whitening and greasy when applied to skin. The ideal sunscreen should protect skin from UV-A and UV-B radiation, bind to the stratum corneum with minimal penetration into the skin, be resistant to heat, sweating, and bathing, and have good cosmetic acceptance by the consumer. Consumers desire innovative sun care products that continue to provide additional benefits; health-conscious consumers are creating a growing demand for "natural" and "functionally based" botanicals. Phytoderived products serve various functions that include, emollients, tanning agents, and sunscreens. Flavonoids in botanicals having active UV absorbing properties have been identified and representative botanicals from this group have been found to enhance the absorption of UVR. For example, at about 282 nm, the flavones account for about 75–98% of the absorbency; *Citrus aurantium* is particularly high in flavonone. To avoid issues of dermal irritation, a unique patented process is used to extract the flavonoids of interest. Naringin, neohesperidin, neoeriocitrin, luteolin, and rutin are among the most desirable components (9) in galangal (*Kaempferia galanga*), a member of the ginger family. Galanga root is a natural source of ethyl *p*-methoxycinnamate. Studies have been conducted demonstrating the ability of galanga extract to "synergistically enhance the UV absorbency of a sunscreen composition." Further, the extract was shown to help make a sunscreen active more "photostable in a topical sunscreen composition," enabling more time to pass before additional application of sunscreen is needed for photoprotection. The synergistic effect of galanga extract with a conventional sunscreen allows a lower percentage of conventional sunscreen to be formulated into the sun care product (10,11). Recently, a process producing "sunscreens from vegetable oil and plant phenols" was disclosed: a lipase-catalyzed transesterification of a triglyceride to yield a feruyl-substituted or coumaryl-substituted acylglycerol with properties suitable for use as a sunscreen agent. Soybean oil is combined with ferulic acid using the enzyme lipase. Other suitable sources of triglycerides are corn, sunflower, canola, and safflower oils. The products of this reaction have UV absorptivity from ~280 nm to ~350 nm and are claimed to be particularly effective in the range of ~310–350 nm, the UV-A range. These products are well suited for waterproof type formulations (12). Other botanicals with UV absorbance are found in Table 32.1 (13).

Table 32.1 Botanically Derived Sunscreens and SPF Boosters

Botanical	Absorption spectrum	Compounds identified
Aloe (*Aloe socoirina*)	Maximum peak at 297 nm, with a second peak at 360 nm	Aloin (liquid and glycolic extracts)
Helichrysum (*Helichrysum italicum*)	275–300 nm	A complex of quinonic flavonoids
Frangula (*Rhamnus frangula*)	270 nm 300 nm	Glucofrangulin Glycolic extract of frangula
Camomille (*Matricaria chamomilla*)	250–300 nm	Gylcolic extract (oily extract had no effective absorption)
Rhatany (*Krameria triadra*)	Shows poor absorption, tannins produce an insoluble complex with proteins in skin	Digalloyltrioleate

Source: Courtesy of R&D Systems, Inc., Minneapolis, MN.

Botanicals as Photochemoprotective Agents

Photochemoprevention is the prevention of photoaging, skin cancer, and photosensitivity diseases of the skin by the use of pharmacological agents that inhibit or reverse the photoaging process. Protection provided by sunscreens is not complete and cannot repair damage to skin that has already occurred. Until recently, the main focus of research was on UV-B radiation, it is now appreciated that UV-A radiation also has significantly detrimental effects to the skin, such as generation of reactive oxygen species, further leading to lipidperoxidation, activation of transcription factors, and generation of DNA strand breaks. UV-A and UV-B exposure to skin has been shown to trigger two other major pathways leading to photoaging: induction of matrixmetalloproteinases (MMPs), resulting in collagen breakdown and mutation of mitochondrial DNA (mtDNA), which results in premature aging (14–17). Current research is investigating the potential of botanicals to function as chemopreventative agents. Green tea (*Camellia sinensis*) polyphenolic (GTP) compounds were among the early agents investigated and were found to be very effective as chemoprotective and chemopreventative agents. The primary antioxidants identified in green tea are epicatechin and epigallocatechin. These antioxidants have been shown to be stronger antioxidants than vitamin E and vitamin C (18–20). Studies have been conducted on human volunteers to observe the ability of green tea polyphenols to inhibit erythema and prevent the formation of thymine dimers, a marker for DNA damage in skin. GTP was found to significantly reduce erythema and DNA damage when taken orally and applied topically prior to volunteers'skin being treated with UV-A and UV-B radiation. Other studies have indicated that mice pretreated with GTP maintained reduced levels of ROS and reduction of inflammatory leukocytes, a marker for inflammation (21–24). Other potential natural antioxidants to be evaluated for photochmoprotective benefits are α-tocopherol from plant oils, apigenin from various fruits and vegetables, carotenoids, caffeic and ferulic acids from vegetables, olives and olive oil, genistein, a phytoestrogen in soy, red clover, Greek oregano and Greek sage, L-ascorbic acid from fruits and vegetables, resveratrol in grape seeds and skin, curcumin, garlic, red clover, and milk thistle (25).

BOTANICALS IN SUN CARE PRODUCTS

The sun care industry can be divided into three categories: sunscreen and sun blocking, sun tanning, and after-sun care products. About 80% of sun care sales take place at mass-market counters, drug stores, and supermarkets. The total US market for 2002 has been estimated to be in excess of $440 million, with the majority of purchases for sunscreen and sun blocking products. Market data indicate that about 45% of the adults in the USA use sun care products. Prime consumers are females between the ages of 25 and 44. Schering-Plough's Coppertone brand is the leading product sold in the USA; Banana Boat and Hawaiian Tropic follow. New sun care products offering benefits beyond SPF protection are emerging as consumers are becoming more aware of the damage to skin caused by exposure to the sun. These additional benefits include antiaging, skin firming ingredients, and ingredients for sensitive skin. Aloe remains the most common botanical used in after-sun products, to promote soothing and rehydration of skin exposed to the sun (Tables 32.2 and 32.3).

QUALITY CONTROL: METHODS OF ANALYSIS

Confirmation of botanical identity is the key responsibility of the botanical supplier. The appearance and active constituents of the botanical may vary with growing conditions and geographically diverse soil conditions. Botanicals formulated in OTC drugs and cosmetics are not regulated and lack of quality control/standardization is common. Adulteration of botanicals tends to become a problem when prices are high or it is difficult to obtain a popular botanical (26).

Botanicals should be evaluated by visual and microscopic inspection. Appearance, color, and odor can be compared to a reference standard. An experienced botanist can evaluate subtle plant structural differences under microscopic evaluation. Sometimes stains may be used to identify a specific botanical.

Table 32.2 Botanicals in Sun Care Products

Product	Botanical component	Suggested purpose or claim
Nivea Sun Care	Alpha flavone	Antiage sun cream
Nature's Gate	Aloe	Antiaging
Laboratories Oenobiol	Carotene, tomato extract	Antiaging
Clarins Sun Care Cream	Aloe, ayapana, silver birch, camellia, shea butter, mimosa, palm, pea, quinquina, and vanilla	Children with sensitive skin
Clairins Hydrating After-sun Moisturizer	Aloe, chamomile, shea, walnut, rosemary, *Siegesbeckia orientalis*, linden, vitamins A and E	After-sun use
ABRA Therapeutics, Collagen PhytoSHield, SPF 15 and SPF 30	Green tea, grape seed extract, vitamins C and E	Maximum solar protection
Aubrey Organics, Saving Face SPF 15	Aloe vera, witch hazel, St. John's wort oil, calendula oil	
Bath & Body Works, Suntan SPF 8	Green tea extract	
Almay Age Decelerating Daily Lotion SPF 15	Kinetin (furfuryladenine), salix nigra (willow) bark extract, aloe, leaf juice, simmondsia chinesis seed oil, *Anthemis nobilis*, salvia sclarea, ferula galbanifula, *Camellia sinesis*, *Rosmarinis officinalis*	Antiaging
Caudalie	Grapeseed polyphenols, resveratrol, passion flower, sesame, shea butter	Antiaging and soothing
L'Oreal, Ambre Solarie	Cactus nutriflavones	Extra miniaturization and softness to skin
Eucerin, Onagrine line	AGR, a plant flavonoid with high antioxidant activity	

(continued)

Table 32.2 *Continued*

Product	Botanical component	Suggested purpose or claim
Boots, Soltan	Aloe vera, watermelon, chamomile	Promotes safer, longer-lasting tans
Nivea/Beiersdorf Perfect Protection SPF 15	Japanese pagoda tree extract	Antioxidant sunscreen protection
MOP Suncare (Modern Organic Products) SPF 15, 30	Quinoa, horsetail extract with vitamins A and E	Natural antioxidants to protect and restore skin
Kiss My Face, Sun Swat SPF 15	Titanium dioxide and oat protein complex, oat beta glucan (1) also contains citronella, bay, cedarwood, lavender, vetivert, patchouli, juniper, tea tree, lemon peel, pennyroyal, tansy, goldenseal (2)	(1) A natural sunscreen blend; (2) Blend of botanicals that help repel bugs and are good for skin
Aveeno (Johnson & Johnson)/Skin Brightening Daily Moisturizer SPF 15	Soy extract	A unique combination of naturally active complexion corrector

Instrumentation used to evaluate chemical constituents include infrared spectroscopy, thin-layer chromatography, gas and liquid chromatography (GC, LC) and, more recently, LC/MS and GC/MS. GC/MS can selectively measure volatile chemical constituents and nonvolatile components such as fatty acids, phytosterols, and terpenoids. Use of instrumentation permits one to build a reference library of compounds to compare lot- to-lot submissions of botanicals. The equipment may be used to develop what is termed a "fingerprint" or "marker compounds," key characteristic components of the botanical under evaluation. The marker compounds will appear as a colored band, known as a chromatogram. Each peak in the chromatogram represents an active constituent or component in the botanical extract. One should be aware that while marker compounds help to identify a specific botanical, it is frequently other components or a synergistic interaction of components in the botanical that are responsible for its activity. In cases where one wishes to evaluate a botanical or combination of botanicals for a synergistic effect, a biological assay may be the preferred method of quality control.

Table 32.3 US Patent Technology

Patent number	Botanical or active in botanical	Application
5,665,367	Flavonoid: naringen and/or quercetin	Treatment of photodamaged skin, wrinkles
US Patent application number 20020176903	Olive plant extract (*Olea europaea* L.)	Skin beautification, antiaging via an antioxidant effect
6,121,243	Alpha-glucosyl rutin and one or more flavonoids and their glycosides, cinnamic/ferulic acid derivatives (obtained from beet crops latex from umbelliferous plants such as *Ferula asafetida*)	Antiaging, antioxidant
6,251,878	Tamarind seed	Inhibition of UV-induced immune suppression and interleukin-10 production
5,861,415	Curcumoids (curcumin, demethoxy curcumin, bis-demethoxy curcumin)—extracted from the roots of tumeric	Antioxidant, anti-inflammatory, antimutagen
5,824,659	Aloe oligosaccharide	Prevents damage to the skin immune system by UVR
6,248,341	Green tea—epigallocatechin, epicatechin gallate	When combined with tyrosinase inhibitors is useful for treatment or prevention of dark circles, melanization, anti-irritant
6,531,165	*Fagus crenata*	Collagen production promotor, repair of collagen damaged from UV exposure

(*continued*)

Table 32.3 *Continued*

Patent number	Botanical or active in botanical	Application
6,596,761	Various flavonoids in combination with cinnamic acid derivatives	Antioxidant, helps to protect skin against UVB and UVA radiation
6,592,911	(−)-Olivil from *Stereospermum personatum*	Antioxidant, comparable to tocopherol
6,589,514	*Morinda citrifolia* (Indian mulberry plant)	Antiaging serum, repair skin damaged by UVR

To ensure safety, botanical shipments should be certified to be free of pesticides, heavy metals, and microbial contamination. Documentation should state the correct Latin name, part of the plant used, season and method of harvest, method of storage, and extraction method used including solvents that may have been removed prior to shipment.

Recent Research Techniques: Biological Assays and Cell Culture

Currently, common industry practice is to standardize botanicals to "marker" compounds. Biological assays (bioassays) enable one to standardize botanical products that have been mixed or contain several components that are responsible for the activity of the plant. Botanicals are considered to have "holistic, functional benefits that are beneficial for more than one body site." For this reason, a biological assay would be considered a preferable approach to standardizing a botanical for a desired activity. Bioassays are desirable when chromatography is unable to separate a compound effectively or chemical analysis does not yield satisfactory results. As the human genome project comes to completion, the herbal industry has benefited by the availability of techniques and instrumentation capable of determining "receptor binding, enzyme inhibition, DNA nicking," and antioxidant activity. Biological assays offer the advantage of rapidly screening large numbers of samples for a specific desired activity.

Cells of the body react to the external environment and each other through a series of complex signaling networks. These networks contain feedback loops with various isolated pathways that have begun to be understood only in recent years. Signal transduction is the process of conversion of "external signals, such as hormones, growth factors, neurotransmitters, and cytokines to a specific internal cellular response, such as gene expression, cell division, or even cell suicide" (27). There are five basic routes for external cell signaling (28):

1. Diffusion of hydrophobic molecules across lipid bilayers of cell membranes
2. Cell surface signaling enzymes located on the interior of cell membranes, for example, tyrosine kinases and Ras proteins; these molecules trigger a signaling cascade while anchored to the plasma membrane
3. Ion channels are specific membrane proteins that permit specific ions to pass through a cell membrane
4. Receptor binding on the cell surface, found on the exterior of the membrane; examples are tumor necrosis factors or cytokines
5. G protein-coupled receptors are seven-transmembrane proteins composed of subunits in triplicate; these molecules traverse both sides of the cell membrane.

Signal transduction initiates at the cell membrane where the release of a chemical signal or other external stimulus stimulates a cascade of enzymatic reactions inside the cell. These reactions eventually cause changes in cell function or identity of the cell through protein interactions. Signal transduction pathways contain "go-no go" control points that, when activated by environmental stresses such as UVR, lead to photoaging, immunological compromise, and possibly skin cancer. Biological signaling is the result of interacting signaling molecules that are mostly protein in nature. SWISS-PROT, an online molecular biology database, lists approximately 1551 human signal proteins and a total of 2986 signal proteins in humans (SWISS-PROT protein database, public release Number 36). Signaling networks exist on several levels of complexity. Hormones and other molecules carried by the circulatory system control activities of organs and tissues; other messenger molecules such as amino acids, peptides, proteins, fatty acids, lipids, nucleosides, and nucleotides act as second messengers to relay signals to other body parts. Ultimately, gene expression is regulated in the process. Cell signaling and detection of the messengers and changes in gene expression through protein interactions are the basis of contemporary drug discovery programs. "Genes control all cellular functions responsible for maintaining human health by serving as blueprints for the production of protein in cells." Gene regulating enzymes are frequently kinases and phosphatases involved in intracellular signaling. Normally, there is a balance between the promoters, activators, and inhibitors in the cascade system that maintains the cells in an optimal state.

Biological Assays of Interest for Screening Botanicals in Sun Care Products

Biochemical assays have been traditionally used to study the enzyme mechanism and in identification of enzyme inhibitors or activators (Table 32.4). Cell-based

Table 32.4 Examples of Biochemical Assays—Measure Enzymatic Reactions or Biological Responses Induced by Immunologic Interactions

Assay	Concept	Comments
Matrix MMPs (e.g., MMP 1, 2, 3, 9,12) (family of endoproteases)	Prolonged exposure to UV-A and UV-B radiation stimulates expression of collagenases, degrades collagen and elastin in dermal layer of skin	Visual immunofluorescence, immunuhistochemistry assay using antibody to MMP Protease activity can be measured by colorimetric activity Fibroblast cell cultures can be used with enzyme-linked immnosorbent assay to measure release of MMP
Elastase inhibition	Elastin is broken down by the enzyme elastase, which is produced by photodamaged skin	Dermal fibroblast cells can be used as a source of elastase; botanical extract can be screened for elastase inhibition as measured by colorimetric activity
Nitric oxide synthase, inducible (iNOS)	Nitric oxide is a free radical that is a biological mediator in many organs of the body	Western blot analysis Immuncohistochemistry with appropriate antibodies
Cyclooxygenase-2 (COX-2)	COX-2 is elevated in cells when inflammation exists	Effect on enzymatic activity, a colorimetric assay Expression of COX-2 activity on mRNA
p38	A series of gene regulating pathways that include mitogen-activating protein kinases, extracellular signal-regulated kinase, c-Jun N-terminal kinase; these regulating family members are believed to be involved in the control of cell proliferation, differientiation, inflammationand apoptosis (cell death) in response to UVR.	Antibodies react with standards and samples from cell lysates to form a colorimetric reaction

Table 32.5 Cell Culture Based Biological Assays—Measure Biochemical or Physiological Response at the Cellular Level

Assay	Concept	Comments
Interleukin 10, 12	Interleukins are pharmacologically active proteins that regulate cell functions such as inflammatory and immune response	Keratinocyte cell cultures have been shown to show an immunologic response upon exposure to UVR
Nuclear factor-kappa beta	A signal transduction protein responsible for immunity, inflammation and cell death	Protein is found in the cell nucleus
Apoptosis (programmed cell death)	Apoptosis is involved in the development and growth of the epidermis Programmed cell death occurs in late stages of keratinocyte differentiation; UV-B radiation is known to induce apoptosis	Sunburn cells are believed to be apoptotic cells
DNA damage	UV radiation damages cell by fragmenting sections of the cell's DNA, these fragments will migrate out of damaged cells under influence of an electric potential	Various methods are available DNA damage can lead to apoptosis
Phosphorylation assays Mitogen-activated protein kinases, extracellular signal-regulated kinases, c-Jun N-terminal kinase	Many functions of cell biology are controlled by a reversible phosphorylation of protein targets by kinases Involved in oxidative stress of cell, cell proliferation, differentiation, and apoptosis	These cellular signals are involved in cellular aging associated with UVR and other disease pathogenesis

assays can be used to evaluate signal transduction events when a cell is stimulated as previously described. Cell-based assays have traditionally been used to evaluate the efficacy and potency of inhibitors that have been previously screened by biochemical assays. Cell-based assays are now becoming more commonly used as the primary screening assay (Table 32.5). Some assays cannot be performed with a biochemical assay. A cell-based assay is necessary for ion channel assay, signal transduction assay, and transporter assay. For these tests, live cells are required to measure the end points (29).

CONCLUSION

It is now acknowledged that cellular damage from UVR and the resulting inflammation contributes to the appearance of aging skin. Furthermore, while it is known that excessive exposure to the sun's radiation is a cause of many forms of skin cancer, the incidence of skin cancer continues to increase dramatically. Sunscreens are designed to protect against sunburning, which is believed to be directly related to skin cancer development. Sunscreens that provide adequate protection against sunburn may not be as effective in providing protection against the immunosuppression caused by UV-A exposure. Some investigators speculate that this may explain why some skin cancers develop on skin in places with little exposure to UVR (30). Research techniques developed during the era of the human genome project have advanced the understanding of cell signaling and normal cellular functioning. Cell signaling serves to regulate gene expression and other cellular functions in response to external stimuli in the environment. Cell signaling and gene regulation are controlled at the molecular level through the formation of protein–protein interactions. Protein–protein and other molecular interactions have enabled molecular biologists to evaluate the ability of botanicals to repair or prevent cell damage from occurring. The study of cell signaling pathways and gene expression resulting in protein interactions connected to the genetic expression is becoming an integral part of an emerging field known as "systems biology." Systems biology is an integrative approach that measures the various biological responses of an entire organism involving genomics, proteonomics, and metabolomics from an interactive "systems" perspective (31). The ability to apply this emerging science to the study of botanical interaction will provide future opportunities to formulate sun care products with "functional" botanicals.

REFERENCES

1. Duman M, Jauberteau-Merchan MO. The protective role of Langerhan's cells and sunlight in multiple sclerosis. Med Hypotheses 2000; 55:517–520.
2. Gilchrest BA. A review of skin aging and its medical therapy. Br J Dermatol 1996; 135:867–875.
3. Muizzuddin N, Shakoori AA, Marenus KD. Effect of antioxidants and free radical scavengers on protection of human skin against UVB, UVA and IR irradiation. Skin Res Technol 1999; 5:260–265.
4. Vayalill PK, Elmets CA, Katiyar SK. Treatment of green tea polyphenols in hydrophilic cream prevents UVB induced oxidation of lipids and proteins, depletion of

antioxidant enzymes and phosphorylation of MAPK proteins in SKH-1 hairless mouse skin. Carcinogenesis 2003; 24(5):927–936.
5. Thiele JT, Dreher F, Packer L. Antioxidant defense systems. In: Elsner P, Maibach HI, eds. Cosmeceutical, Drugs vs. Cosmetics. New York: Marcel Dekker, 2000.
6. Kulms D, Schwartz W. 20 years after-milestones in molecular photobiology. Soc Invest Dermatol 2002; 7(1):46–50.
7. Goldsmith LA, ed. Physiology, Biochemistry, and Molecular Biology of the Skin. 2nd ed. New York: Oxford University Press, 1991.
8. Cruz PD, ed. Active photoprotection from botanical extracts. Dermatol Focus 2003; 22(1).
9. US patent 6,409,996.
10. US patent 6,440,402.
11. US patent 5,000,937.
12. US patent 6,346,236.
13. Proserpio G. Natural sunscreens: vegetable derivatives as sunscreen and tanning agents. Cosmet Toilet 1976; 91:34–46.
14. Berneburg M, Plettenber H, Krutmann J. Photoaging of human skin. Photodermatol Photoimmunol Photomed 2000.
15. Grether-Beck S, Oliazoh-Horn S, Schmitt H, Grewe M, Jahncke A, Johnson JP, Briviba K, Sies H, Krutmann J. Activation of transcription factor AP-2 mediates ultraviolet A radiation and singlet oxygen-induced expression of the human intracellular adhesion molecule gene. Proc Natl Acad Sci USA 1996; 93:14586-14591.
16. Berneburg M, Gattermann N, Stege H, Grewe M, Vogelsang K, Ruzicka T, Knowland J. Chronically ultraviolet-exposed human skin shows a higher mutation frequency of mitochrondrial DNA as compared to unexposed skin and the hematopoietic system. Photochem Photobio 1997; 66:271–275.
17. Bernburg M, Grether-Beck S, Kurten V, Ruzicka T, Briviba K, Sies H, Krutman J. Singlet oxygen mediates the UVA-induced generation of the photoaging-associated mitochrondrial common deletion. J Biol Chem 1999; 274:15345–15349.
18. Katiyar SK, Elmets CA. Green tea polyphenolic antioxidants and skin photoprotection. Int J Oncol 2001; 18:1307–1313.
19. Ahmas N, Mukhtar H. Cutaneous photochemoprotection by green tea: a brief review. Skin Pharmacol Appl Skin Physiol 2001; 14:69–76.
20. Katiyar SK, Matsui MS, Elmets CA, Mukhtar H. Polyphenolic antioxidants (−)-epigallocatechin-3 gallate from green tea reduces UVB-induced inflammatory infiltration of leukocytes in human skin. Photochem Photobiol 1999; 69:148–153.
21. Fguyer S, Araq F, Mukhtar H. Photochemoprevention of skin cancer by botanical agents. Photodermatol Photoimmunol Phototomed 2003; 19:56–72.
22. Afaq F, Adhami VM, Ahmad N, Mukhtar H. Botanical antioxidants for chemoprevention of photocarcinogenesis. Front Biosci 2002; 7:784–792.
23. Katiyar SK, Afaq F, Perez A, Mukhtar H. Green tea polyphenol (−)-epigallocatechin-3-gallate treatment of human skin inhibits ultraviolet radiation-induced oxidative stress. Carcinogenesis 2001; 22:287–294.
24. Katiyar SK, Ahmad N, Mukhtar H. Green tea and skin. Arch Derrmatol 2000; 136:984–994.
25. Cruz PD, ed. Active photochemoprotection from botanical antioxidants. Dermatol Focus 2003; 22(1).

26. D'Amelio FS. Botanicals a Phytocosmetic Desk Reference. New York: CRC Press, 1999.
27. Signal transduction as a drug-discovery platform. Nat Biotechnol 2000; 18(Suppl).
28. Coty C. The new frontier of cell signaling-based therapies. Drug Discov 2003; 6(4):73–77.
29. Miner LK. Biochemical vs. cell-based assays: which one for primary screening? Drug Discov Dev 2003; 6(4):15.
30. Rigel DA. Presentation. American Academy of Dermatology, 2002.
31. Henry CM. Systems biology. Chem Eng News 2003; 8(20):45–55.

33

Antiaging Actives in Sunscreens

Karl Lintner
Sederma, Paris, France

INTRODUCTION

The first and second editions of *Sunscreens* did not contain a chapter equivalent to the present one. Including "antiaging actives" in the present book reflects some of the changes occurring in cosmetic formulations and marketing strategies. As in so many other domains, we see a blurring of frontiers, a mixing of categories, and a (deliberate?) gradual disappearance of clear distinctions and definitions.

Although the title of *Sunscreens* has not changed and certainly suggests to most readers the general category of "cosmetic products used on the skin during extensive sun exposure in order to protect the skin against the deleterious effects of direct sunlight," the apparent simplicity of this description is deceptive. Even more ambiguity is contained in the title of this chapter, with the two powerful, but vague, concepts of "antiaging" and "actives" (or "cosmeceuticals," as these ingredients are sometimes, erroneously, called). It appears therefore necessary to start with a few definitions of our own, that we will use within the scope of this chapter, without prejudice to different meanings in other parts of the book.

Let us call "sunscreens" the finished cosmetic consumer product that bears a clear message of "protection against solar radiation" such as the prevention of erythema, sunburns, sometimes even cancer. This would include in most cases "suntan lotions," "sun care products," "sunblocks," and the like. Generally, it would not include "after-sun lotions" and "self-tanning products." Although the word "sunscreen" is sometimes also used to designate the chemical entity that blocks the sunlight from reaching the skin, these chemicals contained in "sunscreens" should be called ultraviolet (UV) filters or UV reflectors.

Difficulties in nomenclature also arise because of different legislations in different parts of the world (cf. the section on regulatory aspects) and because of technical and marketing considerations: a "sunscreen" of today contains, more and more often, specific skin and/or body care active ingredients, accompanied by a corresponding claim (this is the reason for this chapter); on the other hand, an increasing number of classic "skin care" (i.e., face care, lip care, makeup, body care, and even hair care) products boast sun protection factors (SPFs) in the 5–15 range. These products have primary skin care claims (moisturizing, antiwrinkle, firming, . . .) and offer the sun protection as an additional benefit. So where is the borderline between the two? A "sunscreen" of SPF 15 with an additional antiwrinkle claim is a "sunscreen" (e.g., Biotherm's recent launch with exactly that name: "Antiwrinkle Suncare") because the marketeer positions the product as such (advertising, point of sale, timing of promotional activity), whereas Yves-Saint Laurent's spring launch of Age Expert ("age-defying cream") has an SPF15 but is clearly *not* positioned as a "sunscreen". It claims to contain DHEA-like actives and lycopene as a free radical scavenger and is a "classical" face care product.

In any case, the New Zealand Society of Dermatology proposes on its website that "sunscreens should be applied daily, more often when outdoors." While this makes sense, it is certainly not the daily routine of the general population.

How about "actives"? My opinion and arguments for it can be found in the proceedings of the PCIE conference (1). Briefly, any cosmetic ingredient that has (i) demonstrated cosmetic activity on human skin (or its appendages), (ii) a substantiated claim, and (iii) a plausible "story" to go with it can be considered an active: this encompasses then the wide field of ingredients (such as found in the CTFA/INCI dictionary) from botanicals (various types of plant extracts) to pure chemical entities that possess a function that is clearly different from the galenic purpose (emulsifiers, texturizers, thickeners, preservatives, fragrances etc.). Again, it may occur that an ingredient functions as an "active" in one product (positioned as such by the marketeer) and as a basic ingredient in another product (glycerin, lecithin, and lanolin come to mind). In the main body of this chapter, we shall concentrate on "actives" that are particularly suited or are already in use in the general category of "sunscreens," "actives" that make sense in the context of sun care and skin protection/treatment.

We can therefore now drop the quotation marks from the word active.

Finally, "antiaging" (again with quotation marks): the term is catchy, seductive, but very vague. Some countries have regulations forbidding the use of this "claim" in cosmetic advertising or on the packaging.

As usual, there are two aspects to the concept: prevention and treatment. Antiage prevention implies that a consumer product helps "reduce the speed of the appearance of the clinical signs of (cutaneous) aging," based on the protective active contained in the product. Antiage treatment promises to reverse (some of) the visible signs of skin aging (such as wrinkle reduction, firmness improvement, moisturization of dry skin, etc.), based on actives that "restore, regenerate, repair, ..." skin items such as "barrier, extracellular matrix, collagen fibers, hydrolipid balance" and the like.

If one really wants to get a more *global* perspective of the antiaging field in general, books like *Pharmacological Intervention in Aging and Age-Associated Disorder* (2) are a good place to start. Yu and Yang introduce the discussion there with a "critical evaluation of the Free Radical Theory of Aging" (see in following text, the impact of free radicals and antioxidant strategies). Many articles and references therein are useful for finding ideas in "antiaging".

In the following sections we consider both types of "antiaging" actives and their respective merits in sunscreens.

I apologize for the lengthy introduction and the many quotation marks and hope the reader has thus a clear picture of where this chapter is headed and what the various terms are meant to convey.

In view of the many detailed chapter headings before and after this one in the present book, it would be redundant to repeat much that is described about the dangers of the sun to our skin, about the photobiology, the physics of filters, the differences between chronological aging and photoaging. If modern UV filters are so well suited to protect us against the sun's dangerous rays, for what reason (other than a marketing and/or label claim) should the formulator of a modern sunscreen add antiaging actives to his product?

For one, and most importantly, UV filters are not absolute: even an SPF 60 (not allowed as a claim everywhere) will wear off with time, or may not be applied in sufficient amount from the beginning, or the exposure of the person wearing it continues beyond the period of protection. Any well-chosen additional active in the product will help decrease the damages that are not prevented by the UV filter. For instance, this seems to be particularly true for the combination of UV-A filters with antioxidant protective molecules. The presently available

UV-A filters are rarely (not?) able to block out all of the UVA radiation such as to prevent all free radical generation in the deeper layers of the skin.

Second, the trend in all cosmetic formulas and products goes that way: makeup mascaras, foundations, lip sticks, powders, also cleansers, body care, and scalp care SKUs all contain actives for additional benefits. True skin care needs a global, and continuous, approach. We need the sunlight for the synthesis of vitamin D and for our psychic well-being ("healthy tan"), and we desire silky, youthful skin: for this we need the optimum combination of sunscreen and skin care actives.

Before reviewing the traditional actives used and useful in sunscreens and presenting a few new ideas in the final section, Table 33.1 summarizes the rationale for the different types of actives that might make sense in sunscreens,

Table 33.1 Rationale for Adding Different Types of Actives to Sunscreens

Type of danger/ damage	Type of active proposed	"Cause"	Increased sophistication
Dryness	Moisturizer/humectant	IR, UV-A, UV-B	↓
Dryness	Barrier repair: ceramides	UV-B	
Skin sagging	Firming, elasticity enhancing	UV-A, UV-B	
Wrinkles	Tissue repair: ECM, collagen stimulation, cell metabolism, skin tighteners	UV-A, UV-B	
Skin thinning	Tissue repair: ECM, collagen stimulation, cell metabolism, skin tighteners	UV-A, UV-B	
Roughness	Smoothing, emollients	UV-B	
Inflammation (redness)	Anti-inflammatories, soothing actives	UV-A, UV-B	
Melasma, age spots	Skin "whitening"	UV-A	
Yellowing, elastosis	Elastase inhibitors	UV-A, UV-B	
Telangiectasis	Anticouperose, veinotonic	UV-B	
Blackheads, whiteheads	Antiacne	UV-B	
Free radical damage	Radical scavengers	UV-A	
Lipoperoxidation	Antioxidants	UV-A	
Enzyme damage	Enzymes, pseudoenzymes	UV-A, UV-B	
DNA damage	DNA repair	UV-B	
Apoptosis	Cell repair	UV-B	

although some appear far-fetched. Very roughly, one can partition these actives along the following lines.

UV-B rays generate actinic damages that need antiage treatment (long-term), UV-A radiation needs to be addressed with actives more immediately: to prevent oxidation, to scavenge the radicals, to reduce local inflammation and thus avoid long-term damages of molecular nature to accumulate (antiage Prevention).

STRATEGIES OF ANTIAGING ACTIVES IN SUNSCREENS

Prevention of Damage ("Slowing Down the Aging Process")

Vitamins

One of the first and most widely used categories of actives formulated in sunscreens is the one comprising the vitamins C and E, sometimes A (retinoids) or a few of the B group.

The literature on the effects of vitamins C and E as photoprotective agents in cell cultures (*in vitro*) and on animals is impressively large. Although general consensus is expressed that the protective effect afforded by these molecules "might be beneficial" to human skin, there is astonishingly little documentation of the benefits of vitamin uses in cosmetic finished products, especially sunscreens, on human skin (*in vivo*). Pehr and Forsey concluded in 1993, that "after 44 years of research there is still scant proof of vitamin E's effectiveness [...]; it is of no use in [...] skin damage induced by ultraviolet light" (3). It is not the purpose of this chapter to present an exhaustive review of this topic, as antioxidants will also be discussed in a separate chapter. Such a review can be found, for instance, in Pinnell (4) in the form of a lecture, followed by a quiz.

A rapid overview of the literature however shows that research into the effects of topical vitamin application continues, many papers focusing on combinations of vitamins, such as E and C, E and A.

Vitamin E (α-tocopherol) is a ubiquitous, liposoluble molecule, the major activity of which is as an antioxidant. Although more powerful antioxidants can be found in nature, vitamin E is most accessible, by synthesis or extraction, is colorless and well documented as being toxicologically safe. Ritter et al. (5) show the beneficial effects of tocopherol application *before* UV irradiation on mice. They note an increase in epidermal thickness, which might contribute to the decrease in the number of sunburn cells. The concentration of tocopherol in the vehicle (50% in ethanol) is however quite unrealistic in cosmetic and sunscreen applications. Saral et al. (6) studied vitamin E acetate (the more stable ester form of vitamin E that is preferentially employed in sunscreens) by applying it topically for 3 weeks on guinea pigs before a single UV-B dose. Measuring lipid peroxide levels and enzyme scavenging activity (cf. also following text) these authors find that tocopherol acetate did prevent the UV-B-induced effects. Trevithick et al. (7) studied the application of tocopherol acetate immediately *after* UV-B irradiation on mice and found decreases in sunburn cell number, inflammatory infiltration, and edematous swelling. Even delayed application (8 h after irradiation) afforded some protection, again however at high concentrations (5%).

Another interesting study was carried out on the antioxidant activity of α-tocotrienol in topical application (8). Although it did not address UV irradiation, the oxidant damages were induced by benzylperoxide (10%). Application of a 5% w/v preparation of α-tocotrienol for 7 days reduced the BPO-induced lipid peroxidation significantly. For cosmetic purposes, 5% vitamin E again appears unrealistically high.

Vitamin C has several properties, which make it attractive to the formulator of sunscreens. Not only does the molecule possess antioxidant (reducing) activity, but it also stimulates the synthesis of collagen (*in vitro*) and contributes to the hydroxylation and the correct lay-down of collagen fibers in skin tissue. Its cosmetic use is found particularly in "antiwrinkle" creams (based on the collagen stimulation claim) and in "skin whitening" products (based on the inhibition of melanogenesis).

Darr et al. (9) investigated the topical use of vitamin C on pigskin and found protection against UV-B damages as measured by erythema and sunburn cell formation. As innate vitamin C concentrations decrease as a result of UV irradiation, topical supplementation is a potential strategy to counter this deleterious effect of sunlight. Follow-up studies later confirmed the protective effect of vitamin C, when formulated together with a UV filter (oxybenzone) (10). An even more broad-spectrum protection is achieved with the combination of vitamin C, vitamin E and the sun-filter, as vitamin C affords particular protection against the UV-A-mediated phototoxicity in this animal model.

Some more recent studies suggest benefits to using vitamin C together with vitamin E in topical products such as sunscreens. Moison et al. (11) describe a synergistic effect between the two molecules in protecting the lipids, also on pigskin; moreover, the inherent vitamin C and E content of the skin is maintained at its levels, against depletion by UV-B radiation. Steenvorden and Beijersbergen (12) investigated vitamins C and E independently and conjointly: topical application on mice before UV-B irradiation led to reduced immunosuppression. In their model, no synergy was found, however. Both studies cited showed that vitamin C concentration needed to be about 500–1000 times higher than vitamin E to obtain comparable efficacy.

Human *in vivo* studies were carried out by Dreher et al. (13) using three antioxidant molecules, alone or in combination: vitamin C, vitamin E, and melatonin. Slight synergistic results are obtained by combining the ingredients two by two or in a threesome and applying them in a vehicle 30 min before UV exposure. Skin color and skin blood flow were used as markers for UV-induced damage.

The same authors then studied the effects of these combinations when applied 30 min, 1 h, and 2 h *after* UVR exposure, using the same end-points (14). As no protective effect whatsoever was noted, the authors concluded that UVR-induced skin damage is rapid; antioxidants can alleviate or prevent damages only when present before or during sun exposure. Melatonin is of course used in oral supplementation against jet lag, but Reiter et al. (15) describe in much detail its antioxidant, radical scavenging activity, and life span prolongation! Lin et al. (16) tried a further combination of 15% vitamin C and 1% vitamin E on pig skin and found that repeated application of this cocktail reduced erythema, sunburn cells, as well as thymidin dimers (DNA damage) generated by repeated UV irradiation with a solar simulator. While the protection against this latter aspect is of importance in the prevention of mutations and their consequences, the sunscreen formulator may again have difficulties in incorporating these levels of ingredients in the finished product.

And what about vitamin A and its derivatives? Kligman (17) in 1987 recommended the use of retinoic acid to replenish the inherent pool of this molecule in the skin after its depletion by UV light. Together with Schwartz (18) he also demonstrated that post-UV irradiation treatment with 0.05% retinoic acid stimulated collagen synthesis *in vivo* in albino hairless mice. Ho et al. (19) showed in 1992 that retinoic acid augments UV-induced melanogenesis, an interesting side effect to all other activities known for retinoids. The study was carried out on a specific mouse strain and confirmed on two human volunteers. As retinoic acid is considered a prescription drug in most countries, the cosmetic industry became interested in retinol, retinol esters, and retinaldehyde. Thus, more recently, Boisnic et al. (20) published a study with a retinaldehyde cream, applied to an *ex vivo* human skin model. Eighteen days of regular UV-A exposure simulated photoaging; this was followed by application of the retinaldehyde cream for 2 weeks. The UV-A-induced alterations of collagen and elastic fibers were reversed by the retinaldehyde, and collagen synthesis rates were restored to the levels of unexposed skin. Sorg and colleagues (21,22) have interested themselves in the combination effects of retinoids and vitamin E; they find certain specific benefits, depending on the type of irradiation (UV-A, UV-B), the time of application (before or after exposure), and other parameters.

More data on human volunteers in studies on retinoids in conjunction with UV radiation can be found in Kang et al. (23). One opposing opinion is, however, expressed in Ref. (24) under the aggressive title: "Tretinoin and cutaneous photoaging: new preparation. Guaranteed adverse effects!"

Knowing that the skin contains various antioxidants all together, a more holistic approach was taken by Greul et al. (25) where a combination of β-carotene, lycopene, vitamin C, vitamin E, selenium, and proanthocyanidins was tested in a double-blind placebo-controlled human study involving UV irradiation and skin analysis. Findings concerned significant differences in MMP 1 and MMP 9 expression and a slowdown in the development and grade of UV-induced erythema. This reference is given tongue in cheek (excuse the pun), as the study did not use the antioxidant mixture topically, but orally. Somewhat similar results were obtained in the SUVIMAX study (26).

In summary, "vitamins are good for you." Their use in sunscreens is widespread; based on the numerous studies, even if most of them are animal or *in vitro* studies, their claim to "antiaging" activity is not far-fetched. Vitamins C and E would be considered more of the "preventive" type (antioxidant, to be used before or during sun exposure), vitamin A and derivatives are more the "repair" type, undoing some of the UV-caused damages. Their main drawback is the difficulty in formulating stable vehicles, such that the right amount of efficacious vitamins can be guaranteed for sufficient shelf life.

Botanicals

Like the antioxidants, botanicals, also called plant extracts, are also discussed in another chapter in the present book. Nevertheless, they merit a short mention here, as an increasing number of ingredients of plant origin are offered and used that are tested and positioned as "antiaging" actives, and thus used or useful in sunscreens.

Plant extracts cover the spectrum from hydroglycolic solutions of analytically ill-defined nature to pure, isolated, chemically identified molecules, and all products that present intermediate stages of purification. The reputation of the plant kingdom is one of almost unlimited source of potential healing activities, thousands of substances yet undiscovered.

A closer look reveals, however, that with some notable exceptions, a few broad categories suffice to describe the benefits obtained from plant extracts for cosmetic claims: we find antioxidant activity (polyphenols, vitamins, flavonoids), anti-inflammatory properties (nonsteroidal enzyme inhibitors), tissue repair molecules (di- and triterpenes). All of these activities can be employed for "antiage" claims, all of them make sense in the context of sunscreen formulation. A few references gleaned from the peer-reviewed literature shall illustrate this concept. It is of course impossible to list here all the commercially available plant-derived cosmetic ingredients (cf. CTFA dictionary) that are claimed to be antiaging based on some or another *in vitro*, *ex vivo*, or even *in vivo* test with or without UV irradiation included in the test protocol.

Green tea is a favorite among the botanicals with well-known reputation. *In vitro* scavenging of hydrogen peroxide and prevention of UV-induced oxidative damages on skin cells in culture by various fractions of green and black teas, including purified epigallocatechin gallate (EGCG) were described by Wei et al. (27). The pure molecule enhanced the observed activity and is considered the major active substance in these preparations. An *in vivo* study by Vayalil et al. (28) on hairless mice confirmed the prevention of UV-induced lipid peroxidation by green tea polyphenols, such as EGCG. Interestingly, the authors also quantified the amount of inherent antioxidant enzymes (catalase, glutathione peroxidase): whereas UV irradiation depleted these enzymes in the skin, EGCG application before single UV-B doses prevented this loss by 50–90% (see also following text).

Less well known botanical extracts such as those obtained from methanolic maceration of *Capparis spinosa* L. buds (29), crude ethanol extracts from *Culcitium reflexum* H.B.K. (30), or *Chromolaena odorata* (31), to cite just a few exotic ones, all contain flavonoids, phenolic acids, coumarins and the like. They all show *in vitro* antioxidant activity that can be used for antiage claims in sunscreens. *Prunus persica* Batsch extracts rich in kampferol glycoside derivatives (32) also showed inhibition of UV-induced edema on mouse ear and tumor prevention (33) in UV-B- and UV-C-irradiated mice.

A further aspect, not yet widely recognized or mentioned in this context of sunscreen protection by antiaging products is discussed by Okano et al. (34). It is known that with advancing age, proteins and sugar molecules react, unspecifically, in a process called glycation to give what has been aptly termed, advanced glycation endproducts (AGEs). Okano et al. describe that AGEs are not only inherently a sign of aging skin (less elasticity of the glycated proteins) but also contribute actively to aging by reducing fibroblast proliferation, matrix synthesis, and by generating reactive oxygen species (ROS) during UV exposure! He then describes that unspecified extracts of *Paenia suffruticosa* and *Sanguisorba officinalis* inhibit AGE formation and scavenges hydrogen peroxide at the same time.

A review of photochemoprevention by botanical antioxidants in view of their use in sunscreens is given in Ref. (35).

A typical example of anti-inflammatory activity of a botanical extract useful in a suncare product is described by Hughes-Formella et al. (36). UV-B irradiation, provoking erythema on the back of 30 volunteers was followed by application of a *Hamamelis virginiana* lotion 7, 24, and 48 h after irradiation. Significant differences in erythema values (chromameter, visual scoring) were observed with respect to the vehicle lotion. This type of use is, however, better suited for after-sun products than for the sunscreen itself and we shall not dwell on these applications.

Enzymes

We have cited earlier two studies (6,28) that mentioned antioxidant enzymes of the skin. This aspect has received less attention in the sunscreen and protection field; two reasons may account for this. Technical difficulties in analyzing enzyme activities on human skin, and the inherent instability of enzymes which make them hard to formulate and stabilize in finished cosmetic sunscreens. Nevertheless, basic research into the innate enzyme defense system of the skin has progressed, and a number of *in vitro*, animal and human *in vivo* studies point to the delicate balance that is required between the various enzymes in the skin.

We shall first review the salient facts about cutaneous defense enzymes and then discuss the possibility of using antiaging actives within this scope.

Once again, the problem turns around the free radicals, lipoperoxidation, and other oxidative damages. ROS such as superoxide anion, hydroxyl radical, singlet oxygen, and hydrogen peroxide cause numerous deleterious effects on structural and functional (enzyme) proteins, lipid membranes, tissue polysaccharides, and genetic material (DNA). The molecules present in the skin that are supposed to protect us against these damages are the vitamins (see preceding text), a few other antioxidants (melanin, urocanic acid, glutathione, and ubiquinone) and specific enzymes: essentially superoxide dismutase (SOD), glutathione peroxidase (GPO), and catalase.

It now has become evident that these inherent antioxidant defense systems of the skin are rapidly overwhelmed by the amount of sun exposure we stress them with in today's lifestyle. Not only are vitamins C and E depleted in the skin by UV irradiation, but the same also occurs with the enzymes. Miyachi et al. (37) describe the decrease of SOD activity in mice after a single dose of UV light, Pence and Naylor (38) confirm this observation in hairless mice and add that catalase activity also was significantly depressed. Punnonen et al. (39) extended this observation to human epidermis. A quantitative analysis of the localization of these enzymes (and nonenzymatic antioxidants) in murine skin and their decrease after UV exposure is presented by Shindo et al. (40). These acute effects are in opposition to long-term irradiation, as Okada et al. (41) show: after 36 weeks of regular UV exposure, SOD activity increased with UV-B, but not with UV-A; catalase activity however was strongly depressed by UV-A. Although catalase, which detoxifies hydrogen peroxide into water and molecular oxygen is the enzyme most frequently cited as being necessary in conjunction with SOD, which transforms the superoxide anion into hydrogen peroxide (itself a cytotoxic molecule), the two enzymes do not react in similar ways to long-term UV exposure. A few, more pointed investigations into the details can be found in Shindo and Hashimoto (42), Filipe et al. (43), Aricioglu (44), and Naderi-Hachtroudi et al. (45) and references therein.

A thorough investigation on humans, carried out over winter and summer season, confirms this fact: catalase is easily destroyed by UV-A light in summer, more active in winter (oh, the logic of nature!), whereas SOD is much more resilient (46). This then leads to a potential buildup of hydrogen peroxide in the skin, not necessarily the best thing to occur. The need for a balanced antioxidant enzyme system thus becomes apparent.

Two approaches are possible: (a) to stimulate and/or protect the innate enzyme system, so that even under UV exposure, it retains its efficacy, and (b) to supply the lacking enzymes by topical application, for instance, within a sunscreen, as well as presun or postsun products.

Hoppe and colleagues (47), as well as Maes and coworkers (48) presented examples of the first strategy: they show that molecules such as salicin in skin fibroblasts (Hoppe) and vitamin D derivatives or betulinic acid in keratinocytes (Maes) are able to stimulate the synthesis of heat shock proteins which are able to protect the catalase against UV-induced degradation. These molecules could therefore be used advantageously in sunscreens as antiaging actives in as much as they induce protection of our own antiaging defense systems. Other molecules that induce heat shock could be worthwhile looking for. A more controversial proposal is put forward by Inal et al. (49) who show that treatment of rats with quercetin (a plant-derived molecule) reduces the UV induced damages to SOD, catalase, GPO significantly. Quercetin is often described as mutagenic (based on Ames tests) and its behavior under UV light (photostability) would need investigation.

Once more it may be instructive to refer to orally administered substances such as deprenyl, a monoamine oxidase B inhibitor which upregulates SOD activity and has shown to prolong the "remaining life span of old rats" (50). Antiaging concepts may be found in many strange places.

Strategy (b) has a few limitations. Usually available enzymes such as SOD and catalase (extracted from yeast or other biotech sources) are not easy to stabilize in cosmetic formulas, to say the least. Complicated packaging stratagems or encapsulation techniques may overcome the problem; it is, however, well known that enzymes—relatively large proteins—are inherently unstable in aqueous environments, and also heat and UV sensitive. Furthermore, SOD alone on the skin would lead, at least theoretically, to a buildup of hydrogen peroxide, already described by Maes and colleagues (46) as being the "natural" problem of seasonal variations of these enzyme activities. Adding the fragile catalase is not only difficult, it is also not possible for any formula sold in Europe because of an archaic prohibition of catalase use in cosmetic products (51).

A neat solution to this problem is afforded by antioxidant enzymes originating from organisms that live and thrive under extreme conditions of heat: the "extremophiles." Discovered a little more than a decade ago, these bacteria live close to the hydrothermal vents at the bottom of the ocean, at temperatures that can reach 80–100°C. It is possible today to cultivate these organisms at sea level, in industrial fermenters, and to extract heat-stable antioxidant enzymes that mimic the skin's SOD, catalase and GPO activity. Further, the enzymes are the more active, the hotter it gets, up to 100°C (which is unrealistic from a cosmetic point of view anyway). They are thus ideal for incorporation into sunscreens where the exposure to UV and to the sun's heat will not only not destroy the defensive activity afforded by them, but also even increase it with increasing outside temperature of irradiation. An active ingredient based on this concept is described by Lintner et al. (52,53). *Thermus thermophilus* bacteria, harvested 6000 ft below the California coast, are fermented at 75°C, then extracted and concentrated to yield a high potency solution containing superoxide anion dismutating (SOD), hydrogen peroxide converting, and GPO mimicking activity. *In vitro* tests carried out on this cosmetic ingredient include protection of human fibroblasts in culture, lipoperoxidation inhibition, protection of DNA against the formation of 8-oxo-guanidine, collagen contraction. Studies on human volunteers show the persistence of cutaneous catalase against UV-A irradiation and a decrease in *in vivo* lipoperoxidation of the stratum corneum.

Miscellaneous

A few more (nonexhaustive!) ingredients of diverse nature that might be of interest in photoprotection can be found in the literature. Pinnell and coworkers have reviewed the evidence supporting the antioxidant role of zinc in UV protection

(54), Mitani et al. (55), on the other hand, reminds us that iron is bad for the skin and that Kojic acid treatment prior to sun exposure may help reduce UV-induced wrinkling (in hairless mice).

A complex but very promising concept is presented by Maes and coworkers (56): they found that creatine, the precursor molecule to phosphocreatine (PCr), protects cells from UV damage either by pretreatment or after UV irradiation. The story involves cellular energy, as creatine is neither a filter, nor an antioxidant, but a key molecule in the chemical energy management (ATP, PCr) of the cells. The additional energy reserves afforded by supplementation in the culture medium with creatine allow the repair mechanisms (thymidine dimer excision, for instance) to function more efficiently, thus protecting the cells against apoptosis and further damage. These authors confirm the beneficial effects of creatine in a clinical study where they show that the number of UV-induced sunburnt cells is diminished by topical application of creatine.

An intriguing study from back in 1978 shows that caffeine and theophylline protect mice ears from UV-induced tumors (57). Knowing that these molecules stimulate the pool of cyclic AMP (an essential ingredient in the cellular processes of both melanogenesis and lipolysis), their use in sunscreens has been promoted in Sun Active Body Refiner (SPF 8) by Lancaster/Coty in a recent launch.

Treatment of UV-Induced Age Symptoms

As mentioned in the introduction, "reversing" some of the signs of aging is of course also considered "antiage" activity. Is it realistic? Can anything but retinoic acid reduce some of the wrinkles, the sagging skin, the dryness, and loss of tonus that comes with (photo)aging?

And even if so, does it make sense to include these antiaging actives in sunscreens? Apart from price considerations in the highly competitive market, the relatively seasonal aspect of sunscreen use and the relatively short contact times (when compared with "standard" skin care products) would cast doubt on the proposition.

Whatever the theoretical considerations say, the market has already acted and begun to introduce sunscreens that contain various actives with some type of antiage and repair claims. It is not for us to judge the scientific validity, but to describe possible concepts and ideas that may be useful to the marketeer, if sufficiently documented by experimental evidence.

Once more, it is not possible to review here the enormous mass of antiage and wrinkle repair ingredients of synthetic, marine, botanical, or biotechnological origin proposed on the market, which all might be considered, based on their merit, for inclusion in sunscreens.

We shall examine two major aspects—barrier repair of the skin surface and tissue repair in the deeper layers—and discuss some actives that appear to have clearly perceivable, demonstrated benefits. Contrary to the "prevention type" products discussed above, the interaction between the repair active and the sunscreen and/or the UV irradiation is not compulsory. We shall simply review the "repair" aspect as a possibility to boost sunscreen marketing appeal, an added, but logical, benefit to the use of these products.

Barrier Repair

Scanning the literature on the relationship between skin barrier and UV irradiation, one realizes quickly that the subject is more complex than expected.

First: definitions. For our purpose here, we limit the terms *barrier*, *barrier function*, and *barrier repair* to the epidermis, essentially to the stratum corneum (SC) where ceramides, cholesterol, and corneocytes constitute the cutaneous barrier. Although this is purely arbitrary—and not necessarily consistent with my general view of barrier repair—it is convenient and simple for the purpose at hand.

On one hand, UV-B irradiation stimulates barrier synthesis: the epidermis thickens, ceramide synthesis is increased, involucrine (a distinct marker protein of cell differentiation and cornification) increases (58–60). On the other hand, this seems to be a transient effect, an immediate reaction of the skin to the danger of UV rays. Long-term effects of UV exposure clearly lead, especially in old age, to a diminished barrier function (61,62); all systems of the skin suffer through photoaging, and so does the capacity to repair the important structure that is called stratum corneum: enzymes necessary for the process are fewer in number and less active, lipids are peroxidized, the skin is thinner, and the normal desquamation process is altered.

When should barrier enhancement actives be used in a sunscreen? Only for "mature" skin? Starting when? Or as a preventive (again?) measure, right from the start, even on young skin? Too few *in vivo* studies are available to form a clear prescription. A few ideas may help in making one's own decision on the type of "barrier function antiage" active to use in sunscreens.

Hydroxy acids: Lactic acid, one of the most widely used actives in skin care, is known to stimulate many processes in skin, in particular the proliferation of keratinocytes and barrier repair. A 4-week *in vivo* study by Rawlings et al. (63) showed that L-lactic acid increases ceramide synthesis by 38% over baseline. This is confirmed by a similar study using TEWL as a measure of barrier repair. Rendl et al. (64) investigated more immediate effects in a model of human skin (reconstituted epidermis) and found that lactic acid in a cream increased growth factors (VEGF), and decreased angiogenin secretion. They conclude that the regulation of keratinocyte growth factors and cytokines by AHA may explain some of the therapeutic effects observed in treating photoaged skin with lactic acid. Scott (65) reviewed a large number of AHA and BHA containing preparations and found only a few of them active on photoaged skin. Glycolic acid, found in fruit and milk sugars is described as a cosmetic ingredient with photoprotective activity. Hong et al. (66) describe its inhibition of UV-induced skin tumorigenesis in hairless mice and investigate some of the complex mechanisms involved. However, a more recent study of 2003 by Kaidbey et al. (67) suggests that AHAs can increase the sensitivity of the skin to UV light. After pretreatment for 4 weeks (24 applications of a 10% glycolic acid product or placebo on the back of 29 Caucasian subjects) the skin was irradiated with 1.5 MED. They observed increased sunburn-cell induction and lowered MEDs and conclude that 10% glycolic acid sensitizes the skin to the damaging effects of UV light. Thus, clearly more systematic studies are needed to determine the benefits of hydroxy acids in sunscreens for antiaging purposes.

Ceramides: The large family of complex lipids called ceramides needs no review here. They are the essential element in the cement of cell cohesion of the stratum corneum; long-chain lipids, highly insoluble, ceramides are not so much "biologically active" as structurally important. There is thus less possible controversy about their use in sunscreens. In view of the outdoor activities that go with the use of sunscreens, the abrasion, frequent bathing and the sun exposure, it seems reasonable to use ceramides or ceramide promoting actives in the formula. Any barrier repair contribution will be beneficial to the skin. The improvement of barrier function by ceramides in general has been described in numerous papers (68 and references therein), rarely though in conjunction with UV irradiation. Various studies report the effects of substances that stimulate keratinocyte differentiation and ceramide synthesis: niacinamide (vitamin B3) (69,70), avocadofuran (71), vitamin C (72), calcium (73), mevalonic acid (74), ursolic acid liposomes (75), and others.

The *T. thermophilus* ferment described in the previous section (52,53) has one additional antiaging benefit. Not only does it contain the heat-stable anti-oxidant SOD and catalase-like enzymes to protect the skin against the heat and the free radicals, it also turns out to stimulate keratinocyte differentiation, involucrin synthesis, and barrier repair by increased ceramide and cholesterol production. *In vivo*, this translates to greater resistance of the skin barrier against aggression and to better moisture retention, both important antiage concepts (76).

Tissue Repair

The most important antiage activity, from a cosmetic point of view, is to reduce wrinkles. Wrinkles are of course, as we have said at the outset, a major, visible, consequence of the actinic damages sunlight, rather excessive sunlight, generates in the skin. Does it therefore make biological, physiological, scientific sense, to include antiwrinkle actives in sunscreens? Similar arguments as those used for barrier repair actives in sunscreens hold here, too. Sunscreens, if properly used, are in contact with the exposed skin for quite some time. During the outdoor activities that incite the consumer to use a sunscreen, she or he will hardly use other skin care products. But the benefits of truly active tissue repair, antiage molecules lie in extended use, regular exposure to their action, and constancy.

In the way a good modern skin care (face care) product should offer at least some SPF—even if not positioned as a sunscreen (cf. Introduction), in the same way a sunscreen may offer tissue repair ingredients to bridge the periods between morning face preparation and the night cream.

Two major categories of antiage ingredients are presently of great interest, that follow the wave of hydroxy acids and retinoids discussed earlier: the isoflavones (phytohormones), which are proposed as plant-derived "(pseudo)substitutes" of estrogen, for mature (i.e., postmenopausal) skin, and the matrikines, natural protein fragments with specific, tissue repairing activity which are wound healing research inspired new cosmetic ingredients. We shall limit our discussion mainly to those two fields.

Isoflavones: Although there appears to be an impressive amount of literature on the benefits of isoflavones (genistein, daidzein, puerarin, biochanin A, and others), more of it is again concentrated on demonstrating the antioxidant (and thus protective) effects of these molecules (extracted most often from soy, sometimes from red clover or more exotic plants) than on their wound-healing and tissue repair activities. At least, this is true with respect to peer-reviewed published studies. But hundreds of references to the stimulating and repair activating properties of these molecules—in pure form or presented as enriched extracts—are nevertheless found on websites and in promotional documents. Two recent publications by Widyarini et al. (77) and Kang et al. (78) describe the protective effect of isoflavones against UV-induced inflammation and photoaging. More in the spirit of the present section and of significant interest is the study by Myazaki et al. (79), which shows that topical genistein and daidzein stimulate hyaluronic acid production in human keratinocyte culture and in hairless mice. This is tissue repair of a type that antiaging claims require. Schmid and Zülli (80) have gone further and measured the skin thickness increase by topical application of soy isoflavones in a human, placebo-controlled trial. The most recent document on soy isoflavone activity in human skin is by Kawai (81), demonstrating the ability of these extracts to stimulate collagen synthesis in the skin.

Cosmetic research has most certainly produced many more examples and data about the skin repair benefits of isoflavone ("phytoestrogens"); for reasons of intellectual property and fierce competition, only a small portion of this research sees publications in peer-reviewed journals. It can thus only be surmised that the use of these ingredients in sunscreens helps keep the skin in better (i.e., more youthful) condition.

Matrikines: A whole new concept in tissue repair, and thus in antiaging strategy, is offered by the discovery of matrikines. The term was coined by Macquart (82) to designate protein fragments (peptides) of small size, which are generated by the gradual hydrolysis of natural, structural proteins in the connective tissue. But not just any breakdown product of proteins will be a matrikine. During wound healing and/or inflammation, proteolytic enzymes break down collagen, elastin, fibronectin, and other structure proteins into smaller pieces. Certain peptide sequences, thus released, possess mediator ("kinin") or messenger ($o\rho\mu o\nu\varepsilon$ = "hormone") function: they act on nearby cells (fibroblasts) to stimulate them into neosynthesis of tissue macromolecules, or to attract them to the damaged tissue site (chemotaxis). Like all mediators or signal molecules, these peptides of specific amino acid sequence, act at very low (nano- to micromolar) concentration, but achieve dramatic effects in the rapid regeneration of tissue.

These peptides, derived from the natural sequence of the damaged proteins, are usually in the tri- to hexamer range.

Some of these matrikines have found cosmetic use, for which it was necessary to attach a lipophilic, fatty acid chain in order to assure skin diffusion and bioavailability (83). It has thus been shown that a few parts per million of the tripeptide palmitoyl-Gly-His-Lys (a serum protein fragment) is able to stimulate collagen and GAG synthesis *in vitro*, which translates into skin thickening and antwrinkle effects *in vivo*. Equally low concentrations of palmitoyl-Val-Gly-Val-Ala-Pro-Gly (a fragment of elastin) or palmitoyl-Gly-Gln-Arg-Pro (a fragment of Immunoglobulin IgG) have potent skin repair activities (84,85) that may be used in antiaging compositions.

As a concrete example of cosmetic use of this concept, the matrikine peptide palmitoyl-Lys-Thr-Thr-Lys-Ser shall be presented in more detail in the following.

Discovered by Katayama et al. (86) during wound healing related research on lung cells, it was investigated for skin applications (87) first in *in vitro* studies on normal human fibroblasts which demonstrate the extracellular matrix (ECM) stimulation by the palmitoylated peptide: collagen I and GAG are increased over baseline by amounts varying between 50% and 250%. This is confirmed on full thickness skin tissue where 2 ppm of Pal-KTTKS achieve the same result as 1000 ppm of vitamin C and in clinical, vehicle, or benchmark (retinol, moisturizer) controlled studies using the Pal-KTTKS peptide in topical antiwrinkle creams (87–89). The use of 3–5 ppm of Pal-KTTKS in a topical formula leads to significant, measurable, and consumer perceivable benefits in reducing wrinkle volume, depth, density, and to overall improvement of the facial skin when used for up to 6 months. Skin biopsies that were taken during one of the panel studies (88) on both the Pal-KTTKS treated group and the placebo group, at time points $T = 0$, $T = 2$ months, and $T = 4$ months show that the treated skin has improved collagen IV and elastin fiber assemblies whereas the control group showed no notable changes in the skin samples. Matrikines such as Pal-KTTKS are thus ideal candidates for cosmetic tissue repair.

Nothing in the nature, activity, or mechanism of action of these molecules with true antiaging properties prevents them from being used in sunscreens. They are compatible with any kind of formulation, they are stable, their mode of action is unperturbed by UV and outdoors. They are clearly an additional benefit to sunscreens, as they demonstrably can repair some of the actinic photodamage.

CONCLUSIONS

Some aspects of this chapter may appear somewhat polemic and/or tongue in cheek. Whereas UV absorbing molecules are clearly designated as sun filters and constitute a well-defined category of chemicals, the notion of "antiage" actives (cosmeceuticals?) is much less well characterized, whence the occasional asides.

We have tried to demonstrate that the notion of antiaging actives in sunscreens opens many possibilities to the formulator to improve the basic sunscreen products, to add real benefits and to allow for variety in claims and marketing positioning.

Prevention of sun damages on the skin can be reinforced by some of the antioxidant and photoprotective agents; treatment of sun damage during or immediately after sun exposure with repair actives is also justified. Teaching the consumer on how to "manage" the sunlight (prevention goes beyond using sunscreens and includes wearing adequate clothes, avoiding the hottest hours of the day, etc.) has become part of the marketeer's obligation.

Depending on the country, however, from the USA to Europe to East Asia, the legislations on sunscreens, claims, and formulations, are quite different and complex. Adding antiage actives to these sunscreens makes the legal situation even more complex with respect to advertised claims. Other chapters in this book address the regulatory aspects of sunscreens *per se*: the notion of which actives can legally be called "actives" varies even more. From my understanding, in the USA, a "cosmetic antiaging active" is an oxymoron [if it is physiologically active, it is a drug and not a cosmetic (90)], in Europe, neither sunscreens nor cosmetic actives are specifically regulated other than by the general European directive and its seven amendments (the notion of active is used in the industry, but not in legal texts), in Korea, certain actives (for wrinkle reduction, thus antiage) have become "functional ingredients," that is, quasidrugs, similar to the eponymous Japanese category.

Harmonization seems a far way off in the future. Careful wording of any antiaging claims in sunscreen is thus recommended, no matter how many studies one cites in support of this added benefit.

REFERENCES

1. Lintner K. The role of actives in face care. Proceedings of the PCIE Conference, Düsseldorf, Feb 4–6, 2003. Düsseldorf: Ziolkowsky Verlag Augsburg, published on CD ROM.
2. Yu BP, Yang R. Critical evaluation of the free radical theory of aging. In: Kitani K, Aola A, Goto S, eds. Pharmacological intervention in Aging and Age-Associated Disorders, Proceedings VI Congress Intl. Ass. Biomed. Gerontol. Ann N Y Acad Sci 1996; 786:1–11.
3. Pehr K, Forsey RR. Why don't we use vitamin E in dermatology? Can Med Assoc J 1993; 149(9):1247–1253.

4. Pinnell SR. Cutaneous photodamage, oxidative stress and topical protection. J Am Acad Dermatol 2003; 48(1):1–19.
5. Ritter EF, Axelrod M, Minn KW, Eades E, Rudner AM, Serafin D, Klitzman B. Modulation of ultraviolet light-induced epidermal damage: beneficial effects of tocopherol. Plast Reconstr Surg 1998; 102(5):1785–1786.
6. Saral Y, Uyar B, Ayar A, Naziroglu M. Protective effects of topical alpha-tocopherol acetate on UVB irradiation in guinea pigs: importance of free radicals. Physiol Res 2002; 51(3):285–290.
7. Trevithick JR, Shum DT, Redae S, Mitton KP, Norley C, Karlik SJ, Groom AC, Schmidt EE. Reduction of sunburn damage to skin by topical application of vitamin E acetate following exposure to ultraviolet B radiation: effect of delaying application or of reducing concentration of vitamin E acetate applied. Scanning Microsc 1993; 7(4):1269–1281.
8. Weber SU, Thiele JJ, Han N, Luu C, Valacchi G, Weber S, Packer L. Topical alpha tocotrienol supplementation inhibits lipid peroxidation but fails to mitigate increased transepidermal water loss after benzoyl peroxide treatment of human skin. Free Radic Biol Med 2003; 34(2):170–176.
9. Darr D, Combs S, Dunston S, Manning T, Pinnell S. Topical vitamin C protects porcine skin from ultraviolet radiation-induced damage. Br J Dermatol 1992; 127(3):247–253.
10. Darr D, Dunston S, Faust H, Pinnell S. Effectiveness of antioxidants (vitamin C and E) with and without sunscreens as topical photoprotectants. Acta Derm Venereol 1996; 76(4):264–268.
11. Moison RM, Beijersbergen van Henegouwen GM. Topical antioxidant vitamins C and E prevent UVB-radiation-induced peroxidation of eicosapentaenocic acid in pig skin. Radiat Res 2002; 157(4):402–409.
12. Steenvoorden DP, Beijersbergen van Henegouwen GM. Protection against UV-induced systemic immunosuppression in mice by a single topical application of the antioxidant vitamins C and E. Int J Radiat Biol 1999; 75(6):747–755.
13. Dreher F, Gabard B, Schwindt DA, Maibach HI. Topical melatonin in combination with vitamins E and C protects skin from ultraviolet-induced erythema: a human study in vivo. Br J Dermatol 1998; 139(2):332–339.
14. Dreher F, Denig N, Gabard B, Schwindt DA, Maibach HI. Effect of topical antioxidants on UV-induced erythema formation when administered after exposure. Dermatology 1999; 198(1):52–55.
15. Reiter RJ, Pablos MI, Agapito TT, Guerrero JM. Melatonin in the context of the free radical theory of aging. In: Kitani K, Aola A, Goto S, eds. Pharmacological Intervention in Aging and Age-Associated Disorders, Proceedings VI Congress Intl. Ass. Biomed. Gerontol. Ann N Y Acad Sci 1996; 786: 362–378.
16. Lin JY, Selim MA, Shea CR, Grichnik JM, Omar MM, Monteiro-Riviere NA, Pinnell SR. UV photoprotection by combination topical antioxidants vitamin C and vitamin E. J Am Acad Dermatol 2003; 48(6):866–874.
17. Kligman LH. Retinoic acid and photocarcinogenesis a controversy. Photodermatology 1987; 4(2):88–101.
18. Schwartz E, Cruickshank FA, Mezick JA, Kligman LH. Topical all-*trans* retinoic acid stimulates collagen synthesis in vivo. J Invest Dermatol 1991; 96(6):975–978.
19. Ho KK, Halliday GM, Barnetson RS. Topical retinoic acid augments ultraviolet light-induced melanogenesis. Melanoma Res 1992; 2(1):41–45.

20. Boisnic S, Branchet-Gumila MC, Le Charpentier Y, Segard C. Repair of UVA-induced elastic fiber and collagen damage by 0.05% retinaldehyde cream in an ex vivo human skin model. Dermatology 1999; 199(Suppl. 1):43–48.
21. Sorg O, Tran C, Saurat JH. Cutaneous vitamins A and E in the context of ultraviolet- or chemically-induced oxidative stress. Skin Pharmacol Appl Skin Physiol 2001; 14(6):363–372.
22. Sorg O, Tran C, Carraux P, Didierjean L, Falson F, Saurat JH. Oxidative stress-independent depletion of epidermal vitamin A by UVA. J Invest Dermatol 2002; 118(3):513–518.
23. Kang S, Fisher GJ, Vorhees JJ. Photoaging: pathogenesis, prevention and treatment. Clin Geriatr Med 2001; 17(4):643–659.
24. Anonymous. Tretinoin and cutaneous photoaging: new preparation. Guaranteed adverse effects! Prescrire Int 1999; 8(43):139–140.
25. Greul AK, Grundmann JU, Heinrich F, Pfitzner I, Bernhardt J, Mabach A, Biesalski HK, Gollnick H. Photoprotection of UV-irradiated human skin: an anti-oxidative combination of vitamins E and C, carotenoids, selenium and proanthocyanidins. Skin Pharmacol Appl Skin Physiol 2002; 15(5):307–315.
26. http://www.esculape.com/textes/suvimax_2003.html
27. Wei H, Zhang X, Zhao JF, Wang ZY, Bickers D, Lebwohl M. Scavenging of hydrogen peroxide and inhibition of ultraviolet-light induced oxidative DNA damages by aqueous extracts from green and black teas. Free Radic Biol Med 1999; 26(11/12):1427–1435.
28. Vayalil PK, Elmets CA, Katiyar SK. Treatment of green tea polyphenols in hydrophilic cream prevents UVB-induced oxidation of lipids and proteins, depletion of antioxidant enzymes and phosphorilation of MAPK proteins in SKH-1 hairless mouse skin. Carcinogenesis 2003; 24(5):927–936.
29. Bonina F, Puglia C, Ventura D, Aquino R, Tortora S, Sacchi A, Saija A, Tomaino A, Pellegrino ML, de Caprariis P. In vitro antioxidant and in vivo photoprotective affects of a lyophilized extract of Capparis spinosa L buds. J Cosmet Sci 2002; 53(6):321–335.
30. Aquino R, Morelli S, Tomaino A, Pellegrino M, Saija A, Grumetto L, Puglia C, Ventura D, Bonina F. Antioxidant and photoprotective activity of a crude extract of *Culcitium reflexum* H.B.K. leaves and their major flavonoids. J Ethnopharmacol 2002; 79(2):183–191.
31. Phan TT, Wang L, See P, Grayer RJ, Chan SY, Lee ST. Phenolic compounds of Chromolaena odorata protect cultured skin cells from oxidative damage: implication for cutaneous wound healing. Biol Pharm Bull 2001; 24(12):1373–1379.
32. Kim YH, Yanbg HE, Par BK, Heo MY, Jo BK, Kim HP. The extract of the flowers Prunus persica, a new cosmetic ingredient, protects against solar ultraviolet-induced skin damage in vivo. J Cosmet Sci 2002; 53(1):27–34.
33. Heo MY, Kim SH, Yang HE, Lee SH, Jo BK, Kim HP. Protection against ultraviolet B- and C-induced DNA damage and skin carcinogenesis by the flowers of *Prunus persica* extract. Mutat Res 2001; 496(1/2):47–59.
34. Okano Y, Tamura K, Masaki H. Possible roles of advanced glycation end-products in promoting skin aging, and of plant extracts in inhibiting skin aging. Proceedings XX Congress IFSCC, Cannes, Sep 14–18, 1998. Vol. 1:7–17.
35. Afaq F, Mukhtar H. Photochemoprevention by botanical antioxidants. Skin Pharmacol Appl Skin Physiol 2002; 15(5):297–306.

36. Hughes-Formella BJ, Bohnsack K, Rippke F, Benner G, Rudolph M, Tausch I, Gassmueller J. Anti-inflammatory effect of hamamelis lotion in a UVB erythema test. Dermatology 1998; 196(3):316–322.
37. Miyachi Y, Imamura S, Niwa Y. Decreased skin superoxide dismutase activity by a single exposure of ultraviolet radiation is reduced by liposomal superoxide dismutase pretreatment. J Invest Dermatol 1987; 89(1):111–112.
38. Pence BC, Naylor MF. Effects of single-dose ultraviolet radiation on skin superoxide dismutase, catalase and xanthine oxidase in hairless mice. J Invest Dermatol 1990; 95(2):213–216.
39. Punnonen K, Autio P, Kiistala U, Ahotupa M. In-vivo effects of solar-simulated ultraviolet irradiation on antioxidant enzymes and lipid peroxidation in human epidermis. Br J Dermatol 1991; 125(1):18–20.
40. Shindo Y, Witt E, Packer L. Antioxidant defense mechanisms in murine epidermis and dermis and their responses to ultraviolet light. J Invest Dermatol 1993; 100(3):260–265.
41. Okada K, Takahashi Y, Ohnishi K, Ishikawa O, Miyachi Y. Time-dependent effect of chronic UV irradiation on superoxide dismutase and catalase activity in hairless mice skin. J Dermatol Sci 1994; 8(3):183–186.
42. Shindo Y, Hashimoto T. Antioxidant defence mechanism of the skin against UV irradiation: study of the role of catalase using acatalasaemia fibroblasts. Arch Dermatol Res 1995; 287(8):747–753.
43. Filipe P, Emerit I, vassy J, Rigaut JP, Martin E, freitas J, Fernandes A. Epidermal localization and protective effects of topically applied superoxide dismutase. Exp Dermatol 1997; 6(3):116–121.
44. Aricioglu A, Bozkurt M, Balabanli B, Kilinc M, Nazaroglu NK, Turkozkan N. Changes in zinc levels and superoxide dismutase activities in the skin of acute, ultraviolet-B-irradiated mice after treatment with gingko biloba extract. Biol Trace Elem Res 2001; 80(2):175–179.
45. Naderi-Hachtroudi L, Peters T, Brenneisen P, Meewes C, Hommel C, Razi-Wolf Z, Schneider LA, Schuller J, Wlaschek M, Scharffetter-Kochanek K. Induction of manganese superoxide dismutase in human dermal fibroblasts: a UV-B mediated paracrine mechanism with the release of epidermal interleukin 1 alpha, interleukin 1 beta and tumor necrosis factor alpha. Arch Dermatol 2002; 138(11):1473–1479.
46. Hellemans L, Corstjens H, Neven A, Declercq L, Maes D. Antioxidant enzyme activity in human stratum corneum shows seasonal variation with an age-dependent recovery. J Invest Dermatol 2003; 120(3):434–439.
47. Steckel F, Gieseler R, Pollet D, Hoppe U. Heat shock protein expression and UV-light induced damage in cultured human skin cells. Proceedings XX Congress IFSCC, Cannes, Sep 14–18, 1998. Vol. 1:133–140.
48. Declercq L, Hellemans L, Goyarts E, Gan D, Corstjens H, Sente I, Mammone T, Marenus K, Maes D. Induction of heat shock proteins to protect against seasonal deficiency in antioxidant defense capacity of human stratum corneum. Proceedings XXII Congress IFSCC, Edinburgh, Sep 24–27, 2002. Vol. 2:podium 20.
49. Erden Inal M, Kahraman A, Koken T. Beneficial effects of quercetin on oxidative stress induced by ultraviolet A. Clin Exp Dermatol 2001; 26(6):536–539.
50. Kitani K, Miyasaka K, Kanai S, Carrillo MC, Ivy GO. Upregulation of antioxidant enzyme activities by deprenyl. Implications for life span extension. In: Kitani K,

Aola A, Goto S, eds. Pharmacological Intervention in Aging and Age-Associated Disorders, Proceedings VI Congress Intl. Ass. Biomed. Gerontol. Ann N Y Acad Sci 1996; 786:391–409.

51. Council Directive no. 76/768/CEE of July 27, 1976. (JOCE L 262 of Sep 1976).
52. Mas-Chamberlin C, Lamy F, Mondon P, Scocci S, de Givry L, Vissac F, Lintner K. Heat- and UV-stable cosmetic enzymes from deep sea bacteria. Cosmet Toilet 2002; 117(4):22–30.
53. Lintner K, Lamy F, Mas-Chamberlin C, Mondon P, Scocci S, Buche P, Girard F. IFSCC Mag 2002; 5(3):195–200.
54. Rostan EF, DeBuys HV, Madey DL, Pinnell SR. Evidence supporting zinc as an important antioxidant for skin. Int J Dermatol 2002; 41(9):606–611.
55. Mitani H, Koshiishi I, Sumita T, Imanari T. Prevention of the photodamage in the hairless mouse dorsal skin by kojic acid as an iron chelator. Eur J Pharmacol 2001; 411(1/2):169–174.
56. Maes D, Collins D, Declercq L, Foyouzi-Youssefi R, Gan D, Mammone T, Pelle E, Marenus K, Gedeon H. Improving cellular function through modulation of energy metabolism. Proceedings XXII Congress IFSCC, Edinburgh, Sep 24-27, 2002. Vol. 1:podium 7.
57. Zajdela F, Latarjet R. Inhibition of skin carcinogenesis in vivo by caffeine and other agents. Natl Cancer Inst Monogr 1978; 50:133–140.
58. Lehmann P, Melnik B, Holzle E, Neumann N, Plewig G. The effect of UV-A and UV-B irradiation on the skin barrier. Skin physiologic, electron microscopy and lipid biochemistry studies. Hautarzt 1992; 43(6):344–351 (in German).
59. Magnoni C, Euclidi E, Benassi L, Bertazzoni G, Cossarizza A, Seidenari S, Giannetti A. Ultraviolet B radiation induces activation of neutral and acidic sphingomyelinases and ceramide generation in cultured normal human keratinocytes. Toxicol In Vitro 2002; 16(4):349–355.
60. Coderch L, de Pera M, Fonollosa J, De La Maza A, Parra J. Efficacy of stratum corneum lipid supplementation on human skin. Contact Dermatitis 2002; 47(3):139–146.
61. Elias PM, Ghadially R. The aged epidermal permeability barrier: basis for functional abnormalities. Clin Geriatr Med 2002; 18(1):103–120.
62. Lamaud E, Schalla W. Influence of UV irradiation on penetration of hydrocortisone. *In vivo* study in hairless rat skin. Br J Dermatol 1984; 111(Suppl. 27):152–157.
63. Rawlings AV, Davies A, Carlomusto M, Pillai S, Zhang K, Kosturko R, Verdejo P, Feinberg C, Nguyen L, Chandar P. Effect of lactic acid isomers on keratinocyte ceramide synthesis, stratum corneum lipid levels and stratum corneum barrier function. Arch Dermatol Res 1996; 288:383–390.
64. Rendl M, Mayer C, Weninger W, Tschachler E. Topically applied lactic acid increases spontaneous secretion of vascular endothelial growth factor by human reconstructed epidermis. Br J Dermatol 2001; 145(1):3–9.
65. Scott IR. Real performance in cosmetic antiaging products. Proceedings XXII Congress IFSCC, Edinburgh, Sep 24-27, 2002. Vol. 1: Keynote address.
66. Hong JY, Kim EJ, Ahn KS, Jung KM, Yun YP, Park YK, Lee SH. Inhibitory effect of glycolic acid on ultraviolet-induced skin tumorigenesis in SKH-1 hairless mice and its mechanism of action. Mol Carcinog 2001; 31(3):152–160.
67. Kaidbey K, Sutherland B, Bennett P, Wamer WG, Barton C, Dennis D, Kornhauser A. Topical glycolic acid enhances photodamage by ultraviolet light. Photodermatol Photoimmunol Photomed 2003; 19(1):21–27.

68. Förster T, ed. Cosmetic Lipids and the Skin Barrier. New York: Marcel Dekker, 2002 and references therein.
69. Matts PJ, Oblong JE, Bissett DL. A review of the range of effects of niacinamide in human skin. IFSSC Mag 2002; 5(4):285–289.
70. Tanno O, Ota Y, Kitamura N, Katsube T, Inoue S. Nicotinamide increases biosynthesis of ceramides as well as other stratum corneum lipids to improve the epidermal permeability barrier. Br J Dermatol 2000; 143(3):524–531.
71. Almada AL. New Research on Vitamin E, Soy & Avocado. Functional Food and Neutraceuticals, Nov/Dec 2001.
72. Ramdin LSP, Richardson J, Harding CR, Rosdy M. The effect of ascorbic acid (vitamin C) on the ceramide subspecies profile in the SkinEthic epidermal model. Proceedings of STRATUM CORNEUM III Basel, Sep 12–14, 2001. Poster 40.
73. Elias PM, Nau P, Hanley K, Cullander C, Crumrine D, Bench G, Sideras-Haddad E, Mauro T, Williams ML, Feingold KR. Formation of the epidermal calcium gradient coincides with key milestones of barrier ontogenesis in the rodent. J Invest Dermatol 1998; 110:399–404.
74. Haratake A, Ikenaga K, Katoh N, Uchiwa H, Hirano S, Yasuno H. Topical mevalonic acid stimulates de novo cholesterol synthesis and epidermal permeability barrier homeostasis in aged mice. J Invest Dermatol 2000; 114(2):247–252.
75. Both DM, Goodtzova K, Yarosh DB, Brown DA. Liposome-encapsulated ursolic acid increases ceramides and collagen in human skin cells. Arch Dermatol Res 2002; 293(11):560–575.
76. Lintner K, Lamy F, Mas-Chamberlin C, Mondon P, Scocci S, Buche P, Girard F. Heat-stable enzymes from deep sea bacteria: a key tool for skin protection against UV-A induced free radicals. IFSCC Mag 2002; 5(3):195–200.
77. Widyarini S, Spinks N, Husband AJ, Reeve VE. Isoflavonoid compounds from red clover (*Trifolium pratense*) protect from inflammation and immune suppression induced by UV radiation. Photochem Photobiol 2001; 74(3):465–467.
78. Kang S, Chung JH, Lee JH, Fisher GJ, Wan YS, Duell EA, Voerhees JJ. Topical N-acetyl cysteine and genistein prevent ultraviolet-light induced singaling that leads to photoaging in human skin in vivo. J Invest Dermatol 2003; 120(5):835–841.
79. Miyazaki K, Hanamizu T, Iizuka R, Chiba K. Genistein and daidzein stimulate hyaluronic acid production in transformed human keratinocyte culture and hairless mouse skin. Skin Pharmacol Appl Skin Physiol 2002; 15(3):175–183.
80. Schmid D, Zülli F. Topically applied soy isoflavones increase skin thickness. Cosmet Toilet 2002; 117(6):45–50.
81. Kawai N. Phytoestrogens: applications of soy Isoflavones in skin care. Cosmet Toilet 2003; 118(5):73–80.
82. Maquart FX, Simeon A, Pasco S, Monboisse JC. Regulation of cell activity by the extracellular matrix: the concept of matrikines. J Soc Biol 1999; 193(45):423–428.
83. Lintner K, Peschard O. Biologically active peptides: from a lab bench curiosity to a functional skin care product. Int J Cosmet Sci 2000; 22:207–218.
84. Lintner K. French patent FR03/05705.
85. Lintner K. French patent FR 99/00743 and WO/0043417.
86. Katayama K, Armendariz-Borunda J, Raghow R, et al. A pentapeptide from type I procollagen promotes extracellular matrix production. J Biol Chem 1993; 268(14):9941–9944.

87. Lintner K. Promoting production in the extracellular matrix without compromising barrier. Cutis 2002; 70(6S Suppl.):13–16.
88. Mas-Chamberlin C, Lintner K, Basset L, Revuz P, et al. Relevance of antiwrinkle treatment of a peptide: 4 months clinical double blind study vs excipient. Ann Derm Venereol 129: Proceedings 20th World Congress of Dermatology, Book II, PO 438, Paris, 2002.
89. Robinson L, Fitzgerald NC, Doughty DG, Dawes NC, Berge CA, Bissett DL. Palmitoyl-pentapeptide offers improvement in human photoaged facial skin. Ann Derm Venereol 129: Proceedings 20th World Congress of Dermatology, Book II, PO 179, Paris.
90. Greive K. Cosmetics and life sciences: a continuing courtship. IFSCC Mag 2002; 303–305.

Production and Quality Control

34

The Manufacture of Suncare Products

Timothy Meadows
Farpoint, Inc., Dallas, Texas, USA

INTRODUCTION

For the average private label, contract, or name brand manufacturer, suntan/sunscreen products usually represent between 16% and 35% of their production. With so much production devoted to this category, it is especially important to be aware of any processing techniques that would enable one to bring the production from the initial preweigh to filling as quickly and as efficiently as possible.

Most sunscreen items are considered a seasonal product by the retailers, with the unsold product to be returned at the end of the season. It is very important to have as little overhead in that product as possible. To further complicate this, sunscreens are considered OTC products which require expiration date unless the manufacturer can provide the required long-term stability data.

Although these are primarily marketing concerns, if the product is not manufactured efficiently and according to specifications, both quality and marketing problems may arise.

PRODUCT TYPES

Based on the physical form of a product the method of manufacture may be drastically different. Different viscosities, emulsion types, pHs usually require different manufacturing techniques.

Since a product's SPF value is an efficacy rating and not simply a quantitative measure of a product's UV absorber level, a sunscreen product's physical form is very important. Very often the manufacturing procedure is directly responsible for a sunscreen's efficacy. The same level of UV absorbers in two different bases can produce two very different SPF values. Besides the formula, the method of addition, mixing temperatures, homogenization, etc., can be a major factor in determining the SPF value or whether a product is water resistant or not.

Sunscreen products come in all forms and emulsion types depending on the type of delivery system that the marketer desires. The following are some of the basic categories.

Oil-in-Water Emulsions

This the most basic type of emulsion system. The traditional method of manufacture is to add the oil phase to the water phase at about 80°C. Mix until 45°C, then add the fragrance, vitamins, and any other heat sensitive materials. The usual procedure in making waterproof oil-in-water (o/w) emulsion is to add an oil-soluble film former to the oil phase. The selection of materials is covered in another section of this book, but whatever materials are used, it should be added to the rest of the oil phase from the beginning. Many o/w emulsions use water-soluble thickeners such as the carbomers. These are best dispersed in pure water at room temperature before the rest of the water phase is added. Depending on the formulation, the water phase is neutralized either first, before the addition of the oil phase, or last, after the phases are combined. There are some formulations where the waterproofing ability is totally dependent on when the carbomer is neutralized.

Formulas 1 and 2 show two formulations that use water-soluble polymers for external thickening and emulsification. Formula 1 is neutralized after the

Formula 1 SPF 30 Lotion (Final neutralization)

Percentage	Material
	Phase A
50.85	Water
0.20	Carbomer 934
0.10	Carbomer 941
	Phase B
0.30	Methylparaben
0.1	Propylparaben
0.05	Disodium EDTA
1.00	Proplyene glycol
10.00	Aloe vera gel
0.05	Alpha bisabalol
	Phase C
5.00	Octinoxate
4.00	Oxybenzone
5.00	Octocrylene
0.50	Silicon fluid 200, 350 CS
5.00	Octisalate
4.00	Stearic acid
5.00	Sorbitan isostearate
0.10	Tocopheryl acetate
2.00	Crodaphos CES[a]
	Phase D
0.50	Triethanolamine
	Phase E
QS	Fragrance
100.00	

[a]Croda Chemical Company.

Manufacturing procedure:

1. Disperse the ingredients in *cold* water in phase A.
2. When fully dispersed add phase B to phase A.
3. Begin heating A/B to 80°C.
4. Heat phase C to 80°C.
5. At 80°C add *oil to water* with good agitation.
6. Mix for 15 min.
7. Add phase D.
8. Mix and cool to 45°C.
9. Add fragrance.

Formula 2 SPF 15 Sunscreen Lotion (Water phase neutralized first)

Percentage	Material
	Phase A
69.30	Water
0.20	Carbomer 934
	Phase B
2.50	Glycerin
0.05	Verseen NA
1.00	Disodium EDTA
0.30	Methylparaben
0.10	Propylparaben
0.20	Aloe concentrate (10×)
	Phase C
0.40	Triethanolamine
	Phase D
3.50	Stearic acid
7.50	Octinoxate
40	Oxybenzone
0.30	Silicon 200
1.00	Hydrogenated vegatable oil
1.50	Glyceryl stearate, SE
2.25	Sorbitan stearate
3.00	Octyl palmitate
2.00	Lexoraz 200[a]
0.10	Tocopheryl acetate
	Phase E
QS	Fragrance
100.00	

[a]Inolex Chemicals

Manufacturing procedure:

1. Disperse the carbomer in *cold* water. Mix until fully dispersed.
2. Heat phase A to 80°C. Add phase B.
3. At 80°C neutralize with phase C.
4. Heat phase D to 80°C.
5. With both phases at 80°C. Add phase D to A/B/C
6. Mix and cool to 45°C.
7. Add phase E

phase addition, and in Formula 2 the water phase is neutralized first. Both are water resistant, but Formula 1 requires the addition of the oil-soluble film former.

When manufacturing high-SPF products the oil phase can exceed 40%. This leaves little room for the hydration of water-soluble polymers or gums. Often the small water phase will get too thick, even when unneutralized to heat evenly. The traditional answer to this problem is to add a very small amount of a mineral acid to the water phase (1). This will thin out the solution immediately. However, the appearance of an acid like hydrochloric acid on the label may not be acceptable. There may also be other reactions with some of the other ingredients. In this case the addition of certain botanicals will help. Aloe vera is mildly acidic and as little as 3% in the water phase will thin out the slurry to an acceptable viscosity. Most sunscreen products use aloe in any case. One must be sure that the aloe material used is in fact real aloe vera and not a diluted extract, otherwise it will not thin out the unneutralized carbomer solution (2). Formula 2 uses this technique.

Carbopol 1342™ is often used in waterproof formulations. It is less soluble in water that than other carbomers and is slightly oil soluble, thus making it more difficult to wash off. Dispersing the 1342 in the water can be a problem though. It has a tendency to foam and thicken, even when unneutralized in low percentages. For this reason the addition of 1342 into the heated oil phase is often done. It is important to keep the oil phase mixing during addition to the water phase, otherwise the 1342 will settle to the bottom of the oil tank. Once the phases are blended the 1342 will migrate into the water phase. The batch can then be neutralized. In the case of Formula 3, PEG-8 is used to neutralize the batch. This allows the hydrogen bonding to occur and permits the 1342 to gel, while not creating the salt which is more water soluble and thus less water resistant.

Water-in-Oil Emulsions

Any water-in-oil (W/O) emulsion is usually much more difficult to manufacture than the basic O/W type. Most W/O formulations require some degree of homogenization, which adds to the time and expense of manufacture. The continuous phase (oil) is usually small, often under 50%, making it difficult to heat and mix in a large processing tank.

Spray Emulsions

These types of products have been very popular in Europe for many years, and now here in the USA we are beginning to see more sunscreen products in this form. Since almost all beach and pool suncare products are expected to be waterproof, this is an expected feature for a spray emulsion product as well. Without the physical support of the viscosity of a cream or lotion a high emulsifier level is usually employed in the formula to obtain product stability. However a high level of emulsifiers often results in a sticky or tacky feel. Therefore, emulsification is best achieved by mechanical means.

There are many types of homogenizers available, and most are very expensive. One of the best techniques is to pass the product backward through a centrifugal pump with perforated impellers. The degree of shear can be determined by adjusting the flow rate of the pump (positive displacement

Formula 3 SPF 30 Sunblock Lotion

Percentage	Material
	Phase A
71.60	Water
0.30	Methylparaben
0.10	Propylparaben
0.05	Disodium EDTA
1.00	Aloe vera gel
	Phase B
7.50	Octinoxate
5.00	Oxybenzone
4.00	C12–15 alkyl benzoate
5.00	Octisalate
0.05	Tocopheryl acetate
	Phase C
1.00	DEA cetyl phosphate
	Phase D
0.40	Acrylates/C10–30 alkyl acrylate cross-polymer
	Phase E
4.00	PEG-8
	Phase F
QS	Fragrance
100.00	

Manufacturing procedure:

1. Heat phase A to 80°C.
2. Heat phase B to 90°C.
3. Once phase B is at temperature add phase C to it with mixing.
4. Mix at 90°C until phase C is completely melted.
5. Add phase D to B/C with agitation.
6. *As soon as phase D is dispersed*, combine the phases (oil to water).
7. Mix until smooth, add phase E.
8. Mix and cool to 45°C.
9. Add phase F.

type), which is feeding the centrifugal pump. With this method the pump can be used on various tanks, thus making it far less expensive than the traditional in-tank homogenization. It also cuts down on processing time because the product can be pumped directly from the processing tank into the portable tank or whatever vessel is used to hold the product for filling. Figure 34.1 shows the basic setup of this system.

Formula 4 is an SPF 30 spray product. After initial neutralization and emulsification citric acid is added to disrupt the gel structure of the Carbopol

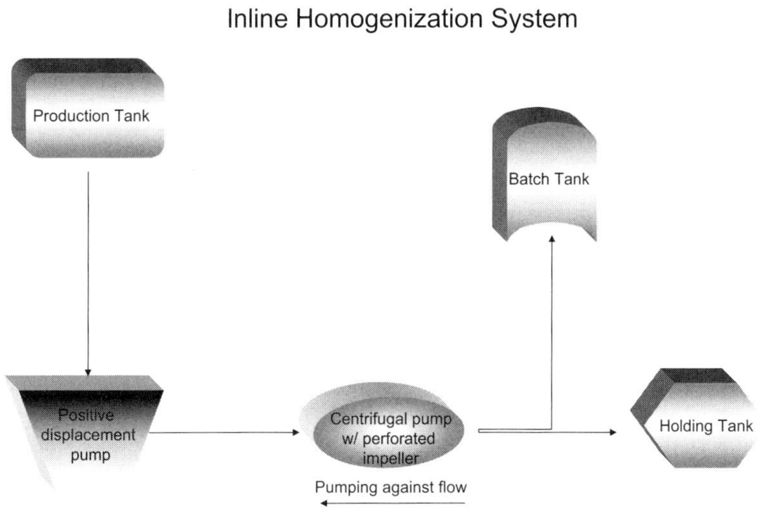

Figure 34.1 Inline homogenization system.

1342. In order to stabilize the product now, it is passed through a homogenization system.

Heavy Creams

Sunscreen creams can be very luxurious and go well in a tube application; however, they are often difficult to produce and fill. Therefore, it is often necessary to cease manufacturing and begin filling the cream at higher temperatures than normal. Since most sunscreen creams derive their high viscosity from an external thickening system such as carbomers, keeping the product warm only slightly reduces its viscosity.

Hydroalcoholic Products

The general perception of the public is that products that are alcohol based are drying to the skin. Even so, there are some great advantages to sunscreen products containing alcohol since most UV absorbers are oil soluble and dissolving them in alcohol permits a more uniform film upon spreading onto the skin.

Obtaining a clear gel or solution is often difficult. In many cases the addition of even the smallest amount of water will cloud the system. Selecting the correct ratio of different UV absorbers is critical here. Each UV absorber has different hydroalcoholic solubility but with all the formulation challenges this class of products offer many advantages. They dry quickly on the skin, feel cool, and are usually waterproof without the use of a film former.

Formula 4 SPF 30 Spray Emulsion

Percentage	Material
	Phase A
69.00	Water
0.05	Disodium EDTA
1.00	Aloe vera gel
	Phase B
7.50	Octinoxate
5.00	Oxybenzone
4.00	C12–15 Alkyl benzoate
5.00	Octisalate
0.05	Tocopheryl acetate
0.10	Cocoa butter
1.00	Sorbitan isostearate
	Phase C
1.00	DEA cetyl phosphate
	Phase D
0.40	Acrylates/C10–30 alkyl acrylate cross-polymer
	Phase E
4.00	PEG-8
	Phase F
0.80	Propylene glycol, methylparaben, propylparaben, and diazolidinyl urea
1.10	Citric acid
	Phase G
QS	Fragrance
100.00	

Manufacturing procedure:

1. Heat phase A to 80°C.
2. Heat phase B to 90°C.
3. With rapid agitation, add phase C to phase B.
4. When the phase C is melted, *quickly* add phase D to phase B.
5. As soon as phase D is dispersed, *immediately* add phase B to phase A.
6. After the phases are combined, mix for 15 min.
7. With good agitation, add phase E to batch.
8. Mix and cool to 65°C.
9. Slowly add phase F to batch.
10. Lower agitation as batch thins out.
11. Cool to 45°C. Add phase G.
12. Cool to 35°C. Run product out through homogenizer.

Obviously, the products flammability is a major consideration during manufacture. All motors must be explosion proof, both in compounding and in filling rooms.

SCALE UP

Many formulations, which work very successfully in the laboratory, do not translate well into full-scale production. There are several factors that come into play when manufacturing a large production batch which are not present in the laboratory.

Mass

When making 500 or 1000 g of a product in the laboratory, the effects of the mass of the product itself or the emulsification and mixing are negligible. But when dealing with thousands of kilograms of a product, it then becomes a factor to consider. Often the shear weight of the product is enough to squeeze out the internal phase of the emulsion resulting in either oiling or watering out of the product. Since many high-SPF formulations have a high internal oil phase the external pressure of the batch can simply push it out. Making the batch size smaller can help to prevent this. This is a trial and error procedure. Continue to decrease the batch size until you achieve the desired results. The maximum batch size will depend on your equipment.

Mixing

High-SPF sunscreens usually have specific gravities greater than 1.00. The mixers should be of sufficient horsepower to be able to move the product in the processing tank. Both side sweep and propeller agitation are required for complete mixing. If the batch is not mixed thoroughly, then proper emulsification cannot occur. There may be a batch size limitation for some types of products. There are many emulsions that simply will not mix together properly at volumes greater than 750 gal. When larger batches of these types of formulas are made, they tend to exhibit some oiling out. The solution is able to mix the product more thoroughly. This is achieved by decreasing the batch size or modifying the equipment.

Cooling

The cooling rate of a batch is just as critical as the mixing efficiency. The rate at which an emulsion is cooled can determine its stability and physical characteristics. Care must be taken not to cool the batch too quickly. The emulsion stability is often dependent on the formation of wax or fat crystallization. If this crystallization process is disrupted, an unstable emulsion may be the result.

This in turn not only will affect the aesthetics of the product but the function as well, such as its water resistance.

Many "very water resistant" lotions are of the water in oil type. These emulsions present a different type of cooling problem. Since the water is in the internal phase, and since water has a higher heat capacity than oil, it requires more cooling time than oil. But since the external phase is the more easily cooled oil part, the initial temperature drop is quick. Then as the internal heat of the water phase comes through, the product begins to heat up again. If the emulsion is cooled down too quickly and pumped out of the tank it can reheat itself, and without the continued mixing, destabilize. Therefore, a slow cooling while mixing is the best way to insure that the product will remain stable after manufacture.

PRODUCTION METHODS

As previously mentioned O/W emulsions are the most common type. They usually have the best feel and have greater stability that W/O emulsions. Most of these emulsions require a water-soluble thickener or film former for stability and water resistance. If the selected thickener or film former requires neutralization, then, there are two ways to do so, either before or after the phases are combined.

By combining the phases as usual at 76–80°C and immediately adding the neutralizing agent, the neutralization will be "shared" between the thickener and any other material in the oil phase like stearic acid. This may create a stable, good-feel product, but if a soap is created (e.g., tea-stearate), then it is unlikely that the emulsion will be waterproof.

By neutralizing the water phase first and allowing it to thicken and then adding the oil phase you can usually create a transitional emulsion, that is, an emulsion that feels like an oil–water type, but upon rubbing it on the skin acts like a water–oil type. Since the W/O type has the best chance of being water resistant, this method of neutralizing is often the best (Formula 2).

If the thickener has no or little emulsification capabilities, however, then the decision of when to add the neutralization agent is not as important.

We have previously touched upon the subject of where and how to incorporate different thickeners or film formers.

In the laboratory, you have all the time you want and a very large ratio of mixing to product volume. It is easy to disperse almost any polymer, but in a 1000 gal tank it may be another story. Foaming is probably the biggest problem in dispersing carbomers, especially Carbopol 1342. It is often easier to add the Carbopol 1342 to the oil phase after it is at emulsifying temperature and the heat is off. Once the Carbopol 1342 is dispersed, the oil phase should immediately be pumped over to the water phase. It should then be neutralized as soon as the phases are combined (Formula 3).

RAW MATERIAL HANDLING

Most of the ingredients used in the formulation of sunscreens are also used in many other types of skin care products. The obvious exception would be the active ingredients, the UV absorbers. Most are oil soluble, a few are water soluble, and two are dispersions of specialized physical pigments. The oil-soluble ones can be treated like any other ingredient in the oil phase. These products are all very stable at high temperatures and pose no special handling problems. The water-soluble materials usually have to be neutralized first in cold water before any of the other ingredients are added. Once they are in solution you can proceed with the batch as usual. Remember though that these are salts and therefore may be incompatible with systems that are salt intolerant.

The most difficult UV absorbing materials are the dispersions on titanium dioxide and zinc oxide. When these dispersions first appeared they were very difficult to work with. They would separate in their drum after only a small amount of time and therefore needed to be mixed up before use. Even with mixing, the powder would settle on the bottom and cake up, not being usable at all. Since then, there are many solvents to choose from as the dispersant and the dispersion itself is far more stable.

It is best to add the oil dispersions to the oil phase after the phase is all melted and at emulsifying temperature. Also, the heating should be over. The dispersion can "burn" and coagulate at the bottom of the vessel. This also holds true for W/O emulsions. The addition of the dispersion into the continuous phase should be handled in the same manner.

Since sunscreen products are OTC drugs, the handling of these raw materials (including labels, bottles, etc.) must be documented in a procedural company handbook for FDA inspection. Form 1 is an example of a procedure used by a manufacturer for handling raw material.

FORM 1

Raw Material Sampling and Approval Procedure

- The warehouse receiving manager informs Quality Control (QC) when a shipment of chemicals or compentry arrives.
- If it is a **chemical raw material** the following procedure is used:
    - The warehouse receiving department notifies QC that a shipment has arrived and brings to the laboratory a copy of all relevant paperwork.
    - QC collects one sample from each lot of material, stickering the containers from which the sample is taken. The materials, item number, identity, lot number, and date received are entered into the QC Raw Material Log Book.

   - Each container is then labeled with the materials item number, lot number, and date received. The sample is analyzed in the laboratory against the manufacturer's certificate of analysis sheet.
   - A sample of the material is labeled and stored.
   - If the material passes the laboratory analysis, the warehouse is notified and the material is put into inventory.
- If the **material is a package** component, the following procedure is used:
   - A representative sample is brought to the laboratory for identification.
   - A capacity test, weight check, and general inspection are performed on the component.
   - If the component passes the tests, the warehouse is notified and the material is transferred to the general warehouse.
- If the material is **labels**, then the following procedure is used:
   - Warehouse receiving notifies QC that labels have arrived.
   - QC collects samples of both front and back labels from each lot.
   - The labels are visually compared to a standard for text, color, etc.
   - The labels are then attached to a piece of paper and retained in a QC standard file.
   - If the labels are approved, the warehouse is notified and they are placed in the inventory.

QUALITY CONTROL OF SUNSCREENS

As dictated by FDA regulations each production facility needs to have a "Master Batch Control Record." This outlines each step of operations of an OTC manufacturing facility (3). The following is an example of the 10 sections of such a record:

1. Master formula including the manufacturing procedure of the product
2. Quality control analysis and release form
3. Tote or portable tank sanitizing report/procedure
4. Filling machine cleaning and sanitizing report/procedure (this documents that the fill machine has been properly cleaned in preparation for the run, and the person responsible)
5. Production setup checklist (this list insures that all the components are available for the fill run and are correct)
6. Daily fill report (it should include work times, fill weight checks, yield analysis, etc.)
7. Daily production quality control report (this is usually the hourly checklist performed by the line inspector, who monitors the fill level, the label placement, and the general appearance of the package)

8. Label check report (at the end of a run, all labels must be accounted for, even the waste)
9. Machine time logs
10. Used tote or portable tank tags (the original tag should be included with the complete batch report).

This Master Batch Control Record not only outlines for any FDA inspector how the company operates, but shows them at a glance the entire process.

Forms 2–4 are some examples of these documents.

To summarize, Form 5 represents the steps in the process from incoming raw materials to product release.

FORM 2

Finished Product Sampling and Approval Procedure

- **Batch approval**
  - When the batch is complete two samples are brought to the laboratory along with the batch sheet, one for evaluation, and one for microtesting.
  - The product specification sheet is pulled out and the appropriate tests are performed on the product. If the product passes the tests, verbal approval is given to compounding and the product is transferred into totes for filling.
  - A bulk sample of the batch is labeled and retained for a period of 1 year.
  - Tote tags containing the batch information are issued to compounding. These tags are placed on the filled totes.
  - The filled totes then are put into the racks until ready for filling into bottles.
  - The QC report is attached to the Batch report and goes into a yield packet.
- **Filling approval**
  - A start-up sample is taken from the tote and given to QC for inspection and microtesting.
  - QC checks the tote tag against the yield packet to verify that the correct product is being filled.
  - Random filled samples are removed from the line for micro-testing during the beginning, middle, and end of the fill run.
  - Random samples are also pulled from the line for weight checks and specific gravity measurements.
  - The product may be released from quarantine if it tests clean after 3 days. All plates are held for 5 days before being discarded.

FORM 3

Finished Product Filling Sampling and Approval Procedure

- A start-up sample is taken from the tote and given to QC for inspection and microtesting.
    - QC checks the tote tag against the yield packet to verify that the correct product is being filled.
    - Random filled samples are removed from the line for microtesting during the beginning, middle, and end of the fill run.
    - Random samples are also pulled from the line for weight checks and specific gravity measurements.
    - The product may be released from quarantine if it tests clean after 3 days. All plates are held for 5 days before being discarded.

FORM 4

Finished Product Filling Procedure

- Once QC has given approval to begin filling, the following procedure is performed:
    - A QC inspector completes the "production set-up list" to insure that all the correct components are present. A separate "label check" is also performed.
    - Throughout the filling process the "machine time log", and the "Daily production QC report" are filled in.
    - The "Daily filling report" is completed in order to keep track of the exact number of bottles filled, fill weights, waste, and final yield.
    - When the fill run is completed all the information is put together in the yield packet.

Stability Testing

Once a batch is manufactured and a sample is submitted to quality control the usual tests should be performed on the batch.

The batch sample should be cooled to room temperature with mixing. Once cooled, the usual tests should be performed. These include viscosity, pH, specific gravity, and general appearance. Since sunscreen products are classified as OTC drug products, chemical analysis of the active ingredients is also required. The overall assay of the UV absorbance using a UV spectrophotometer is a good in-process test for the testing of active ingredients, but the individual assay of the various actives is preferred by the FDA. At this point many other countries

FORM 5

Product Flow Diagram

Receipt for raw materials
↓
Quality control analysis of chemicals and packaging → Rejected materials
↓
Approval of materials
↓
Reweigh chemicals for compounding
↓
Manufacture of product → Batch rejected → Destroyed
↓
Quality control approval of batch
(Batch rejected ↓ Batch corrected → Filling of product)
↓
Filling of product ← Batch corrected
↓
Quality control during filling
↓
5-day microhold on finished product → Rejected ↓ Destroyed
↓
Product released from quarantine
↓
Product shipped

require individual analysis of the actives by HPLC or equivalent analysis. Form 6 is an example of a stability worksheet that should be followed on a production batch. It is recommended that even after the 3-year stability testing is complete you randomly choose a product to test each year.

Analysis by Nonscanning UV Analysis

This method is a good, quick way to check that the total amount of UV absorbers are present in your batch. It does not determine the percentages of each of the UV absorbers, but it will determine if the overall UV absorbance of the product matches your laboratory standard.

Your laboratory sample is scanned at a specific wavelength to determine the degree of absorbance of the product. The ratio between the absorbance at a specific wavelength and the sample size is calculated. This can then be compared to the batch sample. By using a simple ratio and proportion calculation, you can determine the total percentage of UV absorbers in a product.

The procedure and calculation is shown in Form 7 (4).

Once the lab has determined that the batch sample is equivalent to the standard, it can be submitted for the more detailed and specific HPLC analysis.

FORM 6

Annual Product Stability Testing Report

Product:
Formula number:
Manufacture date:

Room Temperature

Test	Specification	Int. results	30 days	90 days	6 months	1 year
Appearance						
Odor						
Viscosity						
pH						
% Actives						
Sp. gravity						
Challenge test						
Other						

Oven (45°C)

Test	Specification	Int. results	30 days	60 days
Appearance				
Odor				
Viscosity				
pH				
% Actives				
Sp. gravity				
Challenge test				
Other				

Freeze–Thaw Cycles

Test	Specification	Int. results	Three cycles
Appearance			
Odor			
Viscosity			
pH			
% Actives			
Sp. gravity			
Challenge test			
Other			

FORM 7

Simple Test for Percent Sunscreen in a Product

EQUIPMENT:

1. Analytical balance
2. UV spectrophotometer
3. 100 mL volumetric flask (two per sample)
4. Quartz glass cuvette
5. 10 mL volumetric flasks
6. 1.0 mL graduated volumetric pipettes
7. 5.0 mL volumetric pipettes
8. Ultrasonic cleaner (for samples)

REAGENTS:

1. Isopropyl alcohol (IPA) (spectrophotometric grade)
2. Sunscreen(s) used in products to be tested

STANDARD PREPARATION:

A. Standard preparation:
   1. Make the standard solution by preparing a solution of IPA and the exact percentage of each sunscreen. For example, for a sunscreen product that has 7.5% octinoxate and 4.0% oxybenzone you would prepare the following solution:

Octinoxate	7.5%
Oxybenzone	4.0%
IPA	88.5%

   2. Take exactly 0.1 mL of the stand solution and dilute to 100 mL in a volumetric flask. Then, take exactly 1.0 mL of this solution and dilute to 10 mL in a 10 mL volumetric flask. This concentration should give an absorbance in the range of 0.4–1.7.

B. Product analysis:

Prepare the sample for analysis in the same manner. Run the absorbance at 310 nm for the standard and sample.

C. Calculation and results:

By using a simple ratio and proportion method you can calculate the total percent sunscreen in a finished product. The equation is as follows:

$$\frac{\text{Std abs.}}{\%\ \text{sunscreen}} = \frac{\text{sample abs}}{X}$$

where X = total percent sunscreen in the product.

Although the UV spectrophotometric method is presumptive, it is able to determine if the total sunscreen percentage in the batch matches the laboratory standard.

Analysis of sunscreens with physical sunscreens is more difficult. Unlike organic UV absorbers, the UV protection of products that utilize physical absorbers is totally dependent on the dispersion of the pigment. No matter how small the particle size of the starting material is, if it agglomerates in the emulsion, its UV absorption qualities will be negligible. Therefore, an analysis that can determine the actual protectiveness of the product is necessary. Simply determining the amount of titanium dioxide or zinc oxide is not sufficient (5).

The Optometrics MPF scanning spectrophotometer can asses the UV absorbance characteristics of the actual product, and not just determine the amount of UV absorbers in the product. UV light is passed through the product, which is spread on a special tape, which simulates skin (6). A detector on the other side of the tape records the level of absorbance at each wavelength.

The manufacturing procedures for products containing pigment dispersions are sometimes very different from those for typical emulsions. The addition of the pigment slurry or powder can be a very tricky maneuver.

If the pigment is dispersed in an oil-soluble material, it should be added to the oil phase after the phase has come to temperature while under good agitation. The dispersion should not be allowed to settle on the bottom of the tank otherwise it has a tendency to agglomerate. If agglomeration still occurs, the addition of the slurry after the phases are combined may work.

There are also aqueous dispersions of these micronized pigments. Since it is the water phase that would contain any acids, bases, or salts, the addition of an aqueous pigment dispersion has to be carefully considered. Like an oil dispersion if agglomeration occurs the dispersion should be added after the phases are together. Formula 5 represents a typical SPF 15 O/W emulsion using a 40% TiO_2 oil dispersion (7).

With both forms of dispersions it is important to continually mix while cooling. The batch should be completely cooled before it is pumped out of the tank.

CONTRACT MANUFACTURING OF SUNCARE PRODUCTS

More and more of the suncare products on the market are controlled or store brand products. That is, they are products made specifically for the retailer, with their name on them. Almost all of the them are national brand equivalent (NBE) products, products that match the popular name brand products. With more and more consumers reading the back labels of products they are comparing what is inside the bottle to the price, and not what is printed on the outside, like label design.

Formula 5 SPF 15 O/W Lotion

Percentage	Material
	Phase A
2.00	Stearyl alcohol
5.00	Octyl palmitate
5.00	Triethylhexanoin
2.00	Polysorbate 60
7.50	Isohexadecane
	Phase B
15.00	Solaveil CT-100[a]
	Phase C
54.80	Water
2.50	Arlatone 2121[a]
0.20	Rewoderm S1333[b]
	Phase D
0.80	Veegum Ultra[c]
0.20	Xanthan GUM
1.00	Germaben II[d]
4.00	Propylene glycol
100.00	

[a]Uniqema.
[b]Witco.
[c]R T Vanderbilt.
[d]ISP.

Manufacturing procedure:

1. Heat phase A to 80°C.
2. At 80°C add phase B while mixing.
3. Heat phase C to 80°C.
4. Premix the ingredients of phase D and add them to phase C.
5. Adjust both phases to 80°C.
6. With good agitation add the oil to the water phase.
7. Homogenize for an appropiate time.
8. Cool to 35°C.

Formulation- and manufacture-wise, this is a reverse engineering exercise. The product must be first formulated to match the physical characteristics of the national brand, using the same ingredients, then it should go through all the safety and performance testing required by the FDA for an OTC drug product. When all this is completed and the product stability is complete, the manufacturer has a product to sell to the store.

The term NBE is used to describe a product that has been reverse engineered to match a national brand. The qualification is usually preformed by an outside testing laboratory which specializes in NBE qualifications.

CONCLUSIONS

The manufacturing of sunscreen products encompasses the worst of both worlds. Being OTC products, they must be made under strict FDA guidelines. This includes detailed product analysis, stability studies, process validation, etc. But they must be manufactured at a low enough cost to be able to compete in a world of close-out/discount stores. As with all cosmetic manufacturing, technique is as much a part of success as science. Knowing the limitations of your equipment and formulas is of paramount importance.

REFERENCES

1. Carbopol Resins Handbook. Cleveland, OH: Noveon Inc.
2. Product Bulletin. Ormond Beach, FL: Concentrated Aloe Corporation.
3. Code of Federal Regulations (CFR), sec. 21, part 211.
4. Analytical Procedure #4A. Ormond Beach, FL: Concentrated Aloe Corporation.
5. Tioveil Product Guide. Unichema Inc. TVI/1.
6. Product Bulletin. Ayer, MA: Optometrics USA Inc.
7. True transparency for Solaveil. Uniqema Product bulletin.

35

Quality Control of Finished Sunscreen Products

Henry T. Kalinoski
L'Oréal USA Products, Inc., Clark, New Jersey, USA

INTRODUCTION

Any description of the techniques for product quality control should start with an agreed definition of the term. The description almost requires that the question

"Why do quality control at all?" be asked. In the modern times of Good Manufacturing Practices (GMP) (1,2), speed to market, just-in-time processes, and government mandated development and production, quality control of the finished product is almost an expensive complication delaying the release of finished products. The reality is that even with the best systems in place, with all of the supplier qualifications completed, with a regular auditing process, and with government oversight, there is still a need to ensure that material produced will meet the expectations of the final consumer. One could probably find many definitions of quality and a number of systems to ensure product quality. For the purposes of this chapter, quality is defined as meeting the customer's expectations every time. Such an approach is described, for example, by Juran and Godfrey (3), who indicate two aspects of quality. The first definition covers the features of products that meet customer needs and thereby provide customer satisfaction. The second is the freedom from deficiencies, which could result in the need for rework or lead to product failure and therefore customer dissatisfaction. This latter aspect has, for the most part, been addressed through conformance to specifications. This grew from a belief that if something meets specifications, it will satisfy the customer. Newer approaches with greater emphasis on customer focus require that a broader view be taken, that quality is not always captured only in specifications. From such a view grows the definition of quality control as a universal managerial process for conducting operations so as to provide stability—to prevent adverse change and to maintain the status quo. The quality control process maintains this stability by evaluating actual performance, comparing actual performance to goals and acting on differences found (3). This chapter does not pretend to cover all of the aspects one must understand, address and control to have a quality system or even a quality control system. It also does not cover quality assurance (defined as verification that control is being maintained), quality improvement, "total quality management," or other extensions of these concepts and philosophies. This is an ever-evolving area and today's definitions are likely to change again in the future. Many volumes have been written on that. Quality control is a program with the steps taken by the developer and manufacturer to support delivery to the customer's expectation. Quality control focuses on control during operations and meeting the goals for operations. Quality assurance is involved at later steps and interacts with a broader range of functions involved in the product life cycle.

For a finished consumer product, quality control begins with an understanding of the customer's expectations. The product marketer wants to demonstrate or be assured that material produced and packaged for sale to and use by the final consumer is equivalent to the material originally developed in the product development process. Further, there is a need to ensure that this material is produced consistently through the life of the product. Taking these views requires that quality control is much more than an after-the-fact inspection. Any quality control testing depends heavily on an appropriate set of product specifications being set and agreed to during the product development process. This reduces the important characteristics of a product to a series of numbers that can be evaluated with an accepted set of test methods. This results in a series of objective standards and tests that can be used and replicated at any point along the product's life cycle. The range of accepted values is determined during the product development process and evaluated during the product life cycle. Characteristics and their associated methods can be grouped into release criteria and other characteristics, those important to know but not essential to meet to allow product to be released to the final consumer. There will be times when certain key characteristics cannot be reduced to a number. These subjective tests require the development and acceptance of suitable standards for each product or formulation. Training of the quality control testing staff is critical to ensure that subjective criteria are met consistently. All of this is coupled with input from the target consumer.

This chapter really focuses more on evaluation of the finished product and does not really address in-process control (inspection, sampling, etc.). Similar tests, characteristics and approaches could be taken but in-process control is a topic all to itself (4). Also, this chapter does not go into the intricacies of the statistical aspects of the quality control process. Such aspects have led to detailed developments in statistical process control (SPC). These areas are topics of great interest in and of themselves (4).

This chapter describes the characteristics of finished sunscreen products that are most often evaluated in the quality control process. This is a general outline and there may be some specific products where a property or performance is key for that particular product but is not included here. Included here are the typical methods used to evaluate these characteristics and some of the parameters that should be controlled or established for proper use of these techniques.

PRODUCT FORMS

The various forms for sunscreen products, oils, lotions, sticks and balms, sprays (alcohol or aqueous, aerosol or pump) are described in some detail elsewhere (this volume, chapter by SaNogueira). It is important to consider that form and associated ingredients may influence the type or range of characteristics of importance for quality evaluation. Techniques or characteristics appropriate for one product form, a lotion, for example, would not necessarily be of much importance for another form such as a stick. Other parameters, such as actives content, would be of importance for all forms. Specific testing or modifications to address particular product forms are not addressed in this chapter.

SAMPLING

Any effort at finished product quality control must include a consideration of the sampling plan (3–5). It must be determined what constitutes a characteristic representation of the total production of a given product. The approaches to the development of a sampling plan are covered in considerable detail in a number of texts (3–5) and requirements are detailed in guidance documents or individual monographs (5,6). In general, a sampling plan should be based on the amount of material produced and it should include sampling from the bulk product as well as product in final packaging. Whether a product is produced in a batch or continuous process will determine some aspects of the sampling plan. The plan should also require sampling from the top, middle, and bottom portions of a tank, drum, tote, or final package and samples from the early, middle, and late parts of a filling run. All these steps are required to ensure representative sampling as well as to gauge whether changes are occurring during production processes. Each step in manufacturing, filling, storage, and transportation can have effects on the "quality" of a product and the sampling plan should be robust enough to acknowledge and address these (7). The time intervals between samplings and after filling but before shipping should be considered in a sampling plan. Sampling should ensure that material tested for quality control purposes is characteristic of the formula and representative of the material to be used by the consumer. If sampling for quality control purposes reveals inconsistencies in product properties (separation, gelling, solidification, liquification), that information must be included in any reporting of quality control results.

PHYSICAL METHODS

These are methods that evaluate the physical, rather than chemical or compositional, characteristics of the finished products. This section does not include the methods used to ensure proper product delivery from the final package (such as spray rate, etc.), although that should be addressed during the product development and manufacturing process. These methods deal with the characterization of the "juice" in the package. Color, odor, appearance, refractive index, specific gravity, viscosity, or more generally rheology, flash point, melting point, particle size analysis (useful for any emulsion product, some application to sunscreen lotions), and perhaps others relate to the properties of the complete product. Some of these physical attributes are influenced by the actives but many are not.

The three initial characteristics (color, odor, and appearance; COA) are most appropriately evaluated in comparison to an accepted standard. This accepted standard is usually production material that is agreed by developers to be "characteristic" of the desired end product. A general product description may be included in the finished product specifications (e.g., thick, creamy-smooth white lotion with no visible oil separation, sandiness or grittiness, with a mild citrus fragrance). It is even better if this comparison standard is from the same batch or lot that has been used for consumer acceptance testing. This practice ensures that production material closely matches material already deemed acceptable by the final consumer. This is a key area of distinction from the characterization or quality control of raw materials or determinations by other test methods. For those other materials, intrinsic properties of the chemicals define these appearance factors. With the final product, the product developer uses the input from the consumer to define what these acceptance criteria will be. For the raw materials, specific values are determined based on raw material or product performance. Acceptable COA parameters for final products are based heavily on consumer acceptance. Hedonics are strong factors in consumer preference for a particular product and the quality control of COA can ensure that consumer preference, established in testing during development, is consistently met by final production material.

In addition to matching a standard, color can also be evaluated using standard colorimetric techniques (7–9). In such evaluations, a representative aliquot of a product is introduced to a colorimeter or spectrophotometer and the color values read directly from the instrument. The instruments function based on the absorption or reflection of light, usually a defined, full-spectrum white light. Color values are a complex combination of the primary colors (blue, red, and yellow) along with light intensity and contributions from reflectance (gloss), transmittance or opacity. This allows for an objective representation of the color of a product. There are a number of accepted, industry-standard approaches to color measurements (7–9) that might be relevant to quality control of sunscreen products. The colorimetric methods would be guided by the accepted product standard agreed to during product development.

Another physical property, refractive index, is also related to how a product interacts with light. Refractive index is a measure of how a material interferes with the transmission of light or, more specifically, the ratio of the velocity of light in air to the velocity of light in the substance (10). The refractive index is related to and can influence both the color and appearance of a product. A measure of refractive index is an objective means to evaluate the more subjective aspects of product appearance. The refractive index of a product is directly determined by the ingredients in the formula but cannot be predicted simply by knowing the product formula. Refractive index is typically measured at 25°C and any quality control testing should specify and record the temperature at which refractive index measurements are made.

Specific gravity [a ratio of the weight of a volume of a liquid relative to an equal volume of pure water, at 25°C, (11)] is also a function of the ingredients that are combined to produce the final product. As the value of specific gravity is dependent on the formula, its measure during a quality control process can give some evaluation that the correct formula has been followed and that processing conditions were appropriate. This value is also related to how the final consumer interacts with the product although the consumer would have no easy means to define that relationship. The specific gravity would have some relationship with the viscosity and overall rheology of a finished product. Specific gravity is a function of temperature and the temperature at which a specific gravity measurement is made should be specified.

Viscosity is probably the most complex physical property of a finished sunscreen product. In the simplest definition, it is a measure of how a material will flow. Many things can affect viscosity and its measurement offers a "snapshot" of a product's life or history. One can take a rather simple (get a number that indicates a sample's "quality") out through a very detailed (know and define every aspect of a product's behavior) view of this characteristic. From the quality control point of view, for product release, it is usually sufficient to obtain a number under a specified set of conditions.

Viscosity is a subset of the more complex area of rheology. A dictionary definition of viscosity is the internal friction of a fluid that makes it resist a tendency to flow. By definition, rheology is the study of change in form and the flow of matter. Viscosity is the measure of the amount of force required to move a layer (shear) of a product (or more correctly, a fluid) relative to the rate at which a stress is applied. The result is that high-viscosity fluids (those having more internal friction) require more force to move than low-viscosity fluids. The viscometer is a tool to measure this internal friction and viscosity can be measured or reported as absolute or apparent viscosity. The behavior of a material under shear conditions is related to properties and composition of the material and allows for classification based on observed properties. These properties will impact how a product can be formulated, processed, packaged, and finally experienced by a consumer. As there is a range of product forms, properties of sunscreen products run the gamut through the range of rheological systems. Products can be solutions in water or mineral oil that will likely exhibit Newtonian properties (12,13). Such systems will show no change in viscosity with added shear with the result being an easy pouring, easy to process, and easy to apply product. More complex rheology runs the range out through pseudoplastic and thixotropic, where the more stress that is encountered, the more the product will change (12,13). Some of these non-Newtonian fluids will change and not return to the original properties after stress is released. The understanding of the rheological behavior of a product is required to ensure straightforward (and economical) processing and consumer-acceptable final product attributes.

For some products, a simple measure of apparent viscosity at a defined stress and shear rate will suffice to define a product for quality control release. More complex rheological measurements of stress/rate relationships, yield curves, and flow curves are more appropriately performed during product development to ensure an acceptable range of product properties will be consistently produced using the given formula under the intended production, processing, filling and application processes. Even the simple apparent viscosity measurement can be influenced by temperature and product "history." Temperature should be controlled and any sample history should be recorded for the quality control record.

These three physical characteristics (refractive index, specific gravity, viscosity) are often used as release parameters as they are easily measured and relate to both formula and function of the finished product. There is no way to calculate or determine beforehand the final values of any of these properties for any given product. They are intrinsic to a particular product, are usually determined during the development of a particular formula and relate closely to how a product is perceived by a consumer. Control and monitoring of these properties should ensure ongoing acceptance of the final product by the consumer.

Physical values such as melting point, boiling point, or flash point might be critical parameters in the identification and characterization of a pure compound or raw material. They are less relevant to the quality control of a finished product. As the finished product is such a complex mixture of ingredients, these measurements do not necessarily yield much useful quality control information on the product. For certain product forms, such as a stick, it might be important to know and control the melting point to ensure performance and stability. For alcohol or oil products, a flash point might be required for packaging or transportation. These determinations should be made during product development and then checked during process validation.

CHEMICAL METHODS

As with some of the physical tests described in the previous section, most chemical tests specified for individual actives (acid value, saponification value, metal content) are not relevant to the finished product. The control and testing of incoming raw materials would limit undesirable impurities such as metals in the finished product. Again the complex nature of finished products limits the utility of many chemical tests.

The pH of a product is a measure of the free hydrogen ion content and can be a very important chemical characteristic. The value of pH is dependent on the materials used in the formulation and their interactions. The pH can affect the use properties of the product as well as the stability of the actives and stability of the overall formula. The pH might be taken directly on the completed formula or on a solution of known concentration of the product in water. In either case, the conditions under which the pH is obtained, including the temperature of the sample, should be monitored and recorded. For some product forms, such as oils, a pH measurement is meaningless.

Water content of a finished product can be critical to long-term stability, actives stability, product use properties, physical properties, and the susceptibility to microbial growth (14). There are generally two techniques to determine the water content of a product. One method, the titrimetric or Karl Fischer method, specifically determines water through a chemical reaction. This is a fairly well defined reaction but it can be complicated if systems and the environment in which the method is conducted are not kept scrupulously dry. The second method is the gravimetric or loss on drying approach (15). This method may be simpler to perform but may include other materials in addition to water in the final value. Any material volatile at the temperature of the determination will evaporate in the test and be reported as part of the loss. This approach is only appropriate for a product where water is known to be the only volatile material in the formula. Water content or loss on drying might be used as a release criterion for a finished product. If the gravimetric approach is used, the temperature and time used for the determination should be recorded.

SPECTROSCOPY

Bulk spectroscopic methods, such as ultraviolet (UV) or infrared (IR) spectroscopy (16–18), are not used as much for finished products as they would be for raw materials. Finished products are quite complex mixtures, the spectroscopic methods are fairly general and it would be difficult to associate specific features, characteristics, or changes to specific product issues or problems. The techniques may be used to evaluate some individual component in a formula, such as a preservative, as some ingredients likely have unique absorbances that could be distinguished in a complex spectrum. This measurement would probably not be a release criterion and release would rely more on microbiological evaluation.

One technique amenable to quality control is near-IR spectroscopy (18). This approach uses only a part of the IR spectrum to characterize a sample. In contrast to full spectrum approach, the near-IR technique uses a portion of the spectrum characteristic of interactions between materials. This allows for a better evaluation of mixtures. More importantly, when coupled with a computer data system and appropriate spectral evaluation software, the technique can yield some simple good/bad, yes/no, or pass/fail determinations. The spectral evaluation and chemometric (19,20) software required for such determinations rely on the development of a data set of spectra of acceptable and unacceptable samples. Once such a comparison data set is produced, the technique is reduced to appropriate sample preparation and introduction. This preparation is usually not complicated and near-IR systems can be installed and used in both the quality control laboratory as well as directly in the production area. This approach permits a much greater in-process control of materials and products.

Spectroscopic techniques are also used for elemental analysis and, as some inorganic actives are used in sunscreen products, atomic absorption (AA) or inductively coupled plasma (ICP) spectroscopy (18) might be used in quality control. The inorganic actives titanium dioxide and zinc oxide are best addressed using one of these techniques. The techniques involve introducing solution samples into a flame or plasma to excite the elements present and then detecting the light absorbed or emitted by the excited elements. The amount of light absorbed or emitted is directly proportional to the amount of an element present. The techniques both require the inorganic material to be present in the elemental form. As both sunscreen actives are used as oxides of the metal, and are present in complex matrices of organic materials in finished products, sample preparation involves digestion of the product and isolation of the inorganic components. This is a harsh procedure that could be hazardous due to the nature of the reagents and conditions used (strong acids, high temperatures). Care must be taken to ensure product samples are thoroughly digested to obtain dependable results without interferences and without getting equipment excessively "dirty." As it is an absorbance technique, AA is usually performed one element at a time using individual wavelengths of light characteristic of the element of interest. The ICP technique relies on light emitted from excited elements and can be conducted for both elements (Ti and Zn) simultaneously. ICP spectroscopy yields better sensitivity but this level of sensitivity is not usually necessary based on the concentrations of sunscreen actives typically employed. The greater sensitivity can allow for the evaluation of a much smaller size sample in ICP, requiring less sample preparation, lower hazard, and less waste disposal. Determination of inorganic actives would be required before product could be released for distribution.

Mass spectrometry (21) would usually be used coupled with chromatography (gas or liquid) to simplify sample preparation or introduction. This technique is most useful for determining the presence or, more specifically, the identity of an unknown material. As it is not likely that unknowns will routinely appear in production materials, and process steps are taken to limit likely occurrences, mass spectrometry is not typically used as a quality control tool.

CHROMATOGRAPHY

Chromatographic separation techniques (22,23) are quite amenable for the quantitation of the actives in finished sunscreen products. Chromatography allows for efficient separation of ingredients in complex formulations followed by selective or sensitive detection of the components of interest. Of the two most widely used chromatographic techniques, gas chromatography (GC) and liquid chromatography (LC), the physical requirements for GC render it less useful for finished product analysis. The technique requires samples be in the gas phase for analysis and many complex sunscreen product formulations contain a variety of low volatility or thermally labile materials. The technique may be more compatible with some product forms (oils or alcohol-based) and it could be used for determination of alcohol content, if that is a critical parameter. GC may be used coupled with headspace sampling for odor analysis or fragrance characterization of finished products. This approach would not likely be used as a release criterion but might be a follow-up if a sample fails a subjective odor analysis.

LC is more likely to be used due to compatibility between the physical properties of samples and the requirements of the technique. In general, reverse phase LC is used, with mobile phase solvents being water-based and modified siloxane based stationary phases used. Many sunscreen product formulations can be readily prepared as solutions in solvents appropriate for LC. As such, sample preparation can be kept as simple as possible (dilute and shoot) and it would be easy to incorporate an appropriate internal standard into a sample solution for precise quantitation. The chemical nature of sunscreen actives also allow for very selective and sensitive detection in LC. This selective detection following separation typically uses UV or diode-array UV absorption, permitting sensitive detection of actives in the presence of a great variety of other formula ingredients. The most critical application of LC would be for organic actives determinations, as most actives are readily amenable to LC and show characteristic UV absorption. It is also possible that preservatives could be quantified using an LC procedure. Determination of actives level would absolutely be a product release test.

Although sunscreen actives and finished products formulations are readily addressed using LC techniques, the process of method development in LC can be quite complicated. The method development process should lead to conditions that give baseline separation of all active components in a formulated product, with good chromatographic peak shape, in a relatively short period of time. The resulting quality control method should also have selective detection of the actives, with a wide concentration range for detection. Finally, the method should be free from interferences from other components in the mixture or in the chromatographic mobile phase. There are a variety of stationary phases available for LC and it is often best to start with a generally applicable phase such an octadecyl-modified (C18) siloxane coating on silica. The primary mobile phase component is water with various organic solvents as mobile phase modifiers. Methanol and acetonitrile are among the solvents often employed. Further mobile phase modification may come from the use of organic acids (such as acetic acid) to adjust the pH of the mobile phase.

VALIDATION

Validation is now required for the methods used to characterize over-the-counter (OTC) products such as sunscreen formulas. Validation is the process of demonstrating and documenting that the described method is appropriate for producing the information used for making a quality decision and applicable to the particular product being evaluated. Requirements for validation are described in a number of national and international regulations and guidance documents (24–29). In general, validation of a method includes documentation that the method is specific, linear, accurate, and precise. The appropriate range of these parameters must be defined and it must include the expected target concentration of the sunscreen active. In addition, the technique or method must be able to be performed under a range of defined conditions that may vary from the original development conditions and it must be able to be performed by different operators in different laboratories or settings. The equipment used to practice a method must also be documented to be appropriate for the method (qualified) and must be in proper working order prior to obtaining any sample characterization or quality release information. This final step is achieved in a process known as system suitability. Many of the details and requirements for validation developed from the evaluation of chromatographic techniques. Some techniques would not require full validation, as they are compendial methods, and proven through wide use to be appropriate. Any chromatographic techniques, however, would need to be validated for the specific formulations and active ingredients in any particular finished sunscreen product.

MICROBIOLOGY

In addition to the physical and chemical characteristics, the impact of biological processes on finished products must also be evaluated. Product integrity, performance, functionality, and safety are all aspects of product quality and are reliant on a product being impervious to microbiological contamination. Consequences of a contaminated or improperly preserved product range from undesirable aesthetics (off-color, odor, separation) through loss of production batches to potential physical harm and illness to consumers. Two tests in microbiology are generally performed, one is appropriate for quality control of finished goods. First there is a need to perform a microbial content test (30–32) to ensure microbial "purity" of produced and packed product. Although sunscreen products are controlled OTC drugs produced under defined GMP conditions, a producer cannot simply rely on GMP regulations to ensure product safety and quality. Product developers may rely on the determination of the presence of preservatives and earlier development work on the establishment of appropriate preservative system to create a robust product. The microbial content test ensures that any given production batch is free from contamination. Microbiology tests can be time-consuming, requiring the growth of living organisms. This time requirement may necessitate establishment of a "micro hold" on material to allow completion of the microbiology tests before a product can be released for distribution. The microbial content test is simply an incubation of a specifically prepared sample of a product in a medium to promote the growth of microorganisms. After a specified time to allow for growth, the sample is evaluated for the presence or absence of organisms. The quality control specification may stipulate that levels for all organisms be under a certain level or that certain extremely hazardous organisms be absent from the production material. Certain product forms by their chemical nature are resistant to microbial infection and may be exempted from microbiological specifications.

The second microbiology test is not standard for every batch. A preservative efficacy or challenge test (33–37) is used to evaluate whether a finished formulation can withstand a microbial insult. The test requires a product to be dosed with a known level of specific microorganisms and the dosed product is observed to determine whether the organisms will grow. Growth of microbes in a dosed system indicates the preservative system is inadequate to control microbiological infection of the product. This type of evaluation is usually performed during product development but may also be checked following first production or during production validation. The long-term efficacy of the preservative system would be a critical component of overall product stability. The preservative challenge test would then be a part of the life cycle stability program for the sunscreen product.

EFFICACY

Efficacy of a sunscreen product would be tested using the sun protection factor (SPF) test, as defined in the Food and Drug Administration (FDA) sunscreen monograph (38–40). This is an *in vivo* test using a number of live subjects. This testing would be performed during product development and would not be appropriate as a quality control test. There are also *in vitro* SPF test procedures (41,42) that are likely performed during product development. This combination of tests would have led to a formulation with an appropriate active level to deliver desired product performance. It would be desirable to evaluate the SPF of production material to ensure that production conditions are not, in some unforeseen manner, influencing the final efficacy of the product. This would be done primarily using the *in vitro* method, comparing results from production batches to those obtained during product development. Efficacy testing, while valuable to ensure that the final product meets the customer's expectations, would not be used as a release criterion for production.

STABILITY

Overall product stability, either real-time or accelerated, is also performed as part of product development. It is useful to perform an accelerated test of production material to verify information on product stability gained during product development. Results from production material, most importantly from initial production and process validation, would be compared to results for materials produced during product development. Again, results of this testing would not be used as release criteria.

SUMMARY

To conduct appropriate quality control, it is important to start with a quality definition that relates to consumer acceptance of the finished sunscreen product. This definition leads to a series of criteria or measurements used to judge the production of a finished formula. The criteria require use or development of accepted methods that can be for product release or to understand other characteristics of the products. All quality parameters and product specifications are based on use and maintenance of acceptable product standards. Quality parameters can be objective (numbers based) or subjective and the training of staff is key to consistently evaluate products certain to meet the customer's expectations.

The key subjective criteria used for finished sunscreen products are color, odor, and appearance. Key physical parameters include specific gravity, refractive index and viscosity. Among the key chemical parameters are water, pH (as appropriate), and actives content. Depending on the types used in a product, actives can be determined by spectroscopy (AA or ICP) for inorganics and liquid chromatography for organic materials. Testing for microbiological content is a critical release parameter for most product formulations. The efficacy and stability of a formula are important to know but are product development, not quality control, determinations.

REFERENCES

1. Code of Federal Regulations 21 CFR Part 210, Current Good Manufacturing Practice in Manufacturing, Processing, Packing, or Holding of Drugs; General and Part 211, Current Good Manufacturing Practice for Finished Pharmaceuticals, April 1996.
2. Code of Federal Regulations 21 CFR 700.35, Cosmetics Containing Sunscreen Ingredients, April 2002.
3. Juran JM, Godfrey AB (co-editors-in-chief). Juran's Quality Handbook. 5th ed. New York: McGraw-Hill, 1999.
4. Montgomery DC. Introduction to Statistical Quality Control. 2nd ed. New York: John Wiley and Sons, 1991.
5. Chow S-C, Liu J-P (eds.). Statistical Design and Analysis in Pharmaceutical Science, Statistics: Textbooks and Monographs. Vol. 143. New York: Marcel Dekker, 1995.
6. Schilling EG. Acceptance Sampling in Quality Control. New York: Marcel Dekker, 1982.
7. ASTM E 1164, Standard Practice for Obtaining Spectrophotometric Data for Object-Color Evaluation, ASTM International. For referenced ASTM standards, visit the ASTM website, www.astm.org, or contact ASTM Customer Service at service@astm.org. For Annual Book of ASTM Standards volume information, refer to the standard's Document Summary page on the ASTM website.
8. ASTM E308-01 Standard Practice for Computing the Colors of Objects by Using the CIE System, ASTM International. For referenced ASTM standards, visit the ASTM website, www.astm.org, or contact ASTM Customer Service at service@astm.org. For Annual Book of ASTM Standards volume information, refer to the standard's Document Summary page on the ASTM website.
9. United States Pharmacopeia, Twenty-Sixth Revision, [1061], The United States Pharmacopeial Convention, Rockville, MD, 2002.
10. United States Pharmacopeia, Twenty-Sixth Revision, [831], The United States Pharmacopeial Convention, Rockville, MD, 2002.
11. United States Pharmacopeia, Twenty-Sixth Revision, [841], The United States Pharmacopeial Convention, Rockville, MD, 2002.
12. Macosko CW. Rheology—Principles, Measurements and Applications. New York: Wiley-VCH, 1994.
13. Larson RG. The Structure and Rheology of Complex Fluids. New York: Oxford University Press, 1999.
14. United States Pharmacopeia, Twenty-Sixth Revision, [921], The United States Pharmacopeial Convention, Rockville, MD, 2002.
15. United States Pharmacopeia, Twenty-Sixth Revision, [731], The United States Pharmacopeial Convention, Rockville, MD, 2002.

16. Silverstein RM, Bassler GC, Morrill TC. Spectrometric Identification of Organic Compounds. 5th ed. New York: John Wiley and Sons, 1991.
17. Silverstein RM, Kiemle D, Webster FX. Spectrometric Identification of Organic Compounds. 7th ed. New York: John Wiley and Sons, 2003.
18. Linden JC (ed.-in-chief), Tranter GE, Holmes JL (eds.). Encyclopedia of Spectroscopy and Spectrometry. New York: Academic Press, 2000.
19. Beebe KR, Pell RJ, Seasholtz MB. Chemometrics. A Practical Guide. New York: John Wiley and Sons, 1998.
20. Sharaf MA, Illman DL, Kowalski BR. Chemometrics. New York: John Wiley and Sons, 1986.
21. Grayson MA (ed.). Measuring Mass—From Positive Rays to Proteins. Philadelphia: Chemical Heritage Press, 2002.
22. Ettre LS, J Chromatogr 1975; 112:1–26.
23. Snyder LR, Kirkland JJ. Introduction to Modern Liquid Chromatography. New York: John Wiley and Sons, 1979.
24. Reviewer Guidance: Validation of Chromatographic Methods, US Dept of Health and Human Services, USFDA, November 1994.
25. Draft Guidance for Industry: Analytical Procedures and Methods Validation, US Dept of Health and Human Services, USFDA, August 2000.
26. ICH Q2B: Validation of Analytical Procedures: Methodology, Federal Register 62(96) 19 May 1997 pp 27463–27467.
27. Guidance for Industry: Bioanalytical Method Validation, US Dept of Health and Human Services, USFDA, May 2001.
28. United States Pharmacopeia, Twenty-Sixth Revision, [1225], The United States Pharmacopeial Convention, Rockville, MD, 2002.
29. United States Pharmacopeia, Twenty-Sixth Revision, [621], The United States Pharmacopeial Convention, Rockville, MD, 2002.
30. Curry AS, Graf JF, McEwen GN Jr. (eds.). Cosmetic, Toiletry and Fragrance Association Technical Guidelines—Microbiology Guidelines, Section M-1. Washington, DC: Cosmetic, Toiletry and Fragrance Association, 2001.
31. United States Pharmacopeia, Twenty-Sixth Revision, [61], The United States Pharmacopeial Convention, Rockville, MD, 2002.
32. Bacteriological Analytical Manual. 8th ed. Gaithersburg, MD: AOAC International, 1995.
33. Curry AS, Graf JF, McEwen GN Jr. (eds.). Cosmetic, Toiletry and Fragrance Association Technical Guidelines—Microbiology Guidelines, Section 13. Washington, DC: Cosmetic, Toiletry and Fragrance Association, 2001.
34. Curry AS, Graf JF, McEwen GN Jr. (eds.). Cosmetic, Toiletry and Fragrance Association Technical Guidelines—Microbiology Guidelines, Section M-3. Washington, DC: Cosmetic, Toiletry and Fragrance Association, 2001.
35. Curry AS, Graf JF, McEwen GN Jr. (eds.). Cosmetic, Toiletry and Fragrance Association Technical Guidelines—Microbiology Guidelines, Section 10. Washington, DC: Cosmetic, Toiletry and Fragrance Association, 2001.
36. United States Pharmacopeia, Twenty-Sixth Revision, [51], The United States Pharmacopeial Convention, Rockville, MD, 2002.
37. Horowitz W (ed.). Official Methods of Analysis of the AOAC International. 17th ed. Gaithersburg, MD: AOAC International, 2003.

38. Code of Federal Regulations 21CFR352.72, General Test Procedures, 281–282, April 2001.
39. Code of Federal Regulations 21CFR352.73, Determination of SPF Values, 282–284, April 2001.
40. Code of Federal Regulations 21CFR352.76, Determination if a Product is Water Resistant or Very Water Resistant, 284–285, April 2001.
41. Diffey BL, Robson J. J Soc Cosmet Chem, 1989; 40:127–133.
42. Spruce SR, Hewitt JP. Euro Cosmetics June 1995, 14–20.

36

Quality Control of Ultraviolet Filters

Nadim A. Shaath
Alpha Research & Development, Ltd., White Plains, New York, USA

INTRODUCTION

The recent rapid growth of the sunscreen market reflects increased consumer awareness concerning the protection against excessive exposure to the sun's damaging ultraviolet (UV) rays (this volume, chapters by Nelson and Diffey). This large-scale introduction of UV filters into a multitude of cosmetic and toiletry products has complicated the task of the quality control chemist.

UV filters are analyzed in their pure form by ingredient suppliers and also by cosmetic companies that purchase those filters for incorporation into their finished products. Once these UV filters are included into cosmetic finished products they also need to be analyzed for both quality control and regulatory compliance.

This chapter deals primarily with the analysis of the UV filters as the pure chemical ingredients supplied by their manufacturers. The analysis of the finished sunscreen products is dealt with in the chapter by Kalinoski (this book) and also in the chapter by Shaath and Flores (this book) dealing with modern analytical techniques in the sunscreen industry.

FDA APPROVED CATEGORY I UV FILTERS

The final monograph (1) published on May 21, 1999 lists 16 UV filters as Category I ingredients as shown:

---

i. Inorganic particulates

1. Titanium dioxide
2. Zinc oxide

ii. Organic filters

UV-A filters	UV-B filters
1. Avobenzone	1. PABA
2. Oxybenzone	2. Cinoxate

ii. Organic filters	
3. Sulisobenzone	3. Octocrylene
4. Dioxybenzone	4. Ocinoxate
5. Meradimate	5. Octisalate
	6. Padimate-O
	7. Homosalate
	8. Ensulizole
	9. Trolamine Salicylate

Of the 14 organic chemical UV absorbers, four are ketones namely avobenzone, oxybenzone, dioxybenzone, and sulisobenzone, and the rest are acids, their salts or esters. These compounds can be easily analyzed using standard physical, chemical, chromatographic, and spectroscopic techniques.

QUALITY CONTROL PROCEDURES

The quality control procedures for all UV filters includes the following:

1. Physical analyses
2. Chemical analyses
3. Chromatographic techniques
4. Spectroscopic techniques.

Listed next are all the possible tests that will verify the purity of a UV filter (2). The analysts should consult the UV filter ingredient supplier for the appropriate battery of tests to undertake to determine the purity of the ingredient in question.

Physical Analyses

Odor

Sunscreen chemicals generally exhibit little or no odor. They should be compared with a standard that is kept in a cool dry place, in an amber bottle free of headspace, and away from heat and light. Request a new standard from your sunscreen supplier every 6–9 months. Odors should be smelled on blotters and not directly from the containers. The sunscreen chemical should not be stored next to a highly odoriferous material to avoid cross contamination of sunscreens that are otherwise odorless, especially if they are viscous liquids or solids.

Color

The color of the sunscreen should be noted on the specifications sheet. Care is to be exercised when comparing the color of the new batch with a sample stored over a period of time. The color of the standard may have changed on standing for more than six months. The chemistry of the sunscreen may be indicative of a potential color problem. For example, cinnamates and PABA derivatives may darken on standing due to air oxidation. Phenolic derivatives, such as salicylates, interact with iron contaminants and form pinkish colorations. Generally, unlined metal drums should be avoided. Restoration of original colors may be possible in some sunscreen liquids through simple chemical treatments, distillations, or otherwise. Sunscreen suppliers should be aware of such procedures and will recommend the most appropriate remedy.

Physical Appearance

Without resorting to any instrumentation, recording the physical appearance alone may be a critical factor in acceptance or rejection of the sunscreen chemical. Observe the nature of the product as to whether it is a solid or liquid, clear or cloudy, viscous or free flowing. Check for particulates, sediments, or foreign substances in the product.

Melting Point

This property is applicable to solid sunscreens such as the benzophenones, avobenzone, ensulizole, and PABA. Record the temperature and melting range in degrees Celsius. Observe the behavior during the melting process. Report any swelling, sweating, charring, or other melting characteristics. This may reveal information on the purity of the sunscreen raw material. The dimer of dihydroxy acetone (DHA) is identified via its melting point.

Refractive Index

The refractive index ($[n]^D$ at 20°C) is the change in direction of a light ray passing from one medium to another of different density. The index of refraction of the substance may also be expressed as the ratio of the velocity of light in vacuum to its velocity in the substance. It varies with the wavelength of the incident light, temperature, and pressure. The usual light source is the D line of sodium and the standard temperature is 20°C. This method applies to liquid sunscreens that are not too viscous to analyze.

Specific Gravity

The specific gravity is the ratio of the density of a substance to the density of a reference substance (water). The temperature should be specified at all times. In the absence of a gas chromatograph, this property is helpful in determining the purity of the sunscreen chemical.

Optical Rotation

The optical rotation (α at 20°C) is the change in direction of the plane of polarized light either to the right or to the left as it passes through a molecule containing one or more asymmetric (chiral) carbon atoms. The optical rotation is measured by the use of a polarimeter. This method applies only to sunscreens that are optically active.

Solubility

The supplier should recommend a procedure for monitoring the solubility behavior of the sunscreen in various solvents. Depending on the application, the sunscreen may be tested at several concentrations in different solvents of various polarities. Usually, a 5% solution of the sunscreen is tested in water, ethanol, mineral oil, isopropyl myristate, corn oil, acetone, isopropyl palmitate, or glycerin.

Moisture Determination

The presence of moisture in the sunscreen product may be detrimental to certain applications. A Karl Fisher titration (manual or automatic) for the determination of moisture content should be performed if it is suspected that the product contains over 0.5% water.

Viscosity

This is a measure of the resistance of fluid sunscreen to flow, expressed in dyne second per square cm or poises. Centipoises, which are 0.01 poises, are also used in the industry.

pH Determination

The pH is a value that represents the acidity or alkalinity of an aqueous solution. It is defined as the logarithm of the reciprocal of the hydrogen ion concentration of a solution pH equals: $\mathrm{pH} = \ln 1/\mathrm{H}^{+}$. The pH of a number of sunscreen acids and their salts should be routinely determined in the quality control laboratory especially ensulizole, trolamine salicylate, PABA, and sulisobenzone.

Flash Point

A closed cup flash point determination in degrees Fahrenheit of the sunscreen is required by the Department of Transportation (DOT) whenever the chemical is to be transported outside of the laboratory facilities. A flashpoint below 140°F is considered to be flammable and possibly combustible.

Chemical Analyses

Saponification Value

This procedure is applicable to the analysis of sunscreen chemicals that are esters. Esters can be converted to carboxylic acids and alcohols by alkaline hydrolysis. The acids can be detected and quantitatively determined by neutralization. The saponification value is defined as the number of milligrams of KOH required for the Saponification of the ester and neutralization of free acids in 1 g of sample (3). Typical values range from 160 to 240.

Acid Value

Some sunscreen products contain carboxylic acids that may be present as unreacted products from the synthesis of the sunscreen (e.g., esterification), as degradation products (e.g., aldehydes), or as part of the compound (e.g., PABA). The amount of acid president is determined by titrating with a standardized base. If the acid value is performed to determine impurity, values lower than 5 should be observed. Some products require a percentage acid as opposed to an acid value.

Functional Group Analysis

In the absence of chromatographic and spectroscopic techniques, many sunscreens containing functional groups may be analyzed with conventional chemical methods. Acetals, acids, aldehydes, esters, ketones, or phenols are analyzed both quantitatively and qualitatively through functional group analyses. For example, hydroxylamine hydrochloride will react with the carbonyl group in ketones, forming oxides and liberating HCl. The amount of ketone can be determined from the amount of HCl liberated (4).

Metal Contents

Zinc oxide and titanium dioxide as well as metal contaminants, such as iron or chromium are analyzed by atomic absorption spectroscopy (5), by ion chromatographic procedures (6) or inductively coupled plasma (7).

Chromatographic Techniques

Chromatography may be defined as the science of separation techniques involving a mobile phase [the solvent in thin layer chromatography (TLC) and high-performance liquid chromatograph (HPLC), or the helium/nitrogen gas in gas liquid chromatography (GC)] passing through a stationary phase (alumina or silica in TLC, C-18 packing in HPLC, silicones or carbowax in GC) (8). The ability to separate various components in a mixture of sunscreen chemicals (owing to the presence of impurities or isomers) is based on selective and preferential partitioning of these components between the mobile phase and the stationary phase. Two advanced automated techniques that are used routinely for the analysis of UV filters are GC and HPLC.

Gas Chromatography

The last 20 years have witnessed an explosion in the use of gas liquid chromatography [also known as gas chromatography (GC) or vapor phase chromatography (VPC)] in the analysis of sufficiently volatile and fairly stable organic chemicals. The supplier should recommend suitable conditions for the analysis by GC. The equipment available, however, maybe the determining factor. The following parameters are crucial in any GC sunscreen analysis (9).

1. *Column*: The type of column (packed or capillary), the packing material (polar or nonpolar) and the length and diameter of the columns must be specified.
2. *Temperature conditions*: The injector, detector, and oven temperature should be noted. Any variations could lead to erroneous results. If temperature programming is available, record the initial and final temperature, as well as the temperature ramp.
3. *Detector*: From the many detectors commercially available, thermo-conductivity detectors (TCDs) and flame ionization detectors (FIDs) are adequate for most analyses.

Other factors that may be important are the carrier gas, flow rate, split ratio, and undercoating of columns. However, as long as the standard and the new batch are analyzed back-to-back, any condition mentioned in the foregoing may be adequate for the analysis. Caution must be exercised in comparing data run on two different machines or on two different days without ensuring that the conditions are identical. The use of internal or external GC standards may be helpful in those circumstances.

A typical set of GC conditions for the analysis of sunscreen chemicals follows:

Sample size	0.1 μL
Oven temp	65–250°C
Program rate	4°C/min
Injection port temperature	210°C
Detector	FID
Carrier flow	1 mL/min
Split ratio	200 : 1
Attenuation	0
Threshold	0
Detector temperature	250°C
Carrier gas	Helium

High-Performance Liquid Chromatography

Liquid chromatography is quite similar to GC except that the mobile phase is a liquid instead of a gas (10). Many laboratories are currently equipped with HPLC machines and are routinely analyzing their products with this procedure. The following conditions have to be specified:

1. *Solvent*: State whether the analysis requires gradient elution or isocratic conditions. If gradient elution is used, the mixing ratio of the binary or ternary solvents must be specified. The use of ultra pure-grade solvents is highly recommended.

2. *Column*: Other than the length and width, the most important factor is the type of packing in the column. Specify whether it is a reverse phase column or a normal phase column.
3. *Detector*: The use of either a UV or refractive index detector is recommended. If a UV detector is used, the exact wavelength should be specified. Other detectors such as conductivity, fluorescence, or electrochemical maybe suitable for particular application.

Unlike GC, HPLC may require extensive preworkup, the use of pure reagents, and generally longer analysis time. However, it is the method of choice if the sunscreen is either thermally unstable or is insufficiently volatile (e.g., PABA or sunscreen salts).

Spectroscopic Techniques

Spectroscopic methods of analysis are excellent methods for the identification of sunscreen chemicals and for the elucidation of their molecular structure (11). This is accomplished by recording the energy absorbed or emitted by the sunscreen chemical in any of the wavelengths of the electromagnetic spectrum in response to excitation by an external energy source.

Ultraviolet Spectroscopy

UV spectroscopy is used in the characterization of sunscreen chemicals which, by definition, are UV radiation absorbers. UV spectroscopy involves the absorption behavior of the chemical and can be either qualitative or quantitative. The qualitative application of absorption spectroscopy depends on the fact that a given molecular species absorbs light in a specific region of the spectrum. Such a display is called an absorption spectrum and serves as a fingerprint for identification purposes. In quantitative applications, the unknown concentration of a given species is determined.

Several useful data may be extracted from the UV spectrum to aid in the identification and characterization of sunscreen active chemicals, namely the UV pattern, the λ_{max}, the molar absorptivity (ε), the K-value, and % purity.

1. *UV pattern*: Pattern recognition of the UV spectrum may provide information for the identification of sunscreen chemicals. Care must be exercised in selecting the appropriate solvent for the analysis at an extremely high purity (ultrapure or spectroscopy-grade solvents). The concentration and dilution techniques have to be carried out carefully since the UV pattern is directly affected by the concentration, as shown in the Beer–Lambert law (12), which governs the UV absorption:

$$\varepsilon = \frac{AM}{bc}$$

where ε is the molar absorptivity in moles per cm (mol/cm) gram and is a constant, characteristic of the solute. The molar of absorptivity is directly proportional to the chemicals ability to absorb UV radiation. Therefore, the greater the absorptivity, the more UV radiation the chemical absorbs; A is the absorbance at the wavelength maximum; M is the molecular weight of the solute in moles per cubic centimeter (mol/cm^3); b is the cell width in centimeters; and c is the concentration of the solute in grams per cubic centimeter (g/cm^3).

2. λ_{max}: The wavelength of maximum absorption, λ_{max} is a characteristic of the sunscreen chemical under investigation, provided that the solvent is clearly defined. The λ_{max}, the extinction coefficient (ε) in ethanol and the percent allowed for the 16 sunscreen chemicals used in the USA are as follows:

FDA-OTC Panel Category I Sunscreens

Sunscreen	Approved %	λ_{max} (ethanol)	Extinction coefficient (ε) (ethanol)
A. Organic absorbers			
UV-A absorbers			
Avobenzone	3	357	30,500
Oxybenzone	6	325	9400
Sulisobenzone	10	324	8400
Dioxybenzone	3	327	10,440
Meradimate	5	336	5600
UV-B absorbers			
PABA	15	283	15,300
Cinoxate	3	305	9000
Octocrylene	10	303	12,600
Ocinoxate	7.5	311	23,300
Octisalate	5	307	4900
Homosalate	15	306	4300
Padimate O	8	311	27,300
Ensulizole	4	310	28,250
Trolamine Salicylate	12	298	3000
B. Inorganic particulates			
Zinc oxide	25	Broad spectrum	
Titanium dioxide	25	Broad spectrum	

3. *Molar absorptivity* (ε): The molar absorptivity (ε), or molar extinction coefficient, is a measure of the radiation's attenuation in an absorbant medium. It is characteristic of the sunscreen chemical and dependent on the wavelength of light, nature of the solvent, concentration and

the temperature. See Shaath (13) for the procedure is used to determine molar absorptivity (ε).

4. *K*-value: The *K*-value is used in the sunscreen industry to rate the effectiveness of the sunscreen chemical. It is the ratio of its maximum absorbance to its concentration in g/L measured in a cell of 1 cm path length.

$$K\text{-value} = \frac{\text{UV absorbance}}{\text{Concentration of sunscreen (g/L)}}$$

   See Shaath (13) for the procedure used to determine *K*-value.

5. *Percentage purity*: Although GC is the best method to determine the purity of a sunscreen chemical, UV spectroscopy could also be used for that purpose provided accurate weighings are performed on an analytical balance and a reference material of known purity is available to calculate molar absorptivity. The UV spectrum of Oxybenzone is shown in Fig. 36.1.

See Shaath (13) for the procedure to calculate the percentage purity.

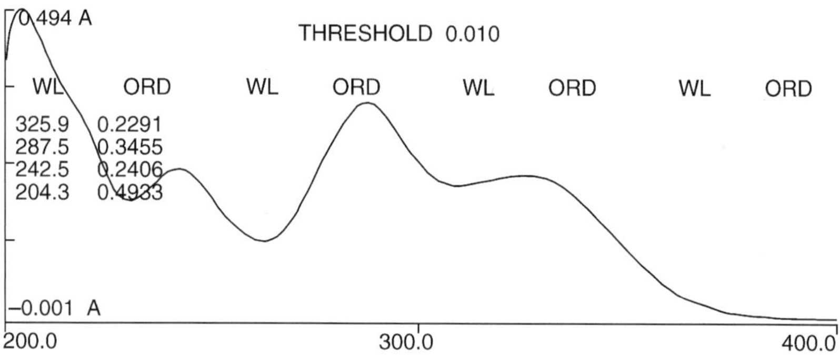

Figure 36.1 Oxybenzone ultraviolet spectrum.

Nuclear Magnetic Resonance Spectroscopy

Nuclear magnetic resonance (NMR) spectroscopy is a powerful technique used to examine the environment of the nuclei of the atoms which make up the sunscreen chemical (14). The nuclear environment depends strongly on the nature of the chemical bonds that hold the atoms together in the molecule and is also dependent on the number of types of other atomic nuclei in the immediate vicinity. Thus, in the NMR experiment the hydrogens (protons) are "seen" and their environment characterized. Figure 36.2 illustrates the NMR spectrum of oxybenzone.

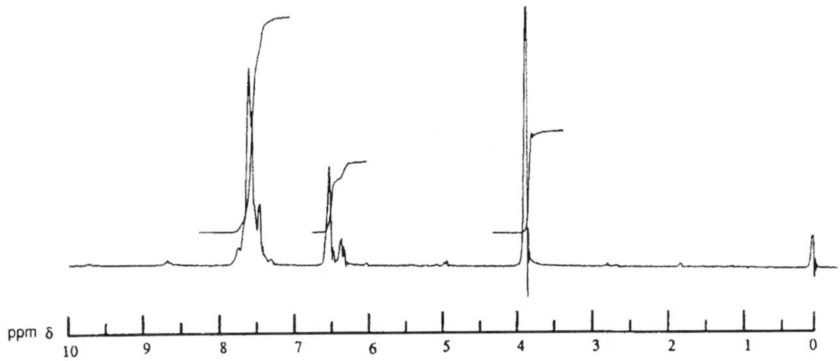

Figure 36.2 Oxybenzone NMR spectrum.

Infrared Spectroscopy

When the sunscreen chemical interacts with infrared (IR) radiation, portions of the incident radiation are absorbed at particular wavelengths. This absorbed energy causes the atoms in the chemical to undergo a series of twisting, bending, rotational, and vibrational motions. These motions, occurring simultaneously, produce a highly complex absorption spectrum that is uniquely characteristic of the functional groups (e.g., carbonyl group, phenolic group) present in the sunscreen molecule and of the overall configuration of the atoms as well. The use of the IR spectrum as a "fingerprint" for the sunscreen chemical provides the analyst with an extremely powerful technique for identification and characterization (15). The IR spectrum of oxybenzone is shown in Fig. 36.3

IR spectroscopy has been used to analyze for the purity of the artificial tanning ingredient, dihydroxy acetone (DHA). The carbonyl group DHA has a peak at 1744 cm^{-1} indicative of the presence of the monomer form of the ingredient. The dimer form has an absorption peak at 1273 cm^{-1} representing the ether bonding. Evaluation of the ratio of the monomer to the dimer will

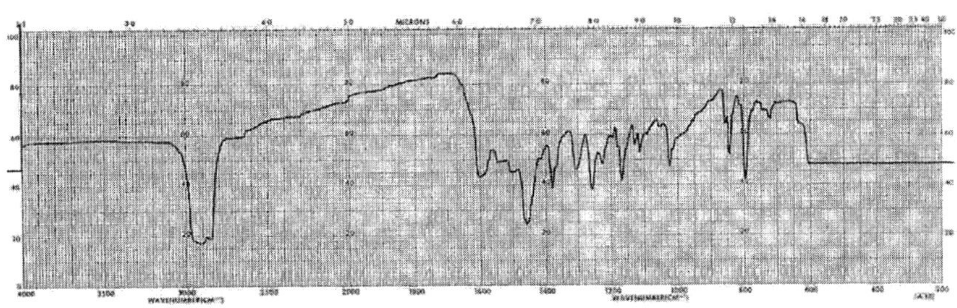

Figure 36.3 Oxybenzone infrared spectrum.

allow the chemist to accurately decipher the exact quality and purity of DHA (16).

Mass Spectrometry

The main advantage of mass spectrometry (MS) is its increased sensitivity over other analytical techniques and its specificity in identifying unknowns and for confirming the presence or absence of suspected compounds (17). The excellent specificity results from characteristic fragmentation patterns, which can give information about molecular weight and molecular structure. The mass spectrum of oxybenzone is shown in Fig. 36.4.

The following table lists typical GC/MS conditions utilizing a quadruple instrument.

GC/MS conditions	Parameter
Sample Size	0.1 μL
Oven temperature	55–250°C
Oven ramp rate	2°C/min
Injection port temperature	250°C
Detector	Total ion chromatogram
Carrier flow	1 mL/min
Split ratio	100 : 1
Peak threshold	30
MS ionization voltage	70 eV
Scan time	108.3 amu/s
Scan start delay	0 s
Start, stop delay	35–400
Electron multiplier voltage	1800 eV

The interfacing of two powerful analytical techniques, namely the separation technique of capillary GC and the identification technique of MS has produced the single most powerful analytical tool to date: the GC/MS. The automation

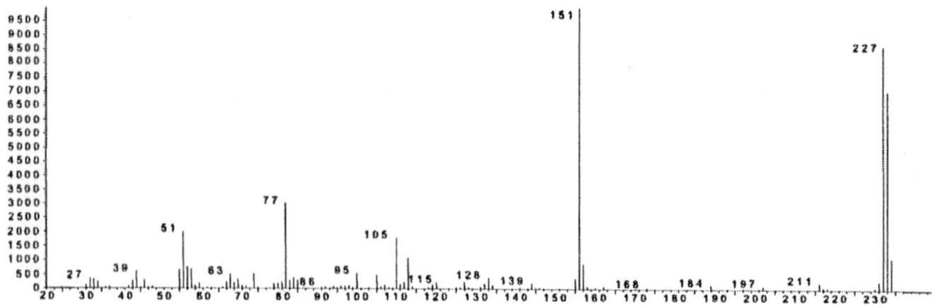

Figure 36.4 Oxybenzone mass spectrum.

and the computerization currently available in the state-of-the-art instrumentation of GC/MS has had a major effect on the flavor and fragrance industry, the food industry, the petroleum industry, the cosmetic and toiletries, sunscreen, and household products industries (18). With the use of a selective ion monitoring (SIM) technique in GC/MS, for example, subparts per million of an impurity can be detected in sunscreen chemicals (19). However, the importance as to the absence or presence of these low-level impurities in the cosmetic and toiletry product is currently considered insignificant and is not measured. Nevertheless, the use of this advanced technique, if available, facilitates the analysis tremendously and decreases the time needed to complete even the most complicated tasks.

For more details see chapter by Shaath and Flores on Modern Analytical Techniques in this book.

Atomic Absorption and Emission Spectroscopy

Atomic absorption (AA) and emission spectroscopy deals with the measurement of the absorption and or emission of electromagnetic radiation by atoms. The wavelength at which electromagnetic radiation is absorbed or emitted is exclusive for a particular element such as titanium or zinc. This amount of light absorbed by a chemical is proportional to the concentration of the mineral element being analyzed as governed by the Beer–Lambert law. This technique is considered to be one of the simplest and best quantitative method for the analysis of metals.

A new addition to the GC's arsenal has been the availability of the atomic emission detector (AED). The strength of the AED lies in the detector's ability to simultaneously determine the atomic emissions of many of the elements in analytes that elute from a GC capillary column.

Inductively Coupled Plasma

Inductively coupled plasma (ICP) is a more advanced technique used to determine the elemental compositions (zinc and titanium) in sunscreens.

An ICP works by injecting a mist from a sample into the center of an argon plasma. The plasma is created from a flow of gas within a high-energy field, which ionizes the gas and causes intense heating. When the mist of the sample enters the plasma field, the intense heat causes the dissociation of most chemical compounds. The energy that the component atoms absorb causes them to undergo excitation and ionization energy transitions which then produce spectral emissions characteristic of the elements being excited. The spectra produced by the plasma is broken down into individual spectral lines by the ICP's spectrometer, and the ICP software translates the spectral lines into concentrations for a specified suite of elements.

For more information on atomic spectroscopy, the reader is urged to read the many references available on this topic (this book, chapter by Shaath and Flores).

CONCLUSIONS

With the rapid growth of the sunscreen industry in both its sales and the number of new product introductions, UV filters are incorporated into a multitude of products used in our daily lives. It has thus become necessary for the quality control chemist to know much more about analytical procedures, the chemical structure of sunscreens and their potential interaction with solvents, impurities, the environment (heat, light, oxygen, or other), and other UV filters. The procedures outlined in this chapter are meant to provide the analyst with the general methods for the analysis of sunscreen chemicals. Sunscreen suppliers should be consulted for the selection of tests appropriate to the ultraviolet filters they offer. The analytical chemist should also research and develop new techniques that can identify impurities, isomers, and other ingredients more accurately.

A new challenge has also been introduced with the incorporation of new forms of zinc oxide and titanium dioxide filters. These ingredients are sold either in their pure form or coated (with silica, dimethicone, aluminum salts, etc.) or are predispersed with a variety of emollients for ease of handling, dispersion, and nonconglomeration of the particles. Thus, the analytical chemist needs to be aware of the properties and impurities of these new forms of inorganic dispersions used in the newer sun care products.

Finally, essential oils, biologically active ingredients, and functional botanical extracts are being incorporated in many new sun and skin care products. This poses a serious challenge to the quality control chemist who has to acquire both the additional skills and techniques as well as the advanced instrumentation to properly analyze the multitude of active and functional ingredients present in the new sun care products.

This increased activity in the sunscreen industry will only increase the burden on the analytical, research, and quality control chemists to meet the new challenges of purity, consistency, accuracy, and, more importantly, claims substantiation.

REFERENCES

1. Federal Register, 27666 (May 21, 1999).
2. Shaath NA. The analysis of sunscreen chemicals. Part 1. Quality control procedures for sunscreen chemicals. Cosmet Toilet 1987; 3:69–81.
3. Association of Official Analytical Chemists. Official Methods of Analysis. Procedure 28.028, 1984.
4. Shriner R, Fuson R, Curtin D, Morrill T. The Systematic Identification of Organic Compounds. New York: John Wiley & Sons, 1980.
5. Willard H, Merrit L, Dean J, Settle F. Instrumental Methods of Analysis. Belmont, CA: Wadsworth Publishing, 1981.
6. Freiser H. Ion Selective Electrodes in Analytical Chemistry. New York: Plenum Press, 1980.
7. http://ral.coafes.umn.edu/icp.htm

8. Poole C, Schuette S. Contemporary Practice of Chromatography. New York: Elsevier, 1984.
9. Jennings W. Gas Chromatography with Glass Capillary Columns. New York: Academic Press, 1980.
10. Snyder L, Krkland J. Introduction to Modern Liquid Chromatography. New York: John Wiley & Sons, 1979.
11. Silverstein R, Bassler GC, Morill T. Spectrometric Identification of Organic Compounds. New York: John Wiley & Sons, 1963.
12. Jaffe H, Orchin M. Theory and Application of Ultraviolet Spectroscopy. New York: John Wiley & Sons, 1972.
13. Shaath NA. Quality control of sunscreens. In: Lowe NJ, Shaath NA, Pathak MA, eds. Sunscreens: Development, Evaluation, and Regulatory Aspects. 2nd ed. New York: Marcel Dekker, 1997:657.
14. Casy AF. PMR Spectroscopy in Medicinal and Biological Chemistry. New York: Academic Press, 1971.
15. Colthup NB, Daly LH, Wilberley SE. Introduction to Infared and Raman Spectroscopy. New York: Academic Press, 1974.
16. Soliance ARD. Dihydroxyacetone Technical File, Soliance Pomacle Fr, 27–42.
17. Jennings W, Shibamoto T. Qualitative Analysis of Flavor and Fragrance Volatiles by Glass Capillary Chromatography. New York: Academic Press, 1980.
18. Chapman J. Computers in Mass Spectrometry. New York: Academic Press, 1978.
19. Agilent 5973N GC/MS System Users Manual 2003.

37

Modern Analytical Techniques in the Sunscreen Industry

Nadim A. Shaath
Alpha Research & Development Ltd., White Plains, New York, USA
Frederick Flores
International Flavors and Fragrances, New York, New York, USA

INTRODUCTION

Excessive exposure to the harmful ultraviolet (UV) rays of the sun leads to premature aging of the skin, photoallergies, and ultimately, malignant melanoma and skin cancer (this volume, chapters by Nelson and Diffey). The increased use of UV filters for protection has become of paramount importance in our daily lives. Scientists have been busy during the last two decades researching novel ingredients and techniques to reduce the spiraling statistics in the proliferation of skin cancer, estimated today to top 1.5 million new cases annually in the USA alone. Primary to this research effort has been the development of new ultraviolet filters. Both organic sunscreens and inorganic sunscreens have been developed and incorporated into a variety of cosmetic formulations containing a plethora of other ingredients to enhance and boost protection.

The sunscreen industry in particular has benefited from the introduction of many new technologically advanced analytical techniques. This chapter will attempt to highlight those developments and also review the classical analytical techniques utilized in the analysis, identification, and quantitation of new and improved ingredients and formulations for the sun care industry (1).

Modern analytical techniques are employed to analyze UV filters and formulations incorporating those sunscreens and a multitude of other cosmetic ingredients. Advanced instrumentation is used for quality control purposes, for research and development purposes and ultimately for regulatory compliance, monitoring, and enforcement. This chapter will first tackle separation techniques followed by identification procedures highlighting both accepted current methodology as well as newer more advanced research techniques.

SEPARATION TECHNIQUES

Cosmetic formulations are by their nature highly sophisticated mixtures of a multitude of ingredients engineered to effectively deliver the UV active components to the skin (this volume, chapter by Klein and Palefski). The UV filters are the ultimate ingredients in a cosmetic preparation that prevent the penetration of the harmful rays of the sun into the skin. Biologically active ingredients have been recently introduced in sun care and skin care formulations to combat other important potential damages of the UV rays (this volume, chapters by Lintner, The Aveda group, Epstein, Chaudhauri and Elmets). These include:

- Moisturizers, humectants, and barrier repair ingredients for dryness, scaling, and chapping.
- Firming, elasticity enhancing, tissue repair, and collagen stimulation ingredients for wrinkles and skin sagging.
- Emollients, anti-inflammatory, and soothing agents for inflammation.
- Radical scavengers, botanicals, and antioxidants for free radical damage and lipoperoxidation.
- Ultimately, DNA and cell repair agents for DNA damage and cell apoptosis.

For the analysis of each of the aforementioned type of ingredients, consult your raw material supplier, specific reference manuals, and Section VII in this book.

Physicochemical Methods

Extractions

The goal of an extraction procedure is to isolate the original ultraviolet filter from the matrix it is incorporated in for analysis and identification (2). This matrix may be hydroalcoholic, oil-based, emulsion, mousse, gel, or shampoo base. The proper selection of solvents is crucial in ensuring the appropriate and complete extraction.

Advanced extraction techniques that have become automated are:

- Sep pack extractions
- Soxhlet extractions
- Supercritical fluid extractions.

For details see section on New Analytical Techniques in this chapter.

Distillations

This is a separation process in which a liquid is converted to vapor, depending on the boiling point of each component (3). The vapor then condenses and each component in the mixture is individually collected. The purpose of distillation is purification, concentration, or separation of the components of a mixture. Procedures are termed either simple or fractional distillations depending upon the presence or absence of a packed column. Other distillation techniques are steam distillation and molecular distillation.

Sublimations

This is the direct passage of the substance from its solid state to its vapor state without passing through the intermediate (liquid) state (4). This method is used in the isolation and purification of select sunscreens in certain emulsions.

Chromatographic Methods

Chromatography may be defined as the science of separation techniques involving a mobile phase passing through a stationary phase. The ability to separate various components of a mixture of organic compounds is based on selective partitioning of these components between the mobile phase and the stationary phase (5).

The sunscreen industry uses all classes of chromatographic procedures, including column chromatography, thin layer chromatography and some techniques described in the following text.

Gas Chromatography

Gas chromatography (GC) is useful for relatively volatile and normally stable organic compounds. This method involves a gaseous mobile phase (helium or nitrogen) and a liquid stationary phase. The sample to be analyzed is injected at a temperature sufficient to vaporize it. The gaseous sample is then partitioned between the stationary liquid phase and the mobile phase causing the separation of the components in the mixture. The separation is a function of both the polarity and volatility of the components of the sample (6).

High-Performance Liquid Chromatography

Liquid chromatography is quite similar to GC, except that the mobile phase is a liquid instead of a gas. Pumps delivering thousands of pounds per square inch push the mobile phase through columns of very fine particles. High-performance liquid chromatography (HPLC) offers advantages of high speed, reusable columns, automatic and continuous solvent addition, reproducible-programmed gradients of solvents, automatic and continuous monitoring of the samples eluted. As the chemicals separate, either a refractive index detector or a UV absorption detector is used for identification. HPLC is primarily used when samples contain components not volatile enough to be detected by GC (7).

Headspace (Purge and Trap)

This method is used when the volatile components to be analyzed are incorporated into a matrix of nonvolatile components. The volatile components are separated from the nonvolatile matrix by purging with helium, collecting this "headspace" fraction of gas on Tenax traps followed by eluting the traps onto the GC for analysis. This method can be employed to separate volatile materials from both liquid and solid matrices, such as purging sunscreens from a plastic packaging matrix (8).

Ion Chromatography

With the advent of the modern ion chromatographs, separations of highly ionic compounds, such as salts, anions, cations, sugars, and phenols, has become routine in instrumentation laboratories. The ion chromatographs use several types of highly sophisticated detectors, such as the suppressed ion conductivity and the pulsed amperometric detectors, which are especially suited for the detection of ionic polar compounds (9).

IDENTIFICATION TECHNIQUES

After a satisfactory separation is achieved, the following identification methods are employed. Most sunscreen chemicals are readily identified by chemical, chromatographic, and spectroscopic techniques that are used in research laboratories.

Chemical Methods

Various chemical tests can be extremely helpful in fully characterizing all the components being investigated. Details of many of the procedures can be found by consulting the many monographs on the subject. The procedures include: alcohol analysis, ester, aldehyde or ketone content, acid value, saponification number, analysis of phenols, derivative formation, and identification (10).

Chromatographic Methods

Gas Chromatography/Retention Time

GC is used as an identification technique. A wealth of information has been accumulated that allows the identification of chemicals by using a relative retention time (RT) library. Information is best when used on the state-of-the-art GC capillary columns (12).

Gas Chromatography/Mass Spectrometry/Data System

The GC interface with the mass spectrometer (MS) data system (DS) is the primary instrument involved in sunscreen identification. A capillary GC column is employed to separate the components of the sample then detected and analyzed by the mass spectrometer. The GC/MS data are automatically stored in the data system computer. After the run is completed, the computer is programmed to search for identifications in the MS library. Libraries are available or can be assembled that contain all available information on sunscreen active chemicals.

High-Performance Liquid Chromatography/Retention Time

HPLC is generally a separation technique, but with an appropriate library it can be an effective identification technique. Initially, a standard is run and the RT is measured. Comparing its chromatogram with that of the standard allows for the identification of the unknown compound.

Headspace/Gas Chromatography/Retention Time

The coupling of two separation techniques, namely, headspace (HS) and GC, permits the analysis of complex matrices from which the volatiles are difficult to extract for direct GC analysis. With the use of a retention index (RT) library of chemicals, identification of sunscreens in normally difficult to analyze products is readily accomplished.

Spectroscopic Methods

Spectroscopy is a branch of analytical chemistry devoted to the identification of elements and the elucidation of atomic and molecular structure. This is accomplished by measurement of the radiant energy absorbed or emitted by a substance in any of the wavelengths of the electromagnetic spectrum in response to excitation by an external energy source (11).

Mass Spectrometry

The mass spectrometer produces charged particles consisting of the parent ion and ionic fragments of the original molecule and sorts these ions according to their mass/charge ratio (10). The mass spectrum is a record of the number of different kinds of ions; the relative numbers of each are characteristic for every compound, including isomers. The main advantages of mass spectrometry as an analytical technique are its increased sensitivity over other analytical procedures and its specificity in identifying unknowns or for confirming the presence of suspected compounds. The excellent specificity results from characteristic fragmentation patterns, which can give information about molecular weight and molecular structure. The tandem technique of MS/MS offers further refinements and improvements in sensitivity and specificity over conventional GC/MS. Also HPLC/MS has increased the sophistication of the separation/identifying technique. Finally, the ratio of the isotopes of carbon, C-12/C-13, can be accurately measured revealing subtle differences as to the biological origin of material.

Infrared Spectroscopy

Infrared (IR) spectroscopy involves the twisting, bending, rotational, and vibrational motions of atoms in a molecule (13). On interaction with IR radiation, portions of the incident radiation are absorbed at particular wavelengths. The multiplicity of vibrations occurring simultaneously produces a highly complex absorption spectrum that is uniquely characteristic of the functional groups that compose the molecule and the overall configuration of the atoms as well. Routinely, chemicals can be separated and collected from cosmetic bases and an IR spectral measurement is performed to assist in the identification of the unknown. With the advent of the more, modern GC/FT-IR (Fourier transform) instruments, separation of a complex mixture followed by rapid infrared analysis can be accomplished in minutes with extremely small (nano- or milligram) samples.

Ultraviolet Spectroscopy

Ultraviolet (UV) spectroscopy involves the absorption behavior of substances and can be either qualitative or quantitative (14). The qualitative application of absorption spectrometry depends on the fact that a given molecular species absorbs light in a specific region of the spectrum indicative of that particular sample. Such a display is called an absorption spectrum of that molecular species, and serves as a fingerprint for identification purposes. The quantitative application is for determining an unknown concentration of a given species. The data derived from a UV spectrum include the λ_{max} (maximum wavelength of absorption), the extinction coefficient (ε), and the K value.

Nuclear Magnetic Resonance Spectroscopy

Nuclear magnetic resonance (NMR) can be used to examine the environment of the nuclei of the atoms that make up a molecule (15). A given nuclear environment depends strongly on the nature of the chemical bonds that hold the atoms together and is also dependent on the number of types of other atomic nuclei in the immediate vicinity. Proton or hydrogen magnetic resonance (PMR), is the most common NMR technique. Other nuclei such as phosphorous and ^{13}C NMR are also utilized. In PMR experiments, the hydrogens in the molecule are "seen" and their environment characterized. A powerful diagnosis of molecular structure can, therefore, be obtained from an NMR experiment. The coupling of this technique with powerful computer manipulations (Fourier transform) permits the analysis of extremely small quantities of chemicals. As the power of the magnets increases, these days exceeding 600 MHz, the H/D ratios can be accurately measured revealing extremely subtle differences as to the biological origin of materials.

The reader is referred to the procedures outlined in an earlier publication for the identification of UV filters in complex cosmetic formulations utilizing an HPLC and GC procedure (1).

IN VITRO SUN PROTECTION FACTOR ANALYZERS

In Vivo sun protection factor (SPF) testing on 20 subjects is a requirement for the FDA's Final Rule (16). UV spectroscopic analyses utilizing dilute solutions in quartz cuvettes of sunscreen formulations suffer from deviations in the Beers–Lambert law (17). They generally provide unreliable data but are currently used to reveal trends for preliminary research purposes. Recently, *In vitro* SPF tests have been developed to provide fast, inexpensive, and reliable data that correlate reasonably well with current *in vivo* techniques on human subjects.

Diffey and Robinson (18) developed, in 1988, a procedure utilizing a surgical tape from 3M Corp., called Transpore tape, as a substrate for *in vitro* SPF measurements. This has now become the basis of a number of commercial instruments, including the Optometrics (19), Lab sphere (20), and the CIBA (this volume, chapter by Herzog) *in vitro* SPF analyzers. A number of improvements have been proposed including the Vitro–skin® by Sottery (21) and the human stratum corneum by Pearse and Edwards (22).

The instruments utilize a continuous UV–Vis source, color compensating filters, diffusion plates, a grating monochromator, and a photomultiplier detector. The quantity of UV-A and UV-B radiation transmitted from a 75-W xenon arc lamp is transmitted through the substrate, with and without sunscreen applied, and the monochromatic protection factor (MPF) is determined automatically by recording photocurrent in 5-nm steps from 290 to 400 nm. Computer calculations are performed to determine the SPF, the UV-A/UV-B ratio as well as the critical wavelength of a cosmetic formulation with ultraviolet filters. Diffey, in 1994, proposed a critical wavelength of 370 nm for all formulations with a significant level of broad-spectrum protection (23).

The *in vitro* SPF analyzers are most capable of analyzing the SPF and critical wavelength as well as the photo stability of an ingredient or a cosmetic formulation (this volume, chapter by Stanfield).

NEW ANALYTICAL TECHNIQUES

There are several specialized techniques that offer the analyst additional insights into any analytical problem on hand. It is beyond the scope of this chapter to describe the details of the procedures beyond the brief description below. The reader, however, should consult the many excellent monographs cited in this chapter.

The specialized chromatographic techniques can be subdivided into three categories:

Use of special detectors in GC (24):
- Thermal conductivity (TC)
- Flame ionization detector (FID)
- Nitrogen phosphorus detector (NPD)
- Mass selective detector (MSD)
- Electron capture detector (ECD)
- Infrared detector (IR)
- Flame photometric detector (FPD)
- Halls detector.

Specialized detectors in HPLC and ion chromatography (25):
- Mass spectrometer detector
- Fluorescence detector
- Coulometric detector
- Suppressed conductivity detector
- Pulse amperometric detector.

Supplementary chromatographic techniques (5):
- Heart cutting
- Trapping
- Headspace—purge and trap
- Split–splitless techniques
- On-column injection
- Dual capillary channels
- New column technology
- Precolumn derivatization
- Postcolumn derivatization.

Recently, new advanced analytical techniques have been commercialized. These include:

1. GC and GC/MS ancillary methods:
   A. Fast GC
   B. Racer GC system
   C. Retention time locking
   D. PTV inlet injection
   E. Simplified 2-D GC
   F. SPME
   G. Gerstel twister and thermodesorption system (TDS)
   H. Mass spectrometer—selective ion monitoring (SIM)
   I. Atomic emission detector (AED)

2. HPLC ancillary methods
   A. Fast HPLC
   B. LC/MS (Electrospray LC)
3. Other methods
   A. Supercritical fluid extractors (SFE)
   B. Inductively coupled plasma (ICP)
   C. X-ray photoelectron spectroscopy (XPS)
   D. X-ray fluorescence spectroscopy (XRF) (Auger)

A brief description of each of these methods follows. The reader is encouraged to seek details of these procedures from equipment suppliers and specialized references.

GC and GC/MS Ancillary Methods

Fast GC

Fast GC is now becoming the norm in the GC field due to the great advantages it offers. Results can be obtained up to 10 times faster than the standard GC without losing the accuracy and consistency compared to a traditional GC run. Savings on operating cost is dramatic. There is less equipment to buy and maintain, therefore maintenance can be done with fewer operators. GC analysts have more time to do interpretation work and quicker results allow them more timely decisions. Other operating cost savings includes the use of less carrier gas, less electricity, and less expensive columns (26).

Fast GC analysis is achieved using small diameter and shorter columns, fast oven temperature ramps, high inlet pressure, and the use of hydrogen as the carrier gas.

GC Racer

GC racer is manufactured and patented by Restek and Zip Scientific (27). It is mainly an auxiliary heating unit controlled by the GC to achieve a rapid oven temperature programming. It offers similar advantages as the fast GC in a less expensive way. With the GC racer unit, it will maintain a temperature program rate of 70°C/min up to 350°C, or a rate of 60°C/min to temperatures as high as 450°C.

Retention Time Locking

Retention time locking (RTL) is a GC software that electronically makes automatic adjustments on the pneumatic pressure controls of the GC, locks a method by making a single injection and enters the retention time locking compound into the software to produce virtually identical chromatograms regardless of the inlet, detector, operator, or location (26). Some of the benefits of RTL are reproducible chromatograms, faster and very accurate identification of compounds once a retention time library is developed, as well as fast and easy comparison of results. It is excellent for routine GC analysis.

Programmable Temperature Vaporizing Inlet

Products such as sunscreen lotions contain minor volatile compounds in this complex matrix. Identification of the volatile compounds generally requires sample preparation and extraction by solvents. Concentration of the extract is often required to detect and quantify the ingredients of importance. A gas chromatograph with programmable temperature vaporizing (PTV) inlet eliminates these time consuming and costly steps. PTV allows you to inject large volume injection of the solvent diluted complex sample to detect analytes at parts per billion or even parts per trillion levels. Other significant advantages of PTV injection over conventional split–splitless or on-column injection are as follows. (a) Avoiding evaporation from the syringe needle, eliminates an important source of discrimination of higher boiling components. (b) Nonvolatiles from the sample injected are retained in the vaporization chamber. This avoids a possible degradation of the column performance due to by-product accumulation (26).

Simplified 2-D GC

This is a GC separation technique which is a simplified Deans switch heart-cutting device for the analysis of complex samples. Peaks of interest from one column are "cut" onto another column having a different stationary phase. As a result, compounds that might co-elute with analytes on the first column are separated from analytes on the second column (26).

Solid Phase Microextraction

Solid phase microextraction (SPME) is an alternative to liquid–liquid extraction or Soxhlet extraction. It has become the technique of choice for separating and concentrating complex matrices in the laboratory. SPME is currently used in a wide variety of applications in the food and flavor, fragrance, environmental, sunscreen, pharmaceutical, and clinical industry.

In SPME a fused silica fibre, coated with a stationary phase is immersed into the sample solution for several minutes. The analytes adsorb onto the stationary phase, which is subsequently pushed into a hot GC injector to rapidly desorb the sample for separation and analysis.

SPME is a sample preparation and introduction method in which analytes partition from the sample into a polymer, coated on a fused silica rod of typically 1 cm length by 100 nm diameter. The fiber is fastened into the end of a fine stainless steel tube contained in a syringe-like device, and protected by an outer stainless steel needle. The device's plunger is depressed to expose the fiber to the sample matrix, retracted at the end of the sampling time, and then depressed again to expose the fiber to a desorption interface for analysis, typically by GC or HPLC (28).

Gerstel Twister and Thermodesorption

The Gerstel twister is a small magnetic stir bar coated with polydimethylsiloxane (PDMS), which is used to analyze organic constituents from aqueous matrices by GC without sample preparation. This technique is also called stir bar sorptive extraction or SBSE. Twister practically came from the SPME technology, therefore it has similar advantages such as total reduction of time, solvents, costly preparation steps, ease of use and lower detection limits. However, it has a sensitivity of up to 1000 times more than SPME (29). The twister is dropped in the aqueous mixture and stirred using a common magnetic stir plate for a short period of time. While stirring, the PDMS coating absorbs the organic constituents. The stir bar can then be soaked in a small amount of extraction solvent such as methylene chloride to extract the analytes or can be directly transferred to a thermodesorption system (TDS).

The TDS is a unit mounted directly to the GC and it is used to trap volatile and semivolatile substances on an adsorbent and for direct thermal extraction of volatile constituents from solids without sample preparation (30).

Mass Spectrometer—Selective Ion Monitoring

A quadruple mass filter can be operated in a scan mode or select ion monitoring (SIM) mode. SIM sets the mass selective detector to repeatedly scan a few selected ions rather than the full range spectrum (scan mode, 40 to 500 amu). This provides the greatest sensitivity and is used for quantitative applications. The analyst has to have a prior knowledge of what ions to expect to use this method. With this procedure, components in the parts per billion concentration range may be detected and quantified.

Atomic Emission Detector

Atomic emission detector (AED) is one of the newest additions to the gas chromatographer's analytical tools. This detector is more expensive than other GC detectors but it is a very powerful alternative.

The AED detects nearly all elements within any volatized compound at very low sensitivities (picogram level). It also has a much wider applicability because it is based on the detection of atomic emissions. The strength of the AED lies in the detector's ability to simultaneously determine the atomic emissions of many of the elements in analytes that elute from a GC capillary column. As the eluants come off the capillary column, they are fed into a microwave powered plasma (or discharge) cavity where the compounds are destroyed and atoms are excited by the energy of the plasma. The light that is emitted by the excited particles is separated into individual lines via a photodiode array detector. The associated computer then sorts out the individual emission lines and can produce chromatograms made up of peaks from eluants that contain only a specific element (31).

HPLC Ancillary Methods

Fast HPLC

Fast HPLC has very similar technical and cost savings advantages as fast GC. It has a setup that typically uses shorter columns with smaller particle size packing and the highest flow rate possible. In addition to length, column inner diameter is the other variable to consider. Optimizing fast separations requires an understanding of the interrelationships of these variables and the compromises involved.

Liquid Chromatography/Mass Spectrometry

An LC/MS is an HPLC system with a mass spectrometer detector. The HPLC separates chemicals by conventional liquid chromatography on a column. Usually the method will be reverse phase chromatography, were the metabolite binds to the column by hydrophobic interactions in the presence of a hydrophilic solvent (e.g., water) and is diluted off by a more hydrophobic solvent (methanol or acetonitrile). As the metabolites appear from the end of the column they enter the mass detector, where the solvent is removed and the metabolites are ionized. The metabolites must be ionized because the detector can only work with ions, not neutral molecules. Ions only fly through very good vacuum, so removal of the solvent is a vital first step. The mass detector then scans the molecules it sees by mass and produces a full high-resolution spectrum, separating all ions that have different masses (32).

Other Methods

Supercritical Fluid Extraction

Supercritical fluid extraction (SFE) is used to extract organics from samples using carbon dioxide (CO_2) as the extracting solvent. It extracts the analytes faster and is more environmentally friendly than typical organic solvents. Another major advantage in using supercritical carbon dioxide fluid extraction is that a small reduction in temperature, or slightly larger reduction in pressure, will result in almost all the solute precipitating out as the supercritical conditions are changed or made subcritical (33). This allows for more efficient separations and extraction of component from complex matrices. Supercritical fluids can produce a product with no solvent residues.

Inductively Coupled Plasma

This is a more advanced technique than atomic absorption spectroscopy and is used to determine the elemental compositions (Zn/Ti) in sunscreen compositions. An inductively coupled plasma (ICP) works by injecting a mist from a liquid into the center of an Argon plasma. A plasma is created from a flow of gas within a high-energy field, which ionizes the gas and causes intense heating. When the mist of the sample enters the plasma, the intense heat causes the dissociation of most chemical compounds, and the energy that the component atoms absorb causes them to undergo excitation and ionization energy transitions. These transitions produce spectral emissions characteristic of the elements being excited. The spectra produced by the plasma is broken down into individual spectral lines by the ICP's spectrometer, and the ICP's computer translates the spectral lines into concentrations for a specified suite of elements (34).

X-Ray Photoelectron Spectroscopy

This is a surface-sensitive chemical analysis technique that provides straightforward data interpretation and chemical bonding information. This can also be used in the elemental analysis (Zn/Ti) of sunscreen formulations (35).

X-Ray Fluorescence Spectroscopy (Auger Electron)

This highly advanced technique is used to measure the elemental composition of sunscreen preparations containing inorganic particulates (Zn/Ti). When a primary X-ray excitation source from an X-ray tube or radioactive source strikes a sample, the X-ray can either be absorbed by the atom or scattered through the material. The process in which an X-ray is absorbed by the atom by transferring all of its energy to an innermost electron is called the "photoelectric effect." During this process, if the primary X-ray had sufficient energy, electrons are ejected from the inner shells, creating vacancies. These vacancies present an unstable condition for the atom. As the atom returns to its stable condition, electrons from the outer shells are transferred to the inner shells and in the process give off a characteristic X-ray whose energy is the difference between the two binding energies of the corresponding shells. Because each element has a unique set of energy levels, each element produces X-rays at a unique set of energies, allowing one to non destructively measure the elemental composition of a sample. The process of emissions of characteristic X-rays is called "X-ray fluorescence," or XRF. Analysis using XRF is called "X-ray fluorescence spectroscopy." In most cases, the innermost K and L shells are involved in XRF detection. A typical X-ray spectrum from an irradiating sample will display multiple peaks of different intensities.

Depending on the application, XRF can be produced by using not only X-rays, but also other primary excitation sources like alpha particles, protons, or high-energy electron beams. Sometimes, as the atom returns to its stable condition, instead of emitting a characteristic X-ray it transfers the excitation energy directly to one of the outer electrons, causing it to be ejected from the atom. The ejected electron is called an "Auger" electron. This process is a competing process to XRF (36).

CONCLUSIONS

The improvements made to the standard chromatographic and spectrophotometric techniques utilized in the sunscreen industry have been outstanding.

Advanced instrumental techniques today have become routine, inexpensive, fast, and reliable. Trace components in the parts per million or even the parts per billion level can now be identified as tell-tale signs of the purity of formulations. Complex mixtures can be isolated more efficiently by SPME and Gerstel twister techniques allowing for a more accurate identification and quantitation of the sunscreen active ingredients.

With the rapid expansion of the new inorganic and organic particulates into the sunscreen formulations of today, more reliable analytical tools need to be investigated and developed. In addition to the standard atomic absorption techniques for the identification of inorganic elements, we have presented a number of novel and advanced methods for the accurate assay of these UV particulates. These methods, which include ICP, XPS, AED, and XRF techniques, will hopefully be developed into fast, reliable, and inexpensive methods for the successful assay of future cosmetic formulations with particulate sunscreen filters.

Modern analytical advanced instrumentation has kept pace with the recent developments and growth of the sun care industry. Their use bodes well for the introduction of more sophisticated and efficient cosmetic formulations that are sorely needed to stem the rise in skin cancer incidence observed today.

REFERENCES

1. Shaath NA, Andemicael G, Griffin P. In: Lowe NJ, Shaath NA, Pathak MA, eds. Sunscreens: Development, Evaluation, and Regulatory Aspects. 2nd ed. New York: Marcel Dekker, 1997:677.
2. Kok M, Young F, Lim G. Rapid extraction method for reproducible of aroma volatiles. J Agric Food Chem 1987; 37:779–781.
3. Maarse H, Belz R. Isolation, Separation and Identification of Volatile Compounds in Aroma Research. Berlin: Akademie-Verlag, 1981.
4. Pavia DL, Lampman GM, Kriz GS, Jr. Introduction to Organic Laboratory Techniques. Philadelphia: W. B. Saunders, 1976.
5. Poole C, Schuette S. Contemporary Practice of Chromatography. New York: Elsevier, 1984.
6. Jennings W, Shibamoto T. Qualitative Analysis of Flavors & Fragrance Volatiles by Capillary Gas Chromatography. New York: Academic Press, 1980.
7. Runner PJ. Maintaining and Troubleshooting HPLC Systems. New York: Wiley, 1981.
8. Kolb B. Applied Headspace Gas Chromatography. London: Heyden, 1980.
9. Weiss J. Handbook of Ion Chromatography. Sunnyvale, CA: Dionex Corporation, 1986.
10. Shriner R, Fuson R, Curtin D, Morrill T. The Systematic Identification of Organic Compounds. 6th ed. New York: John Wiley & Sons, 1980.
11. Silverstein R, Bassler G, Morill T. Spectrometric Identification of Organic Compounds. 3rd ed. New York: John Wiley & Sons, 1963.
12. Smith SL. In: Sandra P, Bicchi C, eds. Capillary Gas Chromatography in Essential Oil Analysis. Heidelberg: Springer-Verlag, 1987:367–384.

13. Startin JR. In: Gilbert J, eds. Applications of Mass Spectrometry in Food Science. New York: Elsevier Applied Science, 1987:289–339.
14. Rao C. Ultraviolet and Visible Spectroscopy. 3rd ed. London: Butterworths, 1975.
15. Casy AF. NMR Spectroscopy in Medicinal & Biological Chemistry. New York: Academic Press, 1971.
16. Federal Register, 27666 (May 21, 1999).
17. Jaffe H, Orchin M. Theory and Application of Ultraviolet Spectroscopy. New York: John Wiley & Sons, 1972.
18. Diffey B, Robson S. J Soc Cosmet Chem 1989; 40:127–133
19. http://www.optometrics.com
20. http://www.labsphere.com
21. Diffey BL. Ultraviolet radiation dosimetry with polysulphone film. In: Diffey BL, ed. Radiation Measurement in Photobiology. London: Academic Press, 1989:135–139.
22. Rontó G, Gáspár S, Gróf P, Bérces A, Gugolya Z. Ultraviolet dosimetry in outdoor measurements based on bacteriophage T7 as a biosensor. Photochem Photobiol 1994; 59:209–214
23. Wilkinson F. Solar simulators for sunscreen testing. In: Matthes R, Sliney D, eds. Measurements of Optical Radiation Hazards. Vienna: International Commission on Non-Ionizing Radiation Protection, 1998:653–684.
24. David DJ. Gas Chromatographic Detector. New York: John Wiley and Sons, 1974.
25. Vickrey M. Liquid Chromatography Detectors. New York: Marcel Dekker, 1983.
26. www.chem.agilent.com
27. www.restek.com
28. Supelco Bulletin 923. Solid phase microextraction: theory and optimization of conditions.
29. Gerstel Publication an-2000–01. A novel extraction technique for aqueous samples: stir bar sorptive extraction
30. www.gerstelus.com/en/667.html
31. www.shsu.edu/~chemistry/AED/AED.html
32. http://www.jic.bbsrc.ac.uk/SERVICES/metabolomics/lcms/why.htm
33. http://www.faqs.org/faqs/sci/chem-faq/part5/section-5.html
34. http://ral.coafes.umn.edu/icp.htm
35. http://www.analytical.org/xps2.html
36. http://www.amptek.com/xrf.html

Analytical Testing Procedures

38

US FDA Protocol for Determining Sun Protection Factor

Toni F. Miller

Essex Testing Clinic, Verona, New Jersey, USA

BACKGROUND OF FDA SUNSCREEN GUIDELINES

The US Food and Drug Administration (FDA) published the "Final" Monograph (1) for sunscreen drug products for over-the-counter human use on May 21, 1999 (64 FR 27666). This Monograph outlined the testing requirements for determining a sun protection factor (SPF) for product labeling. On December 31, 2001 (66 FR 67485) (2) FDA issued a partial stay to 21 CFR Part 352, including Subpart D—Testing Procedures, the part of the Monograph that outlines the testing requirements for establishment of an SPF value.

The anticipated new effective date for FDA's issuance of the SPF testing methodology is 2005 or later. The FDA has proposed that the amended Part 352 will address formulation, labeling, and testing requirements for both ultraviolet-A (UV-A) and ultraviolet-B (UV-B) radiation protection.

Given this regulatory situation, the most recently proposed testing protocols for SPF determination (64 FD 27666) will be addressed, with the knowledge, that these may change when the final monograph is indeed issued.

SUN PROTECTION FACTOR DETERMINATION (64 FR 27666)

The sun protection factor is defined as:

$$\text{SPF value} = \frac{\text{Minimal erythema dose on protected skin}}{\text{Minimal erythema dose on unprotected skin}}$$

The minimal erythema dose (MED) is defined as the quantity of erythema-effective energy (expressed as joules per square meter) required to produce the first perceptible, redness reaction with clearly defined borders.

Light Source: Solar Simulators

The solar simulator used for SPF determination must provide:

- Continuous emission spectrum from 290 to 400 nm similar to sunlight at sea level with the sun at a zenith angle of 10°.
- Less than 1% total energy output from wavelengths shorter than 290 nm.
- Not more than 5% of total energy output from wavelengths longer than 400 nm.
- No significant time-related fluctuations in output after an appropriate warmup time.
- Beam uniformity within 10%.
- Output measured periodically with a calibrated spectroradiometer or equivalent instrument.

Standard Sunscreen

The standard sunscreen will be an 8% homosalate preparation with a mean SPF value of 4.47 (S.D. ± 1.279). The 95% confidence interval for the mean SPF must contain the value 4. Directions for the preparation of the standard appear in the Final Rule (1) and in Steinberg's chapter.

Testing Procedure

Selection of Panel Subjects

Not more than 25 subjects will be chosen to participate on a panel. The number of subjects will be fixed in advance by the study investigator. From this panel, at least 20 subjects must produce valid data for analysis.

Only fair-skin male and female subjects with skin types I, II, and III may be used. Skin type is defined by the response of an individual to the first 30–45 min of sun exposure after a winter season of no sun exposure:

Type I	Always burns easily; never tans (sensitive)
Type II	Always burns easily; tans mimimally (sensitive)
Type III	Burns moderately; tans gradually (light brown) (normal)
Type IV	Burns minimally; always tans well (moderate brown) (normal)
Type V	Never burns; deeply pigmented (insensitive).

The subjects should be in general good health, especially for any skin conditions; should not be taking any medications (topical or systemic) that are known to produce abnormal sunlight response; and should not have any history or known abnormal sunlight responses such as phototoxic or photoallergic reactions.

Subjects should be examined for physical indications of the presence of sunburn, suntan, scars, active dermal lesions, and uneven skin tones on the areas of the back proposed for test sites. The presence of nevi, blemishes, or moles may be acceptable if in the physician's judgment they will not interfere with the study results. If an individual has excess hair, clipping or shaving may have to be undertaken to provide for an acceptable test site.

Informed Consent

Legally effective written informed consent is required for all test subjects.

Skin Test Sites

The skin test site area used for MED determination shall be:

- Located on the back between the beltline and the shoulder blade and lateral to the midline.
- A minimum of 50 cm^2 in area (e.g., 5 cm $\times$ 10 cm), outlined with ink, drawn with the subject in the test position, for example, upright or supine.

Each skin site area shall be:

- Divided into at least three test subsite areas that are at least 1 cm^2.

Usually four or five subsites are used for each test.

Application of Test Materials

Both the test sunscreen product(s) and the standard suncreen shall be applied as:

- Two milligrams per square centimeter
- Spread using a finger cot
- Applied in a blinded, randomized manner
- A period of at least 15 min is required after application and before UV exposure
- If only one sunscreen drug product is being tested, UV radiation doses will be applied in a randomized manner.

Evaluation of Response

The evaluator must be a different person than the person who applied the test products or administered the UV radiation.

The following evaluations must be recorded:

- All immediate responses (e.g., an immediate darkening or tanning; immediate reddening; immediate heat response such as a heat rash).
- The smallest dose that produces erythema reaching the borders of the exposure site at 22–24 h after UV exposure.

Erythema response should be evaluated with:

- Either a tungsten light bulb or a warm white fluorescent light bulb that provides a level of illumination at the test site within the range of 450–550 lux.
- Subjects positioned similarly to when the test site was irradiated.

The goal of the exposure evaluation is to observe some exposures that produce absolutely no effect, and some exposures that produce an effect, with the maximal exposure being no more than twice the total energy of the minimal exposure.

Determination of the MED for Unprotected Skin

- The MED for unprotected skin is determined by administering a geometric series of five exposures represented by $(1.25)^n$ for example, 6, 8, 10, 13, and 16 s.
- Usually a preliminary MED series is administered on the day before the SPF test and the result determines the doses administered to unprotected and sunscreen-protected skin which are used to calculate the SPF.

Rejection of Test Data

The following reasons warrant rejection of the test data:

- An MED response is not elicited on either the treated or unprotected treated skin sites.

- The responses on the treated test sites are randomly absent (indicating that the test substance was not spread evenly).
- The subject(s) were noncompliant (e.g., the subject withdrew from the test due to illness or work conflicts, or the subject did not shield the exposed testing sites from further UV radiation until the MED was read).

Determination of the SPF Value

The erythema action spectrum used to calculate the erythema effective exposure of a solar simulator are:

$$V_i(\lambda) = 1.0\,(250 < \lambda < 298\,\text{nm})$$
$$V_i(\lambda) = 1.0^{0.094(298-\lambda)}(298 < \lambda < 328\,\text{nm})$$
$$V_i(\lambda) = 1.0^{0.015(139-\lambda)}(328 < \lambda < 400\,\text{nm}).$$

Determination of Individual Subject SPF Values

- A series of seven doses is administered to the sunscreen-protected sites. Doses will be determined by the preliminary MED and the expected SPF of the product.
- For products with an expected SPF <8, the exposures will be the preliminary MED of unprotected skin times: $0.64X$, $0.80X$, $0.90X$, $1.00X$, $1.10X$, $1.25X$, and $1.56X$, where X equals the expected SPF of the test product.
- For products with an expected SPF between 8 and 15, the exposures will be the MED of unprotected skin times: $0.69X$, $0.83X$, $0.91X$, $1.00X$, $1.09X$, $1.20X$, and $1.44X$, where X equals the expected SPF of the test product.
- For products with an expected SPF >15, the exposures will be the MED of unprotected skin times: $0.76X$, $0.87X$, $0.93X$, $1.00X$, $1.07X$, $1.15X$, and $1.32X$, where X equals the expected SPF.
- The SPF value of the test sunscreen is then calculated as the ratio of the MED of sunscreen-protected skin to the MED of unprotected skin.

Determination of the Test Product's SPF Value and Product Category Designation

- Use SPF values from at least 20 test subjects.
- Compute the SPF value for each subject.
- Compute the mean SPF value, x, and the standard deviation, s.
- Find the upper 5% point from the t distribution table with $n-1$ degrees of freedom (this is "t").
- Compute $A = ts/\sqrt{n}$

- The label SPF equals the largest whole number less than $(x - A)$. (Typically, a product with a mean SPF of 15 would be labeled 13, by this approach).
- Determine the Product Category designation according to the following chart:

Mean SPF value	Label SPF value	Product category designation
$X < (2 + A)$	<2	Not a sunscreen
$(2 + A) < X < (12 + A)$	2–11	Minimal
$(12 + A) < X < (30 + A)$	12–30	Moderate
$X > (30 + A)$	30(plus/+)	High

Determination of a Water Resistant or Very Water Resistant Product

The general testing procedure used for SPF testing is used except modified in the following way:

- An indoor pool, whirlpool, or jacuzzi maintained at 23–32°C is used during the testing procedure. The pool and air temperature and the relative humidity are recorded.

For a water-resistant claim, the label SPF shall be the label SPF value determined after 40 min of water immersion according to the following procedure:

- Apply the sunscreen test product (followed by the waiting period indicated on the product labeling).
- Subjects maintain a moderate activity in the water for 20 min.
- Subjects maintain a 20-min rest period (without towel drying the test sites).
- Subjects maintain moderate activity in the water for 20 min.
- Air dry test sites without toweling.
- Conduct solar simulator exposure to test site areas.

For a very water resistant claim, the label SPF shall be the label SPF value determined after 80 min of water immersion according to the following procedure:

- Apply the sunscreen test product (followed by the waiting period indicated on the product labeling).
- Subjects maintain a moderate activity in the water for 20 min.
- Allow a 20-min rest period (without towel drying the test sites).
- Subjects maintain moderate activity in the water for 20 min.
- Allow a 20-min rest period (without towel drying the test sites).
- Subjects maintain a moderate activity in the water for 20 min.
- Allow a 20-min rest period (without towel drying the test sites).
- Subjects maintain a moderate activity in the water for 20 min.

- Air dry test sites without toweling.
- Conduct solar simulator exposure to test site areas.

Test Modifications

The US FDA allows alternative testing methods (including automated or *in vitro* procedures) if a formulation or mode of administration of certain products requires testing methodology modification. Any proposed modification or alternative procedure must be submitted to the US FDA as a petition that contains data supporting the modification or data demonstrating that the alternative procedure provides results of equivalent accuracy.

US vs. THE INTERNATIONAL SPF TESTING METHOD

Several countries have SPF determination methods that vary from the USA. An effort to "harmonize" several of these methods was undertaken by The European Cosmetic Toiletry and Perfumery Association, the Cosmetic Toiletry & Fragrance Association of South Africa, and the Japan Cosmetic Industry Association (3). This International testing guideline was issued in 2003. It should be noted that the JCIA has a revised SPF Test Method for SPF determination of products with expected SPFs >30 that is not discussed here. A comparison of the major parameters of the US and International SPF testing methodologies is presented.

	Parameter	US (21 CFR Part 352) (1999)	International Sun Protection Factor (SPF) Test Method (2003)
1.	Selection of test subjects	Medical history of general good health without any abnormal responses to sunlight. Test site free of any interfering skin conditions.	Recommended interview by health professional; no sun exposure for at least 4 weeks prior to testing
2.	Exclusion criteria	–	Recommended interview by health professional; no sun exposure for at least 4 weeks prior to testing
3.	Skin phototypes	I, II, III	I, II, III
4.	Test area	Back between scapulae and lateral to midline	Back (between scapulae line and waist)
5.	Age limitation	–	No children
6.	Frequency interval between tests	–	Not less than 2 months between tests and the site is clear

	Parameter	US (21 CFR Part 352) (1999)	International Sun Protection Factor (SPF) Test Method (2003)
7.	Number of test subjects	Not more than 25 subjects with the number fixed in advance (at least 20 subjects must produce valid data)	10–20 subjects (10 subjects sufficient if 95% CI of the mean is within ±17% of the mean; if not, subjects are increased until met; if not met after 20 of 25, test is rejected)
8.	Reference standard	8% HMS (An SPF 15 control formulation has been proposed and may be adopted in the next monograph publication)	Low SPF standard High SPF standard (if high SPF standard is used, no need to include low SPF standard)
9.	Acceptance limits for standard	SPF value of 4.47 ± 1.279 and the 95% CI must contain 4	2 > SPF > 20 Choose P1 DIN low or HS (SPF = 4) or P2 (SPF = 12) or P3 (SPF = 15) If SPF >30 use P3 (SPF = 15)
10.	Quantity applied	2 mg/cm^2	2 mg/cm^2 ± 2.5% (balance sensitivity at least 0.0001 g)
11.	Mode of delivery	Volumetrically	Syringe/pipette or other quantified means with spreading time of 20–50 s.
12.	Test site (subsite)	At least 1 cm^2	0.5 cm^2
13.	Drying time after application	At least 15 min before exposure	15–30 min
14.	Solar simulator	Specific type not specified	Xenon arc simulator
15.	Solar simulator monitoring	Periodically with a calibrated spectroradiometer or equivalent instrument	Once a year and when physical component is changed; Before each UV site exposure, UV shall be checked with a radiometer.
16.	UV quality	Continuous emission spectrum from 290 to 400 nm similar to	<290 must not exceed 0.1% 290–310 = 49–65% 290–320 = 85–90%

	Parameter	US (21 CFR Part 352) (1999)	International Sun Protection Factor (SPF) Test Method (2003)
		sunlight at sea level with the sun at a zenith angle of 10° <1% total energy output <290 nm. <5% total energy output >400 nm. No significant time-related fluctuations in output after an appropriate warm-up time. Beam uniformity ±10%.	290–330 = 91.5–95.5% 290–340 = 94–97% 290–350 = 95.5–98.5% 290–400 = 100% and total UVA II (320–340) must equal or exceed 20% of total UV (290–400 nm) and UVA I (340–400 nm) must equal or exceed 60%of the total UV
17.	Number of exposure sites	5 for Control; 7 for Test Product	5
18.	Progression of doses	SPF < 8 = MED *x* 0.64*X*, 0.80*X*, 0.90*X*, 1.00*X*, 1.10*X*, 1.25*X*, 1.56*X* SPF = 8–15 = MED *x* 0.69*X*, 0.83*X*, 0.91*X*, 1.00*X*, 1.09*X*, 1.2*X*, 1.44*X* SPF > 15 = MED *x* 0.76*X*, 0.87*X*, 0.93*X*, 1.00*X*, 1.07*X*, 1.15*X*, 1.32*X*	1.12 or 1.25 (1.12 if expected SPF is >25)
19.	Exposure site size	At least 50 cm^2	Minimum 30 cm^2 to maximum 60 cm^2
20.	Skin response	First perceptible unambiguous redness reaction with clearly defined borders	Minimum erythema with defined borders
21.	Observation time post exposure	Immediate and 22–24 h after exposure	16–24 h after exposure
22.	MED determination	Blind	Blind; simultaneous MEDu and MEDp
23.	Individual test response	See Section B.10	95% CI with ≤17% of mean SPF or SEM ≤ 7.5%($n = 10$)
24.	SPF definition for labeling purposes	See Section B.11	Arithmetical mean *x* of SPFi; lower integral number

	Parameter	US (21 CFR Part 352) (1999)	International Sun Protection Factor (SPF) Test Method (2003)
25.	Rejection Criteria	No erythemal response on all subsites Erythemal response absent within an exposure series Subject noncompliant	No erythemal response on all subsites Erythemal response absent within an exposure series All subsites show an erythemal response (If data on five subjects rejected, test is rejected)

REFERENCES

1. Sunscreen drug products for over-the-counter human use. Final Monograph. Fed Reg 1999; 64:27666.
2. Sunscreen drug products for over-the-counter human use. Final Monograph Partial Stay Final Rule. Fed Reg 2001; 66:67485.
3. International Sun Protection Factor (SPF) Test Method. Cosmetic, Toiletry & Fragrance Association of South Africa, The European Cosmetic Toiletry and Perfumery Association (Colipa), and Japan Cosmetic Industry Association. February 2003.

39

SPF Testing in Europe

The International SPF Test Method

Mike Brown
The Boots Company plc, Nottingham, UK

INTRODUCTION

Sun products have been a way of life for many years with some leading brands dating back as far as the 1940s, 1930s, or even the 1920s. However, products from this era provided somewhat limited sunburn protection and were rarely labeled with any reliable measure of their protective efficacy.

The first attempts to realistically describe the protective performance of a sunscreen were made by Ellinger in 1934 (1). Ellinger described an ultraviolet-protective quotient system, which decreased in value as protection increased. However, the system was not particularly attractive as a marketing tool for suncare products since lower performing products achieved higher quotient values. Ellinger's "inverted" quotient was not revised until 1956 when Rudolf Schulze described a method for determining the level of protection provided by a sun product (2). The "Schulze" method, as it became known, described a sunscreen's protection level simply by using the reciprocal of Ellinger's quotient.

The Schulze method was the test method of choice for many European products for several years, but it was not until 1974 that the term "sun protection factor" (SPF) was first introduced by Greiter (3) to describe the outcome of this testing. What is more, it was not until 1977–1978 that a SPF number first appeared on a bottle of a European brand (Piz Buin) of suncare products. Greiter's new SPF rating was simply an alternative application of the method of Schulze but it has since become both widely used and universally recognised as the measure of a sunscreen product's ability to prevent sunburn.

The universal adoption of Greiter's SPF measure was quickly followed by a plethora of attempts to standardise the test procedure. The resulting glut of test methods lead to the situation where SPF numbers in some countries were often significantly different from SPF numbers in other countries, despite the fact that the SPF test was theoretically the same worldwide. Table 39.1 shows a chronological history of worldwide SPF test methodologies and their subsequent revisions which evolved between the 1970s and the present day.

Many European countries initially conducted SPF testing according to the Deutsches Institut für Normung (DIN) method first published in 1985 (4). This method differed in many significant ways from the established test method described in the US FDA's proposed sunscreen monograph, previously published in 1978 (5). A major difference between the two methods was the amount of test product applied to the skin. The DIN method specified an application rate of 1.5 mg/cm^2 whilst the FDA method required application at 2.0 mg/cm^2. This fundamental procedural difference inevitably gave rise to large differences in the measured SPF. In addition to this, the two methods used quite different sources of artificial sunlight (solar simulator), which again had a significant impact on the SPF measured and consequently the SPF labeled.

Because of the incompatibility between the German (DIN) SPF method and that of the US FDA, many Europeans "defected" to the FDA SPF test method, whilst others continued to follow the DIN method. This created an untenable situation in Europe and so the European Trade Association for the Cosmetics and Toiletries Industry (COLIPA) decided to develop a common SPF guideline for all European Union countries. The resulting 1994 COLIPA SPF test method (6)

Table 39.1 A Chronological History of Major Worldwide Methodologies for Sun Protection Factor (SPF) Testing

Year	Issuing authority	Territory
1978	Food and Drug Administration (FDA)	USA
1983	Standards Association of Australia (SAA)	Australia
1985	Deutsches Institut für Normung (DIN)	Germany
1986	Standards Association of Australia (SAA) (revised)	Australia
1991	Commission Internationale De L'Eclairage (CIE)	International
1992	Japanese Cosmetic Industry Association (JCIA)	Japan
1992	South African Bureau of Standards (SABS)	South Africa
1993	Food and Drug Administration (FDA) (revised)	USA
1993	Standards Association of Australia (SAA) (revised)	Australia
1994	The European Cosmetic and Toiletries Trade Association (COLIPA)	Europe
1996	Deutsches Institut für Normung (DIN) (revised)	Germany
1997	Standards Australia/Standards New Zealand (AS/NZS) (revised)	Australia and New Zealand
1998	Korean Pharmaceutical Affairs Committee	Korea
1998	Standards Australia/Standards New Zealand (AS/NZS) (revised)	Australia and New Zealand
1999	Ő Norm	Austria
1999	Japanese Cosmetic Industry Association (JCIA) (revised)	Japan
1999	Food and Drug Administration (FDA) (revised)	USA
2002	South African Bureau of Standards (SABS) (revised)	South Africa
2003	COLIPA/JCIA/SABS—International Method	South Africa, Japan, and Europe

introduced many revisions to the procedures in common use in Europe in order to "move closer" to the newly revised sunscreen tentative final monograph published by the FDA in 1993 (7). The method also proposed a number of advancements and improvements in the test procedure, which were to become standard practice throughout Europe for nearly a decade.

However, even after careful design, the 1994 COLIPA SPF test method still differed sufficiently from other national SPF test methods (specifically the 1993 US FDA tentative final monograph and the various revisions to the Standards Australia/Standards New Zealand SPF Test Method). Consequently, European SPF numbers were still not completely comparable with SPF numbers in other major international markets.

The first steps to address this international incompatibility have now been taken. The European SPF Test Method (1994 COLIPA method) has been completely revised and harmonized with the Japanese Cosmetic Industry Association

(JCIA) SPF Method (8) and the South African Bureau of Standards (SABS) SPF Method (9). The result is a new and improved international SPF test method, which is considerably more compatible with both the final (1999) FDA Sunscreen Monograph (10) and the most recent Standards Australia/Standards New Zealand (AS/NZS) SPF Test Method (11).

THE INTERNATIONAL SPF TEST METHOD

The International SPF Test Method is now the method of choice throughout Europe. In the UK in particular, there is a growing expectation amongst law enforcement authorities that sunscreen products should be labeled according to the "European" method. One of the main objectives of the new method was to help facilitate an eventual complete harmonization with other national SPF methods and so it was designed to be as similar as possible to the US FDA sunscreen monograph. As a consequence, it should now be possible to conduct a single SPF test that would satisfy not only local requirements for SPF testing (e.g. FDA monograph requirements in the USA) but also the requirements of Europe, Japan, and South Africa as laid out in The International SPF Test Method.

The International SPF Test Method has all the main elements of other SPF test methods throughout the world. The procedure requires that the skin of a number of human volunteers be exposed to increasing doses of sunlight simulated ultraviolet radiation, sufficient to elicit minimal erythemal (redness) responses when observed between 16 and 24 h after exposure. For each individual volunteer, a SPF is determined as the ratio of the dose of sunlight simulated ultraviolet (UV) radiation required to produce the first (minimal) erythemal reaction in skin protected by sunscreen product, to the dose of sunlight simulated UV radiation required to produce the first (minimal) erythemal reaction in unprotected skin. The test product's SPF is then simply the mean of all individual SPFs measured. The general outline of the test is as follows:

The SPF test begins with the selection of a panel of suitable human volunteers previously screened against medical, photobiological, and physical exclusion criteria. Investigative work by the European, Japanese, and South African cosmetic and toiletries industry associations (COLIPA, JCIA, and CTFA-SA) suggested that different SPF numbers might be measured on the skin of volunteers with different levels of underlying pigmentation. Fitzpatrick has previously described six generic "skin types" based on natural genotypic pigmentation levels (12). The higher the level of natural skin pigmentation, the more likely this is to interfere with the SPF test. Consequently volunteer selection is restricted to pale skin types (Fitzpatrick types I–III).

A minimum of ten and up to a maximum of 20 volunteers of skin types I–III must complete the study with valid data. The proportions of skin types I, II, and III should reflect a "normal" population to avoid any possible bias toward higher SPF which is thought may occur with lower skin types. Each volunteer is then subjected to the same procedure.

UV light from an artificial source of sunlight simulated ultraviolet radiation is directed onto a number of unprotected 1 cm square sites on the volunteer's back. Both the quality and the intensity of the source of UV light are critical to the accurate measurement of SPF and so these are strictly defined in the International SPF Test Method. Each individual 1 cm square receives an incrementally larger dose of UV light than the previous square, such that a progression of increasing UV exposures is achieved. The intensity of the UV source is usually some 20–50 times the intensity of natural sunlight ultraviolet light, so exposure times are typically within the range of 20 s to 3 min depending on choice of light source. Since UV-induced erythema is a dose-dependent response (13) and not flux dependent (within certain practical limits) the exact UV intensity of the light source is not normally critical, however a close match to "natural" sunlight spectrum is crucial. The starting dose for the series of irradiation exposures is defined by the volunteer's "Fitzpatrick" skin type, their previous exposure history or colorimetric measurement of their resting level of pigmentation.

Sixteen to twenty-four hours after exposure to the incremental doses of simulated sunlight, each of the irradiated sites is visually assessed in order to determine the exposure dose (joules/m^2) that initiated the first perceptible, unambiguous erythema with defined borders appearing over most of the field of exposure. This dose, known as the minimum erythemal dose (MED) acts as reference for the individual's sensitivity to UV light (in unprotected skin). It will be unique for that individual and a function of their skin type and genotype.

Having determined the MED for unprotected skin (MED_u), sun product is applied at the precise application rate of 2.0 mg/cm^2 to an adjacent area of the same volunteer's back. Product application is a major potential source of variability in SPF measurement and so many parameters in the product application procedure are very precisely defined and controlled in the International SPF Test Method.

After application, the product is left to dry for a minimum of 15 min and a maximum of 30 min. Once the product has dried, UV light from the solar simulator is again directed onto a series of at least five 1 cm^2 areas of product-protected skin. As with the unprotected exposures, an incremental progression in UV dose is delivered so that a second series of UV exposure doses is achieved. However, these doses will be considerably greater than those delivered to unprotected skin since the skin should now be protected from burning by the applied sunscreen product. The exact doses delivered are dependent on the previously measured MED_u and the expected SPF of the test product. For example, an SPF10 product should protect the skin 10-fold from UV-induced erythema and so the middle dose in the protected skin incremental exposure series is typically 10 times the unprotected MED.

Sixteen to twenty-four hours after irradiation of the product-protected skin, each exposure site is visually assessed for erythemal response in the same manner as the unprotected MED. The dose of UV light, which initiated the first perceptible unambiguous erythema with defined borders appearing over most of the field of UV exposure, is the MED for product-protected skin (MED_p).

The sun protection factor for each individual volunteer (SPF_i) is then calculated as the ratio:

$$SPF_i = \frac{\text{MED on product protected skin}}{\text{MED on unprotected skin}} = \frac{MED_p}{MED_u}$$

When sufficient volunteers have completed the study with valid SPF_i data, the final SPF for the product is calculated as the arithmetic mean of all valid individual SPF_i values, that is

$$\text{Mean SPF} = \frac{\sum_1^n SPF_i}{n}$$

where SPF_i denotes the individual SPF and n is the total number of individuals with valid data.

The exact number of individual volunteers tested is defined by statistical criteria which address data variability and confidence, but will be between 10 and 25 subjects with between 10 and 20 yielding valid data.

The basic procedure for SPF testing as described above is fundamentally very simple. However, there can be several possible sources of variation at each step in the procedure which when compounded, may lead to significant error in determining a realistic or "correct" SPF number. With any SPF test method, it tends to be the detail which is included in an attempt to control these possible sources of error, that ironically gives rise to the differences between methods.

In Europe, the SPF test method of choice is the International SPF Test Method, a single method shared by industry throughout Europe, Japan, and South Africa. This method is considerably more aligned with other existing national SPF test methods than was the COLIPA (1994) SPF Test Method, but it also retains the strengths of the historical methods of Europe, Japan, and South Africa. However, the International SPF Test Method is not simply a regurgitation of the US FDA final sunscreen monograph, nor is it just a "revamp" of the old COLIPA method. Instead, it addresses what were considered to be the major potential sources of experimental variation in the SPF procedure. The main areas of possible variation identified and addressed were; the definition of the UV-light source, volunteer selection, product application procedure, use of appropriate standard SPF products, UV exposure procedure, MED definition and determination and finally, SPF calculation and statistical acceptance/exclusion criteria.

The UV Light Source

The UV light source, or solar simulator, used to measure a sun product's SPF is critical to the whole test procedure. This arises from the fact that different wavelengths of sunlight have different capacities for inducing erythema in human skin. Consequently, solar simulators that emit different spectra or distributions of

UV wavelengths will have different potentials for causing erythema. This effect is exaggerated when we introduce the filtering effect of a sunscreen product. When the output spectrum of a solar simulator matches the absorption spectrum of the sunscreen, then the sunscreen will be very good at "blocking" the UV light from the solar simulator and it will deliver a high SPF. However, if the solar simulator output spectrum is not aligned to the absorbance spectrum of the sunscreen, then the sunscreen will be less effective and will not be able to block that portion of UV light which falls outside its absorbance range. This will result in a much lower SPF for the same product. This effect is illustrated in Fig. 39.1. The solid curve represents the protection profile of a sunscreen product with its peak UV absorption at approximately 305 nm, typical of a UV-B sunscreen. The dotted curve shows the output spectrum of the UV-B-rich solar simulator by wavelength, expressed in terms of its ability to cause erythema in human skin. This solar simulator produces a peak burning potential at approximately 305 nm, which is matched to the peak of the protection spectrum for the sunscreen. Consequently, the sunscreen will be very effective at reducing the peak burning wavelengths of the solar simulator and the product will measure as having a high SPF.

When we consider the case of the UV-B-depleted solar simulator (hatched curve), we see that it delivers its peak burning effect at a wavelength of approximately 315 nm. Whilst this is only a 10 nm shift, it can be seen that the

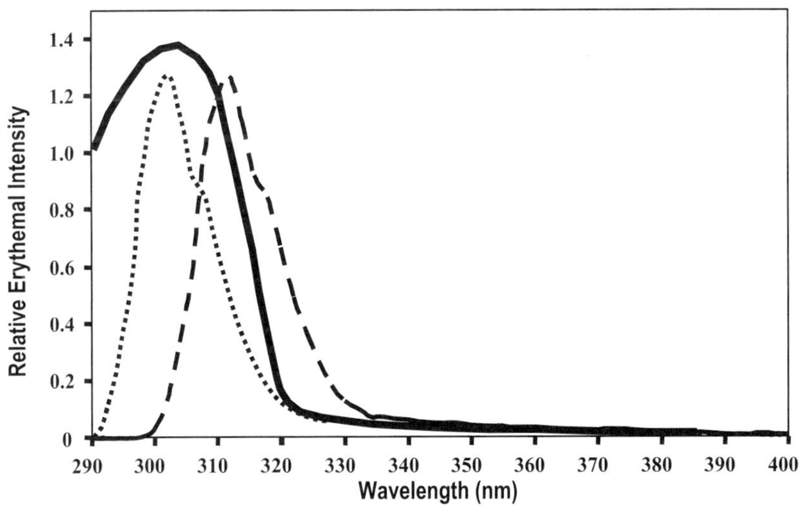

Figure 39.1 Graph to show the importance of solar simulator output spectrum on protective ability of sunscreen product and hence SPF. Solid curve = protection profile of sunscreen product. Dotted curve = UV-B-rich solar simulator erythemal output. Hatched curve = UV-B-depleted solar simulator output.

peak burning wavelength now falls outside of the protective "umbrella" of the sunscreen, that is, the sunscreen product has begun to lose protective performance at the wavelengths where the solar simulator is emitting its most burning radiation. Consequently, the same product will not be able to offer as good protection from this UV-B-depleted solar simulator and hence the product will return a lower SPF in the test.

Because SPF measurement is critically dependent on the output spectrum of the UV light source, the International SPF Test Method defines strict limits of compliance for any light source used in the test. These limits are defined by a parameter known as the relative cumulative erythemal effectiveness (RCEE) of the source. The RCEE is a measure of the spectral distribution of the light source in terms of its capacity to generate erythema and informs which wavelengths of light are contributing what proportion of the total erythemal response. RCEE is described in terms of cumulative erythemal effectiveness by successive wavelength bands from 290 to 400 nm (i.e., all terrestrial UV wavelengths). The erythemal effectiveness for each band of wavelengths is expressed as a percentage of the total erythemal effectiveness of all wavelengths from 290 to 400 nm.

For example, a light source might have a spectrum of emission which contained amounts of UV light in the range 290–300 nm that would contribute, say 10% to the total erythemal response that would result from exposure of skin to this lamp. The source would then be said to have a %RCEE value of 10% for wavelengths 290–300 nm. If a further 30% of total erythema was then contributed by wavelengths between 300 and 310 nm, then the cumulative effect is that the source has a relative cumulative erythemal effectiveness percentage (%RCEE) of 40% for wavelengths in the range 290–310 nm.

The accumulation is continued from 290 to 400 nm until the full 100% UV contribution is achieved. Once all %RCEE values have been calculated for any UV source, they are compared with the maximum and minimum limits for each wavelength band. These are defined within the International SPF Test Method. The limits are based on the practical measurement of the outputs of numerous suitable light sources and on the %RCEE values for known "standard" sunlight spectra, particularly that for Australian sunlight (14). The maximum (upper) and minimum (lower) permitted %RCEE limits for any UV source are shown in Table 39.2, along with representative %RCEE values for a typical solar simulator. As an example, it can be seen that the %RCEE limits for wavelengths of light between 290 and 320 nm (i.e., the UV-B wavelengths) are 85.0% (lower) and 90.0% (upper). This means that a minimum of 85% of any erythema resulting from exposure to a qualifying UV source must have been initiated by wavelengths between 290 and 320 nm and that the maximum contribution to the erythemal response from these wavelengths should be 90%. The "typical" solar simulator shown in the table is a xenon arc source filtered with 1-mm thick Schott® WG320 and UG11 filters. A total of 87.4% of the erythema resulting from exposure to this source is initiated by the wavelengths from 290 to 320 nm.

Table 39.2 Maximum and Minimum Percentage Relative Cumulative Erythemal Effectiveness (%RCEE) Limits for Ultraviolet Light Sources Used in SPF Testing

	%RCEE		
Spectral range (nm)	Lower limit	Upper limit	Typical solar simulator
<290	–	0.1	0.0
290–300	2.0	8.0	4.0
290–310	49.0	65.0	56.7
290–320	85.0	90.0	87.4
290–330	91.5	95.5	93.3
290–340	94.0	97.0	95.3
290–350	95.5	98.5	97.2
290–400	100.0	100.0	100.0

To illustrate the importance of controlling the UV source spectrum, Table 39.3 shows the potential effect of the solar simulator spectrum on the SPF measured. The effect of eight different spectra, each being possible outputs from commercially available solar simulators, is illustrated. The different spectra are identified by their %RCEE value for the wavelength range 290–320 nm. The predicted SPFs shown are calculated from a model incorporating a real SPF35 sunscreen product absorption profile (Fig. 39.2), the solar simulator output spectra corresponding to the various %RCEE values and the CIE (1987) erythemal effectiveness spectrum (15). From Table 39.3 it can be seen that the predicted SPF which is likely to be measured for the SPF35

Table 39.3 Potential Effect of Various Solar Simulator Output Spectra, Described by the Percentage Relative Cumulative Erythemal Effectiveness (%RCEE) Parameter, on the SPF of a Sun Product as Predicted by a Model Incorporating the CIE (1987) Erythemal Effectiveness Spectrum, and the Absorbance Spectrum of the Sunscreen Product Shown in Fig. 39.2

%RCEE (290–320 nm)	Predicted SPF
80	25.8
82	28.0
84	30.0
85	31.4
87	34.6
89	38.5
90	41.0
91	44.4

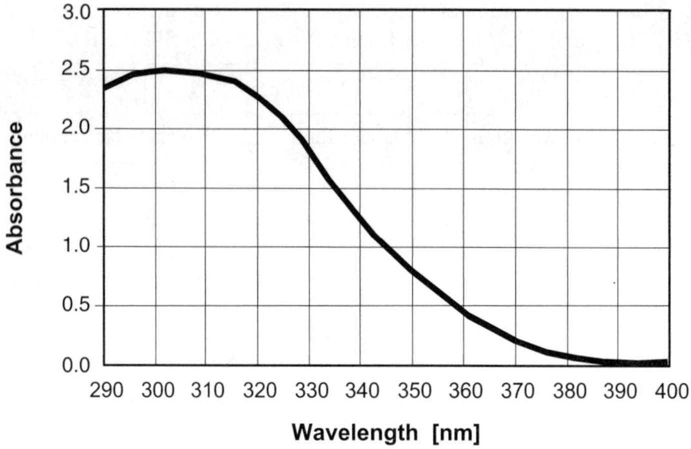

Figure 39.2 Absorbance profile of a commercially available SPF35 sunscreen product, used in the predictive calculation of the effect of UV spectrum on SPF, shown in Table 39.3.

sunscreen product shown in Fig. 39.2 can vary from as low as SPF25.8 and up to as high as SPF44.4. If we were to add to this model calculation, the biological variation that is inherent in any human volunteer study, then the actual SPF range that might be measured could potentially be even larger.

The examples shown are calculated from outputs of real solar simulators (albeit extreme examples) and so they do represent real possibilities for variability. By limiting the acceptable range for solar simulator output to a minimum %RCEE (290–320 nm) of 85.0% and a maximum of 90.0%, we effectively limit the theoretical SPF range for a SPF35 product to SPF31.4–41.0.

In reality, the light source that most readily complies with the limit requirements set out in the International SPF Test Method is the xenon arc lamp. In addition to this, the best way to conform to the additional requirement that wavelengths >400 nm be limited as much as possible is to incorporate a glass cut-off filter such as a Schott® UG11 filter (or similar) which transmits minimal visible or infrared radiation. The standardised use of a visible cut-off filter such as the Schott® UG11 also has the additional benefit of ensuring that all solar simulators have a similar spectral distribution in the UV-A region of the sunlight spectrum. This is important since studies conducted by COLIPA member companies have shown that the UV-A component of a lamp spectrum can have a surprising effect on the determination of the SPF of a sun product. Even though the UV-A wavelengths only contribute about 12.5% of all erythema in unprotected skin, the UV-A contribution to erythema can become quite significant when a sunscreen product is applied to the skin. This effect was demonstrated in a ring-test in which the same solar simulator in each laboratory was first filtered with a Schott® UG5 cut-off filter and then with a UG11. These filters have little impact on the UV-B emission of the solar simulator but can dramatically reshape the UV-A emission without taking the solar simulator outside the permitted %RCEE limits. In the ring-test, the two different filtration systems were used to determine the SPF of several sun protection products and in many cases, different SPF numbers were returned for the UG11 and UG5 filtration. In several instances these differences were significant, although not always large. Consequently, the exclusive use of a Schott® UG11/1 mm filter (or similar) is strongly advised when conducting SPF testing in Europe and xenon arc lamps are the only permitted sources.

Figure 39.3 shows actual emission spectra for two solar simulators, filtered with a Schott® UG11 filter, which comply with the upper and lower spectral limits for lamp output according to the International SPF Test Method. As can be seen from the graph, the permissible variation in light source quality is small.

One final requirement of any light source used in SPF testing in Europe is that the total output intensity (energy) of the source used, should be restricted to that which would not cause an excessive feeling of heat in the skin. As a guide, total irradiance of 120 mW/cm^2 appears not to produce excessive heating and so this would be considered a suitable intensity for total solar simulator output.

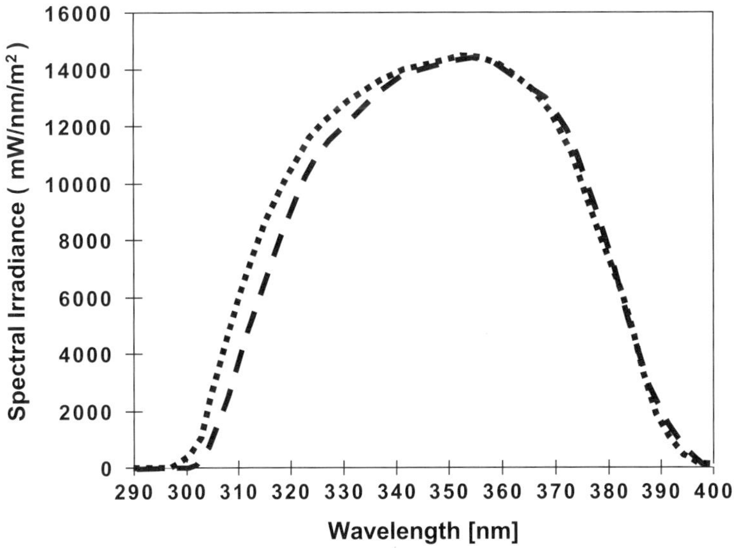

Figure 39.3 Graph to show two typical solar simulator output spectra complying with the upper (dotted curve) and lower (hatched curve) lamp output limits, defined by the International SPF Test Method.

Volunteer Selection

Several laboratories engaged in SPF testing across the world have reported that the SPF measured on dark or tanned skin can often be marginally lower than the SPF for a product tested on white, nontanned skin. For this reason, volunteers who participate in a SPF test in Europe are restricted to those with skin types I, II, or III according to the Fitzpatrick classification (12). In addition to this, the International SPF Test Method also includes an optional selection technique based on reflectance colorimetry. This procedure may be used to exclude deeply tanned type III individuals where an existing tan might threaten to interfere with the measurement of SPF.

A minimum of 10 volunteers and a maximum of 20 volunteers must complete an SPF test with fully valid data. There is provision for rejection of data on the grounds of volunteer noncompliance or incomplete data but rejections are limited to a maximum of five volunteers and must be justified on scientific grounds. Consequently, the maximum number of volunteers which may be tested is 25 and since a maximum of five volunteers may be rejected, the minimum number of volunteers required to produce valid data increases with the total number of volunteers tested according to Table 39.4.

Table 39.4 Minimum Number of Volunteers that Must Produce Valid Data for Varying Numbers of Volunteers Tested in an SPF Test. The Maximum Number of Volunteers That May be Tested is 25 and the Minimum is 10 Provided All Return Valid Data

Number of volunteers tested	Minimum number of volunteers required to produce valid data
10	10
11	10
12	10
13	10
14	10
15	10
16	11
17	12
18	13
19	14
20	15
21	16
22	17
23	18
24	19
25	20

The actual number of volunteers required to complete a test, with valid data, is determined by certain statistical criteria (described later). These criteria govern the acceptable level of variability on the data. If these criteria are satisfied by valid data from 10 volunteers, then the test may end at this point and the SPF is calculated as the mean from these 10 volunteers. However, if the statistical criteria are not achieved after 10 volunteers then testing must continue on additional volunteers until such time as the statistical criteria are met, or until 20 volunteers have returned valid data. Should the criteria not be met after testing the maximum number of 25 volunteers, then the whole test is rejected and the investigator must examine their test procedures for sources of error or noncompliance with methodology.

Product Application Procedure

Product application should be a straightforward and easily controllable parameter in the SPF test, but in fact it is one of the largest, if not the largest, potential source of error. This is because the SPF number measured is extremely dependent on the way in which the sunscreen product is distributed on the surface of the skin. There are two factors which affect surface distribution. These are application rate and spreading technique. The higher the application rate, the higher the SPF that will be measured. This relationship is pseudologarithmic so that the SPF increases approximately logarithmically with increasing application rate. Because of this, it is critical that the amount of product applied to the skin is very accurately controlled. The International SPF Test Method requires that product is applied accurately, at an application rate of 2.0 mg of product per square centimetre of skin. The technique for weighing out the product and transferring it to the skin is strictly defined to ensure that all weighed product is transferred to the skin. All weighing must be carried out to an accuracy of 2.5% on a balance capable of weighing to a sensitivity of 0.1 mg. Whilst this might appear excessive, the reality is that the previously mentioned logarithmic relationship between application amount and SPF, means that overweighing by as little as 2.5% would theoretically lead to a SPF40 product testing as SPF44, that is, a 10% error.

But application rate is not the whole story here. As part of the development of the International SPF Test Method, several laboratories studied the effect of product spreading technique. Two parameters were investigated: spreading time and spreading pressure. Both were found to be possible sources of significant variation in the SPF measured, under certain circumstances. In the spreading-time study, two products were SPF tested following the same procedure but with different product spreading times of 20 s and 40 s. For one of the two products, a significantly higher SPF was measured with the 20 s spreading time than the 40 s spreading time. This is thought to suggest that rubbing some products for too long a time, can transfer too much product into the recesses of the skin's topography, leaving the ridges unprotected and hence leading to a lower measured SPF.

In the spreading-pressure study, two products were SPF tested after spreading with two different forces (~300 and ~50 g). Results for one of the two products showed a significantly higher SPF for the product spread with low pressure (mean SPF = 20.6) compared with that spread with high pressure (mean SPF = 14.7). These results are again consistent with high pressure resulting in more product being transferred to the recesses in the skin's topography, leaving the ridges unprotected.

These studies lead to the introduction of much more explicit guidelines on product application technique in order to ensure that product is applied and spread consistently. Two key stages to the product application technique were defined. The first is the application of the product using a "weighing by loss" technique, which accurately dispenses the correct amount of product. A syringe or micropipette is weighed after filling with the test product and is then weighed again after dispensing the product directly on to the skin in a series of small droplets distributed over the whole product application site. The difference in weights gives the exact amount of product dispensed onto the volunteer's back. The area of skin to which the product is applied must be no less than 30 cm^2 and no more than 60 cm^2. This area was defined from practical experience, which suggested that areas <30 cm^2 required product application volumes which were too small to weigh accurately, whilst areas >60 cm^2 required the applied product to be spread over too large an area of skin to be able to achieve a sufficiently uniform distribution. The second stage of product application requires the product to be rubbed into the skin using "light" pressure for a period of between 20 s and 50 s using either the bare finger or a "finger cot." The product is then left to dry for at least 15 min but no more than 30 min.

The procedures described above, apply to the majority of sun- or UV-protective products that is, those in cream, lotion, milk, oil or gel format. However, it was recognized that a unique product application technique was needed for products in powder format. Therefore, the International SPF Test Method also defines a specific procedure for application of powder products.

Because of the complexity of the product application technique and the difficulty to describe it adequately using only the written word, the International SPF Test Method is accompanied by a CD-ROM based video which illustrates visually, the correct application procedure.

Use of Standard Products

Most SPF test methods incorporate at least one standard product which is included in every SPF study as an internal control to ensure that procedures have been correctly followed. The International SPF Test Method is no exception. It requires one standard product to be tested as part of any SPF test. However the SPF of the products being tested governs the choice of standard. If the products under test are all of expected SPF below SPF20 then any one of four named SPF standards may be used (P1 "DIN Standard"—SPF4; P7

"FDA 8% HMS Standard"—SPF4; P2 "CTFA/JCIA High SPF Standard"—SPF13; or P3 "COLIPA High SPF Standard"—SPF15). However, if any product in the test has an expected SPF of 20 or above, then one of the two high SPF standards (P2 or P3) must be chosen.

The expected mean SPF values for each of the standard products were derived by combining ring-tests carried out by the European Trade Association (COLIPA) during 1993 with an International SPF ring-test conducted in 1996 and are shown in Table 39.5. Since these data are somewhat dated and were obtained following methodologies which preceded the International SPF Test Method, it is the intention of the International Harmonisation Committee to redetermine the SPF values for the standard products in a new ring test likely to be conducted during 2004.

UV Exposure Procedure

The SPF test requires that the back of a human volunteer is exposed to incrementally increasing doses of UV light in order to determine the minimum dose of sunlight simulated light which will induce the first perceptible redness (erythema) response, 16–24 h after exposure. Volunteers may be exposed to the doses of UV radiation in either the seated or the prone position, however, the same position must be maintained for all exposures as well as for the subsequent assessment of erythemal responses.

The minimum area of skin to be exposed to the solar simulated light source is 0.5 cm^2. However, an area of at least 1.0 cm^2 is highly recommended. Each area of exposure should be separated from its adjacent area of exposure by a distance of at least 1.0 cm and each area of skin exposed to the incremental doses of simulated sunlight must be of the same size. In practice, most European laboratories will expose an area of skin equivalent to 1.0 cm^2 to each incremental dose of radiation.

When determining the unprotected MED, a minimum of five sites on the unprotected skin of the volunteer must be exposed to geometrically increasing doses of simulated sunlight UV light, with the increment between the doses

Table 39.5 Expected SPF Values for Standard Products with Indication of Expected Variability According to Historical Ring-Tests Conducted in 1993 and 1996 (To Be Revised)

Standard product	Nominal SPF	Measured SPF (mean)	Standard deviation	SPF Range (±1.65 S.D.)
P1: Low SPF standard	4	4.2	0.2	3.8–4.5
P7: Low SPF standard	4	4.2	0.3	3.8–4.7
P2: High SPF standard	13	12.7	1.2	10.7–14.8
P3: High SPF standard	15	15.3	1.3	13.2–17.4

being either 1.12 or 1.25 times. On product protected sites, a minimum of five separate areas of skin on an adjacent region of the back, must be exposed to geometrically increasing incremental doses of simulated sunlight with the size of the increment being dependent on the expected SPF of the product under test. For products where the expected SPF is less than or equal to SPF25, an increment of no more than 1.25 times should be used. For products where the expected SPF is greater than SPF25, the increment between successive doses of simulated sunlight exposure should be no more than 1.12 times. Smaller increments may be used for any protected MED determination, but the increment must be consistent throughout the whole irradiation sequence.

The requirement for a smaller maximum increment of exposure for high SPF products is intended to increase the sensitivity of the test, whilst also safeguarding the volunteer from exposure to unnecessarily high doses of ultraviolet light (albeit with protection from the test product).

Minimum Erythemal Dose Definition and Determination

A major difference between the new International SPF Test Method and the 1994 COLIPA SPF Test Method, which it will replace, lies in the definition and the determination of the MED. The new definition of an MED is much more akin to that of the US FDA final sunscreen monograph definition and it is the same for both the MED on unprotected skin (MED_u) and for the MED on skin protected by the test product (MED_p). It is defined as "The lowest ultraviolet light dose that produces the first perceptible, unambiguous erythema with defined borders appearing over most of the field of UV-exposure 16 to 24 hours after exposure." There is no longer a requirement for color-matching between the MED_u and MED_p (as was required by the 1994 COLIPA test method) nor for interpolation between two adjacent erythemal responses in order to achieve a color match.

All MED determinations are by visual assessment of the sites exposed to UV radiation, by a trained assessor who has been checked for normal colour vision. The visual assessment is made between 16 and 24 h after exposure, by an assessor who has had no previous involvement in the application of product, delivery of UV exposures or other test design (e.g., randomization of test sites) on that particular volunteer. A minimum of 500 lux illumination is required for the MED assessment, which must be recorded either as the total energy dose delivered to the site (J/m^2 or mJ/cm^2) or the time (in seconds) for which the irradiation was delivered, provided that the solar simulator has been demonstrated to emit a constant output flux.

The International SPF Test Method has introduced specific circumstances under which MED data *must* be rejected. These are shown in Table 39.6. Some circumstances will lead to the rejection of all data from all test products tested on a single individual whilst in other circumstances some of the data may be salvaged. However, if data has to be rejected on more than five different

Table 39.6 Criteria Under Which MED Determinations Are Invalid and Must Be Rejected

Rejection criterion	Unprotected skin	Standard product protected skin	Test product protected skin
The exposure series on a subject fails to elicit any erythemal response on any site, 20 ± 4 h after exposure	Reject all data for all products	Reject all data for all products	Reject all data for the test product affected
Erythemal responses within an exposure series on a subject are randomly absent, 20 ± 4 h after exposure	Reject all data for all products	Reject all data for all products	Reject all data for the test product affected
All subsites in the exposure series on a subject show an erythemal response, 20 ± 4 h after exposure	Reject all data for all products	Reject all data for all products	Reject all data for the test product affected

Note: When multiple products are Tested on one individual and the rejection criterion applies only to the product protected MED for a single product (column 4), then only the data for the affected product are rejected.

individuals, then the whole test is invalid and must be repeated on a completely new panel of 10–25 volunteers.

SPF Calculation and Statistical Acceptance/Rejection Criteria

The International SPF test is similar to other SPF test methods throughout the world in that it requires the outcome of the test to be described by way of an arithmetical mean SPF, calculated from each of the individual SPF_i values measured on every volunteer.

Where the method differs from other methods is in its reliance on a statistical assessment of the variability of the SPF data to define the exact number of individual SPF_i values (from the individual volunteers) from which the mean SPF may be calculated. Another difference lies in the fact that statistical criteria are also used to define a maximum limit of variability that is acceptable on the mean SPF.

The test is initially conducted on 10–15 volunteers in order to generate a minimum of 10 valid individual SPF results after rejection of a maximum of five invalid results. A provisional mean SPF for these first data is calculated together with a 95% confidence interval (95% CI) for the mean. The 95% CI is a statistical estimate of the range within which the population mean SPF might reasonably be expected to fall. Put another way, it represents the range of SPF values within which one might be 95% confident of finding the "true" mean SPF. If the 95% CI for the first 10 valid results falls within a range of $\pm 17\%$ of the measured mean SPF, then the test may be declared valid and complete. However, should the 95% CI exceed $\pm 17\%$ of the mean SPF, then the test must continue by adding further volunteers to reduce variability, until the statistical acceptance criterion (95% CI $\leq$ 17% of mean SPF) is achieved. The number of additional volunteers that should be included can be estimated statistically.

After successfully testing the additional volunteers, a new provisional mean SPF is then calculated with its 95% CI. If this new 95% CI now falls within $\pm 17\%$ of the new provisional mean SPF then the test is valid and may end. If the 95% CI is still greater than $\pm 17\%$ of the new provisional mean SPF then further volunteers are added until a maximum of 20 valid individual SPF results have been determined. If the statistical criterion is still not achieved after 20 volunteers have returned valid data, then the entire test must be rejected and a repeat test will have to be conducted on a new panel of volunteers. Under these circumstances, a full review of experimental technique and equipment would be advisable.

This procedure is best illustrated by example. Table 39.7 shows data from a hypothetical SPF test. Eleven volunteers were required in order to obtain the initial 10 valid individual SPF values. These data are shown in plain font. Each individual SPF was calculated as the ratio of MED_p:MED_u. The mean SPF for these first 10 valid results was SPF20.3 with a standard deviation of 5.8. The calculated 95% CI was SPF16.2–24.5 indicating that there is a 95% probability that the "true" population mean lies somewhere within this range. At its extremes, the range represents a $\pm 20.4\%$ variation on the mean SPF for the first 10 valid results. This does not meet the acceptance criterion for data variability (i.e., within $\pm 17\%$ of mean) and so testing continued on additional volunteers.

Using the standard deviation from the first ten valid results, the *t*-statistic and the $\pm 17\%$ variation target, it was possible to predict that an additional four volunteers were likely to be needed to achieve the acceptance criterion. Four more volunteers were tested (data shown in italic) and individual SPFs were calculated. These were added to the original ten SPF values and a new mean SPF of 20.1 was calculated from all fourteen volunteers who produced valid data, along with a new 95% CI of 17.3–22.9. The extremes of this new 95% CI represent a $\pm 14.1\%$ deviation from the mean SPF and hence were

Table 39.7 SPF Data from a Hypothetical SPF Test Showing Individual MED Doses, Calculated Individual SPF Values, and 95% Confidence Intervals

Vol. no.	Skin type	MED_u (mJ/cm^2)	MED_p (mJ/cm^2)	Individual SPF_i	Mean SPF	SD on mean SPF	Test 95% CI	Target 95% CI (mean ±17%)	Pass or fail 95% CI criterion
1	I	10.2	163.2	16.0	–	–	–	–	–
2	II	20.0	564.0	28.2	–	–	–	–	–
3	III	31.3	626.0	20.0	–	–	–	–	–
4	II	25.0	400.0	16.0	–	–	–	–	–
5	II	16.0	400.0	25.0	–	–	–	–	–
6	III	31.3	500.0	16.0	–	–	–	–	–
7	I	12.8	164.0	12.8	–	–	–	–	–
8	II	16.0	No result	–		Invalid result—data rejected			
9	II	20.0	564.0	28.2	–	–	–	–	–
10	III	25.0	400.0	16.0	–	–	–	–	–
11	III	31.3	783.0	25.0	20.3	5.8	16.2–24.5	16.8–23.8	*Fail*
12	II	*16.0*	*288.0*	*18.0*	–	–	–	–	–
13	II	*20.0*	*450.0*	*22.5*	–	–	–	–	–
14	III	*31.3*	*563.0*	*18.0*	–	–	–	–	–
15	II	*20.0*	*400.0*	*20.0*	*20.1*	*4.9*	*17.3–22.9*	*16.7–23.5*	*Pass*

Note: The mean SPF and 95% CI were initially calculated after the first 10 valid results obtained from the first 11 volunteers tested (plain font). Since the test 95% CI was outside the target 95% CI, then the acceptance criterion was not achieved and a further four volunteers were added (italics). This additional number of volunteers was predicted statistically. A new mean SPF and 95% CI was calculated after the completion of the 15th volunteer and the new 95% CI was found to lie within the new target 95% CI calculated from the revised mean SPF.

within the $\pm 17\%$ target (i.e. SPF16.7–23.5). Consequently, no further testing was required and a mean SPF of 20.1 was reported.

COMPARISON OF THE INTERNATIONAL SPF TEST METHOD AND THE US FDA SPF METHOD

Sunscreen manufacturers in the USA, Europe, or other parts of the world who produce international brands, have historically been seriously encumbered by the fact that the 1994 COLIPA SPF Test Method and the SPF test method described by the US FDA sunscreen monograph were significantly different. This lead to the inevitable situation that products intended for sale in both Europe and the USA, for example, had to be tested twice to comply with local legislation or custom.

The International SPF Test Method has been designed not only as an improvement on preceding methodologies in use in Europe, Japan, and South Africa, but also as an attempt to move closer to common practice elsewhere in the world. The result is that The International SPF Test Method has moved considerably closer to the US FDA and other national SPF methods, whilst still maintaining a certain uniqueness, evidenced by the many small differences that remain. Fortunately, these remaining differences are surmountable and with care, a single SPF test can now be designed, which would comply with both the requirements of the FDA and with European methodology. The data generated from such a test, would still require some degree of different handling and different calculation processes, however, the underlying techniques, procedures, and data generated are now fundamentally compatible.

Table 39.8 summarizes the major elements of any SPF test method and compares the International SPF Test Method with the FDA method described by the 1999 final sunscreen monograph (10). The last column in this table highlights the areas of caution that should be observed, or areas of difficulty that might be encountered by any laboratory attempting to conduct a single SPF test which was intended to comply with both methods.

As a consequence of the introduction of the International SPF Test Method, European SPF testing is now much the same as that elsewhere in the world. The small differences that remain are thought to represent enhancements to the existing procedures of other methodologies and if followed these enhancements would not compromise compliance with other methods but would contribute positively to the accuracy of those existing procedures.

In moving closer to the US FDA SPF test methodology and to other leading international SPF test methods, it is hoped that European SPF testing has taken its first step toward full-scale worldwide harmonization of SPF testing.

SPF LABELING GUIDELINES

The International SPF Test Method does not offer any guidance on sun product labeling. The method is purely a technical procedure for determining the mean

Table 39.8 Comparison of the Major Elements of the 2003 International SPF Test Method and the US FDA 1999 Final Sunscreen Monograph SPF Test Method with Particular Attention to the Areas Where Caution Must Be Exercised in Order to Comply with Both Methods When Conducting a Single, Combined Test

Test parameter	International SPF test	US FDA test	Dual compliance guidance
UV Source	• Xenon arc lamp with UG11 type filtration. Output must be continuous, stable, uniform and comply with erythemal effectiveness limits between 290 and 400 nm • <0.1% of output below 290 nm • Output above 400 nm restricted • Need to avoid excessive heating by restricting total irradiance (≈120 mW/cm²) • Periodic measurement with accurately calibrated spectroradiometer	• Continuous, stable, uniform (within 10%) emission spectrum from 290 to 400 nm similar to sea-level sunlight at 10° zenith angle • < 1% of output below 290 nm • < 5% of output above 400 nm • Periodic measurement with accurately calibrated spectroradiometer	It is possible to design a system comprising a xenon arc lamp that complies with both specifications for output. Sea-level sunlight at 10° zenith angle (FDA) would have a spectrum which fell within the erythemal effectiveness limits of the international method Measurement of exact output spectrum is critical to comply with international method
Test subjects	• Skin types I, II, or III • Minimum number = 10 • Maximum number = 20 • Actual number variable between 10 and 20 according to statistical criteria • Maximum of five rejections • Specific criteria for rejection	• Skin types I, II, or III • Minimum number = 20 • Maximum number = 25 • Actual Number variable between 20 and 25 • Maximum of five rejections • Specific criteria for rejection	To satisfy both methods, 20–25 volunteers must be recruited. All are used for the FDA test but only those that are needed (in chronological order) to achieve the minimum International method acceptance criteria are recorded. Note that data (volunteer) rejection criteria are different

(*continued*)

Table 39.8 *Continued*

Test parameter	International SPF test	US FDA test	Dual compliance guidance
Test site	• The back between scapula line and the waist • Minimum area = 30 cm^2 • Maximum area = 60 cm^2	• The back between beltline and shoulder blade, lateral to the midline • Minimum area = 50 cm^2	Compliance with both methods requires a test site of between 50 and 60 cm^2.
Definition of minimum erythemal dose (MED)	• The lowest UV dose that produces the first perceptible unambiguous erythema with defined borders appearing over most of the field of UV exposure, 16–24 hours after UV exposure.	• The quantity of erythema-effective energy (expressed as joules per cm^2) required to produce the first perceptible, redness reaction with clearly defined borders	This is the same response worded slightly differently
Unprotected MED determination	• Minimum of five exposures • Minimum of 0.5 cm^2 of skin exposed to UV (recommended 1 cm^2) • 1.12 or 1.25 times geometric progression between irradiation doses • Read after 16–24 h under at least 500 lux illumination • Independent assessor	• Exactly five exposures • Minimum of 1.0 cm^2 of skin exposed to UV • 1.25 times geometric progression between irradiation doses • Read after 22–24 h under tungsten or warm white fluorescent light within the range of 450–550 lux • Independent assessor	Only five exposure subsites of 1 cm^2 with 1.25*X* geometric progression between doses in order to comply with both methods. Erythemal responses must be read by an independent assessor at 23 h ± 1 h under tungsten or warm white fluorescent light within the range of 500–550 lux

Test product quantity and application technique	• $2.0\ mg/cm^2 \pm 0.05\ mg$ • Application area = $30–60\ cm^2$ • Apply in 15–30 droplets • Rub-in with light pressure for a period of 20–30 s using finger-cot or bare finger • Drying time 15–30 min	• $2.0\ mg/cm^2$ • Application area $\geq 50\ cm^2$ • Rub-in with a finger cot • Minimum drying time 15 min	With the appropriate technique and application procedure, product can be applied to an area of between 50 and 60 cm^2 and left to dry for 15–30 min. In this way both methods are complied with
Standard sunscreen products	• P1 Low SPF (SPF4) • P7 Low SPF (SPF4) • P2 High SPF (SPF 13) • P3 High SPF (SPF15) • Select one standard from all four if test product SPF <20 or from P2 or P3 if SPF ≥20	• 8% HMS Standard (SPF 4.47)	International SPF Standard P7 is the FDA 8% HMS Standard so this product may be used alone in tests where the test products' SPFs are all less than SPF20. For SPFs ≥20 then the 8% HMS standard *and* either P2 or P3 must be tested in order to comply with both methods
Protected MED determination	• Minimum of 0.5 cm^2 of skin exposed to UV (recommended 1 cm^2) • Minimum of five exposures • Maximum 1.25*X* geometric progression between doses for expected SPFs ≤25 • Maximum 1.12*X* geometric progression between doses for expected SPFs >25	• Minimum of 1.0 cm^2 of skin exposed to UV • Exactly seven exposures • Fixed dose progressions of: 1.25*X* for SPFs <8 1.20*X* for SPF 8–15 1.15*X* for SPFs >15 for irradiation doses 1, 2, 4, 6, and 7. Irradiation doses 3 and 5 to be the midpoint between adjacent doses	For SPFs ≤25 the FDA procedure should be followed, ensuring that erythemal assessments are made under 500–550 lux illumination. This will comply with the International method For SPFs >25, it is not possible to use a single irradiation series and a hybrid series comprising of the International progression of 1.12*X* and the FDA progression of 1.15*X* will need to be used. This is likely

(*continued*)

Table 39.8 *Continued*

Test parameter	International SPF test	US FDA test	Dual compliance guidance
	• Read after 16–24 h under at least 500 lux illumination • Independent assessor	• Read after 22–24 h under tungsten or warm white fluorescent light within the range of 450–550 lux • Independent assessor	to require the exposure of 11 subsites to UV light, when testing SPFs >25
SPF calculation and statistical acceptance	• Total number of volunteers (n) = 10–20 • Calculate arithmetic mean SPF • Calculate the standard deviation on the mean SPF • Calculate 95% CI and check test validity ie 95% CI is less than ±17% of mean SPF	• Total number of volunteers (n) = 20–25 • Calculate arithmetic mean SPF • Calculate standard deviation on the mean SPF • Calculate the lower limit of the 95% CI for the SPF data	Both tests make essentially the same calculations. The FDA test has no limitation on variability (although this will affect labelled SPF). Therefore a joint test must comply only with the International test variability requirement, that is that the 95% CI must be less than ±17% of mean SPF

SPF value for a sunscreen product. However, COLIPA has published an SPF labeling guideline (16) for its European members and the majority of European sunscreen manufacturers do adhere to this guideline.

This guideline is not complex and is summarized below:

- The sun product's SPF must be determined according to the latest SPF test method recognized or issued by COLIPA. The result of the test is reported as the mean SPF with its 95% CI.
- The labeled SPF is the nearest recognized SPF number below the measured mean SPF. COLIPA recommendation number 11 (16) only recognizes certain SPF numbers for product labelling in an attempt to reduce the proliferation of different SPF numbers on sun products. The recognised SPF numbers are SPF 2, 4, 6, 8, 10, 12, 15, 20, 25, 30, 40, 50, and 50+. Only these numbers may be used for labeling the SPF of a sun product. As an example, a product that tested with a mean SPF of 11.8 would be labeled as SPF10 as this is the first recognized SPF number below 11.8.
- The maximum SPF that may be labeled is SPF50+. Products labeled as SPF50+ must have returned a mean SPF of at least SPF 60.
- Product protection category descriptors are optional however if used, then only the following descriptors will be used: "low" (SPFs 2–6); "medium" (SPFs 8–12); "high" (SPFs 15–25); "very high" (SPFs 30–50); and "Ultra" (SPF 50+). The term sunblock will not be used under any circumstances.

WATER RESISTANCE TESTING AND UV-A MEASUREMENT

The International SPF Test Method describes the technique for measuring the static sun protection factor of a sunscreen product only. There are currently no internationally harmonized guidelines or guidelines specific to Europe, which outline how to measure either the water resistance of a sunscreen product or its UV-A protection level.

Of course, European sun products do make claims regarding their water resistance and also their ability to protect against the UV-A component of sunlight ultraviolet light. However, the tests conducted to support these claims are not defined either by legislation or by trade association guidelines.

Most laboratories in Europe now adopt a procedure for water resistance testing which is very similar to that described in the US FDA (1999) sunscreen final monograph; although water resistance labeling of European products can be somewhat different to that in the USA and other territories of the world.

It is usual for the water resistance test to be conducted in a spa-pool. The volunteers are immersed for two separate 20-min immersions in the spa, with each immersion separated by a 10–20-min drying period (no towelling) with the volunteer removed from the spa. At the end of the immersion procedure, the SPF of the product is determined following the International SPF Test

Method to establish the post-immersion SPF number. Unlike the USA and Australia, the labeled SPF for a European water resistance product is the static SPF and not the SPF value after water immersion. When the term water resistance is used in Europe, it is usually considered that the SPF after two 20-min immersions will continue to be at least 50% of the labeled SPF. If the term "extra water resistant" is used, then this usually implies that the product will retain at least 75% of its SPF after water immersion.

COLIPA, the trade association for the cosmetic and toiletries industry in Europe, is currently developing guidelines on water resistant testing which should be completed in the very near future. These guidelines are likely to be extremely similar to that described in the US FDA sunscreen final monograph although the method of labeling of water resistant sunscreen products may not necessarily be the same.

UV-A labeling in Europe is a much more difficult matter. There is no single agreed test method for UV-A measurement in Europe, but UV-A protection is a major area of interest and concern in Europe. Consequently, COLIPA has been trying for many, many years to find a consensus amongst its members, for a UV-A protection measurement technique. One of the major hindrances to progress has been the debate over the appropriateness of *in vitro* techniques versus *in vivo* techniques although there is now some hope that agreement on this issue may be close at hand. COLIPA continues to persevere in its attempt to establish a European guideline on UV-A measurement.

Meanwhile, manufacturers have used their own initiative with UV-A claims in Europe. Consequently, many product UV-A claims are supported by different UV-A test methodologies. The most popular *in vivo* method has been the persistent pigment darkening (PPD) technique, described by Moyal et al. (17,18). This test is essentially the same procedure as the SPF test but utilises a solar simulator, which emits only UV-A light as the irradiation source and the immediate pigmentation response that occurs in pigmented skin after exposure to large doses of UV-A light as the measurement parameter. The method has been adopted by the Japanese Cosmetics Industry Association as their recommended method for UV-A measurement.

In addition to the *in vivo* PPD method, *in vitro* techniques for UV-A measurement are also very popular. In Germany, it is now common practice to test products for UV-A protection level according to the *in vitro* method described in the Australia/New Zealand Standards Association's standard AS/NZS 2604 (11). Products are often labeled as conforming to this standard for UV-A protection. Elsewhere, many investigators rely on techniques based on the *in vitro* transmission method described by Diffey and Robson in 1989 (19). Many variations of this technique are used in Europe, primarily for screening new formulations but in the UK the technique has been adopted with a few adaptations into a UV-A measurement and labeling system, which has been in widespread use for more than a decade. This system, launched by The Boots Company, uses a simple UV-A logo depicting five levels of UV-A performance by means of a series of stars. Each level of performance is determined by the ratio of the sunscreen product's UV-A absorbance to its UV-B absorbance and so, strictly speaking, it is a measure of how "balanced" a product's UV-A absorbance is, compared to its UV-B absorbance. Whilst use of this system is purely voluntary (although under licence) it has become almost universally used in the UK. Any manufacturer who intended to market a sunscreen product in this region of Europe would be well advised to familiarise themselves with the system.

COLIPA continues to seek a consensus on UV-A labeling, which might lead to a single UV-A test procedure for Europe. There is widespread desire in the European cosmetics industry that an *in vitro* UV-A technique be adopted, which would remove the need to subject human volunteers to yet more exposure to ultraviolet light. Progress has recently been good and it is hoped that a COLIPA UV-A test might become a reality in the near future. How similar this test might be to other legislative or advisory UV-A test methods elsewhere in the world is yet to be seen, but it is likely that a harmonization effort in this area may well be needed in the future. But for now, at least we do have an SPF test method that is harmonized across a large proportion of the world and which is similar enough to the other SPF methods of the world to enable a single test to be conducted, which satisfies all national requirements.

ACKNOWLEDGMENTS

The author would like to acknowledge the considerable efforts of friends and colleagues who make up the International SPF Harmonisation Committee and the individual trade associations of Japan (JCIA), South Africa (CTFA-SA), Europe (COLIPA), and the USA (CTFA). Without their hard work and commitment, the International SPF Test Method would never have been possible. Sadly, one person who was highly instrumental in the early European effort never witnessed the completion of the work. This chapter is dedicated to the memory of the late Jack Dupuis.

REFERENCES

1. Henne W. *In vivo* determination of the sunscreen factor of cosmetic preparations, history and the present state of the art. Parf Kosm 1983; 64:415–423.
2. Schulze R. Einige versuche und bemerkungen zum problem der handelsublichen lichtschutzmittel. Parf Kosm 1956; 37:310–315.
3. Greiter F. Sun protection factor—development methods. Parf Kosm 1974; 55:70–75.
4. Deutches Institut für Normung. Experimentelle dermatologische bewertung des erythemschutzes von externen sonnenschutzmittein für die menschliche haut. DIN Standard (1985); 67.501:1-9 and DIN Standard 1996; 67.501.
5. Food and Drug Administration. Sunscreen drug products for over-the-counter human use. Proposed safety, effective and labeling conditions. Federal Register (August 25, 1978 Part II); 43 (No. 166):38205–38269.

6. COLIPA Sun Protection Factor Test Method. COLIPA Publication 94/289 (1994):October 1994.
7. Food and Drug Administration. Sunscreen drug products for over-the-counter human use; tentative final monograph; proposed rule. Federal Register (May 12, 1993); 58(No. 90):28194–28302.
8. Japanese Cosmetics Industry Association. Standard sun protection factor test method, 1999. Available from JCIA.
9. South African Bureau of Standards. Sunscreen Products. SABS Standard 1557 (1992); May 1992.
10. Food and Drug Administration. Sunscreen drug products for over-the-counter human use; final monograph. Federal Register (May 21, 1999); 64(No. 98):27666–27693.
11. Standards Australia/Standards New Zealand. Sunscreen products—evaluation and classification. AS/NZS 2604 (1998):1–32.
12. Wolff K, Gschnait F, Honigsmann H, Konrad K, Parrish JA, Fitzpatrick TB. Phototesting and dosimetry for photochemotherapy. Br J Dermatol 1977; 96:110–122.
13. Sayre RM, Kaidbey KH. Reciprocity for solar simulators used in sunscreen testing. Photodermatol Photoimmunol Photomed 1990; 7:198–201.
14. Bernhard G, Mayer B, Seckmeyer B, Moise A. Measurement of spectral solar UV irradiance in tropical Australia. J Geophys Res 1997; 102(D/7):8719–8730.
15. Commission Internationale De L'Eclairage (CIE). A reference action spectrum for ultraviolet induced erythema in human skin. CIE Research Note 6 (1987).
16. COLIPA. Colipa Recommendation No. 11—SPF Classification/upper limit. COLIPA Document Reference 02/068-AF (June 2002).
17. Moyal D, Chardon A, Kollias N. Determination of UV-A protection factors using the persistent pigment darkening (PPD) as the end point. Part 1. Calibration of the method. Photodermatol Photoimmunol Photomed 2000; 16(6):245–249.
18. Moyal D, Chardon A, Kollias N. UV-A protection efficacy of sunscreens can be determined by the persistent pigment darkening (PPD) method. Part 2. Photodermatol Photoimmunol Photomed 2000; 16(6):250–255.
19. Diffey BL, Robson J. A new substrate to measure sunscreen protection factors throughout the ultraviolet spectrum. J Soc Cosmet Chem 1989; 40:127–133.

40

Balancing UV-A and UV-B Protection in Sunscreen Products: Proportionality, Quantitative Measurement of Efficacy, and Clear Communication to Consumers

Patricia P. Agin
Schering-Plough HealthCare Products Inc., Memphis, Tennessee, USA

Curtis A. Cole
Johnson & Johnson Consumer Products Worldwide, Skillman, New Jersey, USA

Christopher Corbett and Cheryl M. Sanzare
L'Oréal USA Products, Inc., Clark, New Jersey, USA

Kenneth Marenus
Estee Lauder Companies, Melville, New York, USA

John P. Tedeschi
Bath & Body Works, Reynoldsburg, Ohio, USA

Carolyn B. Wills
Mary Kay Inc., Dallas, Texas, USA

INTRODUCTION

In 1996, industry submitted to Food and Drug Administration (FDA) for consideration an *in vitro* UV-A test method called Critical Wavelength (1). That method measured the broadness of the protection provided by a sunscreen product, but did not address either the magnitude of protection or the issue of the appropriate proportionality of UV-A to UV-B protection. The importance of assessing the quantity of UV-A protection provided by sunscreen products was highlighted by the FDA in correspondence relating to the approval of the combination of avobenzone with certain other active ingredients (2,3). In that correspondence, the Agency asked for additional clinical UV-A protection data beyond Critical Wavelength to support the UV-A efficacy of those ingredient combinations. The data that the Agency requested was to be based on the *in vivo* Protection Factor A (PFA) test method (4).

The importance of proportionality between UV-A protection and the SPF was raised at a 1999 feedback meeting between The Cosmetic, Toiletry and Fragrance Association (CTFA) and FDA. At that meeting, FDA asked industry to comment on the requirement for proportionality between the SPF and UV-A protection. The request for information on this point was made again in an FDA letter to CTFA in March 2000. In addition, the importance of the proportionality of UV-A to UV-B was addressed by the American Academy of Dermatology (5) in their April 2000 press statement on UV-A:

> The AAD recommends that an increase in the SPF of a sunscreen must be accompanied by a proportional increase in the UV-A protection value. These "proportional" values should be determined jointly by the FDA and the industry.

The importance of both the measurement of the quantity of UV-A protection in a formulation and the proportionality of UV-A protection to the SPF is clear. However, a final element to consider is the clear communication of both SPF and UV-A protection information to consumers. The American Academy of Dermatology has wisely recommended maintaining the SPF as the primary indicator of overall sunscreen performance. In 1996, CTFA submitted market research to the FDA (6) that showed that the best way to communicate UV-A protection to the consumer was in the form of simple text descriptors, as opposed to utilizing additional numbers or graphics on the package label. This finding continues to be important, and is consistent with the concept of maintaining the SPF as the primary indicator of the protection provided by the sunscreen product, while providing an opportunity to expand label information about product performance.

Another benefit of the adoption of our approach is that voluntary professional labeling information could be provided to physicians, giving details beyond those needed for consumer labeling concerning the quantity and broadness of the UV-A protection offered by a product. This information would allow physicians to recommend sunscreen products for specific needs and conditions, based on individual evaluation of their patients. However, such professional labeling cannot take the place of simple, clear, and comprehensible information on the label for consumers.

The approach presented in this document offers a way to create a comprehensive approach to sun protection which assures not only proportionality of UV-A to UV-B protection levels but also ensures breadth of absorbance for products making UV-A protection claims. More importantly, in the light of concerns expressed by the FDA that high-SPF products may increase sun exposure and consequently UV-A exposure, this proposal also ensures that high-SPF products contain proportionally increased levels of UV-A protection, coinciding with the views expressed by the American Academy of Dermatology. This system also supports communication of the level of UV-A protection in a simple, integrated format consistent with existing SPF labeling.

BACKGROUND ON THE REQUIREMENTS FOR UV-A/UV-B PROPORTIONALITY

The primary use of sunscreen products is to prevent sunburn and other forms of UV damage to skin. According to Urbach (7), the ratio of damage from the UV-B and UV-A components in sunlight over a day is 80% from UV-B and 20% from UV-A. Of the 20% due to UV-A (320–400 nm), 62% of the damage risk has been ascribed to the shorter UV-A II wavelengths (320–340 nm). Diffey (8) and Cole and Van Fossen (9) have described a similar relationship of UV-B to UV-A (4B:1A ratio) for UV-induced biological effects on the skin. Therefore, to provide proportional protection against both UV-A and UV-B, a sunscreen must protect against the 80:20 ratio of UV-B and UV-A in incident sunlight.

The overall SPF is a composite of the UV protection provided by the sunscreen product in both UV-B and UV-A. The biological response of the skin to sunlight can be expressed as MED $= \text{MED}_B + \text{MED}_A$, where one minimal erythemal dose (MED) is composed of the contribution to sunburn from both the UV-B and the UV-A wavelengths present in sunlight at any point in time. Using the 4 : 1 UV-B: UV-A relationship above, we can calculate the minimum UV-A blockage needed to provide UV-A/UV-B protection for any SPF level. Table 40.1 describes the number of MEDs resulting from UV-B radiation and UV-A radiation reflecting that relationship. This table also illustrates the corresponding UV-A blockage needed at each SPF to provide minimum protection in the UV-A against sunburn and other forms of UV-A-induced damage based on the 4B:1A ratio of incident sunlight.

While there are >30 sunburning MEDs per day possible for Fitzpatrick (10) skin type I in the USA, a liberal estimate of the total UV-A MEDs available per day is 4–6 UV-A MEDs, delivered at a fairly constant rate of $\frac{1}{2}$ MED per hour in summer (11,12). However, it is shortsighted to consider only the acute effects of either UV-A or UV-B. Suberythemal doses and chronic doses of UV-A as well as UV-B have been shown to produce measurable damage in the skin. Therefore, considering only the total number of UV-A MEDs available per day may underestimate the ability of UV-A to contribute to and exacerbate long-term UV-B-induced skin damage, including skin cancer and photoaging.

Action spectra for UV damage to skin are also key elements to be considered in determining a method for confirming the UV-A protection provided by sunscreens. If the action spectra for other known forms of damage are compared to the action spectrum for sunburn (Fig. 40.1), it is easy to see why a test method for assessing UV-A protection must include the effects of the shorter-wave UV-A as well as the longer-wave UV-A. *In vivo* responses to UV-A radiation, which can be measured in clinical tests using light sources that include only UV-A wavelengths (320–400 nm), can be used to substantiate protection across the UV-A spectrum [Fig. 40.2(A) and (B)].

Table 40.1 At Each SPF, What Is Required for Proportional Protection?

MEDs incident	SPF required	UVA MEDs	UV-B MEDs	Minimum PFA required
2	2	0.4	1.6	1
4	4	0.8	3.2	1
8	8	1.6	6.4	1.6
12	12	2.4	9.6	2.4
15	15	3	12	3
20	20	4	16	4
25	25	5	20	5
30	30	6	24	6
35	35	7	28	7
40	40	8	32	8
50	50	10	40	10

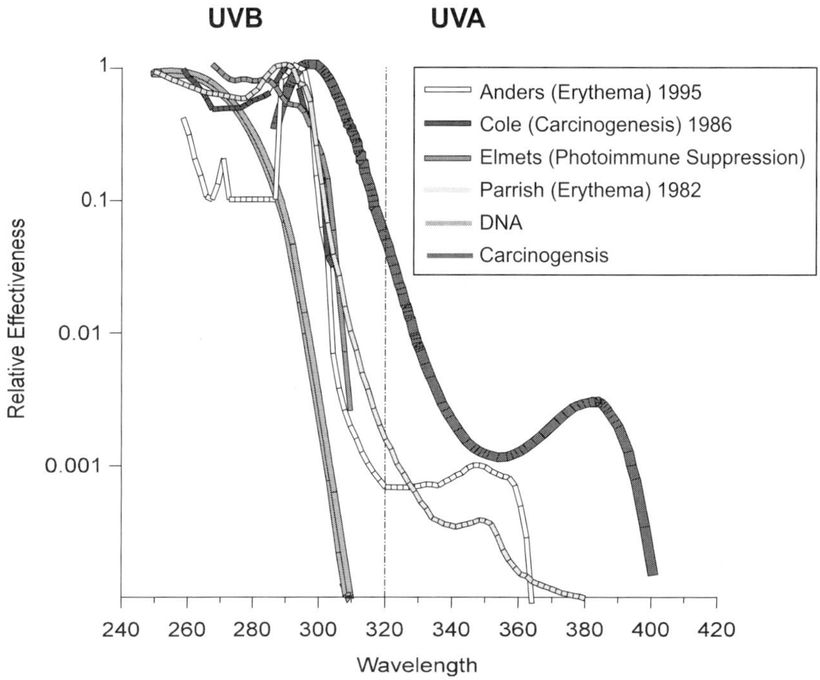

Figure 40.1 On the basis of the comparison of the action spectrum for sunburn to the action spectra for the other known forms of UV damage shown, it is important to include the effects of the shorter-wave UV-A as well as the longer-wave UV-A in any assessment of sunscreen UV-A protection.

Protection Minimums for Proportional UV-A/UV-B Protection

Based on Table 40.1, a PFA $\geq$2 in the UV-A is needed at incident levels of 10 MEDs of sunlight and above. At levels below 10 MEDs, there is no requirement for a PFA of 2 to prevent erythema from UV-A, as the UV-A component of erythema is one MED or less at those levels. Nevertheless, it is desirable to incorporate measurable UV-A protection at all SPF levels; therefore, a minimum PFA of 2 should be a requirement even at low SPF levels for products that claim to protect against UV-A as well as UV-B.

The UV-A wavelengths from 320 to 340 nm have been recognized as wavelengths that can contribute significantly to the development of skin cancer. Studies by Kelfkens et al. (13) have shown that short-wave UV-A ($<$340 nm) is five times more efficient in producing skin cancer than the longer-wavelength UV-A. This is important in light of suggestions that the measurement of sunscreen UV-A effectiveness be limited only to a description of its longwave UV-A protection (i.e., to only its broadness) or that only one "pass–fail" level of UV-A protection be recognized.

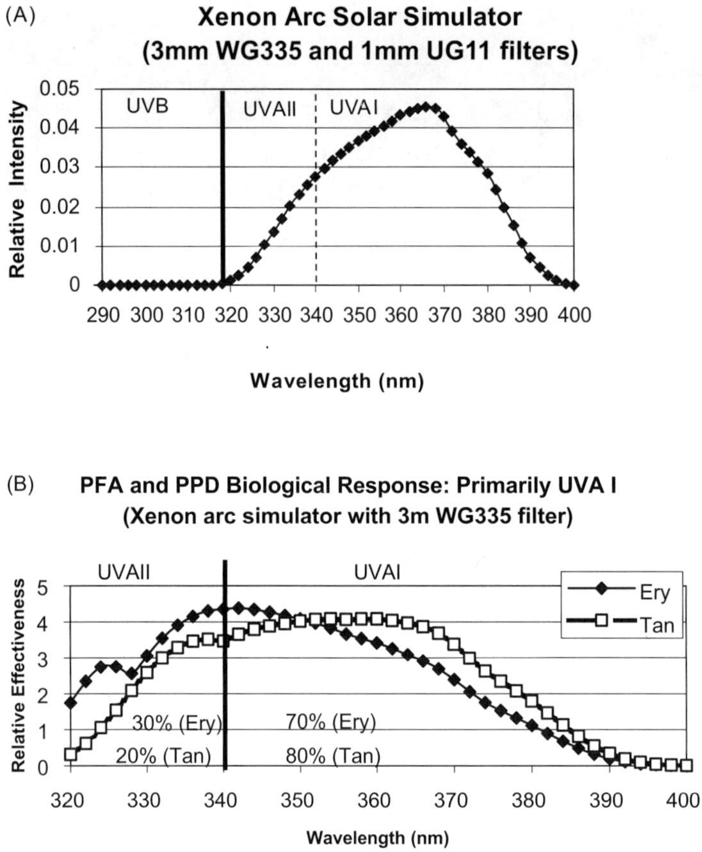

Figure 40.2 (A) Spectral distribution of the UV-A source used in both the PFA and the PPD test methods. Less than 2% of the biological response results from the UV-B contained in the source. (B) The action spectra for erythema (Ery, ◆) (CIE) and PPD (Tan, □), when cross-multiplied with the WG335 3 mm filtered xenon arc solar simulator, clearly show that the predominant biological response is due to the UV-A I portion of the spectrum (340–400 nm). This illustrates that the proposed *in vivo* test methods do not solely test UV-A II and therefore are not redundant with SPF test results.

From an active ingredient perspective, to block the UV-A contribution to sunburn and skin cancer, the absorbance of products of SPF 10 and above must extend beyond the UV-A II region (320–340 nm) to be effective. This is often achieved through the inclusion of oxybenzone or other UV-A absorbers. For higher-SPF products, the UV-A absorbance must extend into the UV-A I region $\geq$360 nm, to achieve the UV-A/UV-B balance needed at those SPF levels. This can be achieved by including combinations of UV-A absorbers or by increasing the content of one or more active ingredients as needed. Products which provide proportional UV-A/UV-B protection should be readily identifiable to consumers, along with those products that include "extra" UV-A protection.

Beyond the Minimum Balance Requirements: Extra UV-A Protection

Based on today's technologies, products can be created such that more UV-A protection is provided at any SPF level than is required from a sunburn protection standpoint. This can be done either to provide extra protection against other forms of potential UV-A damage beyond sunburn or as a consequence of extending the spectrum of absorbance through the inclusion of certain active ingredients which absorb well into the UV-A I (i.e., >360 nm). While the action spectrum for photoaging effects appears to be very similar to the action spectrum for sunburn for some biological end points such as dermal elastosis (14,15), there have been other studies which have shown that long-wave UV-A (>340 nm) may contribute in different ways to premature skin aging. Studies by Lowe et al. (16) and Lavker et al. (17) suggest that repeated exposure to suberythemal doses of UV-A may result in long-term damage, resulting in increased photoaging of the skin. The regular use of sunscreens with effective UV-A and UV-B protection may help to protect against these cumulative, long-term forms of skin damage, as well as the more acute effects.

Honigsmann (18) has suggested that a PFA of 3 (67% UV-A blocked) be incorporated into every sunscreen product above SPF 10. However, it appears from Table 40.1 that if only one protection factor was to be set for all UV-A claims purposes, it would mandate more UV-A protection than is scientifically or medically justifiable in lower-SPF products (SPF 2–8), while allowing less UV-A protection than is actually needed for adequate UV-A protection at SPFs of 12 and above. We propose that the minimum requirement for products that provide "extra UV-A protection" should be a PFA of 3. From there, UV-A protection that *increases* as SPF increases can be incorporated into products based on UV-A protection factors determined *in vivo*, in combination with broadness of protection. Broadness of absorbance alone does not guarantee proportionality of UV-A to UV-B.

Identification and Communication of Two Distinct Levels of UV-A Protection

Based on specific ratios of UV-A to SPF, categories of UV-A protection can be defined to recognize products which provide a basic, proportional UV-A/UV-B protection, and those providing "extra UV-A protection". Breadth of absorbance (i.e., the product has absorbance ≥360 nm[1]) could also be determined to ensure that the broadness of protection was appropriate to support a UV-A protection claim at any SPF level. This could be measured using the critical wavelength method (1) or by a spectrophotometric assessment of the absorbance spectrum.

[1]According to the 1999 Final Monograph (19), p. 27672.

The means to ensure UV-B/UV-A proportionality as SPF rises is shown in Table 40.2. To determine the level of UV-A protection needed at any SPF, the SPF would be multiplied by 0.20. For example, an SPF 20 product would require a PFA of 4 to qualify as a sunscreen providing proportional UV-A/UV-B protection. Table 40.2 also illustrates the increased UV-A protection that would be required for formulations that would qualify for "extra UV-A protection" in comparison to the level of UV-A protection present in formulas that exhibit basic, proportional UV-A/UV-B protection. To qualify for the higher level of claim, a PFA to SPF factor of 0.25 must be reached. An SPF 40 product would require a PFA of 8 for proportional UV-A/UV-B protection, and a PFA of 10 or more to qualify for extra UV-A protection labeling. The ratio of the UV-A protection factor to the SPF can be thought of as the "UV-A index" and readily provides the UV-A labeling category.

Using the UV-B to UV-A relationships shown in Table 40.2, a product could qualify as providing proportional UV-A/UV-B protection, or could qualify for the "extra UV-A protection" claim (e.g., for products which include avobenzone). This method of assessing and communicating protection would serve (along with SPF as the primary indicator of product efficacy) to easily identify products which provide a higher level of protection from UV-A and UV-B, for the most sun sensitive consumers and for dermatology recommendations. It would also serve to allow those who prefer a lower-SPF product to identify and select a product based on their skin type or needs. Not every consumer will want or need only products with extra UV-A protection. A selection of affordable, balanced UV-A/UV-B protection products will continue to remain important, and there should be a readily identifiable UV-A claim for the proportional protection that they provide. This proposal would recognize the basic UV-A protection provided by products which do not choose to utilize

Table 40.2 Providing Proportional Protection: Examples of UV-A Protection Values at Increasing SPFs

	UV-A Protection PFA:SPF factor = 0.20		Extra UV-A Protection PFA:SPF factor = 0.25	
SPF	%UV-A blocked	Minimum PFA	% UV-A blocked	Minimum PFA
<12	50	2	66	3
12	60	2.4	66	3
15	66	3	75	4
25	80	5	84	6.25
30	83	6	87	7.5
40	88	8	90	10
45	89	9	91	11.25
50	90	10	≥92	≥12.5

avobenzone or zinc oxide, but which do exhibit good UV-A protection nonetheless.

The existence of two distinct levels of UV-A protection will not only allow consumer choice, but will also challenge industry to strive to meet the higher category by developing new technologies and new types of formulations. The "extra UV-A protection" category would present true formulation challenges within the limitations of the active ingredient combinations currently allowed, especially at high SPFs. As future technologies are identified and our knowledge of the effects of UV-A progresses, this strategy also provides the flexibility to consider higher levels of sun protection, without altering the familiar labeling that consumers will have come to expect on sunscreen products.

THE NEED TO MEASURE BOTH BREADTH AND QUANTITY OF PROTECTION

Critical Wavelength and similar *in vitro* methods primarily measure the broadness of UV-A absorbance. They do not quantitatively measure the magnitude of protection. This has been illustrated in previous submissions to the docket that showed that two sunscreens with similar critical wavelengths could have very different UV-A absorbance curves and thus provide different protection for consumers. The following figure and table [from Ref. (20)] demonstrate that two formulations with the same SPF can have different absorption curves and very different levels of UV-A protection. Similar findings from a recently conducted study confirm these observations and will be discussed later. To have a complete understanding of the UV-A protection provided by a sunscreen product, both broadness of absorbance and magnitude of UV-A protection must be assessed.

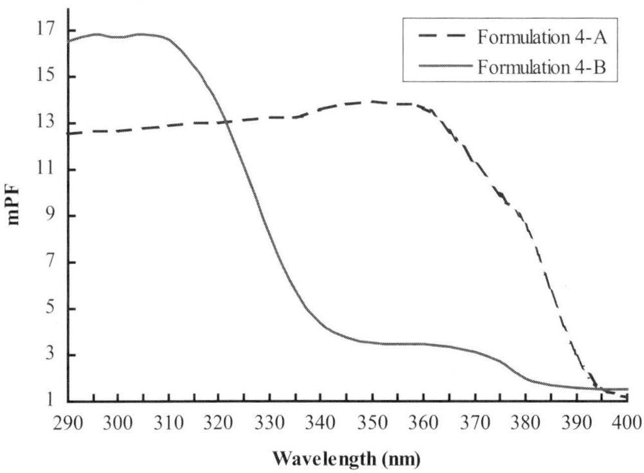

Monochromatic protection factor curves of two prototype formulations.

Product code	SPF (*in vivo*)	λ_c (nm)	UV-A_ePF
4-A	7.5	379	10.2
4-B	7.4	372	5.2

From this discussion the following important points can be made:

1. A minimum 50% UV-A efficacy (a PFA of 2) is appropriate for products below SPF 12 that wish to make basic UV-A protection claims. Higher-SPF products should contain correspondingly higher UV-A protection levels to provide proportional UV-A/UV-B protection.
2. A sliding scale of minimum UV-A efficacies can be proposed so that commensurate UV-A protection is guaranteed at each SPF based on the PFA:SPF ratio of 0.20 (i.e., ensuring that a product provides proportionally balanced protection at *every* SPF).
3. In addition, a higher category of protection based on a higher ratio (PFA:SPF = 0.25) would ensure that products which claim extra UV-A protection on their labeling deliver that benefit from the perspective of both the magnitude of UV-A protection and the breadth of absorbance. For that higher classification, a minimum PFA of 3 would be required at SPFs below 12, with UV-A protection rising with SPF.
4. Broadness of absorbance can be guaranteed for both the "basic" and the "extra" levels of UV-A protection through the requirement that *all* products that make UV-A claims must demonstrate absorbance ≥360 nm.

TESTING FORMULATIONS TO EVALUATE THE REPRODUCIBILITY OF THE PFA AND PERSISTENT PIGMENT DARKENING UV-A TEST METHODS, WITH ADDITIONAL ASSESSMENT OF BROADNESS

CTFA sponsored a study in which seven prototype products representing a wide variety of sunscreen formulation vehicles and active ingredients were used to test the reproducibility of the PFA (4) and persistent pigment darkening (PPD) (21,22) *in vivo* UV-A test methods between laboratories. This test also served to compare the results obtained by using these methods to determine if the two methods could be used interchangeably to measure UV-A protection. In addition, the formulas were evaluated to determine if they met the sunscreen monograph criterion of absorbance ≥360 nm. The *in vitro* method used to assess the broadness of absorbance was the CTFA method previously submitted to the FDA in RPT 9 (1).

The protocols for the PFA and PPD [Japan Cosmetic Industry Association (JCIA)] tests have become standard methods (4,22). In the PFA method, erythema from UV-A is evaluated at 16–24 h post-exposure. In the PPD (JCIA) method, persistent pigment darkening is assessed 2–4 h post-exposure.

Both methods utilize a xenon-arc solar simulator, filtered with a 3 mm WG335 filter, which includes both the UV-A II (320–340 nm) and the UV-A I (340–400 nm) [Fig. 40.2(A)]. The main difference in the two test methods (other than the post-exposure results reading time) lies in the skin types of the subjects tested. Skin types I, II, and III are used for PFA; skin types II, III, and IV are used for PPD. The biological response spectra for the *in vivo* test end points (erythema or pigment darkening/tanning) when tested with this light source are shown in Fig. 40.2(B). Two laboratories conducted both the PFA and the PPD test procedures to determine the *in vivo* UV-A protection provided by each of the seven prototype formulations. One laboratory included an evaluation of the PPD results at 2, 3, and 4 h postexposure.

Two laboratories also assessed the broadness of absorbance using the Critical Wavelength method as submitted by CTFA in 1996 (1). One laboratory provided data on the critical wavelength both before and after sample preirradiation. The other laboratory provided data based both on the labeled SPF of the samples and on the mean (average) SPF of the formulations (however, no differences in critical wavelengths were observed).

RESULTS

The data summary in Table 40.3 shows that for each sunscreen tested, the UV-A protection values determined by the two *in vivo* test methods (PFA and PPD) were comparable, which confirms the results of earlier studies (11,23). These data also demonstrate that clinical test methods for assessing UV-A protection can be used to obtain reliable, reproducible results. Similar conclusions were made based on the multicenter study published on the PFA method by Cole (4). Comparison of the PFA results and the PPD results from the two laboratories is shown in Fig. 40.3(A) and (B). A comparison of the PPD results obtained at 2, 3, and 4 h post-exposure to the PFA data from the same laboratory is shown in Fig. 40.4 and Table 40.4. The correlation of the PPD and PFA results for the seven products is shown in Fig. 40.5.

Six of the seven products met the "broadness" criterion (i.e., absorbance $\geq$360 nm); however, they exhibited a wide range of protection levels *in vivo*, as determined by the PFA and PPD methods. Only formula E, which contained 7% octyl methoxycinnamate with no added UV-A absorber, did not provide a minimum UV-A protection value of 2. Additionally, formula E did not exhibit absorption $\geq$360 nm. These results are shown in Table 40.3 and Fig. 40.6(A) and (B).

Based on the data provided, we suggest that the formulation for product A be used as a control formulation for UV-A testing. This formulation is the same SPF 15 formulation submitted by CTFA as a "high-SPF" control formulation for SPF testing (for which SPF data and methods validation have already been provided to FDA by CTFA November 17, 1992 on and March 6, 2000, respectively).

Table 40.3 Test Value Comparisons

Sample—testing laboratory	Active ingredients, SPF	PPD (JCIA, Ref. 20)	PFA (Cole, Ref. 4)	Critical Wavelength (nm) (CTFA method, Ref. 1)
J—TKL	10% octocrylene,	14.07	13.00	
J—CPT	6% oxybenzone, 5% octyl salicylate, 3% avobenzone	10.80	12.19	379.6
J—IMSI	SPF 30			380
A—TKL	7% Padimate O,	3.18	3.23	
A—CPT	3% oxybenzone	3.24	3.70	360
A—IMSI	SPF 15			362
I—TKL	6% Octyl methoxycin-	2.18	2.59	
I—CPTs	namate, 4% zinc oxide	2.27	2.36	370.4
I—IMSI	SPF 12			374
G—TKL	7% Octyl methoxycin-	4.65	4.4	
G—CPT	namate, 3% avobenzone	3.88	4.73	376.8
G—IMSI	SPF 12			379
F—TKL	5% Oxybenzone	2.95	3.43	
F—CPT	SPF 9	3.23	3.66	360
F—IMSI				362
E—TKL	7% Octyl methoxycin-	1.58	1.79	
E—CPT	namate	1.72	1.75	336
E—IMSI	SPF 8			355
H—TKL	20% Zinc oxide	3.57	4.01	
H—CPT	SPF 4	3.98	4.34	380
H—IMSI				381

DISCUSSION

Six of the seven formulas would qualify for UV-A labeling based on the criterion of absorbance $\geq$360 nm, based on the proposed UV-A protection classification system described in this document. Formula E did not qualify for UV-A labeling based on the criterion of absorbance $\geq$360 nm, nor did it meet the minimum UV-A protection level (PFA or PPD) needed to fulfill the proportionality requirement for basic balanced protection, and thus would not qualify for any UV-A labeling under the proposed plan.

Formula A (SPF 15) would qualify as a product providing basic, proportional UV-A protection, based on meeting the requirements of a PFA:SPF factor of 0.20, with absorbance $\geq$360 nm. This formulation had a PFA or PPD value of 3 and absorbance $\geq$360 nm.

Formula I (SPF 12) appears to be borderline. While its absorbance is $>$360 nm, the PFA values just barely meet the requirements (PFA of 2.4) for

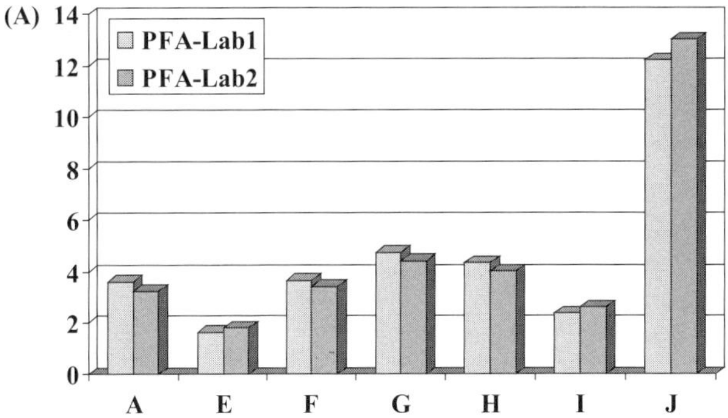

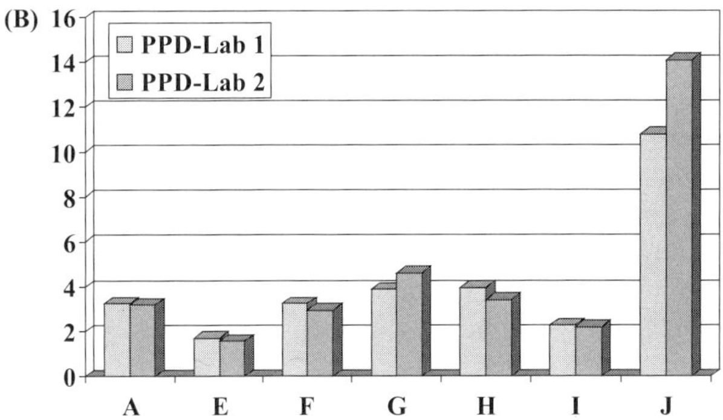

Figure 40.3 (A) Comparison of mean PFA results from two laboratories. (B) Comparison of mean PPD results from two laboratories.

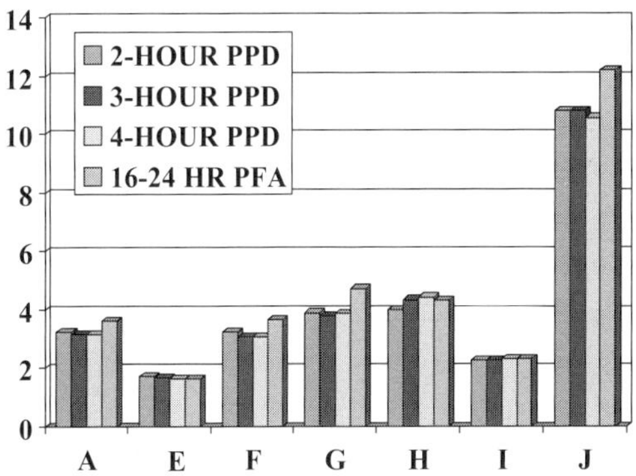

Figure 40.4 Comparison of mean PPD and PFA values from one laboratory.

Table 40.4 Comparison of Mean PPD and PFA Values from One Laboratory

Product	2 h PPD result	3 h PPD result	4 h PPD result	16–24 h PFA result
A	3.24	3.16	>3.16[a]	3.61
E	1.72	1.60	1.64	<1.64[a]
F	3.23	3.06	3.06	3.66
G	3.88	3.78	3.86	4.73
H	3.98	4.35	4.43	4.34
I	2.27	2.27	2.31	2.36
J	10.8	10.8	10.57	12.2

[a]Data sets include one to two inexact values.

the basic level of UV-A protection. The PPD results for this formula would not meet the requirement.

Formulas F, G, H, and J would qualify as formulas that provide extra UV-A protection at their SPF level based on the required PFA:SPF ratio of at least 0.25, as well as exhibiting absorbance ≥360 nm.

The results (Fig. 40.4) from the study on PPD (PPD/JCIA) which included reading of results at 2, 3, and 4 h postexposure show that the biological response is constant over that time period. While the standard time for reading PPD results is 2–4 h postexposure, the data show that this response appears to be very stable,

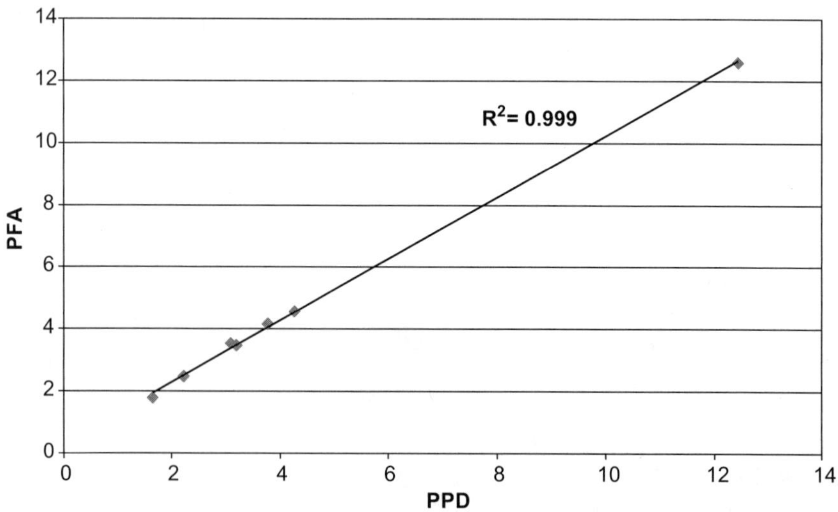

Figure 40.5 For each sunscreen tested, the PPD and PFA *in vivo* tests provided comparable results. These two *in vivo* methods can be used interchangeably to produce reliable data to measure the "quantity" of UV-A protection.

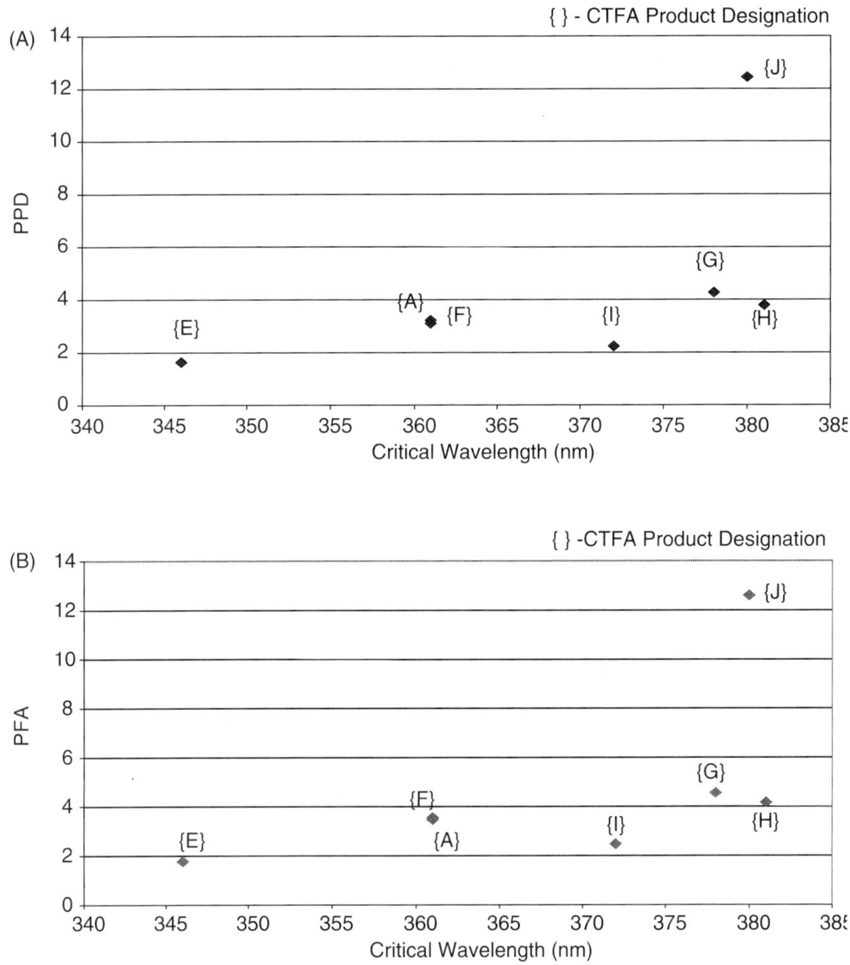

Figure 40.6 Broadness of absorbance alone (as measured by critical wavelength) does not measure the quantity of UV-A protection or fully describe sunscreen product performance in the UV-A.

and that PFA and PPD results are comparable. The data shown in Fig. 40.3(A) and (B) illustrate that the differences between the two laboratories for each end point were also small, for both PFA and PPD.

A comparison of the *in vivo* UV-A protection values to the *in vitro* broadness of absorbance (critical wavelength) shows that it is possible to create formulas with a range of SPFs which can provide significant amounts of UV-A protection as measured by the magnitude of protection (PFA or PPD) and by the broadness of absorbance. However, the data also show that it is not possible to predict the magnitude of UV-A protection from either the SPF or the broadness of absorbance (critical wavelength) at a specific SPF. As shown in Fig. 40.7(A) and (B), when comparing formula I and formula G (both SPF 12 formulations), we can see that formula G has a PFA or PPD value of 4 (blocks 75% of the UV-A damage risk), while formula I has a PFA or PPD value of just over 2, which would block just over 50% of the UV-A risk. Despite its zinc oxide content, formula I falls slightly short in the PPD test for the minimum protection needed to provide proportional UV-A/UV-B protection at that SPF (i.e., it did not reach the required PPD:SPF ratio of 0.20).

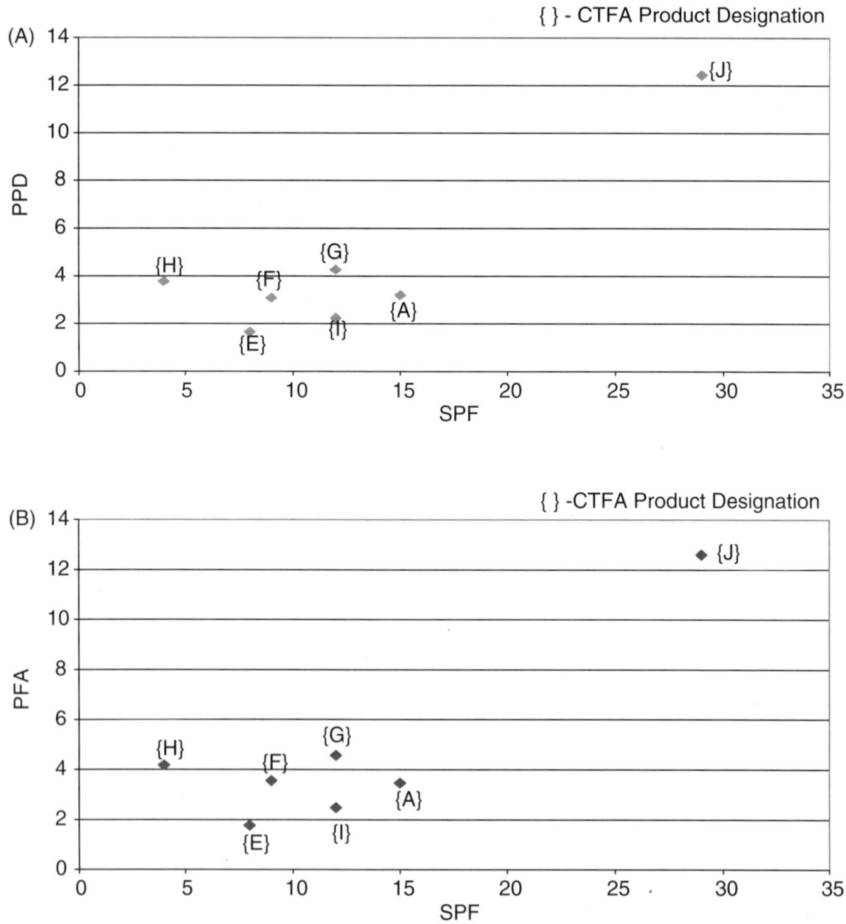

Figure 40.7 Sunscreens with the same SPF can exhibit different levels of UV-A protection. Therefore, the argument that PFA or PPD results are redundant with the information provided by the SPF is not correct.

The data are also relevant to questions raised about the need to assess both the magnitude and the broadness of UV-A protection. As shown earlier and in Table 40.3, it is apparent that two sunscreens with the same SPF can exhibit different levels of UV-A protection. Therefore, the argument that PFA or PPD results are redundant with the information provided by the SPF is not accurate. This is also highlighted by Fig. 2(B), which shows that the predominant biological response of these *in vivo* test methods is due to the UV-A I portion of the spectrum (340–400 nm). This again illustrates that the proposed *in vivo* test methods do not solely test UV-A II and therefore are not redundant with the SPF test results.

It is not possible to predict the level of UV-A protection from the SPF alone, or to predict the quantity of UV-A protection solely from the broadness of the protection (see results for product I, earlier, and in Table 40.3). Comparing the level of protection using the results of either the PFA or the PPD test method to the broadness of absorbance (as measured by critical wavelength) documents the absence of a correlation between broadness and magnitude of protection as both the SPF and the critical wavelength values increase. This finding supports the recommendation of the American Academy of Dermatology, which concluded that measuring broadness alone is not sufficient to accurately describe product performance in the UV-A.

CONCLUSIONS AND RECOMMENDATIONS

1. SPF should retain pre-eminence on the principal display panel, and should continue to be the primary driver of consumer product selection. UV-A labeling should also be displayed on the principal display panel in terms of simple text descriptors, using wording that will allow consumers to identify and select the sunscreen product with the level of SPF and UV-A protection that suits their skin types and sun protection needs.
2. UV-A protection claims should be allowed for sunscreen products with SPFs of 4 and higher. UV-A protection should increase proportionally with higher SPFs, which can be ensured through the use of defined ratios of SPF to PFA or PPD (see Table 40.2). A minimum PFA of 2 (blocks 50% of the UV-A) should be a requirement even at low SPF levels (SPF <12) for products that claim to protect against UV-A as well as UV-B.
3. Sunscreen products can be formulated to provide proportional UV-A/UV-B protection at each SPF level, or to exceed that requirement to provide increased UV-A protection for those who want or need extra UV-A protection. Therefore, two distinct categories of UV-A protection are warranted.
4. Broadness of absorbance alone does not fully measure UV-A protection or describe product performance in the UV-A. A measure of the

"quantity" of UV-A protection provided by a product is needed in addition to an assessment of broadness of absorbance.

5. The PPD and PFA *in vivo* tests provide comparable results. Either method can produce reliable, reproducible data to measure the quantity of UV-A protection. For practical purposes, having the option available of conducting testing for which the results can be read at 2–4 h (PPD) or at 16–24 h (PFA) may be important. For each product, the test method would be selected in advance; all testing for that formulation would be conducted using one method only. An advantage of the PFA method (4) is that it allows inclusion of skin type I subjects, who are those most in need of sun protection and who produce sunburn when exposed to UV-A, whereas the PPD method can only be conducted on darker skin types, who produce pigmentation. The PPD test, however, may be convenient for some laboratories and with its acceptance as the JCIA method, may support ongoing efforts for global harmonization.
6. Voluntary professional labeling can be provided to physicians that will allow them to select or recommend sunscreen products for their patients' needs, based on more detailed information describing the quantity (protection factor) and the broadness of protection.

REFERENCES

1. CTFA/NDMA. CTFA/NDMA Taskforce Report on Critical Wavelength Determination for the Evaluation of the UVA Efficacy of Sunscreen Products. FDA Docket 78N-0038, RPT 9, April 9, 1996.
2. Food and Drug Administration. Letter 167, FDA Docket 78N-0038 to T.S. Elliott, April 8, 1999.
3. Food and Drug Administration. Letter 169, FDA Docket 78N-0038 to T.S. Elliott, November 2, 1999.
4. Cole C. Multicenter evaluation of sunscreen UVA protectiveness with the Protection Factor A test method. J Am Acad Dermatol 1994; 30:729–736.
5. American Academy of Dermatology, Press Release April 20, 2000. Available at "http://www.aad.org/PressReleases/futuresunscreen.html".
6. CTFA/NDMA. Sunscreen UVA Labeling, Market Research Study Report. FDA Docket 78N-0038, February 6, 1996.
7. Urbach F. Ultraviolet A transmission by modern sunscreens: is there a real risk? Photodermatol Photoimmunol Photomed 1993; 9:237–241.
8. Diffey B. Human exposure to ultraviolet radiation. Semin Dermatol 1990; 9:2–10.
9. Cole CA, Van Fossen R. Testing UVA protective agents in man. In: Urbach F, ed. Biological Responses to Ultraviolet A Radiation. Overland Park, KS: Valdenmar Publishing Co., 1992:335–345.
10. Fitzpatrick T. The validity and practicality of sun-reactive skin types I through IV. Arch Dermatol 1998; 124:869–871.

11. Kaidbey K, Gange RW. Comparison of methods for assessing photoprotection against ultraviolet A in vivo. J Am Acad Dermatol 1987; 16:346–353.
12. Sayre RM, Agin PP. A method for the determination of UVA protection in normal skin. J Am Acad Dermatol 1990; 23:429–440.
13. Kelfkens G, de Gruijl FR, van der Leun JC. Tumorigenesis by short-wave ultraviolet A. Carcinogenesis 1991; 12:1377–1382.
14. Kligman LH, Sayre RM. An action spectrum for ultraviolet induced elastosis in hairless mice: quantification of elastosis by image analysis. Photochem Photobiol 1991; 53:237–242.
15. Wulf HC, Poulsen T, Davies RE, Urbach F. Narrow band UV radiation and induction of dermal elastosis and skin cancer. Photodermatology 1989; 6:44–51.
16. Lowe NJ, Meyers DP, Wieder JM, Luftman D, Bourget T, Lehman MD, Johnson AW, Scott IA. Low doses of repetitive UVA induce morphological changes in human skin. J Invest Dermatol 1995; 105:739–743.
17. Lavker RM, Gerberick GF, Veres D, Irwin CJ, Kaidbey KH. Cumulative effects from repeated exposures to suberythemal doses of UVB and UVA in human skin. J Am Acad Dermatol 1995; 32:53–62.
18. Honigsmann H. UVA and human skin. J Photochem Photobiol B 1989; 4:229.
19. Food and Drug Administration. Sunscreen products for over the counter human use; Final Monograph. Fed Reg 1999; 64(98):27666–27693.
20. L'Oreal Research/Cosmair Cosmetics Corp. Comment C545. FDA Docket 78N-0038, May 15, 1998.
21. Chardon A, Moyal D, Hourseau C. Persistent pigment darkening response as a method for evaluation of ultraviolet A protection assays. In: Lowe NJ, Shaath NA, Pathak MA, eds. Sunscreens: Development, Evaluation, and Regulatory Aspects. 2nd ed. New York: Marcel Dekker, 1997:559–582.
22. Japan Cosmetic Industry Association. Measurement Standards for UVA Protection Efficacy, 1998.
23. Stanfield JW, Edmonds SH, Agin PP. An evaluation of methods for measuring sunscreen UVA protection factors. In: Lowe NJ, Shaath NA, Pathak MA, eds. Sunscreens: Development, Evaluation, and Regulatory Aspects. 2nd ed. New York: Marcel Dekker, 1997:537–557.

41

Dosimetry of Ultraviolet Radiation: An Update

B. L. Diffey
Newcastle General Hospital, Newcastle, UK

NATURE OF ULTRAVIOLET RADIATION

Ultraviolet (UV) radiation covers a small part of the electromagnetic spectrum. Other regions of this spectrum include radiowaves, microwaves, infrared radiation (heat), visible light, X-rays, and gamma radiation. The feature that characterizes the properties of any particular region of the spectrum is the wavelength of the radiation. UV radiation spans the wavelength region from 400 to 100 nanometers (abbreviated to nm). Even in the UV portion of the spectrum the biological effects of the radiation vary enormously with wavelength and for this reason the UV spectrum is further subdivided into three regions. The notion to divide the UV spectrum into different spectral regions was first put forward at the Copenhagen meeting of the Second International Congress on Light held during August 1932. It was recommended that three spectral regions be defined as follows:

UV-A: 400–315 nm
UV-B: 315–280 nm
UV-C: 280–100 nm

The subdivisions are arbitrary and differ somewhat depending on the discipline involved. Environmental and dermatological photobiologists normally define the wavelength regions as:

UV-A: 400–320 nm
UV-B: 320–290 nm
UV-C: 290–200 nm

The division between UV-B and UV-C is chosen as 290 nm since UV radiation at shorter wavelengths is unlikely to be present in terrestrial sunlight, except at high altitudes. The choice of 320 nm as the division between UV-B and UV-A is perhaps more arbitrary. Although radiation at wavelengths shorter than 320 nm is generally more photobiologically active than longer wavelength UV, advances in molecular photobiology indicate that a subdivision at 330–340 nm may be more appropriate and for this reason the UV-A region has, more recently, been divided into UV-AI (340–400 nm) and UV-AII (320–340 nm).

QUANTITIES AND UNITS

Quantities of UV radiation are expressed using the radiometric terminology given in the following table:

Term	Unit	Symbol
Wavelength	nm	λ
Radiant energy	J	Q
Radiant flux	W	Φ
Radiant intensity	W sr^{-1}	I
Radiance	W m^{-2} sr^{-1}	L
Irradiance	W m^{-2}	E
Radiant exposure	J m^{-2}	H

Terms relating to a beam of radiation passing through space are the *radiant energy* and *radiant flux.* Terms relating to a source of radiation are the *radiation intensity* and the *radiance.* The term *irradiance*, which is the most commonly used term in photobiology, relates to the object (e.g., patient) struck by the radiation. These radiometric quantities may also be expressed in terms of wavelength by adding the prefix *spectral.* The time integral of the irradiance is strictly termed the *radiant exposure*, but is sometimes expressed as *exposure dose*, or even more loosely as *dose.*

Whilst radiometric terminology is widely used in photobiology, the units chosen vary throughout the literature. For example, exposure doses may be quoted in mJ cm^{-2} or kJ m^{-2}. Examples of the equivalence of these units are:

To convert from	To	Multiply by
J cm^{-2}	mJ cm^{-2}	10^3
J cm^{-2}	J m^{-2}	10^4
J m^{-2}	mJ cm^{-2}	10^7
kJ m^{-2}	J cm^{-2}	10^7
kJ m^{-2}	mJ cm^{-2}	10^{10}

Radiometric Calculations

The most frequent radiometric calculation is to determine the time for which a patient (or other object), who is prescribed a certain dose (in J cm^{-2}), should be exposed when the radiometer indicates irradiance in mW cm^{-2}. The relationship between these three quantities (time, dose, and irradiance) is simply:

$$\text{Exposure time (minutes)} = \frac{1000 \times \text{Prescribed dose (J cm}^{-2}\text{)}}{60 \times \text{Measured irradiance (mW cm}^{-2}\text{)}}.$$

The Standard Erythema Dose

The problem of dosimetry in skin photobiology lies in the fact that the ability of UV radiation to elicit erythema in human skin depends strongly on wavelength, encompassing a range of four orders of magnitude between 250 and 400 nm. Thus a statement that a subject received an exposure dose of 1 J cm^{-2} of UV radiation conveys nothing about the consequences of that exposure in terms of erythema. If the radiation source were a UV-A lamp, no erythemal response would be seen apart from in people exhibiting severe, abnormal pathological photosensitivity. The same dose delivered from an unfiltered xenon arc lamp or fluorescent sunlamp would result in marked erythema in most white skinned individuals. Consequently, there is often a need to express the exposure as an erythemally weighted quantity.

It has been common practice for many years to use the term *minimal erythema dose* (MED) as a "measure" of erythemal radiation. This is absurd because the MED is not a standard measure of anything but, on the contrary, encompasses the variable nature of individual sensitivity to UV radiation.

To avoid further confusing abuse of the term MED, it has been proposed (1) that this term be reserved solely for observational studies in humans and other animals. The term *Standard Erythema Dose* (SED) should be used to refer to erythemal effective radiant exposures from natural and artificial sources of UV radiation. One SED is equivalent to an erythemal effective radiant exposure of 100 J m^{-2} (2). Examples of how the SED can be used are:

- The ambient diurnal exposure on a clear sky summer day in Europe is approximately 30–40 SED
- An exposure dose of 4 SED would be expected to produce moderate erythema on unacclimatized white skin, but minimal or no erythema on previously exposed skin.

DETECTION OF UV RADIATION

Techniques for the measurement of UV radiation fall into three classes: physical, chemical, and biological. In general, physical devices measure power, whilst chemical and biological systems measure energy. The use of chemical and biological methods usually forms the basis of integrating personal ultraviolet dosimeters (see section titled "Measuring Personal Exposure to UV Radiation").

A physical UV radiation detector consists of an element that absorbs the radiation and a means of measuring the resulting change in some property of the element. There are two basic physical types: thermal and photon.

Thermal detectors respond to heat or power and have a broad spectral response with near-uniform sensitivity from the ultraviolet to the infrared, the most common example being the thermopile.

Photon detectors operate on the principle of the liberation of electrons by the absorption of a single quantum of radiation, and consequently have a nonlinear spectral response. Examples of photon detectors include: photoemissive types (vacuum phototube, gas-filled phototube, and photomultiplier tube); junction photodetectors (e.g., Si, GaAsP, GaP photodiodes), which may be operated with a "zero bias" (sometimes called "photovoltaic mode") or a "reverse bias" (sometimes called "photoconductive mode"); and photoconductors (e.g., CdS, CdSe, PbS, InAs).

More detailed descriptions of physical optical radiation detectors can be found elsewhere (3).

DOSIMETRY OF UV RADIATION

Dosimetry is the science of radiation measurement. There are two principal reasons why UV radiation should be measured: to allow consistent radiation exposure of irradiated subjects over many months and years within a local laboratory; and to allow the results of irradiations made in different laboratories to be published and compared.

It is important to distinguish between these two objectives. The first requires *precision*, or reproducibility. The radiometer is used as a monitor to give a reference measurement and so it needs to be stable. *Accuracy*, that is, absolute calibration against some accepted standard, is not essential. The second objective requires both precision and accuracy. Here the radiometer must not only be stable from one day to the next, but also the display (in, say, milliwatts per square centimetre) must be traceable to absolute standards. Whilst electro-optical technology has improved over the years, resulting in the availability of versatile and precise UV radiometric equipment, these improvements have not always been accompanied by improved accuracy due to misunderstandings about calibration.

SPECTRORADIOMETRY

It is common practice to talk loosely of *UV-A lamps* or *UV-B lamps*. However, such a label does not characterize UV lamps adequately, since nearly all UV lamps will emit both UV-A and UV-B, and even UV-C, visible light, and infrared radiation. The only correct way to specify the nature of the emitted radiation is by reference to the spectral power distribution. This is a graph (or table) that indicates the radiated power as a function of wavelength. The data are obtained by a technique known as spectroradiometry. Figure 41.1 shows the UV spectral emission from an optically filtered xenon arc lamp. This combination of lamp and filter produces a spectrum of radiation, which is similar to that of terrestrial sunlight (shown by the broken line in Fig. 41.1). For this reason it is often referred to as a *solar simulator*, and used as a laboratory source for determining

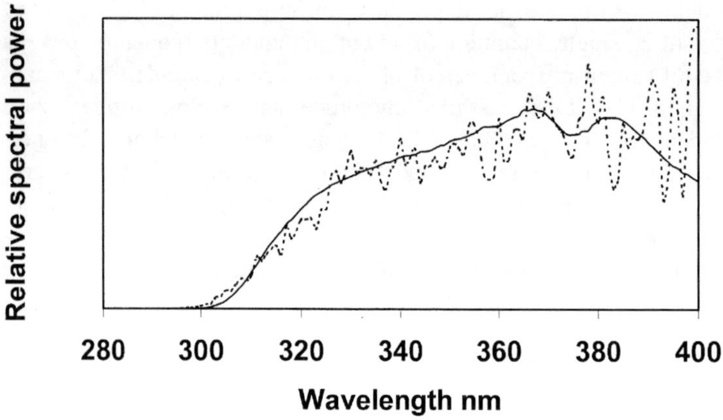

Figure 41.1 The spectral power distribution of clear sky, terrestrial UV radiation measured at around noon in summer at a latitude of 38°S (broken line) and a xenon arc filtered with a WG320 (2 mm thick) and UG5 (1 mm thick) filter (solid line).

photoprotection achieved by sunscreens (see section titled "Simulated Sources of Sunlight").

Components of a Spectroradiometer

The three basic requirements of a spectrometer system are the *input optics*, designed to conduct the radiation from the source into the *monochromator*, which disperses the radiation onto a *detector.*

Input Optics

The spectral transmission characteristics of monochromators depend upon the angular distribution and polarization of the incident radiation as well as the position of the beam on the entrance slit. For measurement of spectral irradiance, particularly from extended sources such as linear arrays of fluorescent lamps or daylight, direct irradiation of the entrance slit should be avoided. There are two types of input optics available to ensure that the radiation from different source configurations is depolarized and follows the same optical path through the system: the integrating sphere or diffusers made of either ground quartz or polytetrafluoroethylene (PTFE). Both these types of input optics produce a cosine-weighted response, since the radiance of the source as measured through the entrance aperture varies as the cosine of the angle of incidence.

Monochromator

A blazed ruled diffraction grating is normally preferred to a prism as the dispersion element in the monochromator used in a spectroradiometer, mainly because of better stray radiation characteristics. High-performance spectroradiometers, used for determining low UV spectral irradiances in the presence of high irradiances at longer wavelengths, demand extremely low stray radiation levels. Such systems may incorporate a double monochromator, that is, two single ruled grating monochromators in tandem, or laser holographically produced concave diffraction gratings can be used in a single monochromator.

Detector

Photomultiplier tubes, incorporating a photocathode with an appropriate spectral response, are normally the detectors of choice in spectroradiometers. However, if radiation intensity is not a problem, solid-state photodiodes may be used, since they require simpler and cheaper electronic circuitry.

Calibration

It is important that spectroradiometers are calibrated over the wavelength range of interest using standard lamps. A tungsten filament lamp operating at a colour temperature of about 3000 K can be used as a standard lamp for the spectral interval 250–2500 nm, although workers concerned solely with the UV region (200–400 nm) may prefer to use a deuterium lamp.

Sources of Error in Spectroradiometry

Accurate spectroradiometry, even where only relative spectral power distributions are used, requires careful attention to detail. Factors that can affect accuracy include wavelength calibration, bandwidth, stray radiation, polarization, angular dependence, linearity, and calibration sources (4).

Commercial Spectroradiometers

Modern spectroradiometers (e.g., model OL754; Optonic Laboratories, Inc., Orlando, FL, USA) incorporate a number of features that include:

- automated computer control of data collection and display
- wavelength accuracy of typically ± 0.2 nm over the spectral range 200–1600 nm
- low stray light rejection level of 1×10^{-8} at 285 nm by using a double holographic grating monochromator in combination with an order blocking filter wheel
- high sensitivity and wide dynamic range
- user selectable bandwidths.

The above type of spectroradiometer operates by stepwise scanning through the required wavelength range at scan speeds of 0.1–2 nm s^{-1}. By using a diode array as the detector in conjunction with a single grating spectrograph, instantaneous spectral power distributions can be obtained in much more compact and portable systems (e.g., Solatell; 4D Controls Ltd, Redruth, Cornwall, UK). What such a device gains in speed, cost and portability, it loses in performance in terms of stray light rejection, which is typically at a level of no better than 1×10^{-4} at 285 nm. This is particularly important in the spectroradiometry of solar UV-B (wavelengths <315 nm), but may not be problem in the spectral characterisation of UV-A lamps in studies where the investigator believes the small UV-B (and possibly UV-C) component is of no biological significance, possibly because of optical filtering.

BROAD-BAND RADIOMETRY

Although spectroradiometry is the fundamental way to characterize the radiant emission from a light source, radiation output is normally measured by techniques of broad-band radiometry. Broad-band radiometers generally combine a detector (such as a vacuum phototube or a solid-state photodiode) with a wavelength-selective device (such as a colour glass filter or interference filter) and suitable input optics (such as a quartz hemispherical diffuser or PTFE window).

Spectral Sensitivity

In order to meet the criterion for a UV-B radiometer, say, the sensor should have a uniform spectral response from 280 to 315 nm (the UV-B waveband) with zero response outside this interval. In other words, the electrical output from the sensor should depend only on the total power within the UV-B waveband received by the sensor and not on how the power is distributed with respect to wavelength. In practice, no such sensor exists with this ideal spectral response (neither does one exist that measures UV-A or UV-C correctly for that matter). All radiometers that combine a photodetector with an optical filter have a nonuniform spectral sensitivity within their normal spectral band. Consequently it is important that broad-band radiometers are calibrated appropriately for every type of UV source (where *type* refers to the spectral power distribution) that it is proposed to measure (5).

Angular Response

Broad-band radiometers are often used to measure the irradiance from extended sources of radiation such as linear fluorescent lamps or the sky. In these instances it is important that the sensor "sees" radiation coming from all parts of the source, and does not have a limited field of view; that is, the sensor is not collimated. Furthermore, the sensor should have a cosine-weighted response; this means that a sensor which is measuring irradiance on a plane must weight the incident flux by the cosine of the angle between the incoming radiation and the normal to the surface. In practice, it is very difficult to achieve a perfect cosine-weighted response, but sensors incorporating a PTFE or quartz input optic can get very close and only diverge significantly from a cosine-weighted response at angles exceeding 70° from the normal.

Radiometers That Simulate Biological Action Spectra

In evaluating sunscreen sun protection factors (SPFs), the delayed erythemal response of the skin is the relevant biological endpoint. It may be desirable therefore to use a radiometer with a spectral sensitivity to match the action spectrum for cutaneous erythema. This can be achieved reasonably well by appropriate choice of detector/filter combination, and the most widely used instrument that has this property is the Robertson–Berger meter (6). The result is that the radiometer can be calibrated to read the erythemally weighted irradiance directly. The reading is then correct for any spectral power distribution with an accuracy limited by the degree to which its spectral response differs from the erythema action spectrum.

WAVELENGTH-INDEPENDENT RADIOMETRY

In this technique, a detector is used that responds equally to all wavelengths of optical radiation, such as a thermopile, and so gives the unweighted irradiance at the point of reference. Until a few years ago, commercial thermopiles were hand-made, expensive, and fragile devices. A major advance came with the production of multiple junction thermopiles based on thin-film technology. These devices are rugged and much less expensive and typified by the Dexter range of thermopiles (Dexter Research Center, Michigan), which have found a role in dermatological photobiology.

Thermopiles measure absolute radiant power and calibration can only be achieved satisfactorily by national standards laboratories, such as the National Physical Laboratory in the UK and the National Bureau of Standards in the USA.

RADIOMETER STABILITY

It should be remembered that the sensitivity of all radiometers changes with time; frequent exposure to high intensity sources of optical radiation will accelerate this change. For this reason, it is always a sound policy to acquire two radiometers, preferably of the same type, one of which has a calibration traceable to a national standards laboratory. This radiometer should be reserved solely for intercomparisons with the other radiometer(s) used for routine purposes. A measurement of the same source is made with each radiometer and a ratio calculated. It is the stability of this ratio over a period of months and years, which indicates long-term stability and good precision.

MEASURING PERSONAL EXPOSURE TO UV RADIATION

In the laboratory, UV radiation is generally measured with bench-top radiometric systems. But in studies where personal exposure to solar UV is required—for example, in assessing the UV dose received by sunscreen compared with nonsunscreen users—this type of instrumentation can be bulky and expensive. Consequently, personal UV radiation dosimeters are available and these can be based on physical, chemical or biological devices.

Physical Dosimeters

The availability of miniature electro-optical UV sensors means that it is possible to construct small UV detectors that can be electrically coupled to a portable data logger carried in a trouser pocket, worn on a belt or clipped to clothing. By this means it is possible to record UV exposure on a second-by-second basis, which permits a clearer understanding of human behavior in sunlight (7,8).

Chemical Dosimeters

The use of chemical methods, which measure the chemical change produced by the radiation, is called *actinometry*. These techniques usually form the basis of integrating personal UV dosimeters. The most commonly used material for studies of personal UV dosimetry has been the thermoplastic, polysulfone. The basis of the method is that when film is exposed to UV radiation at wavelengths principally in the UV-B waveband, its UV absorption increases. The increase in absorbance measured at a wavelength of 330 nm increases with UV dose (9). In practice, the film (40–50 μm thick) is mounted in cardboard or plastic photographic holders. Applications of UV dosimetry with polysulfone film have included:

- sun exposure of children
- sun exposure from different leisure pursuits
- sun exposure from different occupations
- anatomical distribution of sunlight in humans and animals
- clinical photosensitivity studies
- UV exposure of patients from therapeutic light sources
- UV exposure of workers in industry.

Biological Dosimeters

Biological techniques of measurement are generally limited to the use of viruses and micro-organisms. The bacteriophage T7 has been described for use as a UV biosensor (10). It has been used to monitor ambient UV radiation, and when combined with an appropriate optical filter, a spectral response similar to the action spectrum for erythema in human skin can be achieved (11).

SIMULATED SOURCES OF SUNLIGHT

Xenon Arc Lamps

For many experimental studies in sunscreen photobiology, it is simply not practicable to use natural sunlight and so artificial sources of UV radiation designed to simulate the UV component of sunlight are employed. No such source will match exactly the spectral power distribution of sunlight and as the shorter UV wavelengths (less than around 340 nm) are generally more photobiologically active than longer UV wavelengths, the usual goal is to match as closely as possible the UV-B and UV-AII regions.

The classical so-called *solar simulator* consists of an optically filtered xenon arc lamp. This lamp has a smooth continuous spectrum in the UV region and various models of solar simulator are available with input power in the range 75 W to 6 kW and above, from companies that include Oriel Corporation, Solar Light Company, Spectral Energy Corporation and Schoeffel Optical (12). Optical filters and dichroic mirrors are used to shape the spectrum. In most cases, a 1-mm thick Schott type WG320 filter is used to control the short wavelength end of the spectrum. By varying the thickness of the filter from 1 to 1.5 or 2 mm, spectra are obtained that approximate varying solar altitudes. The simulator normally also incorporates an UV-transmitting, visible light absorbing filter (e.g., Schott UG5 or UG11) or other filters or multiple dichroic mirrors to remove visible and infrared wavelengths. The spectrum of a solar simulator is compared with natural sunlight in Fig. 41.1. A comprehensive review of solar simulators, with specific reference to sunscreen testing, is given by Wilkinson (12).

Fluorescent Lamps

A drawback of arc lamp solar simulators is that the irradiation field is generally limited to less than around 15 × 15 cm, although it is possible to achieve uniform flux over a larger area albeit with a reduction in irradiance. This may pose little problem if the object is to irradiate small areas of skin but for studies where a large area of skin or large numbers of experimental animals are to be irradiated, the limited irradiation field is a real problem. Because of this attention has turned to fluorescent lamps as sources of simulated UV (13). One way to evaluate candidate lamps and decide which is the most appropriate approximation to sunlight is to calculate the % relative cumulative erythemal effectiveness (%RCEE) for a number of wavebands and to compare these values with the %RCEE values of a "standard sun" (see Table 41.1). The %RCEE for the spectral range 290 to λ_c is the erythemally effective UV radiation within this waveband expressed as a percentage of the total erythemally effective radiation from 290 to 400 nm. This is calculated mathematically as:

$$\%\text{RCEE} = 100 \times \frac{\sum_{290}^{\lambda_c} E(\lambda)\cdot\varepsilon(\lambda)\cdot\Delta\lambda}{\sum_{290}^{400} E(\lambda)\cdot\varepsilon(\lambda)\cdot\Delta\lambda}$$

Table 41.1 Summer Solar Spectral Irradiance at Noon on Clear Days

λ (nm)	38°N[a] (W m^{-2} nm^{-1})	38°S[b] (W m^{-2} nm^{-1})	λ (nm)	38°N[a] (W m^{-2} nm^{-1})	38°S[b] (W m^{-2} nm^{-1}	λ (nm)	38°N[b] (W m^{-2} nm^{-1})	38°S[b] (W m^{-2} nm^{-1})
290	0.0000	0.0000	327	0.473	0.618	364	0.648	0.808
291	0.0000	0.0000	328	0.501	0.566	365	0.683	0.766
292	0.0000	0.0001	329	0.517	0.629	366	0.718	0.967
293	0.0001	0.0002	330	0.532	0.708	367	0.740	0.911
294	0.0002	0.0004	331	0.533	0.612	368	0.762	0.861
295	0.0007	0.0009	332	0.533	0.632	369	0.764	0.872
296	0.0012	0.0019	333	0.528	0.630	370	0.766	0.975
297	0.0023	0.0030	334	0.523	0.601	371	0.758	0.856
298	0.0033	0.0048	335	0.514	0.667	372	0.750	0.814
299	0.0060	0.0089	336	0.504	0.575	373	0.706	0.787
300	0.0086	0.0111	337	0.502	0.536	374	0.661	0.705
301	0.0161	0.0196	338	0.499	0.617	375	0.664	0.685
302	0.0236	0.0235	339	0.519	0.660	376	0.666	0.845
303	0.0335	0.0513	340	0.539	0.765	377	0.706	0.876
304	0.0435	0.0574	341	0.549	0.650	378	0.746	1.10
305	0.0577	0.0807	342	0.559	0.680	379	0.750	0.917
306	0.0719	0.0812	343	0.547	0.719	380	0.754	0.839
307	0.0844	0.113	344	0.535	0.570	381	0.698	0.957
308	0.0968	0.135	345	0.535	0.640	382	0.642	0.693

309	0.115	0.127	346	0.534	0.642	383	0.614	0.543
310	0.134	0.147	347	0.536	0.680	384	0.585	0.587
311	0.155	0.235	348	0.537	0.638	385	0.605	0.834
312	0.175	0.215	349	0.548	0.640	386	0.626	0.724
313	0.194	0.246	350	0.559	0.724	387	0.649	0.775
314	0.213	0.269	351	0.574	0.743	388	0.672	0.765
315	0.228	0.283	352	0.589	0.717	389	0.715	0.795
316	0.243	0.243	353	0.601	0.695	390	0.757	0.948
317	0.261	0.371	354	0.613	0.829	391	0.737	1.03
318	0.279	0.316	355	0.608	0.832	392	0.716	0.948
319	0.297	0.353	356	0.603	0.757	393	0.686	0.494
320	0.314	0.401	357	0.570	0.603	394	0.655	0.609
321	0.323	0.400	358	0.538	0.582	395	0.668	0.988
322	0.332	0.405	359	0.551	0.594	396	0.681	0.862
323	0.346	0.359	360	0.564	0.854	397	0.741	0.510
324	0.361	0.444	361	0.582	0.669	398	0.801	1.02
325	0.403	0.448	362	0.600	0.671	399	0.906	1.25
326	0.445	0.600	363	0.624	0.795	400	1.01	1.27

[a]Measured in Albuquerque (38°N) at noon on 3 July. Measurements were made at 2-nm intervals and interpolated values have been added here to give points every 1 nm (15).

[b]Measured in Melbourne (38°S) at solar noon on 17 January 1990. Measurements were made at the Australian Radiation Laboratory with a Spex 1680B double monochromator with a resolution of 1 nm (16).

Table 41.2 The UV-B and UV-A Components and the Percentage Relative Cumulative Erythemal Effectiveness (%RCEE) for the Summer Sun and a Number of Fluorescent Lamps

	Sun[a] (%)	A (%)	B (%)	C (%)	D (%)	E (%)
%UV-B (290–315 nm)	3.35	55.64	2.58	4.54	4.30	3.43
% UV-A (315–400 nm)	96.65	44.36	97.42	95.46	95.70	96.57
Lower and upper limits of the %RCEE according to COLIPA (14)						
<290 nm (<1.0%)	0.047	19.6	0.087	0.095	0.000	0.089
290–310 nm (46.0–67.0%)	62.3	77.6	51.4	60.7	42.8	53.4
290–320 nm (80.0–91.0%)	86.4	80.2	79.2	86.7	80.9	81.9
290–330 nm (86.5–95.0%)	91.7	80.4	86.5	92.4	88.8	89.0
290–340 nm (90.5–97.0%)	94.0	80.4	91.0	95.1	93.0	92.8
290–350 nm (93.5–99.0%)	95.8	80.4	94.5	97.1	96.4	95.9

Note: Lamp A, TL-12 ("fluorescent sunlamp"); Philips Lighting, The Netherlands; Lamp B, Bellarium S; Wolff System, Germany; Lamp C, Arimed B; Cosmedico, Germany; Lamp D, CLEO Natural; Philips Lighting, The Netherlands; Lamp E, UV-A-340; Q-Panel Lab Products, Cleveland OH, USA.
[a]Melbourne summer sun (see Table 41.1).

$E(\lambda)$ is the relative spectral power distribution of the UV source and $\varepsilon(\lambda)$ is the effectiveness of radiation of wavelength λ nm in producing erythema in human skin (2). Table 41.2 compares %RCEE values from a number of fluorescent lamps with lower and upper acceptance limits for a "standard sun" given by the European Cosmetic, Toiletry and Perfumery Association (COLIPA) (14). It can be seen that the Arimed B lamp is perhaps the best choice as a source of simulated solar UV radiation from those given, although there is little to chose between this lamp and some of the others. The TL-12 (equivalent spectrum to the Westinghouse sunlamp), a mainstay of photobiological research for many years, is a poor surrogate for solar UV radiation.

REFERENCES

1. Diffey BL, Jansén CT, Urbach F, Wulf HC. The standard erythema dose: a new photobiological concept. Photodermatol Photoimmunol Photomed 1997; 13:64–66.
2. CIE Standard. Erythema reference action spectrum and standard erythema dose. CIE S 007/E-1998. Vienna: Commission Internationale de l'Éclairage, 1998.
3. Wilson AD. Optical radiation detectors. In: Diffey BL, ed. Radiation Measurement in Photobiology. London: Academic Press, 1989:23–45.
4. Saunders RD, Murthy AV. Spectroradiometric basis for irradiance calibration. In: Matthes R, Sliney D, eds. Measurements of Optical Radiation Hazards. Vienna: International Commission on Non-Ionizing Radiation Protection, 1998:473–482.

5. Goodman T. Using broad band radiometers for measurement on sources. In: Matthes R, Sliney D, eds. Measurements of Optical Radiation Hazards. Vienna: International Commission on Non-Ionizing Radiation Protection, 1998:589–601.
6. Berger DS. The sunburning ultraviolet meter: design and performance. Photochem Photobiol 1976; 24:587–593.
7. Diffey BL, Saunders PJ. Behaviour outdoors and its effect on personal ultraviolet exposure rate measured using a portable datalogging dosimeter. Photochem Photobiol 1995; 61:615–618.
8. Autier P, Doré J-F, Reis AC, Grivegnée A, Ollivaud L, Truchetet F, Chamoun E, Rotmensz N, Severi G, Césarini J-P. Sunscreen use and intentional exposure to ultraviolet A and B radiation: a double blind randomized trial using personal dosimeters. Br J Cancer 2000; 83:1243–1248.
9. Diffey BL. Ultraviolet radiation dosimetry with polysulphone film. In: Diffey BL, ed. Radiation Measurement in Photobiology. London: Academic Press, 1989:135–139.
10. Rontó G, Gáspár S, Gróf P, Bérces A, Gugolya Z. Ultraviolet dosimetry in outdoor measurements based on bacteriophage T7 as a biosensor. Photochem Photobiol 1994; 59:209–214.
11. Quintern LE, Furusawa Y, Fukutsu K, Holtschmidt H. Characterization and application of UV detector spore films: the sensitivity curve of a new detector system provides good similarity to the action spectrum for UV-induced erythema in human skin. J Photochem Photobiol 1997; 37:158–166.
12. Wilkinson F. Solar simulators for sunscreen testing. In: Matthes R, Sliney D, eds. Measurements of Optical Radiation Hazards. Vienna: International Commission on Non-Ionizing Radiation Protection, 1998:653–684.
13. Brown DB, Peritz AE, Mitchell DL, Chiarello S, Uitto J, Gasparro FP. Common fluorescent sunlamps are an inappropriate substitute for sunlight. Photochem Photobiol 2000; 72:340–344.
14. COLIPA. Sun Protection Factor Method. Brussels: European Cosmetic Toiletry, and Perfumery Association (COLIPA), 1994.
15. Sayre RM, Cole C, Billhimer W, Stanfield J, Ley RD. Spectral comparison of solar simulators and sunlight. Photodermatol Photoimmunol Photomed 1990; 7:159–165.
16. Gies HP, Roy CR, McLennan A, Diffey BL, Pailthorpe M, Driscoll C, Whillock M, McKinlay AF, Grainger K, Clark I, Sayre RM. UV protection by clothing: an intercomparison of measurements and methods. Health Phys 1997; 73:456–464.

42

Spectral Standardization of Sources Used for Sunscreen Testing: 5 Years of Compliance

Robert M. Sayre and John C. Dowdy

Rapid Precision Testing Laboratories, Cordova, Tennessee and University of Tennessee Center for the Health Sciences, Memphis, Tennessee, USA

INTRODUCTION

In 1978, the US FDA published a report and monograph on sunscreen product testing and labeling (1). This monograph established that a solar simulator would be a source having a continuous emission spectrum from 290 to 400 nm and be filtered for a solar zenith angle of 10° and have less than 1% of its energy contributed by wavelengths shorter than 290 nm. In addition, to avoid purported thermal problems, they also required that the solar simulator could not have more than 5% of its energy contributed by wavelengths longer than 400 nm. The beam uniformity is required to be within 10%. Specifically, latter monographs have recommended that a solar simulator requires periodic remeasurement with a calibrated spectroradiometer to insure the proper spectral distribution (2–4).

Efforts to refine the specifications of the solar simulator used for SPF testing have, over time, resulted in several additional proposed and adopted standards. In1990 Sayre et al. proposed a spectral standard for solar simulators recommending an upper- and lower-wavelength range appropriate for SPF testing (5). A similar, slightly less stringent, implementation of this approach was subsequently adopted in the Australian/New Zealand Standard for evaluation and classification of sunscreen products (6).

In 1994 COLIPA (The European Cosmetic, Toiletry, and Perfumery Association) published a method to test sunscreen products together with specifying a compliance standard for solar simulators (7). In 1999 the US Food and Drug Administration (FDA) was petitioned urging the adoption of the COLIPA Standard for Solar Simulators (8). The latest rendition of the Final Monograph did not formally adopt this recommendation, but as of this writing there is at least one petition to reopen the monograph pending (4).

The COLIPA standard requires that the spectrum of a solar simulator be measured throughout the ultraviolet (UV) from 250 to 400 nm. The spectrum measured is multiplied by the Commission Internationale de l'Éclairage (CIE) (McKinlay–Diffey) erythemal action spectrum to calculate the effective irradiance (9). The solar simulator is specified based on the percentage of erythemal effective radiation within a series of overlapping spectral ranges (Table 42.1), which is termed percent relative cumulative erythemal effectiveness (%RCEE).

An important point to consider about this standard is that unlike natural sunlight, it requires only 1% of the erythemally effective risk to be at UV-A wavelengths longer than 350 nm. The other point about this standard is that

Table 42.1 COLIPA (1994) Solar Simulator Specifications

Percent erythemal effective irradiance (%RCEE) (nm)	Acceptance limits (%)
<290	<1.0
290–310	46.0–67.0
290–320	80.0–91.0
290–330	86.5–95.0
290–340	90.5–97.0
290–350	93.5–99.0

there is no requirement that the source be absolutely continuous and a source with prominent spectral lines is acceptable as long as it meets the overall requirements. One finds that in addition to xenon arcs, mercury metal halide lamps and even fluorescent lamps can meet the standard. SPF testing labs in the USA and Canada, however, almost exclusively use filtered xenon arc Solar Light (Solar Light Co., Inc., Philadelphia, PA) solar simulators of the single port or multiport design.

Unlike Europe, where sunscreens are typically categorized as cosmetics not subject to regulatory mandate, the US FDA regulates sunscreen products as over-the-counter drugs (1–3). Consequently, SPF testing laboratories servicing the US market routinely monitor their solar simulators for compliance with all applicable standards as part of their respective quality assurance programs. This study, presented in part to the 2000 International Congress of Photobiology, presents a retrospective compilation of solar simulator compliance data from six participating North American SPF testing laboratories for the 5-year period from 1995 to 2000 (10).

METHODS

Measurement of a solar simulator requires three separate activities: calibration of the spectroradiometer, measurement of the source, and finally a recheck of the instrument response and recalibration of the system.

Instrumentation

The instrument used for these measurements is an OL-754 double grating spectroradiometer (Optronic Laboratories, Inc., Orlando, FL). For solar simulator spectral measurement the spectroradiometer was configured with an integrating sphere with a 6 mm entrance aperture to collect the radiation and 0.125/1.0/0.125 mm slits. This spectroradiometer comes with a device to check the photometric gain using a small tungsten–halogen source and check the wavelength accuracy using a small fluorescent source. Before each calibration and measurement the wavelength calibration and gain are checked or established.

Calibration Procedures

The OL 754 spectroradiometer was calibrated using a tungsten–halogen spectral irradiance standard lamp annually certified traceable to NIST. The calibration was transferred in 1 nm increments using procedures established by the manufacturer (Optronic Laboratories) of both the spectroradiometer and the NIST traceable tungsten standard source. The calibration spectrum used is the average of three spectral measurements of the standard.

Measurement Procedures

Spectral irradiance measurements were made at 1 nm intervals from 250 to 800 nm. Data were saved to magnetic media and identified using a portion of the solar simulator site/serial number to establish the identity of the system measured. The center of the beam at the site for irradiating human volunteers was selected for spectroradiometric measurement and represents the highest intensity to which a human volunteer might be exposed. A special plug-in aperture was used to position the liquid waveguides of multiport solar simulators.

The final quality control check, conducted after solar simulator spectral irradiance measurements, consisted of repeating all checks performed prior to calibration. The result of this check and the subsequent recalibration of the system with the tungsten standard source indicate that the spectral radiometer functioned the same throughout this period of measurement.

Measurement Uncertainty

Our estimate is that the total possible uncertainty for measuring a solar simulator is less than 12% (Table 42.2). The major sources of uncertainty, potentially up to 10%, is that which may be attributed to reproducible positioning of the spectroradiometer relative to the source and to changing laboratory environments. The uncertainty from changing laboratory environments is due to different levels of electronic noise, temperature, and humidity between laboratories and the same laboratory from visit to visit.

RESULTS

A typical Solar Light single-port solar simulator, used for sunscreen SPF testing, consists of a 150 W ozone-free xenon arc which is filtered with a WG-320 filter

Table 42.2 Measurement Uncertainty Factors

Uncertainty factor	Uncertainty (%)	Uncertainty squared
1. Standard lamp uncertainty to NIST	2	0.0004000
2. Calibration transfer to spectroradiometer	3	0.0009000
3. Stray radiation	0.10	0.0000010
4. Nonlinearity of response throughout measurement range	1	0.0001000
5. Wavelength uncertainty	0.20	0.0000040
6. Wavelength repeatability	1	0.0001000
7. Noise in measurements	0.10	0.0000010
8. Reproducibility of measurements	1	0.0001000
9. Source positioning uncertainty	5	0.0025000
10. Laboratory environment	10	0.0100000
Sum quadrature uncertainties		0.0141060
Uncertainty		11.88%

of appropriate thickness and generally a UG-11 to remove excess visible. A set of representative spectral measurements collected on a typically configured single-port solar simulator (Fig. 42.1) show from year to year that there has not been much change in spectral distribution and only very slight variation in power level. Only one solar simulator using the less common configuration of a UG-5 filter in place of the usual UG-11 (Fig. 42.2) was monitored in this study. Over the years there appear to be some minor changes in the UV-B distribution; however, this variation is not progressing from year to year.

The other type of solar simulator commonly used for sunscreen SPF testing in North America is the Solar Light multiport. It has six complete sets of optics, configured with WG-320 and UG-11 filters, and six waveguides. The multiport's cooling fans force hot air over the waveguides, which consequently show thermal aging over time and periodically must be replaced. Compared to the single-port solar simulators, the multiport systems (Fig. 42.3) show a comparable magnitude of spectral variability per waveguide from year to year.

To compare solar simulators within the framework of COLIPA, we analyzed all data for each solar simulator, or multiport light guide, throughout the period of measurement and calculated the mean COLIPA results along with the standard deviation. This we have replotted (Fig. 42.4) within the %RCEE limits for all COLIPA ranges plus an additional non-COLIPA category for UV-A longer than 350 nm.

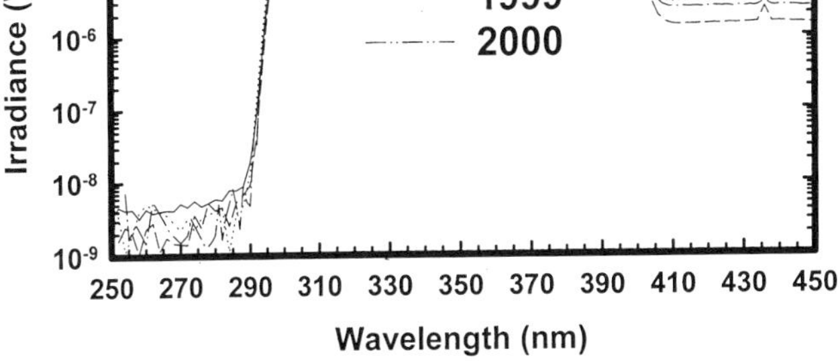

Figure 42.1 Spectral measurements collected on a typically configured Solar Light single-port solar simulator. For over 5 years, with regular maintenance, there was little detectable change in spectral cutoff or distribution over the 290–350 nm range and only slight variation in power level. Typical configuration consists of a 150 W ozone-free xenon arc combined with a WG-320 short-wavelength cutoff filter and a UG-11 UV band pass filter to limit visible emission.

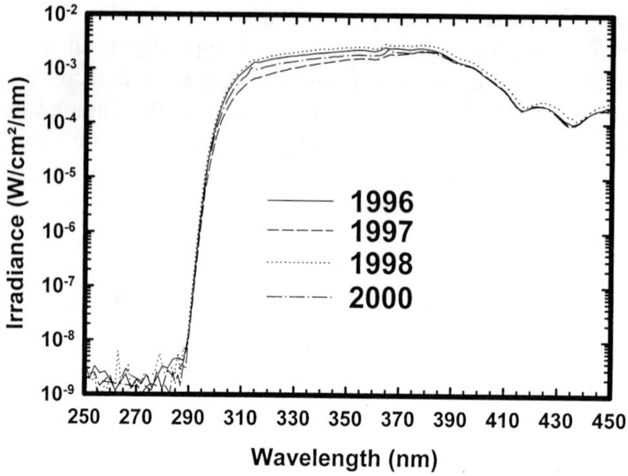

Figure 42.2 Spectral measurement series of a UG-5 single-port solar simulator. Over the measurement period reported, there is some variation in the 295–370 nm range, which does not appear to be a function of measurement interval. This configuration uses a UG-5 bandpass filter which does not limit visible emission to the same extent as the UG-11.

For the single-port solar simulators (Fig. 42.4A), stray radiation of <290 nm is in the lower half of the range allowed. In the 290–310 nm range, some diversity is observed. Over the next four ranges, the data for individual single-port systems are consistently in the upper acceptable range tending to push the limit. For the final non-COLIPA range of UV-A longer than 350 nm, all single-port solar simulators are at the bottom of the range allowed, that is, they have significantly less UV-A-1.

For the multiport solar simulator (Fig. 42.4B), stray radiation of <290 nm for all waveguides is also in the lower half of the range allowed. For the 290–310 nm range, there is some diversity, but unlike the single ports the waveguides all lie at the bottom of the limit range. In the 290–320 nm range, the waveguides lie just below midlimit range. Over the next three ranges, the data for individual waveguides are uniformly in the middle of the acceptable range. For the final non-COLIPA range of UV-A longer than 350 nm, all solar waveguides are at the middle of the range allowed, still there is significantly less UV-A-1.

DISCUSSION

The solar simulators presented in this study are all commercial units. All units are used daily and are well maintained. From the presentation of this set of representative solar simulators at six laboratories, it is clear that these devices not only are consistently compliant but also have changed very little even with extensive

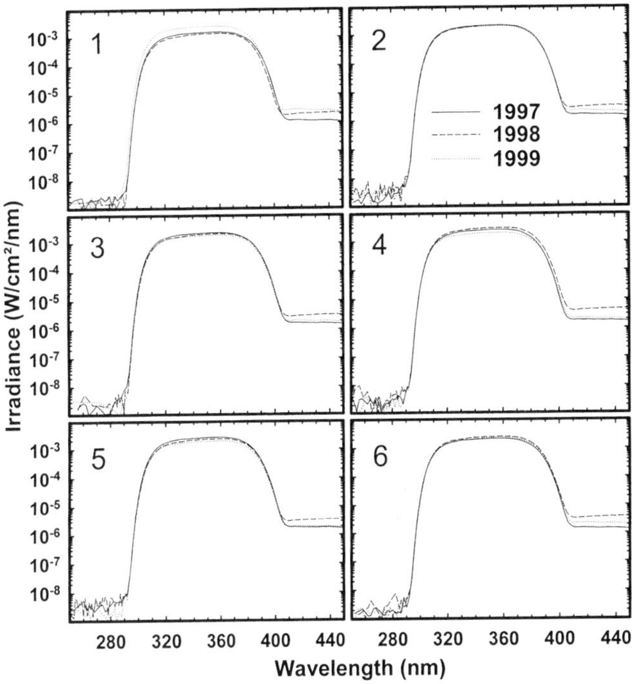

Figure 42.3 Characteristic multiport solar simulator spectral series. This model solar simulator is arrayed with six identical sets of optics (1–6) incorporating liquid light guides in addition to the usual WG-320 and UG-5 filter combination. Through several cycles of annual remeasurement, the multiport solar simulators showed spectral distribution and variability similar to comparably filtered single-port systems.

usage during the years reported. In spite of periodic lamp replacement, the long-term changes to individual solar simulators or between different solar simulators at various locations have all been minor. However, because many systems appear to push limits, it is critical that exacting standards of measurement are followed. It is equally important that the spectral radiometric equipment be rigorously maintained and precise checks performed in association with each measurement made.

It is unlikely that within this particular grouping of instruments, with the possible exception of the UG-5 system, any test might be different because of the particular solar simulator used. However, with only a single multiport solar simulator being included in this review, potentially the multiport type may be less stable from year to year because of the optical complexity of maintaining waveguides and in essence having six independent optical systems potentially aging at different rates.

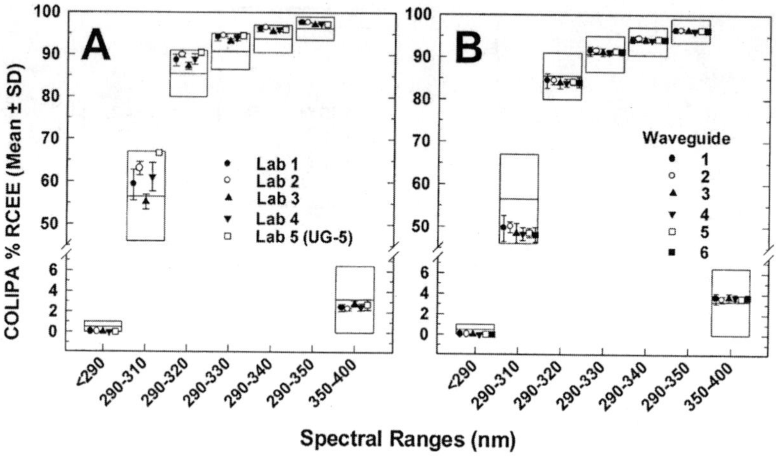

Figure 42.4 Comparison of single-port and multiport solar simulators. To compare solar simulators over time within the framework of COLIPA, we have analyzed all data throughout the period of measurement for each single-port solar simulator (A) or multiport waveguide (B). The mean COLIPA %RCEE results along with the standard deviation calculated are shown within the COLIPA limit range for all ranges. The single-port solar simulators all invariably push the maximum limits of the acceptable COLIPA ranges. An additional non-COLIPA >350 nm range shows that neither type of solar simulator appears to have abundant levels of UV-A-1 radiation.

In this review we have shown that a particular set of solar simulators have successfully been maintained to a rather tight and reproducible spectral profile over a period of years. However, the emission limits of the COLIPA specification have been suggested as being too broad (8). This was demonstrated by the failure of identical products to produce comparable SPFs when tested with solar simulators at opposite ends of the COLIPA acceptance limits (11). With proper maintenance, solar simulators should be able to meet a tighter revised standard in the future.

CONCLUSION

The spectral standardization of solar simulators used for sunscreen SPF testing is important because the resulting SPF of a sunscreen product should be independent of the solar simulator used for testing, the testing location, and the date tested. Spectral standards for solar simulators used for SPF testing are specified within the requirements of the 1978, and subsequent, US FDA sunscreen monographs and the 1994 COLIPA SPF test method. Most solar simulators employed in sunscreen testing by reputable US and Canadian laboratories have been routinely monitored for compliance with applicable standards for many years. This retrospective presents a compilation of solar simulator compliance data from six participating North American SPF testing laboratories over a 5-year period from 1995 to 2000. During this period solar simulators, with proper laboratory maintenance have met the standard(s) and have continued to do so from year to year even when used daily.

REFERENCES

1. Food and Drug Administration. Sunscreen drug products for over-the-counter human use. Fed Reg 1978; 45:38208–38269.
2. Food and Drug Administration. Tentative final monograph. Fed Reg 1993; 58:28194–28302.
3. Food and Drug Administration. Sunscreen Drug Products for Over-the-Counter Human Use. Final Monograph. In: Federal Register, GPO, 1999:27666–27693.
4. Part 352—Sunscreen Drug Products for Over-the-Counter Human Use. In: Code of Federal Regulations, Title 21, US Government Printing Office, 2001:275–285.
5. Sayre RM, Cole C, Billhimer W, Stanfield J, Ley RD. Spectral comparison of solar simulators and sunlight. Photodermatol Photoimmunol Photomed 1990; 7:159–165.
6. Australian/New Zealand Standard. Sunscreen Products—Evaluation and classification. Standards of Australia and Standards of New Zealand, 1998.
7. COLIPA. Colipa Sun Protection Factor Test Method. The European Cosmetic, Toiletry and Perfumery Association—Colipa, 1994.
8. Sunscreen Drug Products for Over-the-Counter Human Use. Final Monograph. Extension of Effective Date: Reopening of Adminstrative Record. In: Federal Register, GPO, 1999:36319–36324.
9. A reference action spectrum for ultraviolet induced erythema in human skin. In: Human Exposure to Ultraviolet Radiation: Risks and Regulations. Proceedings of a seminar held in Amsterdam, March 23–25, 1987. Amsterdam: Excerpta Medica, 1987:83–87.
10. Sayre RM, Dowdy JC, Damstra M, Harrison LB, Lockhart L, Schwartz S, Wood C, Potrebka JL, Shanahan RW. 13th International Congress of Photobiology, San Francisco, 2000:254.
11. Sayre RM, Stanfield J, Bush AJ, Lott DL. Sunscreen standards tested with differently filtered solar simulators. Photodermatol Photoimmunol Photomed 2001; 17:278–283.

43

In Vitro Techniques in Sunscreen Development

Joseph W. Stanfield
Suncare Research Laboratories, LLC, Winston Salem, North Carolina, USA

INTRODUCTION

The ideal index of sunscreen protection would predict product performance in understandable terms for all consumers over the full range of possible conditions of use. Such an index would be measurable with reliability and precision for all product forms and compositions, and its measurement would be rapid and inexpensive and would not require testing on humans or animals. Unfortunately, there is no such index, at present, and the chronic effects of sunlight are not understood sufficiently to permit rigorous definition of the need for sunscreen protection beyond prevention of sunburn.

There is general agreement that the sun protection factor, SPF, is a valid index of protection against acute sunburn, although the SPF measured on human subjects has been reported to vary by as much as 20% among test subjects and by as much as 40% among laboratories (1). Factors that make accurate SPF measurements difficult include the inherent nonuniformity of product application, variability of lamp spectra and the subjectivity of the minimal erythema dose (2,3). At present, the SPF serves as an accepted measure of sunscreen protection and the benchmark for *in vitro* methods of formula assessment.

A common misconception is that the goal of *in vitro* SPF measurement is to quantitate protection against outdoor sunburn. The true goal of *in vitro* SPF measurement is to predict the product SPF measured on humans in the laboratory using an artificial light source. If the SPF measured *in vitro* is sufficiently accurate, the sunscreen formulator has a powerful and economical resource for use in screening new formulas for further testing. If the SPF predicted by *in vitro* measurement matches the SPF measured *in vivo*, it is reasonable to assume that the *in vitro* transmittance spectrum is correct. Then the formulator has a valuable resource that can permit preliminary assessment of product protection against any portion of the solar spectrum for any acute or chronic effect of sunlight having a known action spectrum.

Over the past three decades, *in vitro* measurements of sunscreen SPF have yielded varying degrees of success, particularly for the current generation of sunscreens with high SPFs and finely tuned emulsions, and newer actives such as avobenzone and others that are yet not approved for use in the USA.

This chapter will present basic principles, describe experience to date and discuss problem areas and solutions for *in vitro* measurements of sunscreen protection.

BASIC PRINCIPLES OF *IN VITRO* MEASUREMENTS OF SUNSCREEN PROTECTION

The *in vitro* SPF test simulates the *in vivo* SPF test by measuring the sunburning energy transmitted through a sunscreen on a suitable substrate. This is shown schematically in Fig. 43.1.

The ultraviolet (UV) detector system may be a spectrophotometer, a spectroradiometer, or a photometer with a response corresponding to the erythema action spectrum. For a spectrophotometer the UV source is a built-in xenon arc

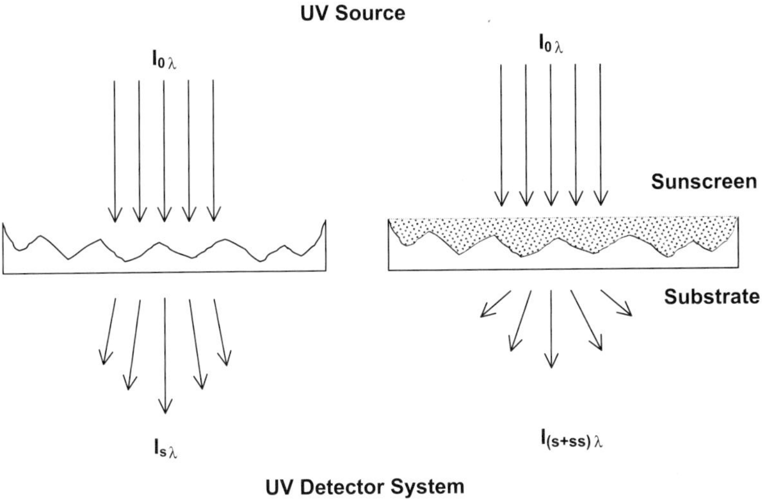

Figure 43.1 Schematic diagram of the *in vitro* SPF test.

or flash lamp or a tungsten lamp. For a spectroradiometer or photometer the source is usually external and may be a xenon arc lamp solar simulator or other type of lamp selected by the user.

The sunscreen spectral transmittance is given by:

$$T_\lambda = \frac{I_{(\mathrm{s+ss})\lambda}}{I_{\mathrm{s}\lambda}} \quad (1)$$

where $I_{(\mathrm{s+ss})\lambda}$ is the spectral irradiance transmitted by the sunscreen/substrate, $I_{\mathrm{s}\lambda}$ is the spectral irradiance transmitted by the substrate alone, and $I_{0\lambda}$ is assumed constant.

The SPF of the sunscreen for a given UV source is then calculated using the expression developed by Sayre et al. (4):

$$\mathrm{SPF} = \frac{\int_{290}^{400} I_{0\lambda} s_\lambda \, \mathrm{d}\lambda}{\int_{290}^{400} I_{0\lambda} T_\lambda s_\lambda \, \mathrm{d}\lambda} \quad (2)$$

where $I_{0\lambda}$ is the spectral irradiance of the UV source and s_λ is the erythemal effectiveness factor for wavelength λ as defined by MacKinlay and Diffey (5). The erythemal effectiveness curve is shown in Fig. 43.2.

Figure 43.3 shows the standard solar spectrum, which represents a maximal solar spectrum for a cloudless sky and high solar elevation angle at 35–40° north latitude (6).

Figure 43.4 shows the spectrum of a typical 150 W xenon arc solar simulator (Model 16S, Solar Light Company, Philadelphia) with a 1 mm WG320 UV-C-blocking filter (Schott), a heat-rejecting dichroic mirror, and a UG-11 visible/infrared-blocking filter (Schott).

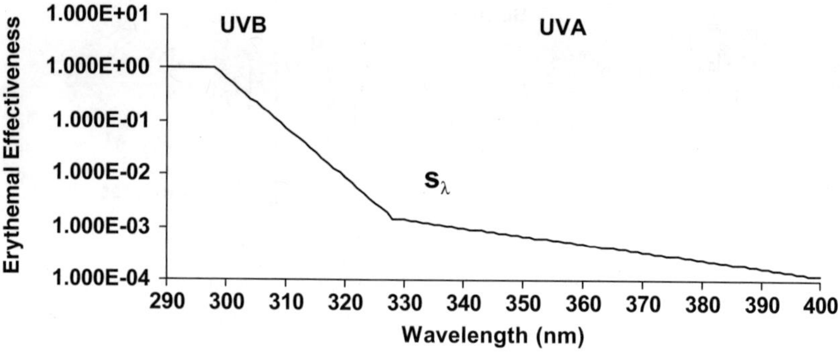

Figure 43.2 The erythemal effectiveness curve. [From McKinlay and Diffey (5).]

From Figs. 43.3 and 43.4, it is apparent that solar simulator spectra may differ significantly from solar spectra, particularly at wavelengths shorter than 300 nm and longer than 370 nm.

EXPERIENCE WITH *IN VITRO* MEASUREMENTS OF SUNSCREEN PROTECTION

Early *In Vitro* Measurements of Sunscreen SPF

In 1978, Sayre and coworkers (4), reported the results of SPF measurements of seven commercially avaliable sunscreens on human volunteers, in isopropanol solutions and from thin films on excised hairless mouse epidermis. The sunscreen formulas had mean SPF values on human volunteers ranging from 4.6 to 17.4, for panels of 10 or 11 volunteers, each. Measurements of sunscreen absorbance

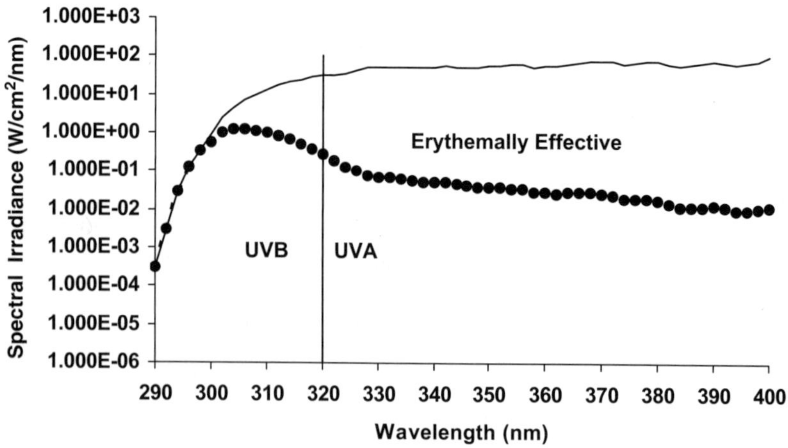

Figure 43.3 The standard solar spectrum. [From COLIPA (6).]

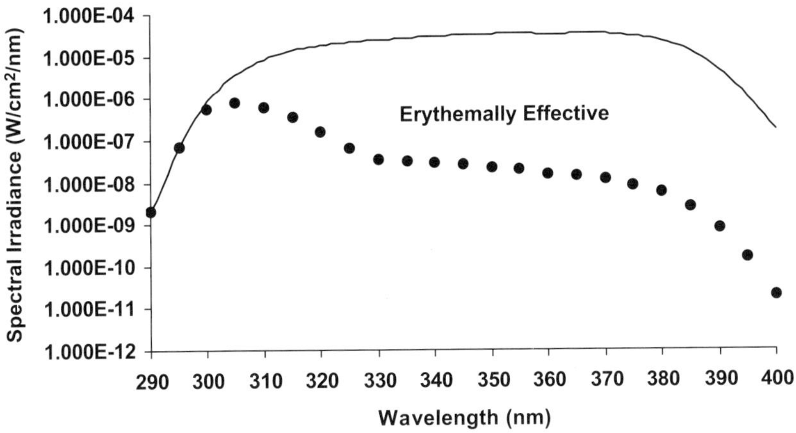

Figure 43.4 A typical solar simulator spectrum.

spectra in isopropanol solutions and computation of SPF for these formulas yielded values from 10 times to 10^{17} times the mean SPF values measured on human volunteers. Measurements of sunscreen absorbance spectra on excised hairless mouse epidermis yielded mean SPF values ranging from 57% to 131% of mean SPF values measured on human volunteers for the same formulas. These results are shown in Table 43.1.

In 1980, Sayre and coworkers (7) reported comparisons of water-resistant SPF measured on hairless mouse epidermis and on human subjects for six sunscreen formulas. The sunscreen formulas had mean SPF values on human subjects ranging from 2.8 to 8.0 for panels of 10–20 volunteers, each, after 40 min of exposure to circulating water or outdoor swimming. Measurements of sunscreen forward scattering spectra on excised hairless mouse epidermis after 40 min of

Table 43.1 SPF from the Human SPF Test, Isopropanol Solutions, and Hairless Mouse Epidermis

Product	SPF from human volunteers[a]	SPF from isopropanol solutions	SPF from hairless mouse epidermis
A	17.4 ± 3.2	3.9×10^{18}	22.8 ± 10.1
C	13.0 ± 4.1	1.4×10^{9}	12.4 ± 9.3
G	12.0 ± 3.1	2.8×10^{2}	6.8 ± 1.5
B	8.2 ± 2.7	8.0×10^{7}	10.2 ± 0.0
E	8.1 ± 2.4	7.9×10^{8}	9.5 ± 4.9
D	6.7 ± 1.7	6.5×10^{6}	6.8 ± 1.2
F	4.6 ± 1.0	6.6×10^{5}	3.4 ± 0.5

[a]$n = 10$ or 11.

Source: From Sayre et al. (4).

Table 43.2 Water Resistant SPF (40 min) Measured on Human Subjects and Hairless Mouse Epidermis

	Product				
	A	B	C	D	E
Human	2.8	3.7	5.1	5.8	8.0
Hairless mouse epidermis	2.5	5.3	4.8	7.8	13.0

Source: From Sayre et al. (7).

exposure to a water bath yielded mean SPF values ranging from 71% to 112% of mean SPF values measured on human subjects for the same formulas. These results are shown in Table 43.2.

Sayre and coworkers measured sunscreen absorbance spectra of sunscreen films by obtaining forward scattering scans of hairless mouse epidermis, with and without the sunscreens. Sunscreens were applied at 2 $\mu L/cm^2$, which was the same amount used for testing on human volunteers. Forward scattering spectra were measured at 5-nm intervals from 250 to 400 nm, using a Beckman spectrophotometer fitted with an integrating sphere. A 2-mm UG-5 filter was used in both the sample beam and the reference beam to remove fluorescence emitted in the visible region by the mouse epidermis and some of the sunscreen ingredients. The authors stated that without this correction the SPF values would have been much less accurate for many of the sunscreens tested.

At that time, there was no satisfactory explanation for the discrepancy between results for solutions of ingredients and SPF values measured on human subjects. Similar discrepancies with SPF values measured on human subjects were seen for measurements on quartz plates and thin film "sandwiches" of products between quartz plates. The failure of these methods was attributed to lack of interactions with the skin surface and even failure of the physical laws governing spectroscopic measurements. The accuracy of results for thin films on a biological substrate was a substantial improvement over solution methods.

The O'Neill Step Film Model

In 1984, O'Neill (8) used an elegant step film model to show that plausible irregularities in sunscreen film thickness can account for large discrepancies in predicted SPF. The step film model is shown schematically in Fig. 43.5 as a uniform, homogeneous film of absorbing material of thickness d and unit length. A portion of the film of length g and thickness fd is removed and added to the remaining portion, as shown by the dashed line. This produces two film fractions with thicknesses d' and $(1-f)d$ and lengths g and $1-g$.

Since the amount of absorbing material stays constant, the expression for d' is:

$$d' = d\left(\frac{fg}{1-g} + 1\right) \tag{3}$$

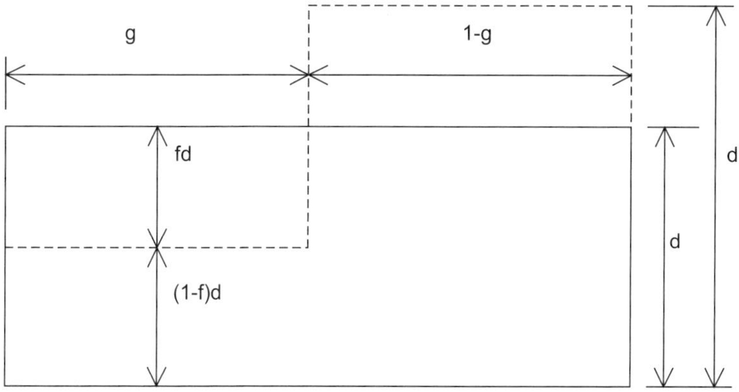

Figure 43.5 O'Neill's step film model.

O'Neill defined the opacity of a sunscreen at a given wavelength λ as:

$$P(\lambda) = (I_0/I)_\lambda = 10^{k(\lambda)cd} \tag{4}$$

where I_0 and I are the intensities of incident and transmitted light, respectively, $k(\lambda)$ is the absorbtivity molar extinction coefficient, c is the molar concentration, and d is the optical path length.

The average intensity of light transmitted by the step film is:

$$I_s = gI_1 + (1 - g)I_2 \tag{5}$$

where I_1 and I_2 are the intensities of light transmitted by the depleted and augmented areas, respectively.

Then the average opacity of the step film, $P_s(\lambda)$, can be written as a function of d, f, and g as:

$$P_s(\lambda) = P_c(\lambda)\left[g \times 10^{-k(\lambda)cdf} + (1 - g)10^{-k(\lambda)cd(fg/(1-g))}\right]^{-1} \tag{6}$$

where $P_c(\lambda)$ is the opacity of the original, undistorted film at wavelength λ.

O'Neill calculated the opacities of step films derived from uniform films with opacities of 10, 1000, and 1,000,000 for values of f and g ranging from 0.1 to 1.0. In all cases, the average opacity of the distorted film was significantly less than that of the original, uniform film. He further noted that the greater the opacity of the original film, the greater the relative decrease in opacity.

The step model is related to sunscreen applied to skin by the fact that a fluid applied to the skin tends to accumulate in the sulci, which are furrows that unfold with body movement, and recede from the plateaus, creating regions of relatively thin coverage and relatively thick coverage. Nonhomogeneity of a sunscreen due to an intact emulsion or poor distribution of absorbing ingredients would have the same effect. The step model permits any number of elements of arbitrary size and shape and is considered valid on the scale of irregularities of thickness or concentration fine enough that the pattern of sunburned and protected skin would be averaged by the eye when evaluating the degree of erythema. O'Neill concluded that a highly absorbing sunscreen with non-uniform coverage would exhibit an overall opacity many orders of magnitude lower than a uniform, homogeneous film.

SPF Predictions Using the Step Film Model

Herzog (9) calibrated the step film parameters using three sunscreen standard formulas [COLIPA Standards P1, P3, and P4 (10)] with known SPF values and demonstrated SPF predictions for 36 different sunscreen formulations. The calibration was accomplished using mean extinction coefficients derived for the combination of active ingredients in the standard formulas to compute values of f and g that approximated their *in vivo* SPF values. Since there was no single set of f and g values that reproduced the *in vivo* SPF values for all three standard sunscreen formulas, Herzog derived a function, Δ_{fg}, that described the overall quadradic deviation of the calculated SPF values from the *in vivo* SPF values. Then, using a 200×200 matrix of f and g values from 0 to 1, calculated the minimum value of Δ_{fg} for the three standard sunscreen formulas by a computerized numerical optimization process. The values of f and g were 0.935 and 0.269, respectively. The calculated SPF value for standard P1 was 5.0 (*in vivo* SPF = 4.2); the calculated SPF value for standard P3 was 10.9 (*in vivo* SPF = 15.5), and the calculated SPF value for standard P4 was 38.5 (*in vivo* SPF = 35.7). Finally, Herzog used the aforementioned values of f and g to calculate the SPFs of 36 sunscreen formulas with known *in vivo* SPF values. From a least squares linear regression curve fit of *in vivo* SPF vs. SPF from the step film model, the slope was 0.83, the intercept on the ordinate was 0.55 and the correlation coefficient, r^2, was 0.8.

Herzog observed that the accuracy of the estimation was in the same range as that for *in vitro* SPF tests (11). Herzog's approach was remarkable in that it predicted synergisms of mixtures of active ingredients using mean extinction coefficients derived for combinations of active ingredients in each formula. Herzog also pointed out that the model does not consider the rheology of emulsions, which determine the homogeneity of sunscreen films, nor does the model consider photostability. Based on the slope of 0.83 for the linear regression line, the method tended to underestimate the *in vivo* SPF. Although the step film model yields valuable insights, its shortcomings described above support the need for accurate and reproducible *in vitro* SPF measurements.

Substrates for *In Vitro* Measurements of Sunscreen Protection

Diffy and Robson (12) introduced the use of a surgical tape known as Transpore® tape (3M Corporation) as a substrate for *in vitro* SPF measurements in 1989. The advantages of Transpore® tape included its transparency, the reservoir effect of holes intended to allow the skin to "breathe" and its availability and economy, compared to hairless mouse skin or human stratum corneum.

In 1993, Sottery (13) introduced Vitro-Skin® as a commercial sunscreen testing substrate, containing protein and lipid components, that was designed to have topography, pH, surface tension, and ionic strength similar to human skin. The manufacturer recommended hydrating the substrate for at least 12 h at approximately 90% relative humidity to ensure simulation of the moisture content of human skin. Sottery compared *in vitro* SPF values obtained using Vitro-Skin® to those obtained using Transpore® tape and Naturalamb® condoms (Church & Dwight, Princeton, NJ). Results for a sunscreen product with an *in vivo* SPF of 12 were SPF values of 4, 10.7, and 14.6, for Transpore® tape, the Naturalamb® condom and Vitro-Skin®, respectively. For a sunscreen product with an *in vivo* SPF of 21.8, results were SPF values of 57.8, 75, and 23.3, for Transpore® tape, the Naturalamb® condom, and Vitro-Skin®, respectively. Another comparison, using a product with an *in vivo* SPF of 19.8, produced values of 81.1 and 54.7, for Transpore® tape and Vitro-Skin®, respectively. Results appeared to favor Vitro-Skin®, and the investigators attributed results, at least for the SPF 12 product, to emulsion breaking behavior on Vitro-Skin® more similar to that on skin than for the other two substrates. There are few literature reports on the use of the Naturalamb® condom substrate, although our laboratory has obtained results similar to those reported above.

Also in 1993, Pearse and Edwards (14) demonstrated the use of human stratum corneum as a substrate for *in vitro* sunscreen testing, although results were not sufficiently improved to justify wide usage.

Tunstall (10) analyzed Transpore® tape and Vitro-Skin® using O'Neill's step model and demonstrated excellent agreement between measured and calculated SPF values for 1%, 2.5%, and 10% solutions of octinoxate applied at 2 $\mu L/cm^2$. Tunstall found that Vitro-Skin® produced more uniform data than Transpore® tape by eliminating the small areas of uncovered substrate present on the latter. Tunstall also pointed out that both Vitro-Skin® and Transpore® tape yield SPF values similar to that of the SPF test on human skin by providing a "sink" for a large portion of the formulation in deep crevices, similar to those on the skin surface. Tunstall reported that Vitro-Skin® absorbed 81% of the formulation and Transpore® tape absorbed 56%, in this manner.

Results are described below for *in vitro* SPF measurements using roughened plexiglass and polymethyl methacrylate (PMMA) substrates. For both substrates, the sunscreen application amount was reduced to compensate for their poor simulation of skin topography.

Critical Wavelength

In 1994, Diffey (15) proposed the use of critical wavelength as an index of the relative UV-A protection provided by sunscreen products. The critical wavelength was defined as the wavelength at which the integral of the absorbance curve reaches 90% of the integral from 290 to 400 nm. The critical wavelength test was designed to provide a rapid, inexpensive, and reliable measure of broad spectrum protection that is essentially independent of SPF, but ensures long-wavelength UV-A protection commensurate with SPF. In 2000, Diffey and coworkers (16) reported results of a study of 59 commercially available and several experimental sunscreen formulas. Sunscreens were applied at 1 mg/cm^2 to hydrated Vitroskin® substrates, preirradiated with a full-spectrum UV dose in J/cm^2 numerically equal to 1/3 of the labeled SPF, to account for any lack of photostability, and then subjected to spectrophotometry. The authors defined a critical wavelength of 370 nm as a "significant" level of broad-spectrum protection and found that $<10\%$ of the commercial formulas satisfied this criterion. They concluded that a recognized long-wave UV-A active ingredient such as titanium dioxide, zinc oxide, or avobenzone is necessary for a sunscreen formula to achieve a critical wavelength $\geq$370 nm. They also found good correlation between the critical wavelength and UV-A protection measured *in vivo* using the phototoxic protection factor. The use of a ratio independent of absolute absorbance is considered attractive, because the amount of sunscreen on the substrate may be adjusted to prevent "saturation" of a spectroradiometer, which occurs when the sunscreen absorbs too much of the sample beam energy to permit measurements.

Simultaneous *In Vitro* Measurement of SPF and Photostability

In the SPF test conducted *in vivo* on human subjects (6,17), UV doses are administered to sunscreen-protected and unprotected skin sites. For sites where the erythemally effective UV dose crosses the threshold for minimally perceptible erythema (MPE), the skin displays erythema responses that are apparent 16–24 h later. The dose that produces MPE is the minimal erythema dose (MED). The sunscreen SPF is the ratio of the MEDs for sunscreen-protected and unprotected skin sites. Since there is no way to observe MPE during the administration of UV doses, a series of progressively increasing doses is administered to sunscreen-protected and unprotected skin sites and results for each UV dose are evaluated the next day.

In 2001, Stanfield and coworkers (18,19) reported an *in vitro* method for simulating the SPF test using a single UV dose administered to a sunscreen applied to a substrate. The method employed a 150-W xenon arc lamp identical to that used for *in vivo* SPF measurement to irradiate the sunscreen after application to 5-cm diameter disks cut from Naturalamb® condom material. The substrate was placed over the aperture of an integrating sphere attached to a spectroradiometer (Model OL 754, Optronic Laboratories, Orlando, FL) and the spectral irradiance of the UV source and spectral transmittance of the substrate were measured from 290 to 400 nm. Then the spectral transmittance of the sunscreen/substrate combination was measured from 290 to 400 nm at 1- or 2-min intervals during irradiation, until the total erythemally effective dose transmitted by the sunscreen exceeded 1 MED, where 1 MED was defined as 0.020 erythemally effective J/cm^2. Each 1- or 2-min interval represented a 2–4 MED increase in the total dose applied by the UV source. This approach permitted recording the time course of SPF during irradiation of the sunscreen. The final cumulative SPF of the sunscreen corresponded to the SPF measured by the *in vivo* SPF test, regardless of whether the SPF was constant during the UV exposure. If the SPF was constant during the UV exposure, the sunscreen was considered photostable and if the SPF decreased significantly during irradiation the sunscreen was considered photolabile.

This approach to *in vitro* SPF measurement is shown schematically in Fig. 43.6.

As shown in Figs. 43.1 and 43.6, the applied spectral irradiance is denoted by $I_{0\lambda}$ and the spectral irradiance transmitted by the substrate is denoted as $I_{s\lambda}$ and is measured before the sunscreen is applied. The spectral transmittance of the substrate, $\tau_{s\lambda}$, is assumed to be constant and is calculated as:

$$\tau_{s\lambda} = I_{s\lambda}/I_{0\lambda} \tag{7}$$

The spectral irradiance transmitted by the sunscreen/substrate combination is denoted by $I_{(s+ss)\lambda}$ and is given by:

$$I_{(s+ss)\lambda} = I_{0\lambda}\tau_{s\lambda}\tau_{ss\lambda} \tag{8}$$

Then

$$\tau_{ss\lambda} = I_{(s+ss)\lambda}/I_{0\lambda}\tau_{s\lambda} \tag{9}$$

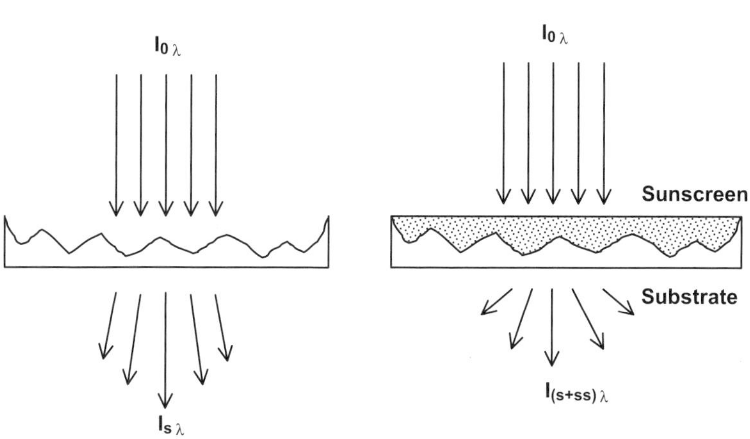

Figure 43.6 Schematic diagram of the *in vitro* SPF test.

and the SPF is computed as:

$$\mathrm{SPF} = \frac{\int_{290}^{400} I_{0\lambda} s_\lambda \, \mathrm{d}\lambda}{\int_{290}^{400} \frac{I_{(\mathrm{s+ss})\lambda} s_\lambda \, \mathrm{d}\lambda}{\tau_{\mathrm{s}\lambda}}} \tag{10}$$

where s_λ is the erythemal effectiveness coefficient (5) for wavelength λ and $\mathrm{d}\lambda$ is the wavelength increment.

The SPF computed using Eq. (10) represents the SPF at a given time during irradiation of the sunscreen/substrate. The spectral irradiance of the UV source, $I_{0\lambda}$, is assumed constant. Since the SPF of the sunscreen may vary with applied UV dose, a more useful concept is the cumulative SPF, $\mathrm{SPF_c}$. To compute $\mathrm{SPF_c}$, it is necessary to replace the erythemally effective spectral irradiance values in Figs. 43.1 and 43.6 with their integrals over time and wavelength, which yields the applied erythemally effective UV energy dose, E_0, the erythemally effective UV dose transmitted by the sunscreen/substrate, $E_{(\mathrm{ss+s})}$, and, with the use of the spectral transmittance of the substrate, the erythemally effective UV dose transmitted by the sunscreen, E_{ss}:

$$E_0 = \int_0^{t_{\mathrm{MED}}} \int_{290}^{400} I_{0\lambda} s_\lambda \, \mathrm{d}\lambda \, \mathrm{d}t \tag{11}$$

$$E_{\mathrm{ss}} = \int_0^{t_{\mathrm{MED}}} \int_{290}^{400} \frac{I_{(\mathrm{s+ss})\lambda} s_\lambda \, \mathrm{d}\lambda}{\tau_{\mathrm{s}\lambda}} \tag{12}$$

The units of $I_{0\lambda}$ and $I_{(\mathrm{ss+s})\lambda}$ are power/unit area/length (W/cm^2/nm), the units of the erythemal effectiveness coefficient, s_λ, are erythemally effective energy per unit area/energy per unit area [erythemally effective (J/cm^2)/(J/cm^2)], the unit of $\mathrm{d}\lambda$ is length (nm) and the unit of $\mathrm{d}t$ is time (s). Therefore, the units of E_0 and E_{ss} are erythemally effective J/cm^2. Since the erythemally effective UV energy dose required to produce minimally perceptible erythema (1 MED) ranges from 15 to 60 erythemally effective mJ/cm^2 (20), E_0 and E_{ss} may be divided by an arbitrary MED value of 20 erythemally effective mJ/cm^2 and expressed in multiples of the MED. Ideally, the MED value chosen would correspond to the mean MED for the subjects of the *in vivo* SPF panel in which the formula is tested.

From the definition of SPF (sunscreen-protected UV dose required to produce minimally perceptible erythema/unprotected UV dose required to produce minimally perceptible erythema), it follows that $\mathrm{SPF_c}$ may be defined as the value of the applied erythemally effective energy required to produce 1 MED of erythemally effective energy transmitted by the sunscreen. Thus, $\mathrm{SPF_c}$ is the value of E_0 at time t_{MED}, when E_{ss} reaches 1 MED. This mimics the sunscreen SPF test on humans, but requires only one UV dose instead of the series of five or seven progressively increasing UV doses used in the human SPF test. Typical transmission curves for photostable and photolabile sunscreens are shown in Fig. 43.7.

UV-A Index

In 2001 Wendel and coworkers (21) proposed the UV-A index as a means of labeling sunscreens according to their relative UV-A protection. The UV-A index was defined as the ratio of the *in vitro* persistent pigment darkening (PPD) factor to the labeled *in vivo* SPF. To determine the UV-A index the sunscreen is applied to a substrate, its spectral transmission, T_λ, is measured for wavelengths from 290 to 400 nm, the *in vitro* SPF is determined using Eq. (1) and the spectral absorbance, A_λ, is calculated for each wavelength as:

$$A_\lambda = -\log(T_\lambda) \tag{13}$$

Then the adjusted spectral transmittance, T^*_λ, is calculated as:

$$T^*_\lambda = 10^{-A\lambda c} \tag{14}$$

where c is adjusted by trial and error until the *in vitro* SPF calculated by Eq. (1) equals the *in vivo* SPF, that is,

$$\textit{In vitro}\ \text{SPF} = \frac{\int_{290}^{400} I_\lambda s_\lambda \, d\lambda}{\int_{290}^{400} I_\lambda T^*_\lambda s_\lambda \, d\lambda} = \textit{In vivo}\ \text{SPF} \tag{15}$$

Then the adjusted spectral transmittance, T^*_λ, is used to calculate the *in vitro* PPD factor as:

$$\text{PPDF} = \frac{\int_{320}^{400} E_\lambda p_\lambda \, d\lambda}{\int_{320}^{400} E_\lambda T^*_\lambda p_\lambda \, d\lambda} \tag{16}$$

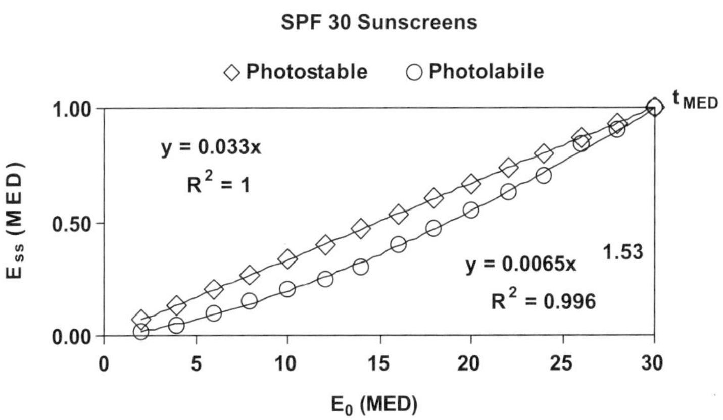

Figure 43.7 Typical transmission curves for photostable and photolabile sunscreens.

where E_λ is the spectral irradiance of the UV-A source and p_λ is the PPD effectiveness factor (22).

Finally, the UV-A index is defined as:

$$\text{UV-A index} = \frac{100\ \text{PPDF}}{\textit{In vivo}\ \text{SPF}} \tag{17}$$

Ring Test of *In Vitro* SPF, PPDPF, and UV-A Index Measurements

In 2002, results were reported for a ring test of *in vitro* SPF, PPDPF, and UV-A Index measurement in seven European test centers using five measuring devices on five commercial sunscreens for which SPFs had been determined independently on human subjects (23). The five measuring devices were spectrophotometers, as described in Table 43.3. The sunscreens included two formulas with organic sunscreens and three formulas with a combination of organic and inorganic sunscreens, and are listed in Table 43.4.

The substrates were roughened Plexiglas® (Type XT, colorless, 24770 UVD, Röhm GmbH, Darnstadt, Germany) plates for single use. A roughened PMMA plate with a uniform layer of glycerin was used as a reference.

Although the method does not require a specific application amount, 0.75 mg/cm^2 of each sunscreen was applied. The sunscreens were spotted evenly across the plate surface and rubbed using a presaturated fingertip or finger cot for 30 s with light pressure. After evaporation of the volatile components, the spreading was continued for another 30 s with significantly higher pressure. Plates were equilibriated in the dark for at least 15 min. The transmittance was then measured from 290 to 400 nm in 1-nm steps. Measurements were performed on at least three plates at four locations per plate.

Results for *in vitro* SPF measurements, PPD protection factor measurements and UV-A index measurements are shown in Tables 43.5–43.7, respectively.

Correlations between *in vitro* and *in vivo* SPF values calculated by this author are shown in Fig. 43.8. The correlation coefficient, R^2, for a linear regression curve fit with a slope of 0.50 was 0.38, which showed poor reproducibility among laboratories. There was a pronounced increase in variability of results with increasing SPF, which is consistent with the greater sensitivity of high SPF values to small changes in transmittance.

Correlations between *in vitro* and *in vivo* PPD protection factors calculated by this author are shown in Fig. 43.9. The correlation coefficient, R^2, for a linear regression curve fit with a slope of 1.01 was 0.93, which shows excellent reproducibility among laboratories. The improvement in reproducibility over the SPF results shown in Fig. 43.8 is attributed to two factors. First, the transmittance spectra of the sunscreens were adjusted to agree with the *in vivo* SPF, removing the variability in the original *in vitro* SPF measurements. Second, the lower numerical values of PPD protection factor are less sensitive to variability in transmittance. The high reproducibility of PPD protection factors demonstrates that a

Table 43.3 UVA Index Ring Test Laboratories and Instruments

Lab	Instrument/type	Type of beam	Light source	Integrating device	Detection system
1	Varian, Cary 3	Double beam, monochromatic	Deuterium D_2/halogen H1	Integrating sphere	Double monochromator before sample + PMT[a]
2	Optometrics SPF290	Single beam, polychromatic	Xenon arc 125 W	Integrating sphere and quartz diffuser	Monochromator + PMT[a]
3	Dr. Kockott	Single beam, polychromatic	Xenon arc 150 W	Integrating sphere or dispersing disk	Grating, spectral detector or integral detector with sensitivity adjusted to erythema action spectrum
4	Optometrics SPF290	Single beam, polychromatic	Xenon arc 125 W	Integrating sphere and quartz diffuser	Monochromator + PMT[a]
5	Optometrics SPF290	Single beam, polychromatic	Xenon arc 125 W	Integrating sphere and quartz diffuser	Monochromator + PMT[a]
6	Varian, Cary 3	Double beam, monochromatic	Deuterium D_2/halogen H1	Integrating sphere	Double monochromator before sample + PMT[a]
7	Perkin Elmer, Lambda 16	Double beam, monochromatic	Deuterium D_2/halogen H1	Integrating sphere	Double monochromator before sample + PMT[a]

[a]Photomultiplier tube.
Source: From Gers-Barlag et al. (23).

Table 43.4 UV-A Index Ring Test Sunscreen Products

Product	Labeled SPF[a]	Type of emulsion	Active ingredients
A	12	O/W[b]	Octinoxate Avobenzone
B	15	W/O[c]	4-Methylbenzylidene camphor[a] Octisalate Avobenzone Octocrylene
C	15	O/W	Octinoxate Zinc oxide Octinoxate
D	24	Hydrodispersion (emulsifier-free)	4-Methylbenzylidene camphor[a] Ethylhexyl triazole[a] Avobenzone Titanium dioxide
E	30	O/W	Octocrylene Titanium dioxide Avobenzone Terephthalylidene dicamphorsulfonic acid[a]

[a]Not approved in the USA.
[b]Oil-in-water.
[c]Water-in-oil.
Source: From Gers-Barlag et al. (23).

simple correction factor applied uniformly across the transmittance spectrum effectively corrects for variability of SPF measurements. The relatively high reproducibility of UV index values reflects the high reproducibility of PPD protection factors.

For the five sunscreen products evaluated, the authors showed that the UV index was a more sensitive measure of broad spectrum sunscreen performance and permits more discrete labeling categories than critical wavelength.

Table 43.5 UV-A Index Ring Test Results for *In Vitro* SPF Measurements

Sample	*In vivo*	Lab 1	Lab 2	Lab 3	Lab 4	Lab 5	Lab 6	Lab 7
A	12	8.3	7.1	6.2	8.4	9.1	8.2	8.2
B	15	9.1	14.2	14.5	13.4	7.7	14.2	13.9
C	15	7.4	5.3	3.6	5.2	3.5	4.5	5.7
D	24	23.8	14.4	10.4	14.4	15.4	14.9	6.9
E	30	17.5	17.6	6.1	16.8	13.8	15.1	26.5

Source: From Gers-Barlag et al. (23).

Table 43.6 UV-A Index Ring Test Results for PPD Protection Factor Measurements

Sample	*In vivo*	Lab 1	Lab 2	Lab 3	Lab 4	Lab 5	Lab 6	Lab 7
A	1.8	2.2	2.2	2	2	2.1	2.1	2.4
B	4.5	6	6.1	5.8	5.8	5.1	6.1	6.3
C	ND	1.9	2.4	2.2	2.2	1.5	2.1	2.3
D	5	6.2	6.7	5.1	5.1	6.5	5.8	7.4
E	10.5	10.3	12.2	10.4	10.4	11.9	9.5	13.5

Source: From Gers-Barlag et al. (23).

European Ring Test of *In Vitro* SPF Measurements

In 2003, results were reported for a ring test of *in vitro* SPF measurement in six European test centers using two SPF calculation approaches and four measuring devices on 10 commercial sunscreens whose SPF had been determined independently on human subjects (24).

The four measuring devices included a spectroradiometer, two spectrophotometers and a photometer, and are described in Table 43.8. The sunscreens included eight formulas with organic sunscreens and two formulas with a combination of organic and inorganic sunscreens, and are listed in Table 43.9.

The substrates were 50 mm × 50 mm PMMA plates (Helioplates, Helioscience, Creil, France) with a 5 μm medium roughness. The sunscreen was spotted evenly on the plate and weighed before spreading or evaporation occurred. Then using light pressure, the product was spread immediately until a uniform distribution was achieved. Samples were allowed to settle at room temperature for 15 min. A roughened PMMA plate with a uniform layer of glycerin was used as a reference.

The transmittance was measured from 290 to 400 nm in 1-nm steps. Up to nine UV transmittance spectra were measured from each substrate at different locations, except for those instruments that measured the whole area of the plate. Five different plates were used for each sunscreen (except Lab 6) for

Table 43.7 Ring Test Results for UV-A Index Measurements

Sample	Lab 1	Lab 2	Lab 3	Lab 4	Lab 5	Lab 6	Lab 7
A	8.3	7.1	6.2	8.4	9.1	8.2	8.2
B	9.1	14.2	14.5	13.4	7.7	14.2	13.9
C	7.4	5.3	3.6	5.2	3.5	4.5	5.7
D	23.8	14.4	10.4	14.4	15.4	14.9	6.9
E	17.5	17.6	6.1	16.8	13.8	15.1	26.5

Source: From Gers-Barlag et al. (23).

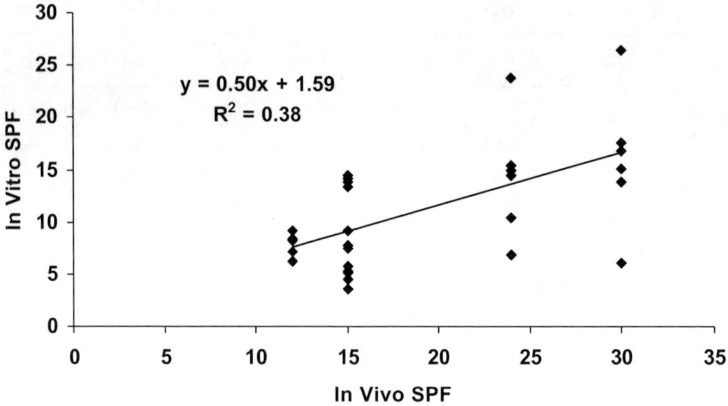

Figure 43.8 Correlations between *in vitro* and *in vivo* SPFs from the UV-A index ring test. [From Gers-Barlag et al. (23).]

calculating average SPF data.The test was conducted in two rounds, the first using an application amount of 1.4 mg/cm^2. The results showed excessively high values for the *in vitro* SPF, so the second round was conducted using a lower application amount of 1.2 mg/cm^2. Results of the first and second rounds are shown in Tables 43.10 and 43.11, respectively.

Correlations between *in vitro* and *in vivo* SPF values calculated by this author are shown for products with *in vivo* SPF values of 40 and lower in Fig. 43.10. The correlation coefficient, R^2, for a linear regression curve fit with a slope of 0.84 was 0.77, which showed good reproducibility among laboratories,

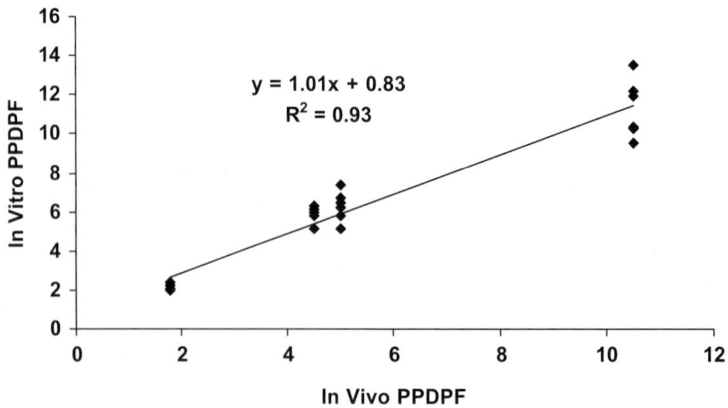

Figure 43.9 Correlations between *in vitro* and *in vivo* PPDs protection factor from the UV-A index ring test. [From Gers-Barlag et al. (23).]

Table 43.8 European Ring Test Laboratories and Instruments

Instrument	Lab	Type	Integrating device	Detection system
OL754[a]	1	Spectroradiometer	Sphere behind sample	Double monochromator PMT
UVIKON 933[b]	3, 4	Spectrophotometer	Sphere behind sample	Single monochromator PMT
UV 1000S[c]	2, 5	Spectrophotometer	Sphere before sample	Diode array
Sunscreen tester[d]	6	Photometer	Sphere behind sample	Integrating detector with spectral sensitivity approximating erythema spectrum

[a]Optronic 754, Optronic Laboratories, Inc. Orlando, FL, USA.
[b]Kontron UVIKON, UVK-LAB Service, Trappes, France.
[c]Labsphere UV 1000S, Labsphere, North Sutton, NH, USA.
[d]Kockott UV Technik, UV technik, Hanau-Steinheim, Germany.
Source: From Pissavini et al. (24).

considering the wide variety of instruments and techniques used. Note that product J, containing octinoxate, octisalate, and avobenzone, showed high variability among laboratories and poor distribution about the linear regression line. This could be explained by a lack of photostability of product J. Other formulas containing similar combinations of ingredients have been observed in our laboratory to have poor photostability. There was also high interlaboratory variability for products with *in vivo* SPF values >17.

Correlations between *in vitro* and *in vivo* SPF values calculated by this author are shown for products with *in vivo* SPF values ≥ 37 in Fig. 43.11. The correlation coefficient, R^2, for a linear regression curve fit with a slope of 0.66 was 0.08, which showed very poor reproducibility between laboratories. The authors pointed out that product E, containing microfine titanium dioxide, octinoxate, benzophenone-3, and octisalate was known to have "physical instability." Again, in our laboratory we have observed poor photostability for at least one formula with a similar combination of active ingredients. The authors also pointed out that product C showed good interlaboratory reproducibility, but had *in vitro* SPF values well below the *in vivo* SPF. This was explained by the presence of "anti-inflammatory" ingredients in the formula, which suppressed erythema in the *in vivo* SPF test and raised the SPF by a mechanism other than absorbing UV energy.

Table 43.9 European Ring Test Sunscreen Products

Product	SPF[a]	Active ingredients
A	6 ± 1.2	Octinoxate
		Avobenzone
		4-Methylbenzylidene camphor[b]
B	7 ± 1.4	Avobenzone
		Methylene bis-benxotriazole[b]
		Tetramethylbutylphenol[b]
D	12 ± 2.4	Avobenzone
		Octinoxate
F	17 ± 3.4	Octinoxate
		Benzophenone-3
		Octisalate
		Avobenzone
J	18 ± 3.6	Octinoxate
		Octisalate
		Avobenzone
I	37 ± 7.4	Microfine titanium dioxide
		Octinoxate
		Benzophenone-3
H	38 ± 7.6	Benzophenone-3
		Avobenzone
		4-Methylbenzylidene camphor[b]
		Diethylhexyl butamido triazone[b]
		Ensulizole
K	40 ± 8.0	Octinoxate
		Isoamyl *p*-methoxycinnamate[b]
		Octisalate
		Benzophenone-3
		Ensulizole
		Avobenzone
		Methylene bis-benzotriazoyle[b]
		Tetramethylbutylphenol[b]
E	58 ± 11.6	Microfine titanium dioxide
		Octinoxate
		Benzophenone-3
		Octisalate
C	79 ± 15.8	Avobenzone
		Octyl triazole[b]
		Octocrylene
		Octinoxate

[a]20 Volunteers ±20%.
[b]Not approved in the USA.
Source: From Pissavini et al. (24).

Table 43.10 European Ring Test Results for *In Vitro* SPF Measurements with Products Applied at 1.4 mg/cm^2

	Product									
	A	B	C	D	E	F	H	I	J	K
In vivo	6	7	79	12	58	17	38	37	18	40
Lab 1	8	6	54	12	67	23	58	46	59	78
Lab 2	8	5	46	10	56	20	46	36	46	74
Lab 3	8	4	42	10	57	16	31	31	42	59
Lab 4	8	8	50	15	103	18	39	49	39	95
Lab 5	8	9	57	15						
Mean	8	6	50	12	71	19	44	40	47	77
SD%	1	32	12	21	31	16	26	21	19	19

Source: From Pissavini et al. (24).

DISCUSSION

Product SPF Values

High SPF values are more sensitive to small changes in transmittance, as shown in Table 43.12. This illustrates the necessity for precise control of the variables discussed above to permit accurate and reproducible *in vitro* measurements for high SPF products.

Product Application and Substrate Considerations

Application of a sunscreen product to the skin involves high shear forces. To spread well over the uneven skin surface, sunscreens are formulated to have a

Table 43.11 European Ring Test Results for *In Vitro* SPF Measurements with Products Applied at 1.2 mg/cm^2

	Product									
	A	B	C	D	E	F	H	I	J	K
In vivo	6	7	79	12	58	17	38	37	18	40
Lab 2	6	4	28	7	37	16	20	21	19	37
Lab 3	4	3	32	5	31	12	23	22	21	34
Lab 4	6	4	33	5	69	17	24	28	21	37
Lab 5	6	6	40	10	59	17	36	40	31	41
Lab 6	6	5	43	8	50	13	30	44	25	28
Mean	6	4	35	7	49	15	27	31	24	36
SD%	17	29	17	34	32	16	23	34	20	14

Source: From Pissavini et al. (24).

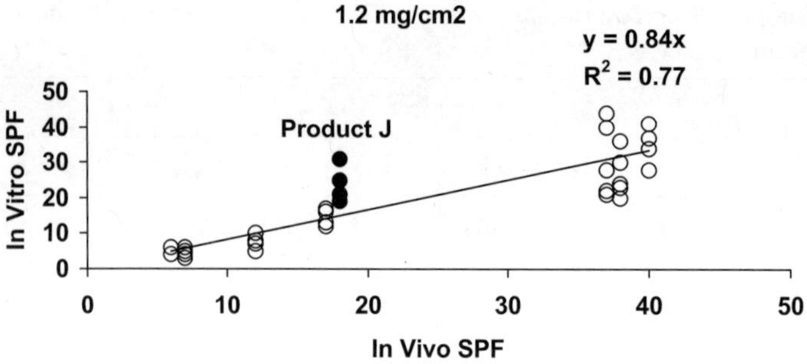

Figure 43.10 Correlation between *in vitro* and *in vivo* SPF values for products with low *in vivo* SPF values. [Modified from Pissavini et al. (24).]

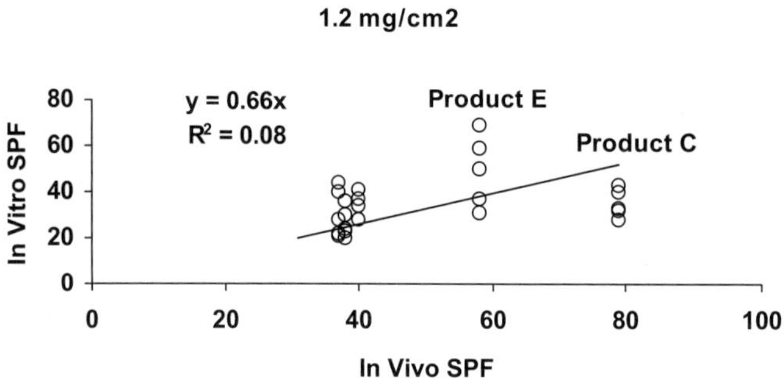

Figure 43.11 Correlation between *in vitro* and *in vivo* SPF values for products with high *in vivo* SPF values. [Modified from Pissavini et al. (24).]

low viscosity at high shear. After the product has been spread over the skin, it should recover its structure quickly to maintain an even film. If the viscosity remains low, the product will flow into the sulci, or crevices, of the skin, resulting in uneven coverage, with a thin layer on the plateaus and a large, ineffective reservoir in the sulci (25). This reduces SPF dramatically, as shown by

Table 43.12 Sensitivity of SPF to Small Changes in Transmittance

	SPF						
	2	8	15	30	45	50	80
Transmittance of erythemally effective energy (%)	50.0	12.5	6.7	3.3	2.2	2.0	1.3
% Decrease in SPF for a 1% increase in transmittance	2	7	13	22	31	33	46

O'Neill (8). The topography of the skin has a strong influence on this process, which is a major reason the substrate for *in vitro* measurements must resemble skin to permit accurate SPF measurements.

Since many highly protective sunscreen products are oil-in-water emulsions with the UV absorbers in the oil phase, the emulsion must break to achieve a continuous film of sunscreen on skin. Surface properties of skin such as salt content influence the behavior of emulsions on skin. Since the water content is significant, the degree of water absorption by skin also plays a large role. The substrate should duplicate the properties of human skin to the maximum extent possible, particularly topography, moisture content, surface protein and lipid components, pH, critical surface tension, and ionic strength (13). The substrate should also be as transparent to UV as possible.

In view of the foregoing considerations, Vitro-Skin® appears to be the best choice of substrate available for *in vitro* SPF measurements.

In the *in vivo* SPF test, 2 $mg/cm^2 \pm 2.5\%$ of each product is applied to the skin by "spotting" droplets of product on the test site with a distribution of approximately one droplet per 2 cm^2, then rubbing lightly with a finger cot for 20–50 s with circular, then linear motion. The amount of product applied must be corrected for the amount lost on the finger cot. Products are allowed to dry without any UV exposure for 15–30 min. The recommended ambient temperature range is 18–26°C (26). Conditions of the *in vitro* SPF test should match those of the *in vivo* SPF test, to the maximum extent possible.

UV Source

For the *in vitro* SPF test, the source of UV energy should be identical to that used in the human SPF test in terms of spectrum, total power, beam uniformity and collimation, and temporal stability. Ideally, the UV source will have a feedback system for regulating output.

Newly published international spectral limits for lamps used for SPF testing are shown in Table 43.13. The total irradiance is required to be below

Table 43.13 Solar Simulator Requirements

Wavelength range (nm)	Measured % relative contribution to erythemal effectiveness: Lower limit	Upper limit	Standard solar spectrum %
<290		<1	0.0
290–300	2.0	8.0	7.2
290–310	49.0	65.0	56.5
290–320	85.0	90.0	84.2
290–400	100.0	100.0	100.0

Source: Modified from Ref. (26).

the threshold for causing pain during UV doses on sunscreen-protected skin, between 120 and 160 mW/cm^2 (26). Most solar simulators used for *in vivo* SPF testing operate at total power levels near 150 mW/cm^2, or 2 erythemally effective mW/cm^2. Typical MEDs on the order of 20 erythemally effective mJ/cm^2 require exposure times on the order of 10–30 s. Undoubtedly, there is local heating of the sunscreen film by the lamp beam, which alters its distribution on skin.

Obviously, the UV sources in many of the systems commonly used for *in vitro* SPF measurements differ significantly from UV sources used for *in vivo* SPF measurements, in spectral distribution of power and total irradiance. This could partially account for discrepancies between *in vitro* and *in vivo* measurements of SPF.

Beam Geometry

Solar simulators irradiate the skin with a collimated beam, which is absorbed, transmitted, and scattered by the sunscreen. Transmitted and forward scattered radiation produces the resulting erythema in the dermis. Forward scattering may occur at more oblique angles when sunscreen is applied to the substrate, as shown in Figs. 43.1 and 43.6. For accurate *in vitro* measurement of sunscreen transmittance, the beam geometry must mimic that of the *in vivo* sunscreen test to the maximum possible extent. It is also essential to collect as much of the forward scattered radiation as possible. This requires the use of an integrating sphere, and that the sunscreen/substrate must be as close to the sphere aperture as possible.

Photostability

Early *in vitro* predictions of the SPFs for sunscreen formulas containing avobenzone yielded erroneously high values. Subsequently it was shown that many sunscreen formulas containing avobenzone were not photostable (27–31). These formulas had high initial SPFs which declined rapidly during irradiation. SPF ratings determined in the human *in vivo* test were valid, but were overestimated by *in vitro* tests. Preirradiation with measured UV doses has permitted more accurate *in vitro* estimates of SPF (29). However, these formulas may be even more unstable in sunlight and significantly less protective for consumers than the label indicates.

The method presented by Stanfield and coworkers described in the section titled "Simultaneous *In Vitro* Measurement of SPF and Photostability" permits assessment of sunscreen photostability using the UV doses encountered in the *in vivo* SPF test. It may be possible to use the same approach with simulated or actual sunlight to assess sunscreen protection of consumers under relevant exposure conditions, particularly when there is concern about the photostability of a particular formulation.

Applications of Sunscreen Transmittance Spectra

Once a valid transmittance spectrum is obtained for a sunscreen formula, it may be possible to adjust the source spectrum to assess protection against sunburn over the course of a day or year or effects of various ozone depletion scenarios. In addition, exploratory assessments of protection against other effects of sunlight that have known action spectra are possible. Preliminary action spectra are available for nonmelanoma skin cancer (32), UV-B-induced immune suppression (33), and photoelastosis (34).

CONCLUSIONS

Accurate and reliable *in vitro* measurement of sunscreen SPF is difficult due to the large number of variables. These variables can be managed to produce acceptable results. The *in vitro* SPF test should incorporate the best available substrate for matching the properties of skin, and the application technique, UV source and beam geometry should mimic those used in the *in vivo* test.

An accurate match of the *in vivo* SPF confirms the accuracy of the sunscreen transmittance spectrum. An accurate sunscreen transmittance spectrum permits evaluation of UV-A protection and useful assessments of sunscreen protection against a wide variety of acute and chronic effects under relevant conditions of UV radiation.

REFERENCES

1. Brown MW. The sun protection factor: test methods and legal aspects. SÖFW 2002; 128:10–18.
2. Lott DL, Stanfield J, Sayre RM, Dowdy JC. Uniformity of sunscreen product application: a problem in testing, a problem for consumers. Photodermatol Photoimmunol Photomed 2003; 19:17–20.
3. Sayre RM, Stanfield J, Lott D, Dowdy JC. Simplified method to substantiate SPF labeling for sunscreen products. Photodermatol Photoimmunol Photomed 2003; 19:254–260.
4. Sayre RM, Poh Agin PA, LeVee GJ, Marlowe E. A comparison of in vivo and in vitro testing of sunscreening formulas. Photochem Photobiol 1979; 29:559–566.
5. McKinlay A, Diffey B. A reference spectrum for ultraviolet induced erythema in human skin. CIE J 1987; 6:17–22.
6. The European Cosmetic, Toiletry, and Perfumery Association. COLIPA Sun Protection Factor Test Method. Brussels, 1994.
7. Sayre RM, Poh Agin P, Desrochers DL, Marlowe E. Sunscreen testing methods: in vitro predictions of effectiveness. J Soc Cosmet Chem 1980; 31:133–143.
8. O'Neill JJ. Effect of skin irregularities on sunscreen efficacy. J Pharm Sci 1984; 7:888–891.
9. Herzog B. Prediction of sun protection factors by calculation of transmissions with a calibrated step film model. J Cosmet Sci 2002; 53:11–26.

10. Tunstall DF. A mathematical approach for the analysis of in vitro sun protection factor measurements. J Cosmet Sci 2000; 51:303–315.
11. Sayre RM. Correlation of in vivo tests, in vitro SPF predictions—a survey of published studies. Cosmet Toilet 1993; 108:111–114.
12. Diffey BL, Robson J. A new substrate to measure sunscreen protection factors throughout the ultraviolet spectrum. J Soc Cosmet Chem 1989; 40:127–133.
13. FDC Reports: "The Rose Sheet"® Toiletries, Fragrances and Skin Care. FDC Reports, Inc. Chevy Chase, MD. Vol. 14, No. 44, November 1, 1993, pp. 15.
14. Pearse A, Edwards C. Human stratum corneum as a substrate for in vitro sunscreen testing. Int J Cosmet Sci 1993; 15:234–244.
15. Diffey BL. A method for broad spectrum classification of sunscreens. Int J Cosmet Sci 1994; 16:47–52.
16. Diffey BL, Tanner PR, Matts PJ, Nash JF. In vitro assessment of the broad-spectrum ultraviolet protection of sunscreen products. J Am Acad Dermatol 2000; 43:1024–1035.
17. US Food and Drug Administration. Sunscreen drug products for over-the-counter human use. Final Monograph; 21CRF Parts 310, 352, 700, and 740. Federal Register 64 (98) May 21, 1999, 27666–27693.
18. Stanfield J, Stanfield W, Stanfield C. Sunscreen photostability assessment and SPF estimation. Thirteenth International Congress on Photobiology, San Francisco, July 3, 2000 (abstract).
19. Stanfield J. Sunscreen photostability and UVA protection. J Cosmet Sci 2001; 52:412–413.
20. Diffey BL, Jansen CT, Urbach F, Wulf HC. The standard erythema dose: a new photobiological concept. Photodermatol Photoimmunol Photomed 2003; 13:64–66.
21. Wendel V, Klette E, Gers-Berlag H. A new in vitro test method to assess the UVA protection performance of sun care products. SÖFW 2001; 127:12–30.
22. Moyal D, Chardon A, Kollias N. Determination of UVA protection factors using the persistent pigment darkening (PPD) as the end point. Part 1. Calibration of the method. Photodermatol Photoimmunol Photomed 2000; 6:245–249.
23. Gers-Barlag H, Wendel V, Klette E, Bimczok R, Springob C, Finkel P, Rudolph T, Gonzenbach HU, Westenfelder H, Schneider P, Kockott D, Heinrich U, Tronnier H, Johncock W, Langner R, Hansjürgen D, Pflücker F, Wünsch T. The reproducibility of an in vitro determination of the UVA index describing the relative UVA protection of sun care products. IFSCC Mag 2003; 5:161–166.
24. Pissavini M, Ferrero I, Alard V, Heinrich U, Tronnier H, Kockott D, Lutz D, Tournier V, Zambonin M, Meloni M. Determination of the in vitro SPF. Cosmet Toilet 2003; 118:63–72.
25. Anderson MW, Hewitt JP, Spruce SR. Broad-spectrum physical sunscreens: titanium dioxide and zinc oxide. In: Lowe NJ, Shaath NA, Pathak MA, eds. Sunscreens: Development, Evaluation, and Regulatory Aspects. 2nd ed. New York: Marcel Dekker, 1997:369–370.
26. Cosmetic, Toiletries and Fragrances Association of South Africa, The European Cosmetic, Toiletry and Perfumery Association (COLIPA), Japan Cosmetics Industry Association (JCIA), International Sun Protection Factor (SPF) Test Method, Final Draft, October 17, 2002.
27. Kammeyer A, Westerhof W, Bolhuis P, Ris A, Hische E. The spectral stability of several sunscreening agents on stratum corneum sheets. Int J Cosmet Sci 1987; 9:125–136.

28. Sayre R, Dowdy J. Photostability testing of avobenzone. Cosmet Toilet 1999; 114:84–90.
29. Diffey B, Stokes R, Forestier S, Mazilier C, Richard A, Rougier A. Suncare product photostability: a key parameter for a more realistic in vitro efficacy evaluation. Part I. In vitro efficacy assessment. In: Rougier A, Schaefer H, eds. Protection of the Skin Against Ultraviolet Radiations. Paris: John Libbey Eurotext, 1998:137–142.
30. Forestier S, Mazilier C, Richard A, Rougier A. Suncare product photostability: a key parameter for a more realistic in vitro efficacy evaluation. Part II. Chromatographic analysis In: Rougier A, Schaefer H, eds. Protection of the Skin Against Ultraviolet Radiations. Paris: John Libbey Eurotext, 1998:143–147.
31. Gonzenbach H, Pittet G. Photostability, a must? Proceedings of Broad Spectrum Sun Protection: The Issues & Status. The Commonwealth Institute, London 1997.
32. de Gruij F, Forbes P. UV-induced skin cancer in a hairless mouse model. BioEssays 1995; 17:651–660.
33. DeFabo EC, Dang V, Noonan FP. UV-induced immunosuppression: wavelength dependency and its implications. In: Matthes R, Sliney D, eds. Measurements of Optical Radiation Hazards. International Commission on Non-Ionizing Radiation Protection and International Commission on Illumination, 1998:115–123.
34. Kligman L, Sayre R. An action spectrum for ultraviolet induced elastosis in hairless mice: quantification of elastosis by image analysis. Photochem Photobiol 1991; 53:237–242.

44

Prediction of Sun Protection Factors and UV-A Parameters by Calculation of UV Transmissions Through Sunscreen Films of Inhomogenous Surface Structure

Bernd Herzog
Ciba Specialty Chemicals Inc., Grenzach-Wyhlen, Germany

INTRODUCTION

The measure of the protection against sunburn achieved by application of sunscreens is the sun protection factor (SPF). The SPF is defined as the ratio of the minimal erythemal doses of solar radiation directed to human skin in the presence and in the absence of a sunscreen (1).

The protection by sunscreen formulations is mainly due to their extinction efficiency. This is linked to the spectral properties and the concentration of the filters inside. In addition, the homogeneity of the sunscreen film distributed on the skin plays an important role. For instance, a film showing blank spots, which may have been left out during distribution of the sunscreen on the skin, will show weak overall extinction even when the concentration and efficiency of the UV absorbers inside would have suggested a stronger effect.

The physical quantity which describes the protection of a layer of absorbing material is the transmission T. The inverse of the transmission defines the factor by which the incoming radiation is attenuated:

$$\frac{1}{T} = \frac{I_0}{I} \tag{44.1}$$

where I_0 is the intensity of light before it penetrates the layer and I the intensity of light after it has passed through the layer (Fig. 44.1). This is reflected in the concept of the so-called monochromatic protection factor (MPF):

$$\text{MPF} = \frac{1}{T(\lambda)} \tag{44.2}$$

which is the protection factor at a certain wavelength. In order to proceed toward an expression for calculating the SPF from transmission data, one has to consider the whole UV spectral range between 290 and 400 nm. Thus, $1/T(\lambda)$ must be

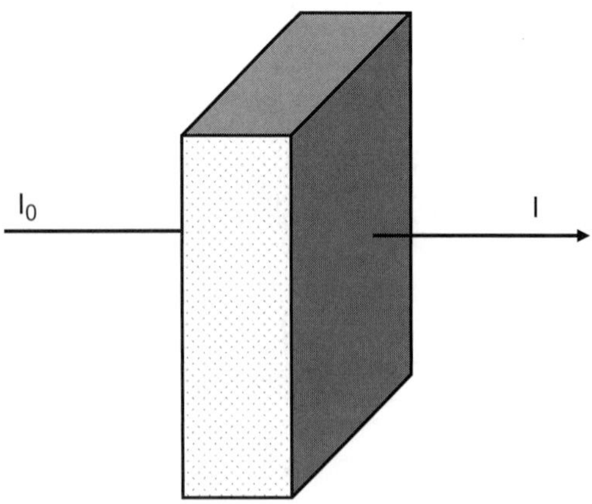

Figure 44.1 Transmission through an absorbing layer.

averaged over this spectral range. Since the intensity of the solar light at the surface of the earth $S(\lambda)$ varies with wavelength as well as the erythemal effect of UV light called the erythemal action spectrum $EA(\lambda)$, the average of $1/T(\lambda)$ has to be weighted by those functions leading to the equation for the SPF first given by Sayre et al. (2):

$$SPF = \frac{\sum_{\lambda=290}^{400} S(\lambda) \cdot EA(\lambda)}{\sum_{\lambda=290}^{400} S(\lambda) \cdot EA(\lambda) \cdot T(\lambda)} \tag{44.3}$$

Data for $S(\lambda)$ and $EA(\lambda)$ are available in the literature (3,4). With *in vivo* measurements of the SPF, an amount of 2 mg/cm^2 is applied on the skin corresponding to a volume of approximately 2 μL/cm^2. The theoretical optical thickness of the resulting film is 20 μm. This thickness may be used to calculate the transmission of a sunscreen formulation, knowing also the concentrations and extinction coefficients of the filters inside and using Lambert–Beer's law:

$$T = 10^{-E} \tag{44.4}$$

with the extinction E, and

$$E = \varepsilon c d \tag{44.5}$$

where ε is the molar decadic extinction coefficient and c the molar concentration. When transmissions are calculated according to Eqs. (44.4) and (44.5) and used for the SPF calculation with Eq. (44.3), the resulting SPF values are a factor of 4–5 higher than would be expected from *in vivo* data. This discrepancy can be overcome when using instead of a film with homogenous thickness a film with a certain inhomogeneity, which may be introduced mathematically. Inhomogenous films are already physically realized with *in vitro* methods for SPF determination, where porous substrates like Transpore™ tape or PMMA plates are used in analogy to the human skin, which has itself an inhomogenous surface structure. In contrast to such *in vitro* methods, reproducibility of results is not a problem when the transmissions are calculated from the UV spectra of the UV absorbers, applying a mathematically defined inhomogenous film structure. It has been shown, that the film structure may be calibrated using sunscreen standards (5), resulting in satisfactory correlations of calculated and *in vivo* SPF data.

MATERIALS AND METHODS

UV Filters and Formulations

The UV filters used are listed in the following table. The International Nomenclature of Cosmetic Ingredients (INCI) names are followed by their abbreviations, which are used throughout this work.

INCI name and abbreviation	Trade name and supplier
UV-B filters	
Ethylhexyl methoxycinnamate (EHMC)	Parsol® MCX (DSM)
2-Phenylbenz-imidazole-5-sulfonic Acid (PBSA)	Eusolex® 232 (Merck)
4-Methylbenzylidene Camphor (MBC)	Eusolex® 6300 (Merck)
Ethylhexyl triazone (EHT)	Uvinul® T150 (BASF)
Padimate O	Eusolex® 6007 (Merck)
Ethylhexyl salicylate (EHS)	Escalol® 587 (ISP)
Titanium dioxide (TiO_2)	Eusolex® T2000 (Merck)
Octocrylene (OCR)	Uvinul® N539 (BASF)
Diethylhexyl butamido triazone (DBT)	Uvsorb HEB (3V Sigma)
Benzylidene malonate polysiloxane (BMP)	Parsol® SLX (DSM)
Broadband and UV-A filters	
Benzophenone-3 (B3)	Uvinul® M40 (BASF)
Butyl methoxydibenzoyl methane (BMDBM)	Parsol® 1789 (DSM)
Bis-ethylhexylphenol methoxyphenyl triazine (BEMT, Bemotrizinol)	Tinosorb® S (Ciba Specialty Chemicals)
Methylene bis-benzotriazolyl Tetramethylbutylphenol (MBBT, Bisoctrizole)	Tinosorb® M, aqueous dispersion of 50% particulate MBBT of particle size <200 nm (Ciba Specialty Chemicals)
Zinc oxide (ZnO)	Nanox®, ZnO with small particle size of about 60 nm (Elementis Specialties)

Sunscreen formulations were of the O/W type and manufactured according to the procedures described in Refs. (5,6).

Measurement of UV Spectra

In order to be able to calculate transmissions through films of inhomogenous structure, UV spectra of the UV absorbers listed in the table have been recorded. The UV spectroscopic measurements were carried out using a Perkin Elmer Lambda 16 spectrometer. For the oil-soluble filters ethanol was used as solvent. UV spectra of particulate UV absorbers in aqueous suspensions were recorded with the same instrument using an integration sphere attachment (Labsphere B009-4012).

While with all soluble UV absorbers an optical pathlength of 1 cm has been employed, the spectra of the particulate filters MBBT, ZnO, and TiO_2, for reasons of dispersion stability, were measured at an optical pathlength of 0.0008 cm (optical cells manufactured by Hellma, Germany) using concentrations of the UV absorber between 0% and 3%. In those cases at each concentration 10 measurements were carried out and the results were averaged (5).

Measurement of UV-A Parameters

The UV-A/UV-B ratio and the critical wavelength were evaluated from transmission measurements with a Labsphere 1000S UV transmittance analyzer (Labsphere, North Sutton, NH). Samples were prepared by distributing the formulations on quartz plates with a rough surface (UQG Ltd., UK) and an area of 40 cm^2 (8 cm $\times$ 5 cm). The plates were cleansed by rinsing first with a solution of a commercial dish washing agent, and then immersing them into concentrated sulfuric acid for 12 h followed by rinsing with deionized water. Formulations were applied as an amount per area of 1 $\mu L/cm^2$. Before taking measurements, the samples were allowed to equilibrate for 15 min. A reference plate was equally prepared by distributing 1 $\mu L/cm^2$ of deionized water in order to reduce the scattering of the incident beam of the transmittance analyzer due to the rough surface of the plate (instead of water, glycerol may also be used, which is recommended when working with scanning analyzers where measurements take longer). First, the transmission of the reference plate was measured, and after that the transmissions of the sample plates. With each sample plate, transmission data were recorded at 11 different locations on the plate. The spectra were depicted as extinction vs. wavelength and the curves with the highest extinction and the lowest extinction were discarded, ending with a set of nine spectra. The experimental error of the extinction in terms of confidence limits based on a significance level of 95% was between 4% and 15%. Extinctions were always below the upper limit ($E \cong 2$) of the linear dynamic range of the Labsphere 1000S UV transmittance analyzer.

INTRODUCTION OF STEP FILM INHOMOGENEITY BY MATHEMATICAL MODELS

Calculation of Average UV Spectra from the Spectra of Individual UV Filters

Before introducing film inhomogeneities one has to know the spectroscopic properties of the respective formulation. With cosmetic sunscreens in most cases several UV absorbers are combined. Considering a mixture of n different UV absorbers, the concentrations of the individual absorbers are most conveniently given as percentages β_i (weight per volume). The corresponding molar extinction coefficients are $\varepsilon(\lambda)_i$, and the molecular weights M_i. The average molar absorption coefficient $\overline{\varepsilon(\lambda)}$ of the mixture can then be calculated according to

$$\overline{\varepsilon(\lambda)} = \frac{\sum_{i=1}^{n} \varepsilon(\lambda)_i \cdot \beta_i / M_i}{\sum_{i=1}^{n} \beta_i / M_i} \tag{44.6}$$

The formation of $\overline{\varepsilon(\lambda)}$ from the spectra of the individual filters is visualized for the COLIPA $P3$ standard in Fig. 44.2.

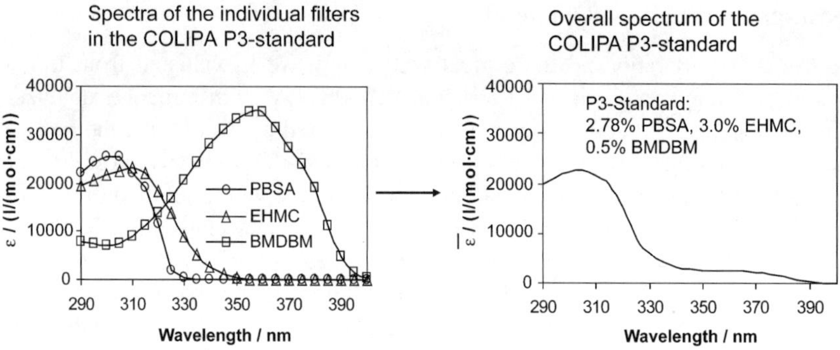

Figure 44.2 Formation of the overall spectrum of the COLIPA *P*3 standard from the spectra of the individual filters.

The Step Film Model by O'Neill

The derivation of the step film model by O'Neill (7) is visualized in Fig. 44.3 as a two-dimensional sketch. The starting point is a homogenous film of absorbing material of a certain thickness d and a horizontal extension of 1. A portion of the homogenous film given by the horizontal extension g and the thickness fd is removed from its original position and added to the remaining thicker part of the film. This results in two film fractions of different thicknesses d' and $(1-f)d$ with horizontal extensions $(1-g)$ and g, respectively. Thus, the step film parameters f and g define the difference in thickness and the relative amounts of the two parts of the film. Both can adopt any value between 0 and 1. In this way transformations of the film geometry can be carried out keeping constant the amount of absorbing material.

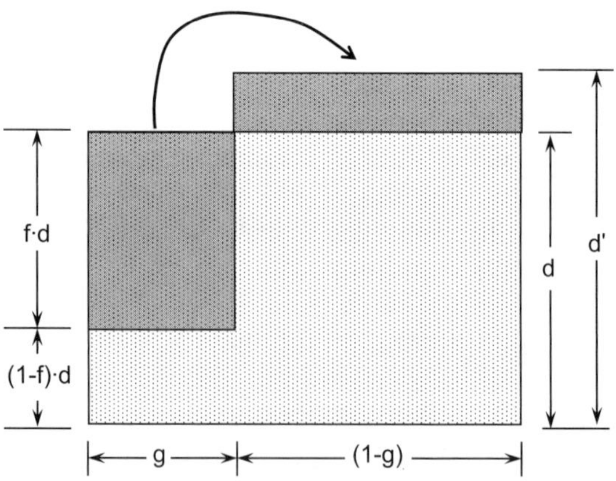

Figure 44.3 Step film model as introduced by O'Neill.

Figure 44.4 shows two extreme cases of possible structures of the step film. Since f defines the depth of the film pores and g the fraction of pores relative to the overall film area, the case of $f \rightarrow 1$ and $g \rightarrow 1$ describes a film with a large fraction of pores where only little of the absorbing material is located resulting in a transmission close to 100%. The bulk of the absorbing material is concentrated on small spots where the transmission is almost blocked completely. Since most of the film transmits nearly 100% of the UV light, the calculated SPF will be much smaller than the *in vivo* SPF. On the other hand, for $f \rightarrow 0$ and $g \rightarrow 0$ the limit of a nearly homogenous film is approached, for which the calculated SPF is much higher than the *in vivo* SPF. However, in between those two extremes there should be values of f and g reproducing the correct *in vivo* SPF.

The transmission as a function of wavelength of a step film $T(\lambda)$ can be written as the sum of the transmissions through the two fractions of the film:

$$T(\lambda)_{g,f} = g10^{-\overline{\varepsilon(\lambda)}\bar{c}d\{1-f\}} + (1-g)10^{-\overline{\varepsilon(\lambda)}\bar{c}d\{gf/(1-g)+1\}} \tag{44.7}$$

where d is the average thickness of the step film. As pointed out before, in accordance with the conditions of *in vivo* determinations of the SPF, this is set to 20 μm. $\overline{\varepsilon(\lambda)}$ is the average molar extinction coefficient calculated according to Eq. (44.6) and $\bar{c}$ is the sum of molar concentrations of the UV absorbers based on the average molecular weight of the UV absorber mixture (5).

Step film transmissions in the spectral range between 290 and 400 nm can be calculated by the use of Eq. (44.7) as a function of g and f. The resulting transmissions are transferred afterward into Eq. (44.3) for calculation of the SPF as function of g and f. This is shown in Fig. 44.5 for the example of the COLIPA *P*3 standard. There is a strong dependence of the calculated SPF on the step film parameters. As discussed before, for $g \rightarrow 1$ and $f \rightarrow 1$ the SPF is approaching unity. For $g \rightarrow 0$ and $f \rightarrow 0$ the SPF is about 70, reflecting the case of a homogenous film. But as is also obvious from Fig. 44.5, there are pairs of step film parameters, which would result in the value of 15.5 representing the *in vivo* SPF of the COLIPA *P*3 standard.

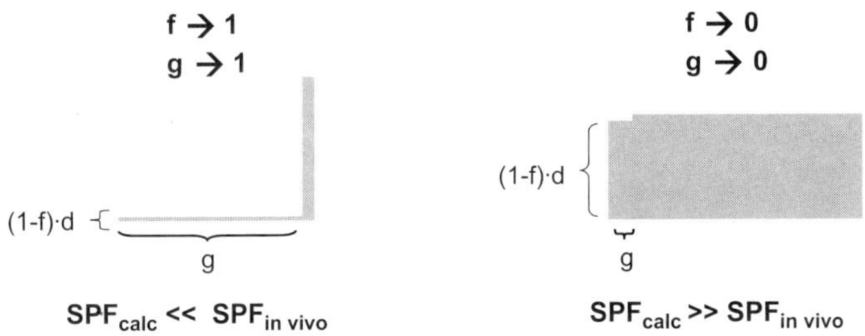

Figure 44.4 Two extreme cases of a step film.

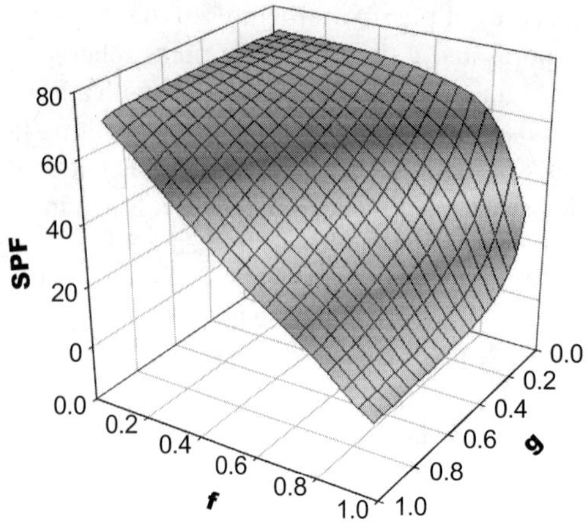

Figure 44.5 SPF of the COLIPA P3 standard from step film calculation as a function of the parameters *g* and *f*; the *in vivo* SPF of the *P*3 standard is 15.5.

It is desirable to identify one set of step film parameters with which sunscreen formulations with a wide range of *in vivo* SPF values would be described satisfactorily. In order to identify those parameters we looked at three sunscreen standards covering a wide range of SPF values. Those were the COLIPA standards *P*1 and *P*3 and a third standard *P*4 manufactured in our laboratory the *in vivo* SPF of which had been measured with 25 volunteers. The *in vivo* SPF of *P*1 and *P*3 had been determined in a multicenter study. Thus, the statistical significance of the corresponding *in vivo* data of those standards is higher than with the normal COLIPA procedure requesting only 10 volunteers. For that reason the standards have been used for the calibration of the film parameters. Their filter contents and *in vivo* SPF values are as follows:

*P*1: 2.7% EHMC, *in vivo* SPF = 4.2 (±0.2).
*P*3: 3.0% EHMC, 0.5% BMDBM, 2.78% PBSA, *in vivo* SPF = 15.5 (±1.5).
*P*4: 5.0% EHMC, 10% MBBT (active ingredient), *in vivo* SPF = 35.7 (±3.2).

The calibration of the model parameters was performed in the following way: First, the SPF values of each sunscreen standard were calculated as a function of both parameters *g* and *f* as described before (see also Fig. 44.5). Then, for each calculated SPF value the square of the difference to the corresponding *in vivo* SPF was determined and summed up for the three standards. Eventually, the pair *g* and *f* was identified, which led to the minimal overall quadratic deviation to the *in vivo* data. Thus, the task was to search the

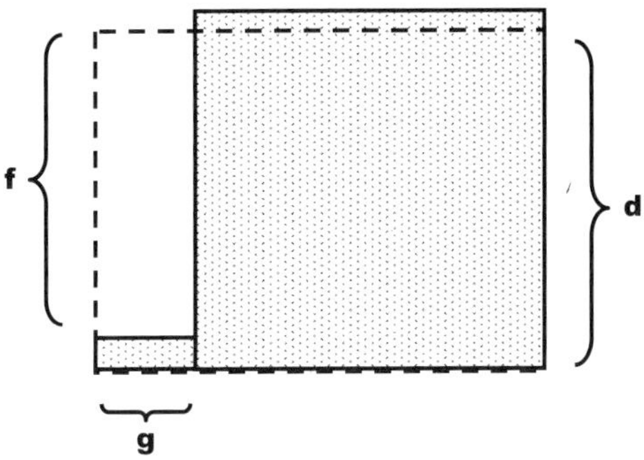

Figure 44.6 Visualization of the calibrated step film model with optimized parameters $g = 0.269$ and $f = 0.935$.

minimum of the following function $\Delta_{g,f}$.

$$\Delta_{g,f} = \left(\frac{\mathrm{SPF}(P1)_{g,f} - 4.2}{4.2}\right)^2 + \left(\frac{\mathrm{SPF}(P3)_{g,f} - 15.5}{15.5}\right)^2 + \left(\frac{\mathrm{SPF}(P4)_{g,f} - 35.7}{35.7}\right)^2 + \left(\frac{[\mathrm{SPF}(P1)_{g,f} - 4.2]}{4.2} + \frac{[\mathrm{SPF}(P3)_{g,f} - 15.5]}{15.5} + \frac{[\mathrm{SPF}(P4)_{g,f} - 35.7]}{35.7}\right)^2 \tag{44.8}$$

The procedure, which is described in more detail elsewhere (5), led to the result of $g = 0.269$ and $f = 0.935$. The result is visualized in Fig. 44.6. For the sunscreen standards described previously. Table 44.1 shows the results of calculated SPF values with these parameters and the corresponding *in vivo* data.

Table 44.1 SPF Values from *In Vivo* Measurements and Calculations with a Calibrated Step Film Model of Sunscreen Standards *P*1, *P*3, and *P*4

UV absorber content	SPF *in vivo*	SPF from step film
*P*1: 2.7% EHMC	4.2 ± 0.2	5.0
*P*3: 2.78% PBSA + 3% EHMC + 0.5% BMDBM	15.5 ± 1.5	10.9
*P*4: 10% MBBT + 5% EHMC	35.7 ± 3.2	38.5

Using a Distribution Function for Introduction of Film Inhomogeneity

An alternative approach to O'Neill's two-step film model would be to introduce a distribution function in order to describe the film inhomogeneity. This was realized using the Gaussian type distribution function $h(i)$:

$$h(i) = A\exp\left[-\left(B\frac{i}{n}\right)^2\right] \tag{44.9}$$

with $i = 1, 2, \ldots, n$, where n is the number of steps which the distribution function is cut into for numerical treatment. A is introduced for normalization (8) and B is the fitting parameter defining the film inhomogeneity. The normalization condition for A is

$$\frac{A}{n}\sum_{i=1}^{n} \exp\left[-\left(B\frac{i}{n}\right)^2\right] = 1 \tag{44.10}$$

With this normalization the total amount of absorbing material is kept constant, irrespective of the structure of the film (which varies with parameter B).

In Fig. 44.7, $h(i)$ is shown as a function of i. The area under this curve is normalized to 1 as expressed by Eq. (44.9), thus being equal to the area under the corresponding homogenous film also drawn (as a dashed line) in the same figure.

The transmission through an inhomogenous layer of a Gaussian distribution of layer thickness can be calculated as the sum of the transmissions through the different steps in which the function is divided. The number of those steps is n. The overall transmission then becomes

$$T(\lambda)_B = \frac{1}{n}\sum_{i=1}^{n} 10^{-\overline{\varepsilon(\lambda)}\bar{c}dh(i)} \tag{44.11}$$

where $\overline{\varepsilon(\lambda)}$ and $\bar{c}$ have the same meaning as in the step film model of O'Neill. Again, the transmission of the inhomogenous film is put into Eq. (44.3) to

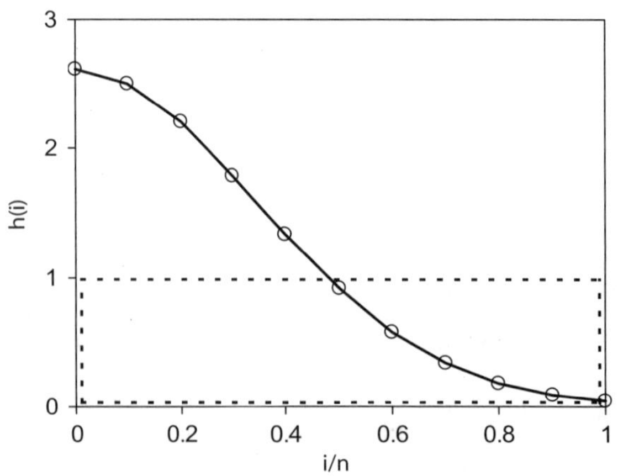

Figure 44.7 Gaussian model of film inhomogeneity with the distribution film thickness $h(i)$ as a solid line; the corresponding homogenous film of the same amount of material is shown as a dashed line.

Table 44.2 SPF Values from *In Vivo* Measurements and Calculations with a Calibrated Gaussian Distribution Model of Sunscreen Standards *P*1, *P*3, and *P*4

UV absorber content	SPF *in vivo*	SPF from Gaussian distribution
*P*1: 2.7% EHMC	4.2 ± 0.2	5.2
*P*3: 2.78% PBSA + 3% EHMC + 0.5% BMDBM	15.5 ± 1.5	11.2
*P*4: 10% MBBT + 5% EHMC	35.7 ± 3.2	35.8

calculate the respective SPF value. The parameter *B* has to be optimized, so that the minimal quadratic deviation between calculated and *in vivo* SPF data of the sunscreen standards *P*1, *P*3, and *P*4 is obtained. Thus, the minimum of the function Δ_B was obtained:

$$\Delta_B = \left(\frac{\mathrm{SPF}(P1)_B - 4.2}{4.2}\right)^2 + \left(\frac{\mathrm{SPF}(P3)_B - 15.5}{15.5}\right)^2 + \left(\frac{\mathrm{SPF}(P4)_B - 35.7}{35.7}\right)^2 + \left(\frac{[\mathrm{SPF}(P1)_B - 4.2]}{4.2} + \frac{[\mathrm{SPF}(P3)_B - 15.5]}{15.5} + \frac{[\mathrm{SPF}(P4)_B - 35.7]}{35.7}\right)^2 \tag{44.12}$$

In the fitting procedure *n* had been set to 10 (see also Fig. 44.7). Larger values of *n* did not lead to significant changes in the results. The result of the fitting was $B = 2.0409$ and the normalization led to $A = 2.6096$.

For the sunscreen standards *P*1, *P*3, and *P*4 the results of the calculated SPF values using these parameters are compared to the *in vivo* data in Table 44.2. The similarity between the results using a Gaussian distribution and those obtained from O'Neill's step film model (Table 44.1) is striking. In contrast to the step film model of O'Neill where two parameters had to be optimized, the Gaussian distribution needs only one adjustable parameter.

CORRELATION OF EXPERIMENTAL AND CALCULATED DATA

Calculated SPF and SPF *In Vivo*

In Tables 44.3–44.5 the *in vivo* SPF results of 56 sunscreen formulations with SPF values ranging between 3 and 36 are compared to the corresponding results of the SPF obtained from calculations with the calibrated step film model as well as with the calibrated Gaussian distribution model. The UV absorbers and their concentrations are specified for each formulation. Tables 44.4 and 44.5 contain data from other authors (9,10) which have been added in order to increase the data pool. Figure 44.8 shows the SPF calculated with the step film model as a function of the SPF *in vivo* for all results listed in Tables 44.1–44.5 ($n = 59$). There is a satisfactory correlation characterized by

Table 44.3 SPF Values from *In Vivo* Measurements of Sunscreen O/W Formulations and the Corresponding Calculations with the Calibrated Step Film Model (11) and the Calibrated Gaussian Distribution Model

UV absorber content	SPF *in vivo*	SPF from step film	SPF from Gaussian distribution
5% EHMC + 1% MBBT	12 ± 4.9[a]	10.8	11.4
5% EHMC + 2% MBBT	12 ± 4.5[a]	12.7	13.7
5% EHMC + 4% MBBT	19 ± 2.8[b]	16.9	18.2
5% EHMC + 8% MBBT	30 ± 7.1[a]	29.3	29.1
2% MBBT	3 ± 0.7[a]	4.9	4.3
4% MBBT	5 ± 2.2[a]	6.5	7.0
8% MBBT	11 ± 2.3[a]	11.3	13.1
5% EHMC+ 2% MBBT + 2% BEMT	29 ± 5.0	24.3	24.8
3% BEMT	7.7 ± 0.8	6.3	6.8
3% BEMT + 4% B3	15.2 ± 2.0	9.9	11.2
3% BEMT + 4% EHT	29.6 ± 2.7	20.4	20.2
3% BEMT + 4% Padimate O	13.3 ± 1.4	14.5	15.5
3% BEMT + 4% MBC	15.5 ± 1.9	13.8	14.8
3% BEMT + 4% EHMC	17.6 ± 1.5	13.2	14.4
3% BEMT + 4% DBT	19.7 ± 1.8	21.7	21.2
3% BEMT + 1% BMDBM	9.4 ± 0.7	7.1	7.8
3% BEMT + 2% BMDBM	9.4 ± 1.0	7.9	8.8
3% BEMT +5% MBBT + 1% BMDBM	15.5 ± 1.9	14.5	16.4
3% BEMT +5% MBBT + 2% BMDBM	13.5 ± 1.1	16.0	17.9
2% BEMT	7.9 ± 1.0	5.2	5.1
2% BEMT + 2.5% MBBT	10.2 ± 0.8	7.7	8.6
2% BEMT + 5% MBBT	13.6 ± 2.0	10.9	12.5
2% BEMT + 7.5% MBBT	16.1 ± 1.9	15.4	17.3
5% BEMT	8.8 ± 0.7	9.2	10.4
5% BEMT + 2.5% MBBT	15.2 ± 1.6	13.4	15.1
5% BEMT + 5% MBBT	30.1 ± 2.8	19.0	20.6
5% BEMT + 7.5% MBBT	30.6 ± 4.3	26.8	27.2
5% EHMC	7.6 ± 1.4	7.1	7.6

[a]*In vivo* results with five volunteers.
[b]*In vivo* results with 20 volunteers.

a correlation coefficient of $r = 0.8941$. The slope of the linear regression is 0.846, indicating the tendency of the model to slightly underestimate the *in vivo* results. Figure 44.9 shows the SPF calculated with the Gaussian distribution model as a function of the SPF *in vivo* again for all the results listed in Tables 44.1–44.5. The correlation coefficient in this case is 0.8917 and the slope of the linear regression is 0.851. Thus, the results of correlations of *in vivo* data and calculated data are very similar with both models. This is also confirmed in Fig. 44.10, where the correlation of the results of both models is shown, which is excellent.

Table 44.4 SPF Values from *In Vivo* Measurements of Sunscreen O/W Formulations (9) and the Corresponding Calculations with the Calibrated Step Film Model and the Calibrated Gaussian Distribution Model

UV absorber content	SPF *in vivo*	SPF from step film	SPF from Gaussian distribution
5% TiO_2	7	9.1	9.9
5% EHMC	9	7.1	7.6
7% OCR	8	6.1	5.2
2% EHT	8	5.0	5.3
3% EHT	9	6.2	6.5
4% MBC	10	6.1	6.4
2% BMDBM	6	4.1	3.4
5% EHMC + 5% TiO_2	20	20.5	19.7
4% MBC + 5% TiO_2	23	18.1	17.8
7% OCR + 5% TiO_2	24	15.9	16.5
2% BMDBM + 5% TiO_2	25	11.5	13.1
2% EHT + 5% TiO_2	21	16.4	16.4
5% EHMC + 7% OCR	10	12.6	12.7
3% EHT + 4% MBC	11	10.1	9.8
3% EHT + 5% EHMC	12	11.7	11.3
5% EHMC + 7% OCR + 2% BMDBM	23	20.7	21.2
3% EHT + 4% MBC + 2% BMDBM	26	23.7	23.2
3% EHT + 5% EHMC + 2% BMDBM	20	26.6	25.5

Table 44.5 SPF Values from *In Vivo* Measurements of Sunscreen O/W Formulations (10) and the Corresponding Calculations with the Calibrated Step Film Model and the Calibrated Gaussian Distribution Model

UV absorber content	SPF *in vivo*	SPF from step film	SPF from Gaussian distribution
7.5% Padimate O + 2% B3	18	14.1	13.4
7.5% Padimate O + 3% B3	19	15.8	15.0
7.5% Padimate O + 4% B3	23	17.5	16.5
7.5% Padimate O + 5% B3	23	19.4	17.9
7.5% Padimate O + 6% B3	28	20.8	19.3
7.5% EHMC + 2% B3	21	13.3	13.1
7.5% EHMC + 3% B3	20	14.8	14.5
7.5% EHMC + 4% B3	22	16.4	15.8
7.5% EHMC + 5% B3	19	17.9	17.2
7.5% EHMC + 6% B3	23	19.6	18.5

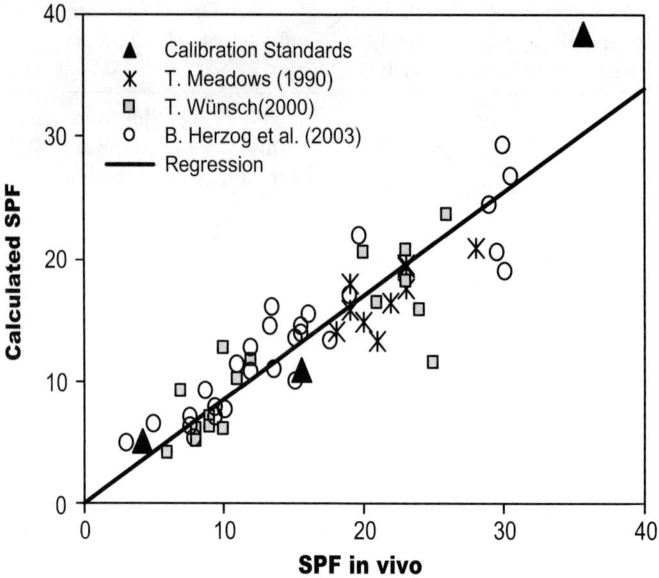

Figure 44.8 Correlation of SPF from step film calculations and *in vivo* data; correlation coefficient = 0.8941, slope = 0.846, $n = 59$.

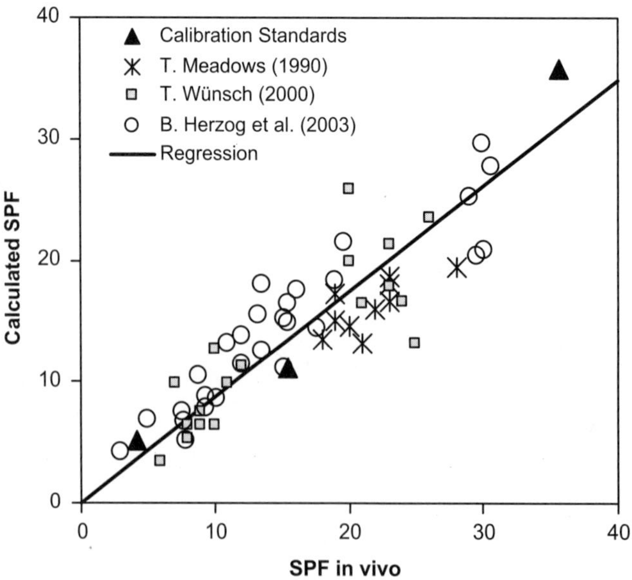

Figure 44.9 Correlation of SPF from Gauss function calculations and *in vivo* data; correlation coefficient = 0.8917, slope = 0.851, $n = 59$.

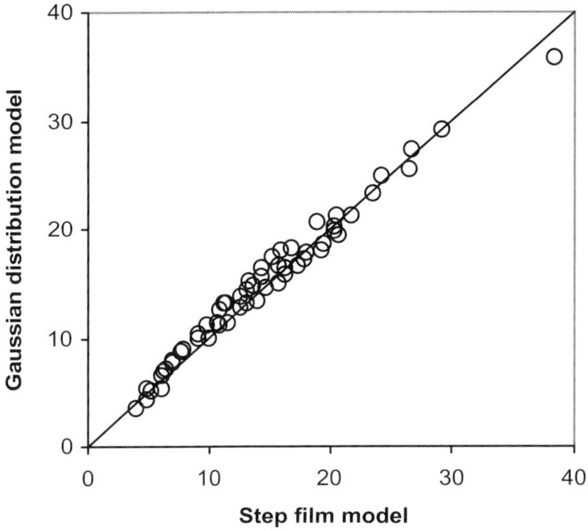

Figure 44.10 Correlation of SPF values calculated according to the Gaussian distribution model and the step film model; correlation coefficient = 0.9905, slope = 1.002, $n = 59$.

Correlation of Calculated UV-A Parameters and UV-A Parameters Measured *In Vitro*

The UV-A/UV-B ratio and the critical wavelength are derived from the extinction spectra of sunscreen formulations (12). Both are reductions of the complete spectral information to one number, characterizing in some way the shape of the spectrum in terms of the amount of UV-A coverage in relation to the amount of UV-B coverage. The UV-A/UV-B ratio is calculated according to Eq. (44.13)

$$\text{UV-A/UV-B ratio} = \frac{\int_{320}^{400} \log(1/T(\lambda))\, d\lambda \big/ \int_{320}^{400} d\lambda}{\int_{290}^{320} \log(1/T(\lambda))\, d\lambda \big/ \int_{290}^{320} d\lambda} \tag{44.13}$$

where $T(\lambda)$ is the transmission at wavelength λ. The integration limits correspond to the respective wavelength ranges (in nm) of the spectra. The UV-A/UV-B ratio typically varies between 0.1 and 1.5. Based on the level of the UV-A/UV-B ratio a classification into five categories had been proposed (12), where the highest rating in terms of relative UV-A protection is obtained with a UV-A/UV-B ratio >0.9.

The critical wavelength λ_c is defined according to Eq. (44.14)

$$\int_{290}^{\lambda_c} \log(1/T(\lambda))\, d\lambda = 0.9 \int_{290}^{400} \log(1/T(\lambda))\, d\lambda \tag{44.14}$$

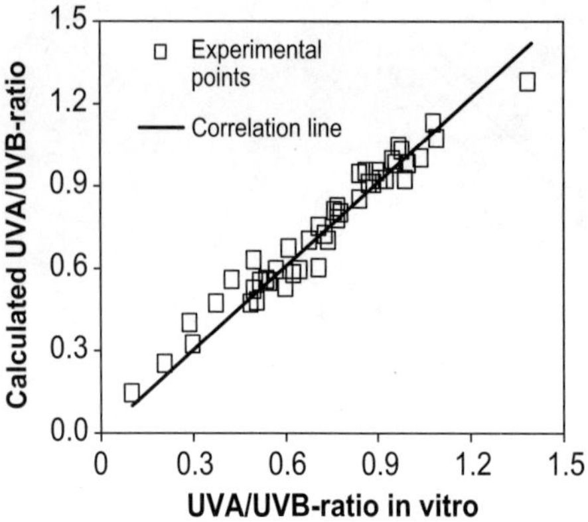

Figure 44.11 Correlation of UV-A/UV-B ratios from step film calculations and corresponding data from *in vitro* measurements; correlation coefficient = 0.9776, slope = 1.015, $n = 47$.

Also, with respect to the critical wavelength a grouping into five categories was suggested (12), where the highest category in terms of a broad-spectrum claim is achieved with $\lambda_c \geq 370$ nm.

As Figs. 44.11 and 44.12 show, there is an excellent correlation between UV-A/UV-B ratios measured *in vitro* and by both types of calculations, according to the step film model and the Gaussian distribution model. The same is true for the critical wavelength results as shown in Figs. 44.13 and 44.14.

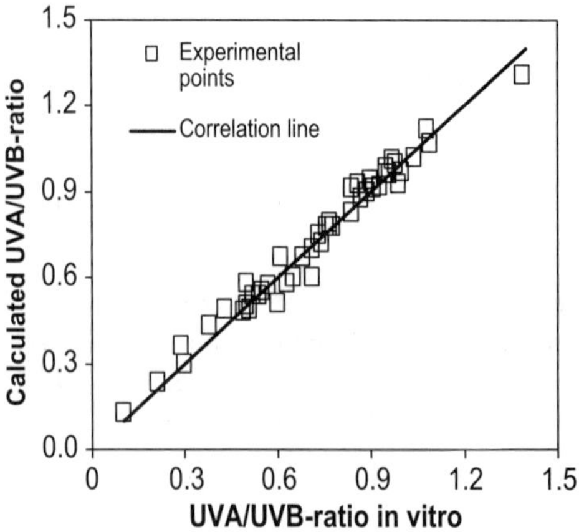

Figure 44.12 Correlation of UV-A/UV-B ratios from Gauss function calculations and corresponding data from *in vitro* measurements; correlation coefficient = 0.9874, slope = 1.001, $n = 47$.

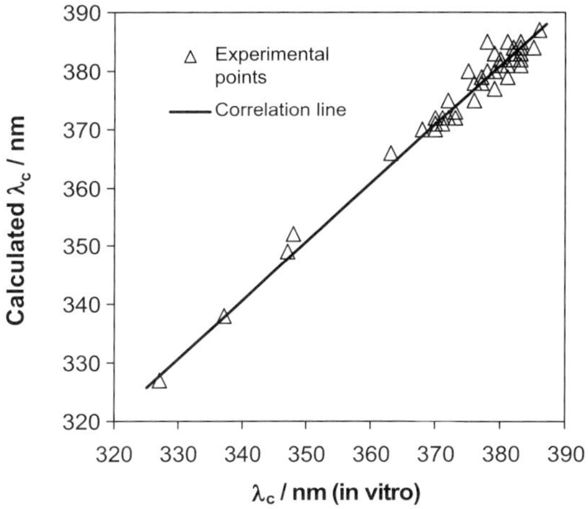

Figure 44.13 Correlation of critical wavelengths λ_c from step film calculations and corresponding data from *in vitro* measurements; correlation coefficient = 0.9883, slope = 1.003, $n = 47$.

Although for both UV-A/UV-B ratio and critical wavelength the same set of 47 formulations were used, the distribution of the correlated data points in the plots is quite different. For the UV-A/UV-B ratio the points are evenly scattered over the whole data range, whereas for the critical wavelength most of the points

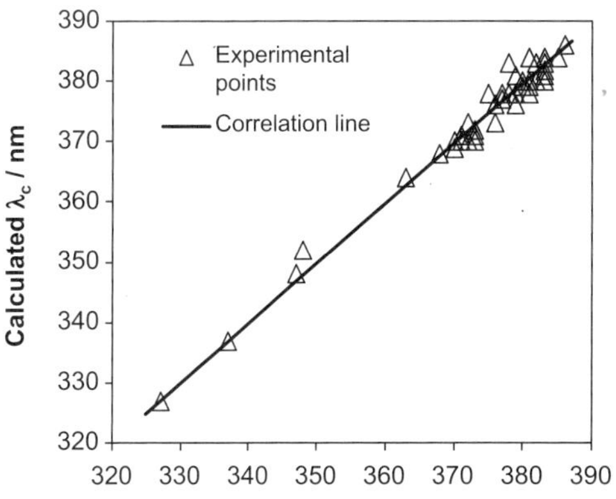

Figure 44.14 Correlation of critical wavelengths λ_c from Gauss function calculations and corresponding data from *in vitro* measurements; correlation coefficient = 0.9889, slope = 0.999, $n = 47$.

are concentrated in the region of higher values. This indicates a limited dynamic range of the critical wavelength compared to the UV-A/UV-B ratio.

In order to tune the UV-A/UV-B ratio or the critical wavelength of a formulation to a certain value, the ratio of the UV-A and UV-B filter concentrations has to be adjusted. This can be calculated rather conveniently using one of the models. In Fig. 44.15 an example is shown with combinations of EHMC and BEMT. The UV-A/UV-B ratio and critical wavelength are plotted as function of the ratio of the concentration of the UV broad-spectrum filter BEMT and the overall UV filter concentration (in %). Since both models lead to nearly the same results, only the step film model calculations are discussed. The calculations are in good accordance with the experimental data. Using such model calculations is a convenient way to study the effect of arbitrary filter combinations on the UV-A parameters of the respective sunscreen formulations.

It is obvious from Fig. 44.15 that in contrast to the UV-A/UV-B ratio the critical wavelength approaches saturation already at low levels of UV-A protection. Again, this indicates a limited dynamic range of the critical wavelength, demonstrating that this parameter is not really suited for the characterization of UV-A protection.

It is also possible to calculate whether the Australian standard will be achieved or not. According to this standard a layer of a broad-spectrum sunscreen product with a thickness of 8 μm shall not transmit more than 10% of radiation at any wavelength from 320 to 360 nm inclusive (13). This criterion can be checked by calculation of transmissions using the averaged molar extinction coefficients from Eq. (44.6) for a homogenous film with a thickness of 8 μm. It has been demonstrated that such calculations are in good accordance with the experimental work (6).

Figure 44.16 shows the concentrations of several UV-A absorbing filters necessary to meet the requirement in the presence and absence of the UV-B absorber EHMC. The presence of EHMC does not have a strong influence on the results for the broad-spectrum filters ZnO, MBBT, and BEMT. However,

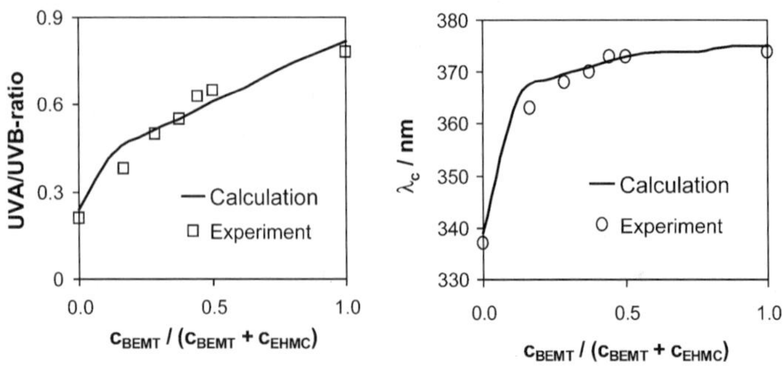

Figure 44.15 Prediction of UV-A parameters for different concentration ratios of a UV broad-spectrum (BEMT) and a UV-B absorber (EHMC).

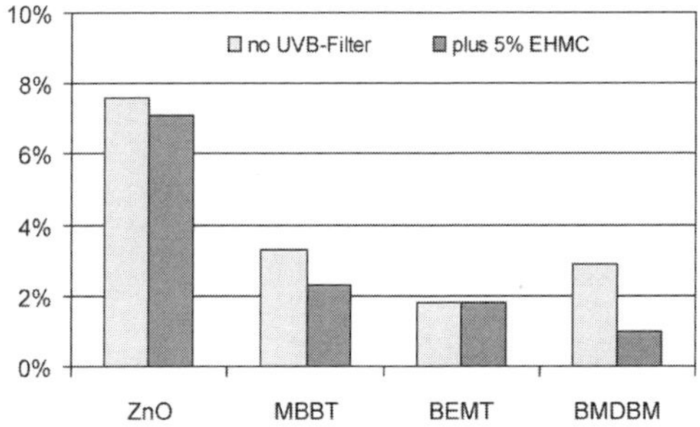

Figure 44.16 Minimum concentrations for achieving the requirements of the Australian Standard calculated from (mixed) spectra using a homogenous film with an optical pathlength of $d = 8$ μm.

there is quite an impact on BMDBM, which is a pure UV-A absorber. Since this compound has weak absorption in the range between 320 and 340 nm, addition of EHMC helps to fill this gap. However, due to a chemical interaction under UV irradiation the combination of BMDBM and EHMC shows increased photo-instability and are not recommended to be used (14,15).

SUMMARY

Mathematical simulation of sun protection factors and UV-A parameters can be performed based on calculation of mixed spectra of the respective sunscreen formulation and on the introduction of a certain inhomogeneity of the sunscreen film. Two mathematical models were employed in order to simulate such inhomogeneities. The first model is the step film model introduced by O'Neill using two parameters, the second one is a Gaussian distribution for the variation of the film thickness with only one parameter. In both models the amount of the film forming material is fixed, while the structure of the film is changed. The model parameters were calibrated using standard sunscreen formulations with well-known *in vivo* SPF values. Both calibrated models are able to estimate realistic SPF values of sunscreen formulations with arbitrary filter combinations and the results of the two models were very close. The simulation of UV-A parameters such as the UV-A/UV-B ratio and critical wavelength works even better. In addition, it is possible to check the Australian Standard criterion by calculating the transmission of the filter mixture of a homogenous film of 8 μm thickness in the spectral range between 320 and 360 nm.

REFERENCES

1. Schulze R. Einige Versuch und Bemerkungen zum Problem der handelsüblichen Lichtschutzmittel. Parfüm Kosmet 1956; 37(6,7):310–315, 365–372.

2. Sayre RM, Agin PP, LeVee GJ, Marlowe E. A comparison of in vivo and in vitro testing of sunscreening formulas. Photochem Photobiol 1979; 29:559–566.
3. Diffey BL, Robson J. A new substrate to measure sunscreen protection factors throughout the ultraviolet spectrum. J Soc Cosmet Chem 1989; 40:127–133.
4. McKinlay AF, Diffey BL. A reference action spectrum for ultraviolet-induced erythema in human skin. CIE Journal 1987; 6:17–22.
5. Herzog B. Prediction of sun protection factors by calculation of transmissions with a calibrated step film model. J Cosmet Sci 2002; 53:11–26.
6. Herzog B, Mongiat S, Deshayes C, Neuhaus M, Sommer K, Mantler A. In vivo and in vitro assessment of UVA protection by sunscreen formulations containing either butyl methoxy dibenzoyl methane, methylene bis-benzotriazolyl tetramethylbutylphenol, or microfine ZnO. Int J Cosmet Sci 2002; 24:170–185
7. O'Neill JJ. Effect of film irregularities on sunscreen efficacy. J Pharm Sci 1984; 73:888–891.
8. Ferrero L, Pissavini M, Marguerie S, Zastrow L. Efficiency of a continuous height distribution model of sunscreen film geometry to predict a realistic sun protection factor. J Cosmet Sci 2003; 54:463–481.
9. Wünsch T. Synergistic effects with high performance UV-filters. Proceedings of the XXIst IFSCC International Congress, 2000:530–535.
10. Meadows T. The effect of various sunscreen combinations on a product's SPF value. J Soc Cosmet Chem 1990; 41:141–146.
11. Herzog B, Mendrok C, Mongiat S, Müller S, Osterwalder U. The sunscreen simulator: a formulator's tool to predict SPF and UVA parameters. SÖFW J 2003; 7:25–36.
12. Diffey BL. A method for broad spectrum classification of sunscreens. Int J Cosmet Sci 1994; 16:47–52.
13. AS/NZS. Australian/New Zealand Standard. AS/NZS, 1998:2604.
14. Rudolph T. Photochemische Aspekte von Lichtschutzstoffen. Behr's Seminar Kosmetische Lichtschutzmittel, 1999.
15. Herzog B, Sommer K. Investigations on photostability of UV-absorbers for cosmetic sunscreens. Proceedings of the 21st IFSCC, Berlin, 2000. Poster P60 (CD ROM).

Marketing and Information

45

Single Sunscreen Application Can Provide Day-Long Protection

Robert M. Sayre

Rapid Precision Testing Laboratories, Cordova, Tennessee and University of Tennessee Center for the Health Sciences, Memphis, Tennessee, USA

John C. Dowdy

Rapid Precision Testing Laboratories, Cordova, Tennessee, USA

William Shields

CCI, Rockledge, Florida, USA

INTRODUCTION

Today it is generally professed that sunscreen users do not apply sufficient sunscreen to achieve all-day protection and that the sun protection actually achieved outdoors is significantly over rated by current sun protection factor (SPF) testing procedures (1–6). Such hypothesis suggests that users of sunscreens are frequently sunburned and consequently sunscreen users are admonished to frequently reapply the sunscreen. In the summer of 2000, we had the opportunity to observe sunscreen usage during a weeklong soccer camp for young adolescent ladies 9–16 years old. Each young lady was required to wear a sunscreen of at least SPF 30 self-applied each morning. They could either use their own sunscreen or were provided a selection of sunscreens. Each camper applied what she believed to be a sufficient amount of sunscreen. The campers were in sunlight from 9 a.m. to noon and then from 1 p.m. to 4 p.m. During these sun-exposed periods, the campers underwent strenuous exercise and activity. This paper reports the results of that experience.

METHODS

Protocol

Volunteers gave informed consent to participate in a study of the protective capabilities of a sunscreen product through outdoor use conditions.

Initial skin grading using a five-point scale (0—no erythema, ?—ambiguous, 1—minimally perceptible, 2—well developed, T—tanned) and photographs showing the volunteer's face, arms, and legs documented that there was no sunburn at the beginning of the study. Before the initial exposure, volunteers applied the sunscreen product to their faces, arms, legs, and other exposed skin areas.

Each participating volunteer received a sunlight dosimeter badge to wear during sunlight exposure. The badge's serial number was recorded. The badge was worn throughout the day on the volunteer's wrist or shirt and returned at the end of the day and logged in. Each day three control dosimeters were also exposed to incident solar radiation for a.m., p.m., and all-day hours.

When the badge was returned, the volunteer's face, arms, and legs were graded for possible erythema using a five-point scale (0, ?, 1, 2, T). Burns on volunteers are not counted unless apparent at the next mornings examination. Burns were only counted once on initial development and persistent erythema, while noted, was not included for statistical analysis. Each day the volunteers were regraded (Table 45.1) and photographed at the beginning of the day and provided with a new badge whose serial number was recorded for the volunteer's use that day. The volunteer then applied the sunscreen. At the day's end, the volunteer was graded and photographed.

Sunlight Exposure Dosimetery

Wearable Ultraviolet Dosimeters for Spectrally Varying Environments, Rapid Precision Testing Laboratories, Patent Pending (Fig. 45.1) were used to measure exposure to ultraviolet (UV) radiation.

Table 45.1 Visual Grading of Major Body Sites

	Day 2		Day 3		Day 4		Day 5	
Soccer camper	Scored sites	Other sites	Scored sites	Other sites	Scored sites	Other sites	Scored sites	Other sites
12	0	1—below eyes	2	1—below eyes	0		0	
10	0		0	1—below eyes	2		0	
1	0		0		0		0	
3	0		0		0		0	1—below eyes 1—tip nose
4	0	1—below eyes	0	1—back neck 1—below eyes	0	2—below eyes 2—top ears 2—tip nose	0	1—tip nose
9	0		0		0	2—below eyes	0	
11	0		0	1—below eyes	0	1—forehead	0	
18	0		1	2—back neck	0		0	1—below eyes
21	0		0		0	1—back neck	0	1—tip nose
2	0		0	1—back neck	NP		0	1—below eyes 1—back neck
20	0	1—below eyes	0	1—below eyes	NP		0	1—tip nose
6	0		0		NP		NP	
13	NP		0		NP		NP	
5	0		NP		NP		NP	
8	0	1—below eyes	NP		NP		NP	
15	0		NP		NP		NP	
19	0	1—below eyes	NP		NP		NP	

(continued)

Table 45.1 *Continued*

Soccer camper	Day 2 Scored sites	Day 2 Other sites	Day 3 Scored sites	Day 3 Other sites	Day 4 Scored sites	Day 4 Other sites	Day 5 Scored sites	Day 5 Other sites
17	NP		NP		0	2—below eyes 2—throat	0	1—below eyes
7	NP		NP		NP		NP	
14	NP		NP		NP		NP	
16	NP		NP		NP		NP	
Product failure	5/224		8/195		8/164		7/179	
p value	1.37×10^{-6}		0.0019		0.0137		0.0021	

Note: Scored sites: 14 body and face sites were evaluated: frontal view—left/right (L/R) face, L/R upper and lower arms, L/R legs. Back view—L/R upper and lower arms, L/R legs. Other sites scored only when evident and included as one additional statistical site. NP indicates nonparticipants, p values based on population proportion of 0.1 (90% unburned).

These dosimeters are based on the UV response of GAFChromic radiographic media (ISP Technologies Inc., product HD-810) which has a spectral response spectrum (7) similar to human UV risk spectra (Fig. 45.2). The dosimeters (Fig. 45.1) consist of two pieces of radiographic film, one of which is covered with a layer of UV-B cut-off filter material, sealed inside an airtight polymer sheath, which transmits sufficiently in the UV-B to allow differential determination of exposure to erythemic radiation in the UV-A and UV-B bands.

Following exposure, the color change of the film pieces were separately evaluated by densitometric scanning (8,9) with the difference between the detected values of total UV exposure and the detected UV-A exposure defining the erythemically significant UV-B exposure. Film response was correlated to solar exposure using calibration curves derived from simultaneous dosimeter exposures and spectroradiometric measurement of sunlight (Fig. 45.3).

Statistical Methods

Response grading involved a series of sites on each volunteer participating each day. The sites, when viewed from the front, were: right and left side of face, right and left upper arm, right and left lower arm, right and left leg. When viewed from the rear the sites were: back right and left upper arm, right and left lower arm, right and left leg. This totaled 14 primary opportunities for each product to fail because of product application, product rub off during the day, or simple product ineffectiveness. It was decided to treat each volunteer test day as a unique individual test and the 14 sites as test replicates adopting a simple burn, no burn binary statistic. Burns that occurred outside these 14 primary sites were combined as one "other" site.

The procedure used is similar to that recently proposed for substantiation that the labeled SPF of a sunscreen is correct (10). Results were evaluated

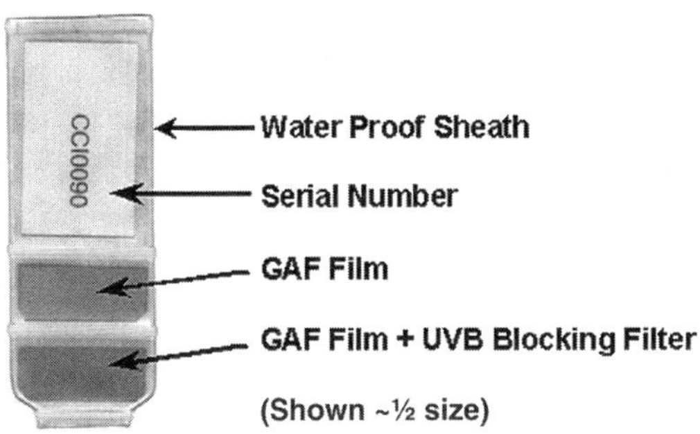

Figure 45.1 Ultraviolet dosimeters. Wearable ultraviolet dosimeters for spectrally varying environments (Rapid Precision Testing Laboratories, Patent Pending) were used to monitor daily exposures. These personal UV dosimeters provide differential monitoring of full-spectrum UV, UV-A, and UV-B (by difference).

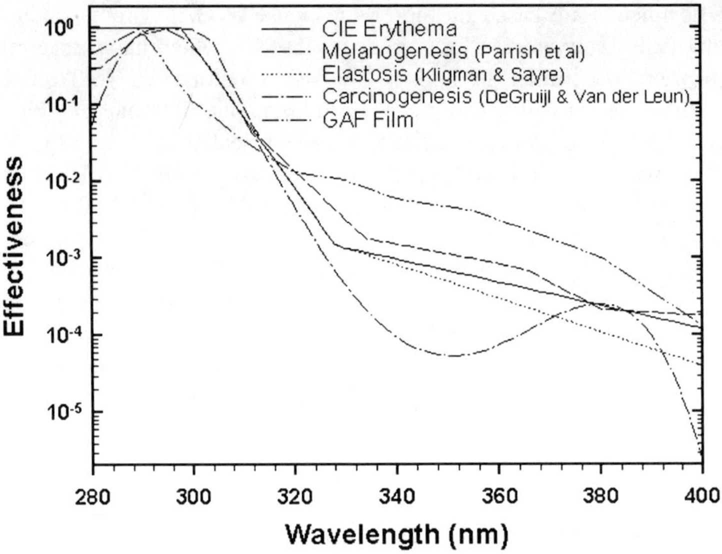

Figure 45.2 Comparison to other action spectra. The GAF film UV action spectrum shows remarkable correlation to several photobiologically important UV action specrta. The response drops almost two orders of magnitude through the UV-B and then drops slightly more than two more orders of magnitude through the UV-A as do most of these reference action spectra.

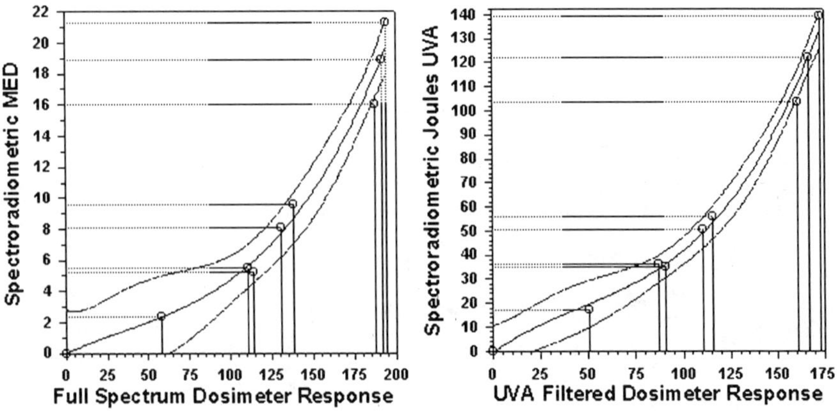

Figure 45.3 Dosimeter calibration curves. Densitometric scans of exposed dosimeters correlated with simultaneous measurement of sunlight with a calibrated spectroradiometer, Optronic Laboratories Model OL-754, traceable to NIST.

using simple binomial statistics, based on the premise that users of high SPF products, self-applied only once at realistic application rates, should expect a reliable chance (90–95%) of all-day protection during an active day of outdoor sunlight exposure. For a given set of exposure site evaluations, if the number of visible responses was lower than a predicted limit, based on the binomial distribution, then the expectation of all day protection was supported. The acceptance level for the number of sites without responses was set for a 95% or greater probability that the actual protection applied was at least as high as the dose accumulated during the exposure day. Look-up tables of cumulative exact binomial probabilities for each day's evaluations were generated for the total number of exposure sites. If the number of sunburned sites was less than or equal to the number that could be reasonably expected ($p < 0.05$), the product is considered adequately protective for all-day use. If there were too many sunburned sites ($p > 0.05$), the product was ruled to be inadequate to provide day-long protection.

RESULTS

On June 19–23, 2000, a soccer camp for young ladies was held in Clearwater, Florida. The ages ranged from approximately 9 to 16 years. Campers were required to apply a sunscreen each day and could either bring their own or use a product supplied by the camp. Those discussed in this report applied Baby Blanket SPF 50+, Sawyer Products System-2 SPF 45, or REI System-2 SPF 45 or Rocky Mountain SPF 50 (supplied by the camp) only once a day, in the morning.

The young ladies participating in the study were in direct sunlight for more than 6 h each day and even when covered by an awning at noon may have received additional scattered exposure. The exposure monitoring indicated that while the campers were engaged in sun exposed activities at least 13 (MED: minimum erythemal dose) MED were available each day with as many as 20 MED on one test day (Fig. 45.4).

While the participating campers ranged from skin types 1–5, none experienced any sunburn where the sunscreen had been applied to their arms and legs. While no swimming occurred, the fact that the subjects were engaged in strenuous soccer activities, sweating and sometimes colliding with each other or the ground, no failure due to these activities was observed. The only product-protected sites where slight sunburn occurred were on the faces of two of the subjects (Table 45.1). This observation may be attributed in part to avoidance of the eyes during application and/or wiping and toweling of sweat from the face. Many individuals seem to miss small areas particularly below their eyes, above their ears, and the tips of their noses (Table 45.2).

The most severe sunburn observed was seen when a young lady applied the sunscreen with her hair down, and sometime during the day's activities tied

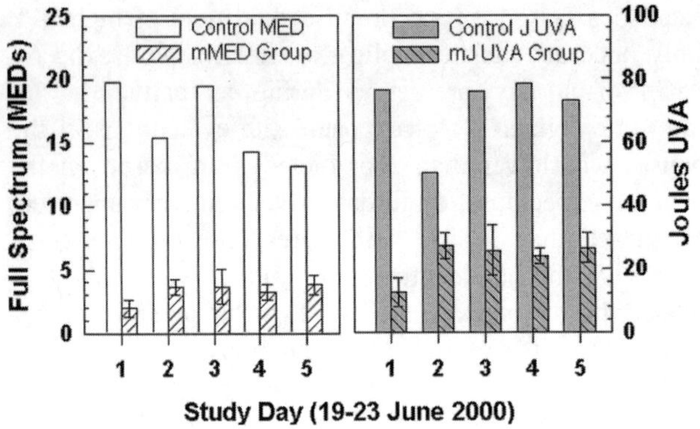

Figure 45.4 Full-spectrum and UV-A dosimetry. Average dosimeter values for each study day are plotted against that day's control dosimeter. Personal dosimeters registered 2–5 MED accumulated dose of the 13–20 MED possible daily exposure. Control dosimeters were exposed face up on a flat surface while personal dosimeters worn on the wrist or pinned onto the shirt were oriented at variable angles to the sun. The relative proportion of UV-A exposure was also significantly less than the control exposures.

her hair up in a ponytail. The sunburn, visible the next morning, was confined to where she failed to apply sunscreen to the back of her neck.

DISCUSSION

Each camper applied the amount of sunscreen she felt necessary without instruction and none of the six 6-oz. sunscreen bottles were emptied during the week's use. This suggests that while reapplication is probably desirable, a single application of a high SPF product used at a realistic application density can provide day-long protection.

Moreover, concerns about a user's ability to uniformly apply sufficient sunscreen to provide all-day protection would appear unfounded. These adolescent

Table 45.2 Cumulative Product Failures at "Other" Localized Sites

	Day 2	Day 3	Day 4	Day 5	Total
Below eyes	5	3	2	3	13
Tip of nose			1	3	4
Throat			1		1
Back of neck		2		1	3
Top of ears			1		1
Forehead			1		1
Number of subjects	16	13	10	11	50

to teenage children were able to apply the product sufficiently to provide adequate protection for extended periods of vigorous athletic exertion in sunlight.

Clearly, a single application the high-SPF sunscreen products used was protective all day. In fact, this single daily application repeatedly provided protection under a variety of different sunlight/cloud conditions. Even young sunscreen users seem to universally apply the sunscreen at adequate levels to completely protect large body areas. However, they miss, sometimes persistently, small particularly sensitive body areas such as below their eyes, above their ears, and the tips of their noses. Missing tops of ears and backs of necks at the hairline could be explained by avoidance of their hair followed by rearranging hair, for example as a ponytail, for outdoor activities.

It is important to realize that while a single sunscreen company sponsored this study, most adolescent soccer campers did not directly participate in the study by using the product supplied. However, they were all required to use the sunscreen of their choice in no case was sunburn observed during the camp on any volunteer. Clearly, many different SPF 30 products were applied adequately and did provide the protection expected. In no instance was inadequate product application observed for large body areas. More importantly, in west-central Florida, in mid-June, there was ample sunlight to cause serious sunburns on anyone who chose to spend the day unprotected or had not applied adequate levels or misapplied sunscreen.

ACKNOWLEDGMENT

This study was supported in part by a grant from Baby Blanket by the Children's Healthcare Research Group.

REFERENCES

1. Wulf HC, Stender IM, Lock-Andersen J. Sunscreens used at the beach do not protect against erythema: a new definition of SPF is proposed. Photodermatol Photoimmunol Photomed 1997; 13:129–132.
2. Bech-Thomsen N, Wulf HC. Sunbathers' application of sunscreen is probably inadequate to obtain the sun protection factor assigned to the preparation. Photodermatol Photoimmunol Photomed 1992; 9:242–244.
3. Azurdia RM, Pagliaro JA, Diffey BL, Rhodes LE. Sunscreen application by photosensitive patients is inadequate for protection. Br J Dermatol 1999; 140:255–258.
4. Diffey BL. Sunscreens, suntans and skin cancer. People do not apply enough sunscreen for protection. Br Med J 1996; 313:942.
5. Stokes R, Diffey B. How well are sunscreen users protected? Photodermatol Photoimmunol Photomed 1997; 13:186–188.
6. Taylor S, Diffey B. Simple dosage guide for suncreans will help users. Br Med J 2002; 324:1526.
7. Dowdy JC, Sayre RM. UV response spectrum of GAF chromic film. Photochem Photobiol 1997; 65:82S.

8. Sayre RM, Sayre DL, Dowdy JC. Determination of the UV transmittance properties of fabrics using UV sensitive film and densitometric techniques (abstract V-3o/04). 6th Congress of the European Society for Photobiology. Churchill College, University of Cambridge, UK, 1995:46.
9. Sayre RM, Dowdy JC. Defining beam uniformity of UV sources using UV sensitive film and densitometric techniques. Photodematol Photoimmunol Photomed 1996; 12:40.
10. Sayre RM, Stanfield J, Lott DL, Dowdy JC. Simplified method to substantiate SPF labeling for sunscreen products. Photodermatol Photoimmunol Photomed 2003; 19:254–260.

46

The Role of Publications in the Industry

Nancy Allured
Allured Publishing Corporation, Carol Stream, Illinois, USA

Getting started on a new research project would be nearly impossible without industry publications. The first step in your search should be to peruse industry publications to get as much current information as possible. Publications are a very important resource. This is true for the general public and also for industry. In the sun products field, there are great resources at our disposal and I will cover them and how best to use these resources.

Publications bring the reader the most current information. When you need the newest and the most up-to-date news, look to trade publications. When you need to research history on a subject, look to technical books and scientific journals to help you look back. There are many levels of publications that we use to keep abreast of the sun products industry and the trends.

There are an extraordinary number of published resources for the sun products researcher. Most chemists start a new project using publications as a first step to develop a new sun product. This field has frequent new technologies being introduced and new research adding knowledge to our category. And, the chemists use these resources heavily to develop the best product for the time.

TRADE PUBLICATIONS

Trade publications are very industry focused but most importantly they are the most current on news and information. Industry publications know the manufacturers, the suppliers, regulatory issues, and the market statistics. The most important service trade magazines provide is keeping the newest information circulating in the industry. Trade publications cover the news—regulatory issues and changes, new ingredients, and new products on the market. And this being an international industry, the magazines cover new developments from around the world.

Trade publications are a part of the industry. This is a distinct difference from other publications. Trade publications are connected to the many resources the industry provides and they are directly a resource to people in the industry. Look to these publications to provide ingredient information, prototype formulations, regulatory restrictions and updates, directories of resources, supplier information, packaging and contract manufacturing services. They can be your practical resource to getting started and keeping connected.

In the sun product category there are many changes happening quickly. It is a very dynamic category. As a result, the trade publications help the industry stay up-to-date on new technologies being developed, and new regulations affecting the category. Due to strong regulatory restrictions on sun products, there is more development taking place in delivery systems and the base product technologies. There is also more development in testing methodologies. The trade publications keep the industry informed on these changes as new discoveries are introduced.

Trade publications provide many of the newest formulas available to try. These prototype formulas are a great starting place to learn new combinations of ingredients and develop new forms of product. As a high-growth category, sun products continue to be the subject of many conferences and seminars. Trade magazines track events and keep calendars current of relevant programs for sun products. These magazines provide a quick overview of everything happening in the industry. They are at the center of information for the industry. It is also very internally focused—industry talks with industry. Readers scan them monthly to keep on top of industry changes. Many researchers file articles by key words to keep information organized for future projects.

SCIENTIFIC JOURNALS

Scientific journals are used in an entirely different way in the sun products category. The journals contain the history and in-depth research. They hold the history of the science behind chemical sunscreens as they are developed, researched, and improved.

Because journals are peer reviewed, the science is scrutinized and evaluated for its integrity before allowing publication. Journals are a forum for pure research. They provide the scientific community a place to present new research and discoveries in sun research. These publications are extremely important for new findings on skin and skin's reaction to photoaging, normal aging, and physiology of skin. These scientific publications carry a lot of research on sun, effects of sun on skin and hair, and the new chemistries in sunscreen development. They also provide insights into many testing methodologies. These papers are also filed by keyword for future projects.

Many researchers watch the scientific journals to see a progression of incremental findings on sun research. This points the way to future sun product discoveries.

TECHNICAL BOOKS

One of the first places a researcher will start in new project is with technical books. Books such as this one on sunscreens offer a tremendous amount of information to get started. It is specifically focused on the project at hand and offers a wide variety of approaches.

Technical books on chemistry, photochemistry, formulations, and ingredients are invaluable. All research chemists working on product development or new research must have technical books at their fingertips.

ELECTRONIC INFORMATION

The Internet is a library at your fingertips. There is a lot of good information available via the Internet. We should never underestimate the value of getting information online. That being said, the Internet is the most difficult to use efficiently and the least organized of all the information resources available to our industry. It is not easy finding the information you want without some experimenting with the use of key words and searching through many websites. But once you become more familiar with the good information out there, it will be a tremendous resource to your work.

Searches using Google can be rewarding in finding some of the latest news or publications available. Some suppliers of sunscreen ingredients have a vast amount of information available online. Web-based compendiums of literature such as STN have a cost but make the use of the Internet more efficient. The Internet can also be a great resource for regulatory and patent information on sun products. Some key websites are the US Patent and Trademark Office (uspto.gov), US Food and Drug Administration (fda.gov), The European Union (europa.eu.int/index-en.htm#), and US Federal Register (archives.gov/federal_register/index.html) to name a few.

Sun product formulations are available online from many of the suppliers of sunscreens. There are also several trade publications that provide hundreds of formulations online with free access.

MORE RESOURCES

There is a wealth of information available in the sun products industry. Suppliers of ingredients conduct regular research for new discoveries. The suppliers publish data, share the data, and many times, provide full booklets on their technical information in print or online. They supply formularies to help chemists develop products and share the scientific data, clinical data, and test results.

And, last but not least is the consumer press. Many women's and men's beauty or lifestyle magazines help us as an industry to keep on top of what the consumer is focused on to help us target our product development more closely to the customer.

This industry has a lot of information available. Through trade publications, scientific journals, the Internet, books, and many other industry resources, quality information is readily available and accessible to those working in the sun product field.

APPENDIX—INDUSTRY PUBLICATIONS

Trade Publications

Chemical & Engineering News—(ACS Publications, USA)

Cosmetic Technology—Technical magazine for the cosmetic industry in Italy (CEC, Italy)

Cosmetics & Toiletries magazine—Technical magazine, peer reviewed, for the international industry (Allured Publishing, USA)

Cosmetics & Toiletries, Portuguese Edition—Technical magazine for the cosmetic industry in Brazil (Tecnopress, Brazil)

Fragrance Journal—Technical magazine for the cosmetic industry in Japan (Fragrance Journal, Japan)

Global Cosmetic Industry magazine—Business magazine for the international cosmetic industry (Allured Publishing, USA)

Happi magazine—Cosmetic and household industry magazine for international industry (Rodman Publishing, USA)

PCA magazine—Cosmetic industry magazine in France (Cosmedia, France)

Rose Sheet newsletter—Weekly news on products, regulations, companies, and events (Elsevier Science, USA)

SOFW journal—Technical magazine for cosmetic and household industry (Verlag H. Ziolkowsky GmbH, Germany)

SPC magazine—Business magazine for the cosmetic industry (Wilmington Press, UK)

Scientific Publications

International Journal of Cosmetic Science—Original papers and review papers in skin and cosmetic research. (Society of Cosmetic Scientists/ Societe Francaise de Cosmetologie, UK and France)

Journal of Applied Cosmetology—Original papers and research reviews on skin and cosmetics. (International Society of Cosmetic Dermatology, Italy)

Journal of Cosmetic Science—Papers on the science underlying cosmetics (Society of Cosmetic Chemists, USA)

Journal of Investigative Dermatology—Original papers and reviews pertinent to the normal and abnormal function of the skin. (Society for Investigative Dermatology, Blackwell, UK)

Journal of Organic Chemistry—(ACS Publications, USA)

Journal of Toxicology—Cutaneous and Ocular Toxicology—Original research papers, short communications and case studies reporting all types of harm to cutaneous and ocular systems from medical products, consumer and household products, as well as environmental and occupational exposures. (Marcel Dekker, USA)

Skin Research and Technology—Clinically oriented journal on biophysical methods and imaging techniques for noninvasive quantification of skin structure and functions. (International Society for Bioengineering and the Skin, Blackwell, UK)

Electronic Information

Dialog.com—a Thomson business
www.nerac.com—Nerac, Inc. (USA)

Consumer Press

Jane—Fairchild Publications (USA)
Cosmopolitan—Hearst magazines (USA)
Vogue—Conde Nast Publications (USA)
Elle—Hachette Filipacchi Media (USA)

Allure—CondéNast (USA)
Lucky—CondéNast (USA)

Regulatory Resources

U.S. Food and Drug Administration (FDA)
5600 Fishers Lane, Rockville, MD 20857-0001 (USA)

Cosmetic, Toiletry, and Fragrance Association (CTFA)
1101 17th Street, NW, Suite 300, Washington, DC 20036-4702 (USA)

Research Institute for Fragrance Materials (RIFM)
Two University Plaza, Suite 406, Hackensack, NJ 07601 (USA)

47

Technical Information in the Expanding Sunscreen Field

Regina Lim
Product Quest, Inc., Daytona Beach, Florida, USA

Christopher D. Vaughan
SPF Consulting Labs, Inc., Pompano Beach, Florida, USA

Edwin D. Leonard, Jr.
Patriot Distributors, Inc., DeLand, Florida, USA

INTRODUCTION

Currently, the spread of new discoveries and scientific studies relating to human protection from ultraviolet (UV) damage is fragmented. Dissemination of publications, and presentations of new techniques, and results in this field has been severely hampered by widespread location of the scientific work. Because of the wide range of disciplines required to address the requirements of UV Protection, information in this field presents a twofold challenge. First, its requirements for expertise are so broad that no scientific journal exists which adopts such broad interests, and second, its technology is covered by much proprietary secrecy, as is typical of any emerging science. Figure 47.1 shows the number of new US patents issued for sunscreens and skin coloring. This pattern usually defines an emerging technology, and it is too early to predict when the technological influx will peak, but it appears that this will not occur for many years.

The technical requirements of the UV protection field include: biologists and physiologists—to study the effects of UV radiation on living creatures; chemists and pharmacists to formulate products to deliver UV protection; physicists to study the effects and response of the UV radiation as it interacts with both formula and skin; lawyers and regulators who assure the safety and effectiveness of UV protection products in the market; and of course, marketers who apply their research to evaluate product acceptability among the population. Sales and marketing professionals are rarely given recognition for their contribution to the delivery of public health. Of course, we know that even the greatest health care advancement is valueless without consumer acceptance. These broad requirements force publication of advancements in sun protection into a wide array of channels.

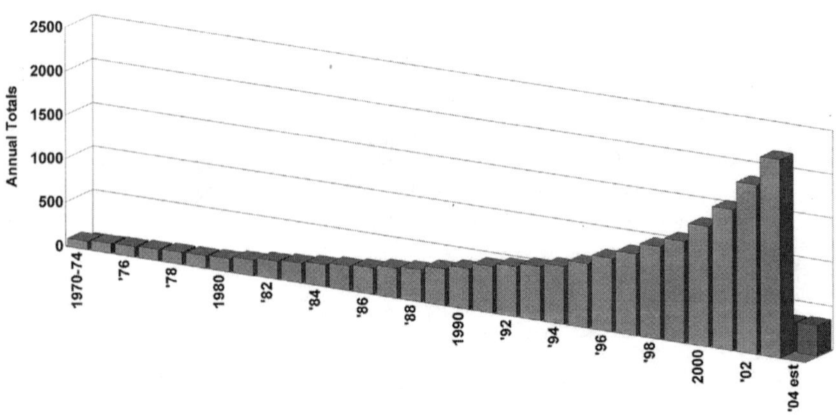

Figure 47.1 Sunscreen patents issued in the USA 1974–2004.

TECHNICAL CONFERENCES

The Florida Sunscreen Symposium

The Florida Sunscreen Symposium ranks first in the field as a source for new information on sunscreen technology. It was the first major sun protection conference, and has been presented continuously over almost 20 years. The Florida Sunscreen Symposium has seen excellent success dealing with the broad range of interests required by UV protection technology. Unfortunately, it is only presented in odd numbered years. Its continual location in Florida places it in a region suited for sun protection study, and recreation. Instigated in 1987 by Ed Leonard Jr. and Chris Vaughan through the Florida Chapter of the Society of Cosmetic Chemists, this conference has become the largest scientific meeting of its kind, and was the first to address the broad range of scientific disciplines required by the field. One of the most successful aspects of this conference arising under the scientific program direction of Regina Lim has been its readiness to air both controversial and problematical aspects arising in sun protection. As a result, much advancement in photostability, optimization of pigmentary reflection, and absorber synergism has been developed.

This three-day conference includes two scientific sessions, usually moderated by Nadim Shaath, and Chris Vaughan, a poster session, an educational seminar course, and a social banquet. This conference regularly attracts approximately 50 suppliers who are limited to presenting materials directed toward sun protection at their booths in the product showcase which is open throughout the conference. Many new ingredients have made a debut in this milieu.

The 8th Symposium was held in 2002 due to the 9/11 tragedy and a simultaneous hurricane in Orlando (in 2001). This conference was rescheduled at Walt Disney World's Coronado Springs Resort in Orlando, Florida. Some of the topics of the scientific sessions covered USP Requirements for Sunscreens, A New way to Characterize Sunscreen Stability, and Thin Film Spectrophotometric Determination of UV-A Protection. The next conference, in September 2003, at Disney's Grand Floridian Hotel & Resort highlighted topics on UV-A Protection, Indoor Tanning Exposure to UV-A, New US Sunscreen Regulations, and the steps ongoing toward Harmonization of International Sunscreen Requirements.

Many new materials and discoveries have debuted at the Florida Symposium, which is sponsored by the Florida Chapter of the SCC each September in odd numbered years. Information may be found on their website: http//www.scconline.org/members/chapters.

The European UV Sunfilters Conference and Exhibition

The European Sunfilters Conference is a privately organized, two-day English language conference held at the Palais de Congress in Paris, France Sponsored by Step Exhibitions, Ltd, Stephouse, North Farm Rd., Tunbridge Wells, Kent,

TN2 3DR, UK. This is a new conference similar to the Florida Symposium. This conference will likely be repeated.

The Sun Protection Conference

This is a new conference organized by the Royal Society in England. It is presented in November, Annually by Summit Events, Ltd., 29–35 Lordship La., London, SE22 8EW, UK who also can be reached on the web at: info@summit-events.com.

EDUCATIONAL COURSES

The Society of Cosmetic Chemists (SCC) sponsors a course (1) twice each year. This course is currently taught by the two of the most respected experts in the field: Ken Klein of Cosmetech, Inc. and David Steinberg of Steinberg Assoc., Their expertise centers on formulation, new technical developments, and regulatory requirements. Both instructors are currently byline contributors and Advisors to *Cosmetics & Toiletries* Magazine. They also manage consulting firms specializing in sunscreens. Information on the time and location of these courses are available from the Society of Cosmetic Chemists, 120 Wall Street, New York, NY 10005, or from their website www.scconline.org.

IMS Testing Group, 282 Quarry Rd., Milford, CT 06460 offers occasional courses on Testing and evaluation of sunscreens, in conjunction with IFSCC, or SCC—John Sottery, PhD is the usual instructor. They can be reached through their website: www.ims-usa.com.

The University of Cincinatti, 3223 Eden Avenue, Cincinatti, OH 45267, is the first of only a few American universities which offer a Masters Degree in Cosmetic Chemistry. Their website http://www.uc.edu provides an Altavista powered search engine, which only turned up two sites when queried for "sunscreen." Neither site directed you to their program on cosmetic science. Nevertheless, this university's School of Pharmacy offers a very active and respected cosmetic science program, which covers all aspects of cosmetic formulation including sunscreen technology. Unfortunately, their website is poorly constructed, and requires perseverance and magnification to glean scraps of information.

Fairleigh Dickinson University, 100 River Road, Teaneck, NJ 07666 also offers an MS in Cosmetic Science. Directed by Dr James Dougherty at their school of Natural Sciences. This university curriculum provides an excellent coverage of sunscreens. Information is available on the web at http://www.fdu.edu, where a fast, and very user friendly search for cosmetic science will provide details.

The Institute for Applied Colloid Technology—directed by Gerd Dahms, PhD also provides instruction in UV protection technology especially with respect to formulation variables and product stability.

SCIENTIFIC SOCIETIES

The American Society for Photobiology (ASP)

This scientific society promotes original research, provides a forum for the integration of various disciplines in the study of photobiology, and provides information on the photobiological aspects of national and international problems. Founded in 1972, they produce a journal, online newsletter, and an annual meeting in July. The basic areas of this society's interest are: photochemistry, photosensory biology, environmental biology, and photosynthesis. They operate from the University of Kansas, and can be contacted at ASP Business office, PO Box 1897, Lawrence, KS 66044. Phone (785) 843-1235x216/Fax (785) 843-1287 or at phot@allenpress.com. Their European counterpart, The European Society for Photobiology (ESP) is associated with the University of Dundee.

The Society of Cosmetic Chemists (SCC)

This scientific society has 18 regional chapters across the USA. Their concentration is in the formulation, function, and testing of UV protecting materials. Their national meetings usually devote one of four scientific sessions to the sunscreen field. These meetings are held early in December in New York City, and mid-year at varying locations. They can be contacted at: SCC, 120 Wall Street, New York, NY 10005. Phone: (212) 668-4088, fax: (212) 668-1504.

The American Academy of Dermatology (AAD)

The AAD is a specialized medical society founded in 1938 with the mission to improve the level of dermatological care. They sponsor a journal, the *Journal of the American Academy of Dermatology*, which publishes cutting edge research in the medical aspects of skin cancer. They also sponsor research on skin cancer treatment and prevention at the Sulzberger Institute. The AAD annual meeting is a fertile forum for the reporting of new skin cancer research results, and treatment discoveries. They can be reached in Shaumberg, IL through their website at: http//www.skincarephysicians.com.

SCIENTIFIC JOURNALS

There is at this time no scientific journal which deals solely with the broad application of science and technology as applied to UV protection. The peer-reviewed journals which most often publish on this topic are:

1. *Photochemistry and Photobiology:* The Journal of the American Society for Photobiology provides the best coverage of new research in the photobiological aspects of sun protection and UV damage. But this journal limits its range to biological interactions with UV.

Abstracts and tables of contents are available free online at www. aspjournal.com.

2. *The Journal of Photochemistry and Photobiology* covers topics on bioluminescense, chronobiology, DNA repair, photocarcinogenesis, photomovement, photoreception, photosynthesis, spectroscopy of biological systems, and UV or visible radiation effects and vision. This independent journal is published by Elseivier Press: 6277 Sea Harbor Drive, Orlando FL 32887-4200, or at PO Box 211, 1000AE Amsterdam, The Netherlands.
3. *Cosmetics & Toiletries Magazine:* This peer-reviewed journal publishes documentary issues specializing in new sunscreen technology, usually twice each year. Its range of topics in the widest of any journal, although it leans toward chemistry of UV interacting systems. It is available from Allured Pulishing, Carol Stream, IL.
4. *IFSCC Magazine* is published quarterly in Germany by Verlag fur Chemische Industrie, PO Box 10 25 65, D-86015 Augsburg, Germany. This journal offers five original scientific papers in each issue. Usually, one or two papers address some aspect of sunscreen technology. It is sponsored by the International Federation of Societies of Cosmetic Chemistry, and can be contacted by email at ifscc.mag@sofw.com.
5. *Photodermatology, Photoimmunology and Photomedicine* is the official publication of the Photomedicine Society. It concentrates on direct and distant effects of electromagnetic radiation mediated through the skin. It is published by Blackwell Ltd. in London, and current abstracts are available online at http://www.blackwellmunksgaard.dk/Journal.
6. *The Journal of Cosmetic Science* (formerly the Journal of the Society of Cosmetic Chemists) is a peer-reviewed journal which generally has one or more UV-related papers in each issue. It is published by the Society of Cosmetic Chemists, New York, NY 10005.

With the exception of the very few focused scientific conferences, and journals mentioned in the aforesaid list, articles on research and new developments in sun protection may occasionally be found scattered amongst the following (re)sources: *Journal of the American Academy of Dermatology*, *British Journal of Dermatology*, *Soap and Cosmetics*, published by Chemical Week Associates, 110 William St., New York, NY. *HAPPI* (*Household & Personal Products Industry*) Published by Rodman Publishing, 17 S.Franklin Tpke., Ramsey, NJ and *The Newsletter of the Florida Chapter of the Society of Cosmetic Chemists*. This newsletter promotes sunscreen technology, and covers recent leading developments in the field. It is circulated to members of the Florida Chapter of the SCC and prior attendees of the Florida Sunscreen Symposium.

SCIENTIFIC BOOKS

This book, *Sunscreens*, has for over 15 years been the only book of its kind addressing the broad field of UV protection issues. It has numerous reference citations (ISI) and 52 US patent citations since its first publication. Other useful books addressing biology and physics of UV light are:

Understanding Physics, Light, Magnetism and Electricity, Issac Asimov, New American Library, (1985) is very readable, and basic.

Waves and Grains, Mark P. Silverman, Princeton University Press, (1998) offers a more advanced explanation of light refraction, reflection, and polarization.

Light in Biology and Medicine, Ron H. Davis, ed., Plenum Press (1991). This book contains 56 peer-reviewed and edited chapters covering the latest topics in photobiology. It is an expensive, but thorough reference.

INTERNET WEBSITES

The Internet has recently become a prime information source (2) for technology transfer. It began its rapid growth in 1990, and surpassed 1 million participating host computers in only 2 years (3). By now, over 20 million computers and 3 billion webpages may be accessed through the Internet.

The ASP website http://www.pol-us.net is named Photobiology Online. They offer news on pertinent publications, and an online textbook.

The US Department of Commerce sponsors the US Patent and Trademark website: http://patft.uspto.gov. This website offers complete text of all US patents since 1974, and currently publishes an average of 10 new patents each week, which can be retrieved by entering "sunscreen" into their internal search engine.

The US Food and Drug Administration currently is enacting a regulatory program which adopts sunscreens into the category of OTC drug products. This herculean effort has been legendary in its tortuosity. Proposed rules have been repeatedly confounded by new scientific discoveries, yet the agency has persevered to respond to the challenge. Most recently, they have expanded their regulatory concern to cover UV-A as well as UV-B radiation. Their website, http://www.fda.gov is a remarkably voluminous and accessible resource. The FDA home page contains a powerful Google-driven search engine which provides current information regarding regulations being developed to control the manufacture, testing, and distribution of sunscreens in the USA.

The United States Pharmacopeia (USP) hosts a slow but searchable website, http://www.usp.org containing official regulatory requirements for the naming (USAN) and testing of Active Pharmaceutical Ingredients (APIs) including the UV absorbers permitted in sunscreens. They are the ones responsible for new shorter drug names, such as Octinoxate, and Ensulizole being recently applied to sunscreen APIs.

COLIPA is the official European Association of Cosmetic Manufacturers available at their web location http://www.colipa.com. This searchable website uses an Atomz search engine, and provides much more unrestricted information than the domestic CTFA site. Through this site COLIPA provides regulatory guidance over the control and harmonization of requirements for sunscreen products throughout Europe. The information available from this agency is absolutely necessary for anyone producing sun protection products designed for sale in Europe. As a reflection of their openness, and in promulgating information, COLIPA has emerged as the world leader in guiding the harmonization and uniformity of sunscreen regulations around the world.

The Cosmetic Toiletries and Fragrance Association (CTFA) is located in Washington, DC. Their website http://www.ctfa.org contains some limited public information on current regulatory issues, but the details of their (sizable) efforts impacting the regulation of sunscreens are only available to members through a password system. The CTFA serves as an industrial lobby protecting the interests of the cosmetic industry in the USA. As such, they have been instrumental in providing FDA both guidance and industrial consensus on many issues surrounding the enactment of regulations.

The Research Institute for Fragrance Materials (RIFM) has a website under construction; http://www.urifm.org, at the time of this writing. Information about RIFM is available through an associated website http://ultrainternational.com/rifm.htm. This organization generates and maintains information on safety and compatibility of fragrance materials as applied to sunscreen products.

Medline—The US National Library of Medicine is the world's largest medical library. It collects material in all major areas of health science. It is a wonderful resource, searchable from the web at http://www.nlm.nih.gov.

Med Scape at www.medscape.com is another huge medical database which requires a password and a one time free registration.

Zebrafish Information Network (http://zfin.org) is a well-organized new biological database (4) from the University of Oregon. The zfin database is divided into nine searchable categories.

Commercial sites of most of the UV absorber manufacturers provide valuable data on their application in sun protection products. Some major industrial suppliers are ISP (info@ispcorp.com), Presperse (samples@presperse.com), Cardre, BASF, Haarman & Reimer, Kobo Products, Degussa (surfactants@de.goldschmidt.com), Roche, Ciba (Gabriella.Kuster@cibasc.com), and others. Major marketers of sun protection products such as L'Oreal, Playtex, Schering Plough, and Hawiian Tropic also sponsor websites which promote their products but also provide excellent information on sunscreen function. Finally, the American Cancer Society and the Skin Cancer Foundation and the National Institutes of Health (especially the National Cancer Institute) support websites and report on research in the field.

CONCLUSIONS

The resources identified in this chapter form the current technological core of the rapidly developing science of sun protection. These are the very same resources we utilize when developing the program for the biennial Florida Sunscreen Symposium Series. To attract the attention, and attendance, of the majority of the sun care scientific community it is necessary to find and recruit the most cutting-edge researchers. The resources enumerated in this chapter allow us to do this. They will also help you access the latest developments in the field. Although our resources have changed over the years, many of the core sources have not only maintained their contact with new developments, but some have gained more power as the technology accelerates. The world wide web of Internet computer servers, has by far produced the biggest change in the way we search for innovation (5). However, it is possible that this resource may become less dynamic, and responsive as the Internet website load increases over time. At the time of this publication website searches for several general sun protection topics, using the Internet search engine; Google (6) provided voluminous responses: "Sun Protection" provided 4,180,000 results; "Skin Cancer" produced 3,158,00 results; "Sunscreen" yielded 743,000 results; "SPF 45" elicited 107,000 results; "UV Absorber" gave up 33,400 responses, and "Sunscreen Book" was cited 17,200 times.

Huge internet responses make searching the web progressively more difficult. For example, no one could hope to read all 17,000 sunscreen book references provided by Google, so in the future Internet, searches must be made more specific. And, simultaneously scientific journal hardcopy is rapidly declining in availability, being replaced by online journal editions. Therefore, it seems apparent that courses and seminars may continue to be the main channel for spreading new sun protection technology. Currently, and in the forseeable future, mining information from many varied sources is the only way to fully maintain cutting-edge technology in the sunscreen field.

REFERENCES

1. Society of Cosmetic Chemists, 120 Wall St, New York, NY 10005 (http//www.scc-online.org/).
2. Plonsker L. Technology transfer. Cosmet Toilet 2001; 116(4):30.
3. Internet Information Superhighway. J NIH Res 1995; 7:72.
4. Surfing for the Best Biotech. Genet Eng News 2001; 21(18):82.
5. Hodel AE. Sharing the chemical industry's little secrets. Chemical Processing, (April, 2001), www.chemical processing.com.
6. Souped up Search Engines. News feature; Nature 2000; 405:112.

48

Recent Sunscreen Market Trends

Nadim A. Shaath and Mona Shaath
Alpha Research & Development, Ltd., White Plains, New York, USA

INTRODUCTION

The sunscreen market is expanding dramatically in response to the alarming increase in the incidence of skin cancer worldwide (this volume, chapter by Nelson). Fears of excessive tanning have done away with the old days of greasing up with coconut fragranced oil for hours motionless under the sun. This, however, has neither quelled the desire for a healthy glow nor has it stopped consumers from pursuing an active lifestyle. A general survey of the sunscreen products currently available reveals a market that mirrors the changing behaviors of today's consumer. Consumers have become more diligent than they once were about sun protection and the industry has responded with creativity in ingredients, packaging, and applications.

Sunscreen products have crossed over the traditional boundaries that once restricted ultraviolet (UV) filters to summertime sunbathing applications and have infiltrated the daily wear skin care market. Although a "sunscreen lotion" may seem to have applications similar to "skin lotion," innovators in the skin care industry and scientists in the sun protection business have only recently joined forces. UV filters, functional botanicals, antioxidants, and other natural ingredients have entered skincare formulations full force, never to be omitted again. Products have evolved into an impressive array of lotions, creams, sprays, gels, and oils that can handle the demands of consumers who wish to simplify their daily beauty routine while maintaining a sunburn protection regimen.

The recent trend in the daily wear sunscreen market is multifunctionality. Now just one jar can contain vitamins, botanicals, and essential oils in an enriched, skin-smoothing body lotion that is hypoallergenic while also providing protection from the harmful UV rays. Consumers want products that both protect and beautify their skin and they do not want to buy too many bottles to get that done. Sunscreens are now an indispensable component of most skin care, lip care, makeup, and even hair care products. In the future, sunscreen products will continue this trend incorporating new and innovative ingredients into their formulations.

One major obstacle to a healthy avoidance of the sun is pale skin. A tanned glow is still considered aesthetically pleasing in our culture and the chances of this preference fading quickly are slim. Again, we find the industry reflecting the needs of the consumer. The sunscreen industry has responded to the consumer demand for color in a number of innovative ways. Most notable of these is the expansion of the industry into self-tanners and bronzers for those who wish to avoid the damaging rays of the sun but who still enjoy a tan.

Even the sunscreen market's traditional core, the familiar recreational use products, has adapted to the new consumer attitudes towards fun in the sun. Fragrances in a typical sunscreen lotion are less overpowering and the product is generally more functional for active lifestyles. Claims of water and sweat resistance and oil-free protection allow the consumer to participate in outdoor activities unencumbered by their method of sun protection. Consumers can pursue sports, including swimming, without excessive reapplications. Again, we find the sunscreen market responding creatively to the needs of the consumer.

Our changing relationships with exposure to the sun have been supported by the sunscreen industry. It is now possible to maintain continual coverage more easily and more pleasingly than it was in the past. This is a responsive industry, continually growing to responsibly meet the needs of consumer. With new consumer demands, advances in technology and new regulatory changes, future sunscreen products will also have to adhere to new guidelines that might necessitate reformulation.

CLASSIFICATION OF THE SUNSCREEN MARKET

The sunscreen market[1] may be classified into three categories:

1. Daily wear skin care with UV filters
2. Tanning products
3. Beach, recreational and sports wear products.

A review of each of these categories in the US market will serve to illustrate the recent trends in the worldwide sunscreen markets. The listing is not intended to be an exhaustive one, listing of all products in the US market and the reader is referred to the many chapters that have tackled marketing issues in their technical presentations.[2]

Daily Wear and Long-Term Protective Products

This multibillion dollar industry has realized the benefits of incorporating UV filters in year-round daily wear and other long-term protective products. Today, UV filters are present in daily-use moisturizers, aftershave and soothing products, antiwrinkle, antiaging and other medical products, in makeup and foundation creams, in lipsticks and lip balms, in a number of hair products including shampoos, conditioners, gels, as well as hair growth and stimulating preparations. Clothing with UV filters has become an industry of its own that is closely governed and regulated (this volume, chapter by Hatch).

In these products, the levels of the UV filters are generally much lower than those present in recreational products, relying heavily on inorganic particulates. The types of cosmetic vehicles are generally simpler and limited to light oil in water emulsions. Harsh emulsifier systems are avoided and the formulation is loaded with moisturizers, antioxidants, vitamins, essential oils, botanical

---

[1]The sun care market includes fabrics with UV filters (Chapter 28) as well as a multitude of after-sun, medicated sunburn treatment products that are outside the scope of this monograph.

[2]SaNogueira cites ACNielsen Scan Track Data reporting sales of almost half a billion dollars for the recreational sunscreen products (Chapter 25). Lott and coauthors list the sales of the mass sunscreen market in the USA to exceed 600 million dollars and classify these products into 12 categories (Chapter 27). Gonzalez and Kalafsky cite IRI Infoscan Review and list the sales of the tanning products on the US market to exceed 100 million dollars annually (Chapter 29). Chaudhuri (Chapter 30) as well as Epstein (Chapter 32) report on consumer products on the market that contain antioxidants, free radical scavengers and other botanical and biologically active ingredients. Buccellato lists the fragrances in a wide variety of sunscreen products (Chapter 23). Shaath and Walele reviewed the cosmetic products in the US market that contain inorganic particulate ultraviolet filters (Chapter 15).

extracts, enzymes, skin lighteners, and other biologically functional ingredients ("cosmeceuticals") including coenzyme Q10, theophyllene, AHA, BHA, retinoids, creatine, isoflavones, matrikines, etc. (1). The products are either fragrance free or are lightly perfumed. The claims are generally more aggressive than those found in recreational products addressing claims of antiaging, antiwrinkle, barrier and tissue repair, hydration, and moisturizing (this volume, chapter by Lentini).

This industry may be classified into premium and specialty brands, mass market brands, and direct sales brands. The products generally contain UV filters along with natural extracts, antioxidants, essential oils, and other important biologically active ingredients to repair the damage of the sun and other environmental agents as well as ingredients to combat the effect of reactive oxygen species (ROS) and free radical damage to the skin (this volume, chapter by Lintner).

Premium and Specialty Brands

These products are generally sold at high-end retail stores, beauty salons, and spas and their prices vary from $30 to over $150 per unit. They include such international brands as Aveda, Bath & Body Works, Biotherm, Clarins, Clinique, Elizabeth Arden, Estee Lauder, Lancome, La Prairie, Origins, Prescriptives, and Shiseido to name only a few.

Aveda has Daily Light Guard SPF15, Tourmaline Charged Protecting Lotion and Sunsource Sunless Tanning, all with specialty extracts and essential oils.

Bath & Body Works has a suntan lotion with an SPF8 and extracts including green tea.

Biotherm has De-Age SPF15 containing olive extracts, grapeseed, and retinol.

Clarins has Suncare Cream with aloe, silver birch, camellia, and palm and also Hydrating after Sun with walnut, linden, and vitamins.

Clinique has a number of products including Anti-gravity with green tea, wheatgerm and Sea whip and Total Turnaround with salicylic acid.

Estee Lauder has the Advanced Night Repair, Resilience SPF15, Light Source, and Day Wear with SPF15.

Lancome has Primordiale Intense, Renergie, and Absolue with specialty ingredients.

La Prairie has Cellular antiwrinkle SPF30, Sun block SPF50, body emulsion SPF30 and Cellular Retinol Complex PM with retinol and coenzyme Q10.

Origins carries Have A Nice Day with gingko, birch extracts, and licorice, Origins Sunshine State SPF20 and Beach Blanket SPF15.

Prescriptives has the Super Line Preventer with vitamins C and E, green tea extract, and hyaluronic acid.

Shiseido has Benefiance with a biohyaluronic complex and Avessa SPF50 PA+++ Neo Sunscreen.

Mass Market Brands

These products are generally sold in drugstores and super markets and their prices range from $10 to $25 per unit. They include such brands as Almay, Beiersdorf, Johnson & Johnson, L'Oreal, Proctor & Gamble, and Schering-Plough.

Almay has the Kinetin skin care line and Milk Plus with tocopheryl acetate, green tea, and other plant extracts.

Beiersdorf carries the Nivea line (Visage) and the Eucerin brands with products such as Antiwrinkle and Firming cream with vitamin E, and Q10 Plus with coenzyme Q10, and Daily Defense with an SPF15, tocopheryl acetate, glucosylrutin and isoquercetin.

Johnson & Johnson carries the Aveeno brand with Skin Brightening Daily treatment and Radiant Skin daily moisturizer with vitamins and soya extract. Their Neutrogena brand has Anti-Wrinkle, Healthy Skin, and Visibly Firm with vitamins.

L'Oreal has the Dermo-expertise line, and the Ombrelle line with vitamins and Ambre Solair with cactus nutriflavones.

Proctor & Gamble has the Olay brand Regenerist with vitamins and green tea extracts and Complete UV Defense moisturizers.

Schering-Plough carries the Endless Summer line with antioxidants and vitamins.

Finally, the lip care market is a significant one that delivers protective balms with ultraviolet filters. This market is dominated by two brands, Blistex and Chapstick.

Blistex has a number of brands with SPF protection, namely, Ultra, Clear Advance, Complete Moisture, Medicated Lip Balm, Liptone, and Silk & Shine.

Chapstick carries Fruit Smoothies, Lipbalm, Lipbalm Ultra, and Lipbalm Moisturizer.

There are many other lip care brands including *Coppertone*, *Hawaiian Tropic*, *Neutrogena*, and *Banana Boat*.

Direct Sales Brands

These products are sold generally online or at-home parties with prices ranging from $10 to $50 and generally contain antioxidants and botanical extracts. They include such brands as Avon, Mary Kay, Nu Skin, and Shaklee.

Avon has Hydrofirming cream with SPF15, Beautifying Morning Revitalising with SPF10, Sun-so-soft SPF30 and 40 for kids.

Mary Kay has Time-Wise with botanicals and vitamin E, Problem Solvers with vitamins C and E and Skin Revival.

Nu Skin has UV Block Hydrator with plankton extracts and Skin Mist with willow herb, algae, mushroom, and cucumber extracts, also Night Supply.

For commercial sunscreen products incorporating inorganic particulates read the chapter by Shaath and Walele (this volume).

Tanning Products

This sector represents sales of about a hundred million dollars in the US sunscreen market and is subdivided into three categories:

A. Sunless tanning products
B. Tanning accelerators
C. Tanning bed products.

The sunless tanners are products that impart a tanned appearance to the skin by the use of colorants or ingredients, mostly dihydroxy acetone (DHA), that interact with the free amino acids on the skins surface. These products are also called bronzers and this category accounts for more than two-thirds of all tanning products sold in the USA. The Maillard (nonenzymatic browning) reaction between DHA and free amino acids on the skin produces colored melanoidins, which are responsible for the bronze appearance of the skin after application. The use of antioxidants, colors, or natural extracts and other ingredients is responsible for imparting the most suitable skin coloration simulating a tanned appearance to the individual. Products are sold for a light, medium, or dark tan.

Tanning accelerators are products that enhance the body's natural tanning processes but have been restricted by FDA's enforcement of any drug claims that these products purport to possess. There are two key enzymes for melanogenesis, namely tyrosinase, which catalyzes the conversion of tyrosine to DOPA (dihydroxy phenyl alanine) and Dopachrome tautomerase which catalyses the DOPA into melanin.

Tanning bed products have increased dramatically with the proliferation of artificial tanning parlors across the country in the last decade. Many tanning salons are also outlets for sunless tanning products where proper application and administration of these products by a professional is crucial for its success. The reader is referred to the chapter on tanning products (this volume, chapter by Gonzalez and Kalafsky).

A review of the three categories, other than the skin lightening products popular in Asia, is given in the following list:

A. Sunless tanning: This category represents about 80% of the dollar sales of all tanning products, and is dominated by Coppertone (Endless Summer), Neutrogena (Instant Bronze Sunless Tanner),

Bain De Soleil (Radiance Eternelle Sunless Tan), and Banana Boat (Sunless Tan).

B. Tanning bed products: This category is dominated by a few companies, including Hawaiian Tropic (Tan 2 Max Tanning Bed), Banana Boat (Tanning Bed), LA Express (Expresso Tanning Bed), and Euro (Optimizer Cobalt Tanning Bed).

C. Tanning accelerators: Few manufacturers in the US market produce formulations in this category. The top brands are Hawaiian Tropic (Tan Accelerator and Ultra Sun), Banana Boat (Tan Accelerator) and other brands such as Ocean Potion Australian Brand, Australian Gold Tan, and Panama Jack Accelerator.

Recreational Products

This ever-expanding, several billion dollar worldwide industry produces a multitude of products primarily designed to protect individuals from the harmful rays of the sun while sunbathing, playing, working, or participating in any sun-exposed activity.

The classification of these products depends upon the degree of sun protection (low, medium to high SPF products), the mode of application (cream, lotion, milk, gel, spray, oil, towelettes, etc.), functionality (water-resistant, sweat-resistant, tanning accelerators, presun and postsun applications, healing products, hair products, etc.) and other specialized products for golfers, tennis and soccer players, skiers, snowboarders, climbers, as well as a number of "combination" products. Combination products for sunscreen include insect repellents, lip care, and antiaging products, where more than one regulatory monograph may need to be satisfied. Natural sunscreen products with little or no synthetic ingredient additives, including "organically" grown ingredients, are part of a rapidly growing sector in this field of sun protection.

Recreational products are generally formulated with multiple UV filters (occasionally exceeding 25% of the total emulsion formulation) and containing water proofing film formers. The emulsifier system is generally a soap system or a nonionic with a high HLB, and contains humectants, shine enhancing emollients and a fragrance (coconut, tropical fruits, orange flower, and rarely, subtle floral types). The claims address protection and prevention as specified by the Final Monograph (2).

The US industry in 2003 dollar figures has exceeded a half billion dollars (this volume, chapter by SaNogueira) and is dominated by four major manufactures, namely, Schering-Plough (Coppertone), Playtex (Banana Boat), Neutrogena and Tanning Research (Hawaiian Tropic).

A. *Schering-Plough* (*Coppertone*): This is the leading sunscreen manufacturer in the USA for recreational and tanning products. Their Coppertone brand has become a household name in the US market. They are constantly introducing new products, brands and line extensions. These include the Shade line, Water Babies and Kids line, Endless Summer, Coppertone brand, and their new brand, Spectra 3, with their marketing campaign that their products reflect, scatter and absorb the harmful UV rays. Some of their specific products include: Coppertone oil free SPF30, Endless Summer SPF30, Ultra Sweat proof SPF30, Sunblock lotion SPF15, Day Oil SPF4, Coppertone Spectra 3 SPF30, Water Babies SPF45, Kids Coppertone SPF30 and 50, and Sports Gel Coppertone.

B. *Playtex (Banana Boat)*: This company had entered the market relatively recently with their Banana Boat line of sunscreen products but managed to earn the distinction of running a close second to Schering-Plough and gaining with each new product introduction. Some of their specific products include: Sports Block SPF50, Kids SPF30, Baby Magic SPF48, Suntannicals, Faces Plus SPF23, Ultra Sun Block SPF30, and Protective Tanning Oils.

C. *Neutrogena*: Neutrogena has developed from a West Coast specialty cosmetics house to a major sunscreen company after being acquired relatively recently by Johnson & Johnson. They formulate products for all of the above three categories in the sunscreen industry. In fact in the sunless tanning market reviewed earlier, six of their products rank in the top ten sellers (Plough's Endless summer holds the first place position). Some of their specific products include: Healthy Defense with SPF30, Neutrogena brand with SPF, Ultra sheer Day Dry Touch SPF30, and Visibly Younger Sunblock lotion SPF30.

D. *Tanning Research (Hawaiian Tropic)*: This Florida-based company originally famous for their beach tanning oils has made substantial contributions to the sunscreen industry by introducing a number of innovative products including products for the children and baby category as well as the tanning accelerator market (holding the top two tanning accelerator products). Some of their specific brands include: Baby Faces SPF50, Sport SPF30, Protection Plus SPF15-45, Ozone SPF70, GoldenTan SPF6, Barbie SPF30, Kids Splash SPF30, and Dark Tan Gel.

There are countless other brands and manufacturers including Ban De Soleil, Blue Lizard, Bullfrog, California Baby, Clearasil, Credentials, DDF, Dermalogica, Dr. Hauschka, Fallene, Fruit of the Earth, Glyderm, Jack Black, Lancaster, M.D.Forte, Dr.Murad, Mustela, Neostrata, No Ad, Nu Derm, Obagi, Peter Thomas Roth, Philosophy, Phytomer, Sea & Ski, Skinceuticals, Ti-silc, Vanicream, Zirh, and many drug store brands.

FUTURE TRENDS

A number of factors will dictate the future development of sunscreen products in the USA. These factors include:

1. New regulations
2. Advances in technology.

New Regulations

With the anticipated publication of the Final Rule by December 2005, a number of changes in future products are imminent (this volume, chapter by Holmann and Shetty). Specifically, two issues will have broad implications on current and future products, namely:

A. *Limits on the SPF label*: Despite the fact that the Tentative Final Monograph and the recently published Final Rule (2) clearly specifies a maximum limit of SPF30+ (plus) for all sunscreen products, the fate of all the current products with SPF >30+ is in question. Marketers and dermatologists all favor values >30+ and today we have seen a significant increase in products labeled 45, 50, 70, and even 100. Those concerned are hoping that the FDA will allow claims of SPF >30+. Despite the lobbying efforts of individual companies, the CTFA and Dermatologists, there are no concrete indications that the FDA will allow claims over 30 in their Final Rule. In any scenario imagined, marketers of sunscreen products will scramble in 2005 or thereabouts to accommodate either the status quo (of SPF 30+) or the hoped for higher SPF values. This could obviously create a major hardship for those companies who may have to withdraw, repackage, relabel, and reformulate their existing products. Change and upheaval in any industry, however, also represents opportunities and challenges for marketers and entrepreneurs, who will be inclined to introduce a number of new products complying with the new regulations.
B. *UV-A and broad-spectrum protection labeling*: Any protocol that the FDA adopts for requiring sunscreen products to be labeled for "UV-A" protection and/or "broad spectrum" protection will favor one way or another those manufacturers who use specific UV-A ingredients and cosmetic formulations. The type of *in vitro* or *in vivo* protocols adopted may have a significant effect on efficacy labeling and cost of compliance with the proposed requirements. Again, this challenge represents both an opportunity and a barrier to a few for the marketing of sunscreen products.

C. *Other regulations*: Other regulations that may have an effect on the marketing of sunscreen products if changed in the Final Rule when it is published in 2005 include:
   a. Photostability of ingredients
   b. Photoreactivity of inorganic particulates
   c. Use of natural UV absorbers
   d. Use of biologically active ingredients
   e. Tanning accelerators and sunless tanning
   f. Medical and drug claims
   g. Worldwide UV testing protocols
   h. "Organic" and "biodynamic" farming certifications
   i. Clothing with sun protection regulations.

Advances in Technology

Despite the fact that the cosmetic industry has made significant strides in the formulation of a multitude of sunscreen products, significant opportunities still exist for technologically advanced new ingredients. Today, we can formulate products with SPFs as high as 100 that are water resistant and aesthetically appealing. Nevertheless, there is a serious shortage of ingredients in the USA for enhanced protection in the future. Specifically:

A. *New UV Filters*: European regulations (COLIPA) have allowed for the adoption of a variety of new filters that have not found their way into the US market. It is totally impractical for a growing industry as the sunscreen industry to introduce new UV filters only through the NDA process. This process is time consuming (3–5 years), expensive (several million dollars) and limited to basically one formulation, with financial rewards that are extremely limited (under 50 million dollars per annum when the ingredient is highly successful). This is unlike the pharmaceutical industry where a patented ingredient with an NDA permit may yield financial returns in the hundreds of millions of dollars per year. It is heartening to see the new TEA process that may allow UV actives with 5-year history of use in foreign countries to be included in the Category I listing of actives (this volume, chapter by Holmann and Shetty). Three ingredients are currently under serious review and their adoption will witness a growth of new cosmetic sunscreen formulations that may incorporate these UV filters.

B. *New cosmetic ingredients*: With reports that emollients and emulsifiers may have an effect on the efficacy of sunscreen products, many new types will be created and marketed in the future (3). These include ingredients that solubilize UV actives, disperse inorganic particulates, increase SPF, assist in waterproofing, improve the film formation of the product on the skin (more uniform, thick and nontransparent film), and ingredients that will reduce the photostability and photoreactivity of UV filters. New sunless tanning ingredients other than DHA will ultimately be developed in combination with new additives and ingredients that will impart a more stable, natural-looking tan.

C. *New packaging*: Our concern for ecologically and environmentally safe packaging should be foremost on the minds of developers. Material that can be recycled and reprocessed is paramount. However, innovations in delivery, durability, practicality, safety, and convenient packaging are key in the promotion of sunscreen products to the consumer. Multicomponent packaging such as those delivering sunless tanning products and other hair and skin multicomponent products will greatly enhance their use and adoption by the consumer.

D. *New biologically active ingredients*: It is inevitable that new biologically active ingredients will be developed that address not only the discomfort of sunburn but the medical problems associated with photodamage. These include both the direct effects of sun damage to the skin such as DNA dimerization and photo adduct formation as well as the indirect effects of producing free radicals and reactive singlet oxygen species (ROS) (this volume, see chapters by Lentini and Epstein). Today we have witnessed a plethora of ingredients from antioxidants such as green tea to vitamins, as well as a variety of antiaging and antiwrinkle ingredients. Many more ingredients will be introduced in the future attempting to rectify a number of biological functions that may be implicated in sun damage and skin cancers. For a discussion on the topic, read the several chapters in this book by Nelson, Diffey, Giacomono, Lintner, Epstein, and Chaudhuri.

E. *New natural ingredients*: The essential oil and botanical extract industry has researched a variety of natural ingredients that provide UV protection, boost SPF and film formation on the skin, and add a variety of functional properties that address a number of consumer concerns. The essential oil and botanical extract industry has experienced major growth in the development of a multibillion dollar industry for aromatherapy, massage and spa products. The use of these ingredients will create new outlets and unconventional avenues for the promotion of new sunscreen products.

We hope that with the unearthing of these natural treasures for incorporation into sunscreen products that extreme care is given to all the concerns of safe mining, sustainability of natural ingredients and the use of renewable resources. We must also support and sustain indigenous people's dependence on these resources, diversify and strengthen the local economies and develop new agricultural techniques for maximizing farming practices such as "organic" and "biodynamic" farming.

An additional word of caution is appropriate with the use of natural ingredients and botanicals in sunscreen products. Their inclusion should be based upon sound medical research and the amounts included should be sufficient to impart the desired biological action. The purity and consistency of those extracts should also be well documented and supported (this volume, see chapters by Epstein, and Shaath and Flores).

CONCLUSIONS

Advances in technology, the impact of imminent regulations, and the publication of new statistics and research on the developing dangers of the UV rays of the sun will clearly fuel research and development projects worldwide. As a result, the sunscreen industry may experience major growth in the future in the following categories:

i. Daily wear and long-term protection.
ii. Specialized products such as children products, antiaging products, sports products, etc.
iii. Reformulations for SPF, water resistance, UV-A and broad-spectrum protection claims, and line extensions.
iv. Sunless tanning and tanning accelerator products.
v. Multifunctional products (e.g., sunscreen and insect repellent, aromatherapy, etc.).
vi. Suncare products with functional biological ingredients.
vii. Suncare products with natural ingredients.

The sunscreen industry is gradually maturing and will reach its zenith in this coming decade with improved, functional products that will address both the concerns of the medical community and those desiring natural ingredients. Pricing, packaging, cosmetically innovative and esthetically appealing products will naturally add to the growth and success of this vital industry.

REFERENCES

1. Kligman A. Cosmeceuticals: Do we need a new category. In: Elsner P, Maibach H, eds. Cosmeceuticals. New York: Marcel Decker, 2000, Chap. I.1.
2. Federal Register, 27666, May 21, 1999.
3. Shaath NA. On the theory of ultraviolet absorption by sunscreen chemicals. J Soc Cosmet Chem 1987; 38:193.

Index